Atlas of
Human
Anatomy

Atlas of Human Anatomy

Bernhard N. Tillmann

Clinical Edition

Walid Elbermani

with drawings by
C. Sperlich, C. Franke, A. Cornford

Mud Puddle Books
NEW YORK

Atlas of Human Anatomy
by Bernhard N. Tillmann

Original German language edition:
Atlas der Anatomie des Menschen
by Bernhard N. Tillmann
Copyright © Springer-Verlag Berlin Heidelberg 2005
Springer is a part of Springer Science + Business Media

English language translation:
Copyright © Mud Puddle, Inc. 2007

Walid Elbermani, Clinical Edition

Catherine McKay, Editor,
English language edition

Mulberry Tree Press, Production,
English language edition

ISBN: 978-1-60311-044-0

Published by
Mud Puddle Books, Inc.
54 W. 21st Street
Suite 601
New York, NY 10010
info@mudpuddlebooks.com

Prof. Dr. med. Bernhard N. Tillmann
Institute of Anatomy of Christian-Albrecht-University in Kiel
Olshausenstr. 40
24098 Kiel

With drawings by
C. Sperlich, Kiel
C. Franke, Kiel
A. Cornford, Reinheim

Illustrations were derived from the following sources:
Braus, H. Anatomie des Menschen. Ein Lehrbuch für Ärzte und Studierende.
Continued by C. Elze. 3rd ed. Vol. I. Berlin: Springer, 1954.
Braus, H. Anatomie des Menschen. Ein Lehrbuch für Ärzte und Studierende.
Continued by C. Elze. 3rd ed. Vol. II. Berlin: Springer, 1956.
Braus, H. Anatomie des Menschen. Continued by C. Elze. 2nd ed. Vol. III.
Berlin: Springer, 1960.
Hafferl. Lehrbuch der topographischen Anatomie, 2nd ed. Berlin: Springer, 1957
Lanz, T. von, and W. Wachsmuth. Praktische Anatomie. Ein Lehr- und Hilfsbuch der
anatomischen Grundlagen ärztlichen Handelns. Vol. I/2: Neck. Berlin: Springer, 1955.
Lanz, T. von, and W. Wachsmuth. Praktische Anatomie. Ein Lehr- und Hilfsbuch der
anatomischen Grundlagen ärztlichen Handelns. 2nd ed. Vol. I/3: Arm. Berlin: Springer, 1959.
Lanz, T. von, and W. Wachsmuth. Praktische Anatomie. Ein Lehr- und Hilfsbuch der anatomischen
Grundlagen ärztlichen Handelns. Vol. I/4: Leg and Statics. Berlin: Springer, 1938.
Lanz, T. von, W. Wachsmuth, von Loeweneck, and Feifel G. Praktische Anatomie. Ein Lehr- und Hilfsbuch der anatomischen
Grundlagen ärztlichen Handelns. Vol. II/6: Abdomen/Berlin: Springer 1993.
Lanz, T. von, and W. Wachsmuth. Praktische Anatomie. Ein Lehr- und Hilfsbuch der
anatomischen Grundlagen ärztlichen Handelns. Vol. II/7: Back. Berlin: Springer, 1982.
Lanz, T. von, and W. Wachsmuth. Praktische Anatomie. Ein Lehr- und Hilfsbuch der
anatomischen Grundlagen ärztlichen Handelns. Vol. II/8: Pelvis. Berlin: Springer, 1984.

Printed and bound in China

Preface
to the original edition

Most anatomical atlases follow a long tradition with regard to their illustrations. When I was asked if I were willing to publish a new atlas of anatomy, I acquiesced under the condition that I be able to diverge from the conventional form of an atlas of anatomy. The atlas was intended to conform in content and didactics to the changes and requirements of anatomical instruction with regard to the new regulations governing the licensing of doctors. This atlas is indeed different from other atlases. For me as a "clinical anatomist," the teaching of the subject of Anatomy is no end in itself. Later, as a clinician, the doctor must be able to apply his knowledge of Anatomy. From this perspective, we have made our preparations and drawn them for the atlas. The illustrations depict the anatomical structures in such a way as to facilitate the reader's understanding of clinical coherences.

The most important characteristic of an anatomical atlas is its illustrations. The goal of the creation of new illustrations for the atlas at hand was to illustrate the close connection between preclinical and clinical content. The new illustrations were created with the help of anatomical preparations which were made from a practical-clinical perspective. The pictures, which were drawn with regard to their clinical application, fit in easily with the classical illustrations of "v. Lanz/Wachsmuth", whose objective is identified as "Practical Anatomy" in the title. The anatomical pictures complement illustrations of modern imaging procedures as examples. The systematics of the pathways is based largely on illustrations of "Anatomie des Menschen" by Braus and Elze, which were revised and amended didactically with the help of modern imaging techniques. Despite the systematic method of illustration, the three-dimensional allocation is preserved and allows for their integration into the topographic-clinical illustrations. The wish of the students was granted by choosing a photograph instead of a drawing for the illustration of the skeleton system.

With this atlas, the students are encouraged to feel motivated to follow their medical curiosity: "Why do I actually have to know this?" That is why the anatomical pictures are annotated with clinical commentaries. Clinicians of all fields, e.g. Otorhinolaryngology, Surgery, or Ophthalmology, have developed and revised these texts together with me. For this reason, you will not find any outdated information in our atlas. We have introduced a modern clinic into the atlas and thereby also fulfill the requirements of the new regulations governing the licensure of doctors. Furthermore, we have made a point of keeping the texts intelligible for students of the preclinical section. Everything has been cross-read by medical students.

Without seeking to go beyond the scope of the usual didactic focus of an atlas, learning aids and clinical advice in select examples were included the atlas. A "Navigation System" in the form of colored markings in the illustration notes and in all tables facilitates use of the atlas, e.g. the learning of branch orders of vessels or the allocation of motor and sensitive nerves. The clinical advice has a direct relationship to the content of the respective illustration; it is designed to inspire curiosity and motivate the students of the preclinical section to independently and continuously further their studies, which is an explicit requirement of the new regulations governing the licensure of doctors. As far as clinically active physicians are concerned, may the clinical advice already known to them rekindle their "passion" for anatomy, the root of all medical activity.

The author and publisher offer this atlas to students of medicine and to physicians with the desire that it may be helpful in their preparation for the occupation or in their practical activities.

—Bernhard N. Tillmann
Kiel, Spring 2004

Portions of this edited Preface are derived from an interview conducted by Christian Schaaf, born in 1978, Student of Human Medicine in Heidelberg

Preface
Clinical Edition

Learning anatomy goes far beyond learning structure. Clinicians must interpret the significance of structure. How does structure enable function? How much alteration is possible without losing function? Interpreting the significance of structure requires and develops the analytical mindset that produces clinical competence.

My training and practice as a thoracic surgeon and subsequent forty-two years of teaching clinical and surgical anatomy have focused me on clinical application as the most effective way to understand anatomy.

The anatomical preparations of Prof. Tillmann and his colleagues and the resulting drawings are outstandingly clear and detailed—which facilitates the understanding of structure. I have added text to deepen the interconnection of structural analysis with diagnosis and intervention.

Analysis and preservation of structure preserve function. An example encountered by runners when injured is replacement of the cruciate ligament by the tendon of the gracilis muscle of the thigh. The replacement diminishes movement and tears under torque. Why doesn't one ligament or tendon fiber substitute satisfactorily for another? The structure of the cruciate ligament is vastly different from that of the gracilis tendon. The fibers of the tendon are straight. But the cruciate ligament, which has to facilitate high torque movement, is formed from fibers that are twisted like rope. By twisting to tighten or loosen, those fibers can accommodate the higher torque that tears straight fibers.

A primary mindset in anatomy is the habit of justifying identifications.

When students ask during dissection, "Is this the x nerve?" I throw back the question, "What are the landmarks for the x nerve? Where does it emerge? What is its course?" I test my students with the "make-a-lesion" game. They have to quickly identify, from topographic landmarks, what functions will be lost if a wound occurs at an indicated place. They should be able to tell immediately what branches emerge from the major nerve beyond where it is damaged and what sensory and/or motor loss would result from those branches being decommissioned. The use of landmarks is another primary mindset in anatomy. Human anatomy is not a one-size-fits-all. What may be x inches on one body is not x inches on another—landmarks are the only reliable guide.

Just as one size does not fit all, one type does not always occur. There is a forty percent chance that the right or left coronary artery will not arise from the corresponding aortic sinus. The celiac trunk divides into three branches in only seventy percent of cases and in ten percent of cases, produces a dorsal pancreatic artery. The liver is supplied from the common hepatic artery only fifty percent of the time. Never make assumptions—anomaly is always lying in wait.

Gross anatomy still has frontiers. I have paid a great deal of attention to presenting the sites of regional nerve blocks. One of the most important developments in surgery is the use of regional anesthesia. Besides being safer and allowing faster recovery, local nerve blocks offer effective, non-narcotic post-procedural pain management. They are also important for immediate response in emergency rooms or where there is limited access to hospitalization for surgical procedures.

For non-medical readers, I hope this atlas will convey the complexity and interconnection of structures and functions of the body you inhabit. Intervention ripples. All interventions have consequences. But knowledge is power. I elaborate on the consequences of treatments because anyone considering a procedure has the responsibility to consider all its possible effects to evaluate alternative interventions and determine what is statistically least risky to his or her individual condition.

For medical readers, anatomy is not a subject that you pass. Anatomy is a mindset that you develop and use as the basis of practice. How you develop that mindset determines your competence as a practitioner.

—Walid Elbermani
Boston, Massachusetts
Spring, 2007

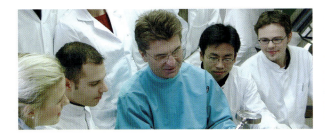 

Vitas

Professor Dr. med. Bernhard Tillmann

Born in 1939. Medical degree from Cologne. Doctorate in Anatomy and Developmental History. Professor for topographic and functional anatomy at the University of Cologne. Appointment as full professor of anatomy at Christian-Albrechts-University, Kiel. Director of the university's Institute of Anatomy. Foundation of Center for Clinical Anatomy, Kiel, main research in functional anatomy, biomechanics of the musculoskeletal system and clinical anatomy. Numerous research awards. First prize in Educational Ranking since the establishment of the evaluation. Chairman of the Anatomical Association.

Associate Professor Walid Elbermani, M.D., Ph.D.

Born in 1937. Medical degree from Baghdad University School of Medicine. Residency and practice in thoracic surgery at Mirjan Chest Hospital, Baghdad. 1969 Ph.D. in Anatomy, Boston University. Assistant Professor of Anatomy, Boston University School of Medicine. Recruited during the Vietnam War to the team for experimental reconstructive surgery at Chelsea Naval Hospital, Boston. 1976 Associate Professor of Anatomy and Cell Biology at Tufts University School of Medicine, Boston. Funded research in innervations of the lung. Provides clinical rotations and postgraduate training in surgical anatomy for general surgery, neurosurgery, neuro-ophthalmologic surgery, orthopaedic surgery, surgery for ob/gyn and regional anesthesia. Received President of Tufts' Outstanding Faculty Achievement Award, yearly Citations for Teaching Excellence from graduating classes, and the Lauro F. Cavazos Prize for Teaching. Director of the Master Degree in Surgical Anatomy given in conjunction with the Department of General Surgery, Tufts-New England Medical Center.

Acknowledgments

From Bernhard N. Tillmann • Kiel, Spring 2004

Preparations for new illustrations were made at the Institute of Anatomy by Mr. G. R. Klaws and Ms. St. Gundlach, who also created preparations for photographs and supervised photography.

Ms. C. Sperlich drew the majority of illustrations and illustrations for the Muscle sections, the pathways and schematic drawings were prepared by Mr. C. Franke with some diagrams by Mr. A Cornford.

Original illustrations and prepared dissections were provided by Professors Dr. A.F. Holstein, Hamburg, Dr. J. Koebke, Cologne, Dr. H. Loeweneck, Munich, Dr. R. Nitsch, Berlin, and Dr. K. Zilles, Düsseldorf.

Colleagues who contributed to clinical depictions were Prof. Dr. L. Mettler, Prof. Dr. I. Schreer, Kiel, Prof. Dr. C. Schmolke, Bonn, Dr. R. Löning, Lübeck, and also from Kiel, Prof. Dr. Dr. H-K. Albers, Dr. H. Bertermann, Private Lecturer Dr. B. Bewig, Private Lecturer Dr. J. Biederer, Dr. J. Blume, Dr. H. Bolte, Dr. M. Bosse, Dr. W. Brenner, Dr. J. M. Doniec, Prof. Dr. U. R. Fölsch, Prof. Dr. M. Heller, Dr. C. Hilbert, Dr. M. Höpfner, Prof. Dr. O. Jansen, Dr. U. Kampen, W. Klüglein, Dr. W. Kroll, Prof. Dr. St. Müller-Hülsbeck, Dr. F. Pries, Dr. S. Schmidt, Dipl. Mathem. A. Schumm, Private Lecturer Dr. A. Thale.

Advice in selection and content of clinical notes came from Dr. U. Thale, Dr. M. Ayub, Private Lecturer Dr. A. Böhle, Private Lecturer Dr. A. Böning, Dr. G. Brademann, Dr. J. M. Doniec, M. Föge, Prof. Dr. Dr. F. Härle, Prof. Dr. J. Pfisterer, Dr. Ch. Schmidt, Private Lecturer Dr. A. Thale, Dr. D. Varoga, Dr. H. Wilms.

Support and advice at the Institute of Anatomy came from Prof. Dr. R. Lüllmann-Rauch, Prof. Dr. F. Paulsen Halle, and Prof. Dr. J. Sievers. Also, preparation for arrangement of illustrations on double pages was facilitated in the photo laboratory by Ms. H. Siebke, Ms. H. Waluk and Ms. R. Worm. Ms. B. Schierhorn typed the tables and a large part of the manuscript, which was completed by Ms. M. Kock.

Former students supplied feedback on use of the atlas, particularly, Dr. Ph. Steven and Th. Zantopp.

Support for the project at Springer Verlag came from Ms. A. Repnow, Mr. S. Spägele and Dr. Th. Hopfe. Dr. U. Osterkamp-Baust prepared the index. Ms. E. Blasig and Mr. P. Bergmann were editors and production was carried out by Ms. M. Uhing, Ms. M. Berg, Ms. A. Metter (amproductions) and Ms. B. Döring (medio Technologies AG).

From Walid Elbermani • Boston, Spring 2007

Thanks for the Clinical Edition go to Gregory Boehm of Mud Puddle Books. He could not have cut his teeth on a more ambitious project. Despite deadlines, he gave unwavering support for definitive excellence. The production designer Joe Gannon carried out modifications to drawings as well as creating additional artwork; he also managed to incorporate the clinical notes while preserving the clarity of the layout that so much facilitates the use of this atlas. The editor Kate McKay made the terminology and the text uniform and concise.

This edition is dedicated to everyone who wants to learn
and
to my never-patient wife and co-writer,
Eva Benedikt

Table of Contents

Editor's Note

This book was originally published in German in 2005 and has been translated into English for this clinical edition. All medical terminology was vetted by Dr. Elbermani to conform to accepted American medical usage. He has also edited the existing clinical notes and added notes, where appropriate, to reflect American clinical practices and procedures. Where necessary, illustrations were adapted or modified to accommodate these differences in approach.

The original German text used a combination of dark and light type to emphasize the importance of the structure depicted; this has also been adopted in the American clinical edition. In this edition, capitalization is used to enhance the visual recognition and memory of structure, terms, and function. Alternate terms are placed in parentheses and figures are labeled using a numerical system related to the chapter number to promote cross-referencing throughout the text. Where relevant, chapters are followed by a Muscle Addendum (MA), which features easily accessed and understood tables detailing the functions, innervations, and blood supply of muscles, in addition to diagrams of muscle origins and insertions.

Every effort has been made to ensure that the translation and terminology used in this atlas is as accurate as possible. However, as with any text of this size and complexity, there may be errors, omissions, or changes in medical knowledge/procedures since the text's preparation and publication. In future editions, these issues will be further minimized and new features added to ensure that *Atlas of Human Anatomy, Clinical Edition* is the most comprehensive reference for the general reader and for medical and health care professionals.

Abbreviations Used:

res.	resected		N.	nerve
var.	variation		Nn.	nerves
A.	artery		rad.	radiologic
Aa.	arteries		V.	vein
Lig.	ligament		Vv.	veins
MA	muscle addendum		VRT	volume rendering technique
M.	muscle		~	approximate
Mm.	muscles			

Key to Symbols:

🅖 Identifies grouping		🅓 Directs to related figure
🅘 Information		♂ Related to man
🅛 Indicates linkage		♀ Related to woman
🅑 Indicates a main branch of an artery, vein, nerve		∿ EKG readout for measurement of heart rate and pulse
🅢 Clinical information		Needle/syringe used for blood sampling, injection to block nerves
➤ and ➤ Indicates the terminal branches of an artery, vein, nerve		

Systematic Anatomy

Regions of the Body

1.1a,b Regions of the Body: Frontal, Anterior, and Ventral Views.

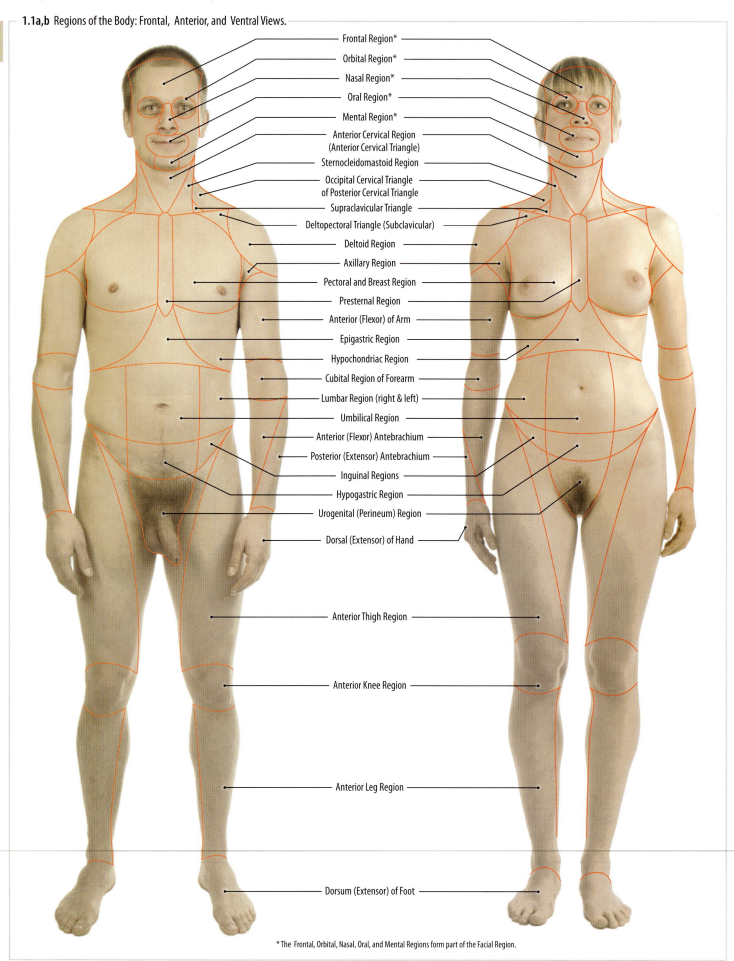

Frontal Region*

Orbital Region*

Nasal Region*

Oral Region*

Mental Region*

Anterior Cervical Region
(Anterior Cervical Triangle)

Sternocleidomastoid Region

Occipital Cervical Triangle
of Posterior Cervical Triangle

Supraclavicular Triangle

Deltopectoral Triangle (Subclavicular)

Deltoid Region

Axillary Region

Pectoral and Breast Region

Presternal Region

Anterior (Flexor) of Arm

Epigastric Region

Hypochondriac Region

Cubital Region of Forearm

Lumbar Region (right & left)

Umbilical Region

Anterior (Flexor) Antebrachium

Posterior (Extensor) Antebrachium

Inguinal Regions

Hypogastric Region

Urogenital (Perineum) Region

Dorsal (Extensor) of Hand

Anterior Thigh Region

Anterior Knee Region

Anterior Leg Region

Dorsum (Extensor) of Foot

* The Frontal, Orbital, Nasal, Oral, and Mental Regions form part of the Facial Region.

1.2a,b Regions of the Body: Occipital View.

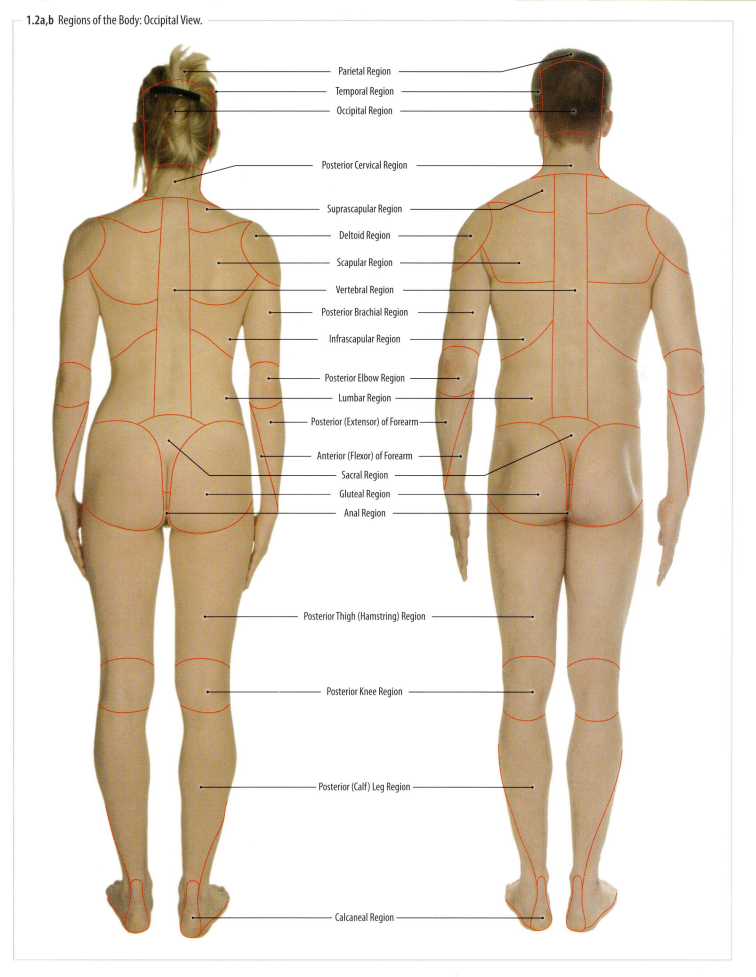

Parietal Region

Temporal Region

Occipital Region

Posterior Cervical Region

Suprascapular Region

Deltoid Region

Scapular Region

Vertebral Region

Posterior Brachial Region

Infrascapular Region

Posterior Elbow Region

Lumbar Region

Posterior (Extensor) of Forearm

Anterior (Flexor) of Forearm

Sacral Region

Gluteal Region

Anal Region

Posterior Thigh (Hamstring) Region

Posterior Knee Region

Posterior (Calf) Leg Region

Calcaneal Region

Orientation Lines and Planes

1.3 Orientation Lines and Planes of the Body: Frontal View.

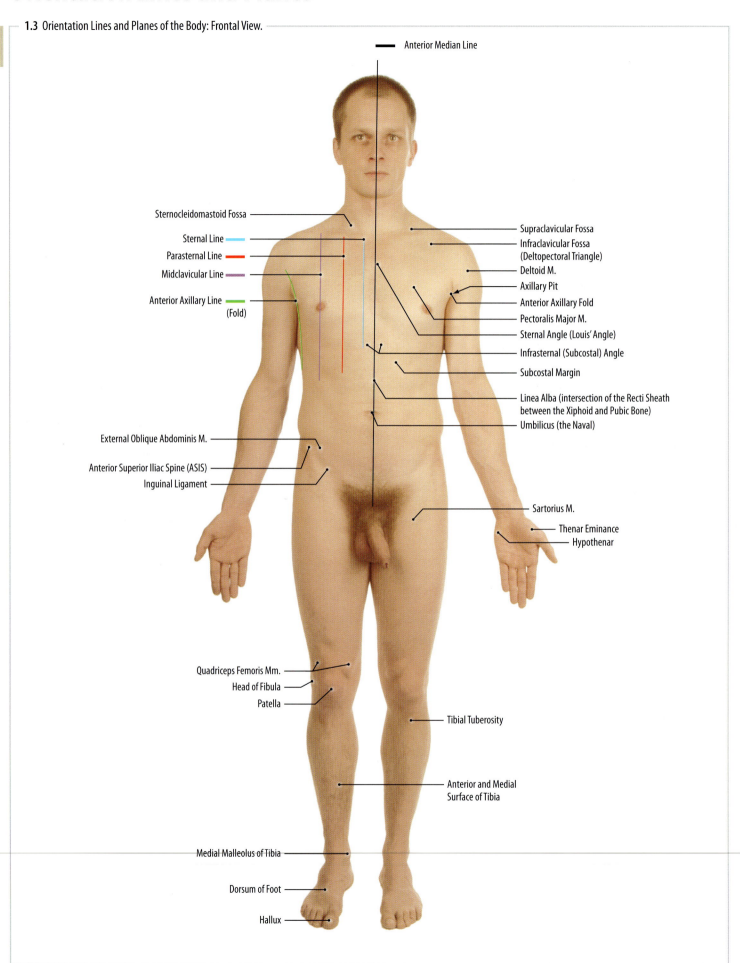

Anterior Median Line

Sternocleidomastoid Fossa

Sternal Line

Parasternal Line

Midclavicular Line

Anterior Axillary Line
(Fold)

External Oblique Abdominis M.

Anterior Superior Iliac Spine (ASIS)

Inguinal Ligament

Quadriceps Femoris Mm.

Head of Fibula

Patella

Medial Malleolus of Tibia

Dorsum of Foot

Hallux

Supraclavicular Fossa

Infraclavicular Fossa
(Deltopectoral Triangle)

Deltoid M.

Axillary Pit

Anterior Axillary Fold

Pectoralis Major M.

Sternal Angle (Louis' Angle)

Infrasternal (Subcostal) Angle

Subcostal Margin

Linea Alba (intersection of the Recti Sheath
between the Xiphoid and Pubic Bone)

Umbilicus (the Naval)

Sartorius M.

Thenar Eminance

Hypothenar

Tibial Tuberosity

Anterior and Medial
Surface of Tibia

Orientation Lines and Planes

1.4 Orientation Lines of the Planes of the Body: Occipital, Posterior, and Dorsal View.

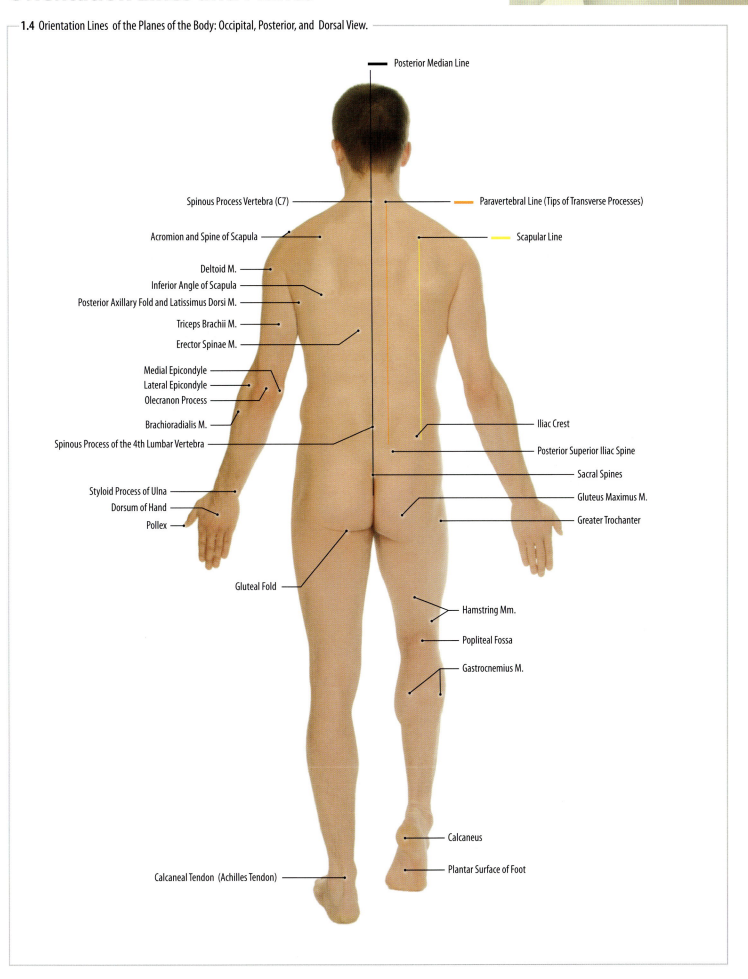

Posterior Median Line

Spinous Process Vertebra (C7)

Paravertebral Line (Tips of Transverse Processes)

Acromion and Spine of Scapula

Scapular Line

Deltoid M.

Inferior Angle of Scapula

Posterior Axillary Fold and Latissimus Dorsi M.

Triceps Brachii M.

Erector Spinae M.

Medial Epicondyle

Lateral Epicondyle

Olecranon Process

Brachioradialis M.

Spinous Process of the 4th Lumbar Vertebra

Iliac Crest

Posterior Superior Iliac Spine

Sacral Spines

Styloid Process of Ulna

Dorsum of Hand

Pollex

Gluteus Maximus M.

Greater Trochanter

Gluteal Fold

Hamstring Mm.

Popliteal Fossa

Gastrocnemius M.

Calcaneus

Plantar Surface of Foot

Calcaneal Tendon (Achilles Tendon)

Axes, Planes, Directions

1.5 Main Axes and Main Planes of the Body, Direction Designations, Position of the Body Parts, and Moving Directions.

Main Axes

1 Vertical or Longitudinal Axis
Runs Lengthwise to the Body

2 Sagittal Axis
Runs Perpendicular to the Vertical and Transversal Axis through the Anterior and Posterior Body Wall

3 Transversal or Horizontal Axis
Runs Across the Body

Direction Designations and Position of the Body Parts

Cranial or Superior	Toward the Head End
Caudal or Inferior	Toward the End of the Trunk
Medial	Toward the Median Plane
Lateral	Away From the Median Plane
Median	Center of the Body Within the Median Plane
Central	Toward the Interior of the Body
Peripheral	Toward the Surface of the Body
Proximal	Toward the Trunk
Distal	Toward the End of the Extremities
Ulnar	Toward the Ulna (Medial Forearm)
Radial	Toward the Radius (Lateral Forearm)
Tibial	Toward the Tibia (Medial of Leg)
Fibular	Toward the Fibula (Lateral of Leg)
Anterior or Ventral	Forward or Toward the Abdomen
Posterior or Dorsal	Backward or Toward the Back
Volar or Palmar	Toward the Palm
Plantar	Toward the Sole of the Foot
Dorsal	The Upper Limb Rotates 90 Degrees Laterally Making the Palm of the Hand Face Anteriorally and Some of the Hand Face Posteriorally. The Lower Limb Rotates 90 Degrees Medially, therefore Making the Sole and the Dorsum of the Foot Face Anteriorally.

Radiological Designations of the Layer Planes

Axial Layer	Transversal Plane
Coronary Layer	Frontal Plane
Sagittal Layer	Sagittal Plane

In Imaging Processes (e.g., Computer Tomography [CT], Magnetic Resonance Imaging [MRI]), the Section Planes are Viewed Cranially (the patient while lying down is viewed from the feet upward). Anatomical Sections are usually Viewed Caudally from the head of the cadaver.

Main Planes

Median Plane
Symmetry Plane which Parts the Body into Two (theoretically) Mirrored Halves

Sagittal Plane
Runs Parallel to the Median Plane

Frontal Plane
Runs Toward the Forehead and Perpendicular to the Sagittal Plane

Transversal Plane
All Section Planes of the Body

Moving Directions

Extension	Move Ventral Surfaces Away from Each Other
Flexion	Move Ventral (Anterior) Surfaces Closer
Abduction	Move the Extremities Laterally Away from the Midline
Adduction	Move the Extemities toward the (Midline) Trunk in the Frontal Plane
Elevation	Move the Pectoral Girdle of the Extremities or Ribs Toward the Head (Superiorly)
Rotation	Medial and Lateral Rotation of the Extremities Around the Longitudinal Axis of the Extremities, Rotation of the Trunk
Circumduction	Movement of the Extremities in a Circular Direction

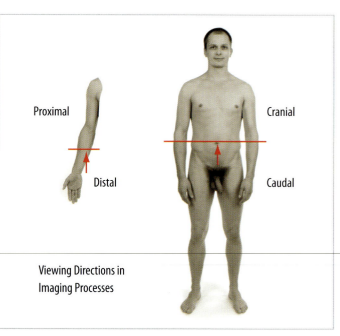

Proximal

Distal

Cranial

Caudal

Viewing Directions in Imaging Processes

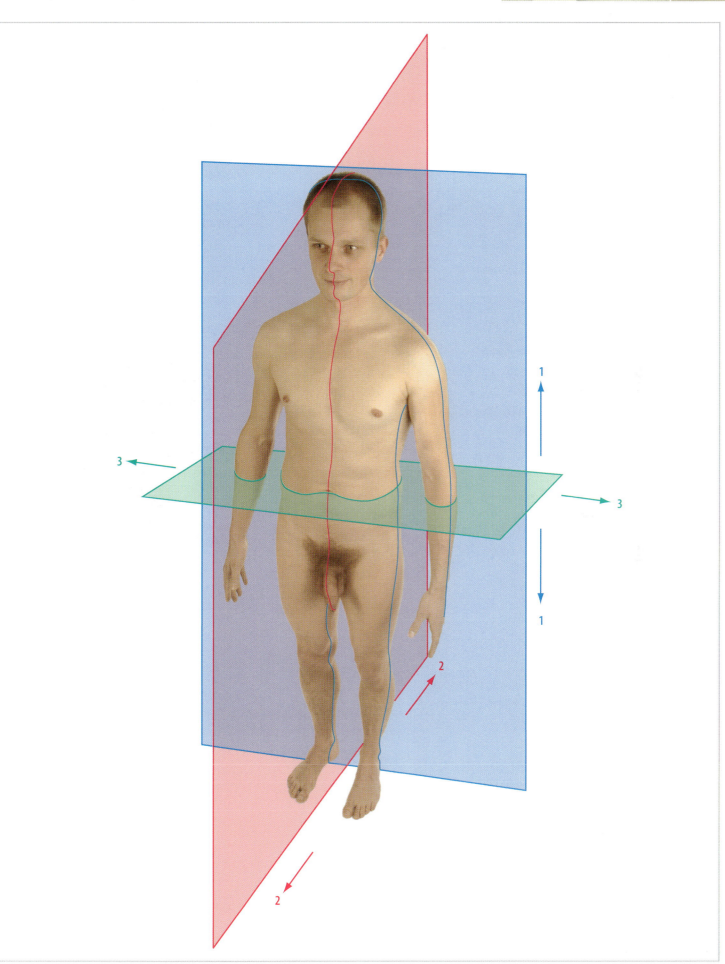

1

1.6 Survey of Bones and Joints: Female Skeleton, Frontoanterior View. [1]

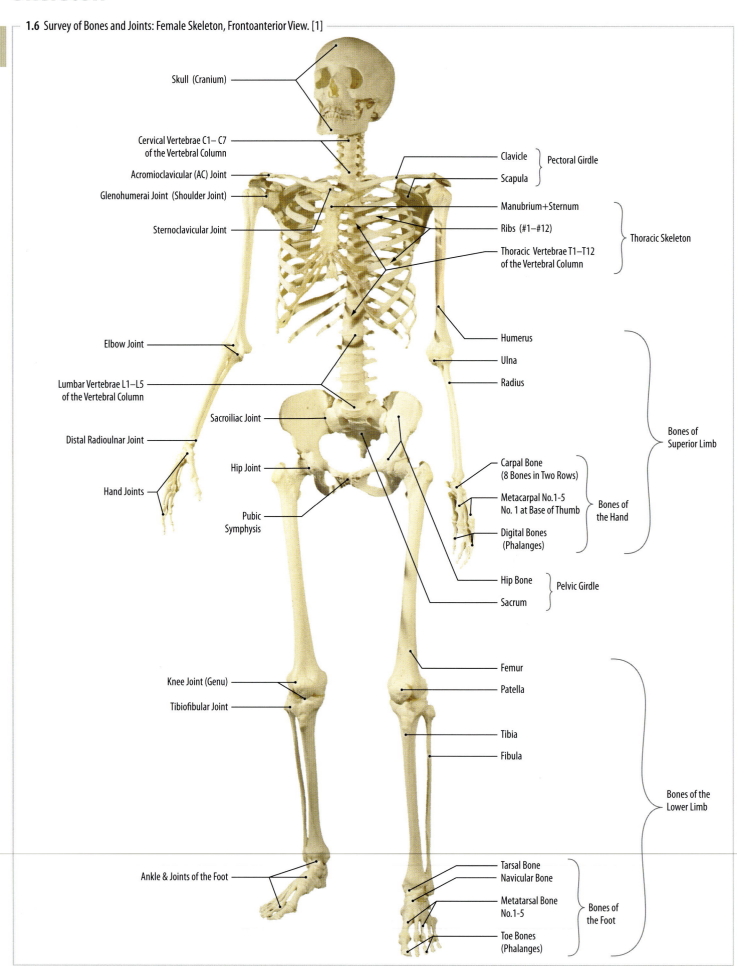

Skull (Cranium)

Cervical Vertebrae C1– C7
of the Vertebral Column

Acromioclavicular (AC) Joint

Glenohumerai Joint (Shoulder Joint)

Sternoclavicular Joint

Elbow Joint

Lumbar Vertebrae L1–L5
of the Vertebral Column

Sacroiliac Joint

Distal Radioulnar Joint

Hip Joint

Hand Joints

Pubic
Symphysis

Knee Joint (Genu)

Tibiofibular Joint

Ankle & Joints of the Foot

Clavicle ⎫
Scapula ⎬ Pectoral Girdle

Manubrium+Sternum

Ribs (#1–#12) ⎫
⎬ Thoracic Skeleton
Thoracic Vertebrae T1–T12 ⎭
of the Vertebral Column

Humerus

Ulna

Radius

Carpal Bone
(8 Bones in Two Rows)

Metacarpal No.1-5
No. 1 at Base of Thumb ⎬ Bones of
the Hand

Digital Bones
(Phalanges)

Hip Bone ⎫ Pelvic Girdle
Sacrum ⎭

Bones of
Superior Limb

Femur

Patella

Tibia

Fibula

Bones of the
Lower Limb

Tarsal Bone
Navicular Bone

Metatarsal Bone
No.1-5 ⎬ Bones of
the Foot

Toe Bones
(Phalanges)

Bone Formations

1.7a–e Bone Form and Structure. [1]

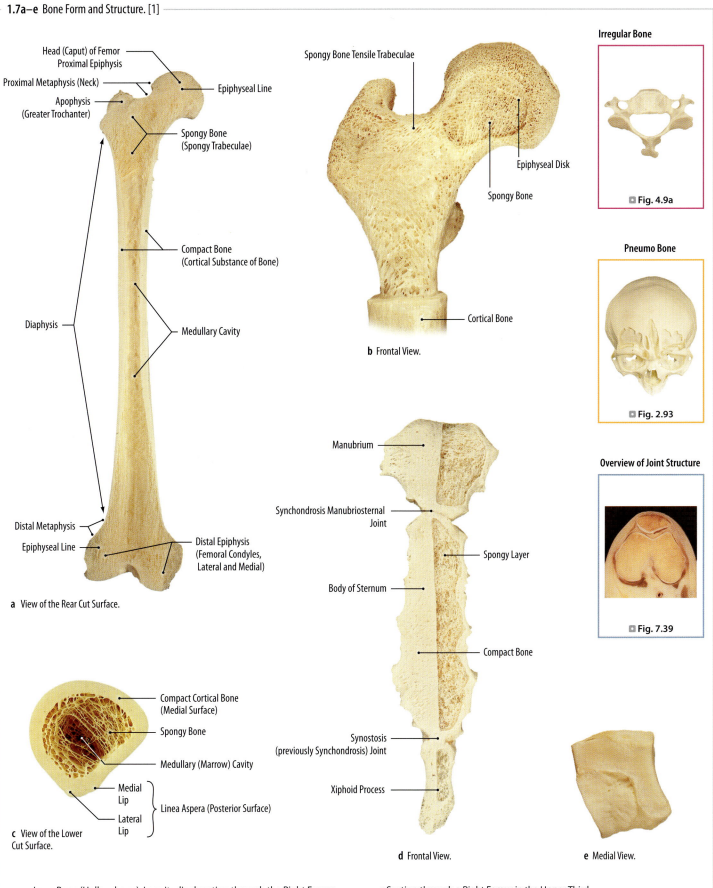

Head (Caput) of Femor
Proximal Epiphysis

Proximal Metaphysis (Neck)

Apophysis
(Greater Trochanter)

Epiphyseal Line

Spongy Bone
(Spongy Trabeculae)

Compact Bone
(Cortical Substance of Bone)

Diaphysis

Medullary Cavity

Distal Metaphysis

Epiphyseal Line

Distal Epiphysis
(Femoral Condyles,
Lateral and Medial)

a View of the Rear Cut Surface.

Spongy Bone Tensile Trabeculae

Epiphyseal Disk

Spongy Bone

Cortical Bone

b Frontal View.

Compact Cortical Bone
(Medial Surface)

Spongy Bone

Medullary (Marrow) Cavity

Medial
Lip

Lateral
Lip

Linea Aspera (Posterior Surface)

c View of the Lower
Cut Surface.

Manubrium

Synchondrosis Manubriosternal
Joint

Spongy Layer

Body of Sternum

Compact Bone

Synostosis
(previously Synchondrosis) Joint

Xiphoid Process

d Frontal View.

e Medial View.

Irregular Bone

◼ Fig. 4.9a

Pneumo Bone

◼ Fig. 2.93

Overview of Joint Structure

◼ Fig. 7.39

a Long Bone (Hollow bone). Longitudinal section through the Right Femur.
b Right Proximal Femur End. To display the Spongy Layer, the Compact Bone was Removed. The Transition Area from the Femoral Head and Femoral Neck was Dissected.

c Section through a Right Femur in the Upper Third.
d Flat Bone. The Sternum and the Spongy Layer were Dissected on the Left Side by Removing the Cortical Bone.
e Short Bone. Right Intermediate Cuneiform Bone.

Circulation Organs

1.8a,b Circulatory Organs. [2]

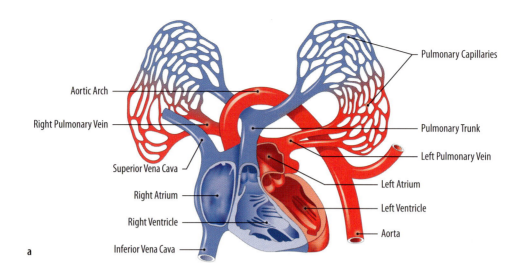

Pulmonary Capillaries

Aortic Arch

Right Pulmonary Vein

Pulmonary Trunk

Left Pulmonary Vein

Superior Vena Cava

Left Atrium

Right Atrium

Left Ventricle

Right Ventricle

Aorta

Inferior Vena Cava

a

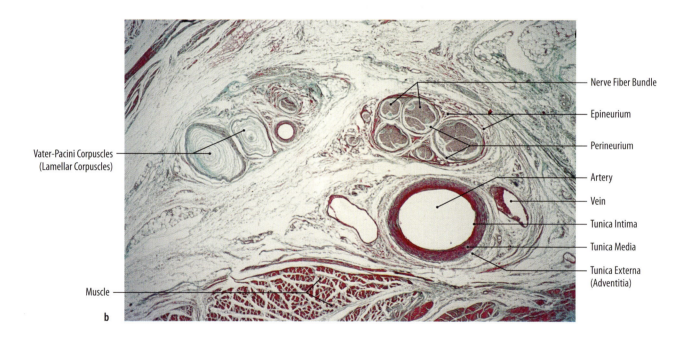

Nerve Fiber Bundle

Epineurium

Perineurium

Vater-Pacini Corpuscles
(Lamellar Corpuscles)

Artery

Vein

Tunica Intima

Tunica Media

Tunica Externa
(Adventitia)

Muscle

b

Aorta and Outlets

Superior Vena Cava and Inferior Vena Cava

Portal Vein Circulation

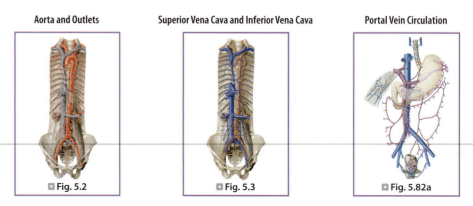

◻ **Fig. 5.2** ◻ **Fig. 5.3** ◻ **Fig. 5.82a**

a Schema of the Heart with Afferent and Efferent Vessels of the General (Greater) Systematic Circulation and the (Lesser) Pulmonary Circulation.
b Vessel Nerve Cord, Histological Section through the Thumb at the Basal Joint. Goldner staining, × 20.

Fetal Circulation

1.9 Fetal Circulation Before and After Birth. [3]

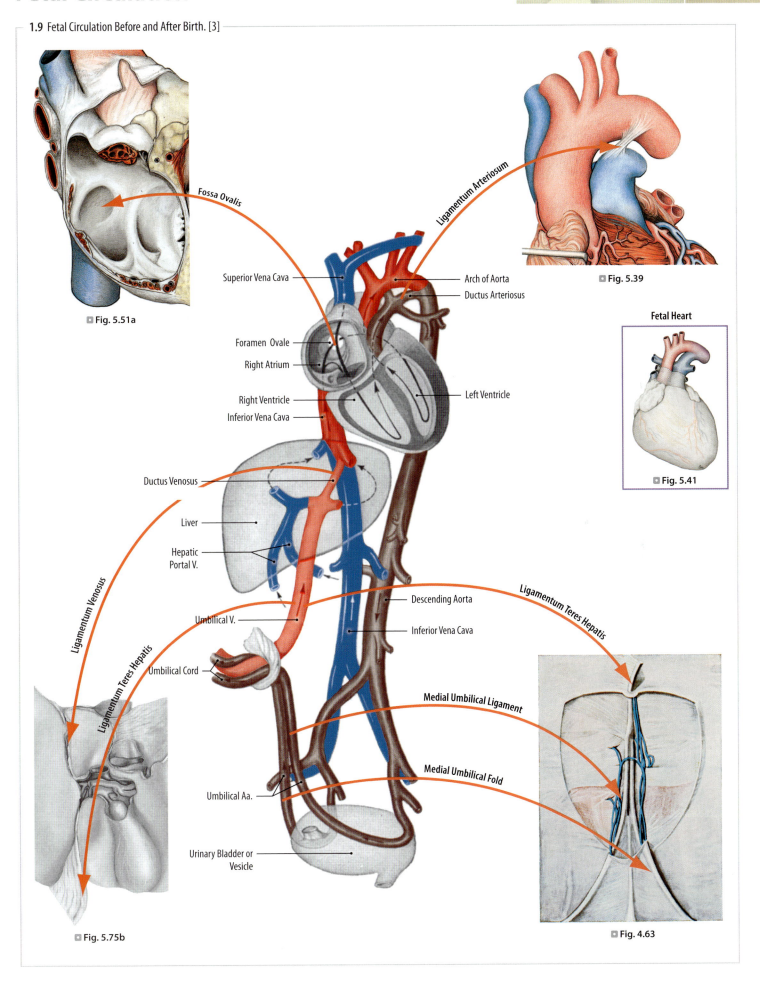

▢ **Fig. 5.51a**

Fossa Ovalis

Ligamentum Arteriosum

▢ **Fig. 5.39**

Superior Vena Cava

Arch of Aorta

Ductus Arteriosus

Fetal Heart

▢ **Fig. 5.41**

Foramen Ovale

Right Atrium

Right Ventricle

Left Ventricle

Inferior Vena Cava

Ductus Venosus

Liver

Hepatic Portal V.

Ligamentum Venosus

Ligamentum Teres Hepatis

Descending Aorta

Ligamentum Teres Hepatis

Umbilical V.

Inferior Vena Cava

Umbilical Cord

Medial Umbilical Ligament

Medial Umbilical Fold

Umbilical Aa.

Urinary Bladder or Vesicle

▢ **Fig. 5.75b**

▢ **Fig. 4.63**

Lymphatic System

1.10a–d Lymphatic System. [a 4, b 5, c 6]

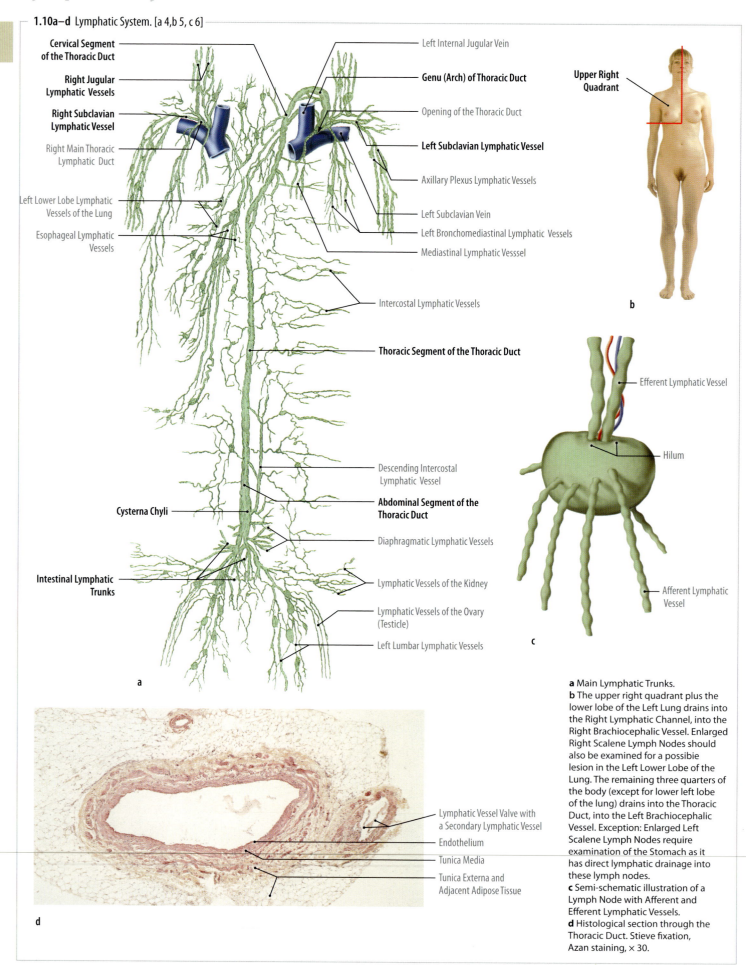

Cervical Segment of the Thoracic Duct

Right Jugular Lymphatic Vessels

Right Subclavian Lymphatic Vessel

Right Main Thoracic Lymphatic Duct

Left Lower Lobe Lymphatic Vessels of the Lung

Esophageal Lymphatic Vessels

Cysterna Chyli

Intestinal Lymphatic Trunks

Left Internal Jugular Vein

Genu (Arch) of Thoracic Duct

Opening of the Thoracic Duct

Left Subclavian Lymphatic Vessel

Axillary Plexus Lymphatic Vessels

Left Subclavian Vein

Left Bronchomediastinal Lymphatic Vessels

Mediastinal Lymphatic Vesssel

Intercostal Lymphatic Vessels

Thoracic Segment of the Thoracic Duct

Descending Intercostal Lymphatic Vessel

Abdominal Segment of the Thoracic Duct

Diaphragmatic Lymphatic Vessels

Lymphatic Vessels of the Kidney

Lymphatic Vessels of the Ovary (Testicle)

Left Lumbar Lymphatic Vessels

a

Upper Right Quadrant

b

Efferent Lymphatic Vessel

Hilum

Afferent Lymphatic Vessel

c

Lymphatic Vessel Valve with a Secondary Lymphatic Vessel

Endothelium

Tunica Media

Tunica Externa and Adjacent Adipose Tissue

d

a Main Lymphatic Trunks.
b The upper right quadrant plus the lower lobe of the Left Lung drains into the Right Lymphatic Channel, into the Right Brachiocephalic Vessel. Enlarged Right Scalene Lymph Nodes should also be examined for a possibie lesion in the Left Lower Lobe of the Lung. The remaining three quarters of the body (except for lower left lobe of the lung) drains into the Thoracic Duct, into the Left Brachiocephalic Vessel. Exception: Enlarged Left Scalene Lymph Nodes require examination of the Stomach as it has direct lymphatic drainage into these lymph nodes.
c Semi-schematic illustration of a Lymph Node with Afferent and Efferent Lymphatic Vessels.
d Histological section through the Thoracic Duct. Stieve fixation, Azan staining, × 30.

Peripheral Nervous System

1.11a,b Peripheral Nervous System, Spinal Nerves, and Plexus Formation. [a 2, b 7]

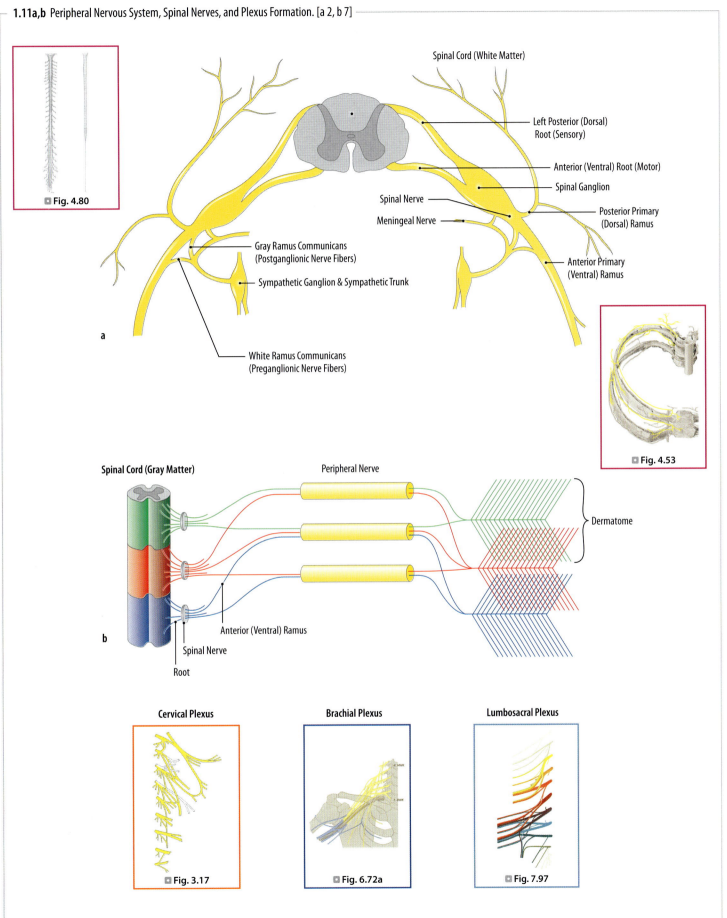

◼ Fig. 4.80

Spinal Cord (White Matter)

Left Posterior (Dorsal) Root (Sensory)

Anterior (Ventral) Root (Motor)

Spinal Ganglion

Spinal Nerve

Meningeal Nerve

Posterior Primary (Dorsal) Ramus

Gray Ramus Communicans (Postganglionic Nerve Fibers)

Sympathetic Ganglion & Sympathetic Trunk

Anterior Primary (Ventral) Ramus

White Ramus Communicans (Preganglionic Nerve Fibers)

a

◼ Fig. 4.53

Spinal Cord (Gray Matter)

Peripheral Nerve

Dermatome

Anterior (Ventral) Ramus

Spinal Nerve

Root

b

Cervical Plexus

◼ Fig. 3.17

Brachial Plexus

◼ Fig. 6.72a

Lumbosacral Plexus

◼ Fig. 7.97

a Composition of the Spinal Nerves.
b Plexus Formation – Radicular Innervation of the Skin – Dermatome Formation.

Cranial Nerves

1.12 Cranial Nerves: Classification, Origin of Nucleus, and Nerve Function.

Sensory Nerves	Nucleus Cells	Function
Olfactory CN I	Sensory Cells in Nasal Mucosa	Smell
Optic CN II	Ganglion Cells of the Retina	Sight
Vestibulocochlear CN VIII		
Vestibular N.	Vestibular Ganglion	Balance
Cochlearis N.	Cochlear Ganglion (Spiral Cochlea)	Hearing

Nerves of the Eye Muscle	Nucleus Cells	Function
Oculomotorius CN III	Oculomotor Nucleus	Somatic motor to: Levator Palpebrae Superioris, Rectus Superior, Rectus Medialis, Rectus Inferior, and Oblique Inferior Mm.
	Oculomotor Nucleus Accessory (autonomics) Edinger-Westphal Nucleus	Visceral motor to: Sphincter Pupillae M. and Ciliary Mm.
Trochlear CN IV	Nucleus of Trochlear N.	Somatic motor to: Superior Oblique M.
Abducent CN VI	Nucleus Abducent	Somatic motor to: Lateral Rectus M.

Branchial Nerves (Branchial/Pharyngeal Arches)	Nucleus Cells	Function
Trigeminus CN V Motor Division	Motor Nucleus Trigeminal N.	Motor to Mm. of Mastication: Masseter; Tensor Tympani; Tensor Veli Palatini; Anterior Belly of the Digastric, Mylohyoid, and Pterygoids Mm.
Sensory Division	Trigeminal N. (semilunar) Gasserian's Ganglion	General sensation: Facial Skin, Dura Mater, Periorbit, Eye, Mucous Membrane of the Nasal and Oral Cavities
	Mesencephalic Trigeminal Nucleus	Proprioception from: Mm. of Mastication, Ocular and Facial Mm.
Facial CN VII with Intermedius N.	Nucleus Facial N.	Motor to Facial Expression Mm: Stylohyoid, Posterior Belly of the Digastric and Stapedius Mm.
	Superior Salivatory Nucleus	Visceral motor (secretory) to: Lacrimal, Nasal, Small Salivary, Sublingual, and Submandibular Salivary Glands
	Geniculate Ganglion	General sensation from: Skin of the Outer Ear Canal, and the Tympanic Membrane
		Special sensation of: Taste to the anterior two thirds of the Tongue
Glossopharyngeal CN IX	Nucleus Ambiguus	Motor to: Pharynx and Larynx Mm.
	Inferior Salivatory Nucleus	Visceral motor (secretory) to: Parotid Gland
	Superior Ganglion	General sensation for: Mucous Membrane of the Tongue, Fauces, Middle Ear, Auditory Tube
	Inferior Ganglion	Special sensation of: Taste to the posterior one third of the Tongue
		Proprioception for: Carotid Sinus
		Chemoreception from: Carotid Body
Vagus CN X	Nucleus Ambiguus	Motor to: Pharynx and the Larynx Mm.
	Dorsal Nucleus of Vagus	Visceral motor to: All Viscera in the Neck, Chest, and Abdomen and to two thirds of the Transverse Colon
	Superior Ganglion (jugular)	General sensation from: Outer Ear Canal and the Dura Mater inside the Skull
	Inferior Ganglion (nodosum)	Visceral sensation from: Fauces, Larynx, Chest, and Abdominal Organ, Special sensation of: Taste of the Laryngeal Aditus
Accessory CN XI		
Cranial Part joins the Vagus Nerve – Internal Branch	Nucleus Ambiguus	Motor to: Pharynx and the Larynx Mm.
Spinal Part – External Branch	Spinal Nucleus Accessory N.	Motor to: Sternocleidomastoideus and Trapezius Mm.
Hypoglossal CN XII	Hypoglossus Nucleus	Intrinsic Muscle of the Tongue
		Motor to the extrinsic muscles: Styloglossus, Hypoglossus, and Genioglossus Mm.

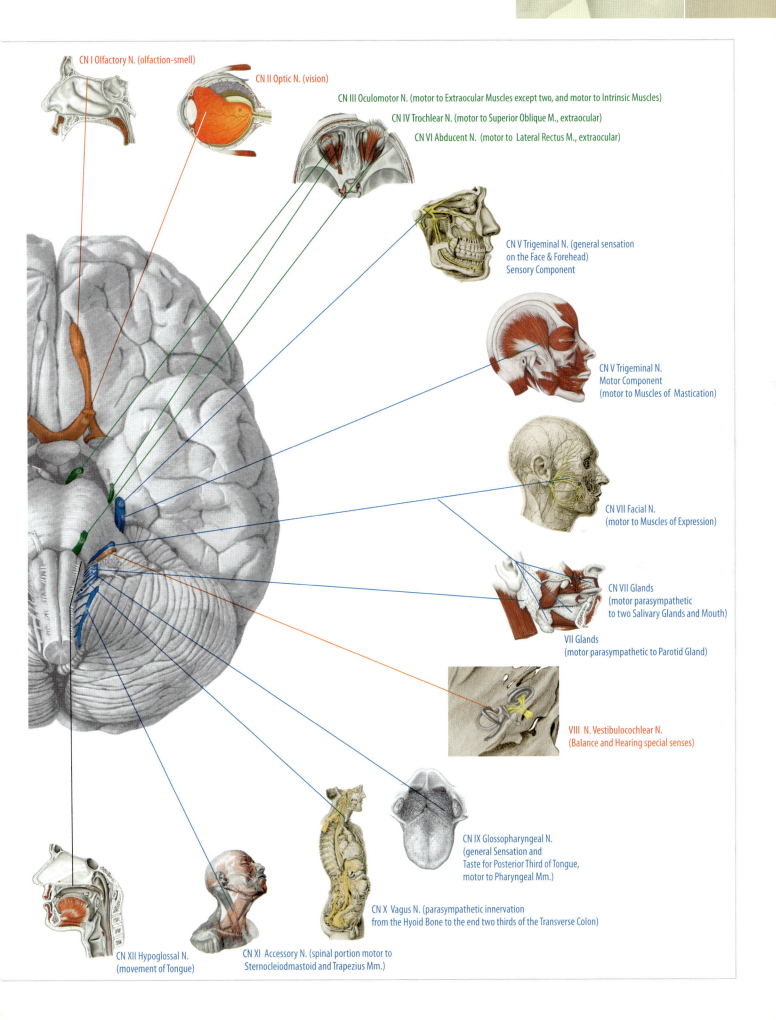

CN I Olfactory N. (olfaction-smell)

CN II Optic N. (vision)

CN III Oculomotor N. (motor to Extraocular Muscles except two, and motor to Intrinsic Muscles)

CN IV Trochlear N. (motor to Superior Oblique M., extraocular)

CN VI Abducent N. (motor to Lateral Rectus M., extraocular)

CN V Trigeminal N. (general sensation on the Face & Forehead) Sensory Component

CN V Trigeminal N. Motor Component (motor to Muscles of Mastication)

CN VII Facial N. (motor to Muscles of Expression)

CN VII Glands (motor parasympathetic to two Salivary Glands and Mouth)

VII Glands (motor parasympathetic to Parotid Gland)

VIII N. Vestibulocochlear N. (Balance and Hearing special senses)

CN IX Glossopharyngeal N. (general Sensation and Taste for Posterior Third of Tongue, motor to Pharyngeal Mm.)

CN X Vagus N. (parasympathetic innervation from the Hyoid Bone to the end two thirds of the Transverse Colon)

CN XII Hypoglossal N. (movement of Tongue)

CN XI Accessory N. (spinal portion motor to Sternocleiodmastoid and Trapezius Mm.)

1.13a,b Vegetative Nervous System, Sympathetic and Parasympathetic Nervous Systems.

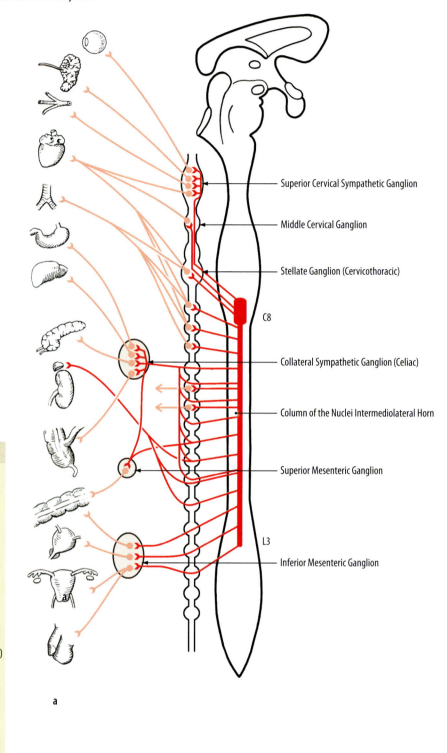

Superior Cervical Sympathetic Ganglion

Middle Cervical Ganglion

Stellate Ganglion (Cervicothoracic)

C8

Collateral Sympathetic Ganglion (Celiac)

Column of the Nuclei Intermediolateral Horn

Superior Mesenteric Ganglion

L3

Inferior Mesenteric Ganglion

a

b

Sympathetic Nervous System

Eye:	Dilator Pupillae M.	▶ Mydriasis
	Tarsal M.	▶ Elevates and depresses the eyelids and widens the palpebral fissure
	Orbitalis M.	▶ Protrusion of the bulb
Salivary Glands:		Watery salivary secretion

Vessels (Skin, Mucous Membrane, Brain; in part, Skeletal Muscles, Intestines):

	Arteries	▶ Vasoconstriction
	Veins	▶ Vasoconstriction
Heart:		
	Coronary Arteries	▶ Vasoconstriction
	Myocardium	▶ Increases heart rate
		▶ Increases power of contraction (ionotropic) of the myocardium
Tracheal & Bronchial Musculature:		▶ Relaxes
Gastrointestinal Tract:		▶ Decreases gland secretion (minor)
		▶ Promotes water resorption
Pancreas (endocrine part):		▶ Decreases insulin secretion
Liver:		▶ Promotes glycogenolysis and gluconeogenesis
Urinary Bladder:		
Internal Sphincter M.		▶ Contraction
Genitals:	Female	▶ Contracts the uterine musculature
	Male	▶ Contracts the smooth musculature of the seminal vesicle, the prostate, and the ductus deferens
Spleen:		▶ Contracts the smooth muscles In the capsule of the spleen
Adrenal Gland:		▶ Secretes adrenalin and noradrenalin

◼ Fig. 5.4

Parasympathetic Nervous System

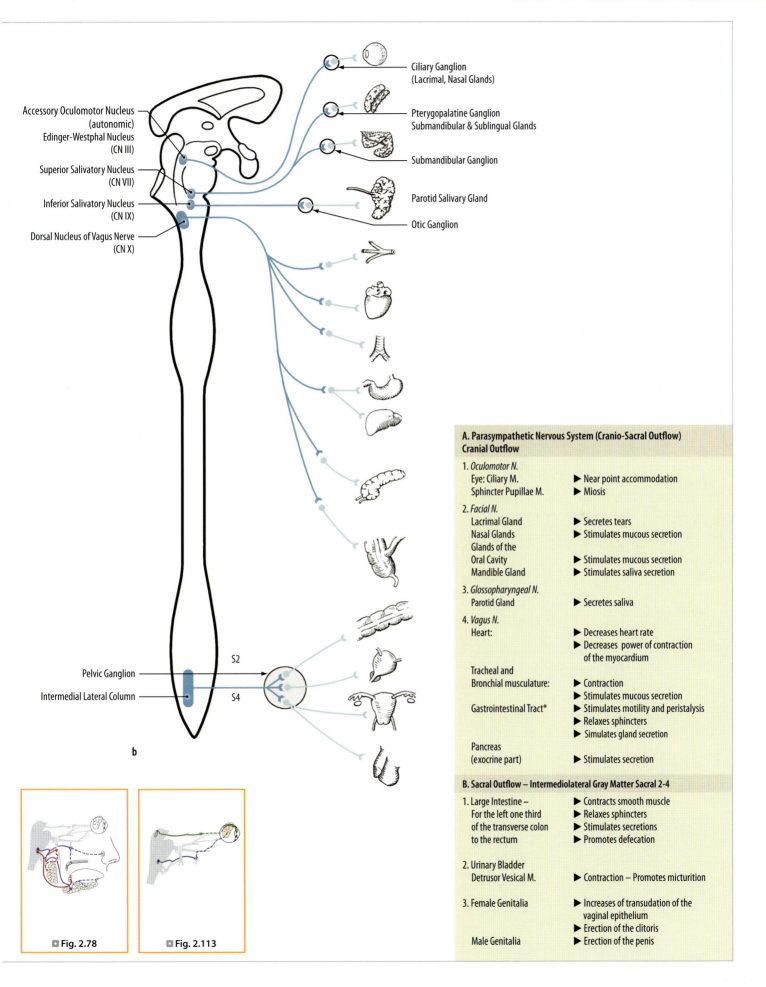

Accessory Oculomotor Nucleus (autonomic)
Edinger-Westphal Nucleus (CN III)

Superior Salivatory Nucleus (CN VII)

Inferior Salivatory Nucleus (CN IX)

Dorsal Nucleus of Vagus Nerve (CN X)

Ciliary Ganglion (Lacrimal, Nasal Glands)

Pterygopalatine Ganglion
Submandibular & Sublingual Glands

Submandibular Ganglion

Parotid Salivary Gland

Otic Ganglion

Pelvic Ganglion

Intermedial Lateral Column

S2

S4

b

□ Fig. 2.78   □ Fig. 2.113

A. Parasympathetic Nervous System (Cranio-Sacral Outflow)
Cranial Outflow

1. *Oculomotor N.*
   Eye: Ciliary M.   ▶ Near point accommodation
   Sphincter Pupillae M.   ▶ Miosis

2. *Facial N.*
   Lacrimal Gland   ▶ Secretes tears
   Nasal Glands   ▶ Stimulates mucous secretion
   Glands of the
   Oral Cavity   ▶ Stimulates mucous secretion
   Mandible Gland   ▶ Stimulates saliva secretion

3. *Glossopharyngeal N.*
   Parotid Gland   ▶ Secretes saliva

4. *Vagus N.*
   Heart: ▶ Decreases heart rate
                              ▶ Decreases power of contraction
                                of the myocardium

   Tracheal and
   Bronchial musculature: ▶ Contraction
                              ▶ Stimulates mucous secretion
   Gastrointestinal Tract*   ▶ Stimulates motility and peristalsis
                              ▶ Relaxes sphincters
                              ▶ Simulates gland secretion

   Pancreas
   (exocrine part)   ▶ Stimulates secretion

B. Sacral Outflow – Intermediolateral Gray Matter Sacral 2-4

1. Large Intestine –   ▶ Contracts smooth muscle
   For the left one third   ▶ Relaxes sphincters
   of the transverse colon   ▶ Stimulates secretions
   to the rectum   ▶ Promotes defecation

2. Urinary Bladder
   Detrusor Vesical M.   ▶ Contraction – Promotes micturition

3. Female Genitalia   ▶ Increases of transudation of the
                                vaginal epithelium
                              ▶ Erection of the clitoris
   Male Genitalia   ▶ Erection of the penis

Skin

1.14a–e Skin (Epidermis and Dermis) and Subcutaneous (Adipose) Tissue.

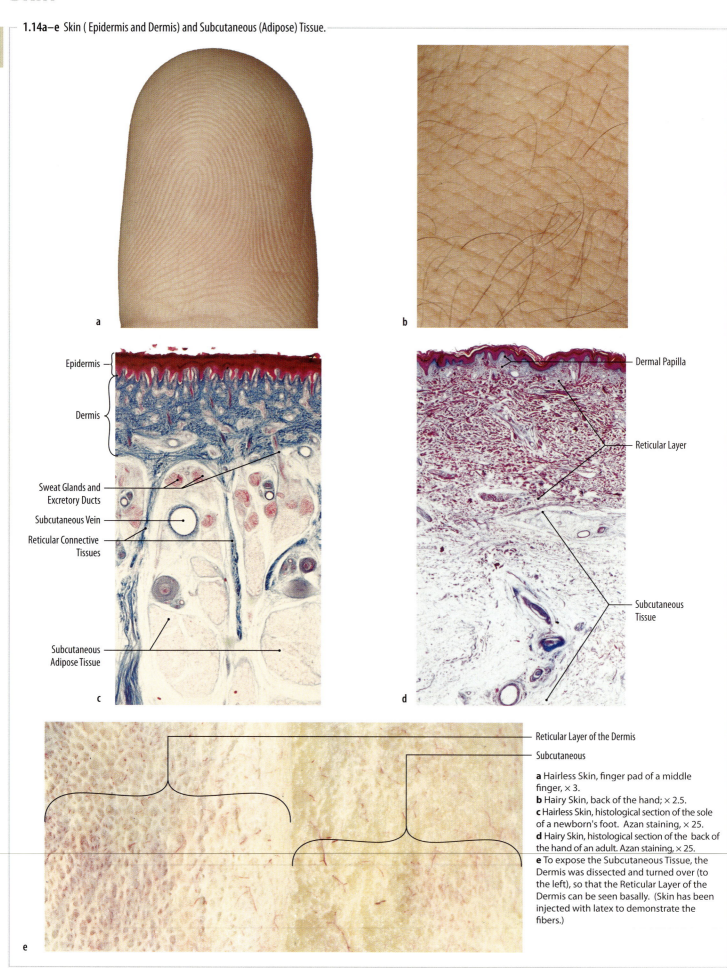

a

b

Epidermis

Dermis

Sweat Glands and
Excretory Ducts

Subcutaneous Vein

Reticular Connective
Tissues

Subcutaneous
Adipose Tissue

c

Dermal Papilla

Reticular Layer

Subcutaneous
Tissue

d

Reticular Layer of the Dermis

Subcutaneous

a Hairless Skin, finger pad of a middle
finger, × 3.
b Hairy Skin, back of the hand; × 2.5.
c Hairless Skin, histological section of the sole
of a newborn's foot. Azan staining, × 25.
d Hairy Skin, histological section of the back of
the hand of an adult. Azan staining, × 25.
e To expose the Subcutaneous Tissue, the
Dermis was dissected and turned over (to
the left), so that the Reticular Layer of the
Dermis can be seen basally. (Skin has been
injected with latex to demonstrate the
fibers.)

e

Head

Skull: Osteogenesis

2.1a–c Fetal Skull (7th Fetal Month): Skeleton Ligament Preparation. [8]

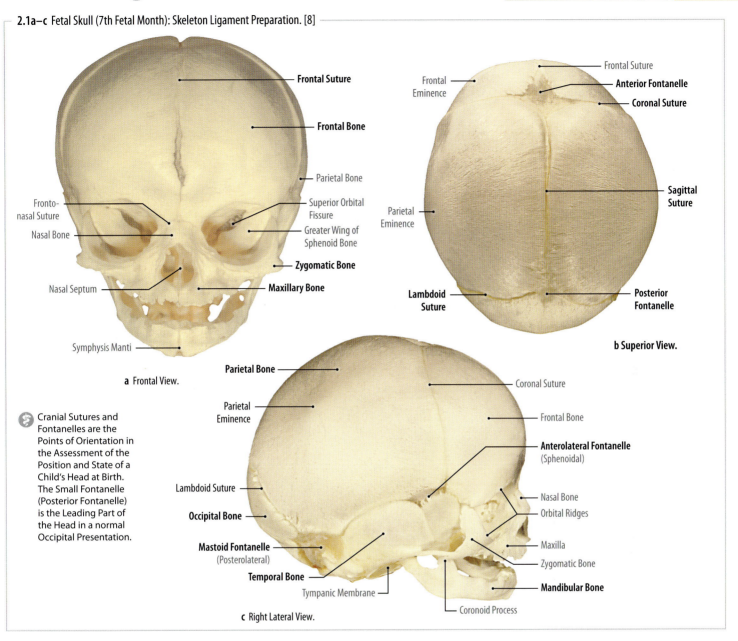

a Frontal View.

Frontal Suture
Frontal Bone
Parietal Bone
Fronto-nasal Suture
Nasal Bone
Superior Orbital Fissure
Greater Wing of Sphenoid Bone
Zygomatic Bone
Nasal Septum
Maxillary Bone
Symphysis Manti

b Superior View.

Frontal Eminence
Frontal Suture
Anterior Fontanelle
Coronal Suture
Parietal Eminence
Sagittal Suture
Lambdoid Suture
Posterior Fontanelle

c Right Lateral View.

Parietal Bone
Parietal Eminence
Coronal Suture
Frontal Bone
Anterolateral Fontanelle (Sphenoidal)
Lambdoid Suture
Nasal Bone
Occipital Bone
Orbital Ridges
Mastoid Fontanelle (Posterolateral)
Maxilla
Temporal Bone
Zygomatic Bone
Tympanic Membrane
Mandibular Bone
Coronoid Process

Cranial Sutures and Fontanelles are the Points of Orientation in the Assessment of the Position and State of a Child's Head at Birth. The Small Fontanelle (Posterior Fontanelle) is the Leading Part of the Head in a normal Occipital Presentation.

2.2 Classification of Cranial Bones and the Type of Osteogenesis.

Cranial Bones (Skull or Cranium)*		
Bones of the Cranium (Neurocranium)		**Bones of the Facial Skeleton (Viscerocranium)**
Frontal Bone	M	**Bones of the Nasal Skeleton**
Parietal Bone	M	– Ethmoid Bone ch
Occipital Bone	M and ch	– Nasal Bone M
Sphenoid Bone	M and ch	– Lacrimal Bone M
Temporal Bone	M and ch	– Inferior Nasal Concha ch
		– Vomer Bone M
		Bones of the Jaw Skeleton
Auditory Ossicles (Auditus/Auditoria)		– Upper Jaw Bone (Maxilla) M
		– Palatine Bone M
Hammer (Malleus)	ch	– Zygomatic Bone M
Incus	ch	– Lower Jaw Bone (Mandible) M and ch**
Stirrups (Stapes)	ch	– Hyoid Bone ch

◻ Fig. 5.180a

M: Membranous (Dermal) Ossification; ch: Chondral Ossification
*   In the literature, the Bones of the Cranium and Part of the Nasal Skeleton are Grouped Together Under the Cranium, and the Bones of the Jaw are Designated as Facial Bone.
** The Secondary Cartilage Areas of the Mandible Ossify Chondrally.
     Hyoid Bone and Auditory Ossicles Emanate from the Skeletal Parts of Meckel's Cartilage, Reichert's Cartilage, and the Pharyngeal Arch.

Skeleton and Joints

2.3 Skull: Frontal Anterior View. [6]

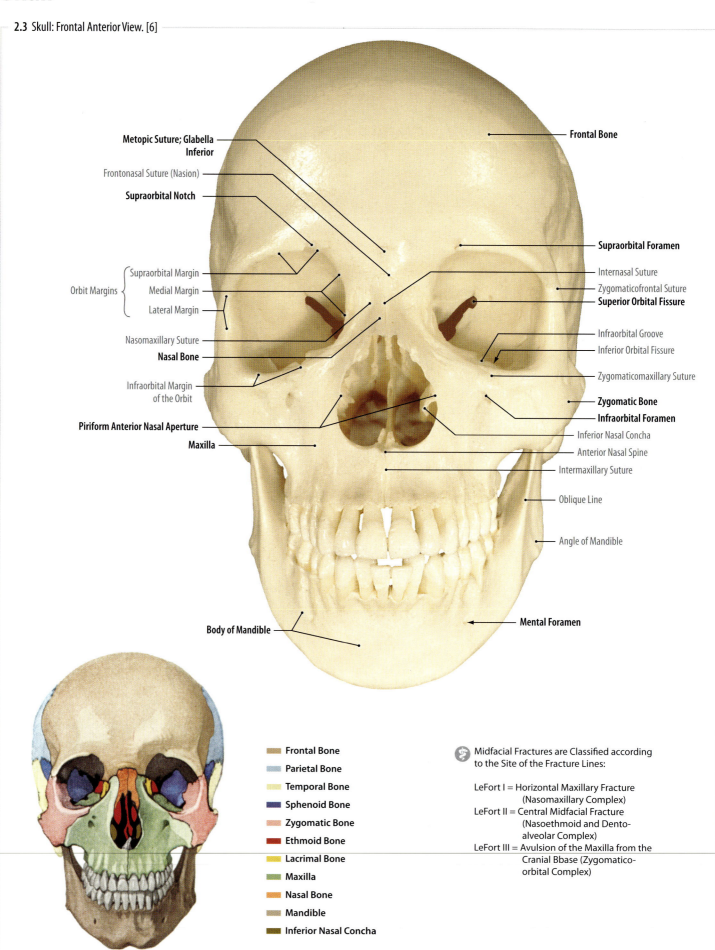

Metopic Suture; Glabella
Inferior

Frontonasal Suture (Nasion)

Supraorbital Notch

Orbit Margins { Supraorbital Margin
Medial Margin
Lateral Margin }

Nasomaxillary Suture

Nasal Bone

Infraorbital Margin
of the Orbit

Piriform Anterior Nasal Aperture

Maxilla

Body of Mandible

Frontal Bone

Supraorbital Foramen

Internasal Suture

Zygomaticofrontal Suture

Superior Orbital Fissure

Infraorbital Groove

Inferior Orbital Fissure

Zygomaticomaxillary Suture

Zygomatic Bone

Infraorbital Foramen

Inferior Nasal Concha

Anterior Nasal Spine

Intermaxillary Suture

Oblique Line

Angle of Mandible

Mental Foramen

Frontal Bone

Parietal Bone

Temporal Bone

Sphenoid Bone

Zygomatic Bone

Ethmoid Bone

Lacrimal Bone

Maxilla

Nasal Bone

Mandible

Inferior Nasal Concha

Midfacial Fractures are Classified according
to the Site of the Fracture Lines:

LeFort I = Horizontal Maxillary Fracture
(Nasomaxillary Complex)
LeFort II = Central Midfacial Fracture
(Nasoethmoid and Dento-
alveolar Complex)
LeFort III = Avulsion of the Maxilla from the
Cranial Bbase (Zygomatico-
orbital Complex)

Skull

2.4 Skull: Right Lateral View. [6]

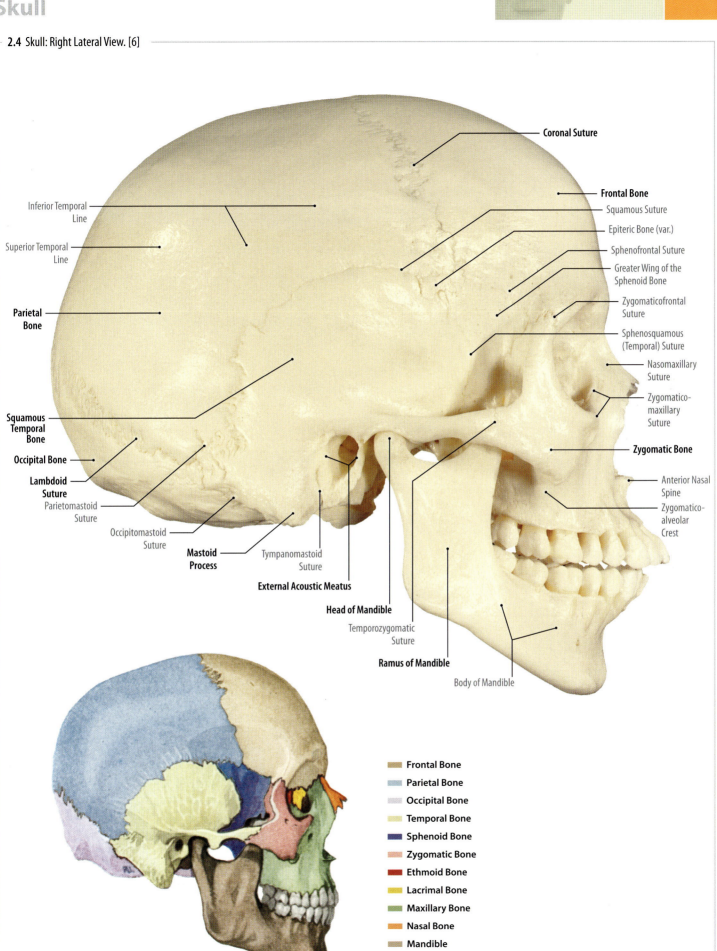

Coronal Suture

Frontal Bone

Squamous Suture

Epiteric Bone (var.)

Sphenofrontal Suture

Greater Wing of the Sphenoid Bone

Zygomaticofrontal Suture

Sphenosquamous (Temporal) Suture

Nasomaxillary Suture

Zygomatico-maxillary Suture

Zygomatic Bone

Anterior Nasal Spine

Zygomatico-alveolar Crest

Inferior Temporal Line

Superior Temporal Line

Parietal Bone

Squamous Temporal Bone

Occipital Bone

Lambdoid Suture

Parietomastoid Suture

Occipitomastoid Suture

Mastoid Process

Tympanomastoid Suture

External Acoustic Meatus

Head of Mandible

Temporozygomatic Suture

Ramus of Mandible

Body of Mandible

- Frontal Bone
- Parietal Bone
- Occipital Bone
- Temporal Bone
- Sphenoid Bone
- Zygomatic Bone
- Ethmoid Bone
- Lacrimal Bone
- Maxillary Bone
- Nasal Bone
- Mandible

Skeleton and Joints

Reference Planes, Anthropological Measuring Points

2.5a–d Skull: Reference Planes (**a**) and Anthropological Measuring Points (**b–d**).

The Tragal-Canthus Plane, Frankfort Horizontal Plane, Camper's Plane, and Mastication Plane are reference planes in dental reconstruction and in the construction of a dental prosthesis.

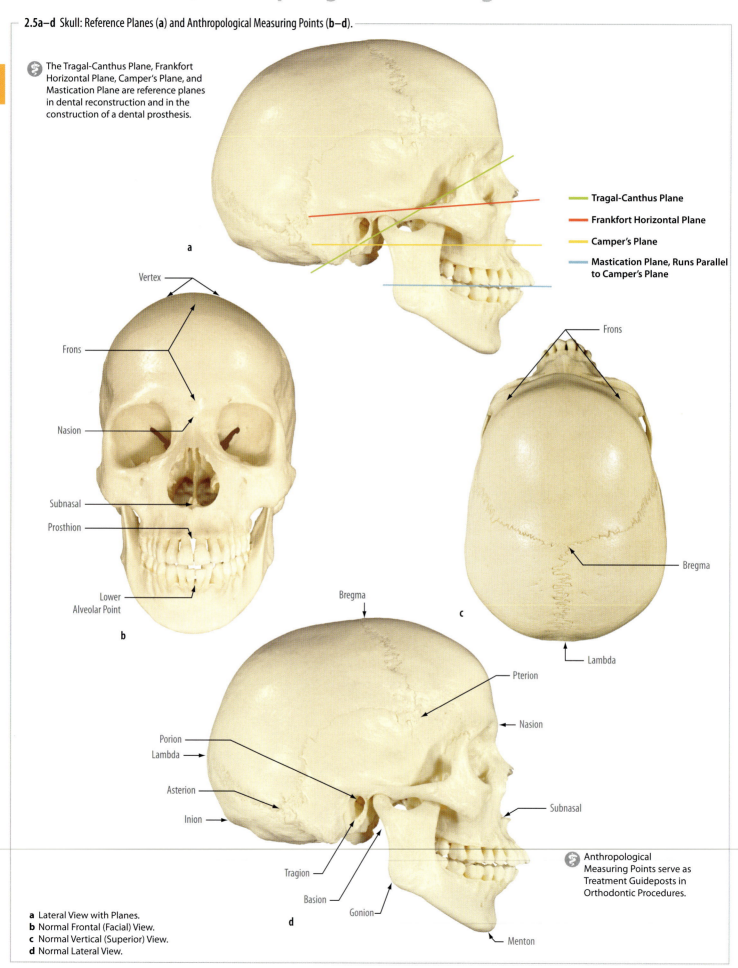

Tragal-Canthus Plane
Frankfort Horizontal Plane
Camper's Plane
Mastication Plane, Runs Parallel to Camper's Plane

Vertex
Frons
Nasion
Subnasal
Prosthion
Lower Alveolar Point
b
a

Frons
Bregma
Lambda
c

Bregma
Pterion
Nasion
Porion
Lambda
Asterion
Inion
Tragion
Basion
Subnasal
Gonion
Menton
d

Anthropological Measuring Points serve as Treatment Guideposts in Orthodontic Procedures.

a Lateral View with Planes.
b Normal Frontal (Facial) View.
c Normal Vertical (Superior) View.
d Normal Lateral View.

2.6a,b Cranial Bone Structure. [8]

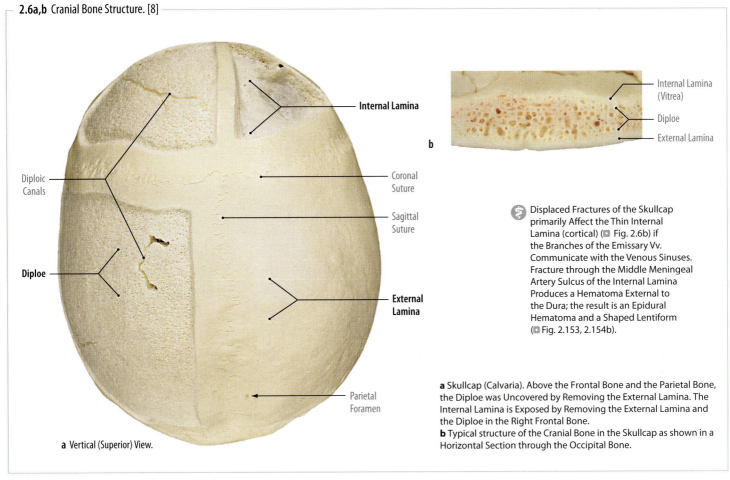

Internal Lamina

Diploic Canals

Diploe

Coronal Suture

Sagittal Suture

External Lamina

Parietal Foramen

a Vertical (Superior) View.

b

Internal Lamina (Vitrea)

Diploe

External Lamina

Displaced Fractures of the Skullcap primarily Affect the Thin Internal Lamina (cortical) (☐ Fig. 2.6b) if the Branches of the Emissary Vv. Communicate with the Venous Sinuses. Fracture through the Middle Meningeal Artery Sulcus of the Internal Lamina Produces a Hematoma External to the Dura; the result is an Epidural Hematoma and a Shaped Lentiform (☐ Fig. 2.153, 2.154b).

a Skullcap (Calvaria). Above the Frontal Bone and the Parietal Bone, the Diploe was Uncovered by Removing the External Lamina. The Internal Lamina is Exposed by Removing the External Lamina and the Diploe in the Right Frontal Bone.
b Typical structure of the Cranial Bone in the Skullcap as shown in a Horizontal Section through the Occipital Bone.

2.7 Skullcap (Calvaria): Internal Surface. [6]

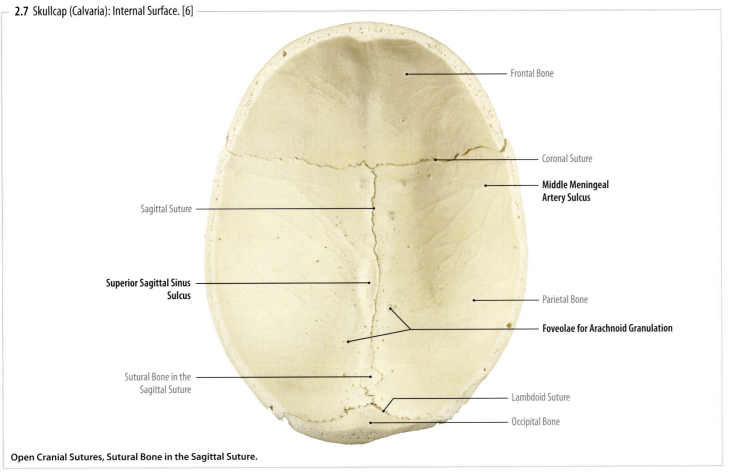

Frontal Bone

Coronal Suture

Middle Meningeal Artery Sulcus

Sagittal Suture

Superior Sagittal Sinus Sulcus

Parietal Bone

Foveolae for Arachnoid Granulation

Sutural Bone in the Sagittal Suture

Lambdoid Suture

Occipital Bone

Open Cranial Sutures, Sutural Bone in the Sagittal Suture.

Skeleton and Joints

2.8 Exterior Cranial Base: Inferior View. [6]

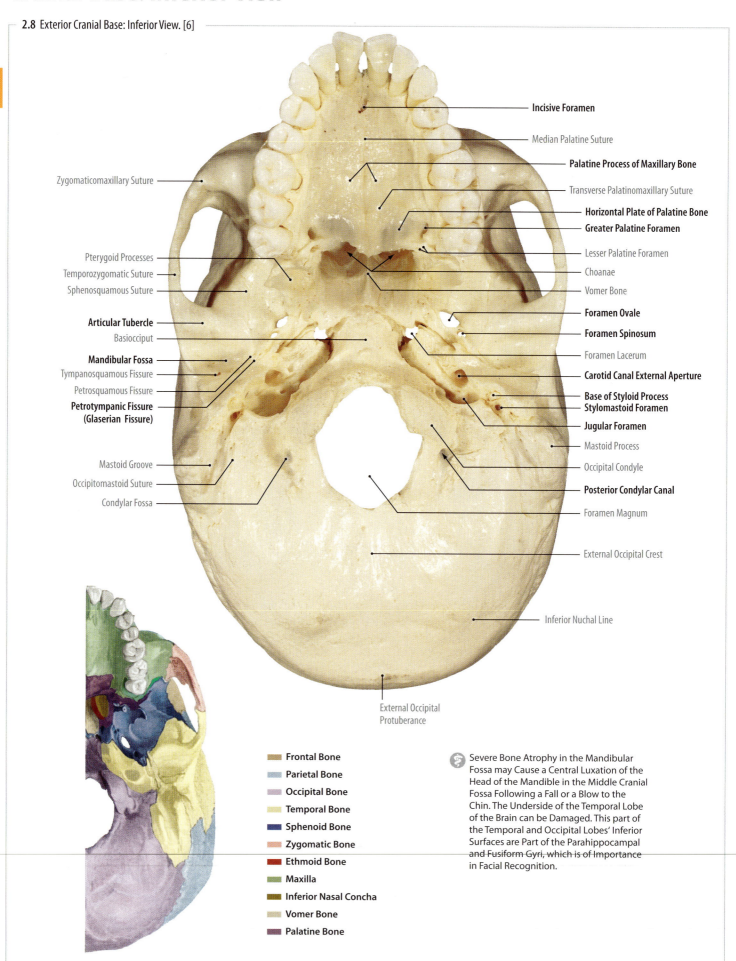

Incisive Foramen

Median Palatine Suture

Palatine Process of Maxillary Bone

Transverse Palatinomaxillary Suture

Horizontal Plate of Palatine Bone

Greater Palatine Foramen

Lesser Palatine Foramen

Choanae

Vomer Bone

Foramen Ovale

Foramen Spinosum

Foramen Lacerum

Carotid Canal External Aperture

Base of Styloid Process
Stylomastoid Foramen

Jugular Foramen

Mastoid Process

Occipital Condyle

Posterior Condylar Canal

Foramen Magnum

External Occipital Crest

Inferior Nuchal Line

External Occipital
Protuberance

Zygomaticomaxillary Suture

Pterygoid Processes
Temporozygomatic Suture
Sphenosquamous Suture

Articular Tubercle
Basiocciput

Mandibular Fossa
Tympanosquamous Fissure
Petrosquamous Fissure
Petrotympanic Fissure
(Glaserian Fissure)

Mastoid Groove
Occipitomastoid Suture
Condylar Fossa

Frontal Bone

Parietal Bone

Occipital Bone

Temporal Bone

Sphenoid Bone

Zygomatic Bone

Ethmoid Bone

Maxilla

Inferior Nasal Concha

Vomer Bone

Palatine Bone

Severe Bone Atrophy in the Mandibular Fossa may Cause a Central Luxation of the Head of the Mandible in the Middle Cranial Fossa Following a Fall or a Blow to the Chin. The Underside of the Temporal Lobe of the Brain can be Damaged. This part of the Temporal and Occipital Lobes' Inferior Surfaces are Part of the Parahippocampal and Fusiform Gyri, which is of Importance in Facial Recognition.

Cranial Fossae: Interior View

2.9 Interior Cranial Fossae: Vertical View. [6]

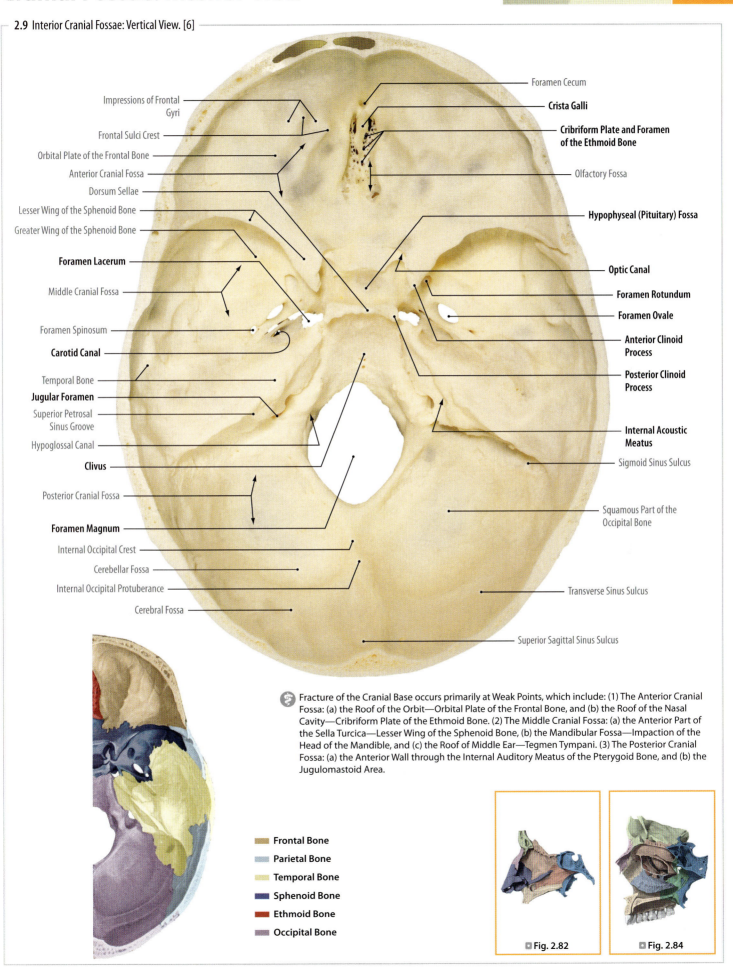

Impressions of Frontal Gyri

Frontal Sulci Crest

Orbital Plate of the Frontal Bone

Anterior Cranial Fossa

Dorsum Sellae

Lesser Wing of the Sphenoid Bone

Greater Wing of the Sphenoid Bone

Foramen Lacerum

Middle Cranial Fossa

Foramen Spinosum

Carotid Canal

Temporal Bone

Jugular Foramen

Superior Petrosal Sinus Groove

Hypoglossal Canal

Clivus

Posterior Cranial Fossa

Foramen Magnum

Internal Occipital Crest

Cerebellar Fossa

Internal Occipital Protuberance

Cerebral Fossa

Foramen Cecum

Crista Galli

Cribriform Plate and Foramen of the Ethmoid Bone

Olfactory Fossa

Hypophyseal (Pituitary) Fossa

Optic Canal

Foramen Rotundum

Foramen Ovale

Anterior Clinoid Process

Posterior Clinoid Process

Internal Acoustic Meatus

Sigmoid Sinus Sulcus

Squamous Part of the Occipital Bone

Transverse Sinus Sulcus

Superior Sagittal Sinus Sulcus

Fracture of the Cranial Base occurs primarily at Weak Points, which include: (1) The Anterior Cranial Fossa: (a) the Roof of the Orbit—Orbital Plate of the Frontal Bone, and (b) the Roof of the Nasal Cavity—Cribriform Plate of the Ethmoid Bone. (2) The Middle Cranial Fossa: (a) the Anterior Part of the Sella Turcica—Lesser Wing of the Sphenoid Bone, (b) the Mandibular Fossa—Impaction of the Head of the Mandible, and (c) the Roof of Middle Ear—Tegmen Tympani. (3) The Posterior Cranial Fossa: (a) the Anterior Wall through the Internal Auditory Meatus of the Pterygoid Bone, and (b) the Jugulomastoid Area.

Frontal Bone

Parietal Bone

Temporal Bone

Sphenoid Bone

Ethmoid Bone

Occipital Bone

Fig. 2.82   Fig. 2.84

Skeleton and Joints

2.10 Disarticulated Skull: Bones of the Cranial Fossae, Vertical View. [9]

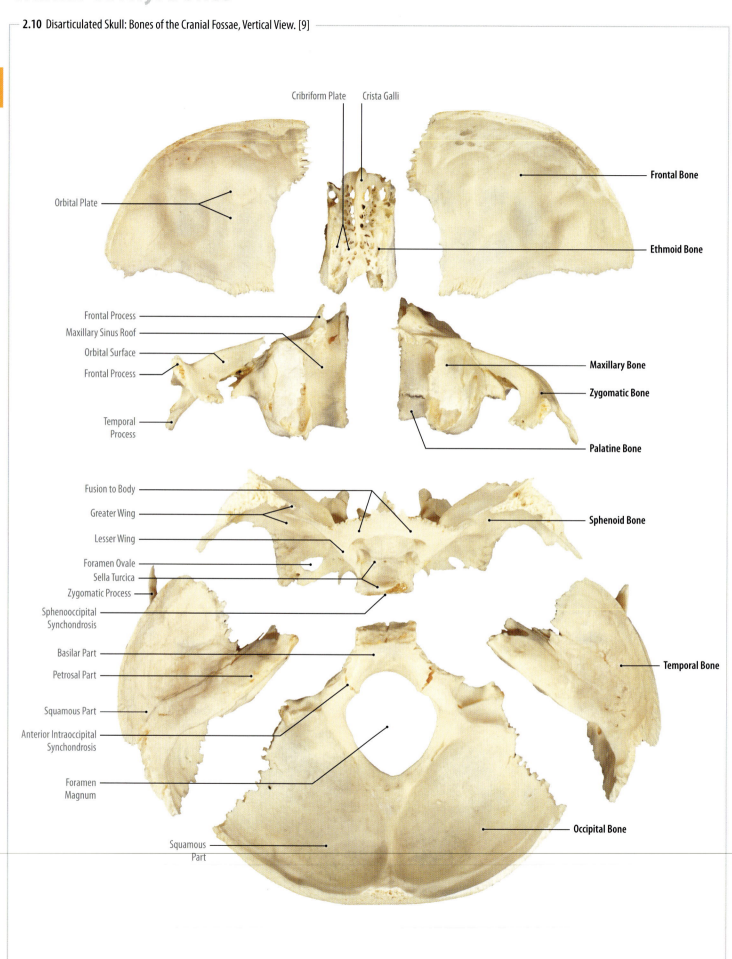

Cribriform Plate

Crista Galli

Frontal Bone

Orbital Plate

Ethmoid Bone

Frontal Process

Maxillary Sinus Roof

Orbital Surface

Frontal Process

Maxillary Bone

Zygomatic Bone

Temporal Process

Palatine Bone

Fusion to Body

Greater Wing

Lesser Wing

Sphenoid Bone

Foramen Ovale

Sella Turcica

Zygomatic Process

Sphenooccipital Synchondrosis

Basilar Part

Petrosal Part

Temporal Bone

Squamous Part

Anterior Intraoccipital Synchondrosis

Foramen Magnum

Occipital Bone

Squamous Part

Frontal Bone

2.11a–c Frontal Bone. [9]

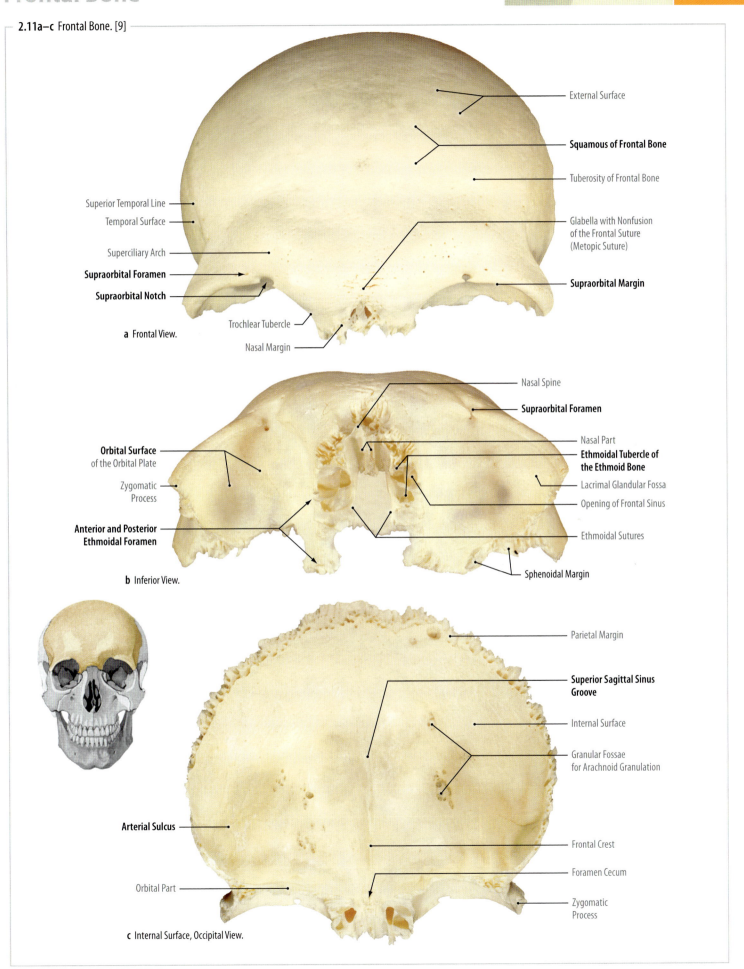

External Surface

Squamous of Frontal Bone

Tuberosity of Frontal Bone

Glabella with Nonfusion
of the Frontal Suture
(Metopic Suture)

Supraorbital Margin

Superior Temporal Line

Temporal Surface

Superciliary Arch

Supraorbital Foramen

Supraorbital Notch

Trochlear Tubercle

Nasal Margin

a Frontal View.

Nasal Spine

Supraorbital Foramen

Nasal Part

**Ethmoidal Tubercle of
the Ethmoid Bone**

Lacrimal Glandular Fossa

Opening of Frontal Sinus

Ethmoidal Sutures

Sphenoidal Margin

Orbital Surface
of the Orbital Plate

Zygomatic
Process

**Anterior and Posterior
Ethmoidal Foramen**

b Inferior View.

Parietal Margin

**Superior Sagittal Sinus
Groove**

Internal Surface

Granular Fossae
for Arachnoid Granulation

Arterial Sulcus

Orbital Part

Frontal Crest

Foramen Cecum

Zygomatic
Process

c Internal Surface, Occipital View.

Skeleton and Joints

Parietal Bone

2.12a,b Left Parietal Bone. [9]

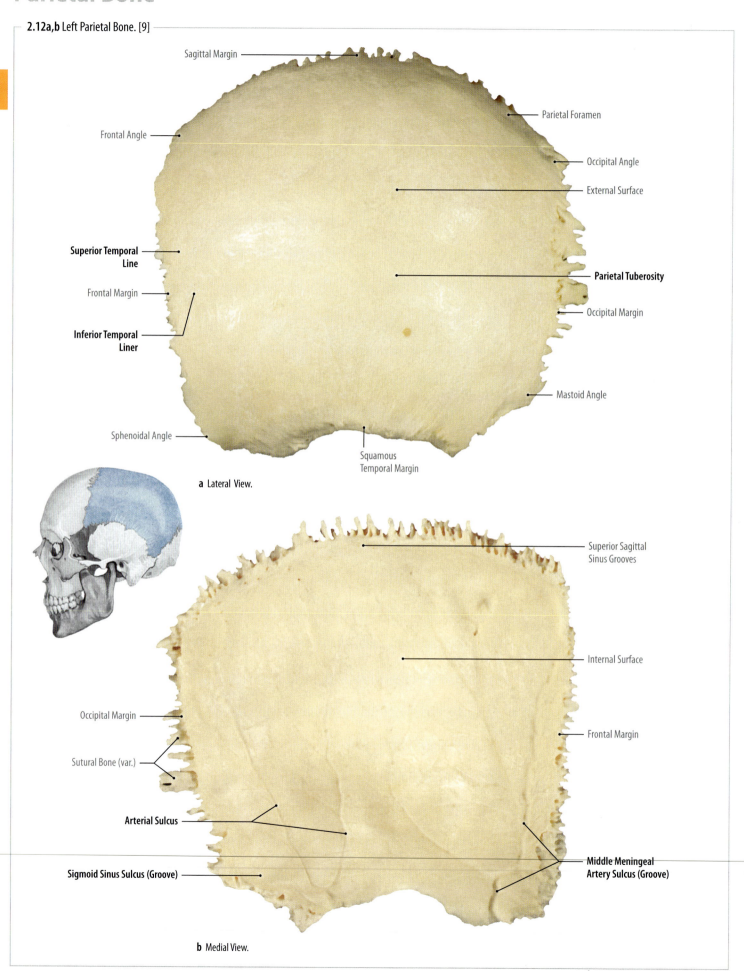

Sagittal Margin

Frontal Angle

Superior Temporal
Line

Frontal Margin

**Inferior Temporal
Liner**

Sphenoidal Angle

Parietal Foramen

Occipital Angle

External Surface

Parietal Tuberosity

Occipital Margin

Mastoid Angle

Squamous
Temporal Margin

a Lateral View.

Superior Sagittal
Sinus Grooves

Occipital Margin

Internal Surface

Sutural Bone (var.)

Frontal Margin

Arterial Sulcus

**Middle Meningeal
Artery Sulcus (Groove)**

Sigmoid Sinus Sulcus (Groove)

b Medial View.

Temporal Bone

2.13a,b Left Temporal Bone. [9]

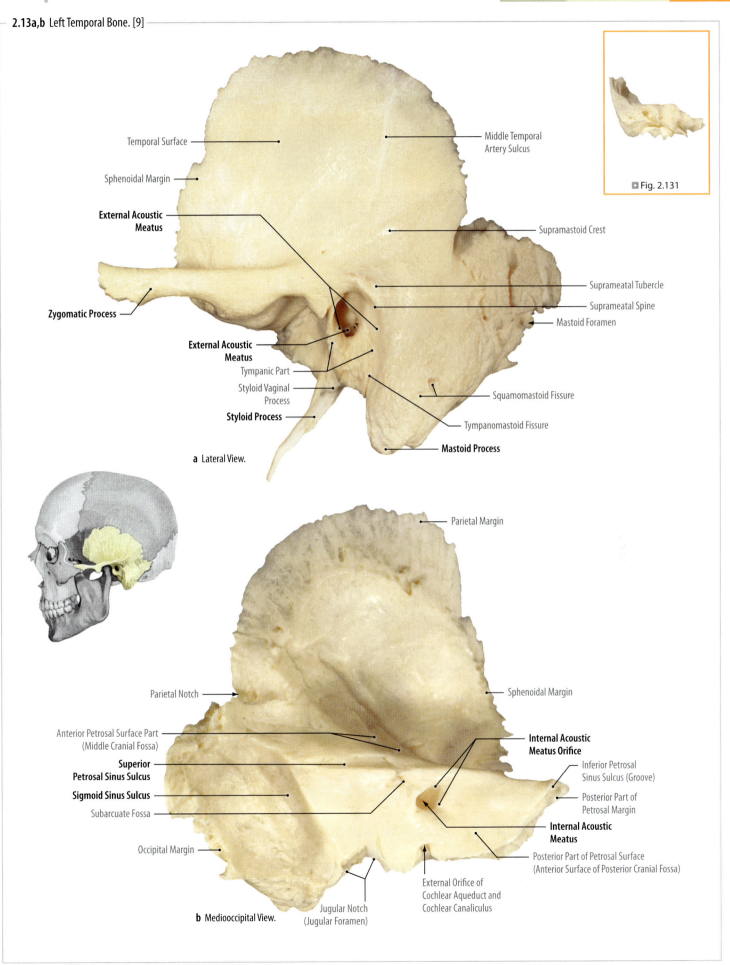

Temporal Surface

Sphenoidal Margin

External Acoustic Meatus

Zygomatic Process

External Acoustic Meatus

Tympanic Part

Styloid Vaginal Process

Styloid Process

a Lateral View.

Middle Temporal Artery Sulcus

☐ Fig. 2.131

Supramastoid Crest

Suprameatal Tubercle

Suprameatal Spine

Mastoid Foramen

Squamomastoid Fissure

Tympanomastoid Fissure

Mastoid Process

Parietal Margin

Parietal Notch

Anterior Petrosal Surface Part (Middle Cranial Fossa)

Superior Petrosal Sinus Sulcus

Sigmoid Sinus Sulcus

Subarcuate Fossa

Occipital Margin

Sphenoidal Margin

Internal Acoustic Meatus Orifice

Inferior Petrosal Sinus Sulcus (Groove)

Posterior Part of Petrosal Margin

Internal Acoustic Meatus

Posterior Part of Petrosal Surface (Anterior Surface of Posterior Cranial Fossa)

b Medioccipital View.

Jugular Notch (Jugular Foramen)

External Orifice of Cochlear Aqueduct and Cochlear Canaliculus

Skeleton and Joints

Occipital Bone

2.14a,b Occipital Bone. [9]

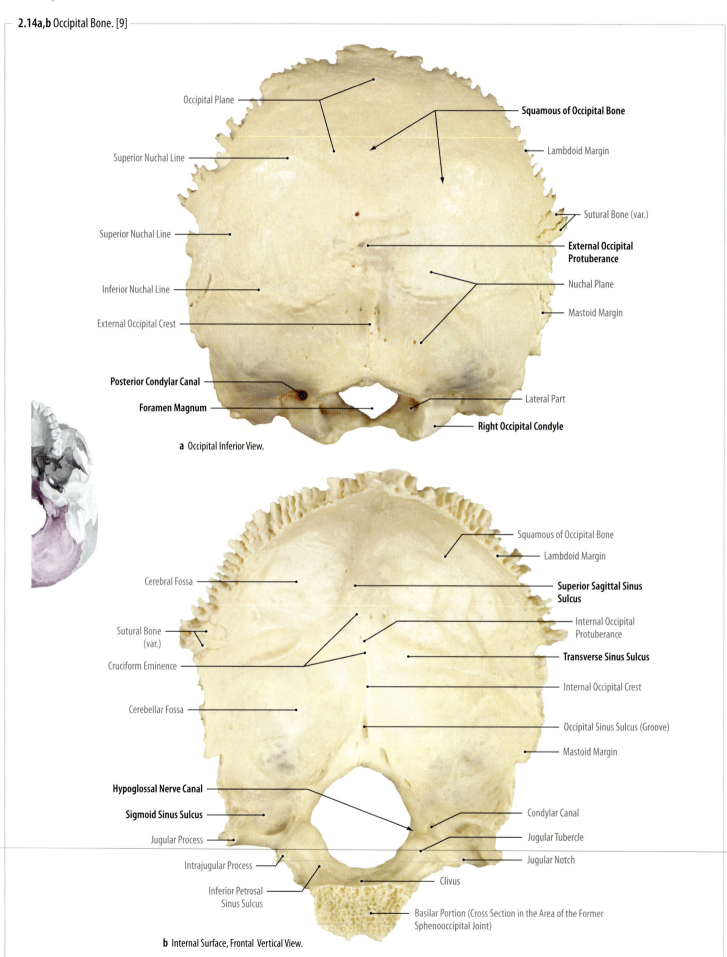

Occipital Plane

Squamous of Occipital Bone

Superior Nuchal Line

Lambdoid Margin

Sutural Bone (var.)

Superior Nuchal Line

External Occipital Protuberance

Inferior Nuchal Line

Nuchal Plane

External Occipital Crest

Mastoid Margin

Posterior Condylar Canal

Foramen Magnum

Lateral Part

Right Occipital Condyle

a Occipital Inferior View.

Squamous of Occipital Bone

Lambdoid Margin

Cerebral Fossa

Superior Sagittal Sinus Sulcus

Sutural Bone (var.)

Internal Occipital Protuberance

Cruciform Eminence

Transverse Sinus Sulcus

Cerebellar Fossa

Internal Occipital Crest

Occipital Sinus Sulcus (Groove)

Mastoid Margin

Hypoglossal Nerve Canal

Sigmoid Sinus Sulcus

Condylar Canal

Jugular Process

Jugular Tubercle

Intrajugular Process

Jugular Notch

Inferior Petrosal Sinus Sulcus

Clivus

Basilar Portion (Cross Section in the Area of the Former Sphenooccipital Joint)

b Internal Surface, Frontal Vertical View.

Sphenoid Bone

2.15a–c Sphenoid Bone. [9]

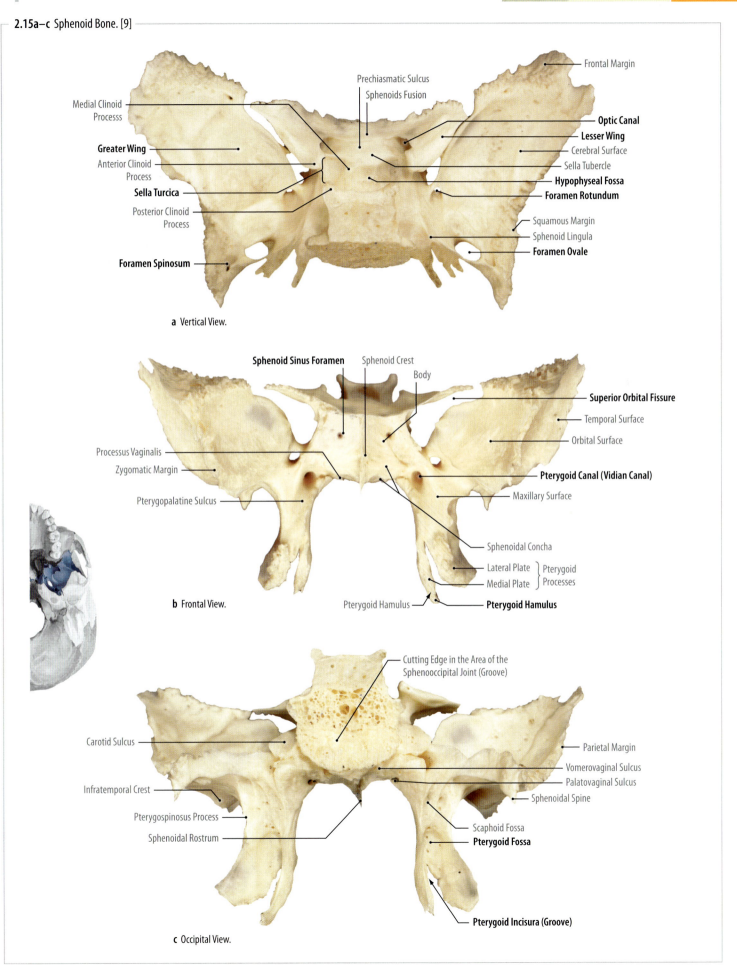

Frontal Margin

Prechiasmatic Sulcus
Sphenoids Fusion

Medial Clinoid
Processs

Optic Canal

Lesser Wing

Cerebral Surface

Greater Wing

Sella Tubercle

Anterior Clinoid
Process

Hypophyseal Fossa

Sella Turcica

Foramen Rotundum

Posterior Clinoid
Process

Squamous Margin

Sphenoid Lingula

Foramen Ovale

Foramen Spinosum

a Vertical View.

Sphenoid Sinus Foramen Sphenoid Crest
Body

Superior Orbital Fissure

Temporal Surface

Orbital Surface

Processus Vaginalis

Zygomatic Margin

Pterygoid Canal (Vidian Canal)

Pterygopalatine Sulcus

Maxillary Surface

Sphenoidal Concha

Lateral Plate } Pterygoid
Medial Plate } Processes

b Frontal View.

Pterygoid Hamulus

Pterygoid Hamulus

Cutting Edge in the Area of the
Sphenooccipital Joint (Groove)

Carotid Sulcus

Parietal Margin

Vomerovaginal Sulcus

Palatovaginal Sulcus

Infratemporal Crest

Sphenoidal Spine

Pterygospinosus Process

Sphenoidal Rostrum

Scaphoid Fossa

Pterygoid Fossa

Pterygoid Incisura (Groove)

c Occipital View.

Skeleton and Joints

Ethmoid Bone · Nasal Concha · Lacrimal Bone

2.16a–c Ethmoid Bone. [9]

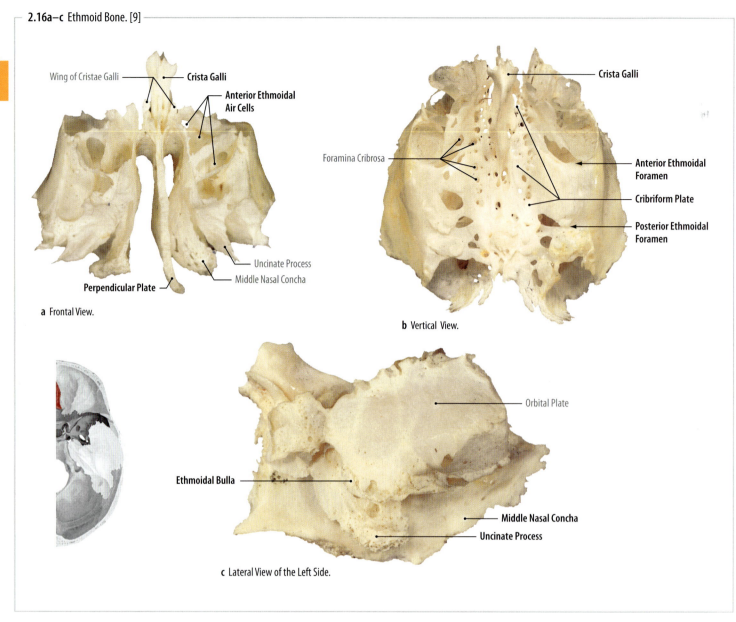

Wing of Cristae Galli — **Crista Galli**

Anterior Ethmoidal Air Cells

Perpendicular Plate

Uncinate Process

Middle Nasal Concha

a Frontal View.

Crista Galli

Foramina Cribrosa

Anterior Ethmoidal Foramen

Cribriform Plate

Posterior Ethmoidal Foramen

b Vertical View.

Orbital Plate

Ethmoidal Bulla

Middle Nasal Concha

Uncinate Process

c Lateral View of the Left Side.

2.17 Right Inferior Nasal Concha: Lateral Surface View. [9]

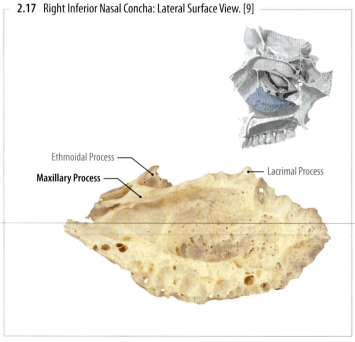

Ethmoidal Process

Maxillary Process

Lacrimal Process

2.18 Right Lacrimal Bone: Anterolateral View. [6]

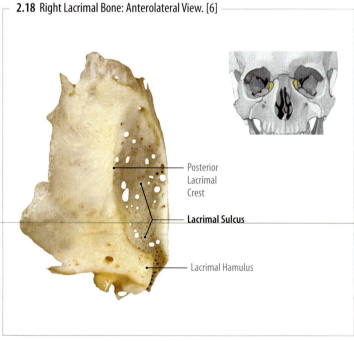

Posterior Lacrimal Crest

Lacrimal Sulcus

Lacrimal Hamulus

Vomer Bone · Nasal Bone · Zygomatic Bone

2.19 Vomer Bone: Left Lateral Surface, Lateral View. [6]

Vomer Cuneiform Processs

Vomer Wing

Vomer Choanal Crest

Vomer Sulcus

2.20a,b Right Nasal Bone. [9]

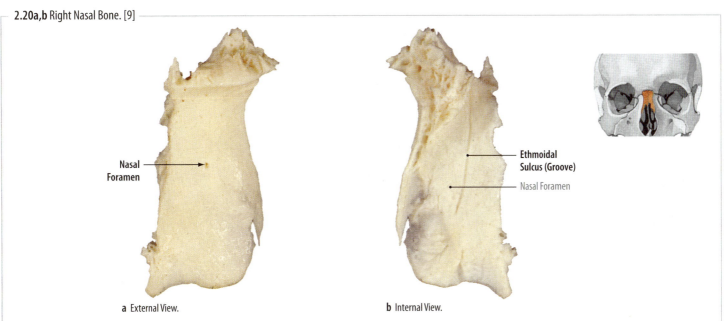

Nasal Foramen

Ethmoidal Sulcus (Groove)

Nasal Foramen

a External View.

b Internal View.

2.21a,b Right Zygomatic Bone. [9]

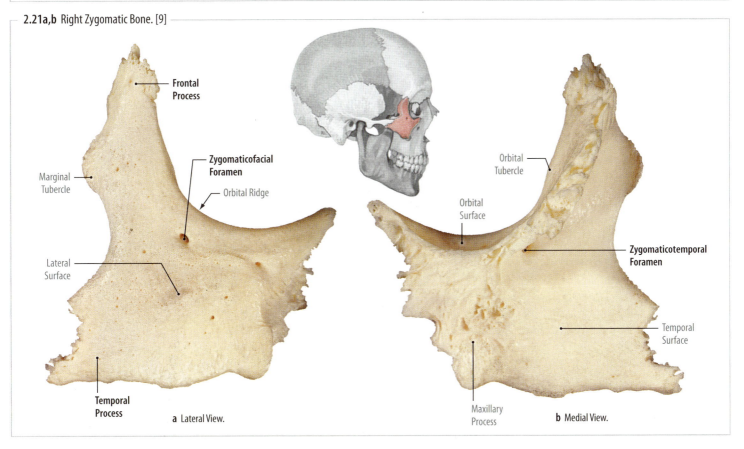

Frontal Process

Marginal Tubercle

Zygomaticofacial Foramen

Orbital Ridge

Lateral Surface

Orbital Tubercle

Orbital Surface

Zygomaticotemporal Foramen

Temporal Surface

Temporal Process

Maxillary Process

a Lateral View.

b Medial View.

Skeleton and Joints

2.22a–c Right Palatine Bone. [9]

2

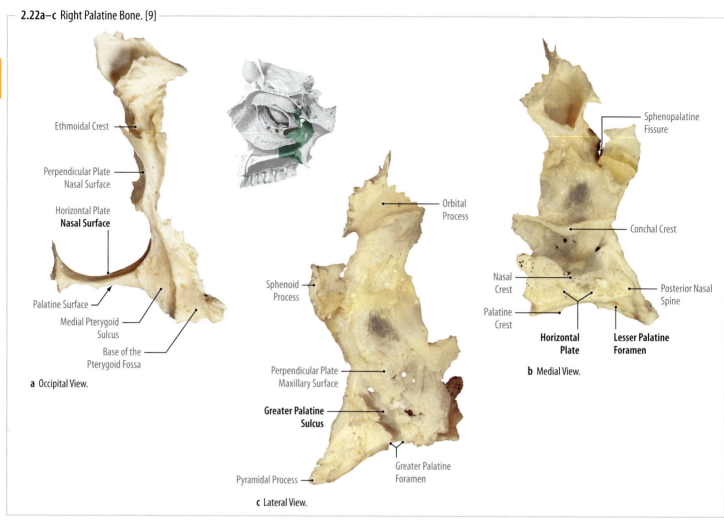

Ethmoidal Crest

Perpendicular Plate
Nasal Surface

Horizontal Plate
Nasal Surface

Palatine Surface

Medial Pterygoid
Sulcus

Base of the
Pterygoid Fossa

a Occipital View.

Orbital
Process

Sphenoid
Process

Perpendicular Plate
Maxillary Surface

**Greater Palatine
Sulcus**

Pyramidal Process

Greater Palatine
Foramen

c Lateral View.

Sphenopalatine
Fissure

Conchal Crest

Nasal
Crest

Palatine
Crest

**Horizontal
Plate**

**Lesser Palatine
Foramen**

Posterior Nasal
Spine

b Medial View.

2.23a,b Right Upper Jaw (Maxilla). [9]

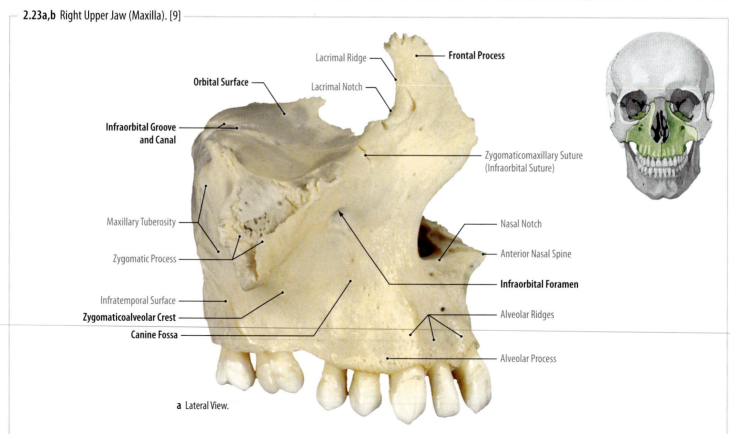

Lacrimal Ridge

Frontal Process

Orbital Surface

Lacrimal Notch

**Infraorbital Groove
and Canal**

Zygomaticomaxillary Suture
(Infraorbital Suture)

Maxillary Tuberosity

Zygomatic Process

Nasal Notch

Anterior Nasal Spine

Infraorbital Foramen

Infratemporal Surface

Zygomaticoalveolar Crest

Canine Fossa

Alveolar Ridges

Alveolar Process

a Lateral View.

Maxilla · Mandible

2.23a,b Right Upper Jaw (Maxilla). [9]

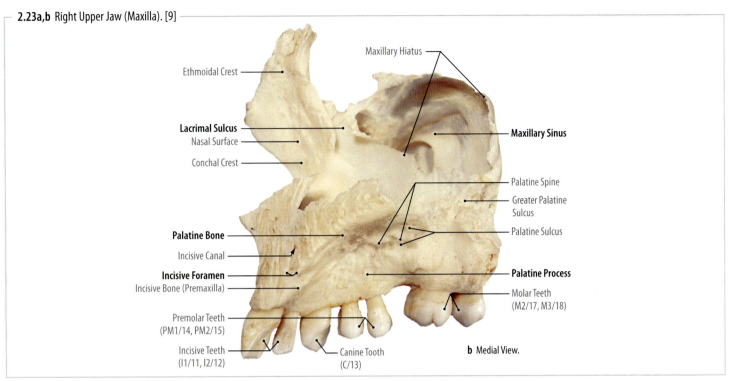

Ethmoidal Crest

Maxillary Hiatus

Lacrimal Sulcus
Nasal Surface
Conchal Crest

Maxillary Sinus

Palatine Spine
Greater Palatine Sulcus

Palatine Bone
Incisive Canal

Palatine Sulcus

Incisive Foramen
Incisive Bone (Premaxilla)

Palatine Process
Molar Teeth (M2/17, M3/18)

Premolar Teeth (PM1/14, PM2/15)

Incisive Teeth (I1/11, I2/12)

Canine Tooth (C/13)

b Medial View.

2.24 Full Teeth Mandible (Mandible): Lateral View, Right Side. [9]

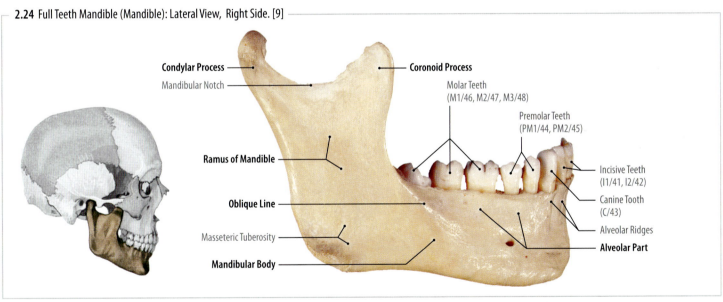

Condylar Process
Mandibular Notch

Coronoid Process

Molar Teeth (M1/46, M2/47, M3/48)

Premolar Teeth (PM1/44, PM2/45)

Ramus of Mandible

Incisive Teeth (I1/41, I2/42)

Oblique Line

Canine Tooth (C/43)

Masseteric Tuberosity

Alveolar Ridges

Mandibular Body

Alveolar Part

2.25 Edentulous (Toothless) Lower Jaw: Lateral View, Left Side. [6]

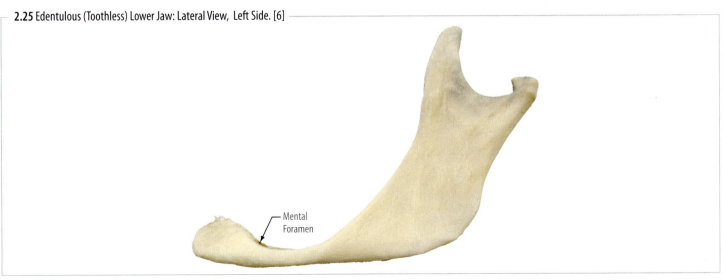

Mental Foramen

Skeleton and Joints

2.26a,b Full Teeth: Lower Jaw (Mandible). [9]

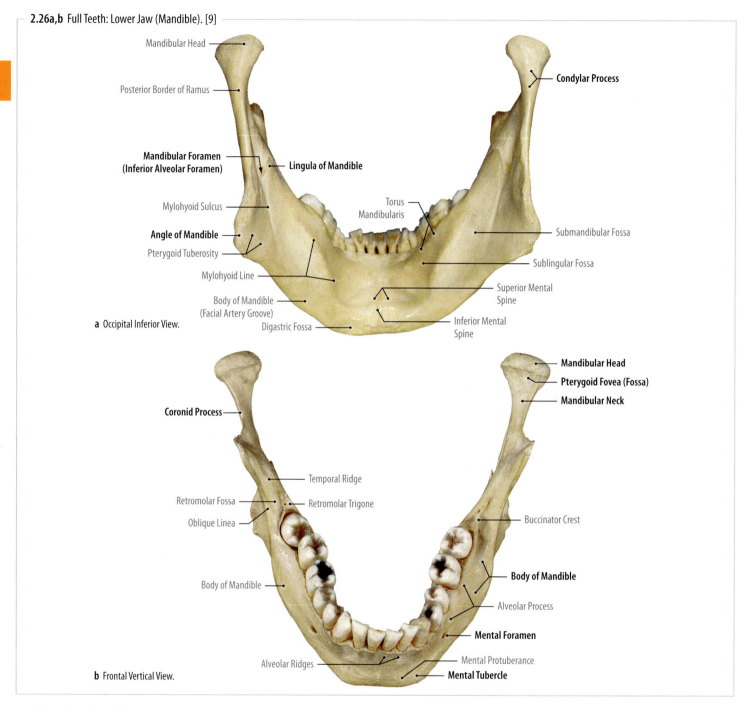

Mandibular Head

Posterior Border of Ramus

Condylar Process

Mandibular Foramen (Inferior Alveolar Foramen)

Lingula of Mandible

Mylohyoid Sulcus

Torus Mandibularis

Angle of Mandible

Submandibular Fossa

Pterygoid Tuberosity

Sublingular Fossa

Mylohyoid Line

Superior Mental Spine

Body of Mandible (Facial Artery Groove)

Inferior Mental Spine

a Occipital Inferior View.

Digastric Fossa

Mandibular Head

Pterygoid Fovea (Fossa)

Coronid Process

Mandibular Neck

Temporal Ridge

Retromolar Fossa

Retromolar Trigone

Oblique Linea

Buccinator Crest

Body of Mandible

Body of Mandible

Alveolar Process

Mental Foramen

Mental Foramen

Alveolar Ridges

Mental Protuberance

b Frontal Vertical View.

Mental Tubercle

2.27a,b Hyoid Bone. [6]

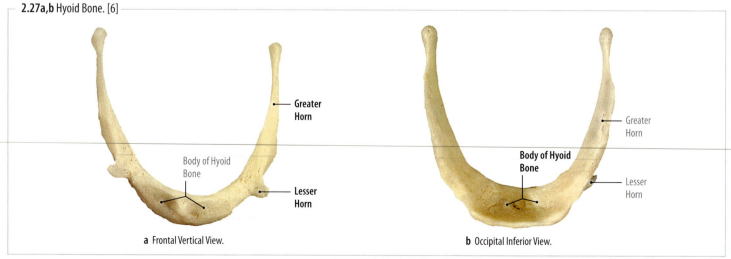

Greater Horn

Greater Horn

Body of Hyoid Bone

Body of Hyoid Bone

Lesser Horn

Lesser Horn

a Frontal Vertical View.

b Occipital Inferior View.

Skull: X-Ray Images

2.28a,b X-Ray Images of the Head of a 34-Year-Old Woman. [10]

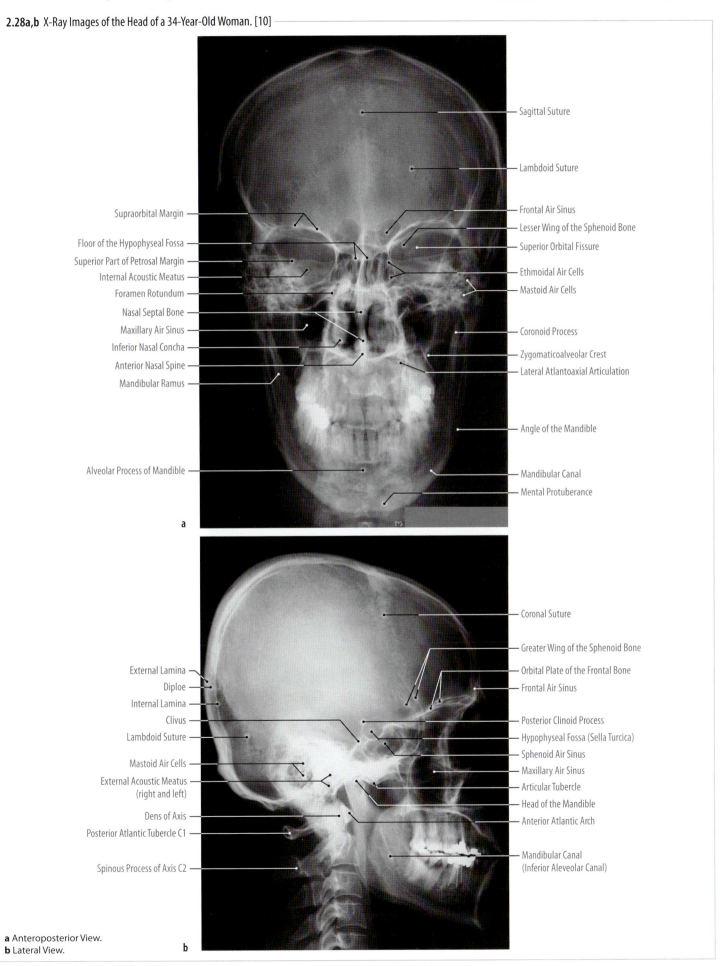

a Anteroposterior View.
b Lateral View.

Labels for image a:
- Sagittal Suture
- Lambdoid Suture
- Frontal Air Sinus
- Lesser Wing of the Sphenoid Bone
- Superior Orbital Fissure
- Ethmoidal Air Cells
- Mastoid Air Cells
- Coronoid Process
- Zygomaticoalveolar Crest
- Lateral Atlantoaxial Articulation
- Angle of the Mandible
- Mandibular Canal
- Mental Protuberance
- Supraorbital Margin
- Floor of the Hypophyseal Fossa
- Superior Part of Petrosal Margin
- Internal Acoustic Meatus
- Foramen Rotundum
- Nasal Septal Bone
- Maxillary Air Sinus
- Inferior Nasal Concha
- Anterior Nasal Spine
- Mandibular Ramus
- Alveolar Process of Mandible

Labels for image b:
- Coronal Suture
- Greater Wing of the Sphenoid Bone
- Orbital Plate of the Frontal Bone
- Frontal Air Sinus
- Posterior Clinoid Process
- Hypophyseal Fossa (Sella Turcica)
- Sphenoid Air Sinus
- Maxillary Air Sinus
- Articular Tubercle
- Head of the Mandible
- Anterior Atlantic Arch
- Mandibular Canal (Inferior Aleveolar Canal)
- External Lamina
- Diploe
- Internal Lamina
- Clivus
- Lambdoid Suture
- Mastoid Air Cells
- External Acoustic Meatus (right and left)
- Dens of Axis
- Posterior Atlantic Tubercle C1
- Spinous Process of Axis C2

Skeleton and Joints

Temporomandibular Joint

2.29 Lower Jaw, Right Condyle: Frontal View. [6]

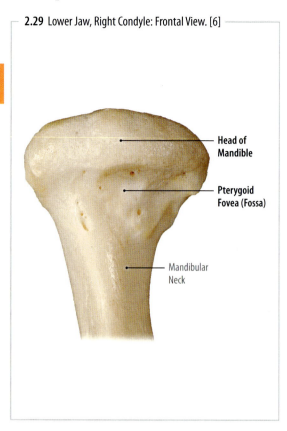

Head of Mandible

Pterygoid Fovea (Fossa)

Mandibular Neck

2.30 Mandible Joint of the Right Side, Articular Fossa and Condyle: Inferior View. [6]

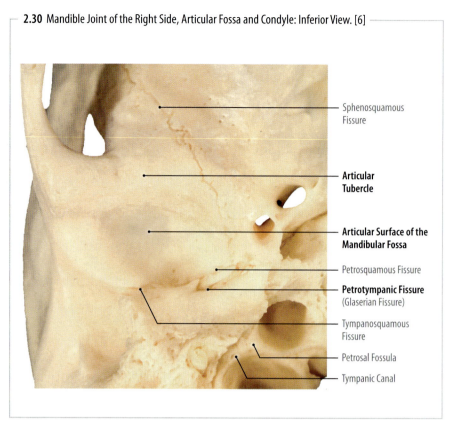

Sphenosquamous Fissure

Articular Tubercle

Articular Surface of the Mandibular Fossa

Petrosquamous Fissure

Petrotympanic Fissure (Glaserian Fissure)

Tympanosquamous Fissure

Petrosal Fossula

Tympanic Canal

2.31 Jaw Joint: Right Articular Disk, Vertical View.

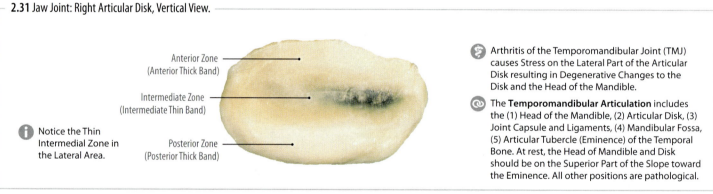

Anterior Zone (Anterior Thick Band)

Intermediate Zone (Intermediate Thin Band)

Posterior Zone (Posterior Thick Band)

Notice the Thin Intermedial Zone in the Lateral Area.

Arthritis of the Temporomandibular Joint (TMJ) causes Stress on the Lateral Part of the Articular Disk resulting in Degenerative Changes to the Disk and the Head of the Mandible.

The **Temporomandibular Articulation** includes the (1) Head of the Mandible, (2) Articular Disk, (3) Joint Capsule and Ligaments, (4) Mandibular Fossa, (5) Articular Tubercle (Eminence) of the Temporal Bone. At rest, the Head of Mandible and Disk should be on the Superior Part of the Slope toward the Eminence. All other positions are pathological.

2.32 Mandibular Joint: Histological Sagittal Section through the Median Area (Resin Embedding, Staining: Methylene Blue, Azure II, and Fuchsin Basic). [11]

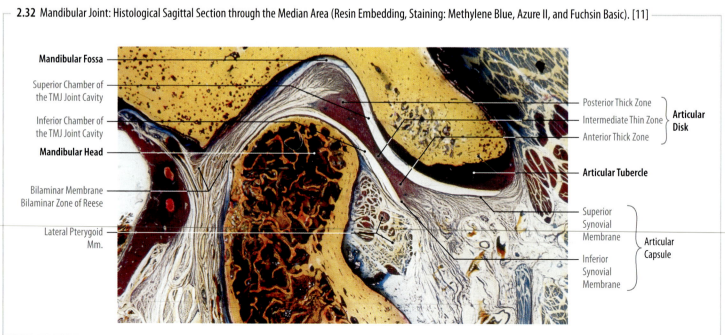

Mandibular Fossa

Superior Chamber of the TMJ Joint Cavity

Inferior Chamber of the TMJ Joint Cavity

Mandibular Head

Bilaminar Membrane Bilaminar Zone of Reese

Lateral Pterygoid Mm.

Posterior Thick Zone

Intermediate Thin Zone

Anterior Thick Zone

Articular Disk

Articular Tubercle

Superior Synovial Membrane

Inferior Synovial Membrane

Articular Capsule

2.33a,b Right Temporomandibular Joint: Joint Capsule and Ligaments. [6]

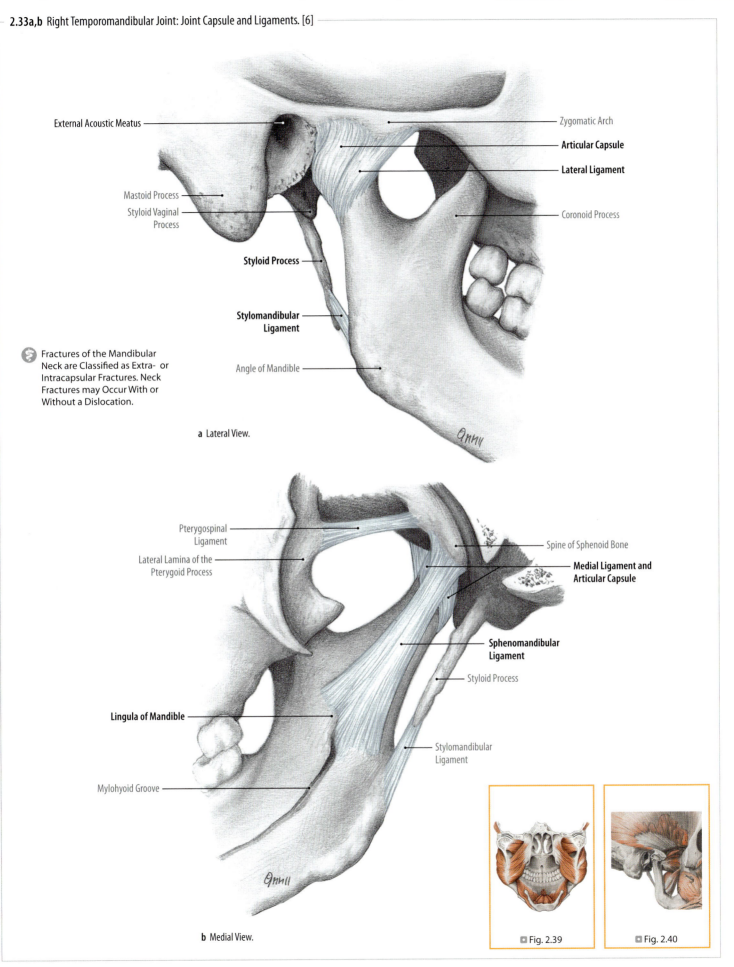

External Acoustic Meatus

Mastoid Process

Styloid Vaginal Process

Styloid Process

Stylomandibular Ligament

Angle of Mandible

Zygomatic Arch

Articular Capsule

Lateral Ligament

Coronoid Process

Fractures of the Mandibular Neck are Classified as Extra- or Intracapsular Fractures. Neck Fractures may Occur With or Without a Dislocation.

a Lateral View.

Pterygospinal Ligament

Lateral Lamina of the Pterygoid Process

Lingula of Mandible

Mylohyoid Groove

Spine of Sphenoid Bone

Medial Ligament and Articular Capsule

Sphenomandibular Ligament

Styloid Process

Stylomandibular Ligament

b Medial View.

⊡ Fig. 2.39

⊡ Fig. 2.40

Skeleton and Joints

Facial Muscles

2.34 Facial Muscles: Superficial Layer of the Left Side, Lateral View. [8]

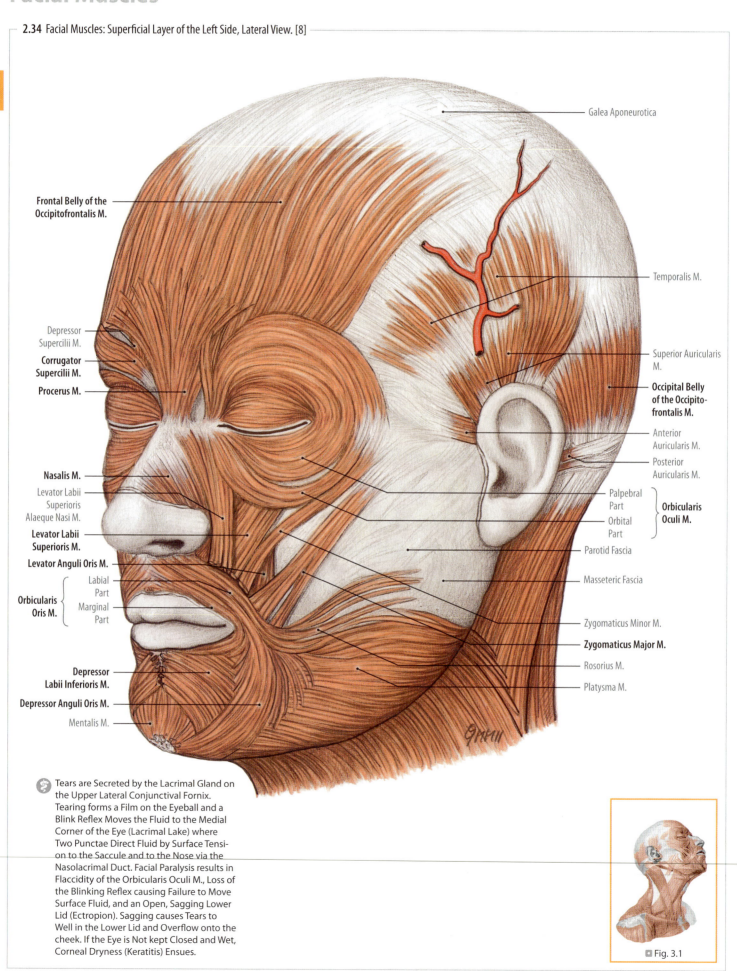

Galea Aponeurotica

Frontal Belly of the
Occipitofrontalis M.

Temporalis M.

Depressor
Supercilii M.

**Corrugator
Supercilii M.**

Procerus M.

Superior Auricularis
M.

**Occipital Belly
of the Occipito-
frontalis M.**

Anterior
Auricularis M.

Posterior
Auricularis M.

Nasalis M.

Levator Labii
Superioris
Alaeque Nasi M.

**Levator Labii
Superioris M.**

Levator Anguli Oris M.

Palpebral
Part

Orbital
Part

}

**Orbicularis
Oculi M.**

Parotid Fascia

Labial
Part

Marginal
Part

Orbicularis
Oris M.

}

Masseteric Fascia

Zygomaticus Minor M.

Zygomaticus Major M.

**Depressor
Labii Inferioris M.**

Depressor Anguli Oris M.

Mentalis M.

Rosorius M.

Platysma M.

🔵 Tears are Secreted by the Lacrimal Gland on
the Upper Lateral Conjunctival Fornix.
Tearing forms a Film on the Eyeball and a
Blink Reflex Moves the Fluid to the Medial
Corner of the Eye (Lacrimal Lake) where
Two Punctae Direct Fluid by Surface Tensi-
on to the Saccule and to the Nose via the
Nasolacrimal Duct. Facial Paralysis results in
Flaccidity of the Orbicularis Oculi M., Loss of
the Blinking Reflex causing Failure to Move
Surface Fluid, and an Open, Sagging Lower
Lid (Ectropion). Sagging causes Tears to
Well in the Lower Lid and Overflow onto the
cheek. If the Eye is Not kept Closed and Wet,
Corneal Dryness (Keratitis) Ensues.

⬛ Fig. 3.1

Facial Muscles and Mastication Muscles

2.35 Facial Muscles and Mastication Muscles: Right Side, Lateral View. [8]

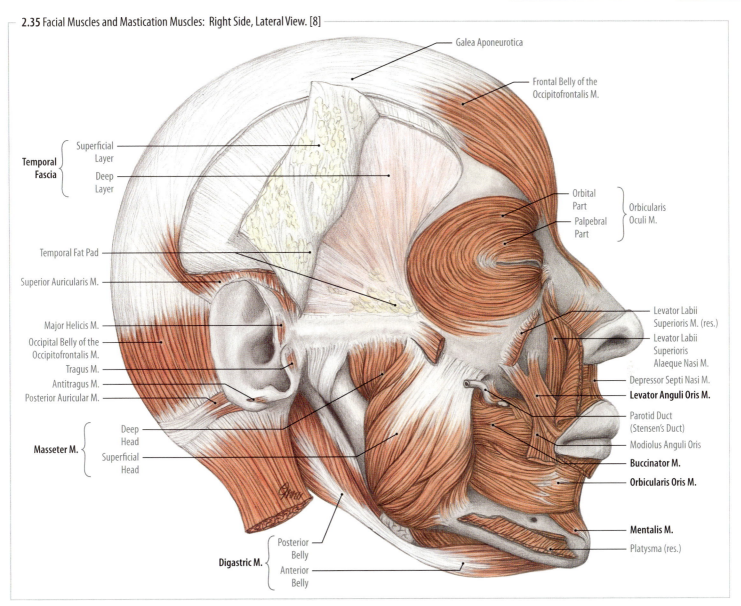

- Galea Aponeurotica
- Frontal Belly of the Occipitofrontalis M.
- **Temporal Fascia**
  - Superficial Layer
  - Deep Layer
- Orbital Part
- Palpebral Part
- Orbicularis Oculi M.
- Temporal Fat Pad
- Superior Auricularis M.
- Levator Labii Superioris M. (res.)
- Levator Labii Superioris Alaeque Nasi M.
- Major Helicis M.
- Occipital Belly of the Occipitofrontalis M.
- Tragus M.
- Antitragus M.
- Posterior Auricular M.
- Depressor Septi Nasi M.
- **Levator Anguli Oris M.**
- Parotid Duct (Stensen's Duct)
- Modiolus Anguli Oris
- **Buccinator M.**
- **Orbicularis Oris M.**
- **Masseter M.**
  - Deep Head
  - Superficial Head
- **Mentalis M.**
- Platysma (res.)
- **Digastric M.**
  - Posterior Belly
  - Anterior Belly

2.36 Orbicularis Oculi Muscle: Right Side, Occipital View. [1]

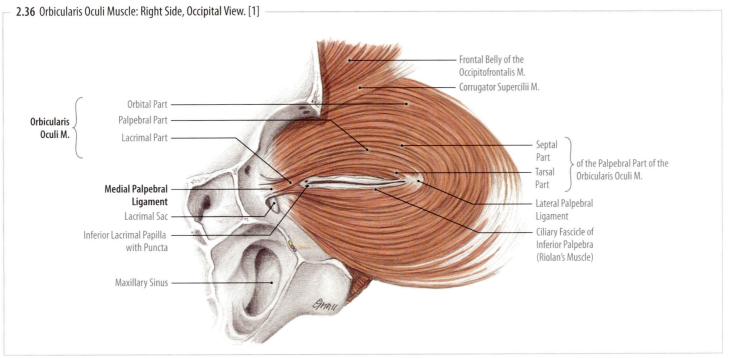

- Frontal Belly of the Occipitofrontalis M.
- Corrugator Supercilii M.
- **Orbicularis Oculi M.**
  - Orbital Part
  - Palpebral Part
  - Lacrimal Part
- **Medial Palpebral Ligament**
- Lacrimal Sac
- Inferior Lacrimal Papilla with Puncta
- Maxillary Sinus
- Septal Part
- Tarsal Part
- of the Palpebral Part of the Orbicularis Oculi M.
- Lateral Palpebral Ligament
- Ciliary Fascicle of Inferior Palpebra (Riolan's Muscle)

Muscles

Facial Muscles and Mastication Muscles

2.37 Facial Muscles (Deep Layer) and Mastication Muscles: Right Side, Lateral View. [8]

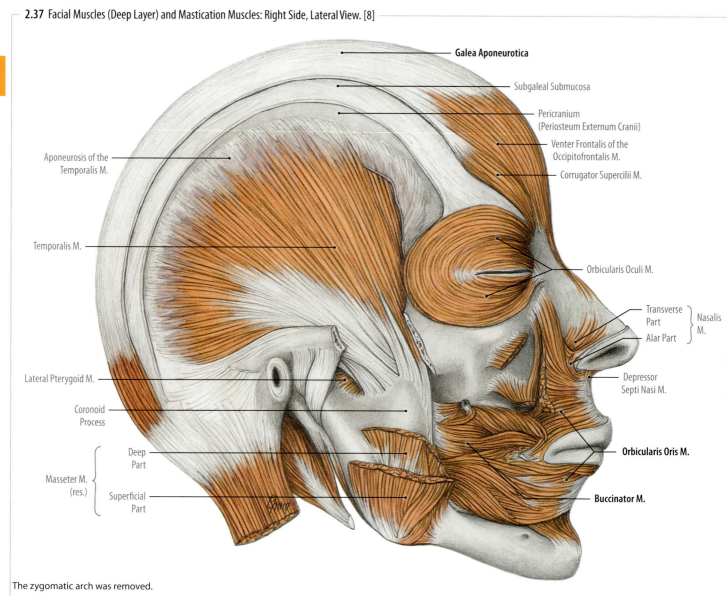

Galea Aponeurotica

Subgaleal Submucosa

Pericranium
(Periosteum Externum Cranii)

Venter Frontalis of the
Occipitofrontalis M.

Corrugator Supercilii M.

Aponeurosis of the
Temporalis M.

Temporalis M.

Orbicularis Oculi M.

Transverse
Part
Alar Part

Nasalis
M.

Lateral Pterygoid M.

Coronoid
Process

Depressor
Septi Nasi M.

Orbicularis Oris M.

Masseter M.
(res.)

Deep
Part

Superficial
Part

Buccinator M.

The zygomatic arch was removed.

2.38 Facial Muscles of the Oral Area (Buccinator M. and Orbicularis Oris M.): Median-Sagittal Section, Medial View of the Left Side. [1]

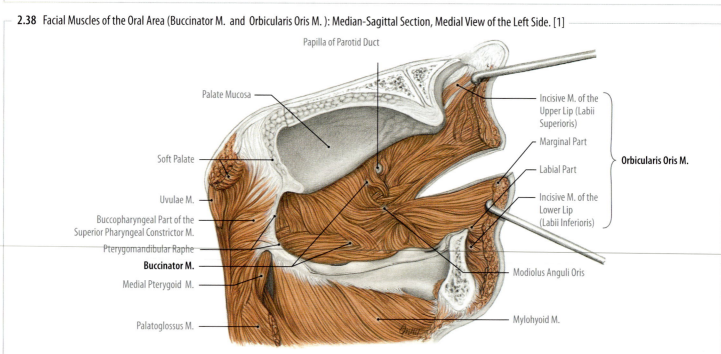

Papilla of Parotid Duct

Palate Mucosa

Incisive M. of the
Upper Lip (Labii
Superioris)

Marginal Part

Soft Palate

Orbicularis Oris M.

Labial Part

Uvulae M.

Incisive M. of the
Lower Lip
(Labii Inferioris)

Buccopharyngeal Part of the
Superior Pharyngeal Constrictor M.

Pterygomandibular Raphe

Buccinator M.

Medial Pterygoid M.

Modiolus Anguli Oris

Palatoglossus M.

Mylohyoid M.

Mastication Muscles: Function

2.39 Mastication Muscles, Upper Hyoid Muscles, and Temporomandibular Joints: Frontal Section through the Head, Occipital View. [1]

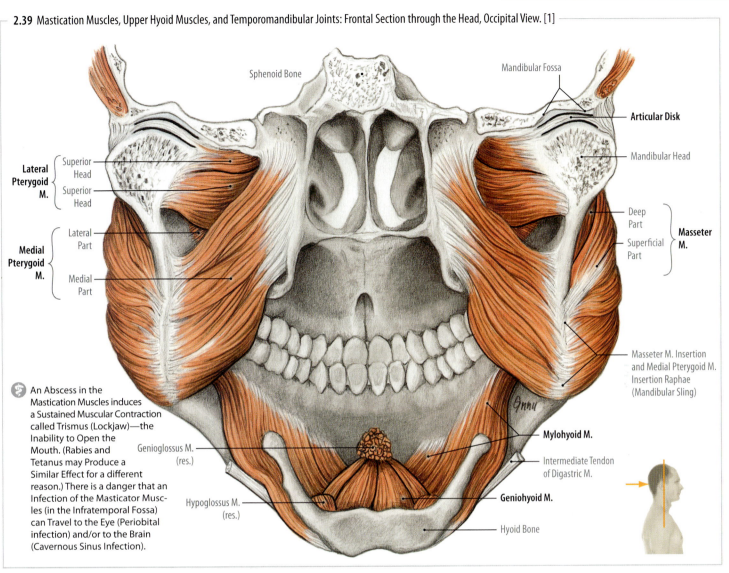

Sphenoid Bone

Mandibular Fossa

Articular Disk

Mandibular Head

Deep Part

Masseter M.

Superficial Part

Lateral Pterygoid M. — Superior Head / Superior Head

Medial Pterygoid M. — Lateral Part / Medial Part

Masseter M. Insertion and Medial Pterygoid M. Insertion Raphae (Mandibular Sling)

Mylohyoid M.

Genioglossus M. (res.)

Intermediate Tendon of Digastric M.

Geniohyoid M.

Hypoglossus M. (res.)

Hyoid Bone

An Abscess in the Mastication Muscles induces a Sustained Muscular Contraction called Trismus (Lockjaw)—the Inability to Open the Mouth. (Rabies and Tetanus may Produce a Similar Effect for a different reason.) There is a danger that an Infection of the Masticator Muscles (in the Infratemporal Fossa) can Travel to the Eye (Periobital infection) and/or to the Brain (Cavernous Sinus Infection).

2.40 Mastication Muscles and Temporomandibular Joint: Right Side, Lateral View. [12]

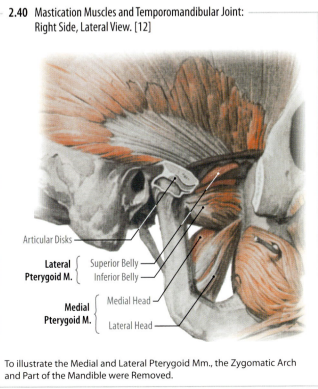

Articular Disks

Lateral Pterygoid M. — Superior Belly / Inferior Belly

Medial Pterygoid M. — Medial Head / Lateral Head

To illustrate the Medial and Lateral Pterygoid Mm., the Zygomatic Arch and Part of the Mandible were Removed.

2.41 Functions of the Mastication Muscles.

Muscles for Elevation (Closing/ Lifting) and Depression (Opening/ Lowering) the Mandible	
Depression (Lowering) (Abduction)	Elevation (Lifting) of the Mandible (Adduction)
Digastric M. Mylohyoid M. Geniohyoid M.	Temporalis M. Masseter M. Medial Pterygoid M.
Lateral Pterygoid M. Inferior Head: Initiation of the Rotation Movement	Lateral Pterygoid M. Superior Head: Fixation (Sliding) of the Head of Mandible on the Slope of the Articular Tubercle

Muscles for Grinding Movement	
Working Side (Lateral Trusion, Rotation Condyle, Resting Condyle)	Balancing Side (Medial Trusions Side, Condylar Translation, Condylar Swing)
Digastric M. Mylohyoid M. Geniohyoid M.	Temporalis M. Medial Pterygoid M. Lateral Pterygoid M. (Inferior Belly)
Temporalis M. (Posterior Part) and Lateral Pterygoid M. (Superior Part): Stabilization of the Mandibular Head	

Muscles

Facial Area: Arteries

2.42 Facial Area: Arteries. [13]

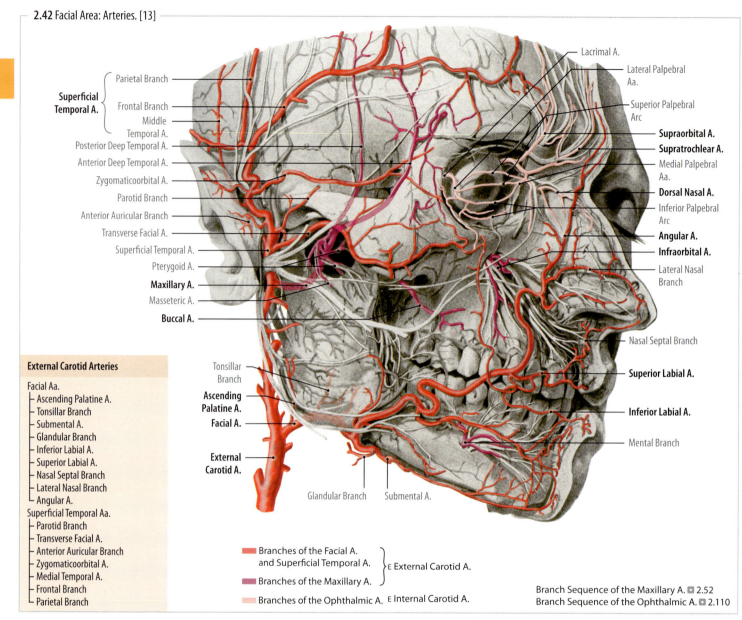

Superficial Temporal A. {
- Parietal Branch
- Frontal Branch
- Middle Temporal A.

Posterior Deep Temporal A.
Anterior Deep Temporal A.
Zygomaticoorbital A.
Parotid Branch
Anterior Auricular Branch
Transverse Facial A.
Superficial Temporal A.
Pterygoid A.
Maxillary A.
Masseteric A.
Buccal A.

Lacrimal A.
Lateral Palpebral Aa.
Superior Palpebral Arc
Supraorbital A.
Supratrochlear A.
Medial Palpebral Aa.
Dorsal Nasal A.
Inferior Palpebral Arc
Angular A.
Infraorbital A.
Lateral Nasal Branch
Nasal Septal Branch
Superior Labial A.
Inferior Labial A.
Mental Branch

Tonsillar Branch
Ascending Palatine A.
Facial A.
External Carotid A.

Glandular Branch
Submental A.

External Carotid Arteries

Facial Aa.
- Ascending Palatine A.
- Tonsillar Branch
- Submental A.
- Glandular Branch
- Inferior Labial A.
- Superior Labial A.
- Nasal Septal Branch
- Lateral Nasal Branch
- Angular A.

Superficial Temporal Aa.
- Parotid Branch
- Transverse Facial A.
- Anterior Auricular Branch
- Zygomaticoorbital A.
- Medial Temporal A.
- Frontal Branch
- Parietal Branch

▮ Branches of the Facial A. and Superficial Temporal A. } E External Carotid A.
▮ Branches of the Maxillary A.
▮ Branches of the Ophthalmic A.   E Internal Carotid A.

Branch Sequence of the Maxillary A. ▣ 2.52
Branch Sequence of the Ophthalmic A. ▣ 2.110

2.43 Craniofacial Bones: Arterial Exits.

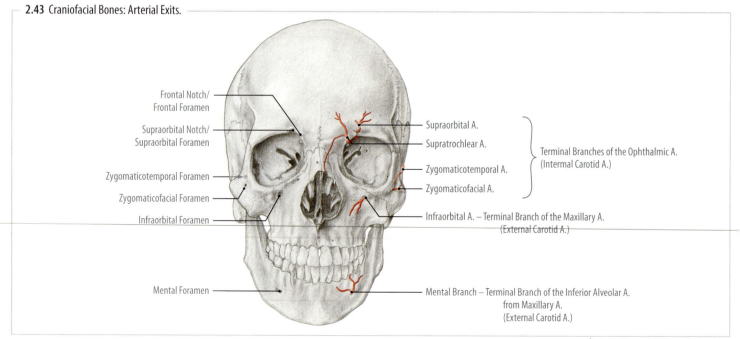

Frontal Notch/ Frontal Foramen
Supraorbital Notch/ Supraorbital Foramen
Zygomaticotemporal Foramen
Zygomaticofacial Foramen
Infraorbital Foramen

Supraorbital A.
Supratrochlear A.
Zygomaticotemporal A.
Zygomaticofacial A.
} Terminal Branches of the Ophthalmic A. (Internal Carotid A.)

Infraorbital A. – Terminal Branch of the Maxillary A. (External Carotid A.)

Mental Foramen

Mental Branch – Terminal Branch of the Inferior Alveolar A. from Maxillary A. (External Carotid A.)

46

Veins: Lymphatic System

2.44 Superficial and Deep Veins of the Head: Right Lateral View. [14]

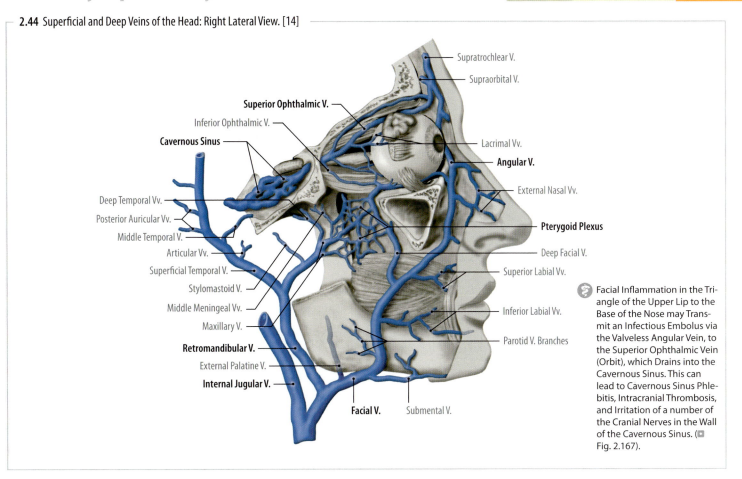

Supratrochlear V.

Supraorbital V.

Superior Ophthalmic V.

Inferior Ophthalmic V.

Cavernous Sinus

Lacrimal Vv.

Angular V.

External Nasal Vv.

Deep Temporal Vv.

Posterior Auricular Vv.

Middle Temporal V.

Pterygoid Plexus

Articular Vv.

Deep Facial V.

Superficial Temporal V.

Superior Labial Vv.

Stylomastoid V.

Middle Meningeal Vv.

Inferior Labial Vv.

Maxillary V.

Parotid V. Branches

Retromandibular V.

External Palatine V.

Internal Jugular V.

Facial V.   Submental V.

Facial Inflammation in the Triangle of the Upper Lip to the Base of the Nose may Transmit an Infectious Embolus via the Valveless Angular Vein, to the Superior Ophthalmic Vein (Orbit), which Drains into the Cavernous Sinus. This can lead to Cavernous Sinus Phlebitis, Intracranial Thrombosis, and Irritation of a number of the Cranial Nerves in the Wall of the Cavernous Sinus. (☐ Fig. 2.167).

2.45 Lymph Nodes of the Head: Right Lateral View. [13]

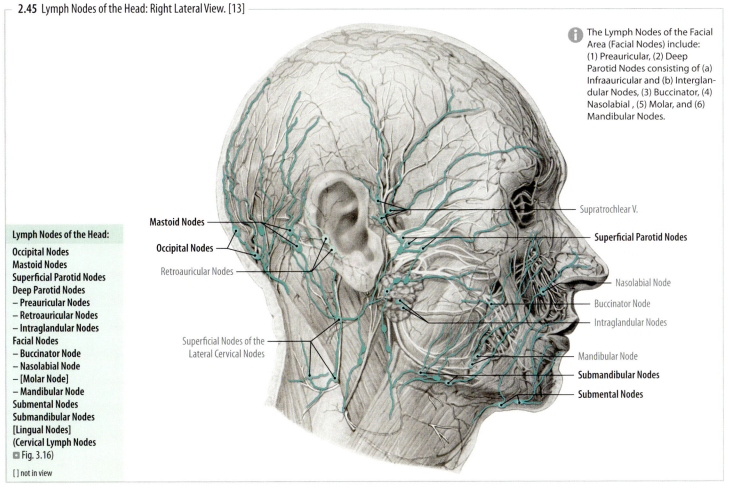

The Lymph Nodes of the Facial Area (Facial Nodes) include: (1) Preauricular, (2) Deep Parotid Nodes consisting of (a) Infraauricular and (b) Interglandular Nodes, (3) Buccinator, (4) Nasolabial , (5) Molar, and (6) Mandibular Nodes.

Supratrochlear V.

Mastoid Nodes

Superficial Parotid Nodes

Occipital Nodes

Retroauricular Nodes

Nasolabial Node

Buccinator Node

Intraglandular Nodes

Superficial Nodes of the Lateral Cervical Nodes

Mandibular Node

Submandibular Nodes

Submental Nodes

Lymph Nodes of the Head:

Occipital Nodes
Mastoid Nodes
Superficial Parotid Nodes
Deep Parotid Nodes
– Preauricular Nodes
– Retroauricular Nodes
– Intraglandular Nodes
Facial Nodes
– Buccinator Node
– Nasolabial Node
– [Molar Node]
– Mandibular Node
Submental Nodes
Submandibular Nodes
[Lingual Nodes]
(Cervical Lymph Nodes
☐ Fig. 3.16)

[ ] not in view

Face

2.46a–c Trigeminal Nerve: Schematic Illustration of the Three Trigeminal Branches. [15]

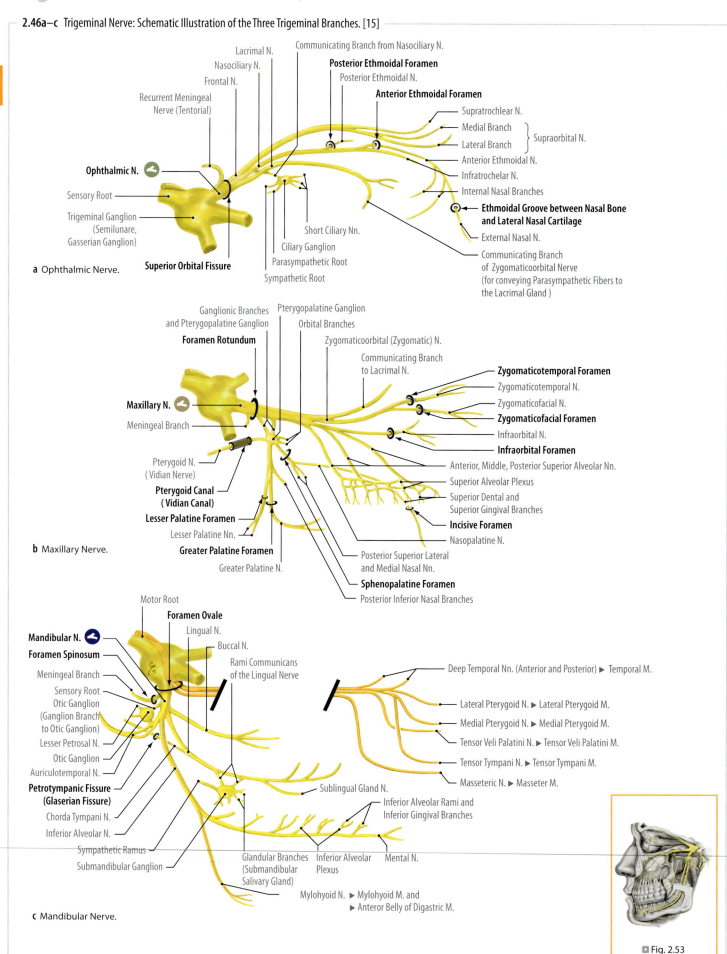

Communicating Branch from Nasociliary N.

Lacrimal N.

Nasociliary N.

Frontal N.

Posterior Ethmoidal Foramen

Posterior Ethmoidal N.

Recurrent Meningeal Nerve (Tentorial)

Anterior Ethmoidal Foramen

Supratrochlear N.

Medial Branch

Lateral Branch } Supraorbital N.

Ophthalmic N.

Anterior Ethmoidal N.

Infratrochelar N.

Sensory Root

Internal Nasal Branches

Trigeminal Ganglion (Semilunare, Gasserian Ganglion)

Ethmoidal Groove between Nasal Bone and Lateral Nasal Cartilage

Short Ciliary Nn.

External Nasal N.

Ciliary Ganglion

Communicating Branch of Zygomaticoorbital Nerve (for conveying Parasympathetic Fibers to the Lacrimal Gland)

Parasympathetic Root

Superior Orbital Fissure

Sympathetic Root

a Ophthalmic Nerve.

Ganglionic Branches and Pterygopalatine Ganglion

Pterygopalatine Ganglion

Orbital Branches

Foramen Rotundum

Zygomaticoorbital (Zygomatic) N.

Communicating Branch to Lacrimal N.

Maxillary N.

Zygomaticotemporal Foramen

Zygomaticotemporal N.

Meningeal Branch

Zygomaticofacial N.

Zygomaticofacial Foramen

Infraorbital N.

Infraorbital Foramen

Pterygoid N. (Vidian Nerve)

Anterior, Middle, Posterior Superior Alveolar Nn.

Superior Alveolar Plexus

Pterygoid Canal (Vidian Canal)

Superior Dental and Superior Gingival Branches

Lesser Palatine Foramen

Incisive Foramen

Lesser Palatine Nn.

Nasopalatine N.

Greater Palatine Foramen

Posterior Superior Lateral and Medial Nasal Nn.

Greater Palatine N.

Sphenopalatine Foramen

b Maxillary Nerve.

Posterior Inferior Nasal Branches

Motor Root

Foramen Ovale

Lingual N.

Mandibular N.

Buccal N.

Foramen Spinosum

Rami Communicans of the Lingual Nerve

Deep Temporal Nn. (Anterior and Posterior) ▶ Temporal M.

Meningeal Branch

Sensory Root

Otic Ganglion (Ganglion Branch to Otic Ganglion)

Lateral Pterygoid N. ▶ Lateral Pterygoid M.

Medial Pterygoid N. ▶ Medial Pterygoid M.

Lesser Petrosal N.

Tensor Veli Palatini N. ▶ Tensor Veli Palatini M.

Otic Ganglion

Tensor Tympani N. ▶ Tensor Tympani M.

Auriculotemporal N.

Masseteric N. ▶ Masseter M.

Petrotympanic Fissure (Glaserian Fissure)

Sublingual Gland N.

Inferior Alveolar Rami and Inferior Gingival Branches

Chorda Tympani N.

Inferior Alveolar N.

Sympathetic Ramus

Submandibular Ganglion

Glandular Branches (Submandibular Salivary Gland)

Inferior Alveolar Plexus

Mental N.

Mylohyoid N. ▶ Mylohyoid M. and ▶ Anteror Belly of Digastric M.

c Mandibular Nerve.

□ Fig. 2.53

2.47 Skin Branches of the Trigeminal Nerve, the Cervical Plexus, and the Dorsal Spinal Nerve Branches: Facial, Cervical, and Occipital Areas. [13]

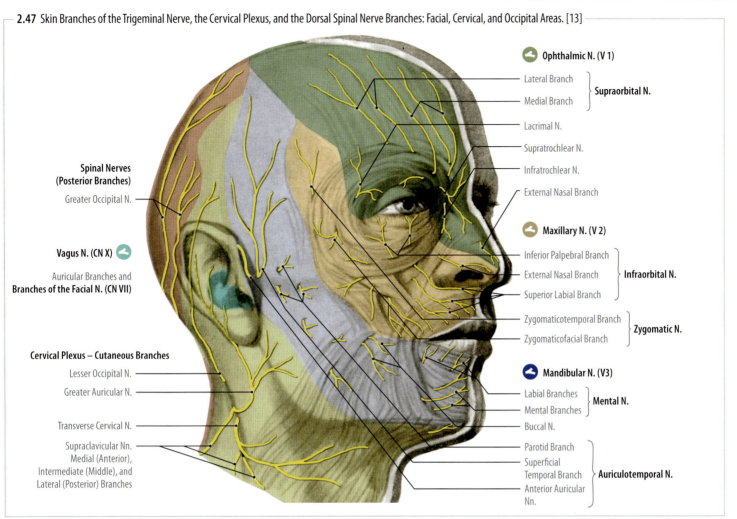

Ophthalmic N. (V 1)

Lateral Branch ⎫
Medial Branch ⎬ Supraorbital N.

Lacrimal N.

Supratrochlear N.

Infratrochlear N.

External Nasal Branch

Maxillary N. (V 2)

Inferior Palpebral Branch ⎫
External Nasal Branch ⎬ Infraorbital N.
Superior Labial Branch ⎭

Zygomaticotemporal Branch ⎫
Zygomaticofacial Branch ⎬ Zygomatic N.

Mandibular N. (V3)

Labial Branches ⎫
Mental Branches ⎬ Mental N.

Buccal N.

Parotid Branch ⎫
Superficial Temporal Branch ⎬ Auriculotemporal N.
Anterior Auricular Nn. ⎭

Spinal Nerves (Posterior Branches)

Greater Occipital N.

Vagus N. (CN X)

Auricular Branches and Branches of the Facial N. (CN VII)

Cervical Plexus – Cutaneous Branches

Lesser Occipital N.

Greater Auricular N.

Transverse Cervical N.

Supraclavicular Nn. Medial (Anterior), Intermediate (Middle), and Lateral (Posterior) Branches

---

2.48 Facial Cranium: Nerve Exit Points of the Trigeminal Branches.

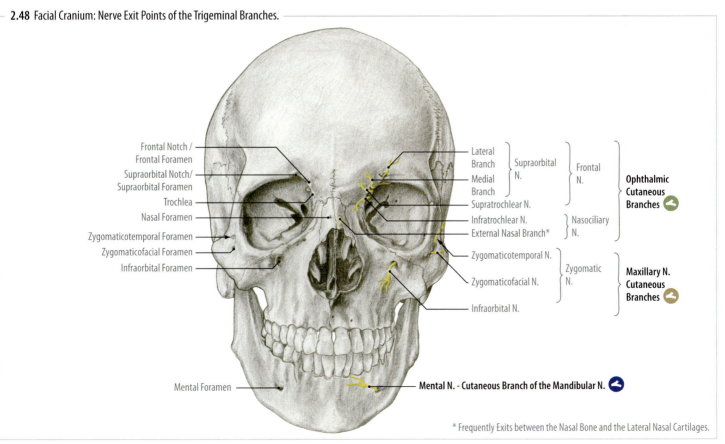

Frontal Notch / Frontal Foramen

Supraorbital Notch/ Supraorbital Foramen

Trochlea

Nasal Foramen

Zygomaticotemporal Foramen

Zygomaticofacial Foramen

Infraorbital Foramen

Lateral Branch ⎫ Supraorbital ⎫
Medial Branch ⎭ N. ⎬ Frontal N. ⎬ Ophthalmic Cutaneous Branches

Supratrochlear N.

Infratrochlear N. ⎫ Nasociliary
External Nasal Branch* ⎬ N.

Zygomaticotemporal N. ⎫ Zygomatic ⎫ Maxillary N.
Zygomaticofacial N. ⎬ N. ⎬ Cutaneous Branches

Infraorbital N.

Mental Foramen

Mental N. - Cutaneous Branch of the Mandibular N.

* Frequently Exits between the Nasal Bone and the Lateral Nasal Cartilages.

Face

2.49 Central and Peripheral Innervation of the Facial Nerve, Parts of the Parasympathetic Nervous System, and Somatosensory Connections to the Facial Nerves

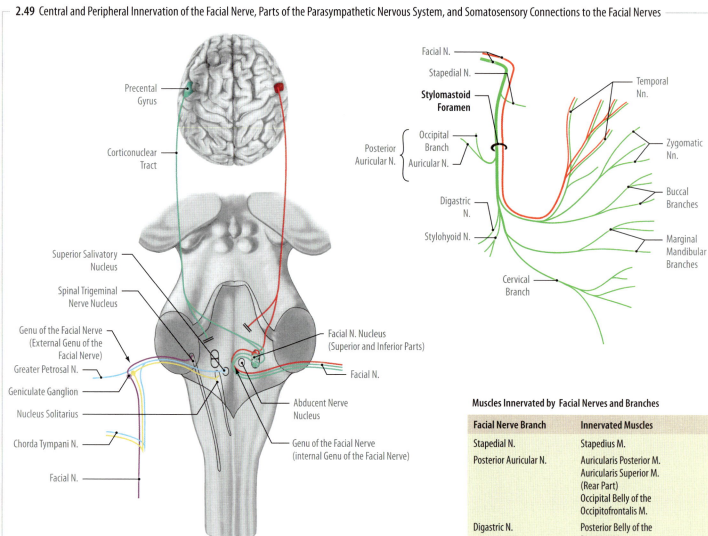

Facial N.

Stapedial N.

Stylomastoid Foramen

Posterior Auricular N. { Occipital Branch / Auricular N.

Digastric N.

Stylohyoid N.

Cervical Branch

Temporal Nn.

Zygomatic Nn.

Buccal Branches

Marginal Mandibular Branches

Precental Gyrus

Corticonuclear Tract

Superior Salivatory Nucleus

Spinal Trigeminal Nerve Nucleus

Genu of the Facial Nerve (External Genu of the Facial Nerve)

Greater Petrosal N.

Geniculate Ganglion

Nucleus Solitarius

Chorda Tympani N.

Facial N.

Facial N. Nucleus (Superior and Inferior Parts)

Facial N.

Abducent Nerve Nucleus

Genu of the Facial Nerve (internal Genu of the Facial Nerve)

Muscles Innervated by Facial Nerves and Branches

Facial Nerve Branch	Innervated Muscles
Stapedial N.	Stapedius M.
Posterior Auricular N.	Auricularis Posterior M. Auricularis Superior M. (Rear Part) Occipital Belly of the Occipitofrontalis M.
Digastric N.	Posterior Belly of the Digastric M.
Stylohyoid N.	Stylohyoid M.
Cervical Branch	Platysma
Temporal Branches	Frontal Belly of the Occipitofrontalis M. Temporoparietalis M. Orbicularis Oculi M. (Superior Palpebra) Corrugator Supercilii M. Depressor Supercilii M. Auricularis Anterior M. Auricularis Superior M. (Anterior Part)
Zygomatic Branch	Orbicularis Oculi M. (Inferior Palpebra) Procerus M. Levator Labii Superioris Alaeque Nasi M. Levator Labii Superioris M. Nasal M. Zygomatic Major and Minor Mm. Depressor Septi M. Levator Anguli Oris M. Orbicularis Oris M. (Upper Lip)
Buccinator N.	Buccinator M. Depressor Anguli Oris M. Risorius M. Orbicularis Oris M. (Corner of the Mouth)
Marginal Mandibular N.	Depressor Labii Inferioris M. Mentalis M. Orbicularis Oris M. (Lower Lip) (Depressor Anguli Oris M.)

2.50 Facial Nerves, Motor Branches: Right Lateral View. [13]

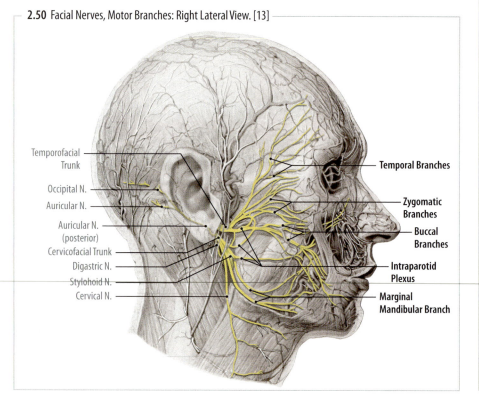

Temporofacial Trunk

Occipital N.

Auricular N.

Auricular N. (posterior)

Cervicofacial Trunk

Digastric N.

Stylohoid N.

Cervical N.

Temporal Branches

Zygomatic Branches

Buccal Branches

Intraparotid Plexus

Marginal Mandibular Branch

Pterygopalatine Fossa: Bones

2.51a,b Bones of the Pterygopalatine Fossa: Left Lateral View. [16]

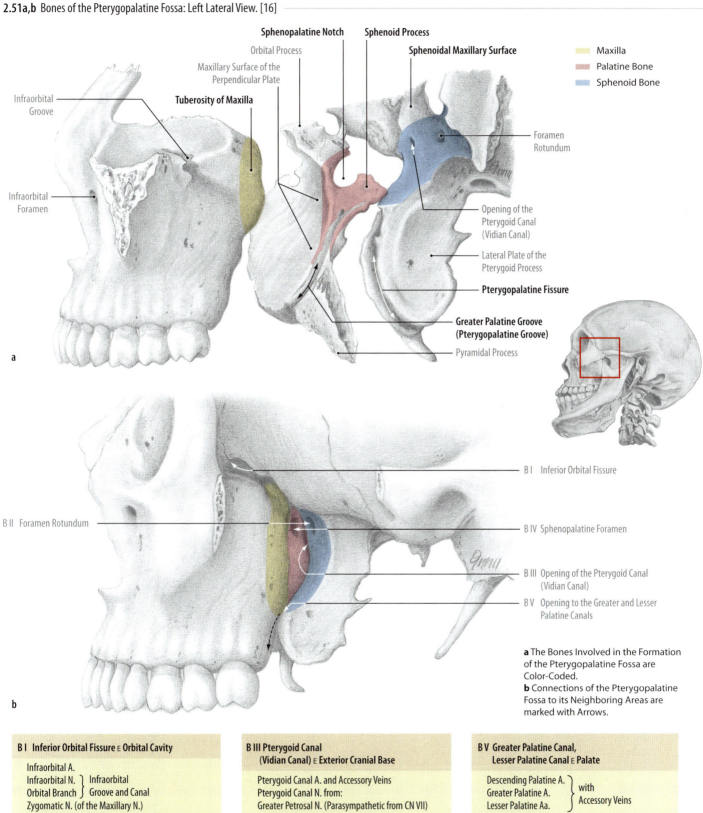

Sphenopalatine Notch

Sphenoid Process

Orbital Process

Sphenoidal Maxillary Surface

Maxillary Surface of the
Perpendicular Plate

Infraorbital
Groove

Tuberosity of Maxilla

Infraorbital
Foramen

Foramen
Rotundum

Opening of the
Pterygoid Canal
(Vidian Canal)

Lateral Plate of the
Pterygoid Process

Pterygopalatine Fissure

**Greater Palatine Groove
(Pterygopalatine Groove)**

Pyramidal Process

Maxilla
Palatine Bone
Sphenoid Bone

a

B I   Inferior Orbital Fissure

B II Foramen Rotundum

B IV Sphenopalatine Foramen

B III Opening of the Pterygoid Canal
(Vidian Canal)

B V   Opening to the Greater and Lesser
Palatine Canals

b

a The Bones Involved in the Formation
of the Pterygopalatine Fossa are
Color-Coded.
b Connections of the Pterygopalatine
Fossa to its Neighboring Areas are
marked with Arrows.

B I Inferior Orbital Fissure E **Orbital Cavity**

Infraorbital A.
Infraorbital N. } Infraorbital
Orbital Branch } Groove and Canal
Zygomatic N. (of the Maxillary N.)
Inferior Ophthalmic V. via Communicating
    Branches to the Pterygoid Plexus

B II Foramen Rotundum E **Medial Cranial Fossa**

Maxillary N. (V II), Recurrent Meningeal N.,
    with Accessory Aa.

**B III Pterygoid Canal
(Vidian Canal)** E **Exterior Cranial Base**

Pterygoid Canal A. and Accessory Veins
Pterygoid Canal N. from:
Greater Petrosal N. (Parasympathetic from CN VII)
    and Deep Petrosal N. (Sympathetic from
    Internal Carotid A. Plexus)

B IV Sphenopalatine Foramen E **Nasal Cavity**

Sphenopalatine A. with Accessory Nerves
(Posterior Lateral Nasal Aa. and
    Posterior Septal Branches)
Posterior Superior Lateral Nasal N.
    and Medially from the Nasopalatine N. of the
    Pterygopalatine Ganglion

**B V Greater Palatine Canal,
Lesser Palatine Canal** E **Palate**

Descending Palatine A.
Greater Palatine A.   } with
Lesser Palatine Aa.   } Accessory Veins
Greater Palatine N.
Lesser Palatine Nn.

Face

2.52 Maxillary Artery: Branch Sequence, Left Lateral View. [17]

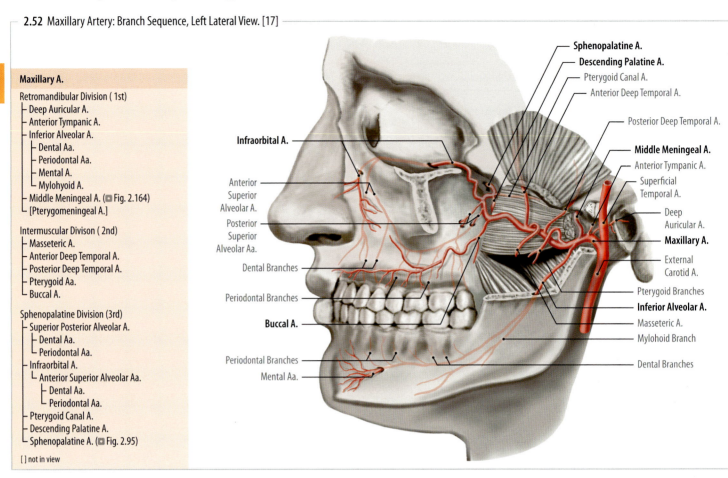

Maxillary A.

Retromandibular Division (1st)
- Deep Auricular A.
- Anterior Tympanic A.
- Inferior Alveolar A.
  - Dental Aa.
  - Periodontal Aa.
  - Mental A.
  - Mylohyoid A.
- Middle Meningeal A. (☐ Fig. 2.164)
- [Pterygomeningeal A.]

Intermuscular Divison (2nd)
- Masseteric A.
- Anterior Deep Temporal A.
- Posterior Deep Temporal A.
- Pterygoid Aa.
- Buccal A.

Sphenopalatine Division (3rd)
- Superior Posterior Alveolar A.
  - Dental Aa.
  - Periodontal Aa.
- Infraorbital A.
  - Anterior Superior Alveolar Aa.
    - Dental Aa.
    - Periodontal Aa.
- Pterygoid Canal A.
- Descending Palatine A.
- Sphenopalatine A. (☐ Fig. 2.95)

[ ] not in view

Labels (figure 2.52): Sphenopalatine A.; Descending Palatine A.; Pterygoid Canal A.; Anterior Deep Temporal A.; Posterior Deep Temporal A.; Middle Meningeal A.; Anterior Tympanic A.; Superficial Temporal A.; Deep Auricular A.; Maxillary A.; External Carotid A.; Pterygoid Branches; Inferior Alveolar A.; Masseteric A.; Mylohoid Branch; Dental Branches; Infraorbital A.; Anterior Superior Alveolar A.; Posterior Superior Alveolar Aa.; Dental Branches; Periodontal Branches; Buccal A.; Periodontal Branches; Mental Aa.

2.53 Trigeminal Nerve: Left Lateral View. [13]

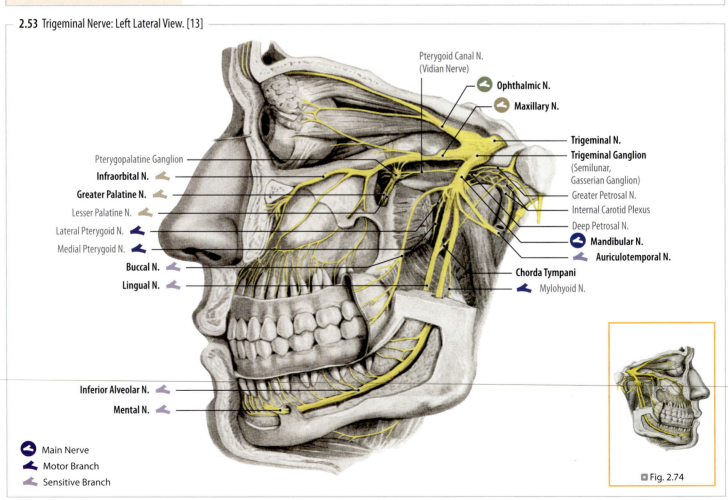

Labels (figure 2.53): Pterygoid Canal N. (Vidian Nerve); Ophthalmic N.; Maxillary N.; Trigeminal N.; Trigeminal Ganglion (Semilunar, Gasserian Ganglion); Greater Petrosal N.; Internal Carotid Plexus; Deep Petrosal N.; Mandibular N.; Auriculotemporal N.; Chorda Tympani; Mylohyoid N.; Pterygopalatine Ganglion; Infraorbital N.; Greater Palatine N.; Lesser Palatine N.; Lateral Pterygoid N.; Medial Pterygoid N.; Buccal N.; Lingual N.; Inferior Alveolar N.; Mental N.

Main Nerve
Motor Branch
Sensitive Branch

☐ Fig. 2.74

Superficial Pathways, Salivary Glands

2.54 Superficial Facial Area, Occipital Area, and Galea: Right Lateral View. [6]

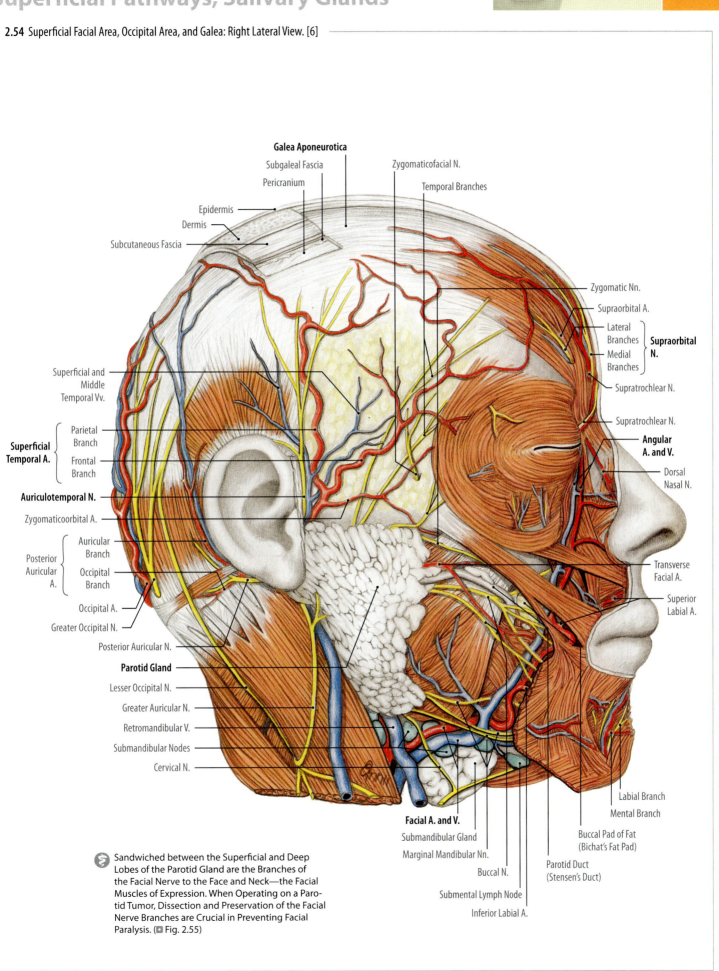

Galea Aponeurotica
Subgaleal Fascia
Pericranium
Epidermis
Dermis
Subcutaneous Fascia

Zygomaticofacial N.
Temporal Branches

Zygomatic Nn.
Supraorbital A.
Lateral Branches
Medial Branches
Supraorbital N.
Supratrochlear N.
Supratrochlear N.
Angular A. and V.
Dorsal Nasal N.

Superficial and Middle Temporal Vv.

Superficial Temporal A.
Parietal Branch
Frontal Branch

Auriculotemporal N.
Zygomaticoorbital A.

Posterior Auricular A.
Auricular Branch
Occipital Branch

Occipital A.
Greater Occipital N.
Posterior Auricular N.

Parotid Gland
Lesser Occipital N.
Greater Auricular N.
Retromandibular V.
Submandibular Nodes
Cervical N.

Transverse Facial A.
Superior Labial A.

Labial Branch
Mental Branch
Buccal Pad of Fat (Bichat's Fat Pad)
Parotid Duct (Stensen's Duct)
Buccal N.
Submental Lymph Node
Inferior Labial A.
Buccal N.
Marginal Mandibular Nn.
Submandibular Gland
Facial A. and V.

Sandwiched between the Superficial and Deep Lobes of the Parotid Gland are the Branches of the Facial Nerve to the Face and Neck—the Facial Muscles of Expression. When Operating on a Parotid Tumor, Dissection and Preservation of the Facial Nerve Branches are Crucial in Preventing Facial Paralysis. (🔲 Fig. 2.55)

Face

Superficial Pathways, Retromandibular Fossa

2.55 Superficial Facial Area and Retromandibular Fossa: Left Lateral View. [6]

The Facial Nerve travels within the Brain (Central) and Exits (Peripheral Route) through the Posterior Cranial Fossa. It then Enters the Facial Canal and the Terminal Branches End on the Face and through the Parotid Gland. Peripheral Facial Palsy leads to Paralysis of All Muscles on the Affected Side. (□ Fig. 2.36, 2.54, 2.56, 2.148).

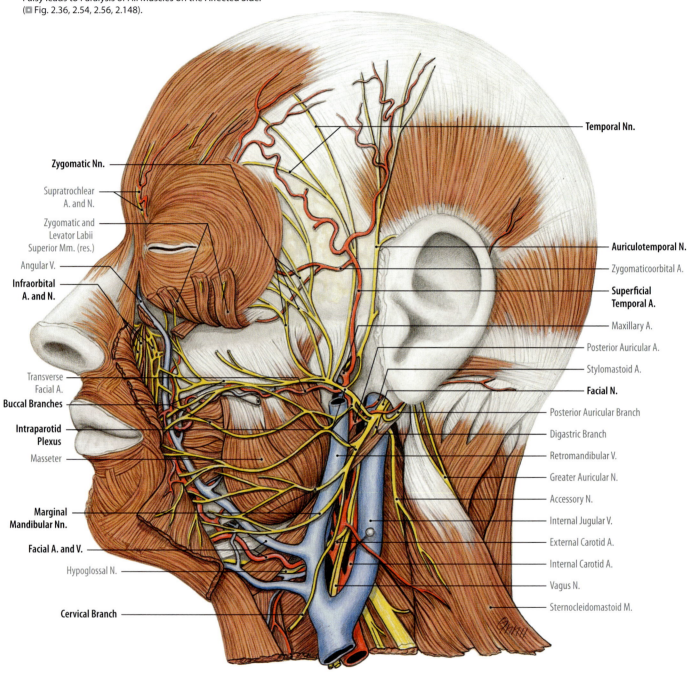

Zygomatic Nn.

Supratrochlear A. and N.

Zygomatic and Levator Labii Superior Mm. (res.)

Angular V.

Infraorbital A. and N.

Transverse Facial A.

Buccal Branches

Intraparotid Plexus

Masseter

Marginal Mandibular Nn.

Facial A. and V.

Hypoglossal N.

Cervical Branch

Temporal Nn.

Auriculotemporal N.

Zygomaticoorbital A.

Superficial Temporal A.

Maxillary A.

Posterior Auricular A.

Stylomastoid A.

Facial N.

Posterior Auricular Branch

Digastric Branch

Retromandibular V.

Greater Auricular N.

Accessory N.

Internal Jugular V.

External Carotid A.

Internal Carotid A.

Vagus N.

Sternocleidomastoid M.

Corticonuclear Fibers Innervate Contralateral Facial Muscles. The Upper (Superior) Part of the Facial Nucleus receives Additional Fibers from the Same (Ipsilateral) Side. Unilateral Paralysis of the Right Facial N. (Central Supranuclear Facial Palsy) results from Stroke. The Stroke may be Hemorrhagic or Result from the Infarction of the Left Corticonuclear Fibers of the Internal Capsule of the Countralateral Side, the Upper Temporal Branches, the Frontalis M., and Orbicularis Oculi. The Upper Eyelid may be Contracted on Both Sides because the Upper Part of the Facial Nucleus receives Extra Corticonuclear Fibers from the Right (Ipsilateral) Internal Capsule. Paralysis of the Right Lower Facial Muscles Innervated by Zygomatic, Buccal, Marginal Mandibular, and Cervical Branches is termed Lower Facial Palsy.

To Dissect the Pathways in the Retromandibular Fossa, the Parotid Gland was Removed.

2.56 Deep Lateral Facial Area: Left Lateral View. [1]

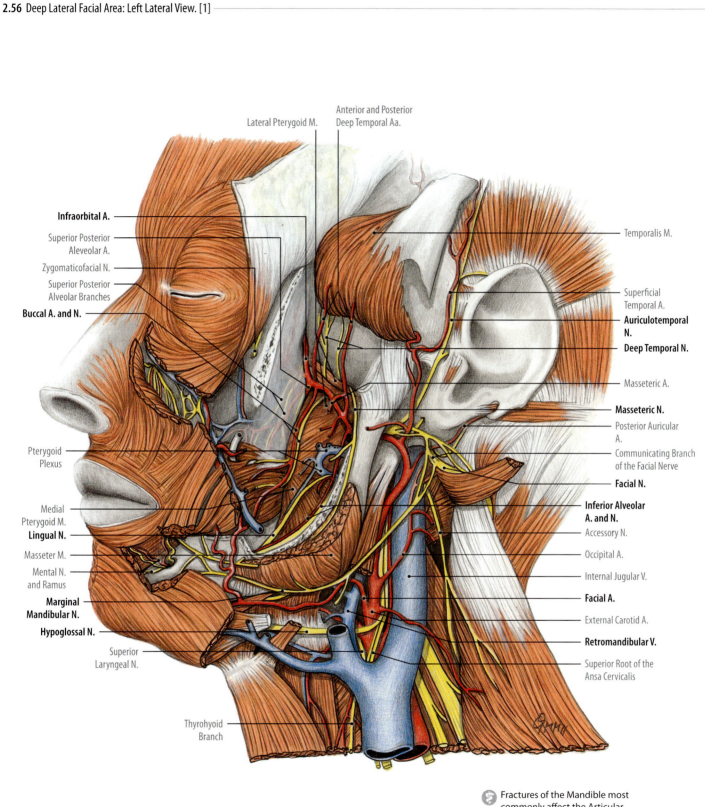

Infraorbital A.

Superior Posterior Aleveolar A.

Zygomaticofacial N.

Superior Posterior Alveolar Branches

Buccal A. and N.

Pterygoid Plexus

Medial Pterygoid M.

Lingual N.

Masseter M.

Mental N. and Ramus

Marginal Mandibular N.

Hypoglossal N.

Superior Laryngeal N.

Thyrohyoid Branch

Lateral Pterygoid M.

Anterior and Posterior Deep Temporal Aa.

Temporalis M.

Superficial Temporal A.

Auriculotemporal N.

Deep Temporal N.

Masseteric A.

Masseteric N.

Posterior Auricular A.

Communicating Branch of the Facial Nerve

Facial N.

Inferior Alveolar A. and N.

Accessory N.

Occipital A.

Internal Jugular V.

Facial A.

External Carotid A.

Retromandibular V.

Superior Root of the Ansa Cervicalis

Fractures of the Mandible most commonly affect the Articular Processes, the Jaw Angle, and the Canines. Extraoral Operational Care of Mandibular Fractures Endangers the Marginal Mandibular Ramus of the Facial N.
Injury of the Nerve Branch causes a Paralysis of the Muscles in the Lower Lip area: The corner of the Mouth Droops.

The Structures of the Infratemporal Fossa are shown following Resection of the Zygomatic Arch and a Part of the Mandible and the Masseter M. The Insertion of the Temporalis M. is Cranially Ectopic.

Face

2.57 Deep Lateral Facial Area: Left Lateral View. [8]

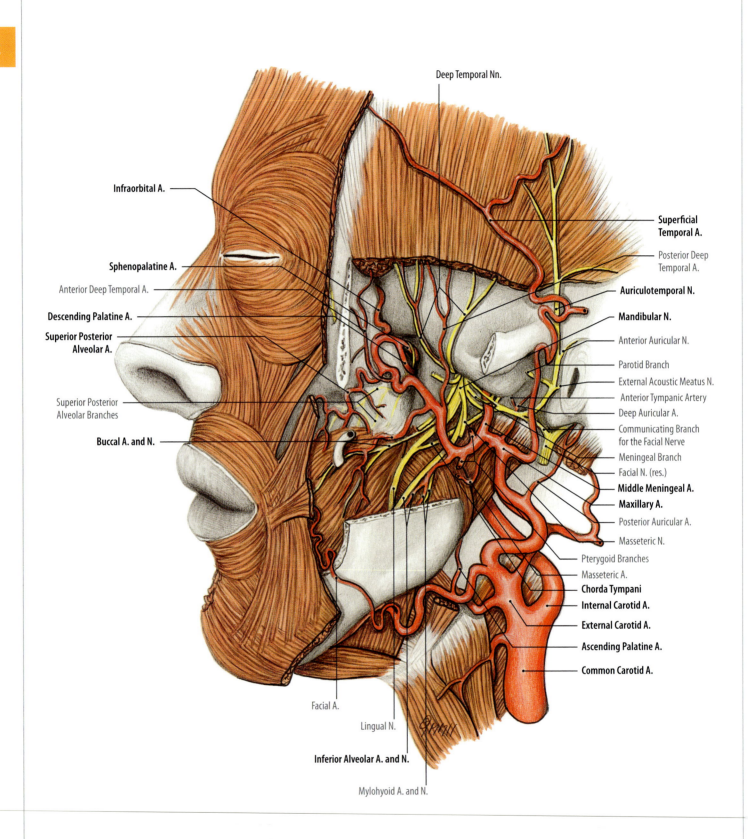

Deep Temporal Nn.

Infraorbital A.

Superficial Temporal A.

Posterior Deep Temporal A.

Sphenopalatine A.

Anterior Deep Temporal A.

Auriculotemporal N.

Descending Palatine A.

Mandibular N.

Superior Posterior Alveolar A.

Anterior Auricular N.

Parotid Branch

External Acoustic Meatus N.

Superior Posterior Alveolar Branches

Anterior Tympanic Artery

Deep Auricular A.

Communicating Branch for the Facial Nerve

Buccal A. and N.

Meningeal Branch

Facial N. (res.)

Middle Meningeal A.

Maxillary A.

Posterior Auricular A.

Masseteric N.

Pterygoid Branches

Masseteric A.

Chorda Tympani

Internal Carotid A.

External Carotid A.

Ascending Palatine A.

Common Carotid A.

Facial A.

Lingual N.

Inferior Alveolar A. and N.

Mylohyoid A. and N.

The structures of the Infratemporal and the Pterygopalatine Fossae were dissected following the resection of the Ramus of the Mandible superior to inferior Alveolar Foramen, the Zygomatic Arch, the Lateral Pterygoid M., and the insertion of the Temporalis M.

Mouth · Lips

2.58 Nasal and Oral Areas: Frontal View.

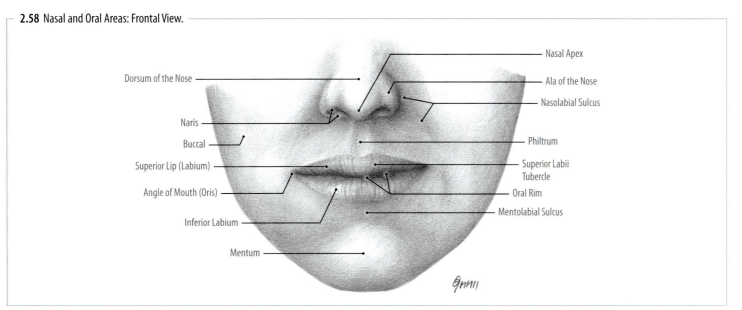

- Dorsum of the Nose
- Nasal Apex
- Ala of the Nose
- Nasolabial Sulcus
- Naris
- Buccal
- Philtrum
- Superior Lip (Labium)
- Superior Labii Tubercle
- Angle of Mouth (Oris)
- Oral Rim
- Inferior Labium
- Mentolabial Sulcus
- Mentum

2.59a Muscles of the Lips. **b** Histological Sagittal Section through the Upper Lip, HE Staining × 4.0 [b 6]

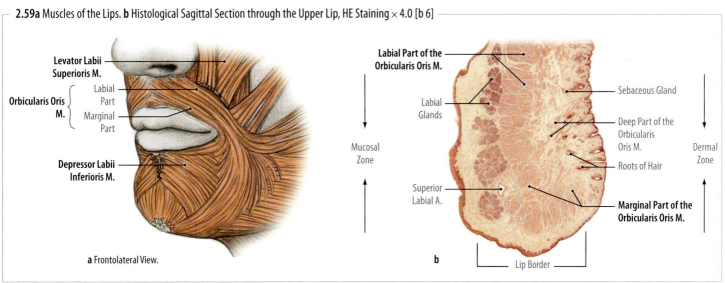

- Levator Labii Superioris M.
- Orbicularis Oris M.
  - Labial Part
  - Marginal Part
- Depressor Labii Inferioris M.

a Frontolateral View.

- Labial Part of the Orbicularis Oris M.
- Labial Glands
- Sebaceous Gland
- Deep Part of the Orbicularis Oris M.
- Roots of Hair
- Superior Labial A.
- Marginal Part of the Orbicularis Oris M.
- Mucosal Zone
- Dermal Zone
- Lip Border

b

2.60a–d Orientation Directions and Viewing Areas of the Teeth: Quadrant Arrangement.

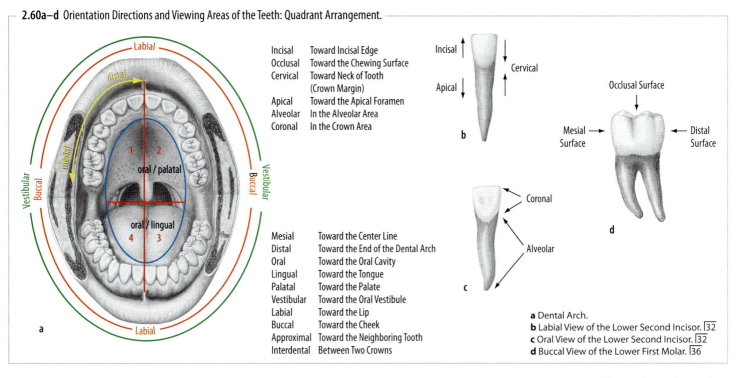

Incisal	Toward Incisal Edge
Occlusal	Toward the Chewing Surface
Cervical	Toward Neck of Tooth (Crown Margin)
Apical	Toward the Apical Foramen
Alveolar	In the Alveolar Area
Coronal	In the Crown Area

Mesial	Toward the Center Line
Distal	Toward the End of the Dental Arch
Oral	Toward the Oral Cavity
Lingual	Toward the Tongue
Palatal	Toward the Palate
Vestibular	Toward the Oral Vestibule
Labial	Toward the Lip
Buccal	Toward the Cheek
Approximal	Toward the Neighboring Tooth
Interdental	Between Two Crowns

a Dental Arch.
b Labial View of the Lower Second Incisor. |32
c Oral View of the Lower Second Incisor. |32
d Buccal View of the Lower First Molar. |36

Mouth and Oral Cavity

2.61 The First Molar of the Mandible with an Illustration of the Periodontium (Parodontium): Sagittal Section, Semi-Schematic Illustration.

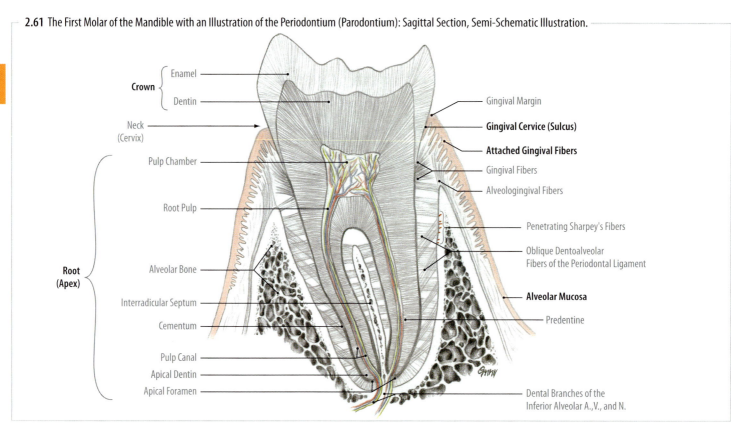

- **Crown** { Enamel / Dentin }
- Neck (Cervix)
- Pulp Chamber
- Root Pulp
- **Root (Apex)**
- Alveolar Bone
- Interradicular Septum
- Cementum
- Pulp Canal
- Apical Dentin
- Apical Foramen
- Gingival Margin
- **Gingival Cervice (Sulcus)**
- **Attached Gingival Fibers**
- Gingival Fibers
- Alveologingival Fibers
- Penetrating Sharpey's Fibers
- Oblique Dentoalveolar Fibers of the Periodontal Ligament
- **Alveolar Mucosa**
- Predentine
- Dental Branches of the Inferior Alveolar A.,V., and N.

2.62 Dentition of the Right Side of Intercuspidation in a Neutral Occlusion: Labial Buccal View.

The Two-Digit System proposed by the Federation Dentaire Internationale (FDI) for Both Primary and Secondary Dentitions has been accepted by WHO and the International Association of Dental Research (IADR).

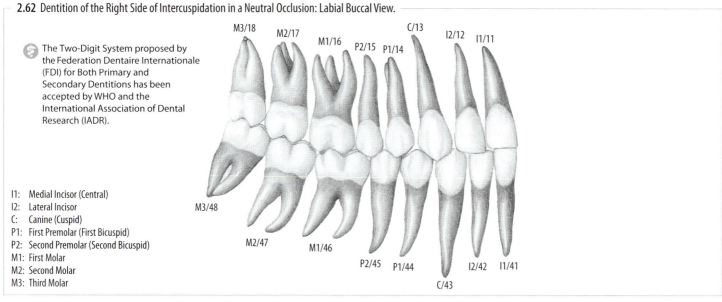

I1: Medial Incisor (Central)
I2: Lateral Incisor
C: Canine (Cuspid)
P1: First Premolar (First Bicuspid)
P2: Second Premolar (Second Bicuspid)
M1: First Molar
M2: Second Molar
M3: Third Molar

M3/18 M2/17 M1/16 P2/15 P1/14 C/13 I2/12 I1/11

M3/48 M2/47 M1/46 P2/45 P1/44 C/43 I2/42 I1/41

2.63 Dental Formula of the Permanent Teeth: Frontal View. [18]

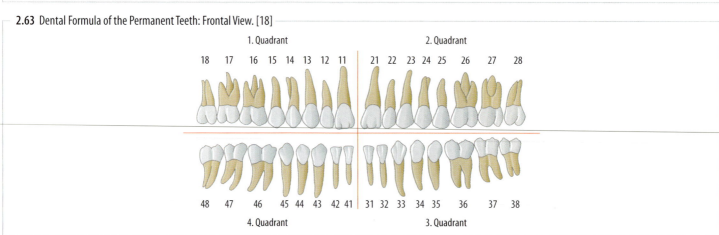

1. Quadrant
18 17 16 15 14 13 12 11

2. Quadrant
21 22 23 24 25 26 27 28

48 47 46 45 44 43 42 41
4. Quadrant

31 32 33 34 35 36 37 38
3. Quadrant

2.64a,b Teeth of the Maxilla and Mandible: Left Side.

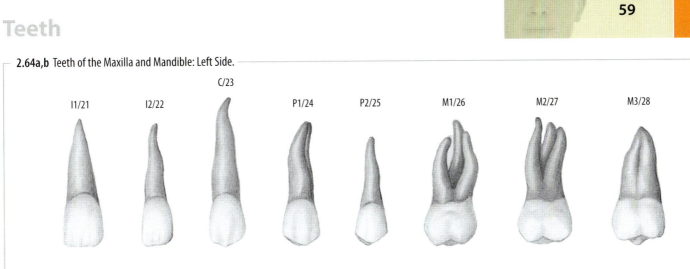

I1/21 I2/22 C/23 P1/24 P2/25 M1/26 M2/27 M3/28

I1/31 I2/32 C/33 P1/34 P2/35 M1/36 M2/37 M3/38

a **Frontal Teeth: Labial View. Lateral Teeth: Buccal View**.

Carabelli's Tubercle

C/23

M3/28 M2/27 M1/26 P2/25 P1/24 I2/22 I1/21

M3/38 M2/37 M1/36 P2/35 P1/34 C/33 I2/32 I1/31

b **Maxillary Teeth, Palatal View. Mandibular Teeth: Lingual View.**

2.65 Oral Vestibule, Oral Cavity, and Isthmus of Fauces: Frontal View. [18]

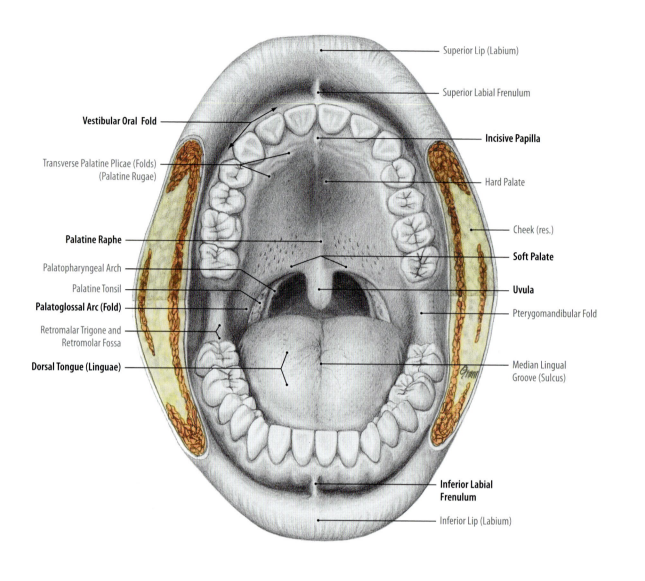

Superior Lip (Labium)

Superior Labial Frenulum

Vestibular Oral Fold

Incisive Papilla

Transverse Palatine Plicae (Folds)
(Palatine Rugae)

Hard Palate

Palatine Raphe

Cheek (res.)

Palatopharyngeal Arch

Soft Palate

Palatine Tonsil

Uvula

Palatoglossal Arc (Fold)

Pterygomandibular Fold

Retromalar Trigone and
Retromolar Fossa

Dorsal Tongue (Linguae)

Median Lingual
Groove (Sulcus)

**Inferior Labial
Frenulum**

Inferior Lip (Labium)

Lips and Cheeks are Incised.

2.66 Structures of the Mouth Floor, Raised Tongue. [19]

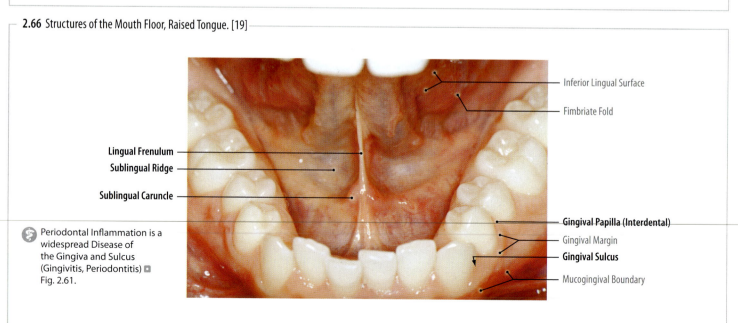

Inferior Lingual Surface

Fimbriate Fold

Lingual Frenulum
Sublingual Ridge

Sublingual Caruncle

Gingival Papilla (Interdental)

Gingival Margin

Gingival Sulcus

Mucogingival Boundary

🔵 Periodontal Inflammation is a
widespread Disease of
the Gingiva and Sulcus
(Gingivitis, Periodontitis) ◻
Fig. 2.61.

Tongue Muscles

2.67 Extrinsic Tongue Muscles: Right Lateral View. [48]

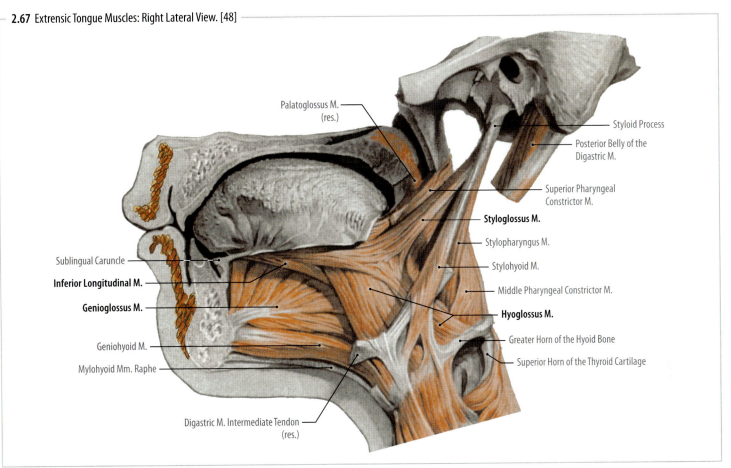

- Palatoglossus M. (res.)
- Styloid Process
- Posterior Belly of the Digastric M.
- Superior Pharyngeal Constrictor M.
- **Styloglossus M.**
- Stylopharyngus M.
- Stylohyoid M.
- Middle Pharyngeal Constrictor M.
- **Hyoglossus M.**
- Greater Horn of the Hyoid Bone
- Superior Horn of the Thyroid Cartilage
- Sublingual Caruncle
- **Inferior Longitudinal M.**
- **Genioglossus M.**
- Geniohyoid M.
- Mylohyoid Mm. Raphe
- Digastric M. Intermediate Tendon (res.)

2.68 Oral Vestibule, Oral Cavity, and Nasopharynx. [6]

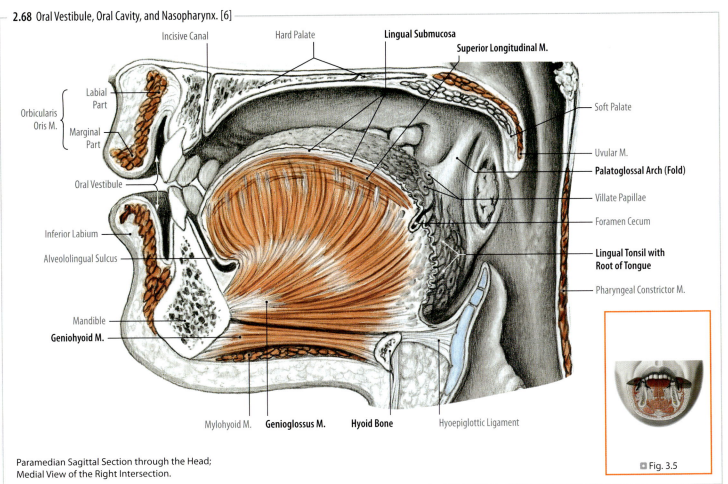

- Incisive Canal
- Hard Palate
- **Lingual Submucosa**
- **Superior Longitudinal M.**
- Orbicularis Oris M.
  - Labial Part
  - Marginal Part
- Soft Palate
- Uvular M.
- **Palatoglossal Arch (Fold)**
- Oral Vestibule
- Villate Papillae
- Foramen Cecum
- Inferior Labium
- Alveololingual Sulcus
- **Lingual Tonsil with Root of Tongue**
- Pharyngeal Constrictor M.
- Mandible
- **Geniohyoid M.**
- Mylohyoid M.
- **Genioglossus M.**
- **Hyoid Bone**
- Hyoepiglottic Ligament

Paramedian Sagittal Section through the Head;
Medial View of the Right Intersection.

☐ Fig. 3.5

Mouth and Oral Cavity

Tongue · Palate

2.69 Back and Root of the Tongue: Vertical View. [6]

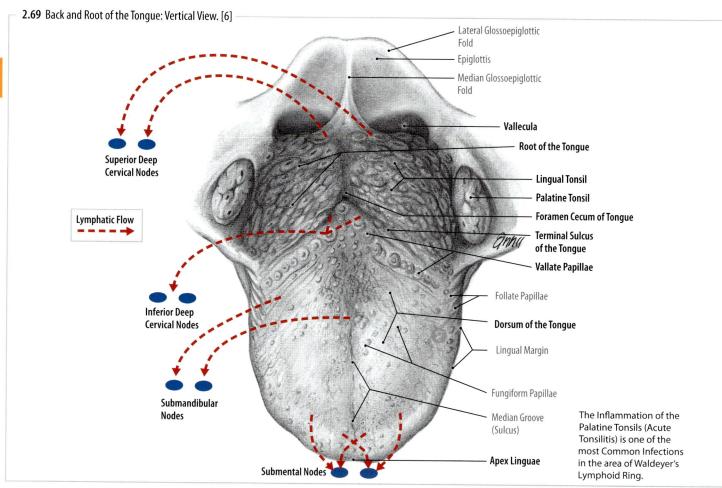

Lateral Glossoepiglottic Fold

Epiglottis

Median Glossoepiglottic Fold

Vallecula

Root of the Tongue

Lingual Tonsil

Palatine Tonsil

Foramen Cecum of Tongue

Terminal Sulcus of the Tongue

Vallate Papillae

Follate Papillae

Dorsum of the Tongue

Lingual Margin

Fungiform Papillae

Median Groove (Sulcus)

Apex Linguae

Superior Deep Cervical Nodes

Lymphatic Flow

Inferior Deep Cervical Nodes

Submandibular Nodes

Submental Nodes

The Inflammation of the Palatine Tonsils (Acute Tonsilitis) is one of the most Common Infections in the area of Waldeyer's Lymphoid Ring.

2.70 Structures and Pathways of the Hard and Soft Palate: Frontal Inferior View. [6]

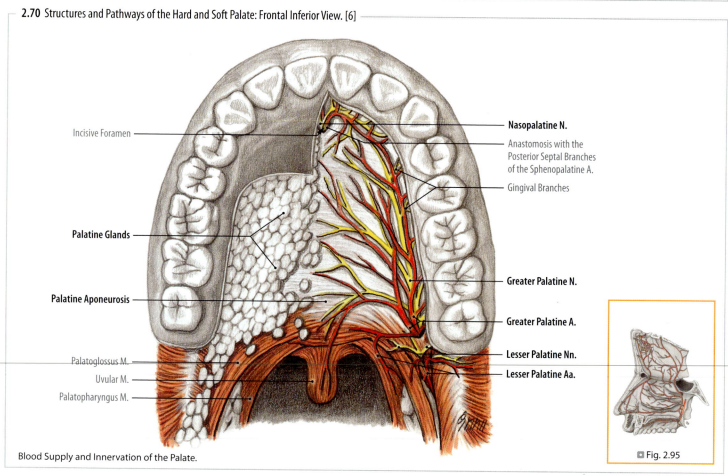

Incisive Foramen

Palatine Glands

Palatine Aponeurosis

Palatoglossus M.

Uvular M.

Palatopharyngus M.

Nasopalatine N.

Anastomosis with the Posterior Septal Branches of the Sphenopalatine A.

Gingival Branches

Greater Palatine N.

Greater Palatine A.

Lesser Palatine Nn.

Lesser Palatine Aa.

▫ Fig. 2.95

Blood Supply and Innervation of the Palate.

Tongue and Floor of the Mouth Vessels

2.71a,b Tongue, Floor of the Mouth, and Tonsillar Area: Arterial (a) and Venous (b) Supply. [20]

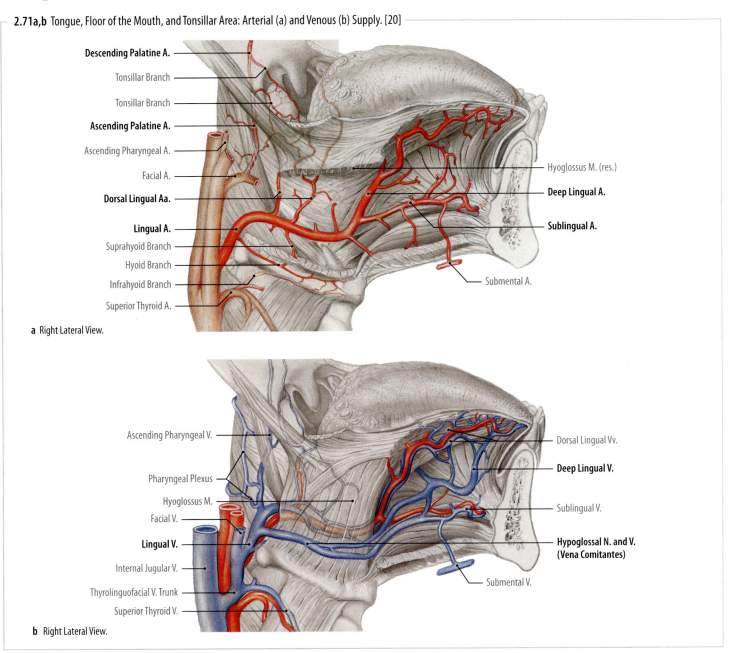

Descending Palatine A.

Tonsillar Branch

Tonsillar Branch

Ascending Palatine A.

Ascending Pharyngeal A.

Facial A.

Dorsal Lingual Aa.

Lingual A.

Suprahyoid Branch

Hyoid Branch

Infrahyoid Branch

Superior Thyroid A.

Hyoglossus M. (res.)

Deep Lingual A.

Sublingual A.

Submental A.

a Right Lateral View.

Ascending Pharyngeal V.

Pharyngeal Plexus

Hyoglossus M.

Facial V.

Lingual V.

Internal Jugular V.

Thyrolinguofacial V. Trunk

Superior Thyroid V.

Dorsal Lingual Vv.

Deep Lingual V.

Sublingual V.

Hypoglossal N. and V. (Vena Comitantes)

Submental V.

b Right Lateral View.

2.72 Tongue, Lips, and Teeth: Lymph Channels and Regional Lymph Nodes. [20]

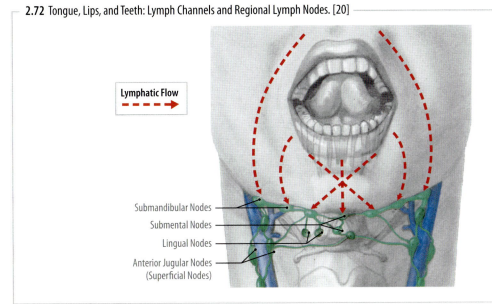

Lymphatic Flow

Submandibular Nodes

Submental Nodes

Lingual Nodes

Anterior Jugular Nodes (Superficial Nodes)

Carcinomas of the Lip and in the Anterior and Medial Areas of the Tongue may Metastasize into the Submental and Submandibular Lymph Nodes.

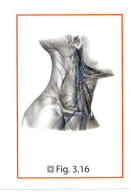

◻ Fig. 3.16

Mouth and Oral Cavity

2.73 Nerves of the Oral Cavity and the Pharynx: Right Lateral View. [13]

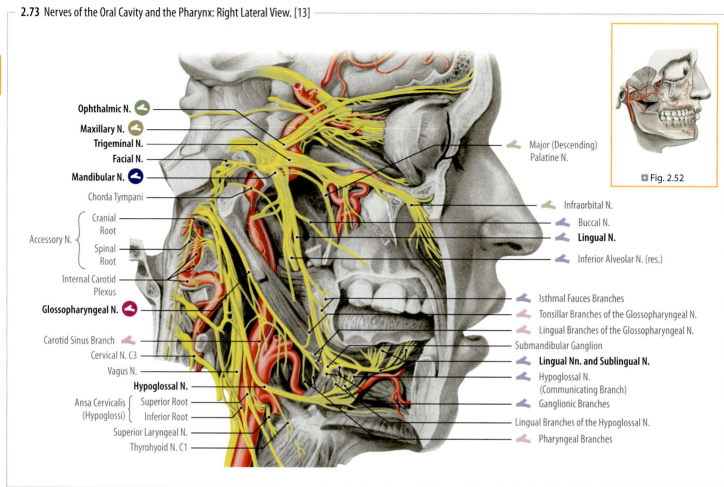

Ophthalmic N.

Maxillary N.

Trigeminal N.

Facial N.

Mandibular N.

Chorda Tympani

Accessory N. { Cranial Root / Spinal Root }

Internal Carotid Plexus

Glossopharyngeal N.

Carotid Sinus Branch

Cervical N. C3

Vagus N.

Hypoglossal N.

Ansa Cervicalis (Hypoglossi) { Superior Root / Inferior Root }

Superior Laryngeal N.

Thyrohyoid N. C1

Major (Descending) Palatine N.

Infraorbital N.

Buccal N.

Lingual N.

Inferior Alveolar N. (res.)

Isthmal Fauces Branches

Tonsillar Branches of the Glossopharyngeal N.

Lingual Branches of the Glossopharyngeal N.

Submandibular Ganglion

Lingual Nn. and Sublingual N.

Hypoglossal N. (Communicating Branch)

Ganglionic Branches

Lingual Branches of the Hypoglossal N.

Pharyngeal Branches

□ Fig. 2.52

2.74 Innervation of the Teeth and Oral Cavity: Right Lateral View. [13]

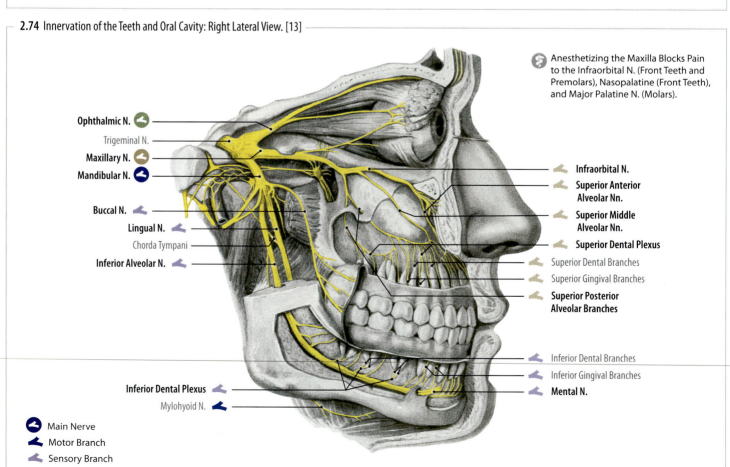

Anesthetizing the Maxilla Blocks Pain to the Infraorbital N. (Front Teeth and Premolars), Nasopalatine (Front Teeth), and Major Palatine N. (Molars).

Ophthalmic N.

Trigeminal N.

Maxillary N.

Mandibular N.

Buccal N.

Lingual N.

Chorda Tympani

Inferior Alveolar N.

Inferior Dental Plexus

Mylohyoid N.

Infraorbital N.

Superior Anterior Alveolar Nn.

Superior Middle Alveolar Nn.

Superior Dental Plexus

Superior Dental Branches

Superior Gingival Branches

Superior Posterior Alveolar Branches

Inferior Dental Branches

Inferior Gingival Branches

Mental N.

Main Nerve

Motor Branch

Sensory Branch

Innervation of the Tongue, Gums, Oral Cavity

2.75 Proprioceptive Sensation of the Tongue Surface (Left Side) and Taste Innervation (Right Side). [21, 70]

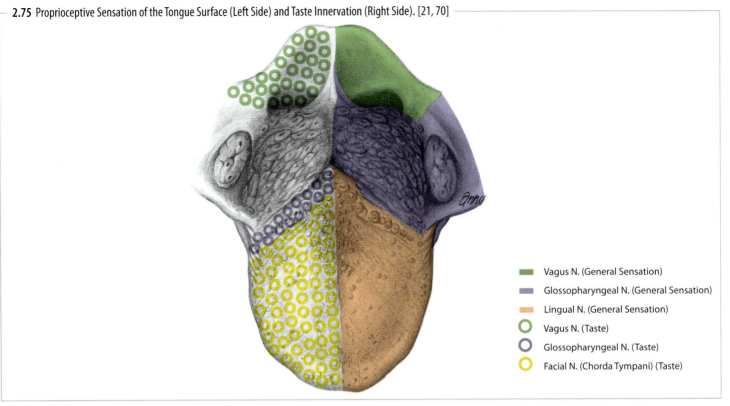

- Vagus N. (General Sensation)
- Glossopharyngeal N. (General Sensation)
- Lingual N. (General Sensation)
- Vagus N. (Taste)
- Glossopharyngeal N. (Taste)
- Facial N. (Chorda Tympani) (Taste)

2.76 Innervation of the Oral Cavity. [13, 70]

Nerve Block of the Oral Cavity

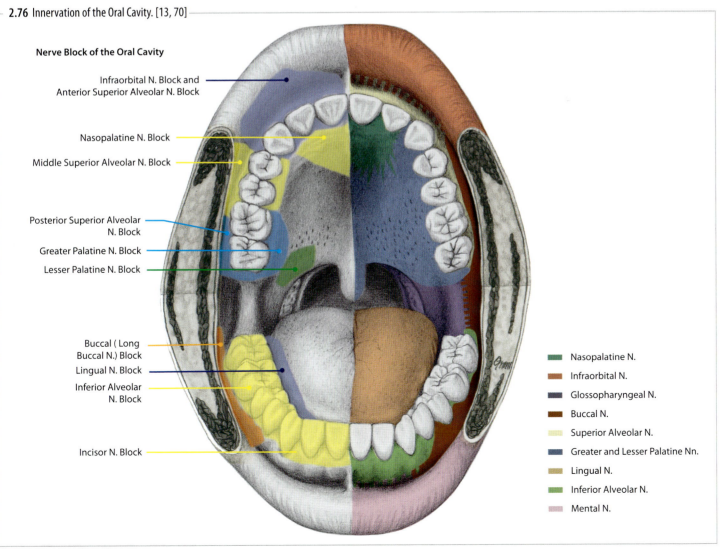

Infraorbital N. Block and Anterior Superior Alveolar N. Block

Nasopalatine N. Block

Middle Superior Alveolar N. Block

Posterior Superior Alveolar N. Block

Greater Palatine N. Block

Lesser Palatine N. Block

Buccal (Long Buccal N.) Block

Lingual N. Block

Inferior Alveolar N. Block

Incisor N. Block

- Nasopalatine N.
- Infraorbital N.
- Glossopharyngeal N.
- Buccal N.
- Superior Alveolar N.
- Greater and Lesser Palatine Nn.
- Lingual N.
- Inferior Alveolar N.
- Mental N.

Mouth and Oral Cavity

2.77 Salivary Glands: Right Lateral View. [1]

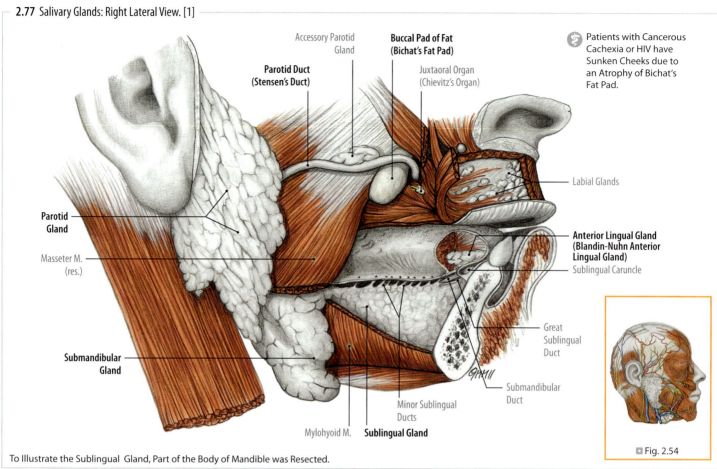

Accessory Parotid Gland

Buccal Pad of Fat (Bichat's Fat Pad)

Juxtaoral Organ (Chievitz's Organ)

Parotid Duct (Stensen's Duct)

Patients with Cancerous Cachexia or HIV have Sunken Cheeks due to an Atrophy of Bichat's Fat Pad.

Parotid Gland

Masseter M. (res.)

Labial Glands

Anterior Lingual Gland (Blandin-Nuhn Anterior Lingual Gland)

Sublingual Caruncle

Great Sublingual Duct

Submandibular Gland

Submandibular Duct

Minor Sublingual Ducts

Mylohyoid M.   **Sublingual Gland**

■ Fig. 2.54

To Illustrate the Sublingual Gland, Part of the Body of Mandible was Resected.

2.78 Innervation of the Glands in the Head Area. [13]

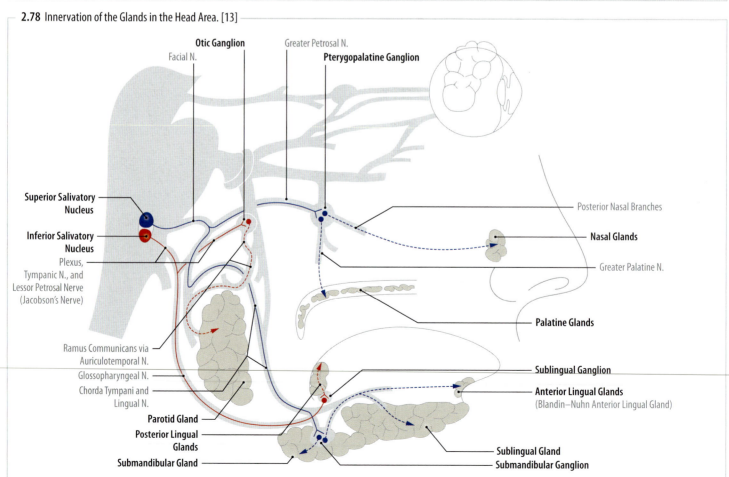

Otic Ganglion   Greater Petrosal N.

Facial N.   **Pterygopalatine Ganglion**

Superior Salivatory Nucleus

Inferior Salivatory Nucleus

Plexus, Tympanic N., and Lessor Petrosal Nerve (Jacobson's Nerve)

Posterior Nasal Branches

Nasal Glands

Greater Palatine N.

Palatine Glands

Ramus Communicans via Auriculotemporal N.

Glossopharyngeal N.

Chorda Tympani and Lingual N.

Sublingual Ganglion

Anterior Lingual Glands (Blandin–Nuhn Anterior Lingual Gland)

Parotid Gland

Posterior Lingual Glands

Sublingual Gland

Submandibular Gland   **Submandibular Ganglion**

2.79 Mandible and Sublingual Area: Right Lateral View. [20]

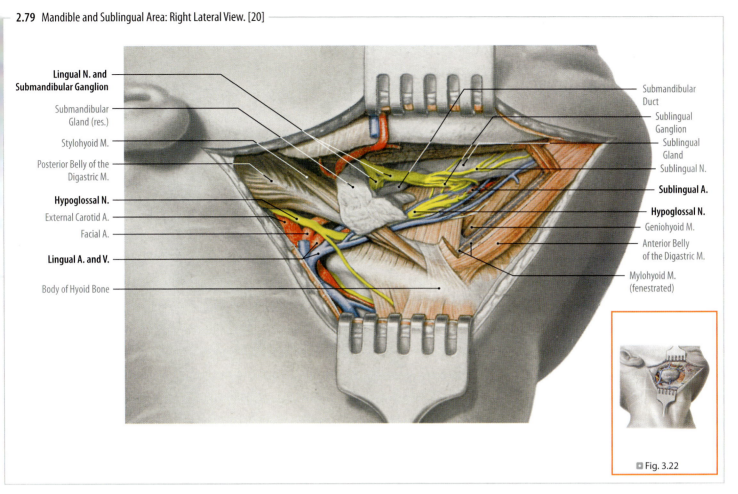

Lingual N. and Submandibular Ganglion

Submandibular Gland (res.)

Stylohyoid M.

Posterior Belly of the Digastric M.

Hypoglossal N.

External Carotid A.

Facial A.

Lingual A. and V.

Body of Hyoid Bone

Submandibular Duct

Sublingual Ganglion

Sublingual Gland

Sublingual N.

Sublingual A.

Hypoglossal N.

Geniohyoid M.

Anterior Belly of the Digastric M.

Mylohyoid M. (fenestrated)

◻ Fig. 3.22

2.80 Sublingual Area and Floor of the Mouth Following Removal of the Mucous Membrane: Frontolateral View. [20]

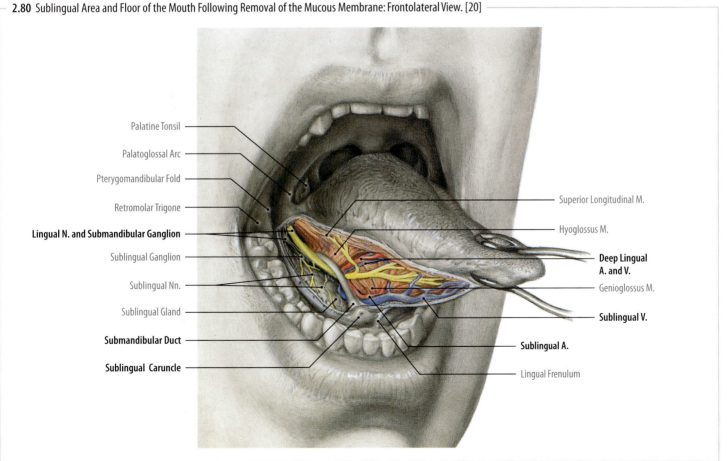

Palatine Tonsil

Palatoglossal Arc

Pterygomandibular Fold

Retromolar Trigone

Lingual N. and Submandibular Ganglion

Sublingual Ganglion

Sublingual Nn.

Sublingual Gland

Submandibular Duct

Sublingual Caruncle

Superior Longitudinal M.

Hyoglossus M.

Deep Lingual A. and V.

Genioglossus M.

Sublingual V.

Sublingual A.

Lingual Frenulum

Mouth and Oral Cavity

Sublingual Area, Oral Cavity

Parotid Duct

Mandibular Ramus and Body (res.)

Lingual N.

Sublingual Process of the Submandibular Gland

Hypoglossal N.

Submandibular Gland

Sublingual Mucosa

Sublingual Gland

Sublingual N.

Sublingual A. and V.

Genioglossus M.

Geniohyoid M.

Anterior Belly of the Digastric M.

Mylohyoid M.

Hyoglossus M.

Hypoglossal Nerve Injury results in Paralysis and Atrophy of Same-Side Muscles. The surface of the Tongue is Wrinkled and Reduced in Size. To test a patient, ask him or her to Protrude the Tongue, you will notice a Drift toward the Paralyzed Side (Ipsilateral Deviation).

a

Masseter M.

Lingual N.

Submandibular Ganglion

Submandibular Gland

Styloglossus M.

Lingual Branches of the Lingual N.

Deep Lingual V.

Sublingual Caruncle

Submandibular Duct

Deep Lingual A.

Sublingual A. and V.

Sublingual N. (res.)

Submental A. and V.

Sublingual Ganglion

Hypoglossal N.

a With Preserved Sublingual Gland.
b Following Removal of the Sublingual Gland.   b

Sialolith (Calculus) develops most commonly in the Submandibular Gland and to a Lesser Degree in the Parotid Duct. It manifests by Swelling, Painful Salivation, and Congestion of the Affected Gland (Sialolithiasis).

2.82 Cartilaginous and Bony Skeleton of the Nasal Septum and Cartilages of the Ala: Left Lateral View. [12]

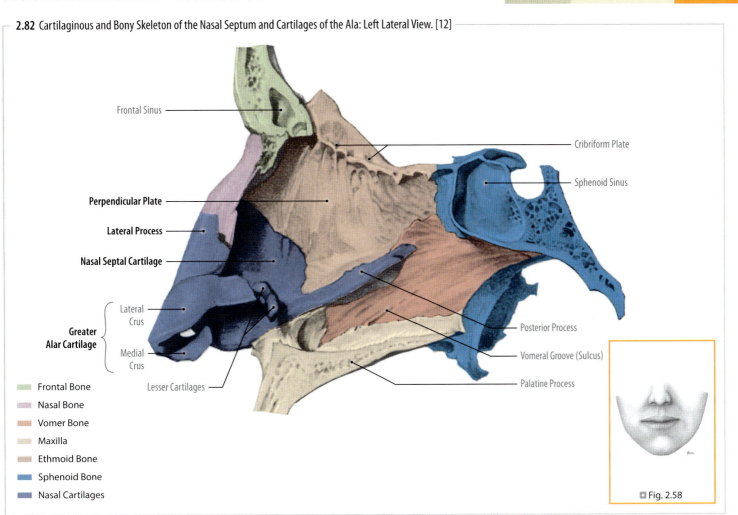

Frontal Sinus

Cribriform Plate

Sphenoid Sinus

Perpendicular Plate

Lateral Process

Nasal Septal Cartilage

Greater Alar Cartilage
- Lateral Crus
- Medial Crus

Lesser Cartilages

Posterior Process

Vomeral Groove (Sulcus)

Palatine Process

- Frontal Bone
- Nasal Bone
- Vomer Bone
- Maxilla
- Ethmoid Bone
- Sphenoid Bone
- Nasal Cartilages

Fig. 2.58

2.83 Mucosal Membrane of the Nasal Septum, Paramedian Sagittal Section: Left Lateral View. [6]

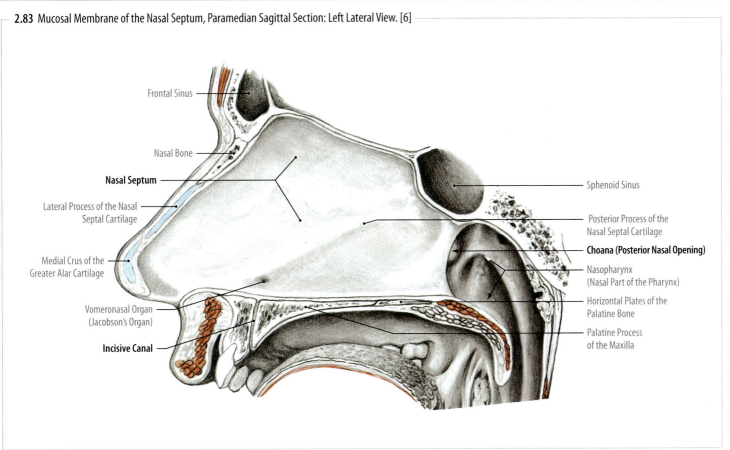

Frontal Sinus

Nasal Bone

Nasal Septum

Lateral Process of the Nasal Septal Cartilage

Medial Crus of the Greater Alar Cartilage

Vomeronasal Organ (Jacobson's Organ)

Incisive Canal

Sphenoid Sinus

Posterior Process of the Nasal Septal Cartilage

Choana (Posterior Nasal Opening)

Nasopharynx (Nasal Part of the Pharynx)

Horizontal Plates of the Palatine Bone

Palatine Process of the Maxilla

Nose

2.84 Bony Skeleton of the Right Lateral Nasal Wall: Median Sagittal Section, Lateral View. [12]

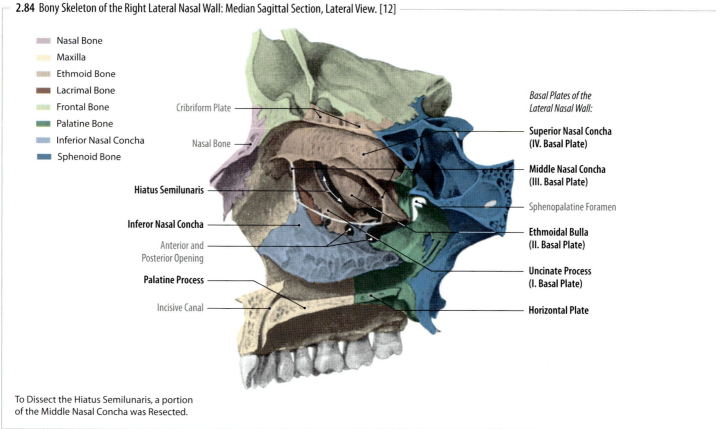

- Nasal Bone
- Maxilla
- Ethmoid Bone
- Lacrimal Bone
- Frontal Bone
- Palatine Bone
- Inferior Nasal Concha
- Sphenoid Bone

Cribriform Plate

Nasal Bone

Hiatus Semilunaris

Inferor Nasal Concha

Anterior and
Posterior Opening

Palatine Process

Incisive Canal

*Basal Plates of the
Lateral Nasal Wall:*

Superior Nasal Concha
(IV. Basal Plate)

Middle Nasal Concha
(III. Basal Plate)

Sphenopalatine Foramen

Ethmoidal Bulla
(II. Basal Plate)

Uncinate Process
(I. Basal Plate)

Horizontal Plate

To Dissect the Hiatus Semilunaris, a portion
of the Middle Nasal Concha was Resected.

2.85 Mucosa of the Right Lateral Nasal Wall: Median Sagittal Section, Right Lateral View. [6]

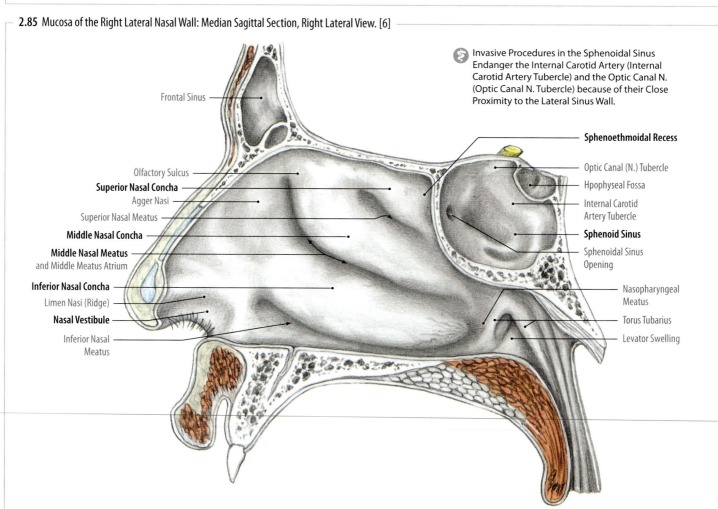

Invasive Procedures in the Sphenoidal Sinus
Endanger the Internal Carotid Artery (Internal
Carotid Artery Tubercle) and the Optic Canal N.
(Optic Canal N. Tubercle) because of their Close
Proximity to the Lateral Sinus Wall.

Frontal Sinus

Olfactory Sulcus
Superior Nasal Concha
Agger Nasi
Superior Nasal Meatus
Middle Nasal Concha
Middle Nasal Meatus
and Middle Meatus Atrium
Inferior Nasal Concha
Limen Nasi (Ridge)
Nasal Vestibule
Inferior Nasal
Meatus

Sphenoethmoidal Recess

Optic Canal (N.) Tubercle
Hpophyseal Fossa
Internal Carotid
Artery Tubercle
Sphenoid Sinus
Sphenoidal Sinus
Opening
Nasopharyngeal
Meatus
Torus Tubarius
Levator Swelling

Nasal Cavity, Paranasal Sinuses

2.86 Frontal Section through the Head in the Area of the Crista Galli: Posterior View. [6]

A Deviated Nasal Septum may Obstruct the Nasal Passage, causing Breathing Difficulty, Hypoosmia, or Anosmia (No Smell), and Headaches. Hematomas of the Septum generally arise From Blunt Trauma (Common in Children). A Septonasal Abscess may Develop as a result of an Inflammation.

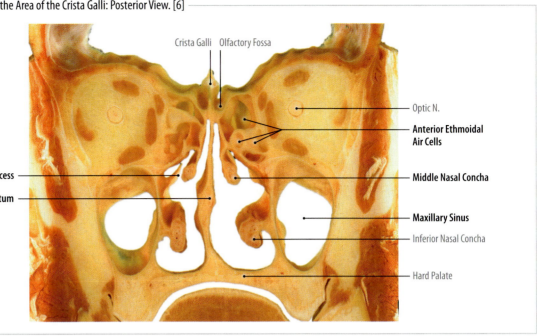

Crista Galli   Olfactory Fossa

Optic N.

Anterior Ethmoidal Air Cells

Uncinate Process — **Middle Nasal Concha**

Nasal Septum — **Maxillary Sinus**

Inferior Nasal Concha

Hard Palate

Section of the Nasal Cavity, Paranasal Sinuses, and Orbits.

2.87 Schematic Illustration of the Bony Structure of the Nasal Cavity and Paranasal Sinuses: Frontal Section. (cf. Fig. 2.86) [14]

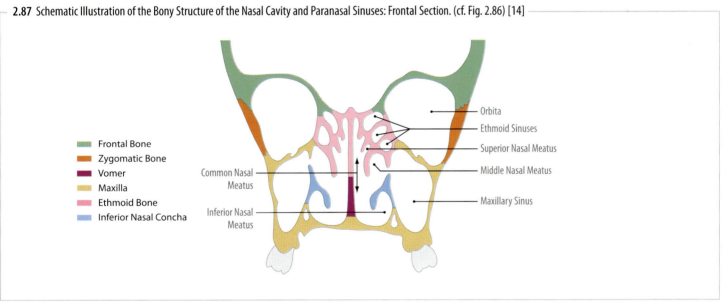

- ■ Frontal Bone
- ■ Zygomatic Bone
- ■ Vomer
- ■ Maxilla
- ■ Ethmoid Bone
- ■ Inferior Nasal Concha

Orbita

Ethmoid Sinuses

Superior Nasal Meatus

Common Nasal Meatus

Middle Nasal Meatus

Maxillary Sinus

Inferior Nasal Meatus

2.88 Histologic Section through the Inferior Nasal Concha, Azan-Staining. [6]

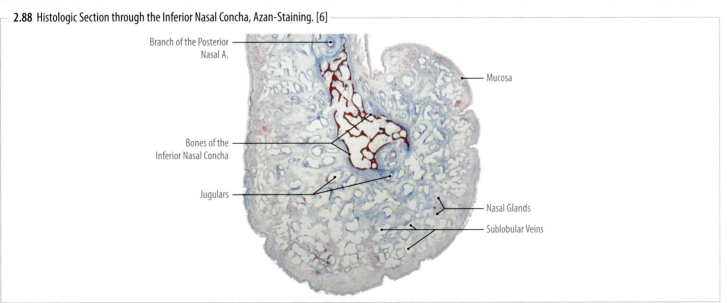

Branch of the Posterior Nasal A.

Mucosa

Bones of the Inferior Nasal Concha

Jugulars

Nasal Glands

Sublobular Veins

Nose

2.89a,b Projection of the Paranasal Sinuses into the Skull. [22, 23]

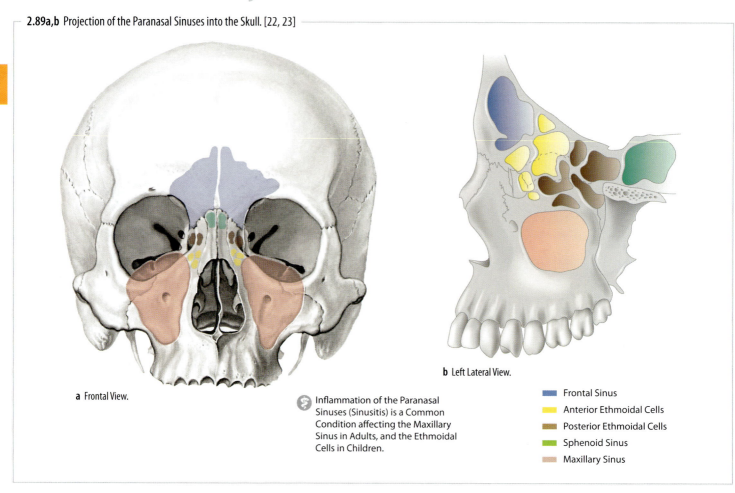

b Left Lateral View.

a Frontal View.

🔎 Inflammation of the Paranasal Sinuses (Sinusitis) is a Common Condition affecting the Maxillary Sinus in Adults, and the Ethmoidal Cells in Children.

■	Frontal Sinus
■	Anterior Ethmoidal Cells
■	Posterior Ethmoidal Cells
■	Sphenoid Sinus
■	Maxillary Sinus

2.90 Nasal Wall: Right Lateral View. Aperture of the Paranasal Sinuses and the Nasolacrimal Duct: Medial View. [15]

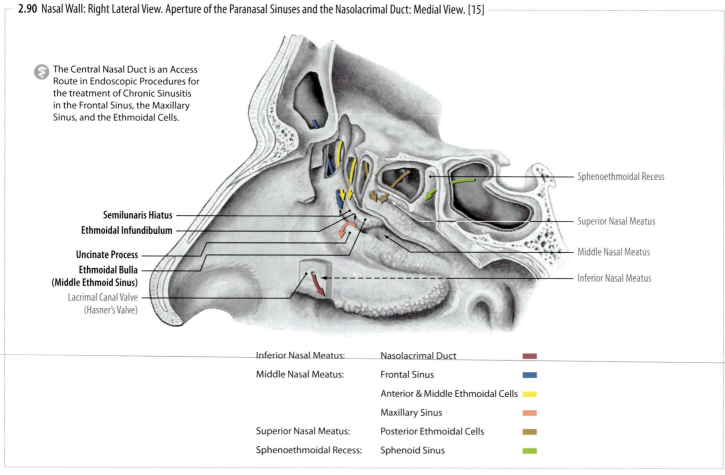

🔎 The Central Nasal Duct is an Access Route in Endoscopic Procedures for the treatment of Chronic Sinusitis in the Frontal Sinus, the Maxillary Sinus, and the Ethmoidal Cells.

Semilunaris Hiatus

Ethmoidal Infundibulum

Uncinate Process

**Ethmoidal Bulla
(Middle Ethmoid Sinus)**

Lacrimal Canal Valve
(Hasner's Valve)

Sphenoethmoidal Recess

Superior Nasal Meatus

Middle Nasal Meatus

Inferior Nasal Meatus

Inferior Nasal Meatus:	Nasolacrimal Duct	■
Middle Nasal Meatus:	Frontal Sinus	■
	Anterior & Middle Ethmoidal Cells	■
	Maxillary Sinus	■
Superior Nasal Meatus:	Posterior Ethmoidal Cells	■
Sphenoethmoidal Recess:	Sphenoid Sinus	■

Paranasal Sinuses

2.91 Frontal Sinus, Anterior, Middle, and Posterior Ethmoidal Cells, and the Sphenoid Sinus. [8]

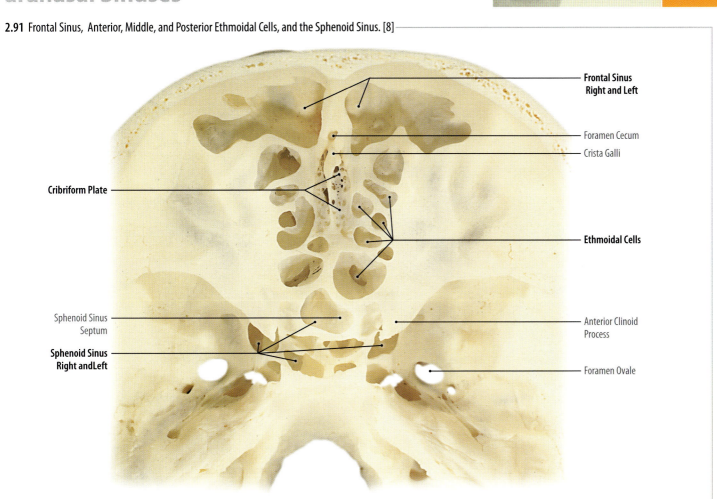

Frontal Sinus
Right and Left

Foramen Cecum

Crista Galli

Cribriform Plate

Ethmoidal Cells

Sphenoid Sinus
Septum

Anterior Clinoid
Process

**Sphenoid Sinus
Right and Left**

Foramen Ovale

Frontal area of the Interior Cranial Fossa; Paranasal Sinuses Opened from Cranial Cavity.

2.92 Ethmoidal Cells: Right Lateral View. [8]

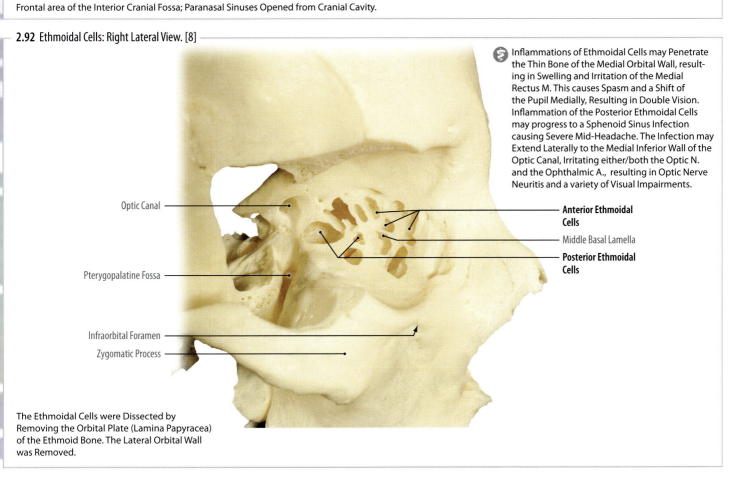

Inflammations of Ethmoidal Cells may Penetrate the Thin Bone of the Medial Orbital Wall, resulting in Swelling and Irritation of the Medial Rectus M. This causes Spasm and a Shift of the Pupil Medially, Resulting in Double Vision. Inflammation of the Posterior Ethmoidal Cells may progress to a Sphenoid Sinus Infection causing Severe Mid-Headache. The Infection may Extend Laterally to the Medial Inferior Wall of the Optic Canal, Irritating either/both the Optic N. and the Ophthalmic A., resulting in Optic Nerve Neuritis and a variety of Visual Impairments.

Optic Canal

Pterygopalatine Fossa

Infraorbital Foramen

Zygomatic Process

**Anterior Ethmoidal
Cells**

Middle Basal Lamella

**Posterior Ethmoidal
Cells**

The Ethmoidal Cells were Dissected by Removing the Orbital Plate (Lamina Papyracea) of the Ethmoid Bone. The Lateral Orbital Wall was Removed.

Nose

Paranasal Sinuses

2.93 Facial Skull with Opened Frontal Sinuses: Frontal View. [8]

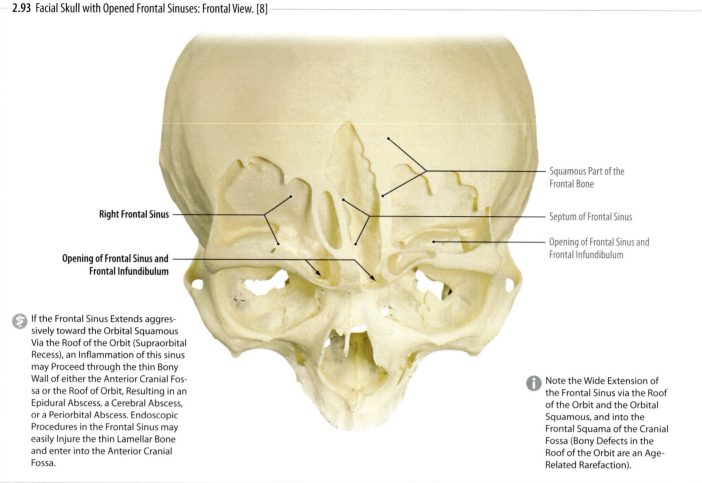

Right Frontal Sinus

Opening of Frontal Sinus and Frontal Infundibulum

Squamous Part of the Frontal Bone

Septum of Frontal Sinus

Opening of Frontal Sinus and Frontal Infundibulum

If the Frontal Sinus Extends aggressively toward the Orbital Squamous Via the Roof of the Orbit (Supraorbital Recess), an Inflammation of this sinus may Proceed through the thin Bony Wall of either the Anterior Cranial Fossa or the Roof of Orbit, Resulting in an Epidural Abscess, a Cerebral Abscess, or a Periorbital Abscess. Endoscopic Procedures in the Frontal Sinus may easily Injure the thin Lamellar Bone and enter into the Anterior Cranial Fossa.

Note the Wide Extension of the Frontal Sinus via the Roof of the Orbit and the Orbital Squamous, and into the Frontal Squama of the Cranial Fossa (Bony Defects in the Roof of the Orbit are an Age-Related Rarefaction).

2.94 Maxillary Sinus: Partial Left Lateral View of a Skull. [1]

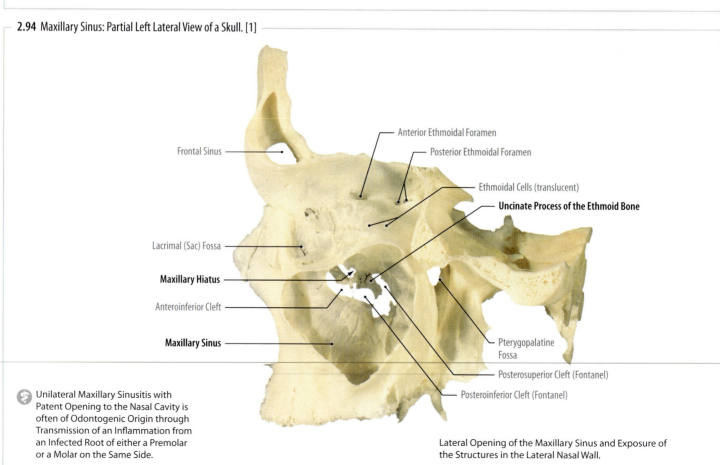

Frontal Sinus

Anterior Ethmoidal Foramen

Posterior Ethmoidal Foramen

Ethmoidal Cells (translucent)

Uncinate Process of the Ethmoid Bone

Lacrimal (Sac) Fossa

Maxillary Hiatus

Anteroinferior Cleft

Maxillary Sinus

Pterygopalatine Fossa

Posterosuperior Cleft (Fontanel)

Posteroinferior Cleft (Fontanel)

Unilateral Maxillary Sinusitis with Patent Opening to the Nasal Cavity is often of Odontogenic Origin through Transmission of an Inflammation from an Infected Root of either a Premolar or a Molar on the Same Side.

Lateral Opening of the Maxillary Sinus and Exposure of the Structures in the Lateral Nasal Wall.

2.95 Arterial Supply of the Nasal Septum (Folded over Cranially) and the Right Lateral Nasal Wall. [18]

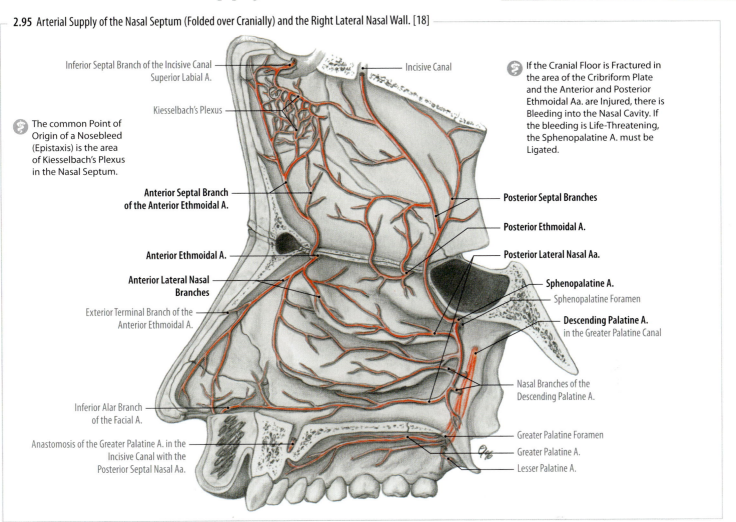

Inferior Septal Branch of the Incisive Canal
Superior Labial A.

Incisive Canal

Kiesselbach's Plexus

The common Point of Origin of a Nosebleed (Epistaxis) is the area of Kiesselbach's Plexus in the Nasal Septum.

If the Cranial Floor is Fractured in the area of the Cribriform Plate and the Anterior and Posterior Ethmoidal Aa. are Injured, there is Bleeding into the Nasal Cavity. If the bleeding is Life-Threatening, the Sphenopalatine A. must be Ligated.

Anterior Septal Branch of the Anterior Ethmoidal A.

Posterior Septal Branches

Posterior Ethmoidal A.

Anterior Ethmoidal A.

Posterior Lateral Nasal Aa.

Anterior Lateral Nasal Branches

Sphenopalatine A.

Sphenopalatine Foramen

Exterior Terminal Branch of the Anterior Ethmoidal A.

Descending Palatine A. in the Greater Palatine Canal

Inferior Alar Branch of the Facial A.

Nasal Branches of the Descending Palatine A.

Greater Palatine Foramen

Anastomosis of the Greater Palatine A. in the Incisive Canal with the Posterior Septal Nasal Aa.

Greater Palatine A.

Lesser Palatine A.

2.96 Sensory Supply of the Nasal Cavity: Medial View of the Right Lateral Nasal Wall. [13]

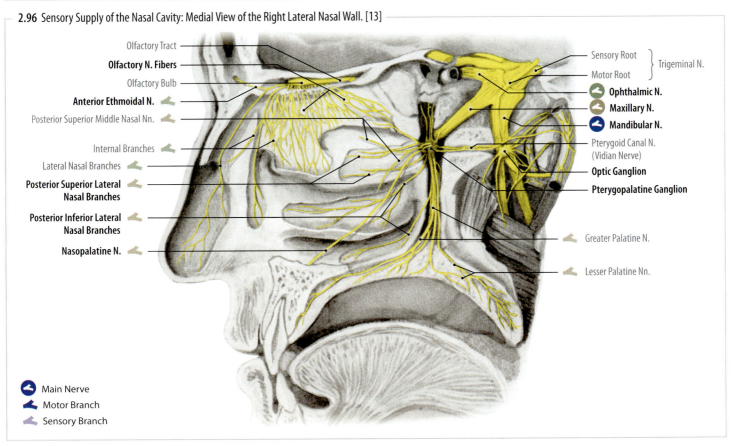

Olfactory Tract

Sensory Root ⎫
Motor Root ⎭ Trigeminal N.

Olfactory N. Fibers

Olfactory Bulb

Ophthalmic N.

Anterior Ethmoidal N.

Maxillary N.

Posterior Superior Middle Nasal Nn.

Mandibular N.

Internal Branches

Pterygoid Canal N. (Vidian Nerve)

Lateral Nasal Branches

Optic Ganglion

Posterior Superior Lateral Nasal Branches

Pterygopalatine Ganglion

Posterior Inferior Lateral Nasal Branches

Greater Palatine N.

Nasopalatine N.

Lesser Palatine Nn.

Main Nerve
Motor Branch
Sensory Branch

Nose

2.97 Computer Tomography (CT): Nasal Cavity, Paranasal Sinuses, and Orbita. [10]

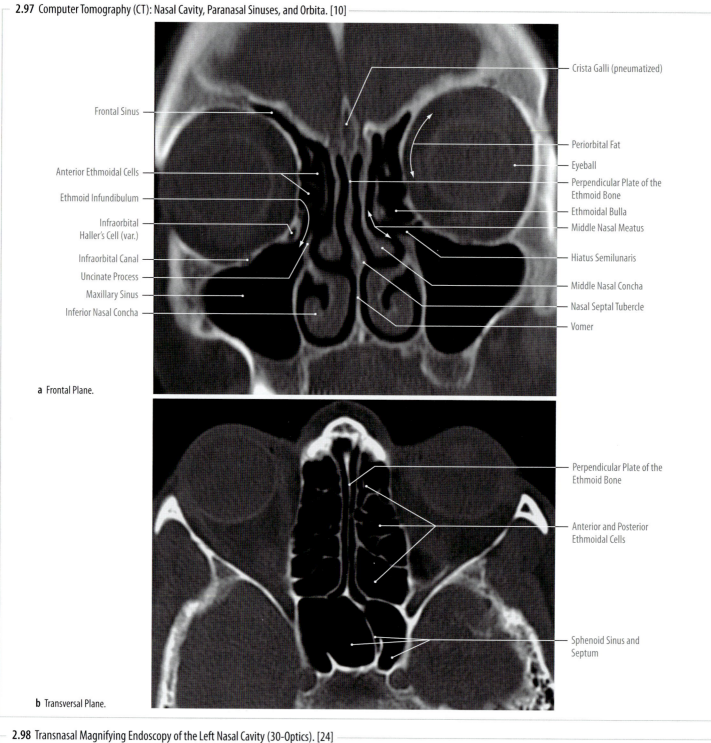

Crista Galli (pneumatized)

Frontal Sinus

Periorbital Fat

Eyeball

Anterior Ethmoidal Cells

Perpendicular Plate of the Ethmoid Bone

Ethmoid Infundibulum

Ethmoidal Bulla

Middle Nasal Meatus

Infraorbital Haller's Cell (var.)

Hiatus Semilunaris

Infraorbital Canal

Uncinate Process

Middle Nasal Concha

Maxillary Sinus

Nasal Septal Tubercle

Inferior Nasal Concha

Vomer

a Frontal Plane.

Perpendicular Plate of the Ethmoid Bone

Anterior and Posterior Ethmoidal Cells

Sphenoid Sinus and Septum

b Transversal Plane.

2.98 Transnasal Magnifying Endoscopy of the Left Nasal Cavity (30-Optics). [24]

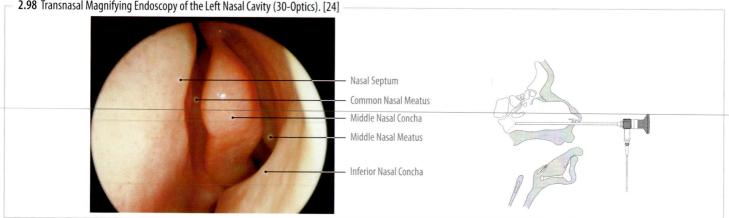

Nasal Septum

Common Nasal Meatus

Middle Nasal Concha

Middle Nasal Meatus

Inferior Nasal Concha

2.99a–c Orbita Area. [25]

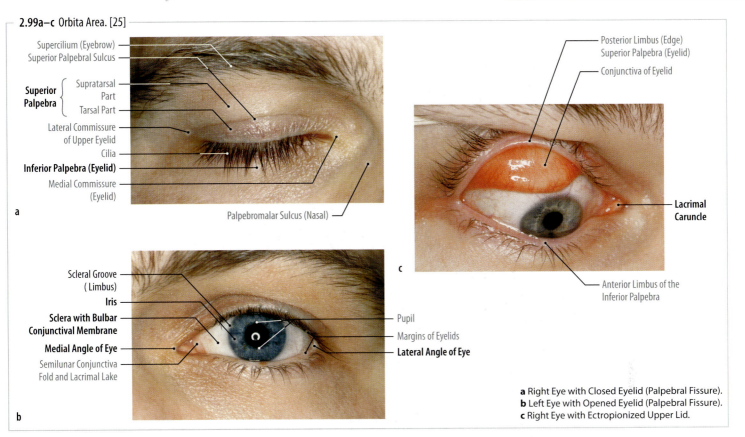

Supercilium (Eyebrow)
Superior Palpebral Sulcus

Superior Palpebra
- Supratarsal Part
- Tarsal Part

Lateral Commissure of Upper Eyelid

Cilia

Inferior Palpebra (Eyelid)

Medial Commissure (Eyelid)

Palpebromalar Sulcus (Nasal)

a

Posterior Limbus (Edge) Superior Palpebra (Eyelid)

Conjunctiva of Eyelid

Lacrimal Caruncle

Anterior Limbus of the Inferior Palpebra

c

Scleral Groove (Limbus)

Iris

Sclera with Bulbar Conjunctival Membrane

Medial Angle of Eye

Semilunar Conjunctiva Fold and Lacrimal Lake

Pupil

Margins of Eyelids

Lateral Angle of Eye

b

a Right Eye with Closed Eyelid (Palpebral Fissure).
b Left Eye with Opened Eyelid (Palpebral Fissure).
c Right Eye with Ectropionized Upper Lid.

2.100 Sagittal Section through the Eyelids and Anterior Eye Segment. [14]

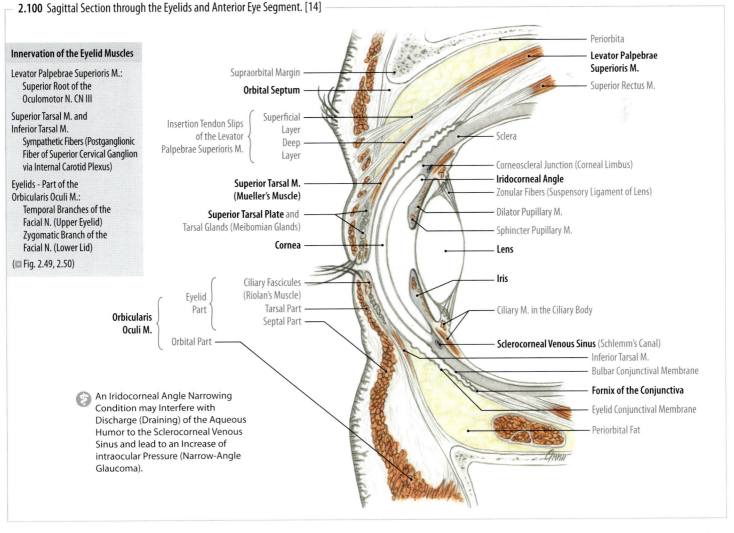

Innervation of the Eyelid Muscles

Levator Palpebrae Superioris M.:
Superior Root of the Oculomotor N. CN III

Superior Tarsal M. and Inferior Tarsal M.
Sympathetic Fibers (Postganglionic Fiber of Superior Cervical Ganglion via Internal Carotid Plexus)

Eyelids - Part of the Orbicularis Oculi M.:
Temporal Branches of the Facial N. (Upper Eyelid)
Zygomatic Branch of the Facial N. (Lower Lid)
(☐ Fig. 2.49, 2.50)

Supraorbital Margin

Orbital Septum

Insertion Tendon Slips of the Levator Palpebrae Superioris M.
- Superficial Layer
- Deep Layer

Superior Tarsal M. (Mueller's Muscle)

Superior Tarsal Plate and Tarsal Glands (Meibomian Glands)

Cornea

Ciliary Fascicules (Riolan's Muscle)

Orbicularis Oculi M.
- Eyelid Part
  - Tarsal Part
  - Septal Part
- Orbital Part

Periorbita

Levator Palpebrae Superioris M.

Superior Rectus M.

Sclera

Corneoscleral Junction (Corneal Limbus)

Iridocorneal Angle

Zonular Fibers (Suspensory Ligament of Lens)

Dilator Pupillary M.

Sphincter Pupillary M.

Lens

Iris

Ciliary M. in the Ciliary Body

Sclerocorneal Venous Sinus (Schlemm's Canal)

Inferior Tarsal M.

Bulbar Conjunctival Membrane

Fornix of the Conjunctiva

Eyelid Conjunctival Membrane

Periorbital Fat

An Iridocorneal Angle Narrowing Condition may Interfere with Discharge (Draining) of the Aqueous Humor to the Sclerocorneal Venous Sinus and lead to an Increase of intraocular Pressure (Narrow-Angle Glaucoma).

Eye and Orbit

Bony Orbit

2.101 Right Orbit: Frontal View. [23]

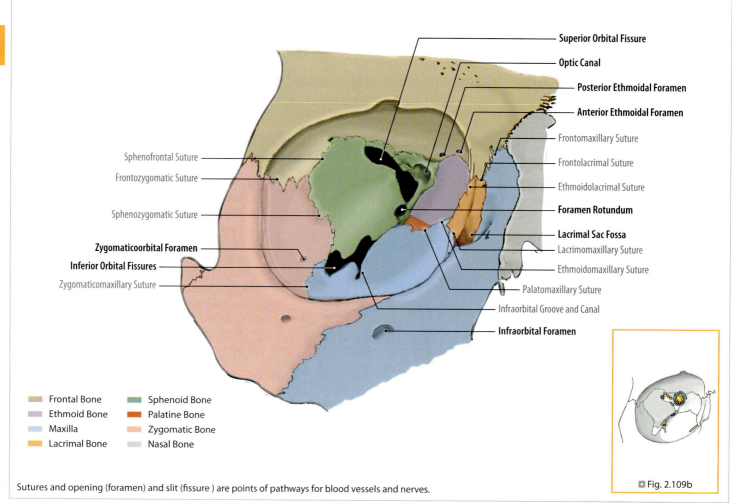

Sphenofrontal Suture

Frontozygomatic Suture

Sphenozygomatic Suture

Zygomaticoorbital Foramen

Inferior Orbital Fissures

Zygomaticomaxillary Suture

Superior Orbital Fissure

Optic Canal

Posterior Ethmoidal Foramen

Anterior Ethmoidal Foramen

Frontomaxillary Suture

Frontolacrimal Suture

Ethmoidolacrimal Suture

Foramen Rotundum

Lacrimal Sac Fossa

Lacrimomaxillary Suture

Ethmoidomaxillary Suture

Palatomaxillary Suture

Infraorbital Groove and Canal

Infraorbital Foramen

Frontal Bone
Ethmoid Bone
Maxilla
Lacrimal Bone

Sphenoid Bone
Palatine Bone
Zygomatic Bone
Nasal Bone

Fig. 2.109b

Sutures and opening (foramen) and slit (fissure) are points of pathways for blood vessels and nerves.

2.102a–d Bony Walls of the Orbit. [23]

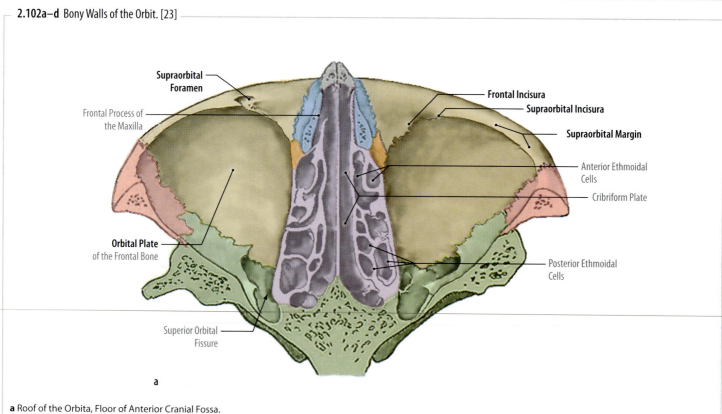

Supraorbital Foramen

Frontal Process of the Maxilla

Orbital Plate of the Frontal Bone

Superior Orbital Fissure

Frontal Incisura

Supraorbital Incisura

Supraorbital Margin

Anterior Ethmoidal Cells

Cribriform Plate

Posterior Ethmoidal Cells

a

a Roof of the Orbita, Floor of Anterior Cranial Fossa.

Bony Orbit

2.102b–d Bony Walls of the Orbit.

Frontal Bone
Ethmoid Bone
Maxilla
Lacrimal Bone
Sphenoid Bone
Palatine Bone
Zygomatic Bone
Nasal Bone

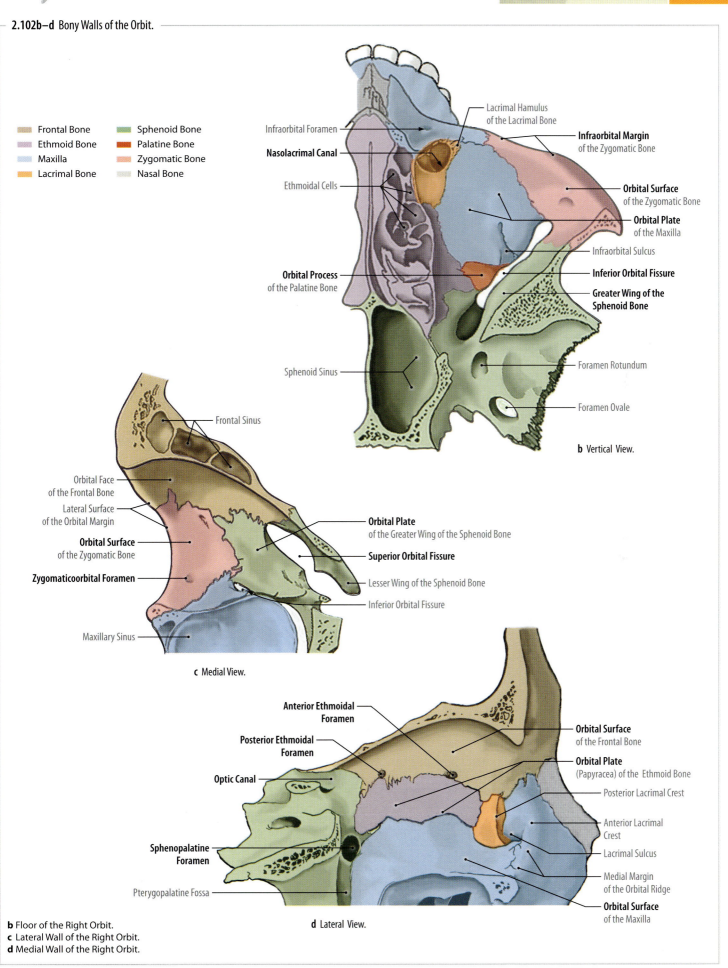

Infraorbital Foramen

Lacrimal Hamulus
of the Lacrimal Bone

Nasolacrimal Canal

Infraorbital Margin
of the Zygomatic Bone

Ethmoidal Cells

Orbital Surface
of the Zygomatic Bone

Orbital Plate
of the Maxilla

Infraorbital Sulcus

Orbital Process
of the Palatine Bone

Inferior Orbital Fissure

**Greater Wing of the
Sphenoid Bone**

Sphenoid Sinus

Foramen Rotundum

Foramen Ovale

b Vertical View.

Frontal Sinus

Orbital Face
of the Frontal Bone

Lateral Surface
of the Orbital Margin

Orbital Surface
of the Zygomatic Bone

Zygomaticoorbital Foramen

Maxillary Sinus

Orbital Plate
of the Greater Wing of the Sphenoid Bone

Superior Orbital Fissure

Lesser Wing of the Sphenoid Bone

Inferior Orbital Fissure

c Medial View.

**Anterior Ethmoidal
Foramen**

**Posterior Ethmoidal
Foramen**

Optic Canal

**Sphenopalatine
Foramen**

Pterygopalatine Fossa

Orbital Surface
of the Frontal Bone

Orbital Plate
(Papyracea) of the Ethmoid Bone

Posterior Lacrimal Crest

Anterior Lacrimal
Crest

Lacrimal Sulcus

Medial Margin
of the Orbital Ridge

Orbital Surface
of the Maxilla

d Lateral View.

b Floor of the Right Orbit.
c Lateral Wall of the Right Orbit.
d Medial Wall of the Right Orbit.

Eye and Orbit

2

2.103 Muscles and Pathways of the Eyelids and of the Periorbital Region: Frontal View. [1]

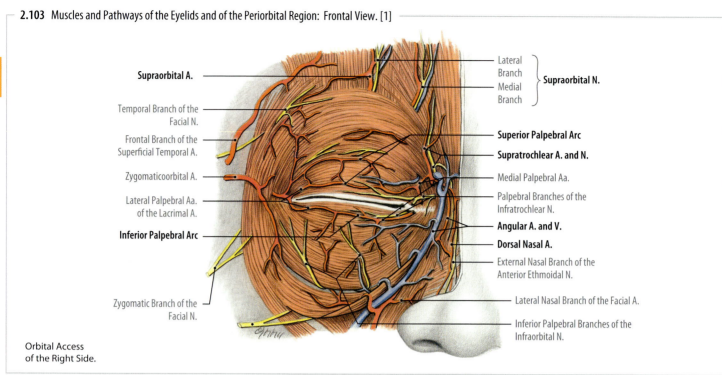

Supraorbital A.

Temporal Branch of the Facial N.

Frontal Branch of the Superficial Temporal A.

Zygomaticoorbital A.

Lateral Palpebral Aa. of the Lacrimal A.

Inferior Palpebral Arc

Zygomatic Branch of the Facial N.

Lateral Branch
Medial Branch
Supraorbital N.

Superior Palpebral Arc

Supratrochlear A. and N.

Medial Palpebral Aa.

Palpebral Branches of the Infratrochlear N.

Angular A. and V.

Dorsal Nasal A.

External Nasal Branch of the Anterior Ethmoidal N.

Lateral Nasal Branch of the Facial A.

Inferior Palpebral Branches of the Infraorbital N.

Orbital Access of the Right Side.

2.104a,b Orbital Access of the Right Side. (a) Orbital Septum, Tarsal Plates, and Palpebral Ligaments; and (b) Lacrimal Gland: Frontal View. [23]

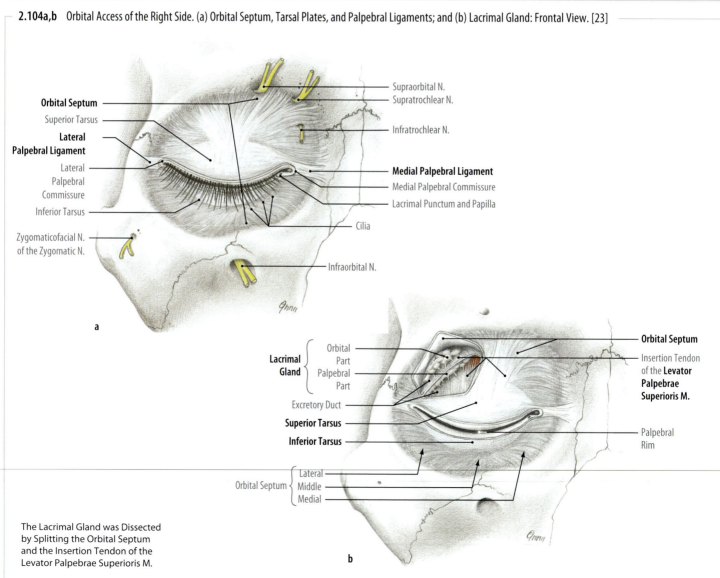

Orbital Septum

Superior Tarsus

Lateral Palpebral Ligament

Lateral Palpebral Commissure

Inferior Tarsus

Zygomaticofacial N. of the Zygomatic N.

Supraorbital N.
Supratrochlear N.

Infratrochlear N.

Medial Palpebral Ligament

Medial Palpebral Commissure

Lacrimal Punctum and Papilla

Cilia

Infraorbital N.

a

Lacrimal Gland
Orbital Part
Palpebral Part

Excretory Duct

Superior Tarsus

Inferior Tarsus

Orbital Septum
Lateral
Middle
Medial

Orbital Septum

Insertion Tendon of the **Levator Palpebrae Superioris M.**

Palpebral Rim

The Lacrimal Gland was Dissected by Splitting the Orbital Septum and the Insertion Tendon of the Levator Palpebrae Superioris M.

b

Conjunctiva and Tear Passages

2.105 Ocular Conjunctiva and Tear Passages of a Right Eye: Frontal View. [23, 26]

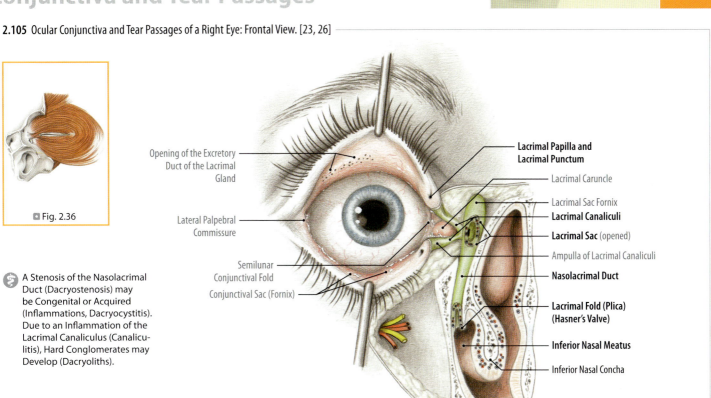

■ Fig. 2.36

Opening of the Excretory Duct of the Lacrimal Gland

Lateral Palpebral Commissure

Semilunar Conjunctival Fold

Conjunctival Sac (Fornix)

Lacrimal Papilla and Lacrimal Punctum

Lacrimal Caruncle

Lacrimal Sac Fornix

Lacrimal Canaliculi

Lacrimal Sac (opened)

Ampulla of Lacrimal Canaliculi

Nasolacrimal Duct

Lacrimal Fold (Plica) (Hasner's Valve)

Inferior Nasal Meatus

Inferior Nasal Concha

A Stenosis of the Nasolacrimal Duct (Dacryostenosis) may be Congenital or Acquired (Inflammations, Dacryocystitis). Due to an Inflammation of the Lacrimal Canaliculus (Canaliculitis), Hard Conglomerates may Develop (Dacryoliths).

Tear Passages have been Exposed by a Frontal Section.

2.106 Catheterization of the Tear Passages via the Canaliculus Inferior: Right Eye, Frontal View. [27]

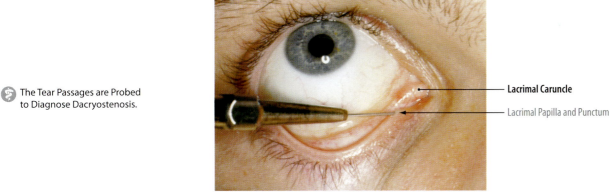

The Tear Passages are Probed to Diagnose Dacryostenosis.

Lacrimal Caruncle

Lacrimal Papilla and Punctum

2.107 Illustration of the Tear Film: Right Eye, Frontal View. [27]

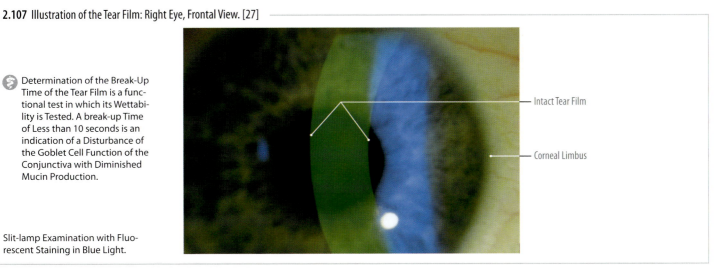

Determination of the Break-Up Time of the Tear Film is a functional test in which its Wettability is Tested. A break-up Time of Less than 10 seconds is an indication of a Disturbance of the Goblet Cell Function of the Conjunctiva with Diminished Mucin Production.

Intact Tear Film

Corneal Limbus

Slit-lamp Examination with Fluorescent Staining in Blue Light.

Eye and Orbit

2.108a–c Eye Muscles. [8, 79]

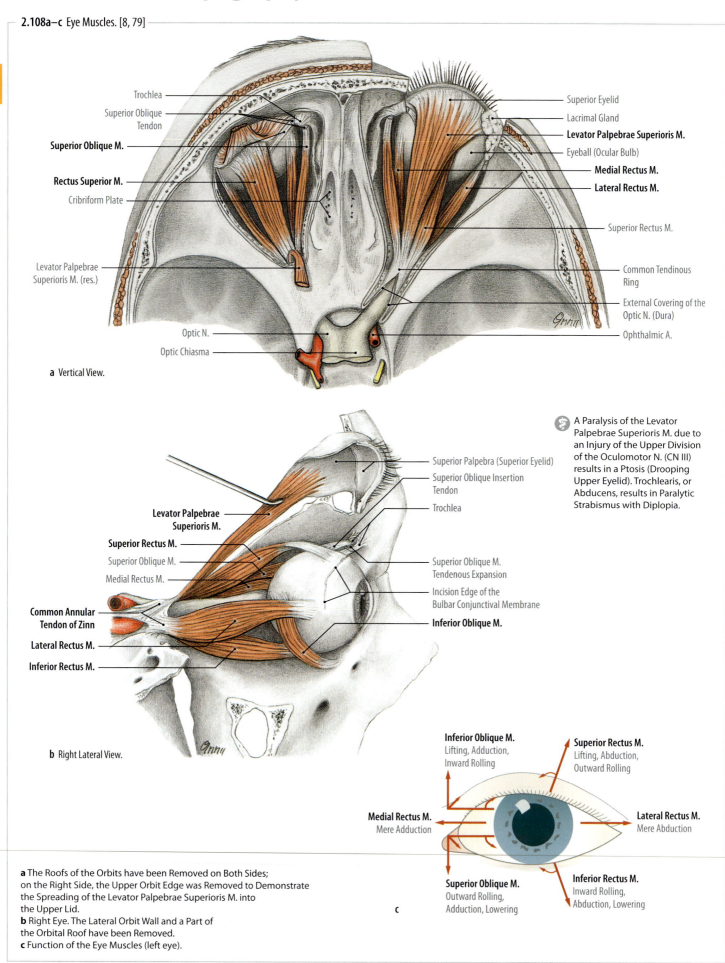

a Vertical View.

Trochlea

Superior Oblique Tendon

Superior Oblique M.

Rectus Superior M.

Cribriform Plate

Levator Palpebrae Superioris M. (res.)

Optic N.

Optic Chiasma

Superior Eyelid

Lacrimal Gland

Levator Palpebrae Superioris M.

Eyeball (Ocular Bulb)

Medial Rectus M.

Lateral Rectus M.

Superior Rectus M.

Common Tendinous Ring

External Covering of the Optic N. (Dura)

Ophthalmic A.

A Paralysis of the Levator Palpebrae Superioris M. due to an Injury of the Upper Division of the Oculomotor N. (CN III) results in a Ptosis (Drooping Upper Eyelid). Trochlearis, or Abducens, results in Paralytic Strabismus with Diplopia.

Superior Palpebra (Superior Eyelid)

Superior Oblique Insertion Tendon

Trochlea

Superior Oblique M. Tendenous Expansion

Incision Edge of the Bulbar Conjunctival Membrane

Inferior Oblique M.

Levator Palpebrae Superioris M.

Superior Rectus M.

Superior Oblique M.

Medial Rectus M.

Common Annular Tendon of Zinn

Lateral Rectus M.

Inferior Rectus M.

b Right Lateral View.

Inferior Oblique M.
Lifting, Adduction, Inward Rolling

Superior Rectus M.
Lifting, Abduction, Outward Rolling

Medial Rectus M.
Mere Adduction

Lateral Rectus M.
Mere Abduction

Superior Oblique M.
Outward Rolling, Adduction, Lowering

Inferior Rectus M.
Inward Rolling, Abduction, Lowering

c

a The Roofs of the Orbits have been Removed on Both Sides; on the Right Side, the Upper Orbit Edge was Removed to Demonstrate the Spreading of the Levator Palpebrae Superioris M. into the Upper Lid.
b Right Eye. The Lateral Orbit Wall and a Part of the Orbital Roof have been Removed.
c Function of the Eye Muscles (left eye).

Ocular Muscles, Pathways

2.109a,b Eye Muscles and Pathways: Frontal View. [23, 15]

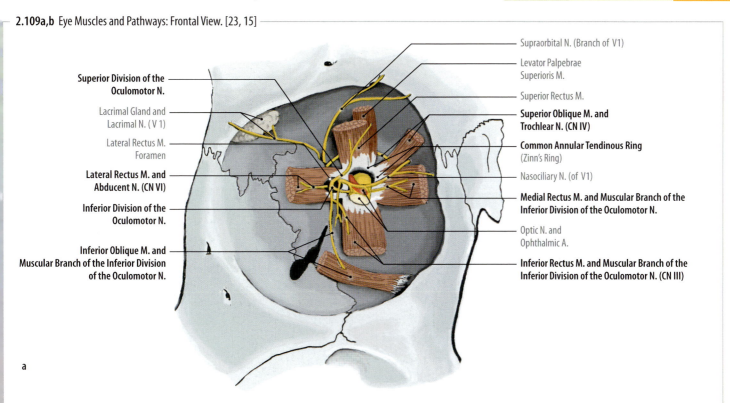

Superior Division of the Oculomotor N.

Lacrimal Gland and Lacrimal N. (V 1)

Lateral Rectus M. Foramen

Lateral Rectus M. and Abducent N. (CN VI)

Inferior Division of the Oculomotor N.

Inferior Oblique M. and Muscular Branch of the Inferior Division of the Oculomotor N.

Supraorbital N. (Branch of V1)

Levator Palpebrae Superioris M.

Superior Rectus M.

Superior Oblique M. and Trochlear N. (CN IV)

Common Annular Tendinous Ring (Zinn's Ring)

Nasociliary N. (of V1)

Medial Rectus M. and Muscular Branch of the Inferior Division of the Oculomotor N.

Optic N. and Ophthalmic A.

Inferior Rectus M. and Muscular Branch of the Inferior Division of the Oculomotor N. (CN III)

a

Eye Muscles, Origin from the Orbit: Frontal View

Levator Palpebrae Superioris M.	E	Head Margin of the Optic Canal on Outside Tendinous Ring from the Lesser Wing of the Sphenoid Bone.
Superior Rectus M.	E	Head Margin of the Optic Canal and Upper of Common Annular Tendinous Ring [Dural Sheath of the Optic N.]
Medial Rectus M.	E	Common Annular Tendinous Ring Medially [Dural Sheath of the Optical N.]
Lateral Rectus M.	E	Greater Wing of Sphenoid Bone and Common Annular Tendinous Ring by Two Heads
Inferior Rectus M.	E	Common Annular Tendinous, Inferiorly
Superior Oblique M.	E	Body of Sphenoid Medially, little Anterior to Optic Canal and Common Annular Tendinous Ring [Dural Sheath of the Optic N.]
Inferior Oblique M.	E	Medial Orbital of the Maxilla Laterally from the Lacrimal Incisura [Lacrimal Sac]

Nerve		Muscle
Oculomotor N.	E	Superior Rectus M.
		Inferior Rectus M.
		Medial Rectus M.
		Inferior Oblique M.
Trochlear N.	E	Superior Oblique M.
Abducent N.	E	Lateral Rectus M.

Optic Canal

Optic N. CN II Special Sensory Vision
Ophthalmic A. Branch of Internal Carotid A.

Superior Orbital Fissure

Outside of the Common Annular Tendinous Ring (Zinn's Ring)
Superior Ophthalmic V.
Lacrimal N.
Frontal N.
Trochlear N.
Within the Common Annular Tendinous Ring through the Lateral Rectum Foramen and Fissure
Oculomotor N.
Nasociliary N. of V1
Abducent N.
[Sympathetic Nn. to Ciliary Ganglion]

Inferior Orbital Fissure

Inferior Ophthalmic V.
Infraorbital A.
Infraorbital N.
Zygomatic N.

Levator Palpebrae Superioris M.

Superior Rectus M.

Lacrimal N.

Superior Ophthalmic V.

Frontal N.

Trochlear N.

Oculomotor N.

Abducent N.

Infraorbital N. and A.

Superior Oblique M.

Optic N.

Medial Rectus M.

Ophthalmic A.

Inferior Rectus M.

Nasociliary N.

Lateral Rectus M.

Inferior Oblique M.

Inferior Ophthalmic V.

Zygomatic N.

b

a Insertions on the Common Annular Tendinous Ring (Zinn's Ring) and Entering Pathways.
b Localization of the Muscle Origin and Position of the Pathways on their Entrance into the Orbit.

Eye and Orbit

2.110 Arteries of the Eye and the Orbit: Vertical View. [17]

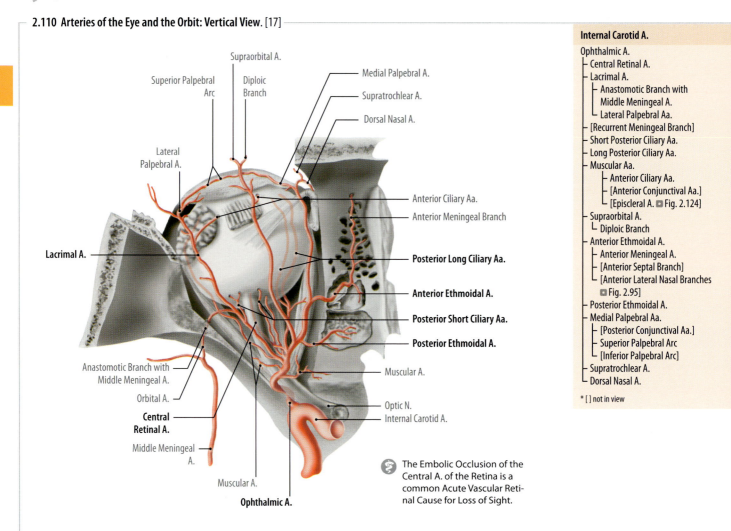

Supraorbital A.
Superior Palpebral Arc
Diploic Branch
Medial Palpebral A.
Supratrochlear A.
Dorsal Nasal A.
Lateral Palpebral A.
Anterior Ciliary Aa.
Anterior Meningeal Branch
Lacrimal A.
Posterior Long Ciliary Aa.
Anterior Ethmoidal A.
Posterior Short Ciliary Aa.
Posterior Ethmoidal A.
Muscular A.
Anastomotic Branch with Middle Meningeal A.
Orbital A.
Optic N.
Internal Carotid A.
Central Retinal A.
Middle Meningeal A.
Muscular A.
Ophthalmic A.

The Embolic Occlusion of the Central A. of the Retina is a common Acute Vascular Retinal Cause for Loss of Sight.

Internal Carotid A.

Ophthalmic A.
– Central Retinal A.
– Lacrimal A.
   ├ Anastomotic Branch with Middle Meningeal A.
   └ Lateral Palpebral Aa.
– [Recurrent Meningeal Branch]
– Short Posterior Ciliary Aa.
– Long Posterior Ciliary Aa.
– Muscular Aa.
   ├ Anterior Ciliary Aa.
   ├ [Anterior Conjunctival Aa.]
   └ [Episcleral A. ▣ Fig. 2.124]
– Supraorbital A.
   └ Diploic Branch
– Anterior Ethmoidal A.
   ├ Anterior Meningeal A.
   ├ [Anterior Septal Branch]
   └ [Anterior Lateral Nasal Branches ▣ Fig. 2.95]
– Posterior Ethmoidal A.
– Medial Palpebral Aa.
   ├ [Posterior Conjunctival Aa.]
   ├ Superior Palpebral Arc
   └ [Inferior Palpebral Arc]
– Supratrochlear A.
└ Dorsal Nasal A.

* [ ] not in view

2.111 Nerves of the Orbit and the Eye: Vertical View. [13]

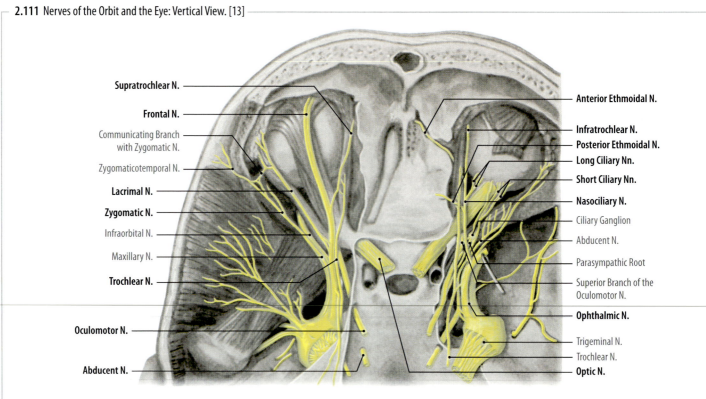

Supratrochlear N.
Frontal N.
Communicating Branch with Zygomatic N.
Zygomaticotemporal N.
Lacrimal N.
Zygomatic N.
Infraorbital N.
Maxillary N.
Trochlear N.
Oculomotor N.
Abducent N.

Anterior Ethmoidal N.
Infratrochlear N.
Posterior Ethmoidal N.
Long Ciliary Nn.
Short Ciliary Nn.
Nasociliary N.
Ciliary Ganglion
Abducent N.
Parasympathic Root
Superior Branch of the Oculomotor N.
Ophthalmic N.
Trigeminal N.
Trochlear N.
Optic N.

Orbital Roof on Right is Opened; the Bones of the Roof of the Orbit and Anterior Wall of the Middle Cranial Fossa on the Left side were Removed.

Innervation Ocular Muscles, Lacrimal Gland

2.112a,b Nerves of the Right Orbit and the Eye: Lateral View. [13]

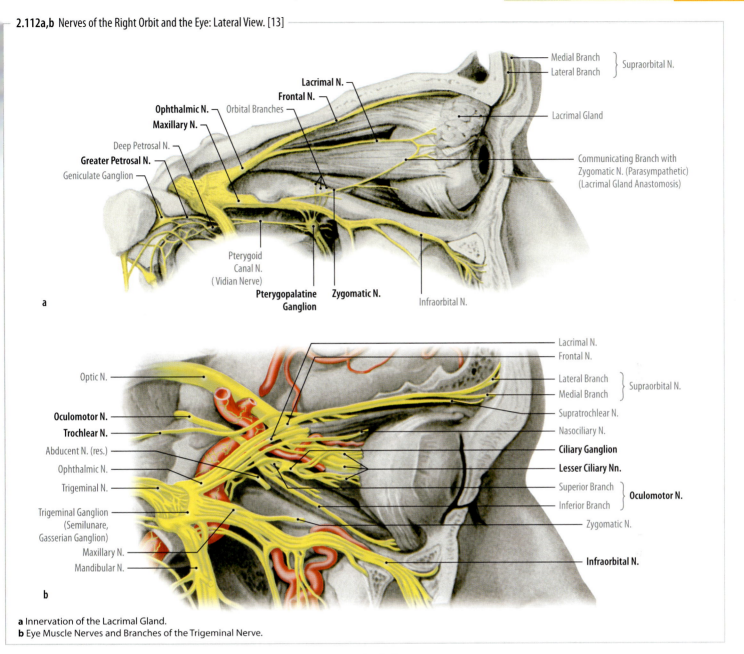

Medial Branch
Lateral Branch } Supraorbital N.

Lacrimal N.
Frontal N.
Ophthalmic N.
Maxillary N.
Orbital Branches
Lacrimal Gland
Deep Petrosal N.
Greater Petrosal N.
Geniculate Ganglion
Communicating Branch with Zygomatic N. (Parasympathetic) (Lacrimal Gland Anastomosis)
Pterygoid Canal N. (Vidian Nerve)
Pterygopalatine Ganglion
Zygomatic N.
Infraorbital N.

a

Optic N.
Lacrimal N.
Frontal N.
Lateral Branch
Medial Branch } Supraorbital N.
Oculomotor N.
Trochlear N.
Abducent N. (res.)
Ophthalmic N.
Trigeminal N.
Supratrochlear N.
Nasociliary N.
Ciliary Ganglion
Lesser Ciliary Nn.
Superior Branch
Inferior Branch } Oculomotor N.
Trigeminal Ganglion (Semilunare, Gasserian Ganglion)
Maxillary N.
Mandibular N.
Zygomatic N.
Infraorbital N.

b

a Innervation of the Lacrimal Gland.
b Eye Muscle Nerves and Branches of the Trigeminal Nerve.

2.113 Parasympathetic Innervation of the Lacrimal Gland and the Intrensic Eye Muscles. [13]

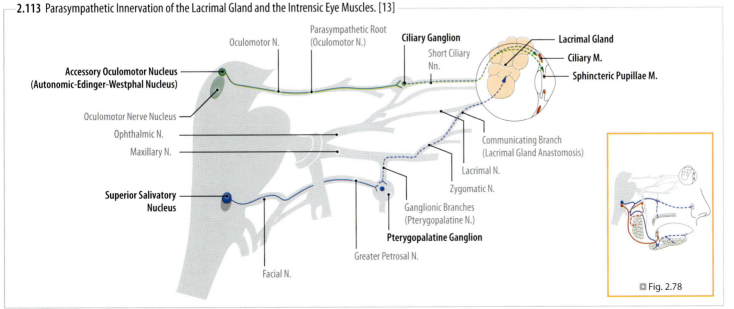

Parasympathetic Root (Oculomotor N.)
Oculomotor N.
Ciliary Ganglion
Lacrimal Gland
Short Ciliary Nn.
Ciliary M.
Accessory Oculomotor Nucleus (Autonomic-Edinger-Westphal Nucleus)
Sphincteric Pupillae M.
Oculomotor Nerve Nucleus
Ophthalmic N.
Maxillary N.
Communicating Branch (Lacrimal Gland Anastomosis)
Lacrimal N.
Zygomatic N.
Superior Salivatory Nucleus
Ganglionic Branches (Pterygopalatine N.)
Pterygopalatine Ganglion
Greater Petrosal N.
Facial N.

□ Fig. 2.78

Eye and Orbit

2

2.114 Topographical Relations of the Orbit. [6]

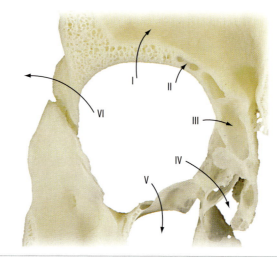

Inflammations and Tumors of the Orbit may Penetrate into the Neighboring Areas (and, in part, vice versa):
I.   Anterior Cranial Fossa (Superior)
II. Frontal Sinus (Superiorly Medially)
III. Ethmoidal Cells (Medial)
IV. Nasal Cavity (Medially Inferiorly)
V. Maxillary Sinus (Inferior)
VI. Temporal Fossa (Laterally)

A Frontal Section through the Skull in the area of the Crista Galli, view of the Posterior Section, Right Side.

2.115 Frontal Section through the Retrobulbar Area of the Right Orbit of the Right Side: Anterior View. [23]

If the Orbital Floor is Fractured, the Content of the Orbit may Penetrate into the Maxillary Sinus (so-called Orbital Hernia). Due to an Entrapment of the Inferior Rectus and Inferior Oblique Mm., the Motility of the Bulb of the Eye is Restricted (Double Images, Ocular Paresis Upward, Enophthalmos). If the Infraorbital N. is Involved, Sensory Disturbances in the area of the Maxilla may Occur (■ Fig. 2.47, 2.53).

Superior Ophthalmic V.
Levator Palpebrae Superioris M.
Frontal N.
Superior Rectus M.
Superior Division of the Oculomotor N.
Lacrimal N., V., and A.
External Sheath
Internal Sheath
Lateral Rectus M. and Abducent N.
Lateral Retinaculum
Posterior Short Ciliary Aa.
Periorbita

Superior Oblique M. and Trochlear N.
Ophthalmic A.
Nasociliary N.
Medial Retinaculum
Optic N.
Central Retinal A. and V.
Medial Rectus M.
Intervaginal Spatium
Bulbar Suspensory Ligament (Lockwood's Ligament)
Inferior Rectus M. and Inferior Branch of the Oculomotor N.

2.116 Sagittal Section through the Middle Area of the Right Orbit: Lateral View. [23]

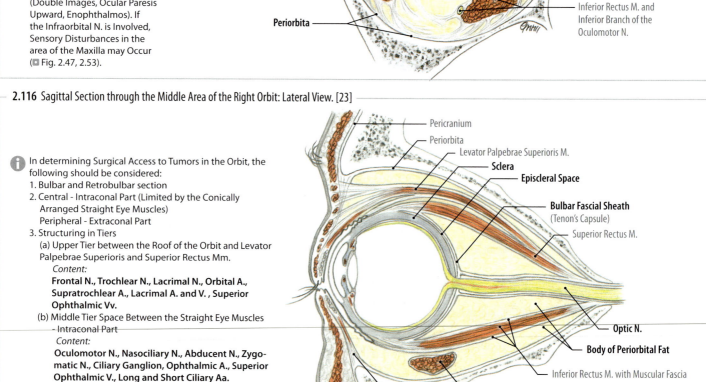

In determining Surgical Access to Tumors in the Orbit, the following should be considered:
1. Bulbar and Retrobulbar section
2. Central - Intraconal Part (Limited by the Conically Arranged Straight Eye Muscles)
   Peripheral - Extraconal Part
3. Structuring in Tiers
   (a) Upper Tier between the Roof of the Orbit and Levator Palpebrae Superioris and Superior Rectus Mm.
      Content:
      Frontal N., Trochlear N., Lacrimal N., Orbital A., Supratrochlear A., Lacrimal A. and V., Superior Ophthalmic Vv.
   (b) Middle Tier Space Between the Straight Eye Muscles - Intraconal Part
      Content:
      Oculomotor N., Nasociliary N., Abducent N., Zygomatic N., Ciliary Ganglion, Ophthalmic A., Superior Ophthalmic V., Long and Short Ciliary Aa.
   (c) Lower Tier between Inferior Rectus and Inferior Oblique Mm. and the Floor of the Orbit
      Content:
      Infraorbital N., Infraorbital A., Inferior Ophthalmic V.

Pericranium
Periorbita
Levator Palpebrae Superioris M.
Sclera
Episcleral Space
Bulbar Fascial Sheath (Tenon's Capsule)
Superior Rectus M.
Optic N.
Body of Periorbital Fat
Inferior Rectus M. with Muscular Fascia
Inferior Oblique M.
Orbital Septum

2.117 Topography of the Orbita: Vertical View. [8]

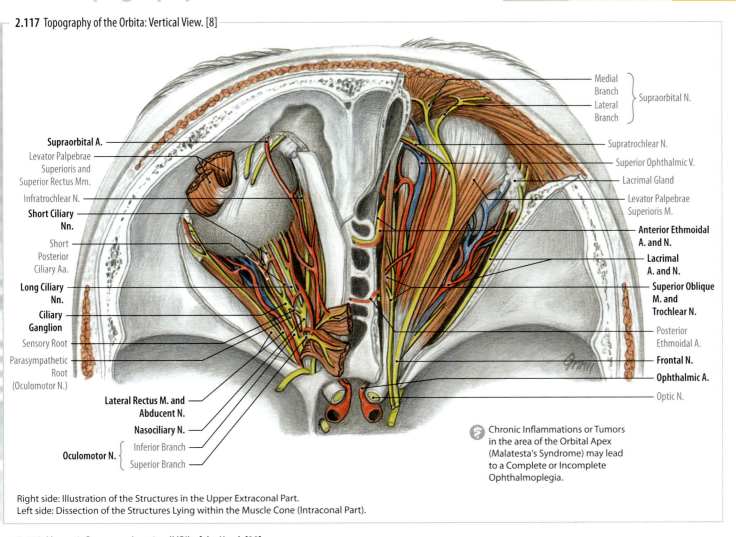

Medial Branch
Lateral Branch } Supraorbital N.

Supraorbital A.
Levator Palpebrae Superioris and Superior Rectus Mm.
Infratrochlear N.
Short Ciliary Nn.
Short Posterior Ciliary Aa.
Long Ciliary Nn.
Ciliary Ganglion
Sensory Root
Parasympathetic Root (Oculomotor N.)
Lateral Rectus M. and Abducent N.
Nasociliary N.
Oculomotor N. { Inferior Branch
Superior Branch

Supratrochlear N.
Superior Ophthalmic V.
Lacrimal Gland
Levator Palpebrae Superioris M.
Anterior Ethmoidal A. and N.
Lacrimal A. and N.
Superior Oblique M. and Trochlear N.
Posterior Ethmoidal A.
Frontal N.
Ophthalmic A.
Optic N.

Chronic Inflammations or Tumors in the area of the Orbital Apex (Malatesta's Syndrome) may lead to a Complete or Incomplete Ophthalmoplegia.

Right side: Illustration of the Structures in the Upper Extraconal Part.
Left side: Dissection of the Structures Lying within the Muscle Cone (Intraconal Part).

2.118 Magnetic Resonance Imaging (MRI) of the Head. [28]

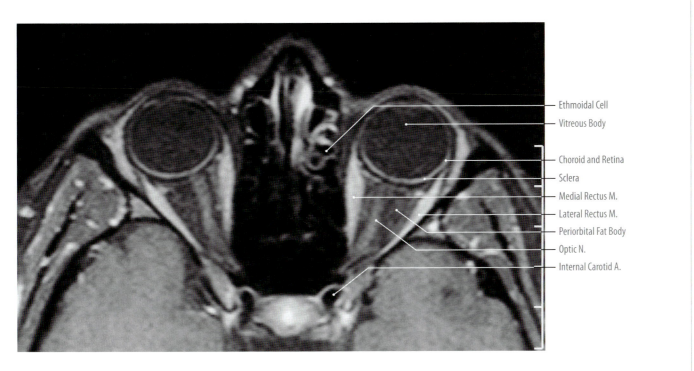

Ethmoidal Cell
Vitreous Body

Choroid and Retina
Sclera
Medial Rectus M.
Lateral Rectus M.
Periorbital Fat Body
Optic N.
Internal Carotid A.

Transverse Section in T1-Weighted MRI following Intravenous Administration of Radiopaque Material, layer thickness 3 mm.

Eye and Orbit

Eyeball

2.119 Eyeball (Bulbus Oculi), Semischematic Illustration: Left Lateral View. [70]

An Ablation of the Retina (Ablatio) develops between the Retinal Pigmented Epithelium (RPE) and the Neurosensory Retina.

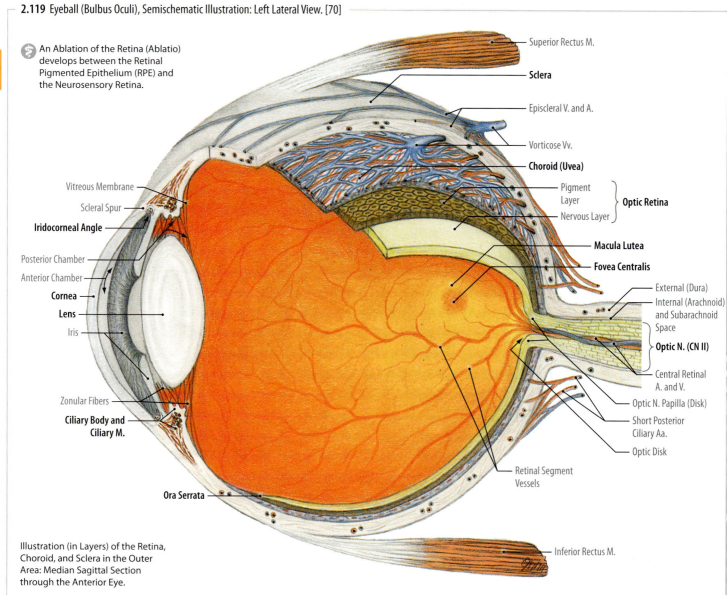

Superior Rectus M.

Sclera

Episcleral V. and A.

Vorticose Vv.

Choroid (Uvea)

Pigment Layer

Nervous Layer

Optic Retina

Macula Lutea

Fovea Centralis

External (Dura)

Internal (Arachnoid) and Subarachnoid Space

Optic N. (CN II)

Central Retinal A. and V.

Optic N. Papilla (Disk)

Short Posterior Ciliary Aa.

Optic Disk

Retinal Segment Vessels

Vitreous Membrane

Scleral Spur

Iridocorneal Angle

Posterior Chamber

Anterior Chamber

Cornea

Lens

Iris

Zonular Fibers

Ciliary Body and Ciliary M.

Ora Serrata

Inferior Rectus M.

Illustration (in Layers) of the Retina, Choroid, and Sclera in the Outer Area: Median Sagittal Section through the Anterior Eye.

2.120 Sonographic Examination of the Eye in B-Scan: Right Axial Section, Sketch. [29]

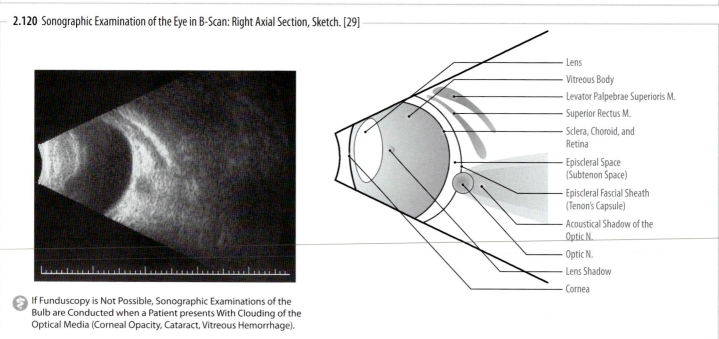

Lens

Vitreous Body

Levator Palpebrae Superioris M.

Superior Rectus M.

Sclera, Choroid, and Retina

Episcleral Space (Subtenon Space)

Episcleral Fascial Sheath (Tenon's Capsule)

Acoustical Shadow of the Optic N.

Optic N.

Lens Shadow

Cornea

If Funduscopy is Not Possible, Sonographic Examinations of the Bulb are Conducted when a Patient presents With Clouding of the Optical Media (Corneal Opacity, Cataract, Vitreous Hemorrhage).

Eyeball

2.121 Horizontal Section through the Eyeball. [13]

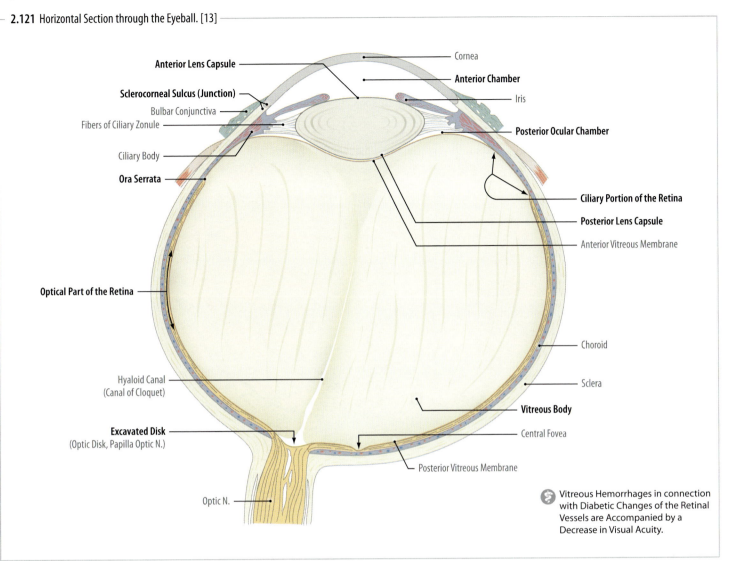

- Cornea
- **Anterior Lens Capsule**
- **Anterior Chamber**
- **Sclerocorneal Sulcus (Junction)**
- Iris
- Bulbar Conjunctiva
- Fibers of Ciliary Zonule
- **Posterior Ocular Chamber**
- Ciliary Body
- **Ora Serrata**
- **Ciliary Portion of the Retina**
- **Posterior Lens Capsule**
- Anterior Vitreous Membrane
- **Optical Part of the Retina**
- Choroid
- Hyaloid Canal (Canal of Cloquet)
- Sclera
- **Excavated Disk** (Optic Disk, Papilla Optic N.)
- **Vitreous Body**
- Central Fovea
- Posterior Vitreous Membrane
- Optic N.

🔷 Vitreous Hemorrhages in connection with Diabetic Changes of the Retinal Vessels are Accompanied by a Decrease in Visual Acuity.

2.122 Slit-Lamp Microscopy of the Right Eye: Optical Section through the Cornea. [27]

Anterior Area of the Cornea | Posterior Area of the Cornea

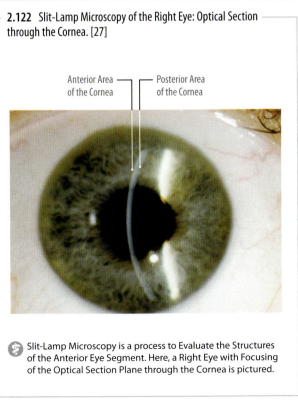

🔷 Slit-Lamp Microscopy is a process to Evaluate the Structures of the Anterior Eye Segment. Here, a Right Eye with Focusing of the Optical Section Plane through the Cornea is pictured.

2.123 Ciliary Body and Lens: Occipital View. [6]

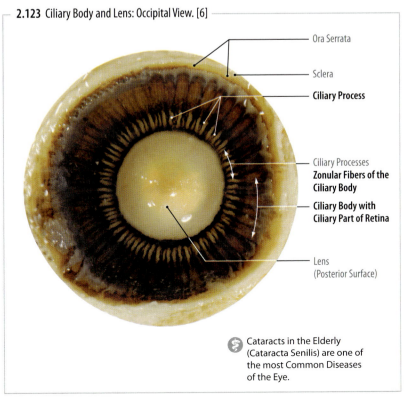

- Ora Serrata
- Sclera
- **Ciliary Process**
- Ciliary Processes **Zonular Fibers of the Ciliary Body**
- **Ciliary Body with Ciliary Part of Retina**
- Lens (Posterior Surface)

🔷 Cataracts in the Elderly (Cataracta Senilis) are one of the most Common Diseases of the Eye.

Eye and Orbit

2.124a,b Blood Vessels of the Eye. [30]

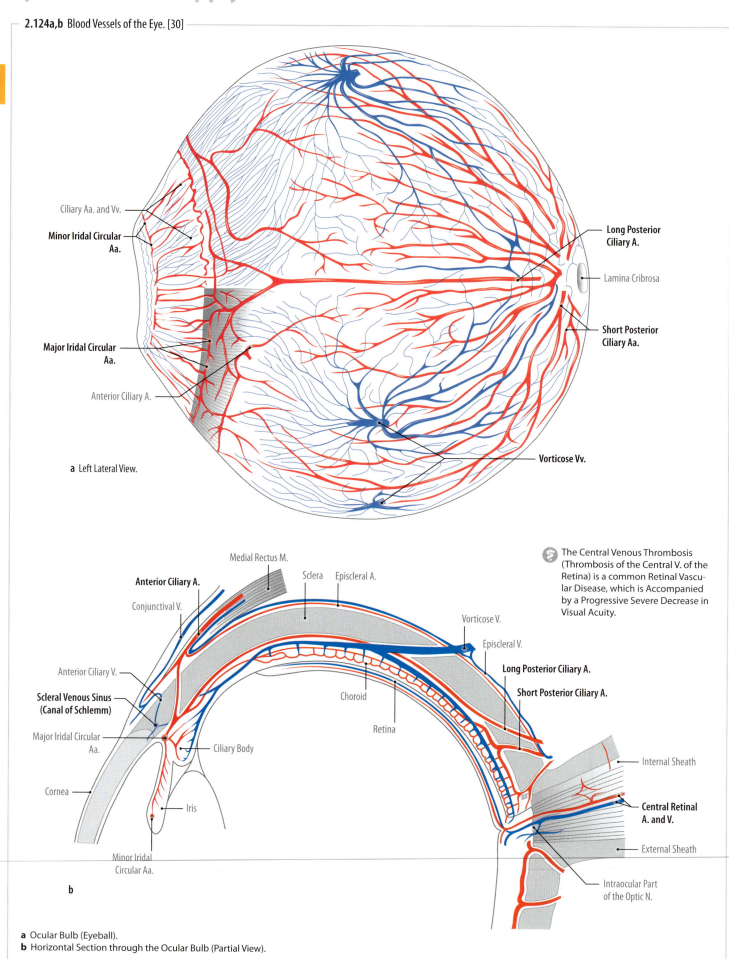

Ciliary Aa. and Vv.

Minor Iridal Circular Aa.

Long Posterior Ciliary A.

Lamina Cribrosa

Short Posterior Ciliary Aa.

Major Iridal Circular Aa.

Anterior Ciliary A.

Vorticose Vv.

a Left Lateral View.

Medial Rectus M.

Sclera   Episcleral A.

Anterior Ciliary A.

Conjunctival V.

Vorticose V.

Episcleral V.

Anterior Ciliary V.

Long Posterior Ciliary A.

Short Posterior Ciliary A.

Scleral Venous Sinus (Canal of Schlemm)

Choroid

Retina

Major Iridal Circular Aa.

Ciliary Body

Internal Sheath

Cornea

Iris

Central Retinal A. and V.

Minor Iridal Circular Aa.

External Sheath

Intraocular Part of the Optic N.

b

The Central Venous Thrombosis (Thrombosis of the Central V. of the Retina) is a common Retinal Vascular Disease, which is Accompanied by a Progressive Severe Decrease in Visual Acuity.

a Ocular Bulb (Eyeball).
b Horizontal Section through the Ocular Bulb (Partial View).

Eyeground, Retina Vessels

2.125a–c Ocular Fundus and Vessels of the Retina. [a 13,b,c 27]

Superior Temporal
Retinal Arteriole and Venule

Optic Disk

Macula Lutea

Fovea Centralis

Foveola

Medial Macular
Arteriole and Venule

Inferior Temporal
Retinal Arteriole and Venule

Superior Macular
Arteriole and Venule

Superior Nasal Retinal
Arteriole and Venule

Disk **(Optic Nerve Papilla)**

Inferior Nasal Retinal
Arteriole and Venule

Inferior Macular
Arteriole and Venule

a

An Ophthalmoscopy (Fundus-
copy) Examines the Papilla
(Marginal Acuity, Color, and
Papilla Level), Retinal Vessels,
Macula, and the Peripheral
Retina for Pathologic Changes.
The Fluorescent Angiography
aids in the Diagnosis of Retinal
and Choroidal Vascular Di-
seases or Anomalies.
Macular Degeneration is the
most common Cause for the
Loss of Sight in the Western
World.

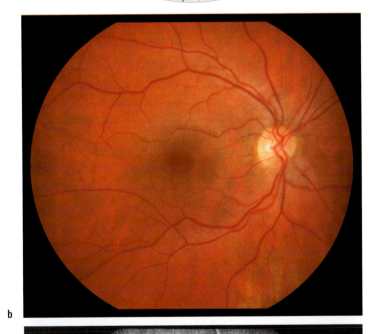

b

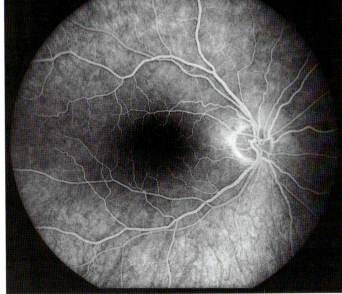

a Schematic Illustration, Right Eye.
b Scout Film, Right Eye.
c Fluorescent Angiography of a Right Eye
in the Arteriovenous Phase.

c

Eye and Orbit

Auricle: Structure · Arteries

2.126 Right Ear of a Young Man: Lateral View. [25]

The Auricle is frequently Affected by Malignant Skin Tumors (Squamous Cell Carcinoma, Basiloma, Melanoma).

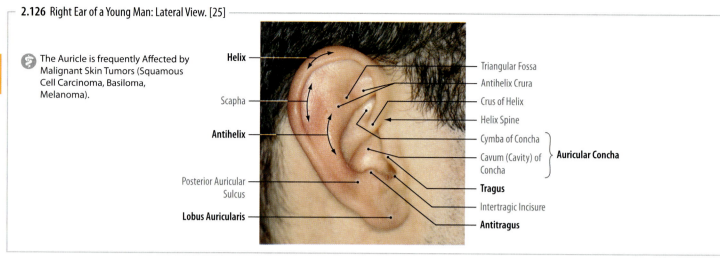

Helix

Scapha

Antihelix

Posterior Auricular Sulcus

Lobus Auricularis

Triangular Fossa

Antihelix Crura

Crus of Helix

Helix Spine

Cymba of Concha

Cavum (Cavity) of Concha } Auricular Concha

Tragus

Intertragic Incisure

Antitragus

2.127a,b Muscles and Cartilage of the Auricle: Right Side. [1, 18]

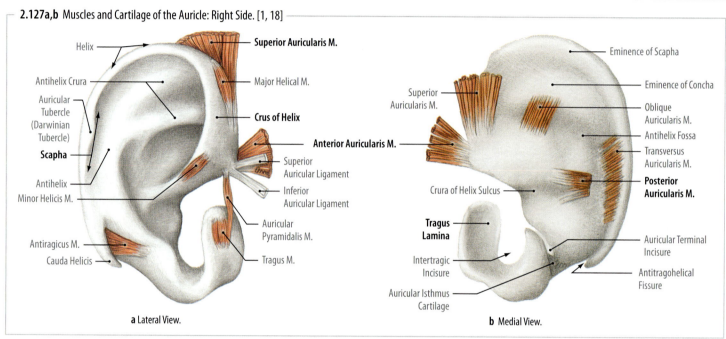

Helix

Antihelix Crura

Auricular Tubercle (Darwinian Tubercle)

Scapha

Antihelix

Minor Helicis M.

Antiragicus M.

Cauda Helicis

Superior Auricularis M.

Major Helical M.

Crus of Helix

Anterior Auricularis M.

Superior Auricular Ligament

Inferior Auricular Ligament

Auricular Pyramidalis M.

Tragus M.

Superior Auricularis M.

Crura of Helix Sulcus

Tragus Lamina

Intertragic Incisure

Auricular Isthmus Cartilage

Eminence of Scapha

Eminence of Concha

Oblique Auricularis M.

Antihelix Fossa

Transversus Auricularis M.

Posterior Auricularis M.

Auricular Terminal Incisure

Antitragohelical Fissure

a Lateral View.

b Medial View.

2.128 Arteries in the Right Auricle: Lateral View. [2]

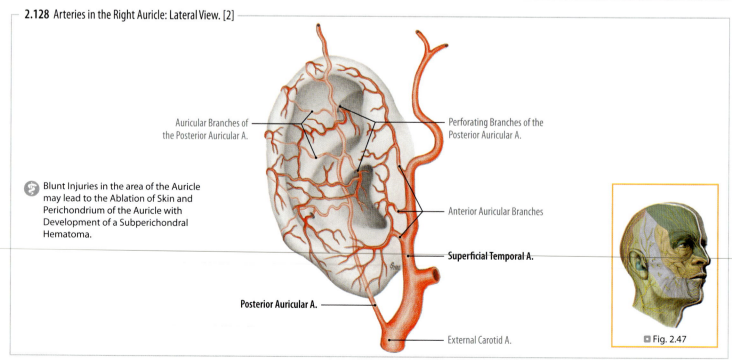

Blunt Injuries in the area of the Auricle may lead to the Ablation of Skin and Perichondrium of the Auricle with Development of a Subperichondral Hematoma.

Auricular Branches of the Posterior Auricular A.

Perforating Branches of the Posterior Auricular A.

Anterior Auricular Branches

Superficial Temporal A.

Posterior Auricular A.

External Carotid A.

■ Fig. 2.47

2.129 External Ear, Sagittal Section through the Auditory Canal, Middle Ear, and Pharyngotympanic Tube. Illustration of the Internal Ear: Right Side, Frontal View. [13]

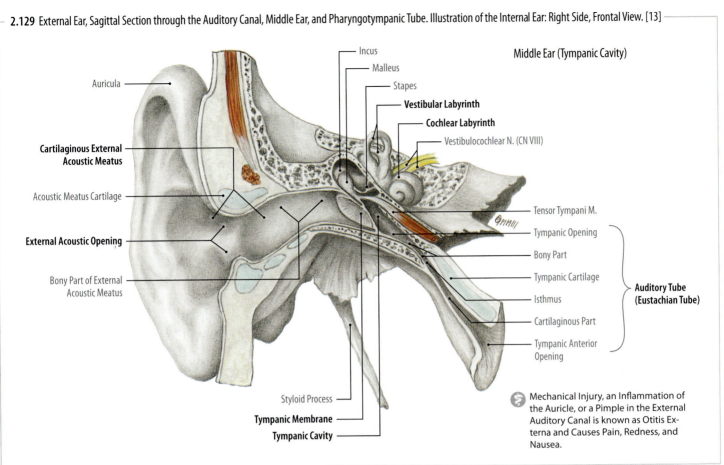

Incus

Malleus

Stapes

Vestibular Labyrinth

Cochlear Labyrinth

Vestibulocochlear N. (CN VIII)

Middle Ear (Tympanic Cavity)

Auricula

**Cartilaginous External
Acoustic Meatus**

Acoustic Meatus Cartilage

External Acoustic Opening

Bony Part of External
Acoustic Meatus

Tensor Tympani M.

Tympanic Opening

Bony Part

Tympanic Cartilage

Isthmus

Cartilaginous Part

Tympanic Anterior
Opening

**Auditory Tube
(Eustachian Tube)**

Styloid Process

Tympanic Membrane

Tympanic Cavity

Mechanical Injury, an Inflammation of
the Auricle, or a Pimple in the External
Auditory Canal is known as Otitis Externa and Causes Pain, Redness, and
Nausea.

2.130 Tympanic Part of the External Auditory Canal. [6]

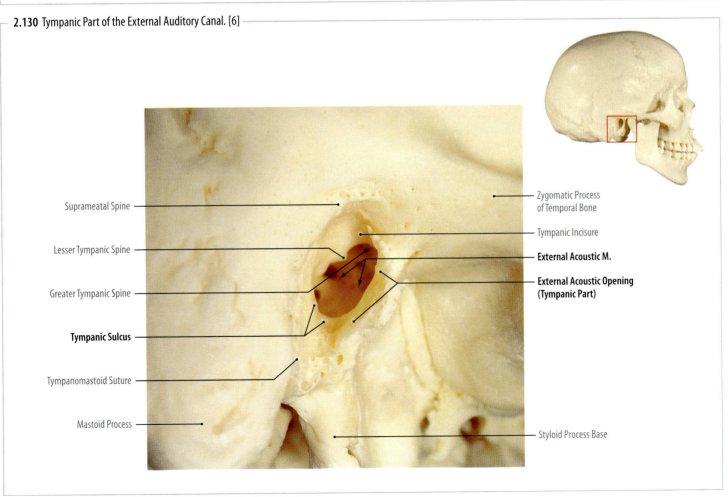

Suprameatal Spine

Lesser Tympanic Spine

Greater Tympanic Spine

Tympanic Sulcus

Tympanomastoid Suture

Mastoid Process

Zygomatic Process
of Temporal Bone

Tympanic Incisure

External Acoustic M.

**External Acoustic Opening
(Tympanic Part)**

Styloid Process Base

Ear

Medial Wall of Tympanic Cavity

2.131 Bones of the Medial Wall of the Tympanic Cavity. [1]

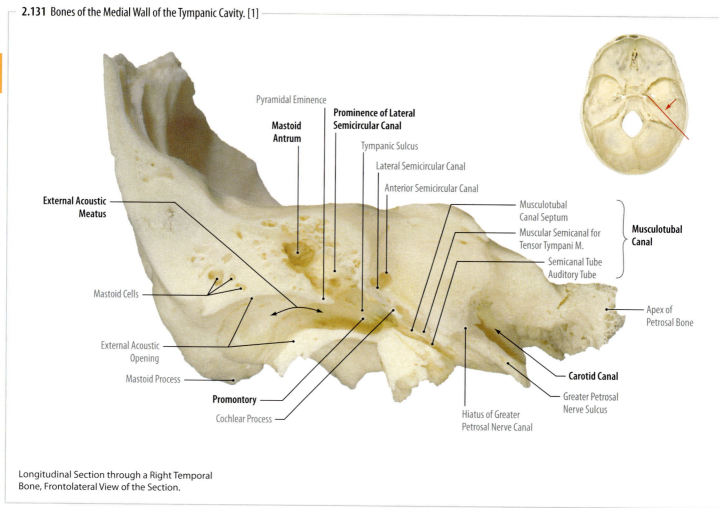

Pyramidal Eminence

Mastoid Antrum

Prominence of Lateral Semicircular Canal

Tympanic Sulcus

Lateral Semicircular Canal

Anterior Semicircular Canal

External Acoustic Meatus

Musculotubal Canal Septum

Muscular Semicanal for Tensor Tympani M.

Musculotubal Canal

Semicanal Tube Auditory Tube

Mastoid Cells

Apex of Petrosal Bone

External Acoustic Opening

Mastoid Process

Promontory

Cochlear Process

Hiatus of Greater Petrosal Nerve Canal

Carotid Canal

Greater Petrosal Nerve Sulcus

Longitudinal Section through a Right Temporal Bone, Frontolateral View of the Section.

2.132 Medial Wall of the Tympanic Cavity: Frontal View. [23]

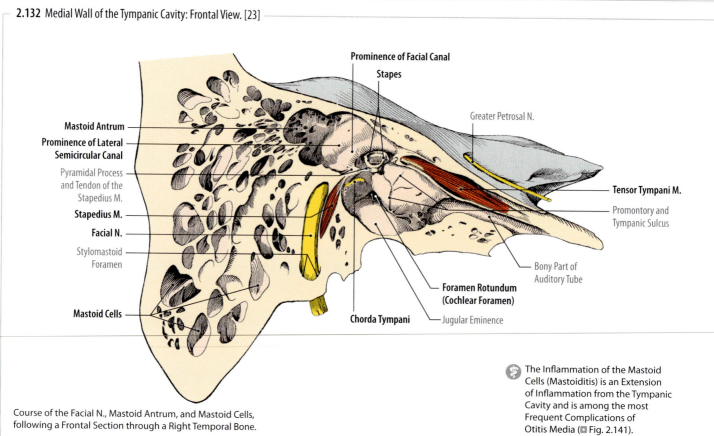

Prominence of Facial Canal

Stapes

Greater Petrosal N.

Mastoid Antrum

Prominence of Lateral Semicircular Canal

Pyramidal Process and Tendon of the Stapedius M.

Stapedius M.

Facial N.

Stylomastoid Foramen

Tensor Tympani M.

Promontory and Tympanic Sulcus

Mastoid Cells

Chorda Tympani

Foramen Rotundum (Cochlear Foramen)

Jugular Eminence

Bony Part of Auditory Tube

Course of the Facial N., Mastoid Antrum, and Mastoid Cells, following a Frontal Section through a Right Temporal Bone.

The Inflammation of the Mastoid Cells (Mastoiditis) is an Extension of Inflammation from the Tympanic Cavity and is among the most Frequent Complications of Otitis Media (Fig. 2.141).

Auditory Ossicles

2.133 Auditory Ossicles (Middle Ear Ossicles): Left Side. [6]

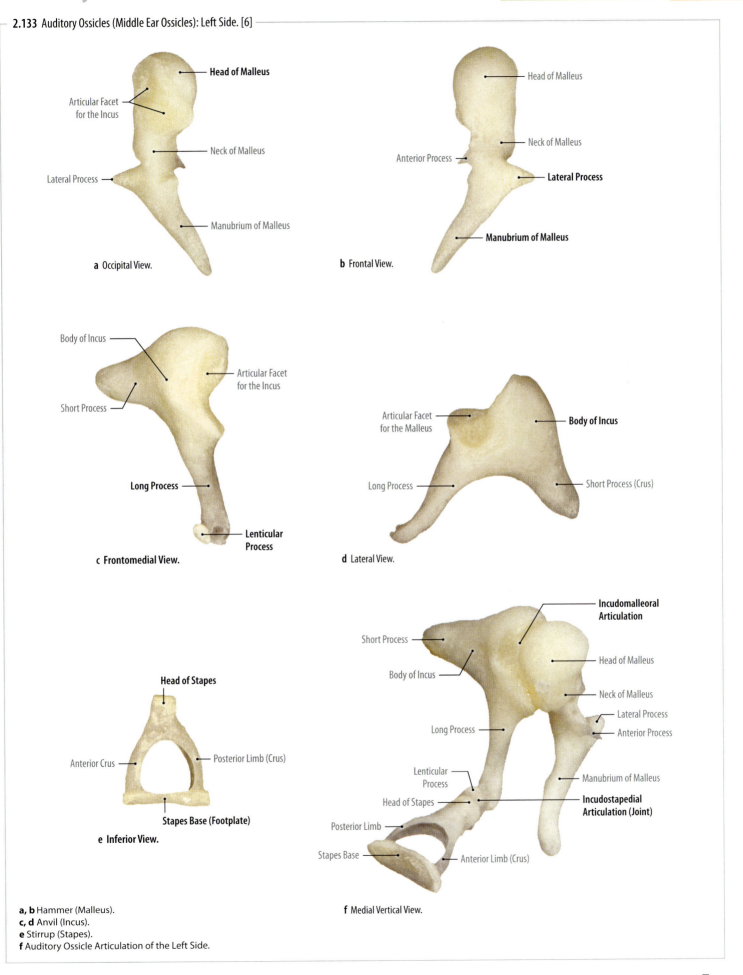

Head of Malleus

Articular Facet
for the Incus

Neck of Malleus

Lateral Process

Manubrium of Malleus

a Occipital View.

Head of Malleus

Anterior Process

Neck of Malleus

Lateral Process

Manubrium of Malleus

b Frontal View.

Body of Incus

Articular Facet
for the Incus

Short Process

Long Process

**Lenticular
Process**

c Frontomedial View.

Articular Facet
for the Malleus

Body of Incus

Long Process

Short Process (Crus)

d Lateral View.

Head of Stapes

Anterior Crus

Posterior Limb (Crus)

Stapes Base (Footplate)

e Inferior View.

**Incudomalleoral
Articulation**

Short Process

Head of Malleus

Body of Incus

Neck of Malleus

Lateral Process

Anterior Process

Long Process

Lenticular
Process

Manubrium of Malleus

Head of Stapes

**Incudostapedial
Articulation (Joint)**

Posterior Limb

Stapes Base

Anterior Limb (Crus)

f Medial Vertical View.

a, b Hammer (Malleus).
c, d Anvil (Incus).
e Stirrup (Stapes).
f Auditory Ossicle Articulation of the Left Side.

Ear

2.134 The Tympanic Cavity and Auditory Ossicles: Frontal Section. [23]

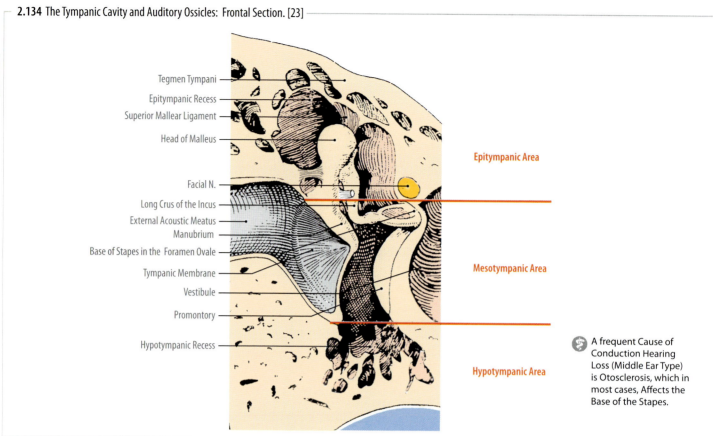

Tegmen Tympani
Epitympanic Recess
Superior Mallear Ligament
Head of Malleus

Epitympanic Area

Facial N.
Long Crus of the Incus
External Acoustic Meatus
Manubrium
Base of Stapes in the Foramen Ovale
Tympanic Membrane
Vestibule
Promontory

Mesotympanic Area

Hypotympanic Recess

Hypotympanic Area

A frequent Cause of Conduction Hearing Loss (Middle Ear Type) is Otosclerosis, which in most cases, Affects the Base of the Stapes.

2.135 Tympanic Membrane of the Right Side with Quadrant Allocation. I = Posterior Upper Quadrant; II = Anterior Upper Quadrant; III = Anterior Lower Quadrant; IV = Posterior Lower Quadrant. [24]

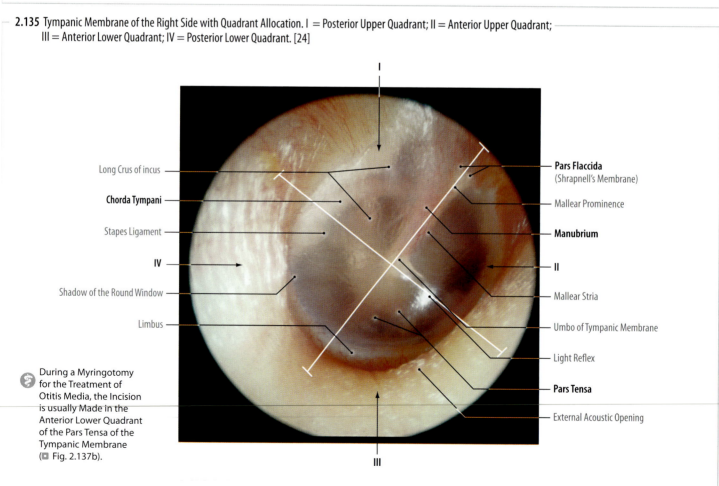

I

Long Crus of incus
Chorda Tympani
Stapes Ligament
IV
Shadow of the Round Window
Limbus

Pars Flaccida (Shrapnell's Membrane)
Mallear Prominence
Manubrium
II
Mallear Stria
Umbo of Tympanic Membrane
Light Reflex
Pars Tensa
External Acoustic Opening

III

During a Myringotomy for the Treatment of Otitis Media, the Incision is usually Made in the Anterior Lower Quadrant of the Pars Tensa of the Tympanic Membrane (■ Fig. 2.137b).

Tympanic Cavity · Tympanic Membrane

2.136 Right Tympanic Membrane: Occipital Vertical View of the Interior. [31]

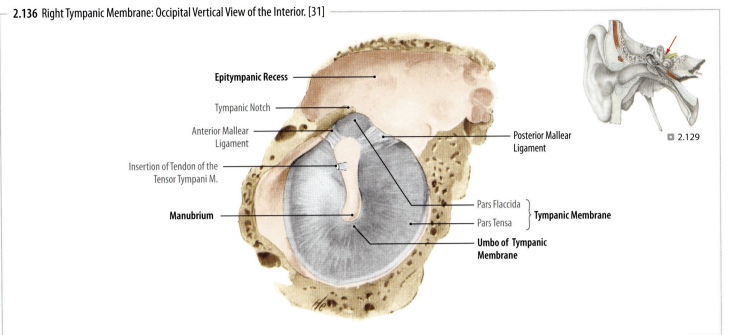

Epitympanic Recess

Tympanic Notch

Anterior Mallear Ligament

Insertion of Tendon of the Tensor Tympani M.

Manubrium

Posterior Mallear Ligament

Pars Flaccida
Pars Tensa } **Tympanic Membrane**

Umbo of Tympanic Membrane

2.129

2.137a,b Tympanic Cavity: Right Side. [a 31, b 13]

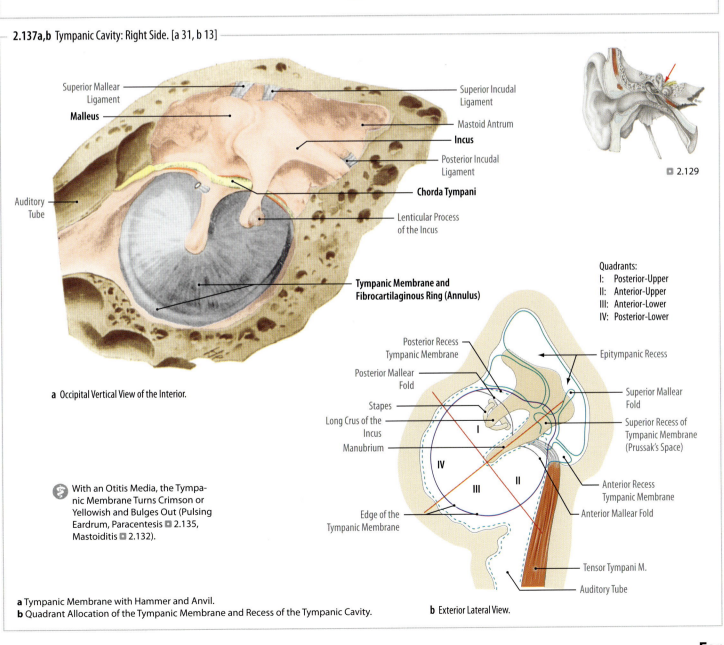

Superior Mallear Ligament

Malleus

Auditory Tube

Superior Incudal Ligament

Mastoid Antrum

Incus

Posterior Incudal Ligament

Chorda Tympani

Lenticular Process of the Incus

Tympanic Membrane and Fibrocartilaginous Ring (Annulus)

2.129

a Occipital Vertical View of the Interior.

Quadrants:
I: Posterior-Upper
II: Anterior-Upper
III: Anterior-Lower
IV: Posterior-Lower

Posterior Recess Tympanic Membrane

Posterior Mallear Fold

Stapes

Long Crus of the Incus

Manubrium

Epitympanic Recess

Superior Mallear Fold

Superior Recess of Tympanic Membrane (Prussak's Space)

Anterior Recess Tympanic Membrane

Anterior Mallear Fold

Edge of the Tympanic Membrane

Tensor Tympani M.

Auditory Tube

With an Otitis Media, the Tympanic Membrane Turns Crimson or Yellowish and Bulges Out (Pulsing Eardrum, Paracentesis ◘ 2.135, Mastoiditis ◘ 2.132).

a Tympanic Membrane with Hammer and Anvil.
b Quadrant Allocation of the Tympanic Membrane and Recess of the Tympanic Cavity.

b Exterior Lateral View.

Ear

Labyrinth

2.138 Position of the Labyrinth in the Petrous Bone: Partial Vertical View of the Interior Cranial Base. [70]

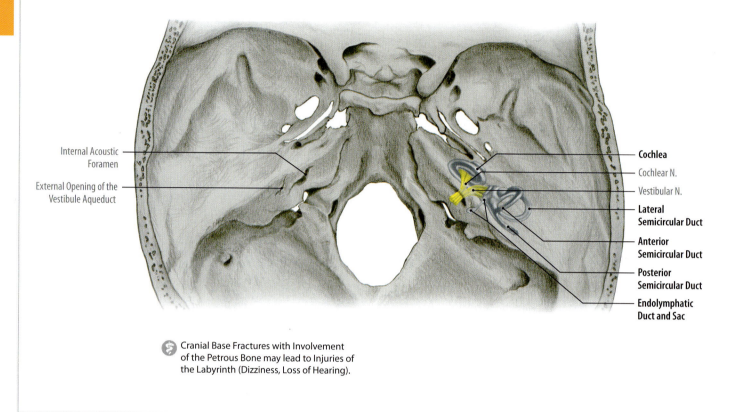

Internal Acoustic Foramen

External Opening of the Vestibule Aqueduct

Cochlea

Cochlear N.

Vestibular N.

Lateral Semicircular Duct

Anterior Semicircular Duct

Posterior Semicircular Duct

Endolymphatic Duct and Sac

Cranial Base Fractures with Involvement of the Petrous Bone may lead to Injuries of the Labyrinth (Dizziness, Loss of Hearing).

2.139 Schematic Illustration of the Bony and Membranous Labyrinth. [31]

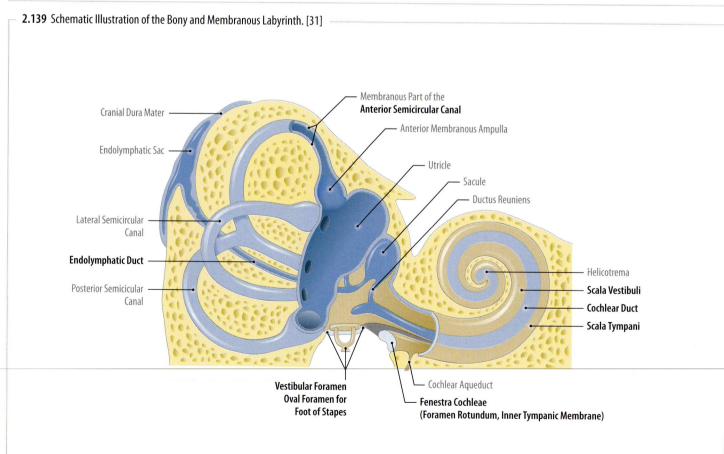

Cranial Dura Mater

Endolymphatic Sac

Lateral Semicircular Canal

Endolymphatic Duct

Posterior Semicicular Canal

Membranous Part of the **Anterior Semicircular Canal**

Anterior Membranous Ampulla

Utricle

Sacule

Ductus Reuniens

Helicotrema

Scala Vestibuli

Cochlear Duct

Scala Tympani

Vestibular Foramen Oval Foramen for Foot of Stapes

Cochlear Aqueduct

Fenestra Cochleae (Foramen Rotundum, Inner Tympanic Membrane)

Bony Labyrinth

2.140 Semicircular Canals and Cochlea: Partial Vertical Medial View of a Right Temporal Bone. [1]

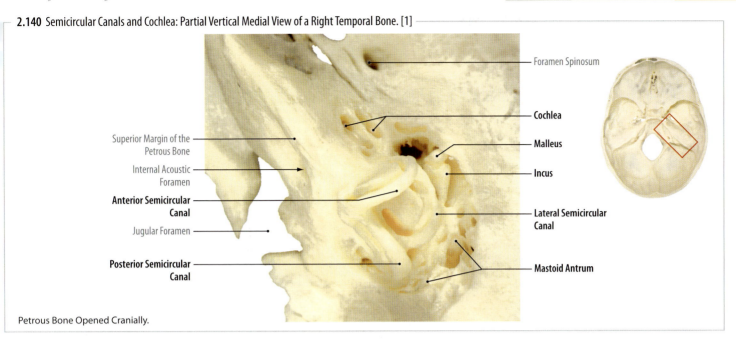

Foramen Spinosum

Cochlea

Malleus

Superior Margin of the Petrous Bone

Internal Acoustic Foramen

Incus

Anterior Semicircular Canal

Jugular Foramen

Lateral Semicircular Canal

Posterior Semicircular Canal

Mastoid Antrum

Petrous Bone Opened Cranially.

2.141 Osseous (Bony) Labyrinth. [1]

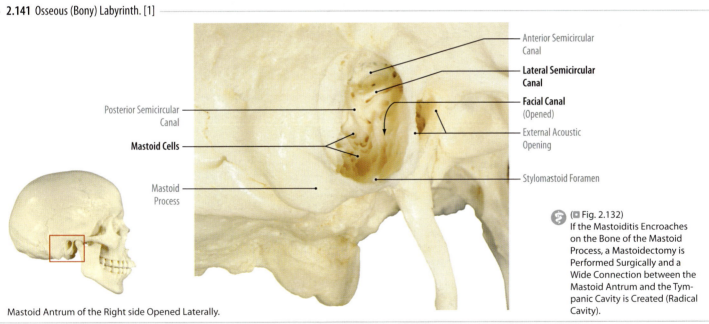

Anterior Semicircular Canal

Lateral Semicircular Canal

Posterior Semicircular Canal

Facial Canal (Opened)

Mastoid Cells

External Acoustic Opening

Mastoid Process

Stylomastoid Foramen

(🔲 Fig. 2.132)
If the Mastoiditis Encroaches on the Bone of the Mastoid Process, a Mastoidectomy is Performed Surgically and a Wide Connection between the Mastoid Antrum and the Tympanic Cavity is Created (Radical Cavity).

Mastoid Antrum of the Right side Opened Laterally.

2.142 Interior Auditory Canal, Internal Acoustic Meatus. [8]

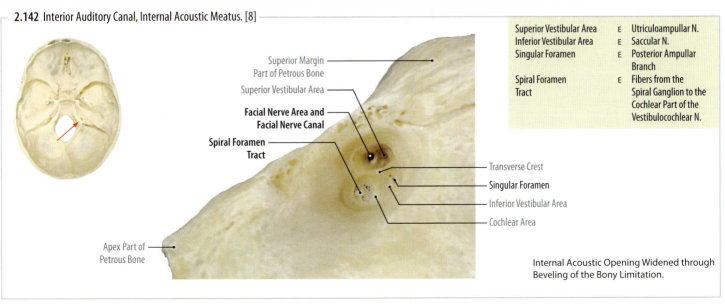

Superior Margin Part of Petrous Bone

Superior Vestibular Area

Facial Nerve Area and Facial Nerve Canal

Spiral Foramen Tract

Apex Part of Petrous Bone

Transverse Crest

Singular Foramen

Inferior Vestibular Area

Cochlear Area

Superior Vestibular Area	E	Utriculoampullar N.
Inferior Vestibular Area	E	Saccular N.
Singular Foramen	E	Posterior Ampullar Branch
Spiral Foramen Tract	E	Fibers from the Spiral Ganglion to the Cochlear Part of the Vestibulocochlear N.

Internal Acoustic Opening Widened through Beveling of the Bony Limitation.

Ear

2.143a–c Outlet of a Right Bony Labyrinth. [a 31, b,c 2]

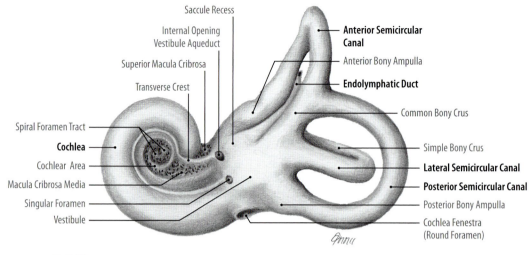

Saccule Recess

Internal Opening
Vestibule Aqueduct

Superior Macula Cribrosa

Transverse Crest

Spiral Foramen Tract

Cochlea

Cochlear Area

Macula Cribrosa Media

Singular Foramen

Vestibule

**Anterior Semicircular
Canal**

Anterior Bony Ampulla

Endolymphatic Duct

Common Bony Crus

Simple Bony Crus

Lateral Semicircular Canal

Posterior Semicircular Canal

Posterior Bony Ampulla

Cochlea Fenestra
(Round Foramen)

a Medial View.

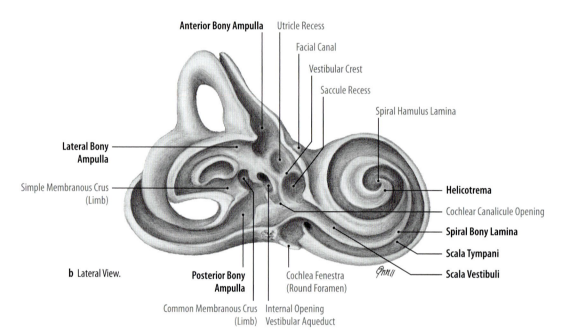

Anterior Bony Ampulla

Utricle Recess

Facial Canal

Vestibular Crest

Saccule Recess

Spiral Hamulus Lamina

**Lateral Bony
Ampulla**

Simple Membranous Crus
(Limb)

Helicotrema

Cochlear Canalicule Opening

Spiral Bony Lamina

Scala Tympani

b Lateral View.

**Posterior Bony
Ampulla**

Cochlea Fenestra
(Round Foramen)

Scala Vestibuli

Common Membranous Crus
(Limb)

Internal Opening
Vestibular Aqueduct

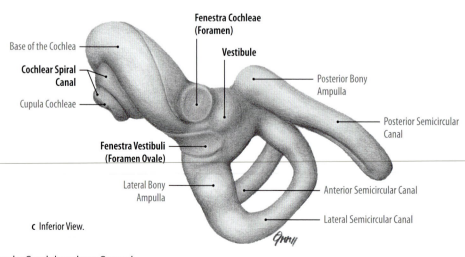

**Fenestra Cochleae
(Foramen)**

Base of the Cochlea

Vestibule

**Cochlear Spiral
Canal**

Cupula Cochleae

Posterior Bony
Ampulla

Posterior Semicircular
Canal

**Fenestra Vestibuli
(Foramen Ovale)**

Lateral Bony
Ampulla

Anterior Semicircular Canal

Lateral Semicircular Canal

c Inferior View.

b Cochlea and Semicircular Canals have been Opened.

Bony Labyrinth · Cochlea

2.144 Longitudinal Section through the Cochlea: Semi-Schematic Illustration of the Organ of Corti with Endolymph and Perilymph Spaces. The Arrows Indicate the Movement of the Perilymphs in the Scala Tympani and in the Scala Vestibuli. [32]

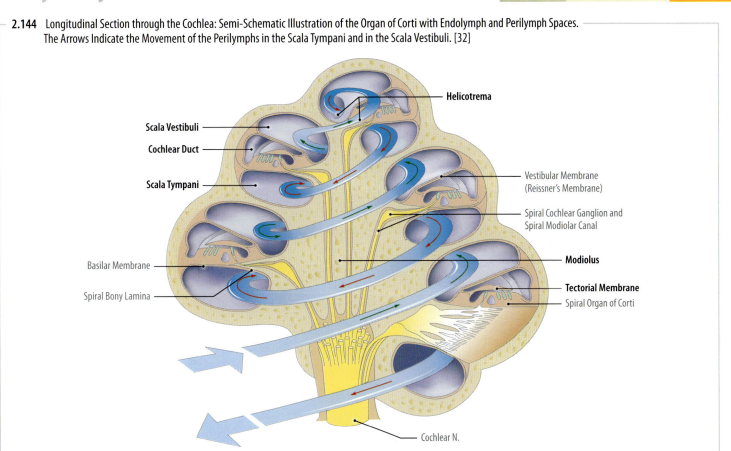

- **Helicotrema**
- Scala Vestibuli
- Cochlear Duct
- Scala Tympani
- Vestibular Membrane (Reissner's Membrane)
- Spiral Cochlear Ganglion and Spiral Modiolar Canal
- Basilar Membrane
- Spiral Bony Lamina
- **Modiolus**
- **Tectorial Membrane**
- Spiral Organ of Corti
- Cochlear N.

2.145 Bony Labyrinth, Section of the Modiolus in the Longitudinal Axis: Lateral View, Medial Section. [1]

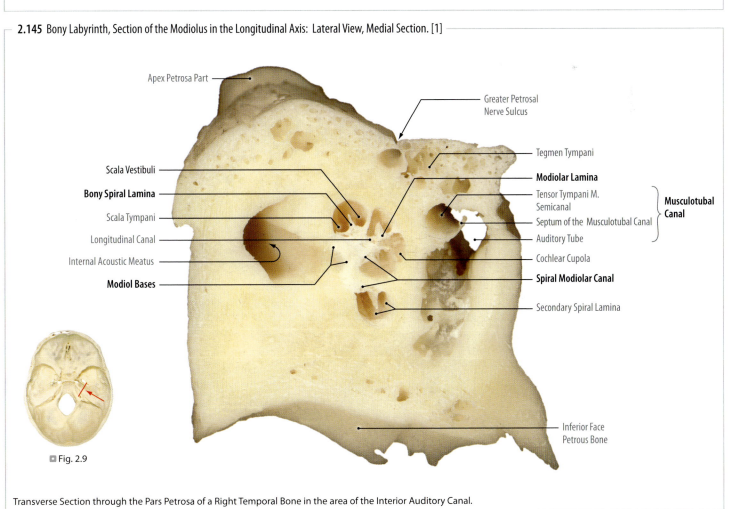

- Apex Petrosa Part
- Greater Petrosal Nerve Sulcus
- Tegmen Tympani
- **Modiolar Lamina**
- Scala Vestibuli
- **Bony Spiral Lamina**
- Scala Tympani
- Longitudinal Canal
- Internal Acoustic Meatus
- **Modiol Bases**
- Tensor Tympani M. Semicanal
- Septum of the Musculotubal Canal
- Auditory Tube
- Musculotubal Canal
- Cochlear Cupola
- **Spiral Modiolar Canal**
- Secondary Spiral Lamina
- Inferior Face Petrous Bone

▫ Fig. 2.9

Transverse Section through the Pars Petrosa of a Right Temporal Bone in the area of the Interior Auditory Canal.

Ear

2.146 Right Temporal Bone with Middle and Internal Ear: CT Multiplanar Reconstruction (1-mm-Layer Thickness, 0.5-mm Reconstruction Increment), Horizontal Plane. [33]

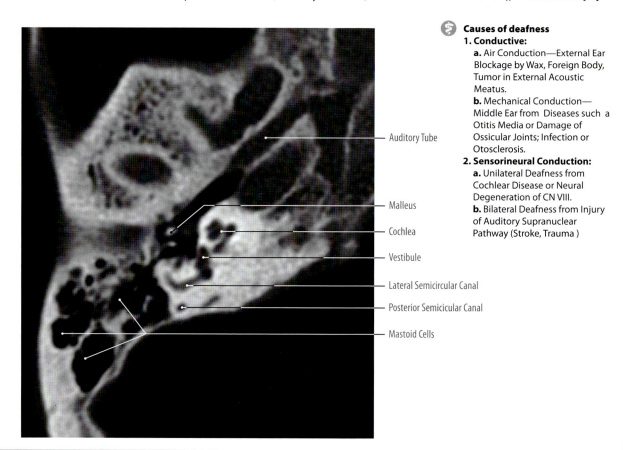

Causes of deafness
1. **Conductive:**
   a. Air Conduction—External Ear Blockage by Wax, Foreign Body, Tumor in External Acoustic Meatus.
   b. Mechanical Conduction—Middle Ear from Diseases such a Otitis Media or Damage of Ossicular Joints; Infection or Otosclerosis.
2. **Sensorineural Conduction:**
   a. Unilateral Deafness from Cochlear Disease or Neural Degeneration of CN VIII.
   b. Bilateral Deafness from Injury of Auditory Supranuclear Pathway (Stroke, Trauma)

Auditory Tube

Malleus

Cochlea

Vestibule

Lateral Semicircular Canal

Posterior Semicicular Canal

Mastoid Cells

2.147 Blood Supply and Nerve Supply of the Hearing and Equilibrium Organs: Right Side, Medial View. [13]

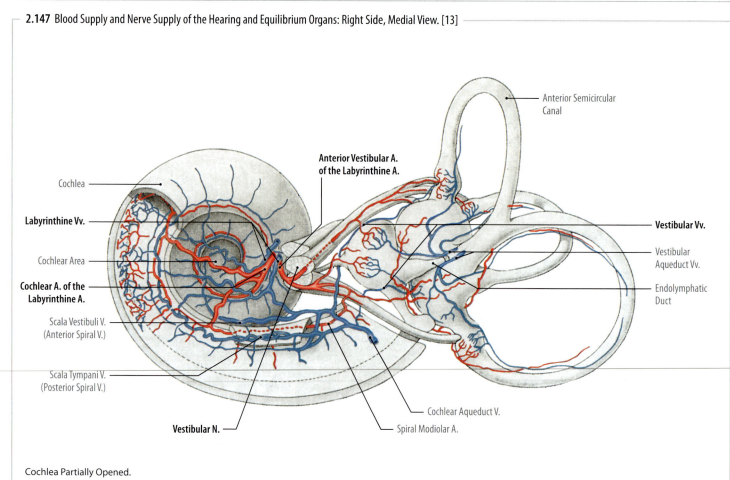

Cochlea

Labyrinthine Vv.

Cochlear Area

Cochlear A. of the Labyrinthine A.

Scala Vestibuli V. (Anterior Spiral V.)

Scala Tympani V. (Posterior Spiral V.)

Vestibular N.

Anterior Vestibular A. of the Labyrinthine A.

Anterior Semicircular Canal

Vestibular Vv.

Vestibular Aqueduct Vv.

Endolymphatic Duct

Cochlear Aqueduct V.

Spiral Modiolar A.

Cochlea Partially Opened.

Temporal Bone: Pathway of the Nerves

2.148 Section through a Right Temporal Bone in the Area of the Middle Ear with Illustration of the Nerves. [34]

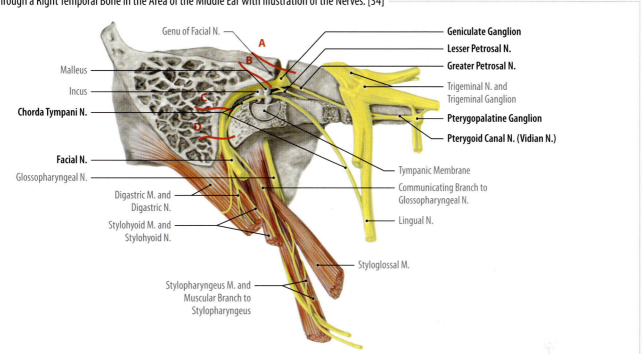

Genu of Facial N.
A
B
Malleus
Incus
C
Chorda Tympani N.
D
Facial N.
Glossopharyngeal N.
Digastric M. and Digastric N.
Stylohyoid M. and Stylohyoid N.
Stylopharyngeus M. and Muscular Branch to Stylopharyngeus

Geniculate Ganglion
Lesser Petrosal N.
Greater Petrosal N.
Trigeminal N. and Trigeminal Ganglion
Pterygopalatine Ganglion
Pterygoid Canal N. (Vidian N.)
Tympanic Membrane
Communicating Branch to Glossopharyngeal N.
Lingual N.
Styloglossal M.

2.149 Right Temporal Bone Opened Vertically. [34]

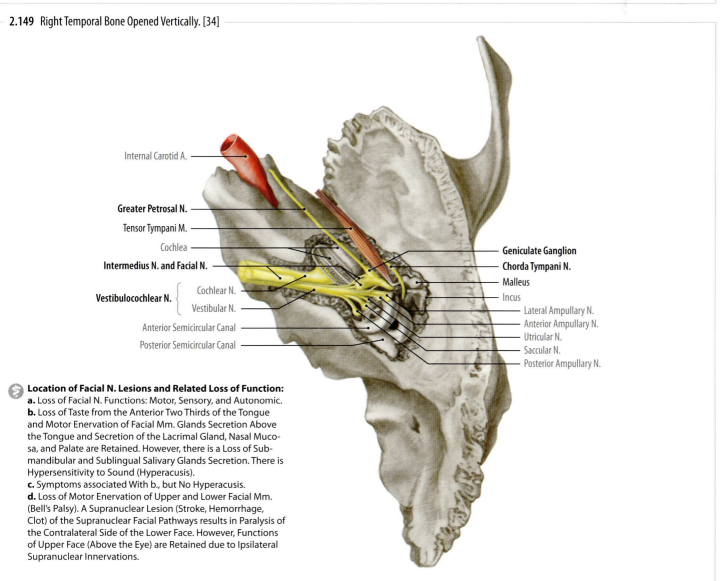

Internal Carotid A.
Greater Petrosal N.
Tensor Tympani M.
Cochlea
Intermedius N. and Facial N.
Vestibulocochlear N. { Cochlear N.
Vestibular N.
Anterior Semicircular Canal
Posterior Semicircular Canal

Geniculate Ganglion
Chorda Tympani N.
Malleus
Incus
Lateral Ampullary N.
Anterior Ampullary N.
Utricular N.
Saccular N.
Posterior Ampullary N.

Location of Facial N. Lesions and Related Loss of Function:
a. Loss of Facial N. Functions: Motor, Sensory, and Autonomic.
b. Loss of Taste from the Anterior Two Thirds of the Tongue and Motor Enervation of Facial Mm. Glands Secretion Above the Tongue and Secretion of the Lacrimal Gland, Nasal Mucosa, and Palate are Retained. However, there is a Loss of Submandibular and Sublingual Salivary Glands Secretion. There is Hypersensitivity to Sound (Hyperacusis).
c. Symptoms associated With b., but No Hyperacusis.
d. Loss of Motor Enervation of Upper and Lower Facial Mm. (Bell's Palsy). A Supranuclear Lesion (Stroke, Hemorrhage, Clot) of the Supranuclear Facial Pathways results in Paralysis of the Contralateral Side of the Lower Face. However, Functions of Upper Face (Above the Eye) are Retained due to Ipsilateral Supranuclear Innervations.

2.150a,b Arteries and Their Points of Passage at the Cranial Base. [6, 18]

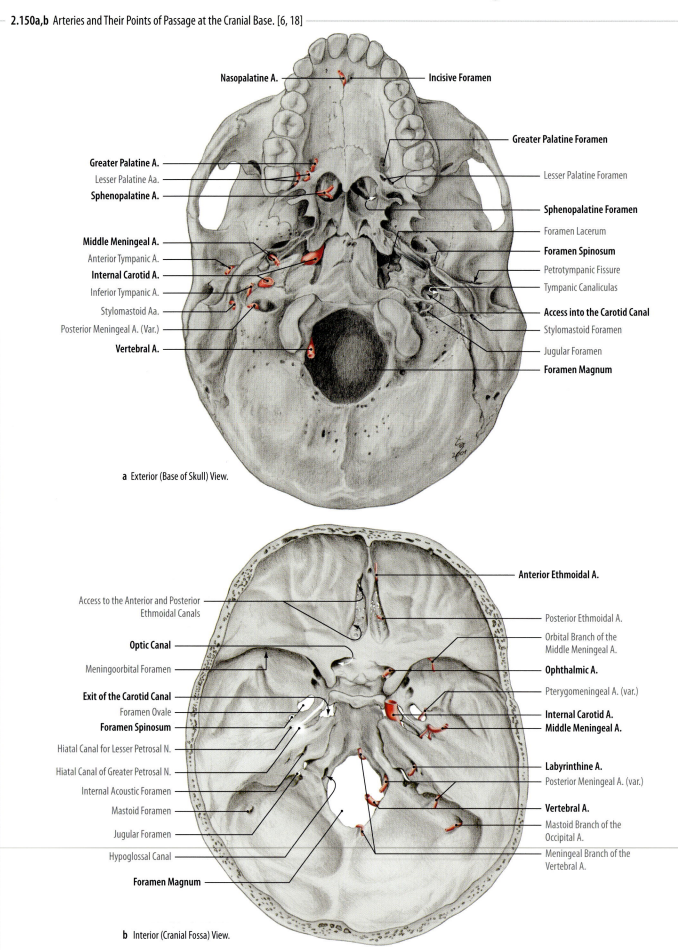

Nasopalatine A. — Incisive Foramen

Greater Palatine Foramen

Greater Palatine A.
Lesser Palatine Aa.
Sphenopalatine A.

Lesser Palatine Foramen

Sphenopalatine Foramen

Foramen Lacerum

Middle Meningeal A.
Anterior Tympanic A.
Internal Carotid A.
Inferior Tympanic A.
Stylomastoid Aa.
Posterior Meningeal A. (Var.)
Vertebral A.

Foramen Spinosum
Petrotympanic Fissure
Tympanic Caniculas
Access into the Carotid Canal
Stylomastoid Foramen
Jugular Foramen
Foramen Magnum

a Exterior (Base of Skull) View.

Anterior Ethmoidal A.

Access to the Anterior and Posterior Ethmoidal Canals

Posterior Ethmoidal A.

Orbital Branch of the Middle Meningeal A.

Optic Canal
Meningoorbital Foramen
Exit of the Carotid Canal
Foramen Ovale
Foramen Spinosum
Hiatal Canal for Lesser Petrosal N.
Hiatal Canal of Greater Petrosal N.
Internal Acoustic Foramen
Mastoid Foramen
Jugular Foramen
Hypoglossal Canal
Foramen Magnum

Ophthalmic A.
Pterygomeningeal A. (var.)
Internal Carotid A.
Middle Meningeal A.
Labyrinthine A.
Posterior Meningeal A. (var.)
Vertebral A.
Mastoid Branch of the Occipital A.
Meningeal Branch of the Vertebral A.

b Interior (Cranial Fossa) View.

Cranial Base: Nerve Points of Passage

2.151a,b Nerves and Their Points of Passage at the Cranial Base. [6, 18]

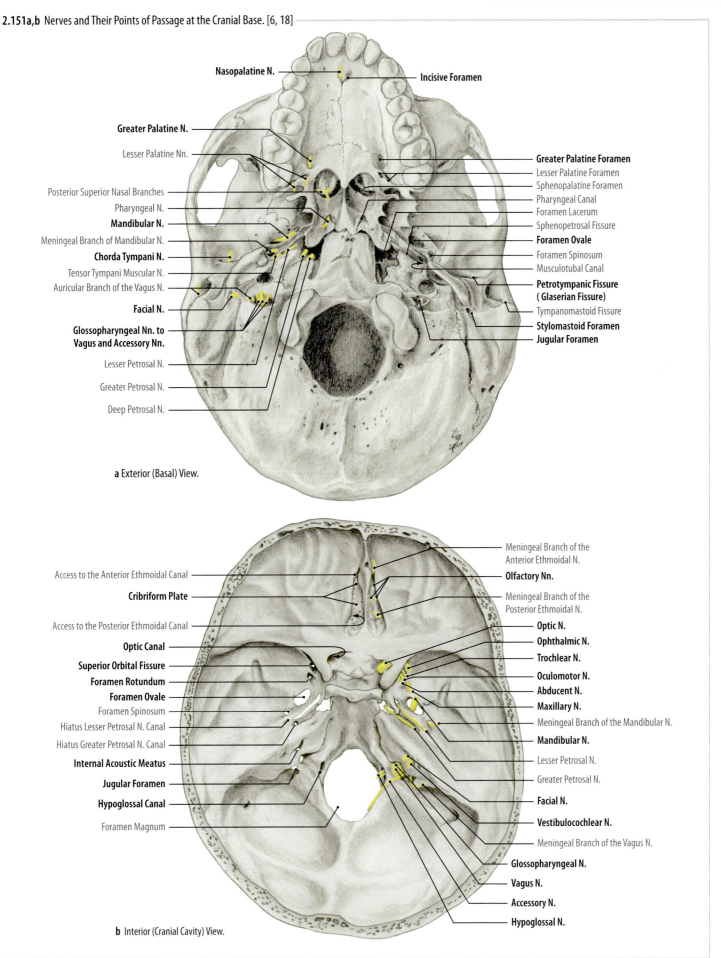

Nasopalatine N. — Incisive Foramen

Greater Palatine N.

Lesser Palatine Nn.

Posterior Superior Nasal Branches

Pharyngeal N.

Mandibular N.

Meningeal Branch of Mandibular N.

Chorda Tympani N.

Tensor Tympani Muscular N.

Auricular Branch of the Vagus N.

Facial N.

Glossopharyngeal Nn. to Vagus and Accessory Nn.

Lesser Petrosal N.

Greater Petrosal N.

Deep Petrosal N.

Greater Palatine Foramen
Lesser Palatine Foramen
Sphenopalatine Foramen
Pharyngeal Canal
Foramen Lacerum
Sphenopetrosal Fissure
Foramen Ovale
Foramen Spinosum
Musculotubal Canal
Petrotympanic Fissure (Glaserian Fissure)
Tympanomastoid Fissure
Stylomastoid Foramen
Jugular Foramen

a Exterior (Basal) View.

Access to the Anterior Ethmoidal Canal

Cribriform Plate

Access to the Posterior Ethmoidal Canal

Optic Canal

Superior Orbital Fissure

Foramen Rotundum

Foramen Ovale

Foramen Spinosum

Hiatus Lesser Petrosal N. Canal

Hiatus Greater Petrosal N. Canal

Internal Acoustic Meatus

Jugular Foramen

Hypoglossal Canal

Foramen Magnum

Meningeal Branch of the Anterior Ethmoidal N.
Olfactory Nn.
Meningeal Branch of the Posterior Ethmoidal N.
Optic N.
Ophthalmic N.
Trochlear N.
Oculomotor N.
Abducent N.
Maxillary N.
Meningeal Branch of the Mandibular N.
Mandibular N.
Lesser Petrosal N.
Greater Petrosal N.
Facial N.
Vestibulocochlear N.
Meningeal Branch of the Vagus N.
Glossopharyngeal N.
Vagus N.
Accessory N.
Hypoglossal N.

b Interior (Cranial Cavity) View.

Brain In Situ

2.152 Diploic and Emissary Vv. with Their Connections to the Superficial Veins: Left Side View. [18, 2]

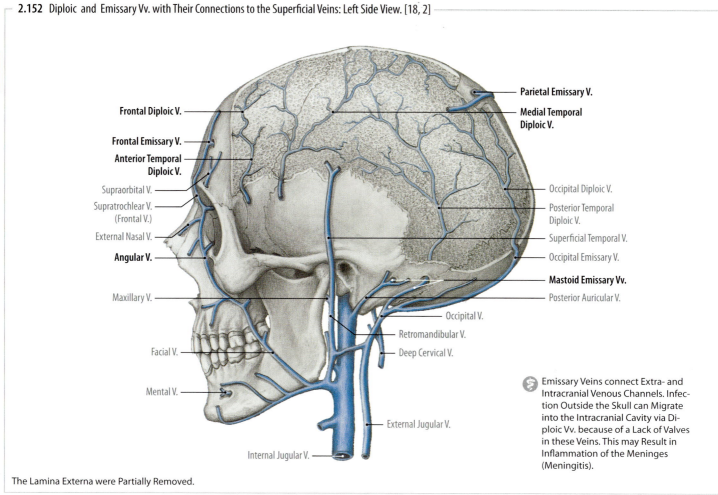

Parietal Emissary V.

Frontal Diploic V.

Medial Temporal Diploic V.

Frontal Emissary V.

Anterior Temporal Diploic V.

Supraorbital V.

Supratrochlear V. (Frontal V.)

External Nasal V.

Angular V.

Maxillary V.

Facial V.

Mental V.

Occipital Diploic V.

Posterior Temporal Diploic V.

Superficial Temporal V.

Occipital Emissary V.

Mastoid Emissary Vv.

Posterior Auricular V.

Occipital V.

Retromandibular V.

Deep Cervical V.

External Jugular V.

Internal Jugular V.

Emissary Veins connect Extra- and Intracranial Venous Channels. Infection Outside the Skull can Migrate into the Intracranial Cavity via Diploic Vv. because of a Lack of Valves in these Veins. This may Result in Inflammation of the Meninges (Meningitis).

The Lamina Externa were Partially Removed.

2.153 Meninges and Subarachnoid Space: Schematic Illustration. [23]

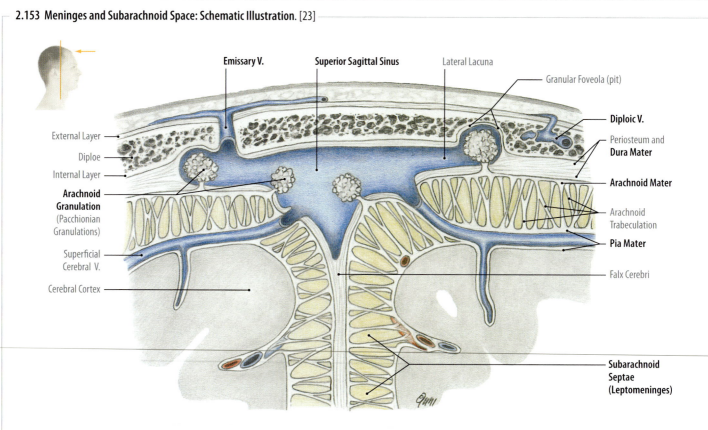

Emissary V.

Superior Sagittal Sinus

Lateral Lacuna

Granular Foveola (pit)

External Layer

Diploe

Internal Layer

Arachnoid Granulation (Pacchionian Granulations)

Superficial Cerebral V.

Cerebral Cortex

Diploic V.

Periosteum and **Dura Mater**

Arachnoid Mater

Arachnoid Trabeculation

Pia Mater

Falx Cerebri

Subarachnoid Septae (Leptomeninges)

Frontal Section through the Head in the area of the Superior Sagittal Sinus.

Dura Mater and Dural Venous Sinuses

2.154a,b Cranial Dura Mater (Encephali), Dural Venous Sinuses, and Veins of the Interior Cranial Cavity. [a 13, b 23]

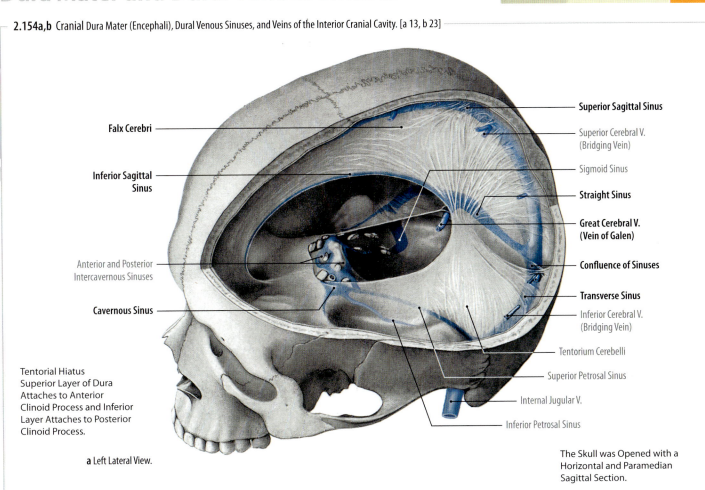

Falx Cerebri

Inferior Sagittal Sinus

Anterior and Posterior Intercavernous Sinuses

Cavernous Sinus

Superior Sagittal Sinus

Superior Cerebral V. (Bridging Vein)

Sigmoid Sinus

Straight Sinus

Great Cerebral V. (Vein of Galen)

Confluence of Sinuses

Transverse Sinus

Inferior Cerebral V. (Bridging Vein)

Tentorium Cerebelli

Superior Petrosal Sinus

Internal Jugular V.

Inferior Petrosal Sinus

Tentorial Hiatus Superior Layer of Dura Attaches to Anterior Clinoid Process and Inferior Layer Attaches to Posterior Clinoid Process.

a Left Lateral View.

The Skull was Opened with a Horizontal and Paramedian Sagittal Section.

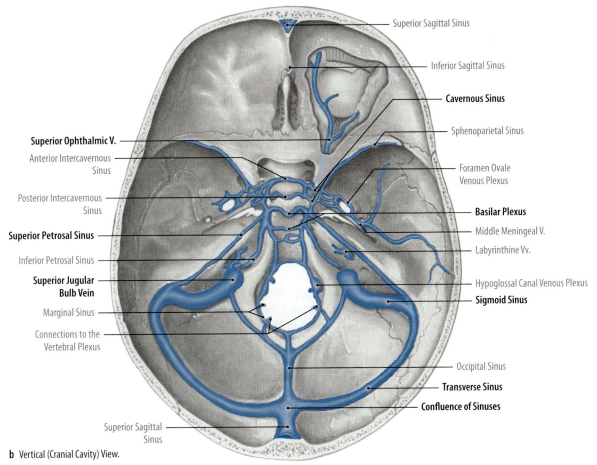

Superior Sagittal Sinus

Inferior Sagittal Sinus

Cavernous Sinus

Sphenoparietal Sinus

Superior Ophthalmic V.

Anterior Intercavernous Sinus

Posterior Intercavernous Sinus

Superior Petrosal Sinus

Inferior Petrosal Sinus

Superior Jugular Bulb Vein

Marginal Sinus

Connections to the Vertebral Plexus

Foramen Ovale Venous Plexus

Basilar Plexus

Middle Meningeal V.

Labyrinthine Vv.

Hypoglossal Canal Venous Plexus

Sigmoid Sinus

Occipital Sinus

Transverse Sinus

Confluence of Sinuses

Superior Sagittal Sinus

b Vertical (Cranial Cavity) View.

Brain In Situ

2.155 Sensory Supply of the Dura Mater Cranial. [13]

Concomitant Symptoms of Meningitis are Headaches (Meningeal Branches of the Trigeminal N.), Nausea, and Vomiting (Meningeal Branches of the Vagus N.), as well as Neck Stiffness (Meningeal Branches of the Cervical C1 and C2 Nn. not pictured here).

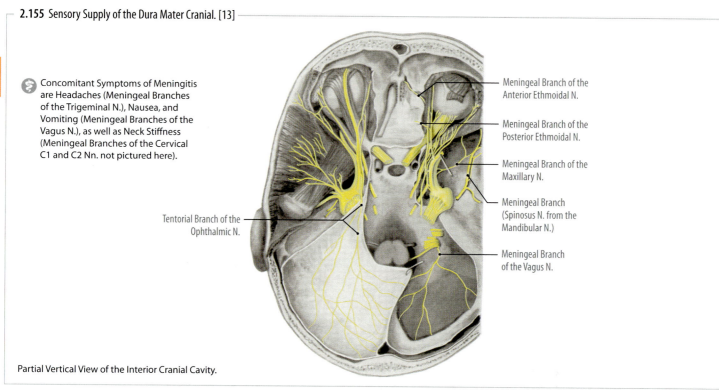

Tentorial Branch of the Ophthalmic N.

Meningeal Branch of the Anterior Ethmoidal N.

Meningeal Branch of the Posterior Ethmoidal N.

Meningeal Branch of the Maxillary N.

Meningeal Branch (Spinosus N. from the Mandibular N.)

Meningeal Branch of the Vagus N.

Partial Vertical View of the Interior Cranial Cavity.

2.156 Paramedian Sagittal Section through the Head with Preserved Nasal Septum: Right Section View. [6]

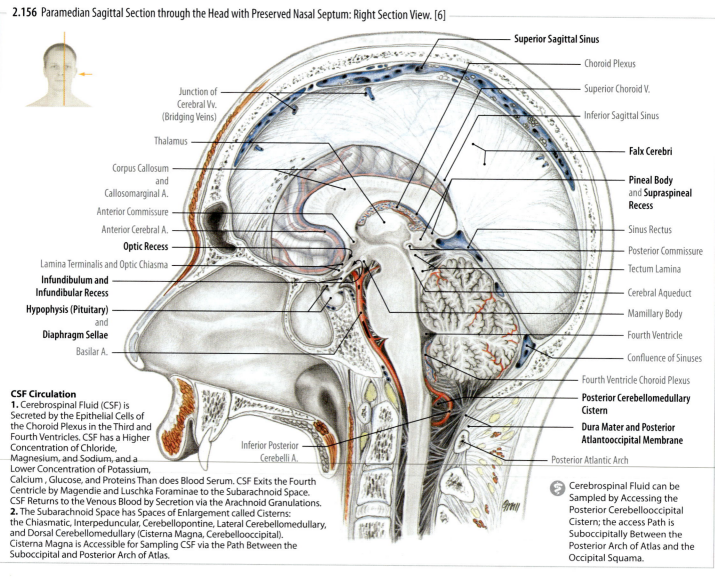

Junction of Cerebral Vv. (Bridging Veins)

Thalamus

Corpus Callosum and Callosomarginal A.

Anterior Commissure

Anterior Cerebral A.

Optic Recess

Lamina Terminalis and Optic Chiasma

Infundibulum and Infundibular Recess

Hypophysis (Pituitary) and **Diaphragm Sellae**

Basilar A.

Superior Sagittal Sinus

Choroid Plexus

Superior Choroid V.

Inferior Sagittal Sinus

Falx Cerebri

Pineal Body and **Supraspineal Recess**

Sinus Rectus

Posterior Commissure

Tectum Lamina

Cerebral Aqueduct

Mamillary Body

Fourth Ventricle

Confluence of Sinuses

Fourth Ventricle Choroid Plexus

Posterior Cerebellomedullary Cistern

Dura Mater and Posterior Atlantooccipital Membrane

Posterior Atlantic Arch

Inferior Posterior Cerebelli A.

CSF Circulation
1. Cerebrospinal Fluid (CSF) is Secreted by the Epithelial Cells of the Choroid Plexus in the Third and Fourth Ventricles. CSF has a Higher Concentration of Chloride, Magnesium, and Sodium, and a Lower Concentration of Potassium, Calcium, Glucose, and Proteins Than does Blood Serum. CSF Exits the Fourth Centricle by Magendie and Luschka Foraminae to the Subarachnoid Space. CSF Returns to the Venous Blood by Secretion via the Arachnoid Granulations.
2. The Subarachnoid Space has Spaces of Enlargement called Cisterns: the Chiasmatic, Interpeduncular, Cerebellopontine, Lateral Cerebellomedullary, and Dorsal Cerebellomedullary (Cisterna Magna, Cerebellooccipital). Cisterna Magna is Accessible for Sampling CSF via the Path Between the Suboccipital and Posterior Arch of Atlas.

Cerebrospinal Fluid can be Sampled by Accessing the Posterior Cerebellooccipital Cistern; the access Path is Suboccipitally Between the Posterior Arch of Atlas and the Occipital Squama.

Subarachnoid Spaces · MRI

2.157 Subarachnoid Space and Ventricles of the Brain, Paramedian Sagittal Section: Right Section, Medial View. [23]

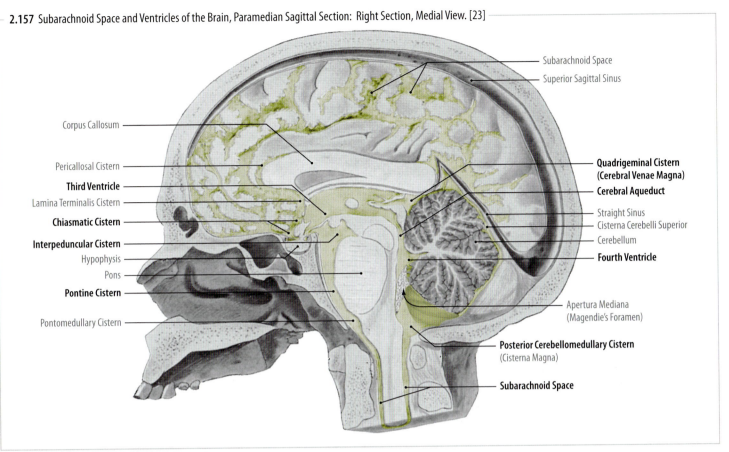

Corpus Callosum

Pericallosal Cistern

Third Ventricle

Lamina Terminalis Cistern

Chiasmatic Cistern

Interpeduncular Cistern

Hypophysis

Pons

Pontine Cistern

Pontomedullary Cistern

Subarachnoid Space

Superior Sagittal Sinus

Quadrigeminal Cistern (Cerebral Venae Magna)

Cerebral Aqueduct

Straight Sinus

Cisterna Cerebelli Superior

Cerebellum

Fourth Ventricle

Apertura Mediana (Magendie's Foramen)

Posterior Cerebellomedullary Cistern (Cisterna Magna)

Subarachnoid Space

2.158 Magnetic Resonance Imaging (MRI) of the Head: Median Sagittal Section. [28]

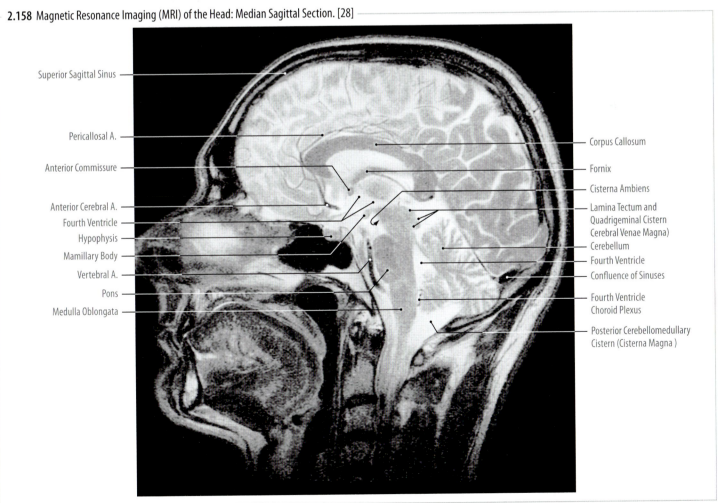

Superior Sagittal Sinus

Pericallosal A.

Anterior Commissure

Anterior Cerebral A.

Fourth Ventricle

Hypophysis

Mamillary Body

Vertebral A.

Pons

Medulla Oblongata

Corpus Callosum

Fornix

Cisterna Ambiens

Lamina Tectum and Quadrigeminal Cistern Cerebral Venae Magna)

Cerebellum

Fourth Ventricle

Confluence of Sinuses

Fourth Ventricle Choroid Plexus

Posterior Cerebellomedullary Cistern (Cisterna Magna)

Brain In Situ

2.159 Meninges, Meningeal and Cerebral Vessels: Vertical View. [35]

Meningiomas are Slow-Growing Tumors Formed by Clusters of Arachnoid Cells at sites Found in Veli where Cranial Nerves or Blood Vessels Pass Through the Dura. At the Base of the Skull, at the Cribriform Plate near the Olfactory N. (Anosmia) and Lateral Cerebral Dura, the Pressure of a Tumor Mass may Affect the Functions of Adjacent Areas.

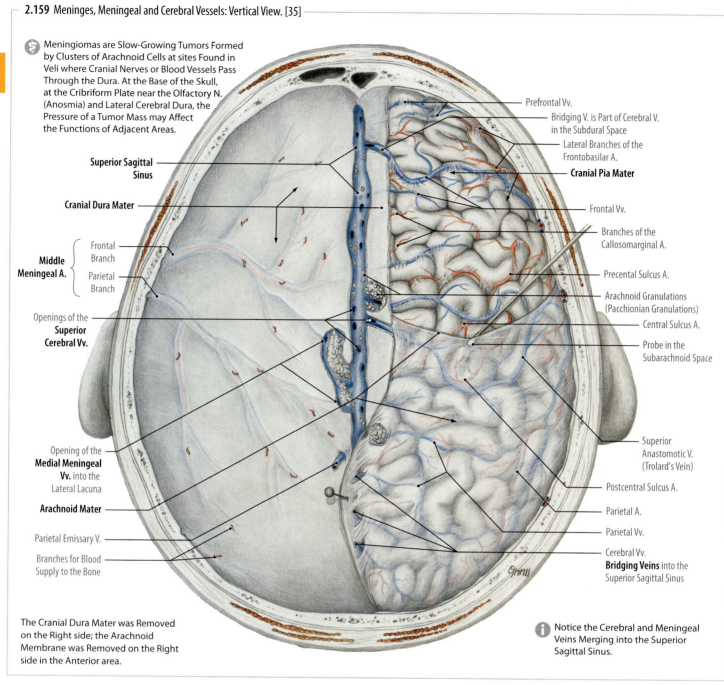

Prefrontal Vv.

Bridging V. is Part of Cerebral V. in the Subdural Space

Lateral Branches of the Frontobasilar A.

Cranial Pia Mater

Frontal Vv.

Branches of the Callosomarginal A.

Precental Sulcus A.

Arachnoid Granulations (Pacchionian Granulations)

Central Sulcus A.

Probe in the Subarachnoid Space

Superior Anastomotic V. (Trolard's Vein)

Postcentral Sulcus A.

Parietal A.

Parietal Vv.

Cerebral Vv.

Bridging Veins into the Superior Sagittal Sinus

Superior Sagittal Sinus

Cranial Dura Mater

Middle Meningeal A.
Frontal Branch
Parietal Branch

Openings of the **Superior Cerebral Vv.**

Opening of the **Medial Meningeal Vv.** into the Lateral Lacuna

Arachnoid Mater

Parietal Emissary V.

Branches for Blood Supply to the Bone

The Cranial Dura Mater was Removed on the Right side; the Arachnoid Membrane was Removed on the Right side in the Anterior area.

Notice the Cerebral and Meningeal Veins Merging into the Superior Sagittal Sinus.

2.160 Projection of the Frontal Branches and Parietal Branches of the Middle Meningeal A. onto the Lateral Cranial Wall. [23, 36]

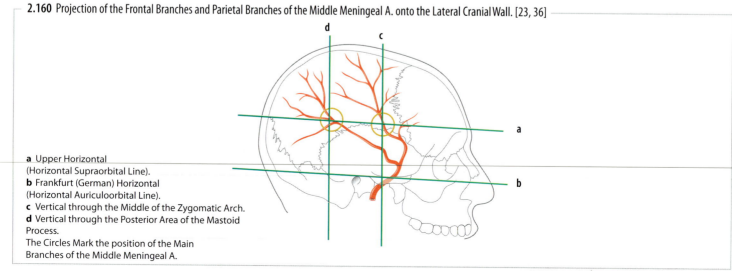

a Upper Horizontal
(Horizontal Supraorbital Line).
b Frankfurt (German) Horizontal
(Horizontal Auriculoorbital Line).
c Vertical through the Middle of the Zygomatic Arch.
d Vertical through the Posterior Area of the Mastoid Process.
The Circles Mark the position of the Main Branches of the Middle Meningeal A.

Brain In Situ: Corpus Callosum & Ventricles

111 | 2

2.161 Brain in Situ, Corpus Callosum, and Ventricles: Vertical View. [35]

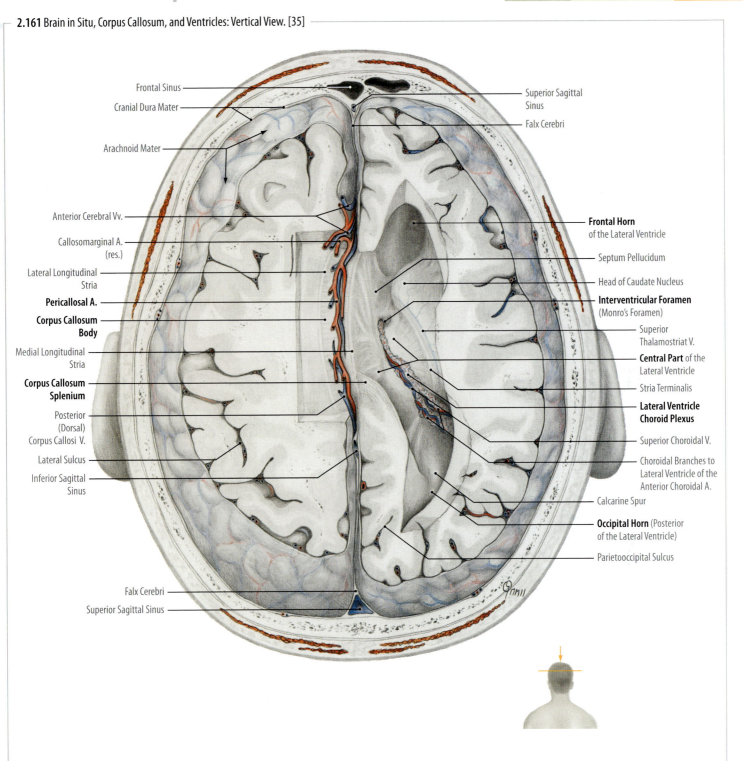

Frontal Sinus

Cranial Dura Mater

Arachnoid Mater

Anterior Cerebral Vv.

Callosomarginal A. (res.)

Lateral Longitudinal Stria

Pericallosal A.

Corpus Callosum Body

Medial Longitudinal Stria

Corpus Callosum Splenium

Posterior (Dorsal) Corpus Callosi V.

Lateral Sulcus

Inferior Sagittal Sinus

Falx Cerebri

Superior Sagittal Sinus

Superior Sagittal Sinus

Falx Cerebri

Frontal Horn of the Lateral Ventricle

Septum Pellucidum

Head of Caudate Nucleus

Interventricular Foramen (Monro's Foramen)

Superior Thalamostriat V.

Central Part of the Lateral Ventricle

Stria Terminalis

Lateral Ventricle Choroid Plexus

Superior Choroidal V.

Choroidal Branches to Lateral Ventricle of the Anterior Choroidal A.

Calcarine Spur

Occipital Horn (Posterior of the Lateral Ventricle)

Parietooccipital Sulcus

On the Left side, the Brain has been Removed up to the Corpus Callosum; on the Right side, the Anterior Horn, the Central Part, and the Posterior Horn of the Lateral Ventricle were Dissected.

Lesions in the Intracranial Space (Tumors, Cerebral Abscesses, Hemorrhages) cause Increased Pressure with symptoms of Headache, Nausea, Vomiting, Pupillary Constriction, and Nerve Damage—most frequently to the Abducent Nn.

2.162 In Situ Brain, Ventricles, and Cerebellum: Vertical View. [35]

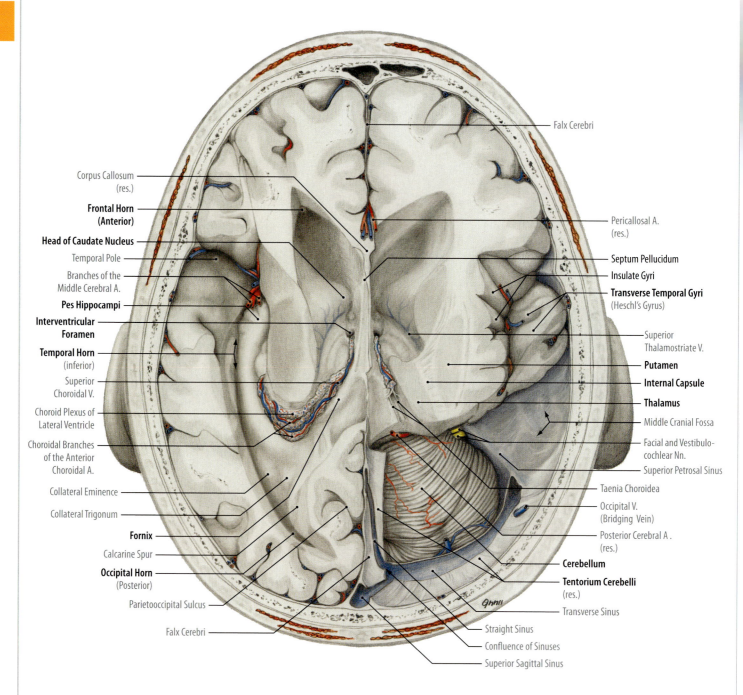

Corpus Callosum (res.)

Frontal Horn (Anterior)

Head of Caudate Nucleus

Temporal Pole

Branches of the Middle Cerebral A.

Pes Hippocampi

Interventricular Foramen

Temporal Horn (inferior)

Superior Choroidal V.

Choroid Plexus of Lateral Ventricle

Choroidal Branches of the Anterior Choroidal A.

Collateral Eminence

Collateral Trigonum

Fornix

Calcarine Spur

Occipital Horn (Posterior)

Parietooccipital Sulcus

Falx Cerebri

Falx Cerebri

Pericallosal A. (res.)

Septum Pellucidum

Insulate Gyri

Transverse Temporal Gyri (Heschl's Gyrus)

Superior Thalamostriate V.

Putamen

Internal Capsule

Thalamus

Middle Cranial Fossa

Facial and Vestibulo-cochlear Nn.

Superior Petrosal Sinus

Taenia Choroidea

Occipital V. (Bridging Vein)

Posterior Cerebral A. (res.)

Cerebellum

Tentorium Cerebelli (res.)

Transverse Sinus

Straight Sinus

Confluence of Sinuses

Superior Sagittal Sinus

On the Left side, the Lateral Ventricle, including the Inferior Horn with the Hippocampus, was Dissected; on the Right side, the Right Cerebellar Hemisphere is Visible Following Resection of the Occipital Lobe and the Largest Part of the Temporal Lobe and the Tentorium Cerebelli in the Posterior Cranial Fossa.

Hydrocephalus is an Increase in Cerebrospinal Fluid (CSF) Volume and Pressure In or Around the Brain (Ventricles or Subarachnoid Space).
1. Internal hydrocephalus causes an Explosion of the Brain by CSF Accumulation in the Ventricles when the Foramenae of Magendie and Luschka are Closed (Dilatation of Ventricles as seen on MRI).
2. External Hydrocephalus is an Implosion of the Brain, caused by Blockage of the CSF through the Arachnoid Granulations and Back Up into the Subarachnoidal Spaces to Blocked Venous Sinuses (Collapse of the Ventricle as seen on MRI). (□ Fig. 2.190).

2.163 Brainstem, Midbrain, and Basal Ganglia, as well as Interior Cranial Base and Upper Section of the Vertebral Canal: Occipital View. [37]

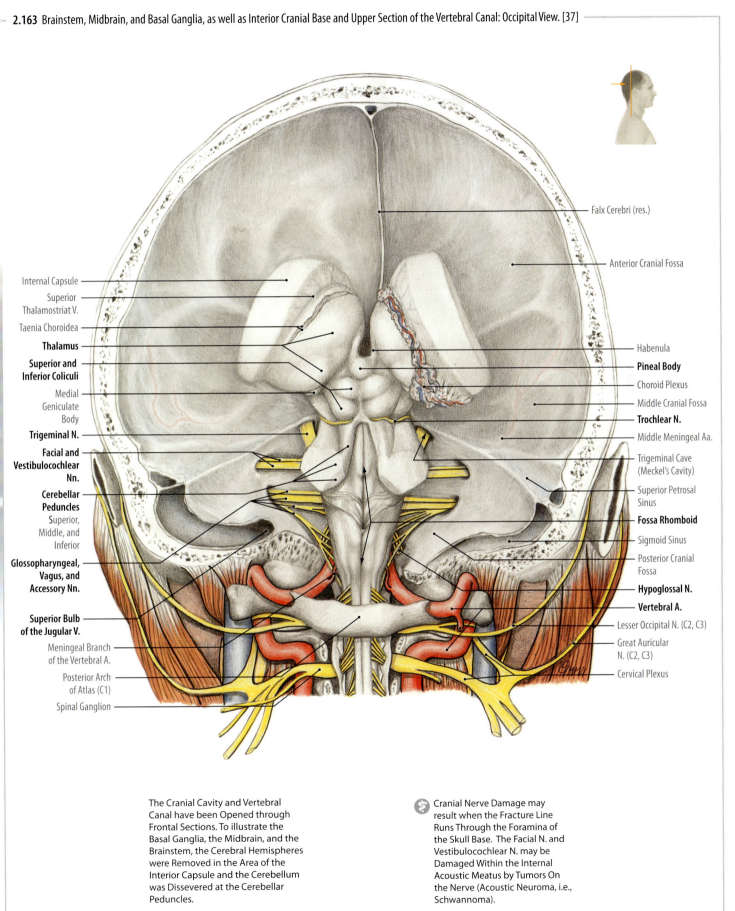

Internal Capsule

Superior
Thalamostriat V.

Taenia Choroidea

Thalamus

**Superior and
Inferior Coliculi**

Medial
Geniculate
Body

Trigeminal N.

**Facial and
Vestibulocochlear
Nn.**

**Cerebellar
Peduncles**
Superior,
Middle, and
Inferior

**Glossopharyngeal,
Vagus, and
Accessory Nn.**

**Superior Bulb
of the Jugular V.**

Meningeal Branch
of the Vertebral A.

Posterior Arch
of Atlas (C1)

Spinal Ganglion

Falx Cerebri (res.)

Anterior Cranial Fossa

Habenula

Pineal Body

Choroid Plexus

Middle Cranial Fossa

Trochlear N.

Middle Meningeal Aa.

Trigeminal Cave
(Meckel's Cavity)

Superior Petrosal
Sinus

Fossa Rhomboid

Sigmoid Sinus

Posterior Cranial
Fossa

Hypoglossal N.

Vertebral A.

Lesser Occipital N. (C2, C3)

Great Auricular
N. (C2, C3)

Cervical Plexus

The Cranial Cavity and Vertebral
Canal have been Opened through
Frontal Sections. To illustrate the
Basal Ganglia, the Midbrain, and the
Brainstem, the Cerebral Hemispheres
were Removed in the Area of the
Interior Capsule and the Cerebellum
was Dissevered at the Cerebellar
Peduncles.

Cranial Nerve Damage may
result when the Fracture Line
Runs Through the Foramina of
the Skull Base. The Facial N. and
Vestibulocochlear N. may be
Damaged Within the Internal
Acoustic Meatus by Tumors On
the Nerve (Acoustic Neuroma, i.e.,
Schwannoma).

Brain Situs

Cranial Nerves and Vessels of the Interior Cranial Base

2.164 Cranial Nerves and Vessels of the Interior Cranial Base: Vertical View. [1]

Skull fracture can Damage the Meningeal A. or V., resulting in Bleeding Between Dura and Skull, Forming a Lentiform-shaped Epidural Hematoma. A sudden Shake to an Elderly Person may Result in Rupture of the Bridging Vein (Cerebral V., crossing Between the Arachnoid and Dural Sinuses) Causing Elliptical (crescentic) Subdural Hematoma. Rupture of the Cerebral Vv. in Subarachnoid Space can Cause a Brush-Stroke Image (MRI).

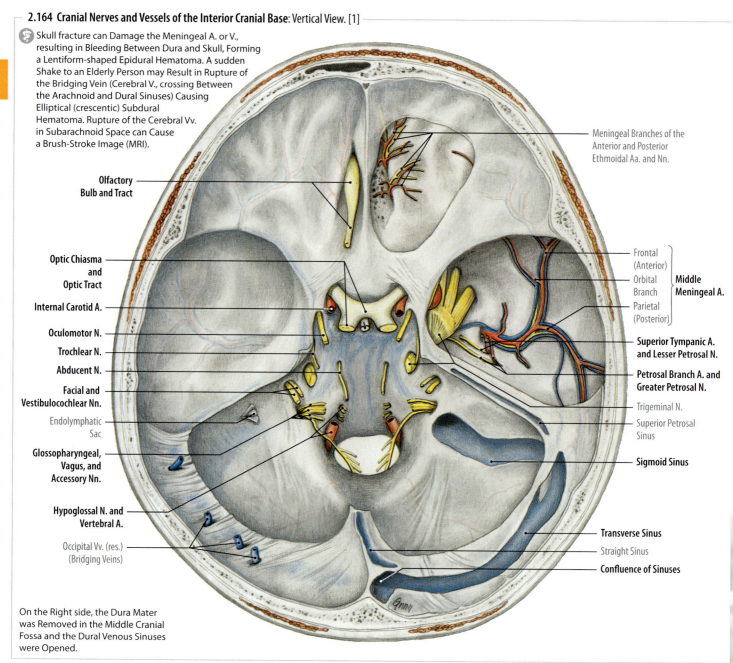

Olfactory Bulb and Tract

Optic Chiasma and Optic Tract

Internal Carotid A.

Oculomotor N.

Trochlear N.

Abducent N.

Facial and Vestibulocochlear Nn.

Endolymphatic Sac

Glossopharyngeal, Vagus, and Accessory Nn.

Hypoglossal N. and Vertebral A.

Occipital Vv. (res.) (Bridging Veins)

Meningeal Branches of the Anterior and Posterior Ethmoidal Aa. and Nn.

Frontal (Anterior)
Orbital Branch   **Middle Meningeal A.**
Parietal (Posterior)

Superior Tympanic A. and Lesser Petrosal N.

Petrosal Branch A. and Greater Petrosal N.

Trigeminal N.

Superior Petrosal Sinus

Sigmoid Sinus

Transverse Sinus

Straight Sinus

Confluence of Sinuses

On the Right side, the Dura Mater was Removed in the Middle Cranial Fossa and the Dural Venous Sinuses were Opened.

2.165 Trigeminal Ganglion (Semilunar Ganglion, Gasserian Ganglion): Right Side, Vertical View. [13, 38]

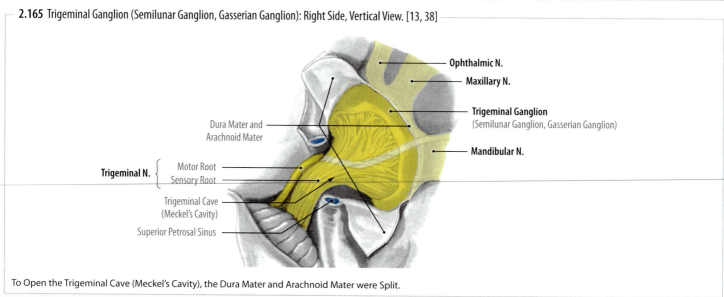

Ophthalmic N.

Maxillary N.

Trigeminal Ganglion (Semilunar Ganglion, Gasserian Ganglion)

Mandibular N.

Dura Mater and Arachnoid Mater

Trigeminal N. { Motor Root
Sensory Root

Trigeminal Cave (Meckel's Cavity)

Superior Petrosal Sinus

To Open the Trigeminal Cave (Meckel's Cavity), the Dura Mater and Arachnoid Mater were Split.

Cavernous Sinus · Internal Carotid A.

2.166 Hypophysis Area, Cavernous Sinus, and Basilar Plexus: Partial Vertical View of the Cranial Cavity. [1]

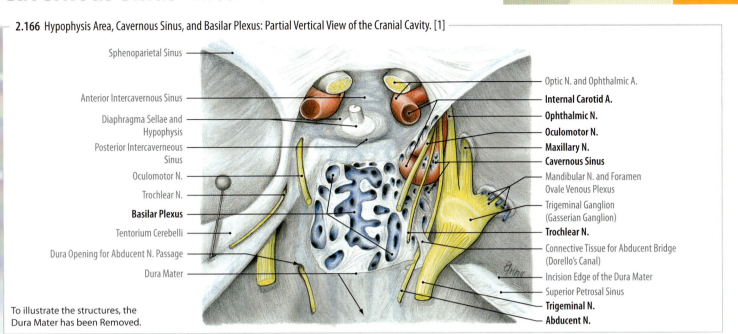

Sphenoparietal Sinus
Anterior Intercavernous Sinus
Diaphragma Sellae and Hypophysis
Posterior Intercaverneous Sinus
Oculomotor N.
Trochlear N.
Basilar Plexus
Tentorium Cerebelli
Dura Opening for Abducent N. Passage
Dura Mater

Optic N. and Ophthalmic A.
Internal Carotid A.
Ophthalmic N.
Oculomotor N.
Maxillary N.
Cavernous Sinus
Mandibular N. and Foramen Ovale Venous Plexus
Trigeminal Ganglion (Gasserian Ganglion)
Trochlear N.
Connective Tissue for Abducent Bridge (Dorello's Canal)
Incision Edge of the Dura Mater
Superior Petrosal Sinus
Trigeminal N.
Abducent N.

To illustrate the structures, the Dura Mater has been Removed.

2.167 Frontal Section through the Cavernous Sinus in the Area of the Hypophysis: Right Side, Occipital View. [23]

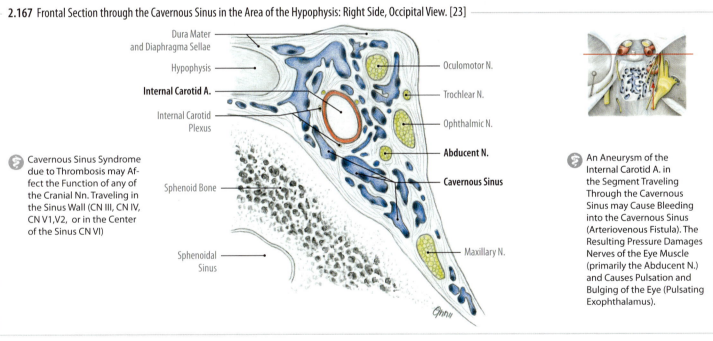

Dura Mater and Diaphragma Sellae
Hypophysis
Internal Carotid A.
Internal Carotid Plexus
Sphenoid Bone
Sphenoidal Sinus

Oculomotor N.
Trochlear N.
Ophthalmic N.
Abducent N.
Cavernous Sinus
Maxillary N.

Cavernous Sinus Syndrome due to Thrombosis may Affect the Function of any of the Cranial Nn. Traveling in the Sinus Wall (CN III, CN IV, CN V1,V2, or in the Center of the Sinus CN VI)

An Aneurysm of the Internal Carotid A. in the Segment Traveling Through the Cavernous Sinus may Cause Bleeding into the Cavernous Sinus (Arteriovenous Fistula). The Resulting Pressure Damages Nerves of the Eye Muscle (primarily the Abducent N.) and Causes Pulsation and Bulging of the Eye (Pulsating Exophthalamus).

2.168 Sections of the Internal Carotid Artery. [39]

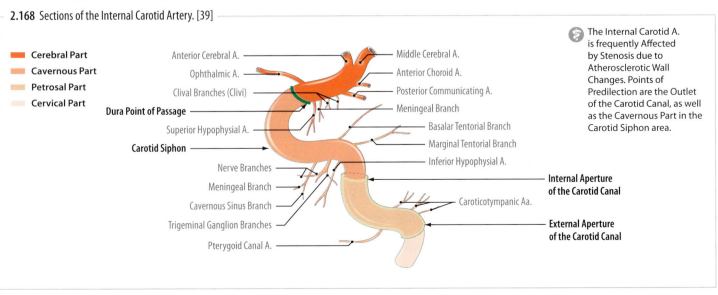

- **Cerebral Part**
- **Cavernous Part**
- **Petrosal Part**
- **Cervical Part**

Anterior Cerebral A.
Ophthalmic A.
Clival Branches (Clivi)
Dura Point of Passage
Superior Hypophysial A.
Carotid Siphon
Nerve Branches
Meningeal Branch
Cavernous Sinus Branch
Trigeminal Ganglion Branches
Pterygoid Canal A.

Middle Cerebral A.
Anterior Choroid A.
Posterior Communicating A.
Meningeal Branch
Basalar Tentorial Branch
Marginal Tentorial Branch
Inferior Hypophysial A.
Internal Aperture of the Carotid Canal
Caroticotympanic Aa.
External Aperture of the Carotid Canal

The Internal Carotid A. is frequently Affected by Stenosis due to Atherosclerotic Wall Changes. Points of Predilection are the Outlet of the Carotid Canal, as well as the Cavernous Part in the Carotid Siphon area.

Brain In Situ

Brain: Development, Classification

2.169 Head of a 4-Month-Old Fetus: Right Lateral View. [8]

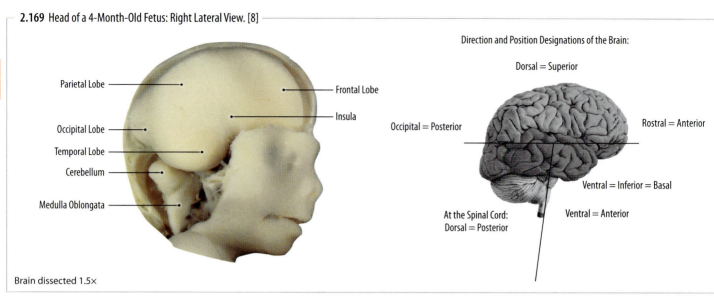

Parietal Lobe

Frontal Lobe

Insula

Occipital Lobe

Temporal Lobe

Cerebellum

Medulla Oblongata

Direction and Position Designations of the Brain:

Dorsal = Superior

Occipital = Posterior

Rostral = Anterior

Ventral = Inferior = Basal

At the Spinal Cord:
Dorsal = Posterior

Ventral = Anterior

Brain dissected 1.5×

2.170a,b Structure of the Brain. [7]

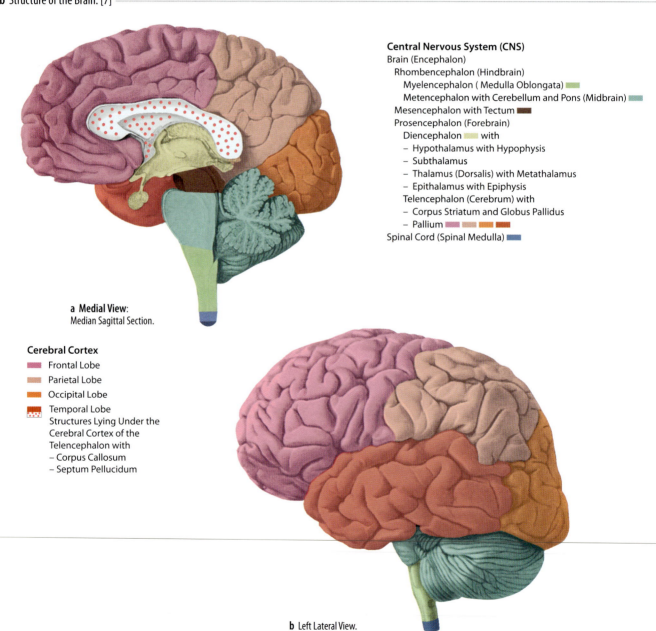

Central Nervous System (CNS)
Brain (Encephalon)
  Rhombencephalon (Hindbrain)
    Myelencephalon (Medulla Oblongata)
    Metencephalon with Cerebellum and Pons (Midbrain)
  Mesencephalon with Tectum
  Prosencephalon (Forebrain)
    Diencephalon with
    – Hypothalamus with Hypophysis
    – Subthalamus
    – Thalamus (Dorsalis) with Metathalamus
    – Epithalamus with Epiphysis
    Telencephalon (Cerebrum) with
    – Corpus Striatum and Globus Pallidus
    – Pallium
Spinal Cord (Spinal Medulla)

a Medial View:
Median Sagittal Section.

Cerebral Cortex
Frontal Lobe
Parietal Lobe
Occipital Lobe
Temporal Lobe
Structures Lying Under the
Cerebral Cortex of the
Telencephalon with
– Corpus Callosum
– Septum Pellucidum

b Left Lateral View.

Cerebral Cortex

2.171 Brain: Vertical View. [6]

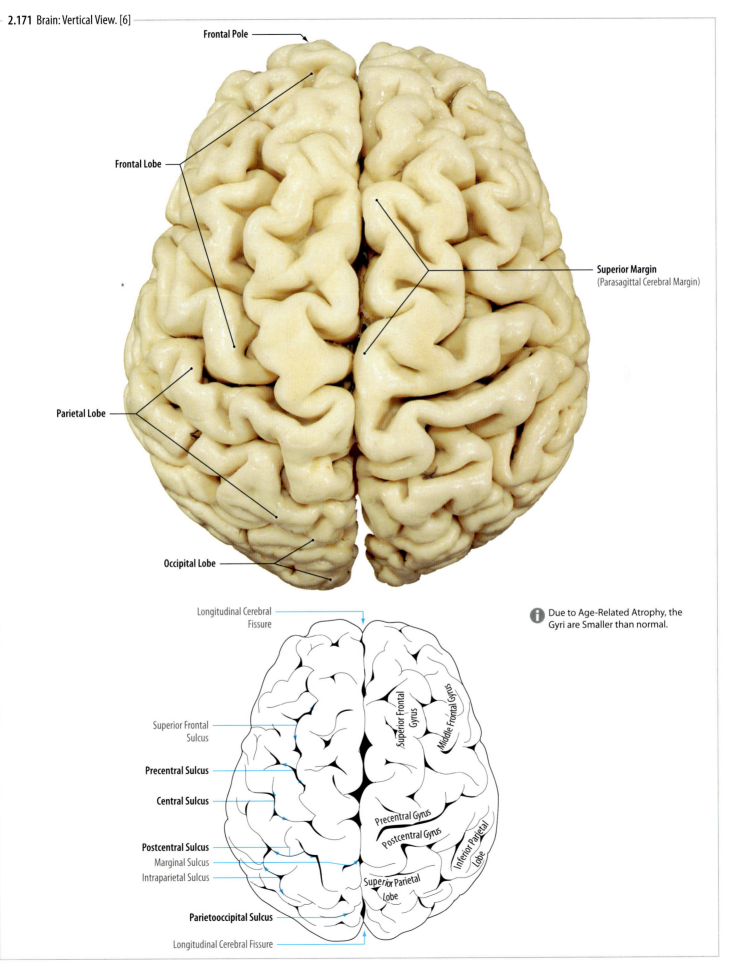

Frontal Pole

Frontal Lobe

Superior Margin
(Parasagittal Cerebral Margin)

Parietal Lobe

Occipital Lobe

Longitudinal Cerebral
Fissure

ⓘ Due to Age-Related Atrophy, the
Gyri are Smaller than normal.

Superior Frontal
Sulcus

Superior Frontal Gyrus

Middle Frontal Gyrus

Precentral Sulcus

Central Sulcus

Precentral Gyrus

Postcentral Gyrus

Inferior Parietal Lobe

Postcentral Sulcus

Marginal Sulcus

Intraparietal Sulcus

Superior Parietal Lobe

Parietooccipital Sulcus

Longitudinal Cerebral Fissure

Cerebral Cortex

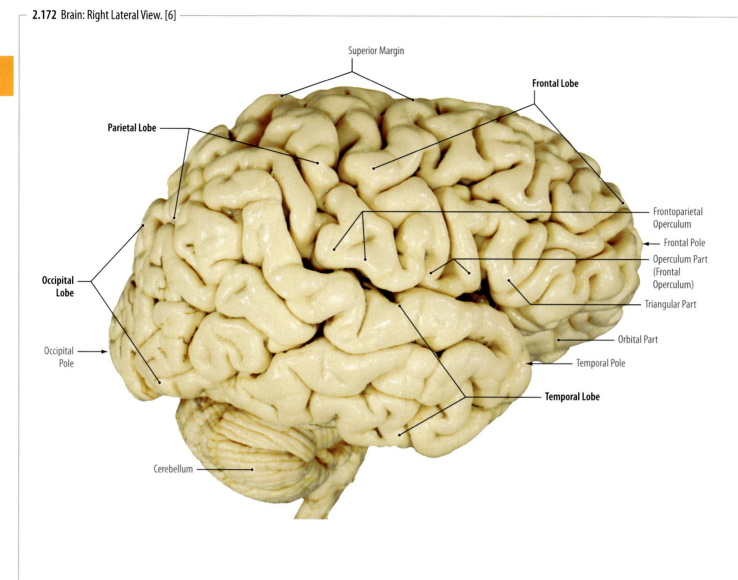

Superior Margin

Frontal Lobe

Parietal Lobe

Frontoparietal Operculum

← Frontal Pole

Operculum Part (Frontal Operculum)

Triangular Part

Occipital Lobe

Orbital Part

Temporal Pole

Occipital Pole →

Temporal Lobe

Cerebellum

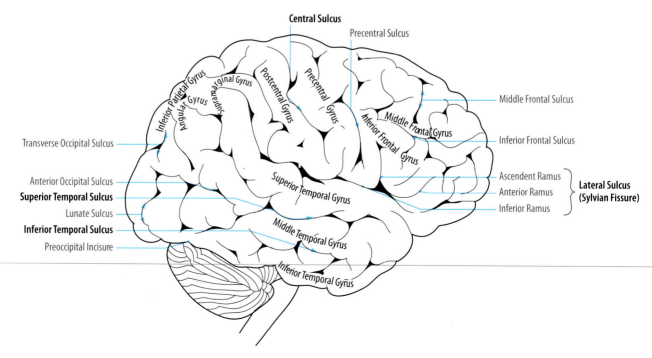

Central Sulcus

Precentral Sulcus

Inferior Parietal Gyrus

Angular Gyrus

Supramarginal Gyrus

Postcentral Gyrus

Precentral Gyrus

Middle Frontal Gyrus

Inferior Frontal Gyrus

Middle Frontal Sulcus

Transverse Occipital Sulcus

Inferior Frontal Sulcus

Anterior Occipital Sulcus

Superior Temporal Sulcus

Lunate Sulcus

Inferior Temporal Sulcus

Preoccipital Incisure

Superior Temporal Gyrus

Middle Temporal Gyrus

Inferior Temporal Gyrus

Ascendent Ramus

Anterior Ramus

Lateral Sulcus (Sylvian Fissure)

Inferior Ramus

2

2.173 Insular Lobe and Heschl's Gyrus of the Temporal Lobe, Brain: Left Lateral View. [40]

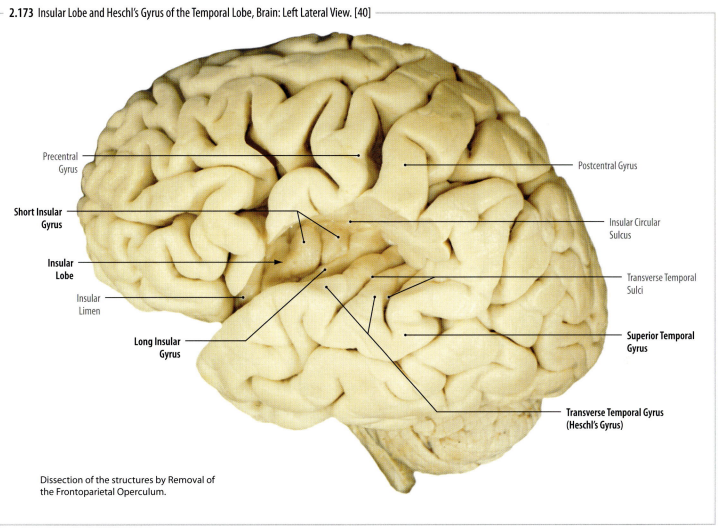

Precentral Gyrus

Short Insular Gyrus

Insular Lobe

Insular Limen

Long Insular Gyrus

Postcentral Gyrus

Insular Circular Sulcus

Transverse Temporal Sulci

Superior Temporal Gyrus

Transverse Temporal Gyrus (Heschl's Gyrus)

Dissection of the structures by Removal of the Frontoparietal Operculum.

2.174 Nerves, Nuclei, and Pathways of the Acoustic System: Occipital View. [41]

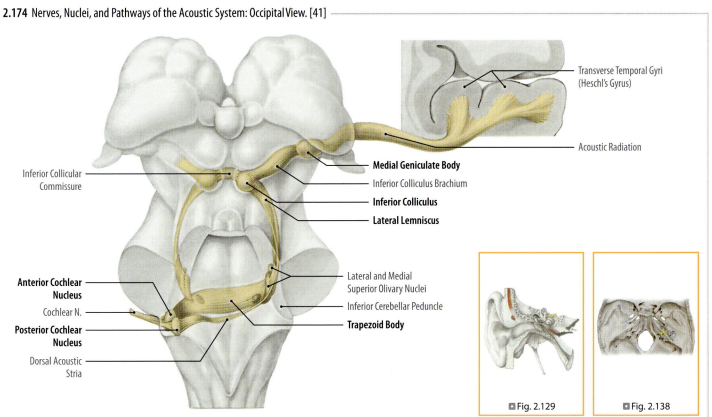

Transverse Temporal Gyri (Heschl's Gyrus)

Acoustic Radiation

Medial Geniculate Body

Inferior Colliculus Brachium

Inferior Colliculus

Lateral Lemniscus

Inferior Collicular Commissure

Lateral and Medial Superior Olivary Nuclei

Inferior Cerebellar Peduncle

Trapezoid Body

Anterior Cochlear Nucleus

Cochlear N.

Posterior Cochlear Nucleus

Dorsal Acoustic Stria

■ Fig. 2.129

■ Fig. 2.138

Brain

2

2.175 Left Hemisphere of the Brain: Median Sagittal Section, Medial View. [6]

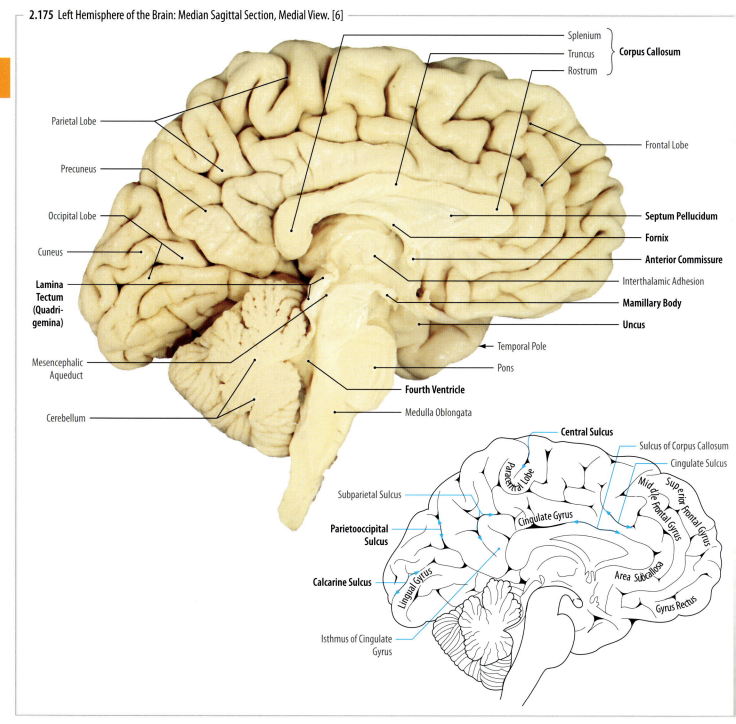

Splenium ⎤
Truncus ⎬ **Corpus Callosum**
Rostrum ⎦

Parietal Lobe

Frontal Lobe

Precuneus

Occipital Lobe

Septum Pellucidum

Cuneus

Fornix

Anterior Commissure

Interthalamic Adhesion

Lamina Tectum (Quadri-gemina)

Mamillary Body

Uncus

Temporal Pole

Mesencephalic Aqueduct

Pons

Fourth Ventricle

Cerebellum

Medulla Oblongata

Central Sulcus

Sulcus of Corpus Callosum

Paracentral Lobe

Cingulate Sulcus

Subparietal Sulcus

Middle Frontal Gyrus

Superior Frontal Gyrus

Parietooccipital Sulcus

Cingulate Gyrus

Calcarine Sulcus

Area Subcallosa

Lingual Gyrus

Gyrus Rectus

Isthmus of Cingulate Gyrus

2.176 Circumventricular Organs: Median Sagittal Section through the Brain. [7]

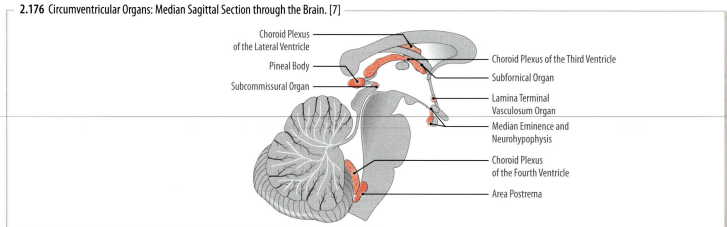

Choroid Plexus of the Lateral Ventricle

Choroid Plexus of the Third Ventricle

Pineal Body

Subfornical Organ

Subcommissural Organ

Lamina Terminal Vasculosum Organ

Median Eminence and Neurohypophysis

Choroid Plexus of the Fourth Ventricle

Area Postrema

The Brain and Cranial Nerves: Basal View

2.177a Brain. [6]

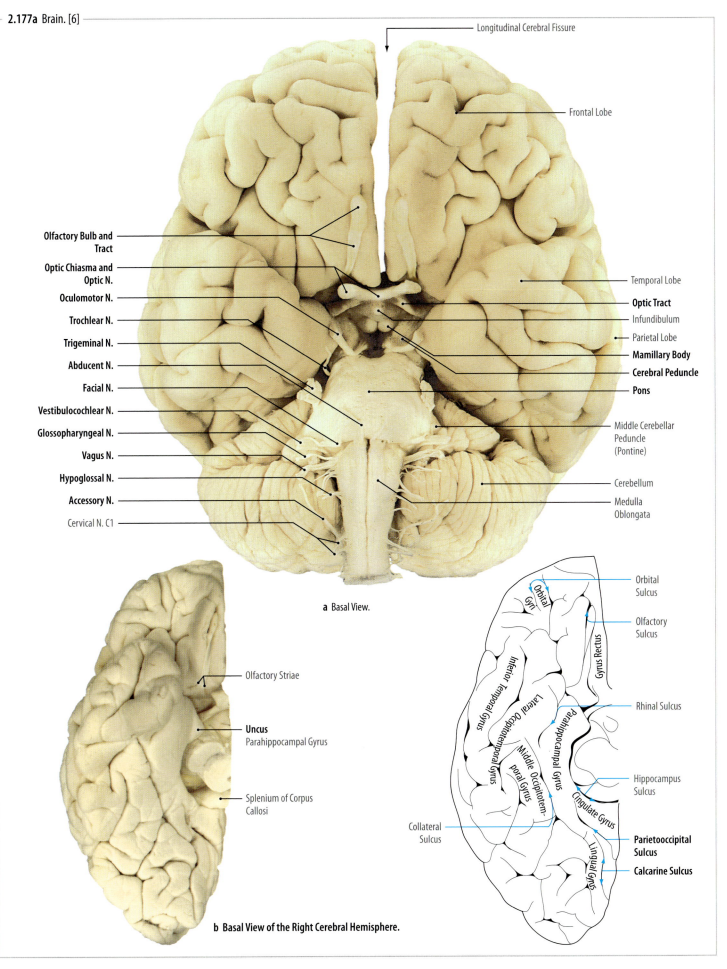

Longitudinal Cerebral Fissure

Frontal Lobe

Olfactory Bulb and Tract

Optic Chiasma and Optic N.

Oculomotor N.

Trochlear N.

Trigeminal N.

Abducent N.

Facial N.

Vestibulocochlear N.

Glossopharyngeal N.

Vagus N.

Hypoglossal N.

Accessory N.

Cervical N. C1

Temporal Lobe

Optic Tract

Infundibulum

Parietal Lobe

Mamillary Body

Cerebral Peduncle

Pons

Middle Cerebellar Peduncle (Pontine)

Cerebellum

Medulla Oblongata

a Basal View.

Olfactory Striae

Uncus
Parahippocampal Gyrus

Splenium of Corpus Callosi

Orbital Sulcus

Orbital Gyri

Olfactory Sulcus

Gyrus Rectus

Inferior Temporal Gyrus

Lateral Occipitotemporal Gyrus

Parahippocampal Gyrus

Rhinal Sulcus

Middle Occipitotemporal Gyrus

Hippocampus Sulcus

Cingulate Gyrus

Collateral Sulcus

Lingual Gyrus

Parietooccipital Sulcus

Calcarine Sulcus

b Basal View of the Right Cerebral Hemisphere.

Brain

Cerebral Cortex Areas

2.178a,b Regions of the Cerebral Cortex. [42]

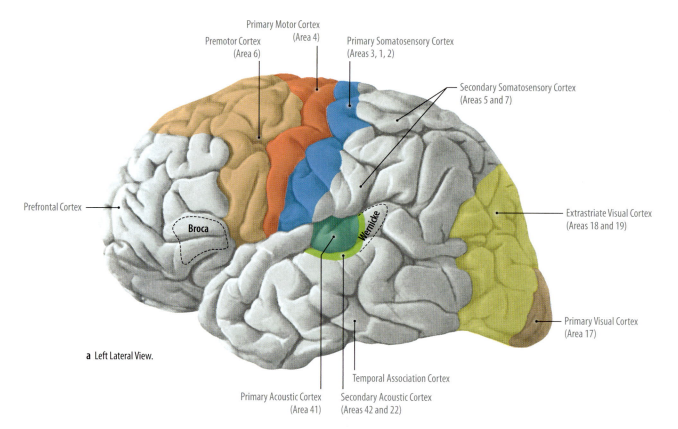

Primary Motor Cortex
(Area 4)

Premotor Cortex
(Area 6)

Primary Somatosensory Cortex
(Areas 3, 1, 2)

Secondary Somatosensory Cortex
(Areas 5 and 7)

Prefrontal Cortex

Broca

Wernicke

Extrastriate Visual Cortex
(Areas 18 and 19)

Primary Visual Cortex
(Area 17)

a Left Lateral View.

Primary Acoustic Cortex
(Area 41)

Secondary Acoustic Cortex
(Areas 42 and 22)

Temporal Association Cortex

ⓘ Generation of Brain Maps according to Integrated Positron Emission Tomography (PET) studies and Cytoarchitectural Findings.

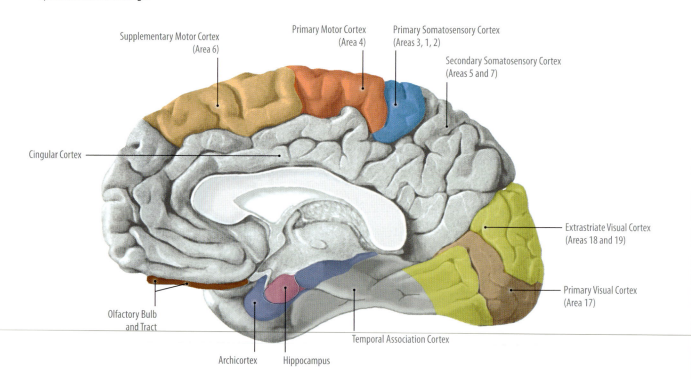

Supplementary Motor Cortex
(Area 6)

Primary Motor Cortex
(Area 4)

Primary Somatosensory Cortex
(Areas 3, 1, 2)

Secondary Somatosensory Cortex
(Areas 5 and 7)

Cingular Cortex

Extrastriate Visual Cortex
(Areas 18 and 19)

Primary Visual Cortex
(Area 17)

Olfactory Bulb
and Tract

Temporal Association Cortex

Archicortex

Hippocampus

b Medial View of the Right Section.

a Cerebrum.
b Median Sagittal Section.

2.179a,b Hippocampus Area. [35]

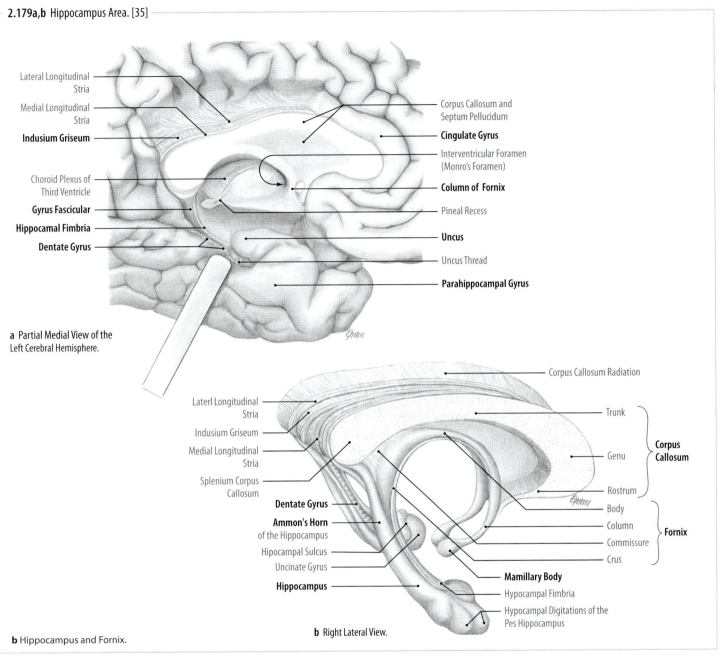

Lateral Longitudinal Stria

Medial Longitudinal Stria

Indusium Griseum

Choroid Plexus of Third Ventricle

Gyrus Fascicular

Hippocamal Fimbria

Dentate Gyrus

Corpus Callosum and Septum Pellucidum

Cingulate Gyrus

Interventricular Foramen (Monro's Foramen)

Column of Fornix

Pineal Recess

Uncus

Uncus Thread

Parahippocampal Gyrus

a Partial Medial View of the Left Cerebral Hemisphere.

Corpus Callosum Radiation

Laterl Longitudinal Stria

Indusium Griseum

Medial Longitudinal Stria

Splenium Corpus Callosum

Dentate Gyrus

Ammon's Horn of the Hippocampus

Hipocampal Sulcus

Uncinate Gyrus

Hippocampus

Trunk

Genu

Rostrum

Body

Column

Commissure

Crus

Mamillary Body

Hypocampal Fimbria

Hypocampal Digitations of the Pes Hippocampus

Corpus Callosum

Fornix

b Right Lateral View.

b Hippocampus and Fornix.

2.180 Association Pathways and Semicircular Fibers of a Left Hemisphere: Lateral View. [13, 7]

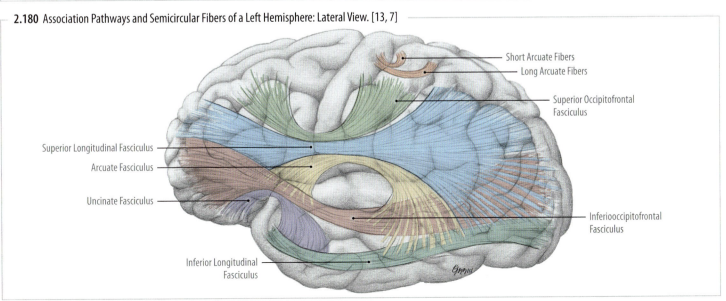

Short Arcuate Fibers

Long Arcuate Fibers

Superior Occipitofrontal Fasciculus

Superior Longitudinal Fasciculus

Arcuate Fasciculus

Uncinate Fasciculus

Inferiooccipitofrontal Fasciculus

Inferior Longitudinal Fasciculus

Brain

2.181 Commissures, the Radiation of the Corpus Callosum, and Cingulum of the Left Hemisphere: Medial View. [13]

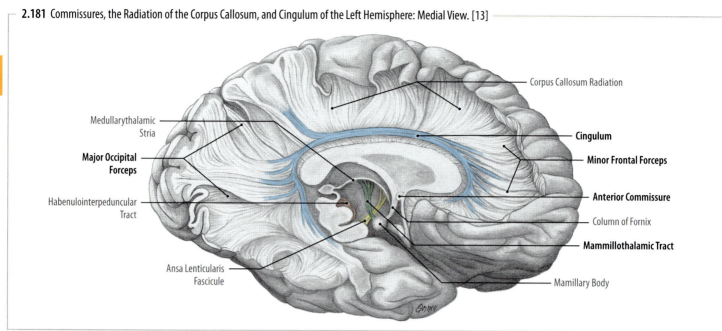

Medullarythalamic
Stria

**Major Occipital
Forceps**

Habenulointerpeduncular
Tract

Ansa Lenticularis
Fascicule

Corpus Callosum Radiation

Cingulum

Minor Frontal Forceps

Anterior Commissure

Column of Fornix

Mammillothalamic Tract

Mamillary Body

2.182 Visual System: Basal View. [6]

If a Pituitary Tumor Damages the Crossing
Fibers of the Optic Chiasma, there is a
Bilateral Loss of Nasal Retina, presented
as Bitemporal Hemianopia, Narrowing the
Visual Field (Tunnel Vision). Aneurysm
of the Distal Part of the Internal
Carotid A. causes Lateral
Side Pressure on the
Chiasma with Loss
of the Ipsilateral
Nasal Field.

Unilateral Damage to
the Optic Tract causes
Same-Side Loss of the
Nasal Visual Field and
Contralateral Loss of
the Temporal Visual
Field (Homonymous
Hemianopia).

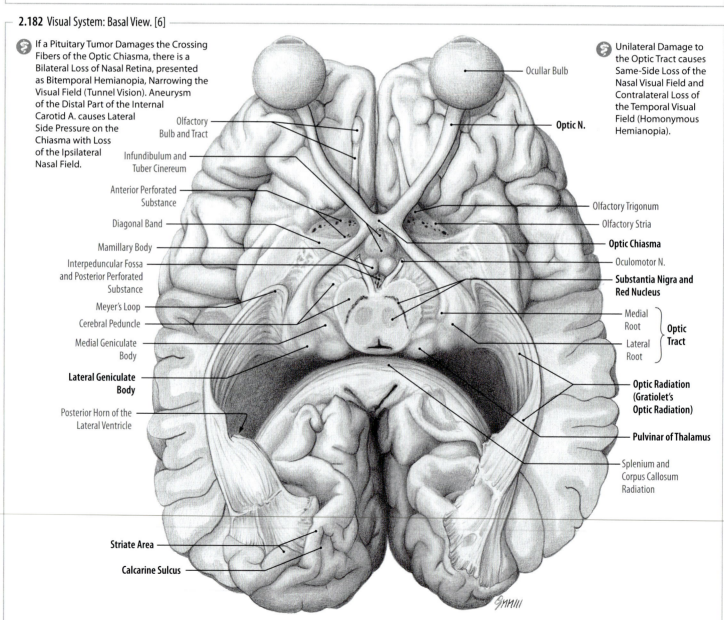

Olfactory
Bulb and Tract

Infundibulum and
Tuber Cinereum

Anterior Perforated
Substance

Diagonal Band

Mamillary Body

Interpeduncular Fossa
and Posterior Perforated
Substance

Meyer's Loop

Cerebral Peduncle

Medial Geniculate
Body

**Lateral Geniculate
Body**

Posterior Horn of the
Lateral Ventricle

Striate Area

Calcarine Sulcus

Ocullar Bulb

Optic N.

Olfactory Trigonum

Olfactory Stria

Optic Chiasma

Oculomotor N.

**Substantia Nigra and
Red Nucleus**

Medial
Root

Lateral
Root

**Optic
Tract**

**Optic Radiation
(Gratiolet's
Optic Radiation)**

Pulvinar of Thalamus

Splenium and
Corpus Callosum
Radiation

2.183a,b Motor Pathways. [41]

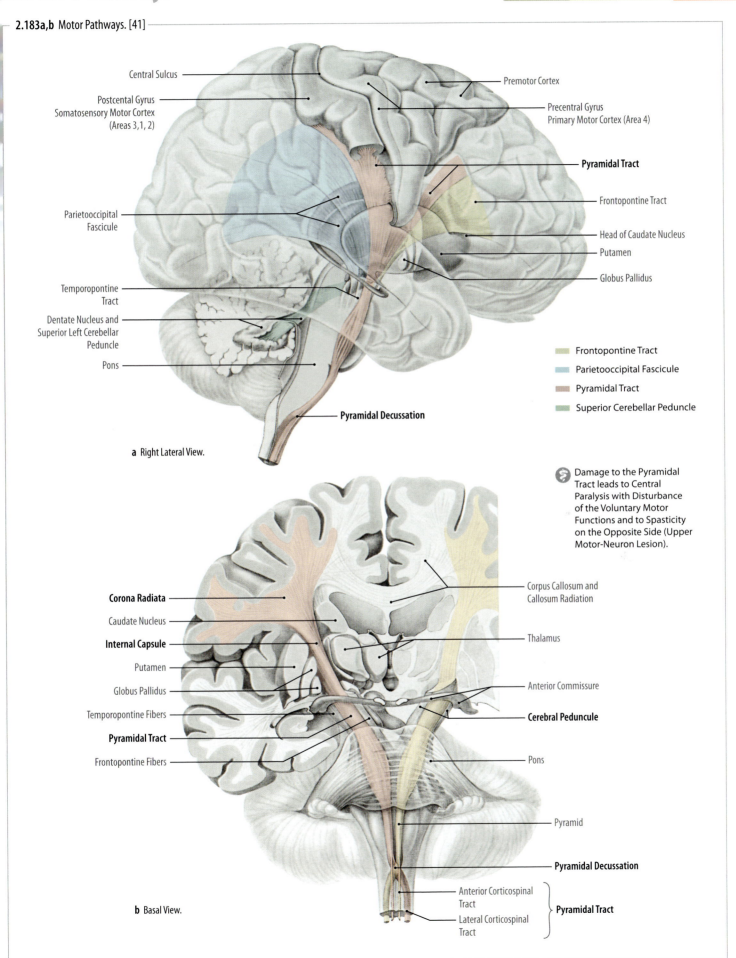

Central Sulcus

Postcental Gyrus
Somatosensory Motor Cortex
(Areas 3,1, 2)

Premotor Cortex

Precentral Gyrus
Primary Motor Cortex (Area 4)

Pyramidal Tract

Frontopontine Tract

Parietooccipital
Fascicule

Head of Caudate Nucleus

Putamen

Globus Pallidus

Temporopontine
Tract

Dentate Nucleus and
Superior Left Cerebellar
Peduncle

Pons

Pyramidal Decussation

a Right Lateral View.

Frontopontine Tract

Parietooccipital Fascicule

Pyramidal Tract

Superior Cerebellar Peduncle

Damage to the Pyramidal
Tract leads to Central
Paralysis with Disturbance
of the Voluntary Motor
Functions and to Spasticity
on the Opposite Side (Upper
Motor-Neuron Lesion).

Corona Radiata

Caudate Nucleus

Internal Capsule

Putamen

Globus Pallidus

Temporopontine Fibers

Pyramidal Tract

Frontopontine Fibers

Corpus Callosum and
Callosum Radiation

Thalamus

Anterior Commissure

Cerebral Peduncle

Pons

Pyramid

Pyramidal Decussation

Anterior Corticospinal
Tract

Lateral Corticospinal
Tract

Pyramidal Tract

b Basal View.

Brain

Cerebellum

2

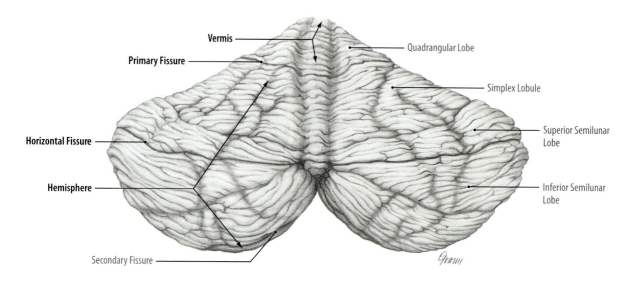

Vermis

Primary Fissure

Quadrangular Lobe

Simplex Lobule

Superior Semilunar Lobe

Horizontal Fissure

Inferior Semilunar Lobe

Hemisphere

Secondary Fissure

a Dorsal View.

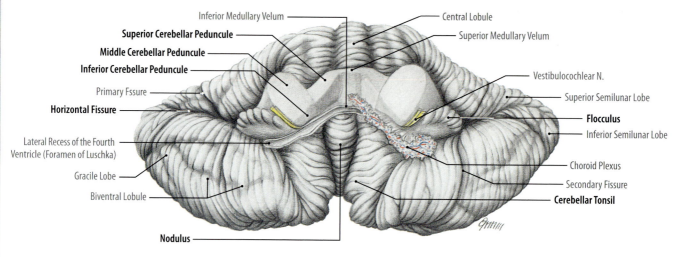

Inferior Medullary Velum

Central Lobule

Superior Cerebellar Peduncule

Superior Medullary Velum

Middle Cerebellar Peduncule

Inferior Cerebellar Peduncule

Vestibulocochlear N.

Primary Fssure

Superior Semilunar Lobe

Horizontal Fissure

Flocculus

Lateral Recess of the Fourth Ventricle (Foramen of Luschka)

Inferior Semilunar Lobe

Gracile Lobe

Choroid Plexus

Biventral Lobule

Secondary Fissure

Cerebellar Tonsil

Nodulus

b Ventral View.

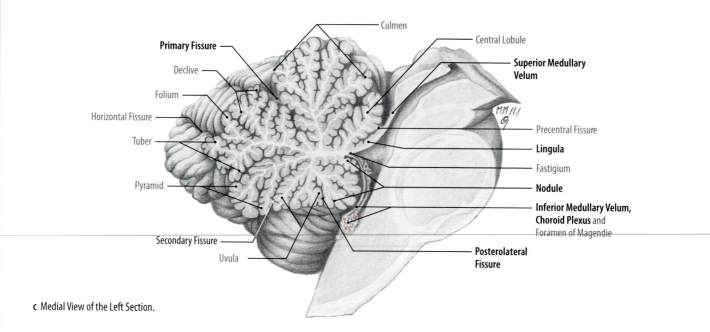

Culmen

Central Lobule

Primary Fissure

Superior Medullary Velum

Declive

Folium

Horizontal Fissure

Precentral Fissure

Tuber

Lingula

Fastigium

Pyramid

Nodule

Inferior Medullary Velum, Choroid Plexus and Foramen of Magendie

Secondary Fissure

Uvula

Posterolateral Fissure

c Medial View of the Left Section.

2.185a,b Structure of the Cerebellum. [18]

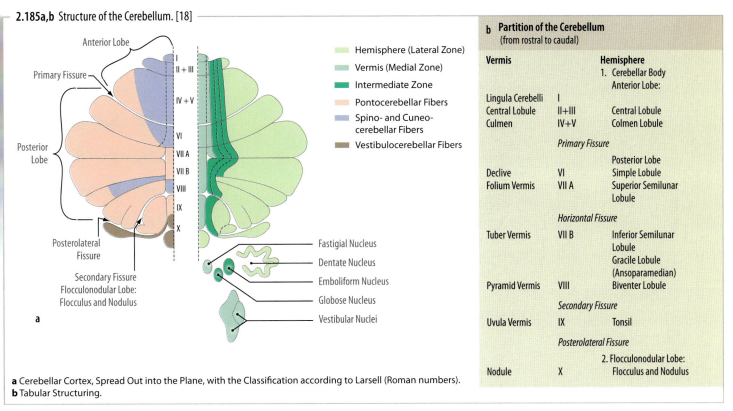

Legend:
- Hemisphere (Lateral Zone)
- Vermis (Medial Zone)
- Intermediate Zone
- Pontocerebellar Fibers
- Spino- and Cuneo- cerebellar Fibers
- Vestibulocerebellar Fibers

Labels (left diagram):
- Anterior Lobe
- Primary Fissure
- Posterior Lobe
- Posterolateral Fissure
- Secondary Fissure
- Flocculonodular Lobe: Flocculus and Nodulus
- I, II + III, IV + V, VI, VII A, VII B, VIII, IX, X

Labels (right diagram):
- Fastigial Nucleus
- Dentate Nucleus
- Emboliform Nucleus
- Globose Nucleus
- Vestibular Nuclei

a

b Partition of the Cerebellum
(from rostral to caudal)

Vermis		Hemisphere
		1. Cerebellar Body Anterior Lobe:
Lingula Cerebelli	I	
Central Lobule	II+III	Central Lobule
Culmen	IV+V	Colmen Lobule
		Primary Fissure
		Posterior Lobe
Declive	VI	Simple Lobule
Folium Vermis	VII A	Superior Semilunar Lobule
		Horizontal Fissure
Tuber Vermis	VII B	Inferior Semilunar Lobule
		Gracile Lobule (Ansoparamedian)
Pyramid Vermis	VIII	Biventer Lobule
		Secondary Fissure
Uvula Vermis	IX	Tonsil
		Posterolateral Fissure
		2. Flocculonodular Lobe:
Nodule	X	Flocculus and Nodulus

a Cerebellar Cortex, Spread Out into the Plane, with the Classification according to Larsell (Roman numbers).
b Tabular Structuring.

2.186 Projection Fibers of the Cerebellum, Cerebellar Peduncles, Fiber Preparation: Left Lateral View. [13]

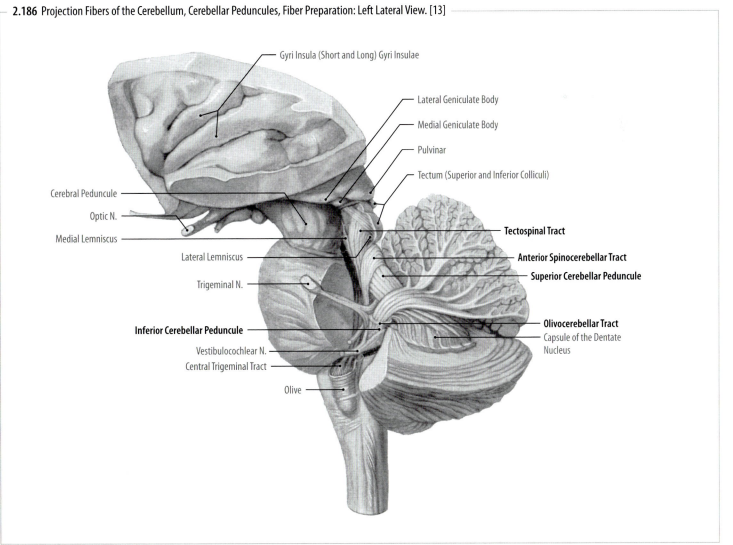

Labels:
- Gyri Insula (Short and Long) Gyri Insulae
- Lateral Geniculate Body
- Medial Geniculate Body
- Pulvinar
- Tectum (Superior and Inferior Colliculi)
- Cerebral Peduncule
- Optic N.
- Medial Lemniscus
- **Tectospinal Tract**
- Lateral Lemniscus
- **Anterior Spinocerebellar Tract**
- **Superior Cerebellar Peduncule**
- Trigeminal N.
- **Inferior Cerebellar Peduncule**
- **Olivocerebellar Tract**
- Capsule of the Dentate Nucleus
- Vestibulocochlear N.
- Central Trigeminal Tract
- Olive

Brain

2.187a,b Brainstem and Interbrain. [a 37, b 6]

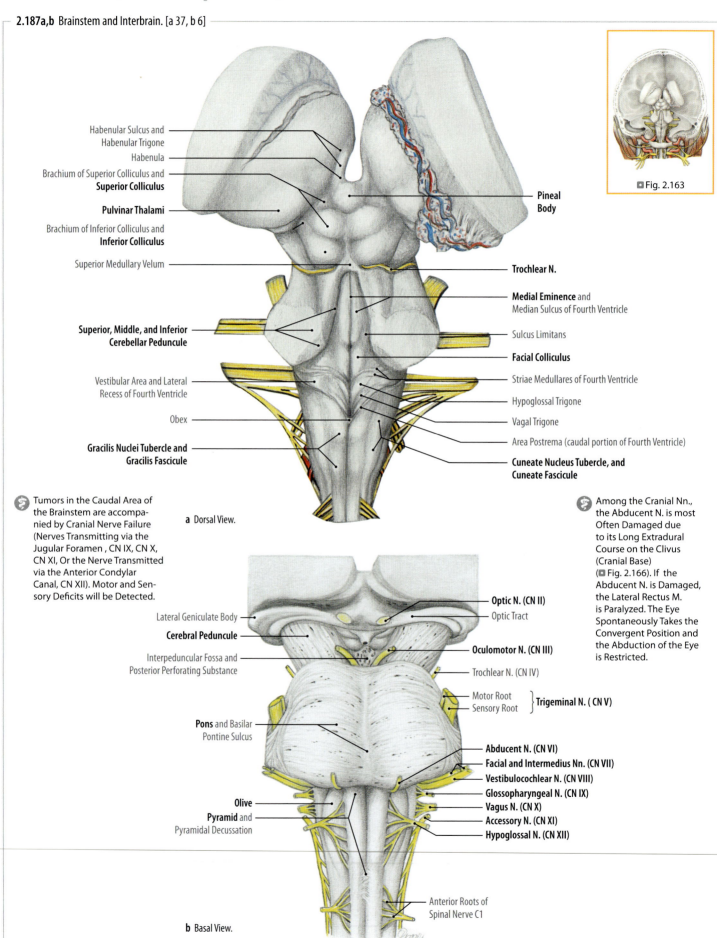

Habenular Sulcus and Habenular Trigone

Habenula

Brachium of Superior Colliculus and **Superior Colliculus**

Pulvinar Thalami

Brachium of Inferior Colliculus and **Inferior Colliculus**

Superior Medullary Velum

Superior, Middle, and Inferior Cerebellar Peduncule

Vestibular Area and Lateral Recess of Fourth Ventricle

Obex

Gracilis Nuclei Tubercle and Gracilis Fascicule

Pineal Body

Trochlear N.

Medial Eminence and Median Sulcus of Fourth Ventricle

Sulcus Limitans

Facial Colliculus

Striae Medullares of Fourth Ventricle

Hypoglossal Trigone

Vagal Trigone

Area Postrema (caudal portion of Fourth Ventricle)

Cuneate Nucleus Tubercle, and Cuneate Fascicule

☐ Fig. 2.163

a Dorsal View.

Tumors in the Caudal Area of the Brainstem are accompanied by Cranial Nerve Failure (Nerves Transmitting via the Jugular Foramen , CN IX, CN X, CN XI, Or the Nerve Transmitted via the Anterior Condylar Canal, CN XII). Motor and Sensory Deficits will be Detected.

Among the Cranial Nn., the Abducent N. is most Often Damaged due to its Long Extradural Course on the Clivus (Cranial Base) (☐ Fig. 2.166). If the Abducent N. is Damaged, the Lateral Rectus M. is Paralyzed. The Eye Spontaneously Takes the Convergent Position and the Abduction of the Eye is Restricted.

Lateral Geniculate Body

Cerebral Peduncule

Interpeduncular Fossa and Posterior Perforating Substance

Pons and Basilar Pontine Sulcus

Olive

Pyramid and Pyramidal Decussation

Optic N. (CN II)

Optic Tract

Oculomotor N. (CN III)

Trochlear N. (CN IV)

Motor Root
Sensory Root } **Trigeminal N. (CN V)**

Abducent N. (CN VI)

Facial and Intermedius Nn. (CN VII)

Vestibulocochlear N. (CN VIII)

Glossopharyngeal N. (CN IX)

Vagus N. (CN X)

Accessory N. (CN XI)

Hypoglossal N. (CN XII)

Anterior Roots of Spinal Nerve C1

b Basal View.

2.188 Cranial Nuclei. [13]

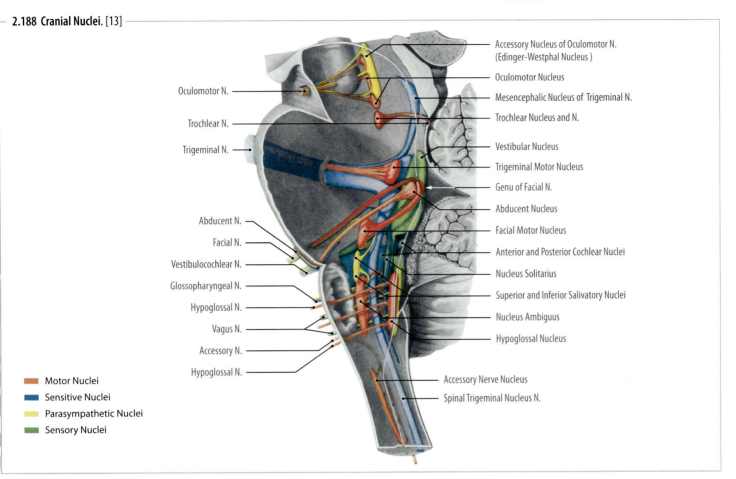

Oculomotor N.
Trochlear N.
Trigeminal N.
Abducent N.
Facial N.
Vestibulocochlear N.
Glossopharyngeal N.
Hypoglossal N.
Vagus N.
Accessory N.
Hypoglossal N.

Accessory Nucleus of Oculomotor N. (Edinger-Westphal Nucleus)
Oculomotor Nucleus
Mesencephalic Nucleus of Trigeminal N.
Trochlear Nucleus and N.
Vestibular Nucleus
Trigeminal Motor Nucleus
Genu of Facial N.
Abducent Nucleus
Facial Motor Nucleus
Anterior and Posterior Cochlear Nuclei
Nucleus Solitarius
Superior and Inferior Salivatory Nuclei
Nucleus Ambiguus
Hypoglossal Nucleus
Accessory Nerve Nucleus
Spinal Trigeminal Nucleus N.

- Motor Nuclei
- Sensitive Nuclei
- Parasympathetic Nuclei
- Sensory Nuclei

2.189 Sensory Pathways: Dorsal View. [41]

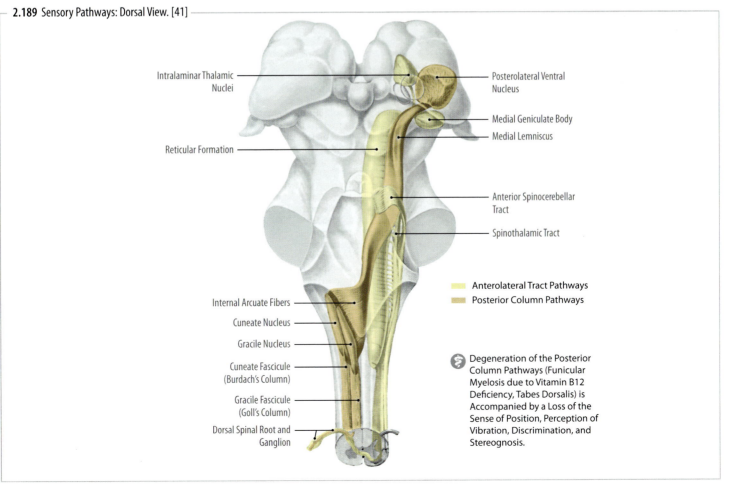

Intralaminar Thalamic Nuclei

Reticular Formation

Internal Arcuate Fibers
Cuneate Nucleus
Gracile Nucleus
Cuneate Fascicule (Burdach's Column)
Gracile Fascicule (Goll's Column)
Dorsal Spinal Root and Ganglion

Posterolateral Ventral Nucleus
Medial Geniculate Body
Medial Lemniscus
Anterior Spinocerebellar Tract
Spinothalamic Tract

Anterolateral Tract Pathways
Posterior Column Pathways

Degeneration of the Posterior Column Pathways (Funicular Myelosis due to Vitamin B12 Deficiency, Tabes Dorsalis) is Accompanied by a Loss of the Sense of Position, Perception of Vibration, Discrimination, and Stereognosis.

Brain

Ventricular System

2.190a–c Ventricles of the Brain. [a,b 1; c 78]

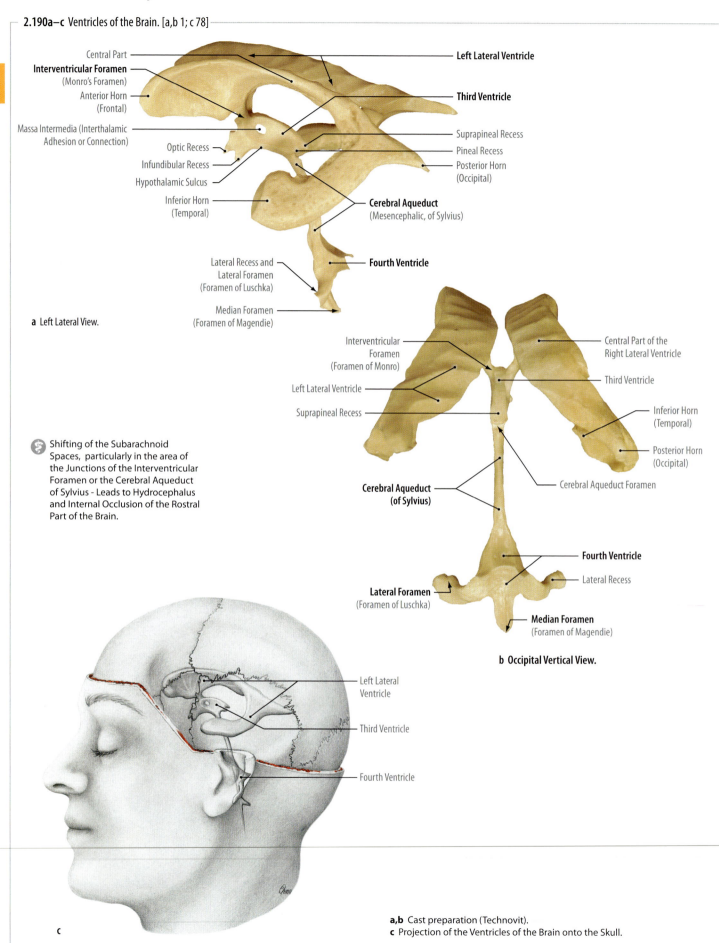

a **Left Lateral View.**

- Central Part
- **Interventricular Foramen** (Monro's Foramen)
- Anterior Horn (Frontal)
- Massa Intermedia (Interthalamic Adhesion or Connection)
- Optic Recess
- Infundibular Recess
- Hypothalamic Sulcus
- Inferior Horn (Temporal)
- Lateral Recess and Lateral Foramen (Foramen of Luschka)
- Median Foramen (Foramen of Magendie)
- **Left Lateral Ventricle**
- **Third Ventricle**
- Suprapineal Recess
- Pineal Recess
- Posterior Horn (Occipital)
- **Cerebral Aqueduct** (Mesencephalic, of Sylvius)
- **Fourth Ventricle**

Shifting of the Subarachnoid Spaces, particularly in the area of the Junctions of the Interventricular Foramen or the Cerebral Aqueduct of Sylvius - Leads to Hydrocephalus and Internal Occlusion of the Rostral Part of the Brain.

- Interventricular Foramen (Foramen of Monro)
- Left Lateral Ventricle
- Suprapineal Recess
- Central Part of the Right Lateral Ventricle
- Third Ventricle
- Inferior Horn (Temporal)
- Posterior Horn (Occipital)
- Cerebral Aqueduct Foramen
- **Cerebral Aqueduct** (of Sylvius)
- **Fourth Ventricle**
- Lateral Recess
- **Lateral Foramen** (Foramen of Luschka)
- **Median Foramen** (Foramen of Magendie)

b **Occipital Vertical View.**

- Left Lateral Ventricle
- Third Ventricle
- Fourth Ventricle

c

a,b Cast preparation (Technovit).
c Projection of the Ventricles of the Brain onto the Skull.

Histological Frontal (Coronal) Sections

2.191a,b Histological Frontal (Coronal) Section through the Brain. [43]

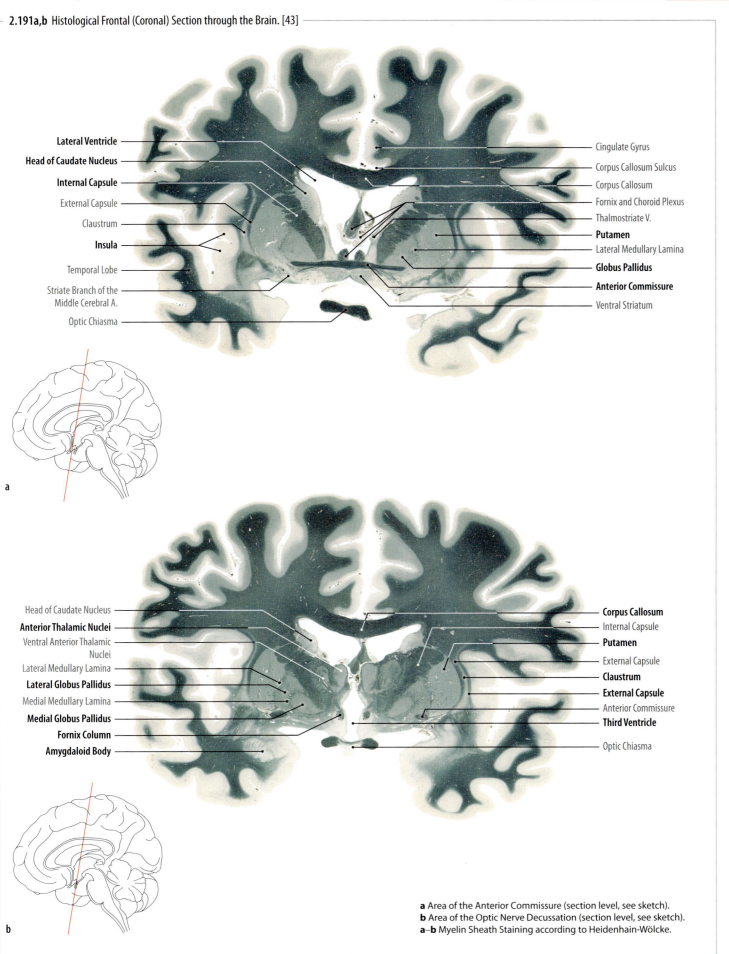

Lateral Ventricle
Head of Caudate Nucleus
Internal Capsule
External Capsule
Claustrum
Insula
Temporal Lobe
Striate Branch of the Middle Cerebral A.
Optic Chiasma

Cingulate Gyrus
Corpus Callosum Sulcus
Corpus Callosum
Fornix and Choroid Plexus
Thalmostriate V.
Putamen
Lateral Medullary Lamina
Globus Pallidus
Anterior Commissure
Ventral Striatum

a

Head of Caudate Nucleus
Anterior Thalamic Nuclei
Ventral Anterior Thalamic Nuclei
Lateral Medullary Lamina
Lateral Globus Pallidus
Medial Medullary Lamina
Medial Globus Pallidus
Fornix Column
Amygdaloid Body

Corpus Callosum
Internal Capsule
Putamen
External Capsule
Claustrum
External Capsule
Anterior Commissure
Third Ventricle
Optic Chiasma

b

a Area of the Anterior Commissure (section level, see sketch).
b Area of the Optic Nerve Decussation (section level, see sketch).
a–b Myelin Sheath Staining according to Heidenhain-Wölcke.

Brain

2.191c,d Histological Frontal (Coronal) Sections through the Brain. [43]

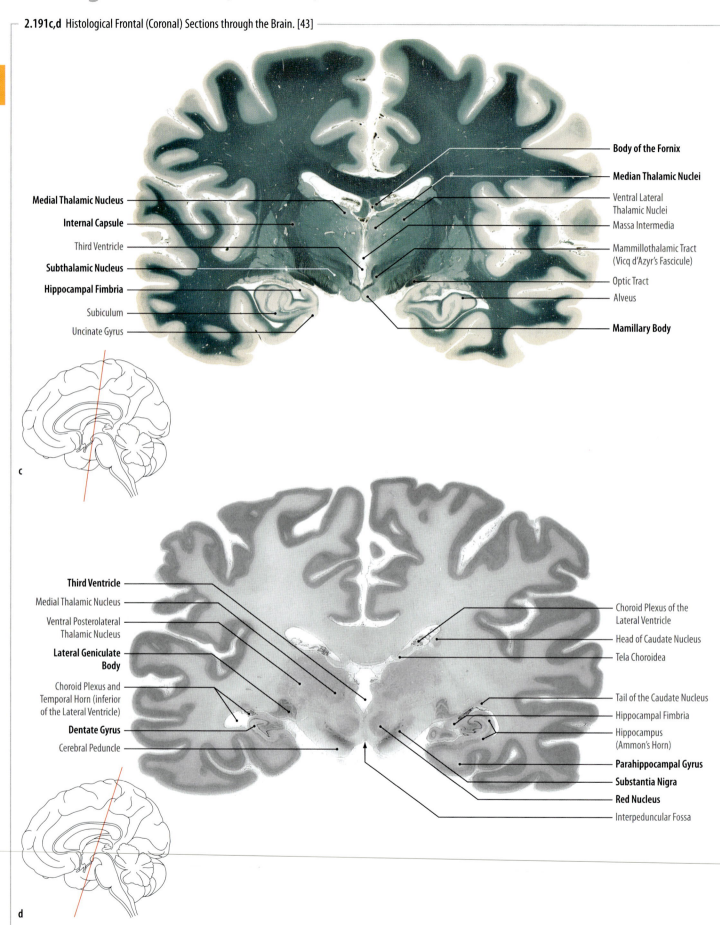

Body of the Fornix

Median Thalamic Nuclei

Ventral Lateral Thalamic Nuclei

Massa Intermedia

Mammillothalamic Tract (Vicq d'Azyr's Fascicule)

Optic Tract

Alveus

Mamillary Body

Medial Thalamic Nucleus

Internal Capsule

Third Ventricle

Subthalamic Nucleus

Hippocampal Fimbria

Subiculum

Uncinate Gyrus

c

Third Ventricle

Medial Thalamic Nucleus

Ventral Posterolateral Thalamic Nucleus

Lateral Geniculate Body

Choroid Plexus and Temporal Horn (inferior of the Lateral Ventricle)

Dentate Gyrus

Cerebral Peduncle

Choroid Plexus of the Lateral Ventricle

Head of Caudate Nucleus

Tela Choroidea

Tail of the Caudate Nucleus

Hippocampal Fimbria

Hippocampus (Ammon's Horn)

Parahippocampal Gyrus

Substantia Nigra

Red Nucleus

Interpeduncular Fossa

d

c Area of the Mamillary Bodies (section level, see sketch), Myelin Sheath Staining according to Heidenhain-Wölcke.
d Area of the Cerebral Peduncules (section level, see sketch), Silver Staining according to Merker, Modified according to Blohm.

Histological Frontal (Coronal) Sections

2.191e,f Histological Frontal (Coronal) Sections through the Brain. [43]

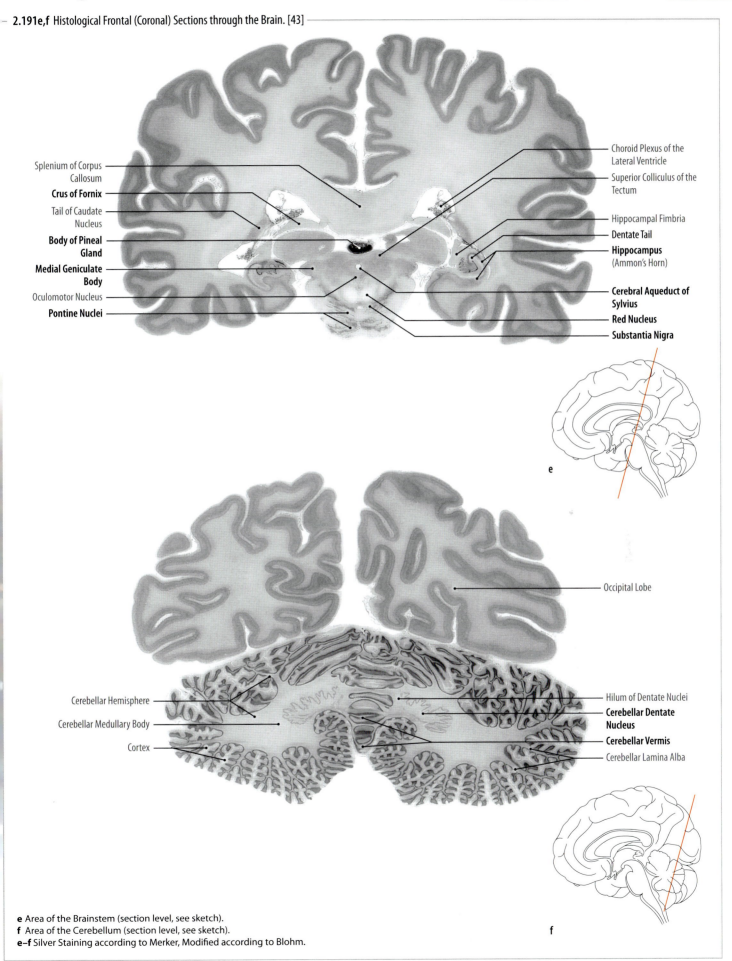

Splenium of Corpus Callosum

Crus of Fornix

Tail of Caudate Nucleus

Body of Pineal Gland

Medial Geniculate Body

Oculomotor Nucleus

Pontine Nuclei

Choroid Plexus of the Lateral Ventricle

Superior Colliculus of the Tectum

Hippocampal Fimbria

Dentate Tail

Hippocampus (Ammon's Horn)

Cerebral Aqueduct of Sylvius

Red Nucleus

Substantia Nigra

e

Cerebellar Hemisphere

Cerebellar Medullary Body

Cortex

Occipital Lobe

Hilum of Dentate Nuclei

Cerebellar Dentate Nucleus

Cerebellar Vermis

Cerebellar Lamina Alba

f

e Area of the Brainstem (section level, see sketch).
f Area of the Cerebellum (section level, see sketch).
e–f Silver Staining according to Merker, Modified according to Blohm.

Brain

2.192a Histological Horizontal Section through the Brain. [43]

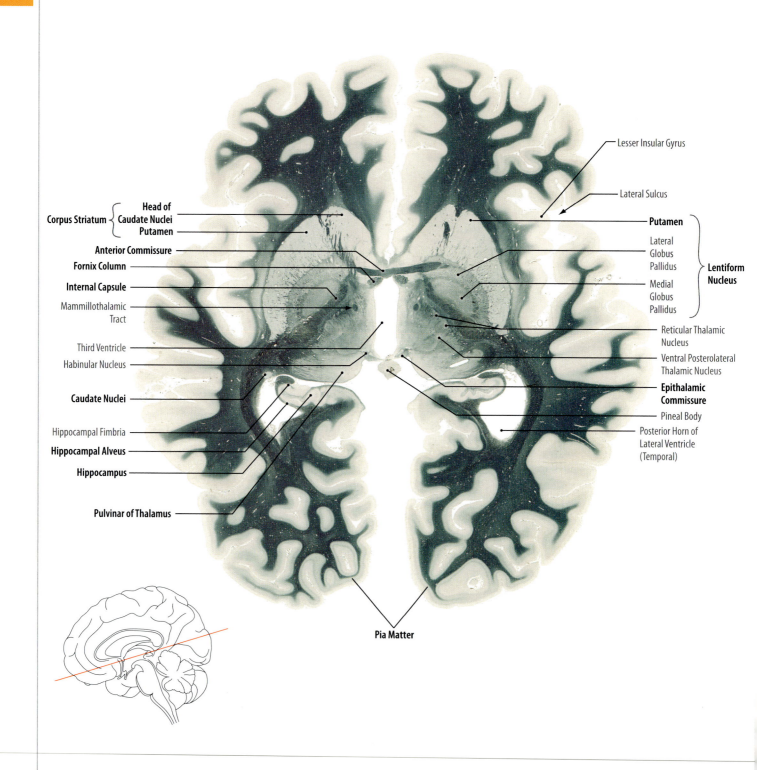

Lesser Insular Gyrus

Lateral Sulcus

Corpus Striatum {
Head of
Caudate Nuclei
Putamen

Putamen

Lateral
Globus
Pallidus

**Lentiform
Nucleus**

Anterior Commissure

Fornix Column

Medial
Globus
Pallidus

Internal Capsule

Mammillothalamic
Tract

Reticular Thalamic
Nucleus

Third Ventricle

Ventral Posterolateral
Thalamic Nucleus

Habinular Nucleus

**Epithalamic
Commissure**

Caudate Nuclei

Pineal Body

Hippocampal Fimbria

Posterior Horn of
Lateral Ventricle
(Temporal)

Hippocampal Alveus

Hippocampus

Pulvinar of Thalamus

Pia Matter

a Area of the Anterior Commissure, Myelin Sheath Staining according to Heidenhain-Wölcke (section level, see sketch).

Histological Horizontal Sections

2.192b Histological Horizontal Section through the Brain. [43]

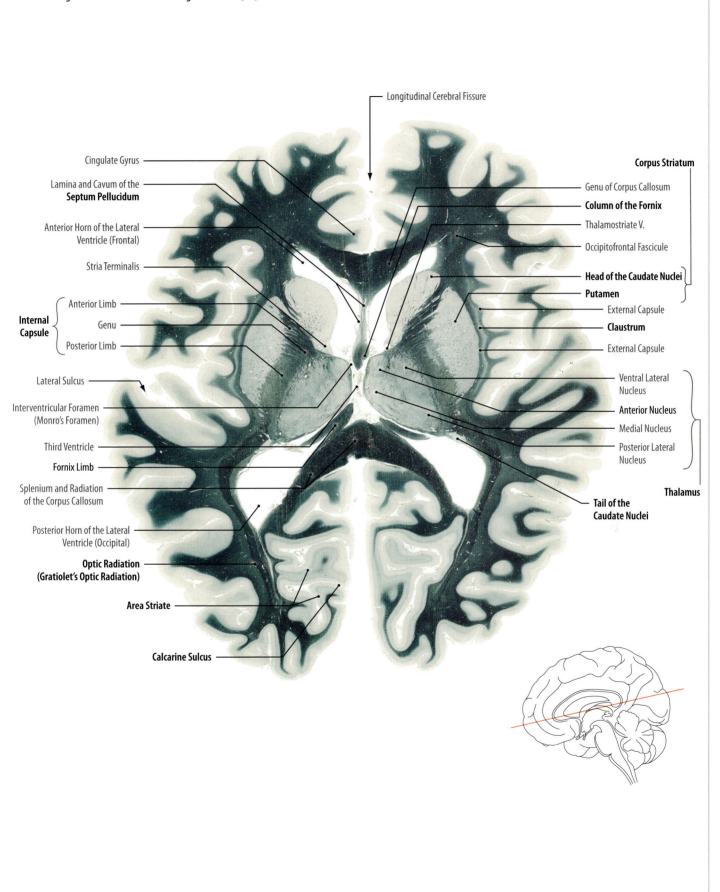

Longitudinal Cerebral Fissure

Cingulate Gyrus

Lamina and Cavum of the
Septum Pellucidum

Anterior Horn of the Lateral
Ventricle (Frontal)

Stria Terminalis

**Internal
Capsule** { Anterior Limb
Genu
Posterior Limb }

Lateral Sulcus

Interventricular Foramen
(Monro's Foramen)

Third Ventricle

Fornix Limb

Splenium and Radiation
of the Corpus Callosum

Posterior Horn of the Lateral
Ventricle (Occipital)

**Optic Radiation
(Gratiolet's Optic Radiation)**

Area Striate

Calcarine Sulcus

Corpus Striatum

Genu of Corpus Callosum

Column of the Fornix

Thalamostriate V.

Occipitofrontal Fascicule

Head of the Caudate Nuclei

Putamen

External Capsule

Claustrum

External Capsule

Ventral Lateral
Nucleus

Anterior Nucleus

Medial Nucleus

Posterior Lateral
Nucleus

Thalamus

**Tail of the
Caudate Nuclei**

b Area of the Genu and Bulge of the Corpus Callosum, Myelin Sheath Staining according to Heidenhain-Wölcke (section level, see sketch).

Brain

2.193a,b Histological Sagittal Sections through the Brain. [43]

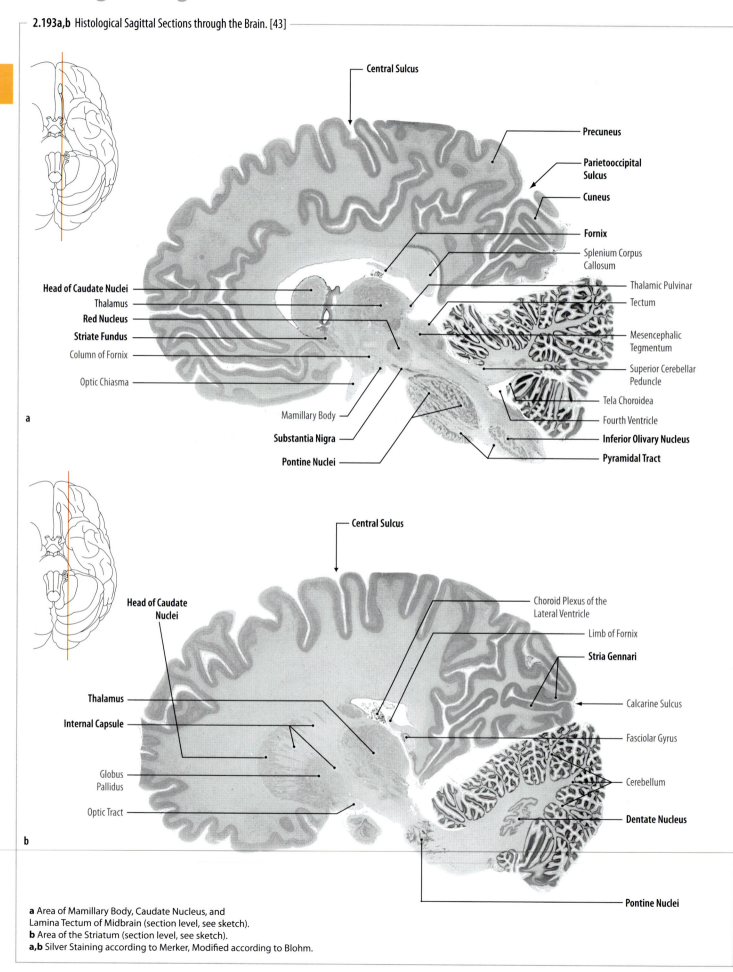

Central Sulcus

Precuneus

Parietooccipital Sulcus

Cuneus

Fornix

Splenium Corpus Callosum

Head of Caudate Nuclei

Thalamus

Red Nucleus

Striate Fundus

Column of Fornix

Optic Chiasma

Thalamic Pulvinar

Tectum

Mesencephalic Tegmentum

Superior Cerebellar Peduncle

Tela Choroidea

Fourth Ventricle

Mamillary Body

Substantia Nigra

Pontine Nuclei

Inferior Olivary Nucleus

Pyramidal Tract

a

Central Sulcus

Head of Caudate Nuclei

Choroid Plexus of the Lateral Ventricle

Limb of Fornix

Stria Gennari

Thalamus

Internal Capsule

Calcarine Sulcus

Fasciolar Gyrus

Globus Pallidus

Optic Tract

Cerebellum

Dentate Nucleus

Pontine Nuclei

b

a Area of Mamillary Body, Caudate Nucleus, and Lamina Tectum of Midbrain (section level, see sketch).
b Area of the Striatum (section level, see sketch).
a,b Silver Staining according to Merker, Modified according to Blohm.

Cerebral Arteries

2.194a–d Cerebral Arteries: Middle Area of the Interior Cranial Cavity with Arteries of the Cerebral Base and Cranial Nerves [a1, b14, c18]

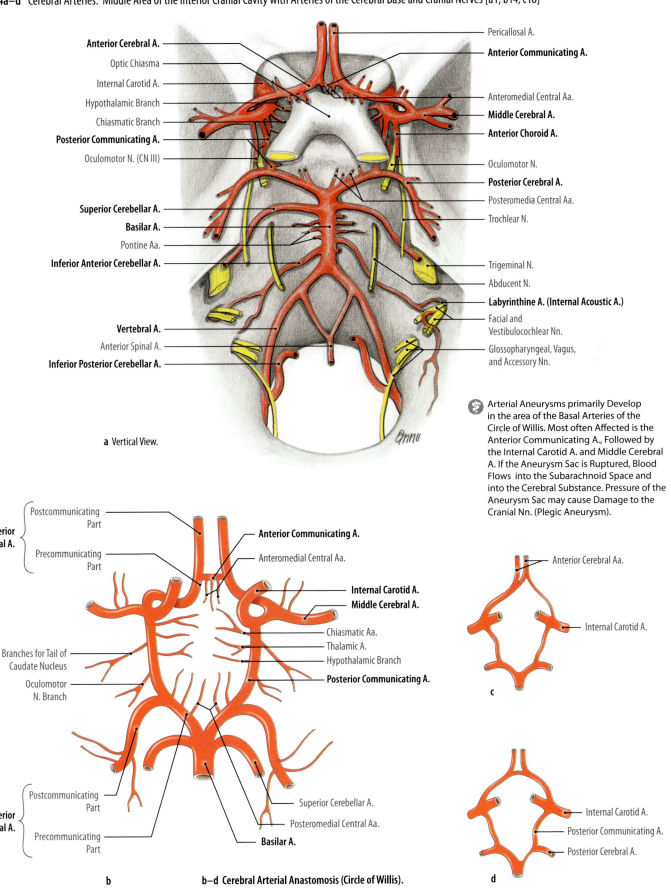

Anterior Cerebral A.
Optic Chiasma
Internal Carotid A.
Hypothalamic Branch
Chiasmatic Branch
Posterior Communicating A.
Oculomotor N. (CN III)

Superior Cerebellar A.
Basilar A.
Pontine Aa.
Inferior Anterior Cerebellar A.

Vertebral A.
Anterior Spinal A.
Inferior Posterior Cerebellar A.

Pericallosal A.
Anterior Communicating A.

Anteromedial Central Aa.
Middle Cerebral A.
Anterior Choroid A.

Oculomotor N.
Posterior Cerebral A.
Posteromedia Central Aa.
Trochlear N.

Trigeminal N.
Abducent N.
Labyrinthine A. (Internal Acoustic A.)
Facial and Vestibulocochlear Nn.

Glossopharyngeal, Vagus, and Accessory Nn.

a Vertical View.

Arterial Aneurysms primarily Develop in the area of the Basal Arteries of the Circle of Willis. Most often Affected is the Anterior Communicating A., Followed by the Internal Carotid A. and Middle Cerebral A. If the Aneurysm Sac is Ruptured, Blood Flows into the Subarachnoid Space and into the Cerebral Substance. Pressure of the Aneurysm Sac may cause Damage to the Cranial Nn. (Plegic Aneurysm).

Anterior Cerebral A.
Postcommunicating Part
Precommunicating Part

Branches for Tail of Caudate Nucleus
Oculomotor N. Branch

Posterior Cerebral A.
Postcommunicating Part
Precommunicating Part

Anterior Communicating A.
Anteromedial Central Aa.
Internal Carotid A.
Middle Cerebral A.
Chiasmatic Aa.
Thalamic A.
Hypothalamic Branch
Posterior Communicating A.

Superior Cerebellar A.
Posteromedial Central Aa.
Basilar A.

Anterior Cerebral Aa.
Internal Carotid A.

c

Internal Carotid A.
Posterior Communicating A.
Posterior Cerebral A.

d

b

b–d Cerebral Arterial Anastomosis (Circle of Willis).

b Normal Case.
c Variant: Origin of the Anterior Cerebral Aa. From the Internal Carotid A. of one side (~10% of all cases).
d Variant: Outlet of the Posterior Cerebral A. via the Posterior Communicating A. From the Internal Carotid A. (~10% of all cases).

Brain

Cerebral Base: Arteries and Veins

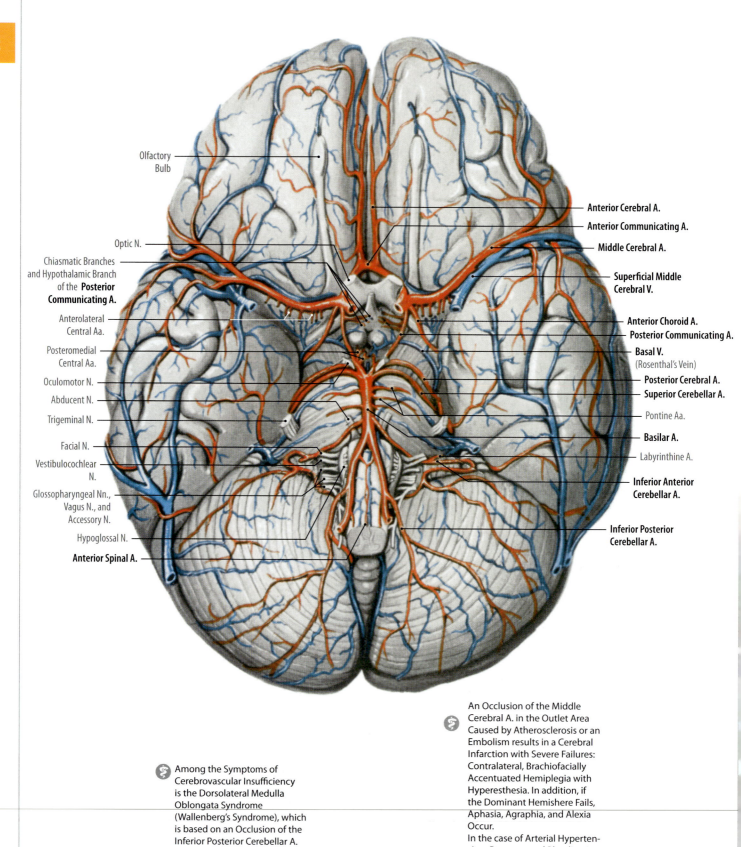

Olfactory Bulb

Optic N.

Chiasmatic Branches and Hypothalamic Branch of the **Posterior Communicating A.**

Anterolateral Central Aa.

Posteromedial Central Aa.

Oculomotor N.

Abducent N.

Trigeminal N.

Facial N.

Vestibulocochlear N.

Glossopharyngeal Nn., Vagus N., and Accessory N.

Hypoglossal N.

Anterior Spinal A.

Anterior Cerebral A.

Anterior Communicating A.

Middle Cerebral A.

Superficial Middle Cerebral V.

Anterior Choroid A.

Posterior Communicating A.

Basal V.
(Rosenthal's Vein)

Posterior Cerebral A.

Superior Cerebellar A.

Pontine Aa.

Basilar A.

Labyrinthine A.

Inferior Anterior Cerebellar A.

Inferior Posterior Cerebellar A.

Among the Symptoms of Cerebrovascular Insufficiency is the Dorsolateral Medulla Oblongata Syndrome (Wallenberg's Syndrome), which is based on an Occlusion of the Inferior Posterior Cerebellar A. Symptoms include Nystagmus, Dizziness, Dysphagia, Hiccups, Dysphonia, and Nausea.

An Occlusion of the Middle Cerebral A. in the Outlet Area Caused by Atherosclerosis or an Embolism results in a Cerebral Infarction with Severe Failures: Contralateral, Brachiofacially Accentuated Hemiplegia with Hyperesthesia. In addition, if the Dominant Hemishere Fails, Aphasia, Agraphia, and Alexia Occur.
In the case of Arterial Hypertension, Ruptures and Bleeding into the Cerebral Tissue (Massive Cerebral Hemorrhage), in particular in the area of the Basal Ganglia, may Occur due to Wall Damage of the Cerebral Arteries.

Brain: Arteries and Veins · Arteriogram

2.196 Arteries and Veins of the Brain: Right Lateral View. [13]

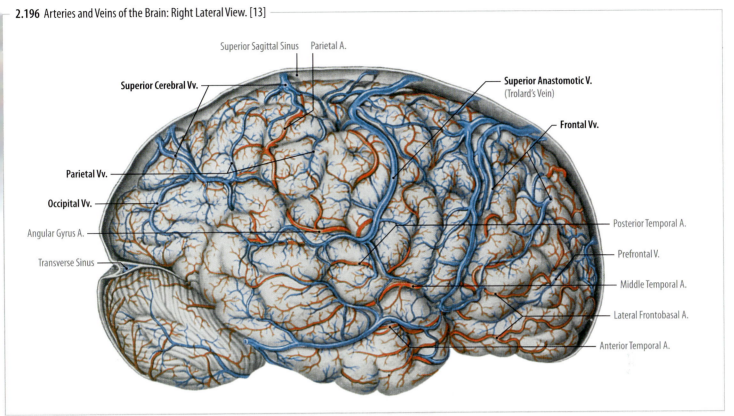

Superior Sagittal Sinus · Parietal A.

Superior Cerebral Vv.

Superior Anastomotic V.
(Trolard's Vein)

Frontal Vv.

Parietal Vv.

Occipital Vv.

Angular Gyrus A.

Posterior Temporal A.

Transverse Sinus

Prefrontal V.

Middle Temporal A.

Lateral Frontobasal A.

Anterior Temporal A.

2.197 Arteriogram of the Cerebral Arteries. [10]

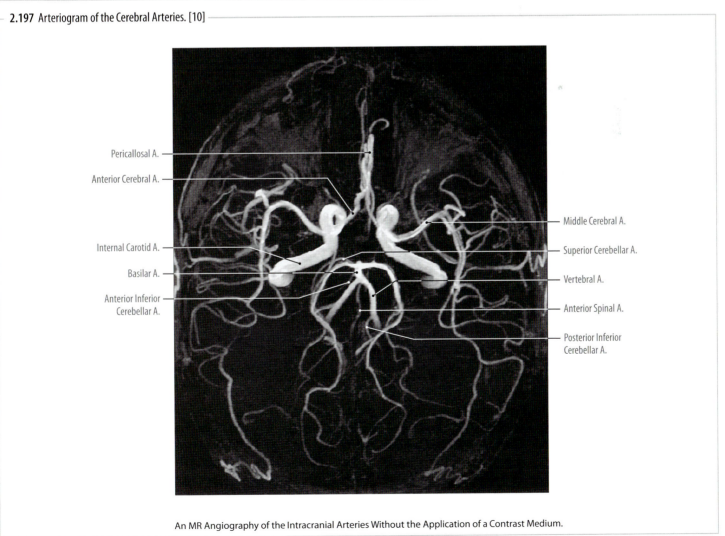

Pericallosal A.

Anterior Cerebral A.

Middle Cerebral A.

Internal Carotid A.

Superior Cerebellar A.

Basilar A.

Vertebral A.

Anterior Inferior
Cerebellar A.

Anterior Spinal A.

Posterior Inferior
Cerebellar A.

An MR Angiography of the Intracranial Arteries Without the Application of a Contrast Medium.

Brain

Cerebral Arteries

2.198a,b Arteries of the Brain. [7, 79]

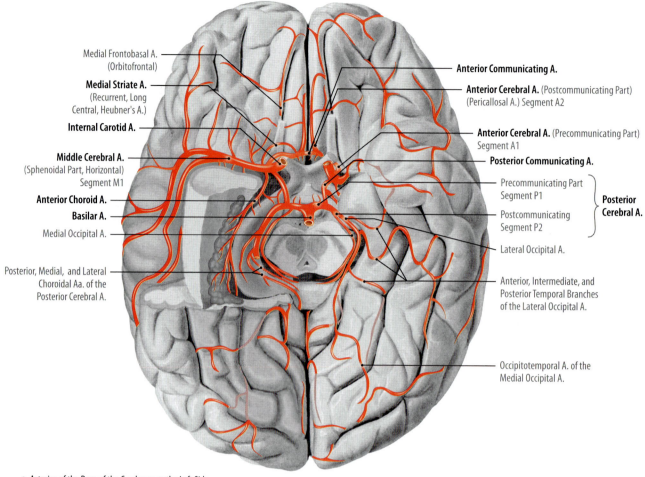

Medial Frontobasal A.
(Orbitofrontal)

Medial Striate A.
(Recurrent, Long
Central, Heubner's A.)

Internal Carotid A.

Middle Cerebral A.
(Sphenoidal Part, Horizontal)
Segment M1

Anterior Choroid A.

Basilar A.

Medial Occipital A.

Posterior, Medial, and Lateral
Choroidal Aa. of the
Posterior Cerebral A.

Anterior Communicating A.

Anterior Cerebral A. (Postcommunicating Part)
(Pericallosal A.) Segment A2

Anterior Cerebral A. (Precommunicating Part)
Segment A1

Posterior Communicating A.

Precommunicating Part
Segment P1

Postcommunicating
Segment P2

} **Posterior Cerebral A.**

Lateral Occipital A.

Anterior, Intermediate, and
Posterior Temporal Branches
of the Lateral Occipital A.

Occipitotemporal A. of the
Medial Occipital A.

a Arteries of the Base of the Cerebrum on the Left Side.

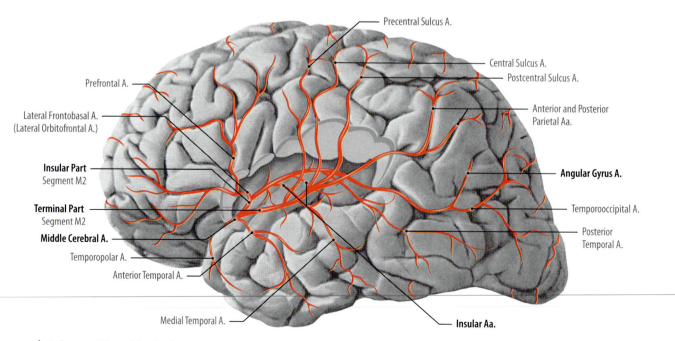

Precentral Sulcus A.

Prefrontal A.

Lateral Frontobasal A.
(Lateral Orbitofrontal A.)

Insular Part
Segment M2

Terminal Part
Segment M2

Middle Cerebral A.

Temporopolar A.

Anterior Temporal A.

Medial Temporal A.

Central Sulcus A.

Postcentral Sulcus A.

Anterior and Posterior
Parietal Aa.

Angular Gyrus A.

Temporooccipital A.

Posterior
Temporal A.

Insular Aa.

b Left Lateral View of the Cerebrum.

a To illustrate the Arterial Supply of the Choroid Plexus of the Lateral Ventricle, Part of the Temporal Lobe on the Right side was Removed.
b To illustrate the Frontal, Parietal, and Temporal Branches of the Middle Cerebral A., the Operculum Frontoparietal was Removed.

2

2.199 Arteries of the Brain. [7, 79]

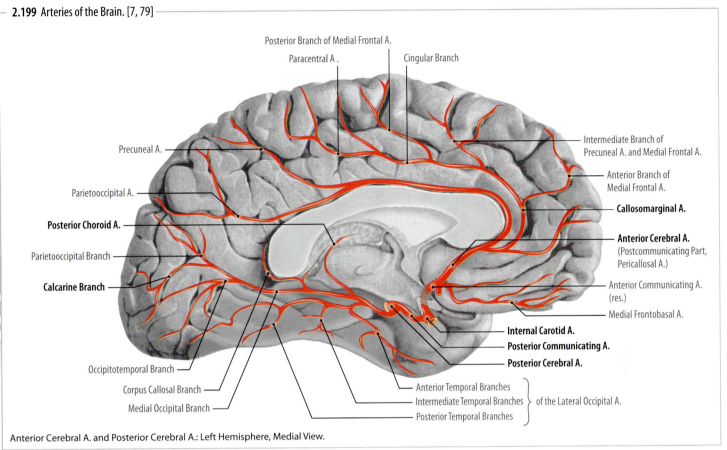

Posterior Branch of Medial Frontal A.

Paracentral A .

Cingular Branch

Precuneal A.

Parietooccipital A.

Posterior Choroid A.

Parietooccipital Branch

Calcarine Branch

Intermediate Branch of Precuneal A. and Medial Frontal A.

Anterior Branch of Medial Frontal A.

Callosomarginal A.

Anterior Cerebral A.
(Postcommunicating Part, Pericallosal A.)

Anterior Communicating A. (res.)

Medial Frontobasal A.

Internal Carotid A.

Posterior Communicating A.

Posterior Cerebral A.

Occipitotemporal Branch

Corpus Callosal Branch

Medial Occipital Branch

Anterior Temporal Branches

Intermediate Temporal Branches } of the Lateral Occipital A.

Posterior Temporal Branches

Anterior Cerebral A. and Posterior Cerebral A.: Left Hemisphere, Medial View.

2.200a,b Artertial Supply of the Cerebral Cortex. [15]

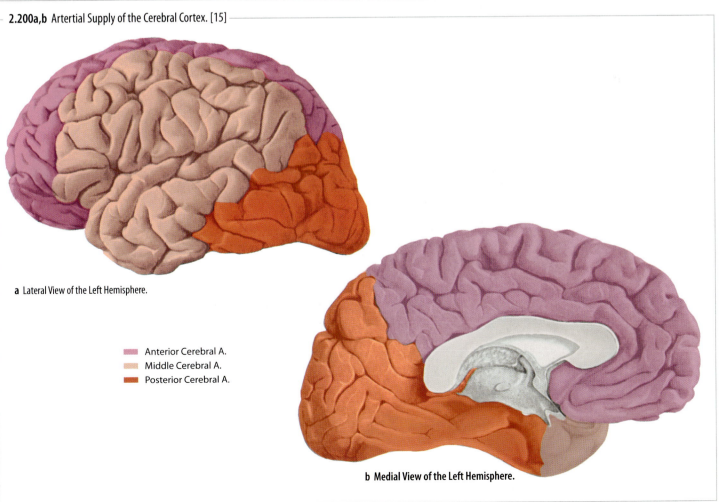

a Lateral View of the Left Hemisphere.

- ▮ Anterior Cerebral A.
- ▮ Middle Cerebral A.
- ▮ Posterior Cerebral A.

b Medial View of the Left Hemisphere.

Brain

Cerebral Arteries

2.201 Arteries of the Cerebrum, the Brainstem, the Thalamus, and the Corpus Striatum: Left Lateral View. [6, 13]

Posterior Cerebral A.

Insular Aa.

Lateral and Medial
Posterior Choroidal Aa.

Superior Cerebellar A.

**Lenticulostriate Aa. of
Middle Cerebral A. (M1)**

Anterior Communicating A.

Internal Carotid A.

Posterior Communicating A.

Pontine Aa.

**Anterior Inferior
Cerebellar A.**

Labyrinthine A.

Basilar A.

Posterior Inferior Cerebellar A.

Vertebral A.

Anterior Spinal A.

Posterior Spinal A.

2.202 Arterial Supply of the Cerebral Cortex, Basal Ganglia, and Internal Capsule. [15]

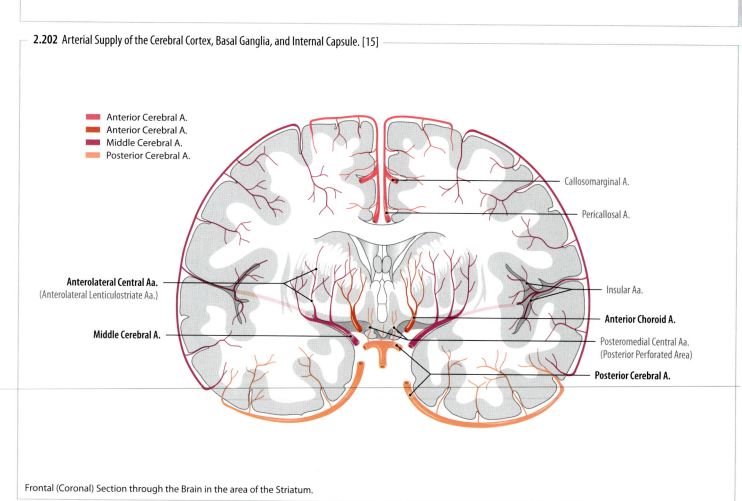

- Anterior Cerebral A.
- Anterior Cerebral A.
- Middle Cerebral A.
- Posterior Cerebral A.

Callosomarginal A.

Pericallosal A.

Anterolateral Central Aa.
(Anterolateral Lenticulostriate Aa.)

Insular Aa.

Anterior Choroid A.

Middle Cerebral A.

Posteromedial Central Aa.
(Posterior Perforated Area)

Posterior Cerebral A.

Frontal (Coronal) Section through the Brain in the area of the Striatum.

Cerebral Veins

2.203a,b Cerebral Veins. [7]

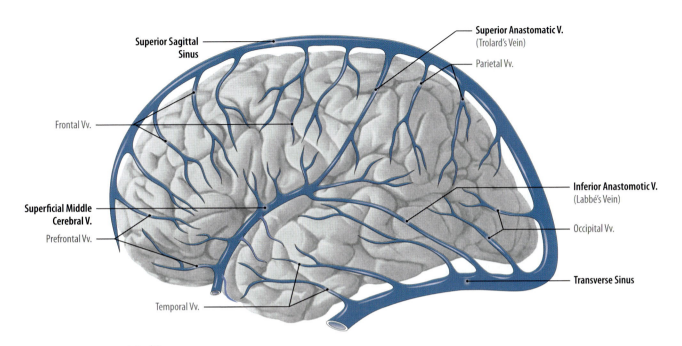

Superior Sagittal Sinus

Superior Anastomatic V. (Trolard's Vein)

Parietal Vv.

Frontal Vv.

Inferior Anastomotic V. (Labbé's Vein)

Superficial Middle Cerebral V.

Occipital Vv.

Prefrontal Vv.

Transverse Sinus

Temporal Vv.

a Lateral View.

Formation and Drainage of Venous Sinuses
1. The Superior Sagittal Sinus (SSS) is Formed by the Nasal Emissary V. Plus the Lateral Cerebral Vv.
2. The Inferior Sagittal Sinus (ISS) is Formed by Right and Left Medial Cerebral Vv.
3. The Straight Sinus (SS) is Formed by the ISS and the Great Cerebral V. of Galen.
4. The Transverse Sinus (TS) is Formed by the SSS, SS, and the Occipital Sinus.
5. The Cavernous Sinus is Formed by the Superior Ophthalmic V. and Sphenoparietal Sinus. (The Cavernous Sinus Drains via Superior and Inferior Petrosal Sinuses.)
6. The Sigmoid Sinus is Formed by the Superior Petrosal Sinus and TS.
7. The Internal Jugular V. is formed by the Inferior Petrosal Sinus and Sigmoid Sinus.

Thrombosis of the Venous Sinuses and/or Veins (Septic or Aseptic) results in Brain Edema and Hemorrhagic Infarction. Initial clinical Symptoms are Headache and Extreme Nausea, Uncontrollable Temperature, and possible Epileptic Seizure.

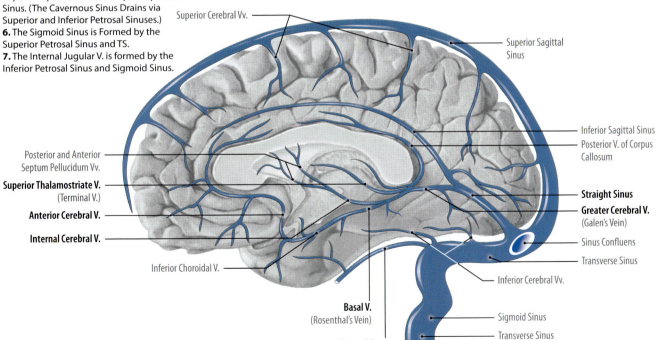

Superior Cerebral Vv.

Superior Sagittal Sinus

Inferior Sagittal Sinus

Posterior V. of Corpus Callosum

Posterior and Anterior Septum Pellucidum Vv.

Superior Thalamostriate V. (Terminal V.)

Straight Sinus

Anterior Cerebral V.

Greater Cerebral V. (Galen's Vein)

Internal Cerebral V.

Sinus Confluens

Inferior Choroidal V.

Transverse Sinus

Inferior Cerebral Vv.

Basal V. (Rosenthal's Vein)

Sigmoid Sinus

Superior Petrosal Sinus

Transverse Sinus

b Medial View.

a Left Hemisphere.
b Right Hemisphere.

Brain

Cerebral Veins

2.204 Basal Cerebral Veins, Hindbrain, Midbrain and Insula: Right Lateral View (The Cerebellum Was Removed). [13, 30]

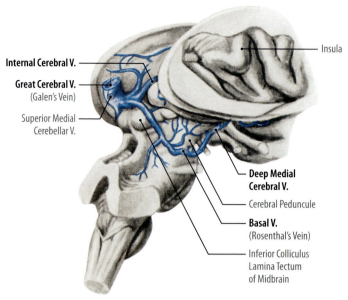

Internal Cerebral V.

Great Cerebral V.
(Galen's Vein)

Superior Medial
Cerebellar V.

Insula

Deep Medial
Cerebral V.

Cerebral Peduncule

Basal V.
(Rosenthal's Vein)

Inferior Colliculus
Lamina Tectum
of Midbrain

2.205 Veins of the Ventricular System, the Basal Ganglia, and the Internal Capsule. [31, 6]

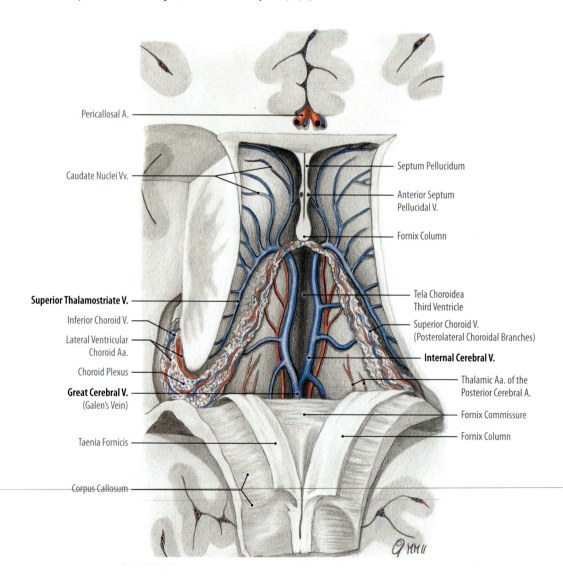

Pericallosal A.

Caudate Nuclei Vv.

Superior Thalamostriate V.

Inferior Choroid V.

Lateral Ventricular
Choroid Aa.

Choroid Plexus

Great Cerebral V.
(Galen's Vein)

Taenia Fornicis

Corpus Callosum

Septum Pellucidum

Anterior Septum
Pellucidal V.

Fornix Column

Tela Choroidea
Third Ventricle

Superior Choroid V.
(Posterolateral Choroidal Branches)

Internal Cerebral V.

Thalamic Aa. of the
Posterior Cerebral A.

Fornix Commissure

Fornix Column

Corpus Callosum and Fornix have been Detached and Displaced Backward.

Cerebral Veins: Imaging

2.206 Superficial Cerebral Veins and Their Confluence into the Superior Sagittal Sinus in a Child: Vertical View. [33]

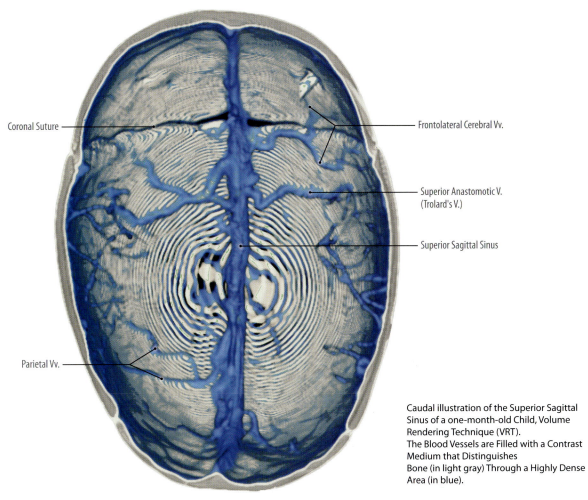

Coronal Suture

Frontolateral Cerebral Vv.

Superior Anastomotic V. (Trolard's V.)

Superior Sagittal Sinus

Parietal Vv.

Caudal illustration of the Superior Sagittal Sinus of a one-month-old Child, Volume Rendering Technique (VRT).
The Blood Vessels are Filled with a Contrast Medium that Distinguishes Bone (in light gray) Through a Highly Dense Area (in blue).

2.207 Cerebral Veins and Venous Blood Vessels. [28]

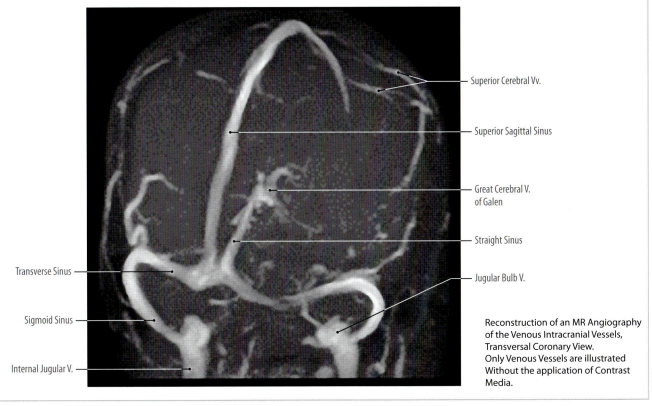

Superior Cerebral Vv.

Superior Sagittal Sinus

Great Cerebral V. of Galen

Straight Sinus

Transverse Sinus

Jugular Bulb V.

Sigmoid Sinus

Internal Jugular V.

Reconstruction of an MR Angiography of the Venous Intracranial Vessels, Transversal Coronary View.
Only Venous Vessels are illustrated Without the application of Contrast Media.

Brain

2.Aa Muscles of the Head (Mastication Muscles): Origins on the Frontal, Parietal, Temporal, Zygomatic and Sphenoid as well as on the Maxilla; Insertions on the Mandible, Right Lateral View.

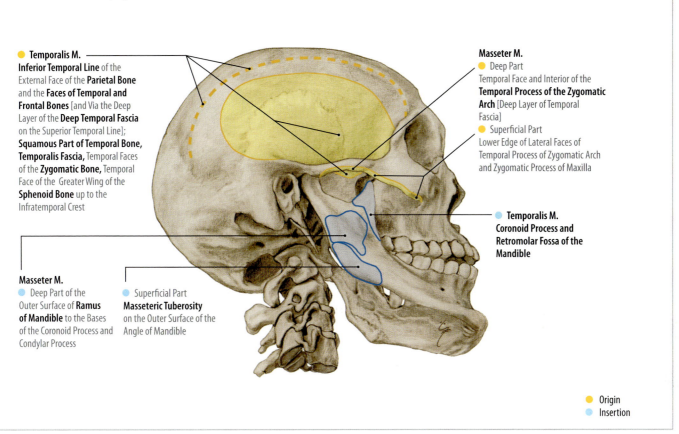

● **Temporalis M.**
Inferior Temporal Line of the
External Face of the **Parietal Bone**
and the **Faces of Temporal and
Frontal Bones** [and Via the Deep
Layer of the **Deep Temporal Fascia**
on the Superior Temporal Line];
**Squamous Part of Temporal Bone,
Temporalis Fascia,** Temporal Faces
of the **Zygomatic Bone,** Temporal
Face of the Greater Wing of the
Sphenoid Bone up to the
Infratemporal Crest

Masseter M.
● Deep Part of the
Outer Surface of **Ramus
of Mandible** to the Bases
of the Coronoid Process and
Condylar Process

● Superficial Part
Masseteric Tuberosity
on the Outer Surface of the
Angle of Mandible

Masseter M.
● Deep Part
Temporal Face and Interior of the
**Temporal Process of the Zygomatic
Arch** [Deep Layer of Temporal
Fascia]
● Superficial Part
Lower Edge of Lateral Faces of
Temporal Process of Zygomatic Arch
and Zygomatic Process of Maxilla

● **Temporalis M.**
**Coronoid Process and
Retromolar Fossa of the
Mandible**

● Origin
● Insertion

2.Ac Muscles of the Head (Mastication Muscles): Origins on the Parietal, Temporal, Zygomatic, and Sphenoid, as well as on the Maxilla, Inferior View.

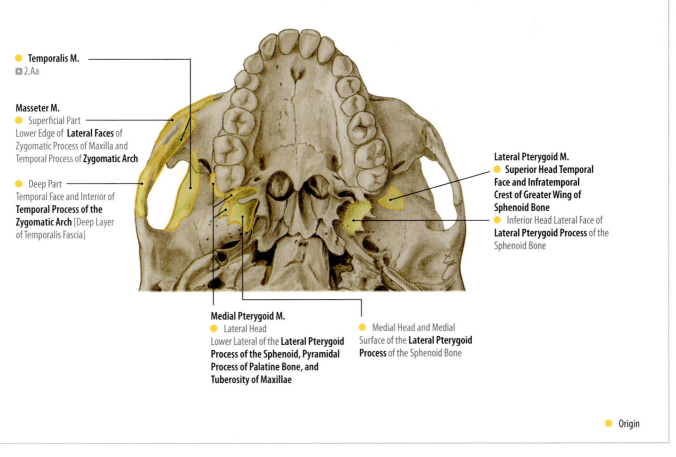

● **Temporalis M.**
▶ 2.Aa

Masseter M.
● Superficial Part
Lower Edge of **Lateral Faces** of
Zygomatic Process of Maxilla and
Temporal Process of **Zygomatic Arch**

● Deep Part
Temporal Face and Interior of
**Temporal Process of the
Zygomatic Arch** [Deep Layer
of Temporalis Fascia]

Lateral Pterygoid M.
● **Superior Head Temporal
Face and Infratemporal
Crest of Greater Wing of
Sphenoid Bone**
● Inferior Head Lateral Face of
Lateral Pterygoid Process of the
Sphenoid Bone

Medial Pterygoid M.
● Lateral Head
Lower Lateral of the **Lateral Pterygoid
Process of the Sphenoid, Pyramidal
Process of Palatine Bone,** and
Tuberosity of Maxillae

● Medial Head and Medial
Surface of the **Lateral Pterygoid
Process** of the Sphenoid Bone

● Origin

2.Ab Muscles of the Head (Mastication Muscles): Insertions on the Mandible, Lateral View.

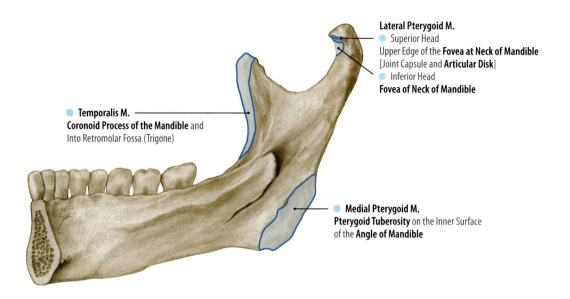

Lateral Pterygoid M.
● Superior Head
Upper Edge of the **Fovea at Neck of Mandible**
[Joint Capsule and **Articular Disk**]
● Inferior Head
Fovea of Neck of Mandible

● **Temporalis M.**
Coronoid Process of the Mandible and
Into Retromolar Fossa (Trigone)

● **Medial Pterygoid M.**
Pterygoid Tuberosity on the Inner Surface
of the **Angle of Mandible**

● Insertion

Function	Innervation	Blood Supply

Temporalis M.
Bilateral Activity: Lifting (Adduction) of the Mandible
  Retrusion of the Mandible
Unilateral Activity:
  Grinding Movement – *Working side:* Stabilization of the Head of Mandible
Grinding Movement – *Balancing side:* Relocation of the Head of Mandible toward the front and rotation to the contralateral side
	Deep Temporal Nn.
	of the Mandibular N. (Mandibular Division) of Trigeminal N. CN V3
		Anterior and Posterior Deep Temporal Aa.
		of the Maxillary A. and less from the Superficial Temporal A.

Masseter M. Lifting (Closing, Adduction) of Mandible Protrusion of the Mandible	Masseteric N. of Mandibular N. (Mandibular Division) of Trigeminal N. CN V3	Masseteric A. of the Maxillary A. Facial A. Transverse Facial A. of the Superficial Temporal A. Buccal A. of the Maxillary A.
Medial Pterygoid M. Bilateral Activity: Lifting (Closing, Adduction) of the Mandible Protrusion of the Mandible Unilateral Activity: Grinding Movement – *Balancing side:* Relocation of the Head of Mandible toward the front and rotation to the contralateral side	Medial Pterygoid N. of Mandibular N. (Mandibular Division) of Trigeminal N. CN V)	Superior Alveolar A. Inferior Alveolar A. Buccal of the Maxillary A.
Lateral Pterygoid M. **Superior Head** Bilateral Activity: Fixation of the Mandibular Head on the Tubercle Declive when lifting (adduction) the Mandible Unilateral Activity: Grinding Movement – *Working side:* Stabilization of the Head of Mandible **Inferior Head** Bilateral Activity: Lowering (abduction) of the Mandible (initiation of the movement) Unilateral Activity: Grinding Movement – *Balancing side:* Relocation of the Head of Mandible toward the front and rotation to the contralateral side	Lateral Pterygoid N. of Mandibular N. (Division) of Trigeminal N. CN V3	Pterygoid Branches of Maxillary A.

Facial Muscles | pp. 42–44, 149

2.Ba Muscles of the Head (Facial Muscles): Frontal View.

Orbicularis Oculi M.
● Orbital Part (Upper Lid)
Anterior Lacrimal Crest
and Frontal Process of the
Maxilla [Medial Palpebral Ligament]
● Palpebral Part
[Medial Palpebral Ligament]
● Lacrimal Part
(Horner's Muscle)
Posterior Lacrimal Crest of the
Lacrimal Bone [Lacrimal Sac]
● Orbital Part (Lower Lid)
[Lateral Palpebral Ligament (Lateral
Palpebral Raphe) on the Zygomatic
Bone]
● Palpebral Part*
Lateral Palpebral Ligament (Lateral
Palpebral Raphe)
● Lacrimal Part
(Horner's Muscle)
Lacrimal Canaliculi

Procerus M.
● Nasal Bone, Lateral Nasal Cartilage
[Aponeurosis of the Transverse Part of the Nasal M.]
● Skin of the Glabella

Corrugator Supercilii M.
● Frontal Bone Above the Frontomaxillary
Suture, Glabella, Superciliary Arch
● Skin Above the Median Third of the
Eyebrow, Galea Aponeurotica

Depressor Supercilii M.
● Medial Part of the Orbicularis Oculi M.
● Insertion in the Medial Part of the
Eyebrow

**Levator Labii Superioris M.
Alaeque Nasi**
● Frontal Process of the Maxilla,
Infraorbital Margin
● Upper Lip, Skin of Ala of the Nose

Levator Labii Superior M.
● Infraorbital Margin of the Maxilla
Above the Infraorbital Foramen
● Skin of the Upper Lip and the Ala of
the Nose, Orbicularis Oris M.

Nasalis M.
● Transverse Part
Lateral to Incisive Fossa of
Canine Tooth of the Maxilla
● Alar Part
Above the Alveolar Fossa of
the Incisor Tooth
● Transverse Part
Aponeurosis Above the Bridge
of the Nose
● Alar Part
Skin of the Nasal Opening
and the Nasal Septum

Levator Anguli Oris M.
● Canine Fossa Below the Infraorbital
Fossa
● Skin and Mucous Membrane of the
Area of the Corner of the Mouth,
Modiolus Anguli Oris, Orbicularis Oris M.

Orbicularis Oris M.
● Marginal Part
● Labial Part
Alveolar Fossae of the Upper and Lower
Canine Teeth [Modiolus Anguli Oris]
● Marginal Part
● Labial Part
Skin of the Upper and Lower Lips

Depressor Septi Nasi M.
● Above the Median Incisor Tooth
● Cartilaginous Part of the
Nasal Septum

Mentalis M.
● Alveolar Fossa of the Lateral Incisor
Tooth of Mandible
● Skin of the Chin

Depressor Labii Infirioris M.
● Mandibular Base Below the Mental Foramen
[Connection to the Platysma]
● Skin and Mucous Membrane of the Lower Lip,
Skin of the Chin Bulge, Orbicularis Oris M.

* Muscle fibers of the edge of the lid are referred to as
Ciliary Fasciculus (Riolan's Muscle).

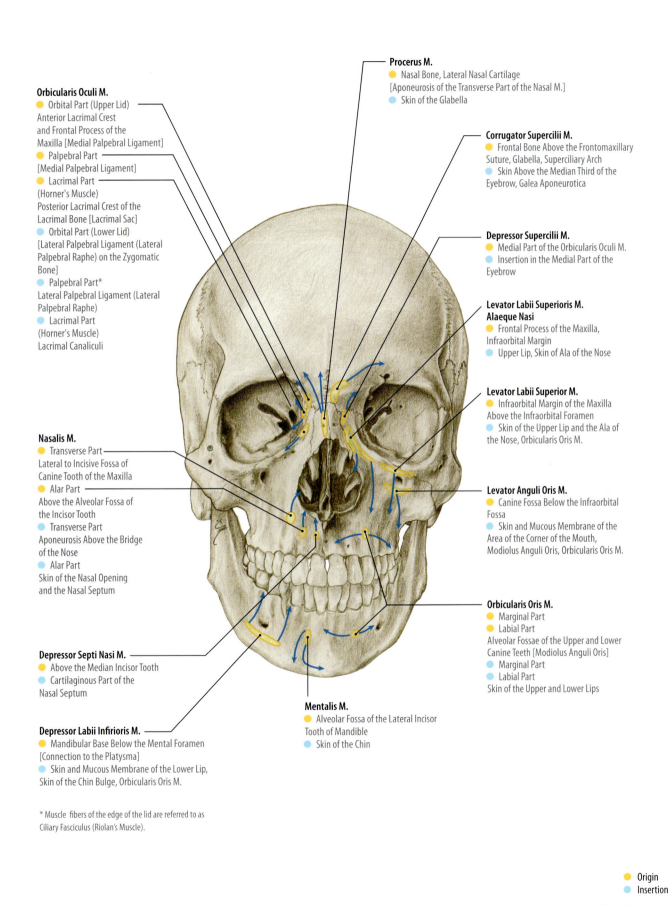

● Origin
● Insertion

Muscles of the Head

2.Bb Muscles of the Head (Facial Muscles): Right Lateral View.

2

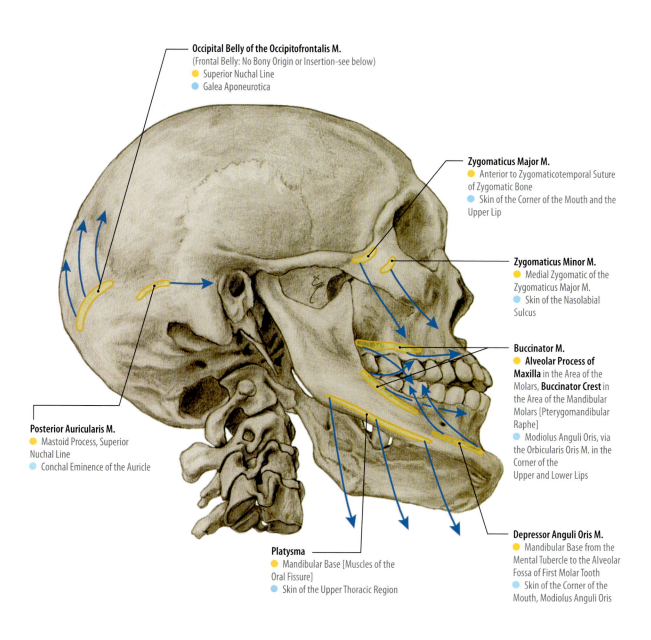

Occipital Belly of the Occipitofrontalis M.
(Frontal Belly: No Bony Origin or Insertion-see below)
- Superior Nuchal Line
- Galea Aponeurotica

Zygomaticus Major M.
- Anterior to Zygomaticotemporal Suture of Zygomatic Bone
- Skin of the Corner of the Mouth and the Upper Lip

Zygomaticus Minor M.
- Medial Zygomatic of the Zygomaticus Major M.
- Skin of the Nasolabial Sulcus

Buccinator M.
- **Alveolar Process of Maxilla** in the Area of the Molars, **Buccinator Crest** in the Area of the Mandibular Molars [Pterygomandibular Raphe]
- Modiolus Anguli Oris, via the Orbicularis Oris M. in the Corner of the Upper and Lower Lips

Posterior Auricularis M.
- Mastoid Process, Superior Nuchal Line
- Conchal Eminence of the Auricle

Depressor Anguli Oris M.
- Mandibular Base from the Mental Tubercle to the Alveolar Fossa of First Molar Tooth
- Skin of the Corner of the Mouth, Modiolus Anguli Oris

Platysma
- Mandibular Base [Muscles of the Oral Fissure]
- Skin of the Upper Thoracic Region

Muscles Without Origin on the Cranial Bone:

Occipitofrontalis M. Frontal Belly	● Via Tendons of Neighboring Muscle in the Area of the Nasal Part of Frontal Bone ● Galea Aponeurotica
Risorius M.	● Masseteric Fascia ● Skin of the Upper Lip, Mucous Membrane of the Vestibule of the Mouth, Modiolus Anguli Oris
Anterior Auricularis M.	● Temporal Fascial Fascia ● Helical Spine of the Auricle
Superior Auricular M.	● Temporal Fascia ● Posterior Surface of the Auricle in the Area of the Eminence Fossa, Triangular Area, and Helical Spine
Posterior Auricular M.	● Nuchal Line and Fascia of Occipital Belly of Occipitofrontalis M. ● Lower of Concha
Temporoparietalis M.	● Temporal Fascia ● Galea Aponeurotica

● Origin
● Insertion

Function	Innervation	Blood Supply
Muscles of the Skullcap (Calvaria)		
Epicranial Muscles		
Occipitofrontalis M.	Temporal Branch of the Facial N. (CN VII)	Supraorbital A.
Frontal Belly (Frontalis M.)		Supratrochlear A., Lacrimal A.
Sole Activity of the Frontal Belly:		Frontal Branch of the
Lifting the eyebrows, frowning (expression of attention, surprise or joy)		Superficial Temporal A.
Occipital Belly (Occipitalis M.)	Occipital Branch of the Posterior Auricular N. of the Facial N.	Occipital A.
With Alternating Activities of Both Muscle Bellies: Moving the Galea Aponeurotica with the scalp to the front and back		
Temporoparietalis M.	Temporal Branches of the Facial N.	Superficial Temporal A.
Fixation of the scalp		
Muscles of the Palpebral Fissure		
Orbicularis Oculi M .	Temporal Branches (area of the upper lid), Zygomatic Branches of the Facial N. (area of lower lid)	Facial A.
Orbital Part		Frontal Branch of the
Firm occlusion of the Palpebral Fissure through movement of the Skin and the Subcutaneous Tissue		Superficial Temporal A.
		Transverse Facial A.
Palpebral Part		Supraorbital A.
Stabilization of the lower lid for the maintenance of the Lacrimal Lake		Lacrimal A.
Blinking to distribute the tear fluid		Supratrochlear A.
Occlusion of the Palpebral Fissure (protective function in the event of strong incidence of light)		Infraorbital A.
Lacrimal Part (Horner's Muscle)		
Furtherance of lacrimation through the Lacrimal Ducts into the Lacrimal Sac and Nasolacrimal Duct		
Corrugator Supercilii M.	Temporal Branches of the Facial N.	Supraorbital A.
Displacement of the Eyebrow Skin in an inferior medial direction and development of a perpendicular skinfold between the root of the Nose and the forehead (protective function in the event of strong incidence of light, expression of pain or meditation – "Thinker Forehead")		Supratrochlear A. Frontal Branch of the Superficial Temporal A.
Depressor Supercilii M.	Temporal Branch of the Facial N.	Supratrochlear A.
(Separation of the Orbital Part of the Orbicularis Oculi M.)		Supraorbital A.
Displacement of the skin of the root of the Nose to a transverse fold		
Muscles in the Area of the Nose		
Procerus M.	Zygomatic Branch of the Facial N.	Dorsal Nasal A.
Displacement of the Skin above the Glabella in an inferior direction and development of a transverse fold above the root of the Nose) together with the Corrugator Supercilii M. (expression of threat or decisiveness)		Supratrochlear A. Branches of the Anterior Ethmoidal A.
Nasalis M.	Zygomatic Branch of the Facial N.	Angular A.
Transverse Part		Dorsal Nasal A.
Pulling the Ala of the Nose and the tip of the Nose downward, slight constriction of the Nostril, depression of the groove of the Ala of the Nose (expression of surprise, joviality, or lustfulness)		Branches of the Anterior Ethmoidal A.
Alar Part		
Dilatation of the Nostril		
Depressor Septi Nasi M.	Zygomatic and Buccal Branches of the Facial N.	Superior Labial A. of the Facial A.
Pulling the tip of the Nose downward		
Levator Labii Superioris Alaeque Nasi M.	Zygomatic Branches of the Facial N.	Infraorbital A.
(Angular Head of the Quadratus Labii Superioris M.)		Superior Labial A.
Lifting of the Ala of the Nose and upper lip		Branches of the Angular A.
Dilatation of the Nostrils (expression of dissatisfaction or arrogance – "wrinkling one's nose")		▶

Muscles of the Head

2

Function	Innervation	Blood Supply
Muscles in the Area of the Mouth		

Orbicularis Oris M.
(Superior Incisive Labii Superioris and Inferior Incisive Labii Mm. – Parts of the Orbicularis Oris M. originating on the Maxilla and Mandible), narrowing and closing of the Mouth, creation of Lip tension, influence on the shape of the Lips and the Mouth in service of ingestion and articulation,
Isolated activity of the Marginal Part:
    Retracting of the red of the Lips
Isolated activity of the Labial Part:
    Bulging out of the Lips (expression of taciturnity, anger, or suspicion)
	Zygomatic Branches of the Facial N. in the area of the upper Lip
	Buccal Branch of the Facial N. in the area of the corner of the Mouth
	Marginal Mandibular Branch of the Facial N. in the area of the lower Lip
		Superior and Inferior Labial Aa. of the Facial A.

Buccinator M. Transportation of food from the Oral Vestibule between the rows of Teeth and into the Oral Cavity, shaping of the bite, creation of Cheek tension and pulling the corners of the Mouth in a lateral direction (expression of laughter or crying)	Buccal Branches of the Facial N.	Branches of the Facial A. and the Superficial Temporal A. Buccal A. and Superior Posterior Alveolar A. of the Maxillary A.
Zygomaticus Major M. **Zygomaticus Minor M.** (Zygomatic Head of the Quadratus Labii Superioris M.) Lifting of the corners of the Mouth outward and upward Depression of the Nasolabial Groove (expression of joy – "laughing muscles")	Zygomatic Branches of the Facial N.	Zygomaticoorbital A. Superficial Temporal A. Branches of the Facial A.
Risorius M. Pulling the corners of the Mouth in a lateral direction Depression of the Nasolabial Groove, creation of "cheek pit" (expression of joy and happiness)	Buccal Branches of the Facial N.	Branches of the Facial A.
Levator Labii Superioris M. (Infraorbital Head of the Quadratus Labii Superioris M.) Lifting of the upper Lip, creation of a fold above and lateral of the Ala of the Nose (expression of dissatisfaction and expression while crying)	Zygomatic Branches of the Facial N.	Infraorbital A. Superior Labial A. Branches of the Angular A.
Levator Anguli Oris M. (Caninus M.) Lifting of the corners of the Mouth in a cranial medial direction	Zygomatic Branches of the Facial N.	Branches of the Angular A. Infraorbital A. Superior Labial A.
Depressor Anguli Oris M. (Triangularis M.) Pulling the corners of the Mouth downward and in a lateral direction, elongation of the Nasolabial Fold (expression of dissatisfaction or mourning)	Buccal Branches of the Facial N. Variable: Marginal Mandibular Branch	Branches of the Facial A. Inferior Labial A.
Depressor Labii Inferioris M. (Quadratus Inferioris M.) Pulling the lower Lip downward and in a lateral direction, bulging out of the red of the Lips (expression of reluctance)	Marginal Mandibular Branch of the Facial N.	Inferior Labial A.
Mentalis M. Displacement of the Skin of the Chin upward Creation of the Chin-Lip groove and of the "chin pit," together with the Depressor Labii Inferioris M. creation of the "puss" at the beginning of crying	Marginal Mandibular Branch of the Facial N.	Inferior Labial A.
Muscles in the Area of the External Ear		
Anterior Auricularis M. Low-grade pulling of the Auricle forward	Temporal Branches of the Facial N.	Superficial Temporal A.
Superior Auricularis M. Low-grade pulling of the Auricle upward	Temporal Branches and Auricular Branches of the Posterior Auricular N. of the Facial N.	Superficial Temporal A. Posterior Auricular A.
Posterior Auricularis M. Low-grade pulling of the Auricle backward	Auricular Branch of the Posterior Auricular N. of the Facial N.	Posterior Auricular A. Auricular Branch of of the Occipital A.
Muscles of the Neck		
Platysma Tenses the Skin of the Neck and furthers venous backflow	Cervical Branch of the Facial N.	Superficial Branch of the Transverse Cervical A. (Superficial Cervical A.) Submental A. of the Facial A.

Neck

Cervical, Facial Muscles

3.1 Superficial Cervical and Facial Muscles: Right Lateral View. [12]

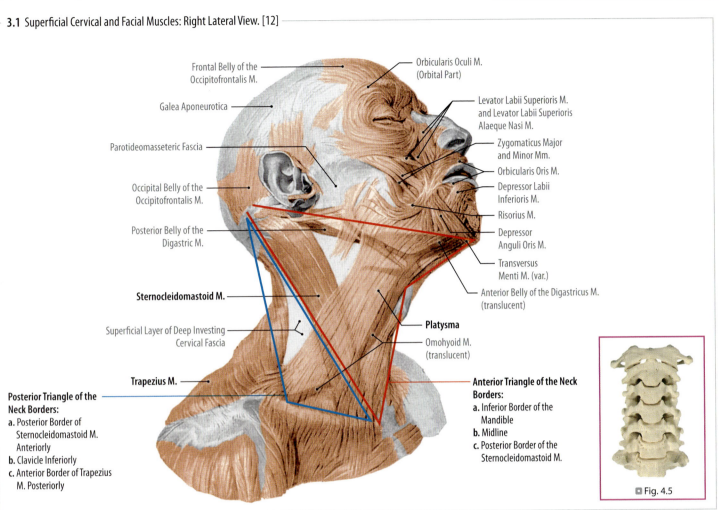

Frontal Belly of the Occipitofrontalis M.

Galea Aponeurotica

Parotideomasseteric Fascia

Occipital Belly of the Occipitofrontalis M.

Posterior Belly of the Digastric M.

Sternocleidomastoid M.

Superficial Layer of Deep Investing Cervical Fascia

Trapezius M.

Posterior Triangle of the Neck Borders:
a. Posterior Border of Sternocleidomastoid M. Anteriorly
b. Clavicle Inferiorly
c. Anterior Border of Trapezius M. Posteriorly

Orbicularis Oculi M. (Orbital Part)

Levator Labii Superioris M. and Levator Labii Superioris Alaeque Nasi M.

Zygomaticus Major and Minor Mm.

Orbicularis Oris M.

Depressor Labii Inferioris M.

Risorius M.

Depressor Anguli Oris M.

Transversus Menti M. (var.)

Anterior Belly of the Digastricus M. (translucent)

Platysma

Omohyoid M. (translucent)

Anterior Triangle of the Neck Borders:
a. Inferior Border of the Mandible
b. Midline
c. Posterior Border of the Sternocleidomastoid M.

◻ Fig. 4.5

3.2 Cervical Muscles: Frontal View. [20]

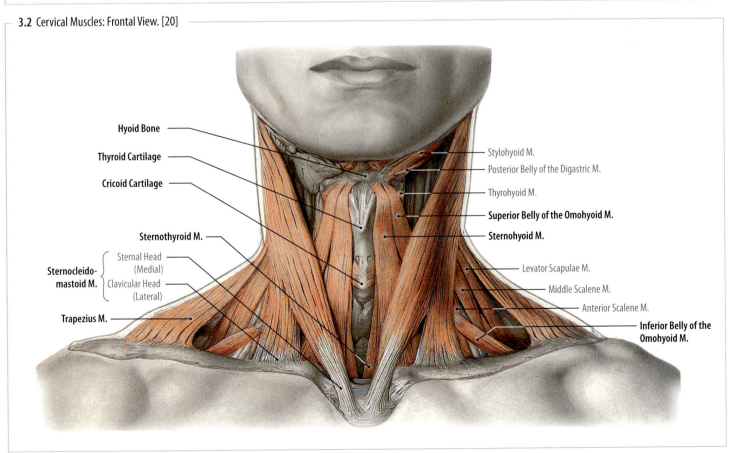

Hyoid Bone

Thyroid Cartilage

Cricoid Cartilage

Sternothyroid M.

Sternocleido-mastoid M. { Sternal Head (Medial) / Clavicular Head (Lateral)

Trapezius M.

Stylohyoid M.

Posterior Belly of the Digastric M.

Thyrohyoid M.

Superior Belly of the Omohyoid M.

Sternohyoid M.

Levator Scapulae M.

Middle Scalene M.

Anterior Scalene M.

Inferior Belly of the Omohyoid M.

Muscles

Cervical Muscles

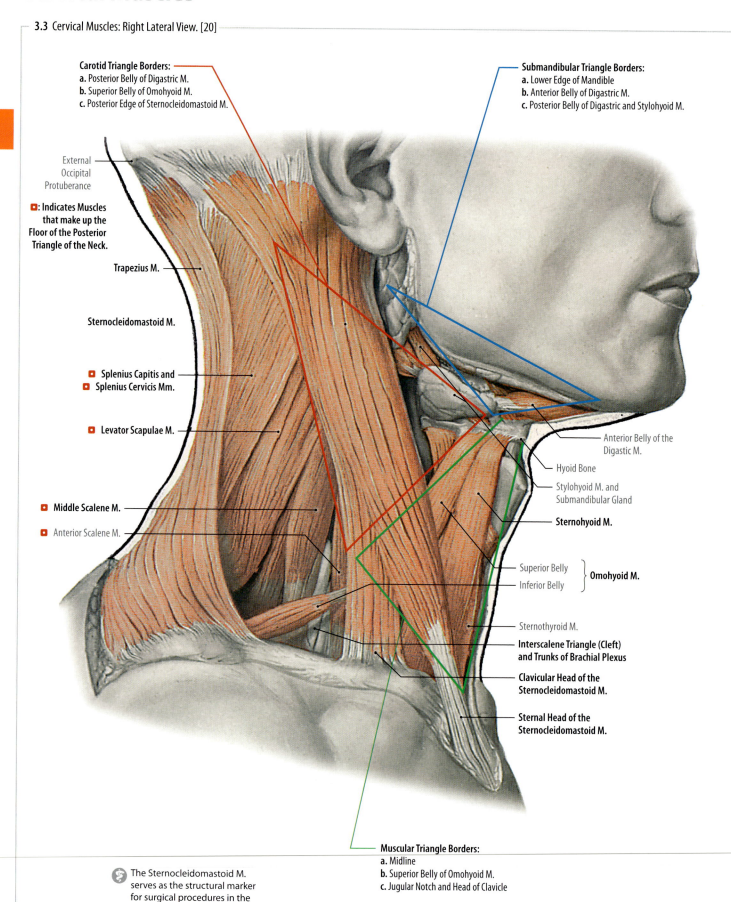

Carotid Triangle Borders:
a. Posterior Belly of Digastric M.
b. Superior Belly of Omohyoid M.
c. Posterior Edge of Sternocleidomastoid M.

Submandibular Triangle Borders:
a. Lower Edge of Mandible
b. Anterior Belly of Digastric M.
c. Posterior Belly of Digastric and Stylohyoid M.

External Occipital Protuberance

■ : Indicates Muscles that make up the Floor of the Posterior Triangle of the Neck.

Trapezius M.

Sternocleidomastoid M.

■ **Splenius Capitis and**
■ **Splenius Cervicis Mm.**

■ **Levator Scapulae M.**

■ **Middle Scalene M.**

■ Anterior Scalene M.

Anterior Belly of the Digastic M.

Hyoid Bone

Stylohyoid M. and Submandibular Gland

Sternohyoid M.

Superior Belly
Inferior Belly
} **Omohyoid M.**

Sternothyroid M.

Interscalene Triangle (Cleft) and Trunks of Brachial Plexus

Clavicular Head of the Sternocleidomastoid M.

Sternal Head of the Sternocleidomastoid M.

Muscular Triangle Borders:
a. Midline
b. Superior Belly of Omohyoid M.
c. Jugular Notch and Head of Clavicle

The Sternocleidomastoid M. serves as the structural marker for surgical procedures in the cervical area.

3.4 Superior Hyoid Muscles: Right Lateral View. [20]

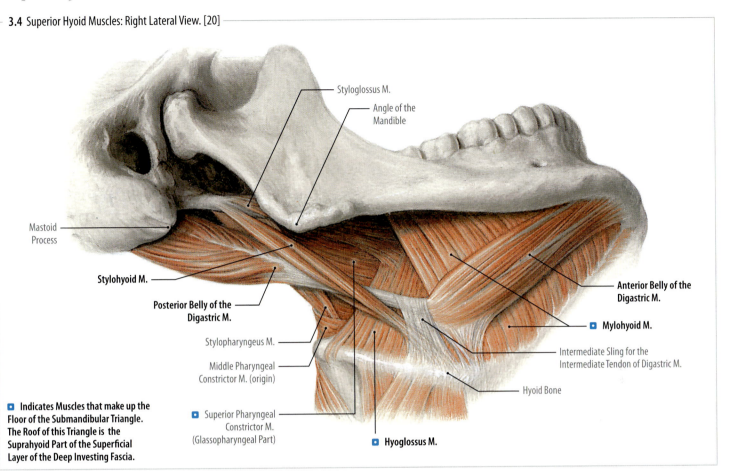

Styloglossus M.

Angle of the Mandible

Mastoid Process

Stylohyoid M.

Posterior Belly of the Digastric M.

Stylopharyngeus M.

Middle Pharyngeal Constrictor M. (origin)

Anterior Belly of the Digastric M.

◨ **Mylohyoid M.**

Intermediate Sling for the Intermediate Tendon of Digastric M.

Hyoid Bone

◨ **Indicates Muscles that make up the Floor of the Submandibular Triangle. The Roof of this Triangle is the Suprahyoid Part of the Superficial Layer of the Deep Investing Fascia.**

◨ Superior Pharyngeal Constrictor M. (Glassopharyngeal Part)

◨ **Hyoglossus M.**

3.5 Frontal Section through the Head in the Area of the Premolars, Section of the Suprahyoid Muscles. [20]

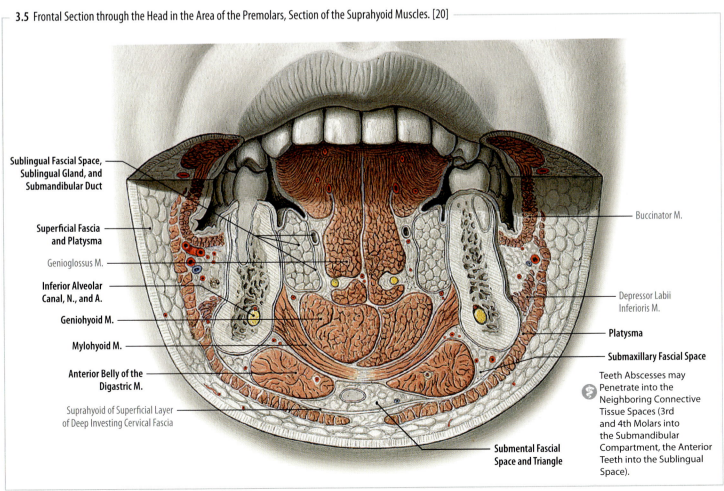

Sublingual Fascial Space, Sublingual Gland, and Submandibular Duct

Superficial Fascia and Platysma

Genioglossus M.

Inferior Alveolar Canal, N., and A.

Geniohyoid M.

Mylohyoid M.

Anterior Belly of the Digastric M.

Suprahyoid of Superficial Layer of Deep Investing Cervical Fascia

Buccinator M.

Depressor Labii Inferioris M.

Platysma

Submaxillary Fascial Space

Teeth Abscesses may Penetrate into the Neighboring Connective Tissue Spaces (3rd and 4th Molars into the Submandibular Compartment, the Anterior Teeth into the Sublingual Space).

Submental Fascial Space and Triangle

Muscles

Hyoid Muscles: Function

3.6a,b Suprahyoid and Infrahyoid Muscles. [20, 44]

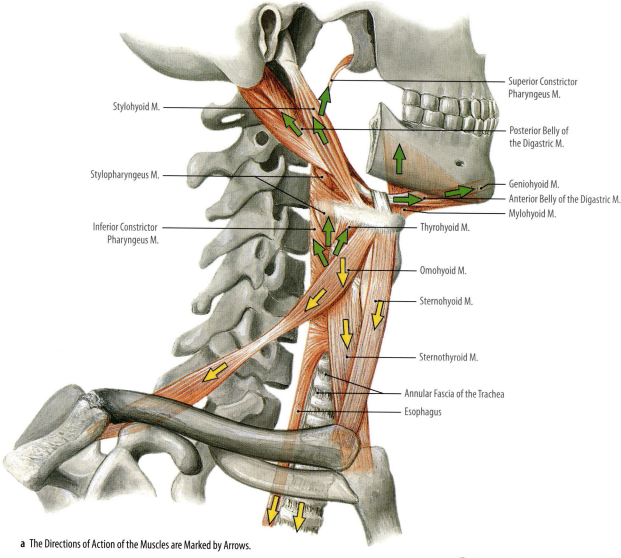

Stylohyoid M.

Stylopharyngeus M.

Inferior Constrictor Pharyngeus M.

Superior Constrictor Pharyngeus M.

Posterior Belly of the Digastric M.

Geniohyoid M.
Anterior Belly of the Digastric M.
Mylohyoid M.

Thyrohyoid M.

Omohyoid M.

Sternohyoid M.

Sternothyroid M.

Annular Fascia of the Trachea

Esophagus

a The Directions of Action of the Muscles are Marked by Arrows.

ℹ️ The Hyoid Bone and Larynx Hang in an Unstable Balance between the Muscle Loops of the Suprahyoid and Infrahyoid Muscles.

b The Mandible must be Locked by the Masticator Mm. to Allow the Elevator Muscle of the Hyoid/Thyroid to Promote Swallowing. The Sternum and Clavicle must be Fixed to Depress the Hyoid/Thyroid Bone and Counteract the Elevator Mm. for the Continuation of the Swallowing Process.

🟩 **Elevator of the Hyoid Bone:**
Superior and Middle
Pharyngeal Constrictor Mm.
Stylohyoid M.
Geniohyoid M.
Digastric M.
Mylohyoid M.

🟩 **Elevator of the Thyroid Cartilage:**
Palatopharyngeus M.
Stylopharyngeus M.
Thyrohyoid M.
Inferior Pharyngeal
    Constrictor M.

🟨 **Depressor of the Hyoid Bone:**
Thyrohyoid M.
Omohyoid M.
Sternothyroid M.
Sternohyoid M.

🟨 **Depressor Thyroid Bone:**
Sternothyroid M.
Traction of the Esophagus
    and the Trachea

Deep Lateral Cervical and Prevertebral Muscles

3.7 Prevertebral and Deep Lateral Cervical Muscles: Frontal Lateral View. [6]

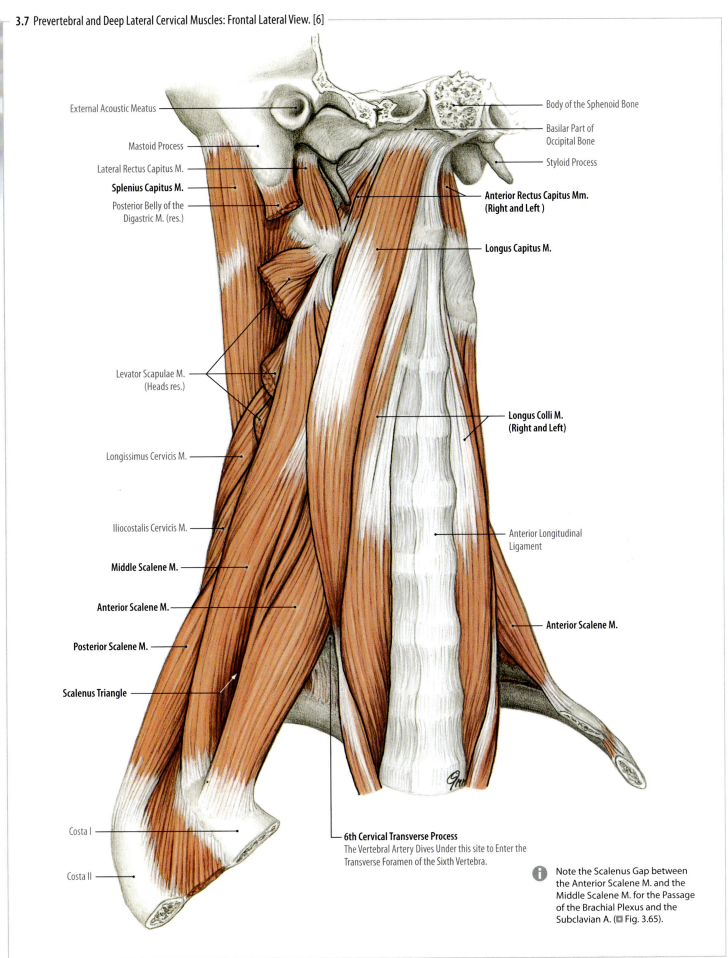

External Acoustic Meatus

Mastoid Process

Lateral Rectus Capitus M.

Splenius Capitus M.

Posterior Belly of the
Digastric M. (res.)

Levator Scapulae M.
(Heads res.)

Longissimus Cervicis M.

Iliocostalis Cervicis M.

Middle Scalene M.

Anterior Scalene M.

Posterior Scalene M.

Scalenus Triangle

Costa I

Costa II

Body of the Sphenoid Bone

Basilar Part of
Occipital Bone

Styloid Process

**Anterior Rectus Capitus Mm.
(Right and Left)**

Longus Capitus M.

**Longus Colli M.
(Right and Left)**

Anterior Longitudinal
Ligament

Anterior Scalene M.

6th Cervical Transverse Process
The Vertebral Artery Dives Under this site to Enter the
Transverse Foramen of the Sixth Vertebra.

ⓘ Note the Scalenus Gap between
the Anterior Scalene M. and the
Middle Scalene M. for the Passage
of the Brachial Plexus and the
Subclavian A. (◱ Fig. 3.65).

Muscles

Cervical Fasciae

3

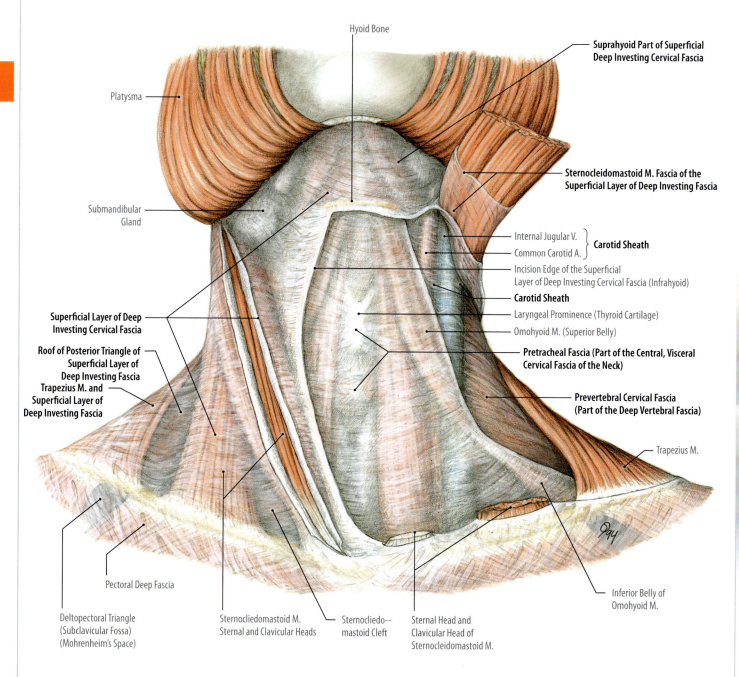

Hyoid Bone

Suprahyoid Part of Superficial Deep Investing Cervical Fascia

Platysma

Sternocleidomastoid M. Fascia of the Superficial Layer of Deep Investing Fascia

Submandibular Gland

Internal Jugular V.
Common Carotid A. } Carotid Sheath

Incision Edge of the Superficial Layer of Deep Investing Cervical Fascia (Infrahyoid)

Carotid Sheath

Superficial Layer of Deep Investing Cervical Fascia

Laryngeal Prominence (Thyroid Cartilage)

Omohyoid M. (Superior Belly)

Roof of Posterior Triangle of Superficial Layer of Deep Investing Fascia Trapezius M. and Superficial Layer of Deep Investing Fascia

Pretracheal Fascia (Part of the Central, Visceral Cervical Fascia of the Neck)

Prevertebral Cervical Fascia (Part of the Deep Vertebral Fascia)

Trapezius M.

Pectoral Deep Fascia

Inferior Belly of Omohyoid M.

Deltopectoral Triangle (Subclavicular Fossa) (Mohrenheim's Space)

Sternocliedomastoid M. Sternal and Clavicular Heads

Sternocliedo--mastoid Cleft

Sternal Head and Clavicular Head of Sternocleidomastoid M.

The Platysma was Removed on Both Sides and Shifted Cranially. On the Right Side of the body, the Superficial Layer of the Cervical Fascia over the Sternocleidomastoid (SCM) M. was Opened. On the Left Side of the body, the SCM M. was Cut Near its Origin and Shifted Cranially. To illustrate the Middle Layer of the Cervical Fascia and the Perivascular Nerve Sheath, the Superficial Layer of the Deep Cervical Fascia was Partially Removed.

The Neck is structured into Two Concentric Compartments defined by the Deep and Superficial Fascia.
1. The Superficial Fascia contains the Platysma M. and the Cutaneous Nn. and Blood Vessels.
2. The Deep Cervical Fascia is organized into Three Investing Sheaths, Two Central, Surrounded by a Third Layer.
(a) Central Posterior Tube: Vertebral Deep Cervical Fascia (Blue).
(b) Central Anterior Tube: Visceral Deep Cervical Fascia (Yellow).
(c) Surrounding Peripheral Tube: Superficial Layer of Deep Cervical Fascia (Green).
(d) Carotid Sheaths are formed by Contributions from the Above Three Layers (Orange).
*The Superficial Layer of Deep Cervical Fascia Splits Twice to Envelop both the Trapezius M. and SCM M. The Fused Layer between Trapezius and SCM Mm. forms the Roof of the Posterior Triangle of the Neck. The Anterior Triangle Roof is the Fused Layer between the Right and Left SCM Mm.

3.9 Reconstruction of the Fasciae and Facial Spaces of the Neck in a Horizontal Section.

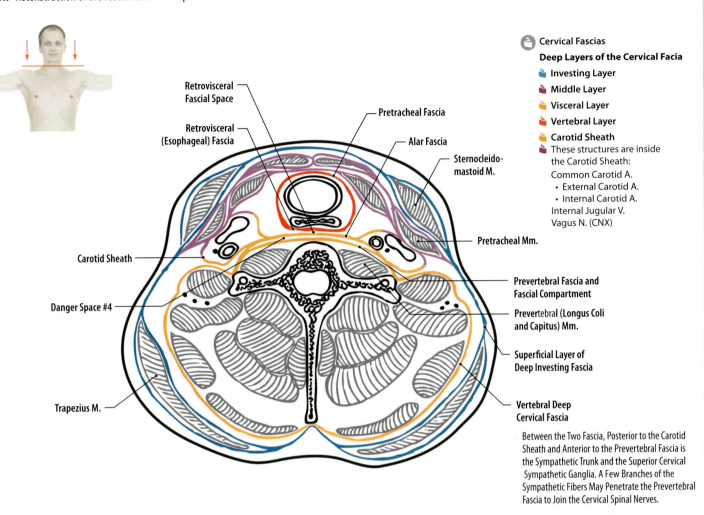

Retrovisceral Fascial Space

Retrovisceral (Esophageal) Fascia

Pretracheal Fascia

Alar Fascia

Sternocleido-mastoid M.

Carotid Sheath

Danger Space #4

Trapezius M.

Pretracheal Mm.

Prevertebral Fascia and Fascial Compartment

Prevertebral (Longus Coli and Capitus) Mm.

Superficial Layer of Deep Investing Fascia

Vertebral Deep Cervical Fascia

Cervical Fascias
Deep Layers of the Cervical Facia
- Investing Layer
- Middle Layer
- Visceral Layer
- Vertebral Layer
- Carotid Sheath
- These structures are inside the Carotid Sheath:
  Common Carotid A.
  - External Carotid A.
  - Internal Carotid A.
  Internal Jugular V.
  Vagus N. (CNX)

Between the Two Fascia, Posterior to the Carotid Sheath and Anterior to the Prevertebral Fascia is the Sympathetic Trunk and the Superior Cervical Sympathetic Ganglia. A Few Branches of the Sympathetic Fibers May Penetrate the Prevertebral Fascia to Join the Cervical Spinal Nerves.

3.10 Sagittal Section through the Neck at the Level of the Larynx. [15]

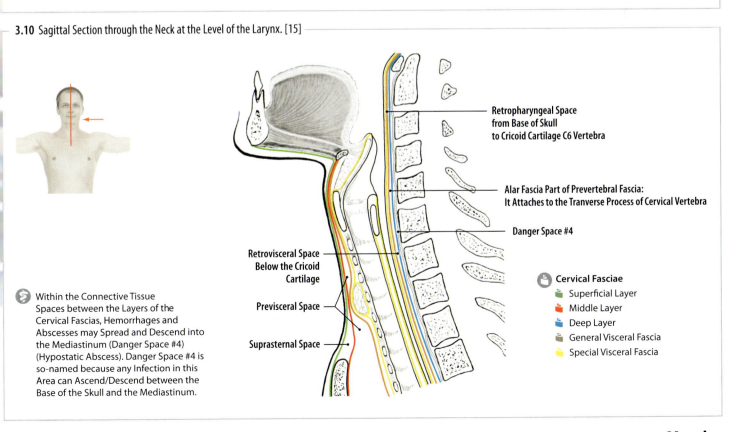

Retropharyngeal Space from Base of Skull to Cricoid Cartilage C6 Vertebra

Alar Fascia Part of Prevertebral Fascia: It Attaches to the Tranverse Process of Cervical Vertebra

Danger Space #4

Retrovisceral Space Below the Cricoid Cartilage

Previsceral Space

Suprasternal Space

Within the Connective Tissue Spaces between the Layers of the Cervical Fascias, Hemorrhages and Abscesses may Spread and Descend into the Mediastinum (Danger Space #4) (Hypostatic Abscess). Danger Space #4 is so-named because any Infection in this Area can Ascend/Descend between the Base of the Skull and the Mediastinum.

Cervical Fasciae
- Superficial Layer
- Middle Layer
- Deep Layer
- General Visceral Fascia
- Special Visceral Fascia

Muscles

Cervical Arteries

3.11 Branches of the Subclavian A. and the External Carotid A.: Right Lateral View. [20]

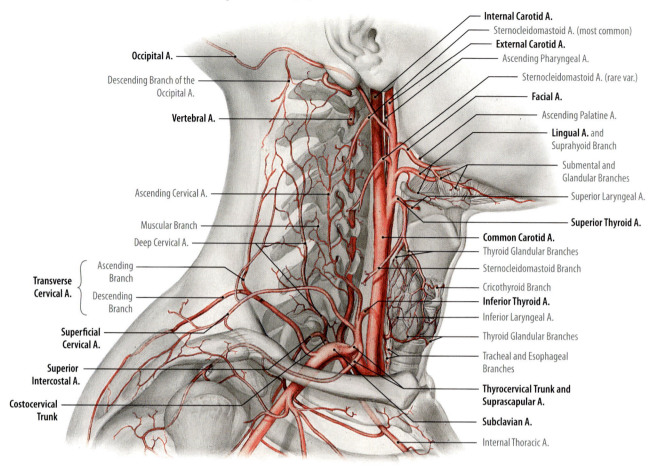

- Occipital A.
- Descending Branch of the Occipital A.
- Vertebral A.
- Ascending Cervical A.
- Muscular Branch
- Deep Cervical A.
- Transverse Cervical A.
  - Ascending Branch
  - Descending Branch
- Superficial Cervical A.
- Superior Intercostal A.
- Costocervical Trunk

- Internal Carotid A.
- Sternocleidomastoid A. (most common)
- External Carotid A.
- Ascending Pharyngeal A.
- Sternocleidomastoid A. (rare var.)
- Facial A.
- Ascending Palatine A.
- Lingual A. and Suprahyoid Branch
- Submental and Glandular Branches
- Superior Laryngeal A.
- Superior Thyroid A.
- Common Carotid A.
- Thyroid Glandular Branches
- Sternocleidomastoid Branch
- Cricothyroid Branch
- Inferior Thyroid A.
- Inferior Laryngeal A.
- Thyroid Glandular Branches
- Tracheal and Esophageal Branches
- Thyrocervical Trunk and Suprascapular A.
- Subclavian A.
- Internal Thoracic A.

The Common Carotid A. splits in 60–70% of cases at the level of the Cervical Vertebra 3/4 (C4 , and at the Upper Border of Thyroid Cartilage) into the External and Internal Carotid Aa.

External Carotid A.
Superior Thyroid A. (1st.)
- [Infrahyoid Branch]
- Sternocleidomastoid A.
- Superior Laryngeal A.
- Cricothyroid A.
- Anterior Glandular A.
- Posterior Glandular A.
- Lateral Glandular A.
Ascending Pharyngeal A. (2nd)
- [Posterior Meningeal A.]
- [Pharyngeal Aa.]
- [Inferior Tympanic A.]

Lingual A. (◫ Fig. 2.71)
Facial A. (◫ Fig. 2.42)
Occipital A. (◫ Fig. 2.54)
- [Mastoid A.]
- [Auricular A.]
- [Sternocleidomastoid Aa.]
- [Occipital Aa.]
  - [Meningeal A. (var.)]
- Descending A.
[Superficial Temporal A.](terminal)
(◫ Fig. 2.42)
[Maxillary A.] (◫ Fig. 2.52)(terminal)

Subclavian A. (◫ Fig. 6.70)
Vertebral A. (◫ Fig. 3.31)
Internal Thoracic A.
(◫ Fig. 4.96)
Thyrocervical Trunk
- Interior Thyroid A.
  - Inferior Laryngeal A.
  - Thyroid Glandular Aa.
  - [Pharyngeal Aa.]
  - Esophageal Aa.
  - Tracheal Aa.
- Ascending Cervical A.
  - [Spinal Aa.]

- Suprascapular A.
  - [Acromial A.]
- Transverse Cervical A.

[ ] not in view

Variation in the Area of the Transverse Cervical A.:

- Transverse Cervical A.
  - Superficial Cervical A. with independent opening
    - Ascending Branch
    - Descending Branch
  - Deep A. (Dorsal Scapular A. with independent origin)

3.12 Branch Sequence of the External Carotid A.

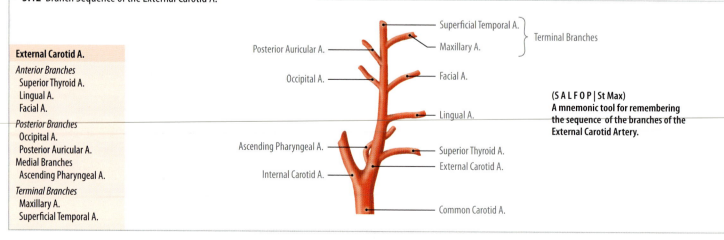

External Carotid A.

Anterior Branches
  Superior Thyroid A.
  Lingual A.
  Facial A.
Posterior Branches
  Occipital A.
  Posterior Auricular A.
Medial Branches
  Ascending Pharyngeal A.
Terminal Branches
  Maxillary A.
  Superficial Temporal A.

- Superficial Temporal A.
- Maxillary A.
- Terminal Branches
- Posterior Auricular A.
- Occipital A.
- Facial A.
- Lingual A.
- Ascending Pharyngeal A.
- Superior Thyroid A.
- External Carotid A.
- Internal Carotid A.
- Common Carotid A.

(S A L F O P | St Max)
A mnemonic tool for remembering the sequence of the branches of the External Carotid Artery.

Cervical Arteries

3.13 Branches of the Vertebral A. and the Costocervical Trunk: Frontal View. [13]

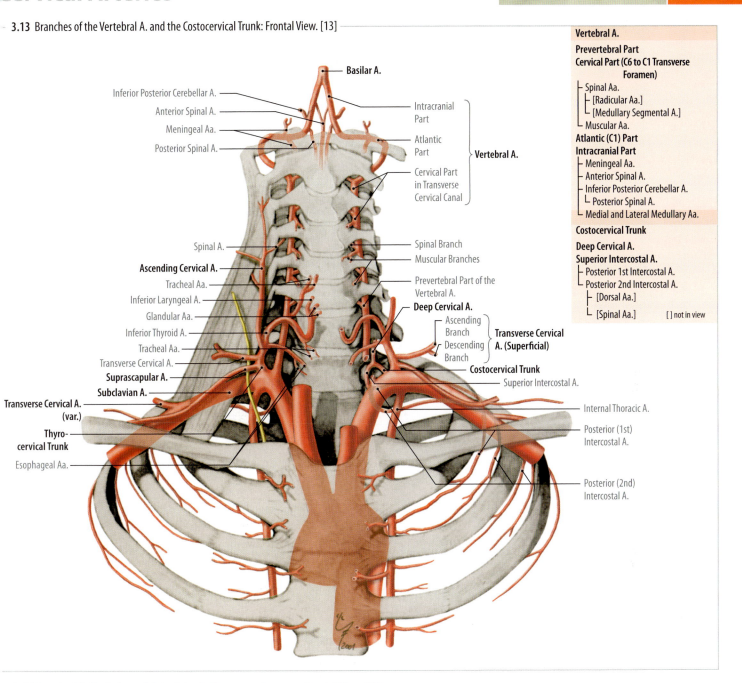

Basilar A.

Inferior Posterior Cerebellar A.

Anterior Spinal A.

Meningeal Aa.

Posterior Spinal A.

Intracranial Part

Atlantic Part

Vertebral A.

Cervical Part in Transverse Cervical Canal

Spinal A.

Ascending Cervical A.

Tracheal Aa.

Inferior Laryngeal A.

Glandular Aa.

Inferior Thyroid A.

Tracheal Aa.

Transverse Cervical A.

Suprascapular A.

Subclavian A.

Transverse Cervical A. (var.)

Thyro-cervical Trunk

Esophageal Aa.

Spinal Branch

Muscular Branches

Prevertebral Part of the Vertebral A.

Deep Cervical A.

Ascending Branch

Descending Branch

Transverse Cervical A. (Superficial)

Costocervical Trunk

Superior Intercostal A.

Internal Thoracic A.

Posterior (1st) Intercostal A.

Posterior (2nd) Intercostal A.

Vertebral A.
Prevertebral Part
Cervical Part (C6 to C1 Transverse Foramen)
├ Spinal Aa.
│ ├ [Radicular Aa.]
│ └ [Medullary Segmental A.]
└ Muscular Aa.
Atlantic (C1) Part
Intracranial Part
├ Meningeal Aa.
├ Anterior Spinal A.
├ Inferior Posterior Cerebellar A.
└ Posterior Spinal A.
└ Medial and Lateral Medullary Aa.
Costocervical Trunk
Deep Cervical A.
Superior Intercostal A.
├ Posterior 1st Intercostal A.
└ Posterior 2nd Intercostal A.
├ [Dorsal Aa.]
└ [Spinal Aa.]   [ ] not in view

3.14 Vertebral A., Variations of Entry into the Transverse Foramen: Frontal View. [20]

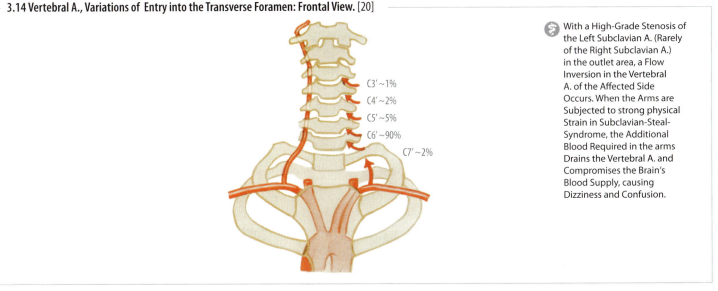

C3′ ~1%

C4′ ~2%

C5′ ~5%

C6′ ~90%

C7′ ~2%

With a High-Grade Stenosis of the Left Subclavian A. (Rarely of the Right Subclavian A.) in the outlet area, a Flow Inversion in the Vertebral A. of the Affected Side Occurs. When the Arms are Subjected to strong physical Strain in Subclavian-Steal-Syndrome, the Additional Blood Required in the arms Drains the Vertebral A. and Compromises the Brain's Blood Supply, causing Dizziness and Confusion.

Pathways

3.15 Veins of the Neck: Right Lateral View. [20]

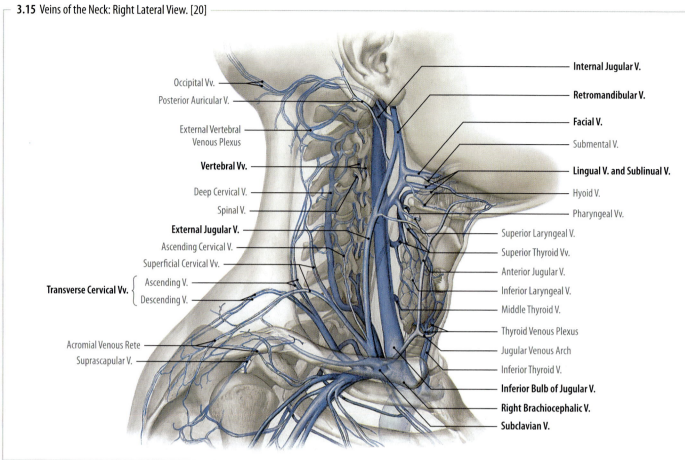

Occipital Vv.
Posterior Auricular V.
External Vertebral Venous Plexus
Vertebral Vv.
Deep Cervical V.
Spinal V.
External Jugular V.
Ascending Cervical V.
Superficial Cervical Vv.
Transverse Cervical Vv. { Ascending V.
Descending V.
Acromial Venous Rete
Suprascapular V.

Internal Jugular V.
Retromandibular V.
Facial V.
Submental V.
Lingual V. and Sublinual V.
Hyoid V.
Pharyngeal Vv.
Superior Laryngeal V.
Superior Thyroid Vv.
Anterior Jugular V.
Inferior Laryngeal V.
Middle Thyroid V.
Thyroid Venous Plexus
Jugular Venous Arch
Inferior Thyroid V.
Inferior Bulb of Jugular V.
Right Brachiocephalic V.
Subclavian V.

3.16 Lymph Nodes of the Neck (Cervical Lymph Nodes): Right Lateral View. [20]

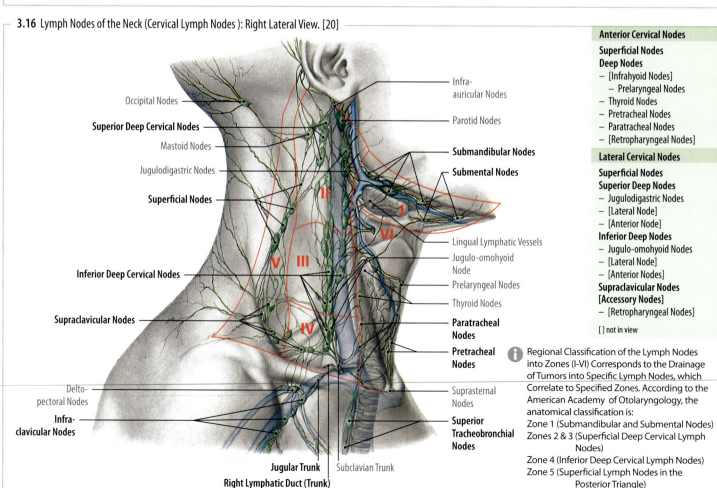

Occipital Nodes
Superior Deep Cervical Nodes
Mastoid Nodes
Jugulodigastric Nodes
Superficial Nodes
Inferior Deep Cervical Nodes
Supraclavicular Nodes
Delto-pectoral Nodes
Infra-clavicular Nodes

Infra-auricular Nodes
Parotid Nodes
Submandibular Nodes
Submental Nodes
Lingual Lymphatic Vessels
Jugulo-omohyoid Node
Prelaryngeal Nodes
Thyroid Nodes
Paratracheal Nodes
Pretracheal Nodes
Suprasternal Nodes
Superior Tracheobronchial Nodes

Jugular Trunk
Subclavian Trunk
Right Lymphatic Duct (Trunk)

Anterior Cervical Nodes
Superficial Nodes
Deep Nodes
– [Infrahyoid Nodes]
– Prelaryngeal Nodes
– Thyroid Nodes
– Pretracheal Nodes
– Paratracheal Nodes
– [Retropharyngeal Nodes]

Lateral Cervical Nodes
Superficial Nodes
Superior Deep Nodes
– Jugulodigastric Nodes
– [Lateral Node]
– [Anterior Node]
Inferior Deep Nodes
– Jugulo-omohyoid Nodes
– [Lateral Node]
– [Anterior Nodes]
Supraclavicular Nodes
[Accessory Nodes]
– [Retropharyngeal Nodes]

[ ] not in view

Regional Classification of the Lymph Nodes into Zones (I–VI) Corresponds to the Drainage of Tumors into Specific Lymph Nodes, which Correlate to Specified Zones. According to the American Academy of Otolaryngology, the anatomical classification is:
Zone 1 (Submandibular and Submental Nodes)
Zones 2 & 3 (Superficial Deep Cervical Lymph Nodes)
Zone 4 (Inferior Deep Cervical Lymph Nodes)
Zone 5 (Superficial Lymph Nodes in the Posterior Triangle)

3.17 Motor Innervation from the Cervical Plexus and from the Brachial Plexus Roots. [18]

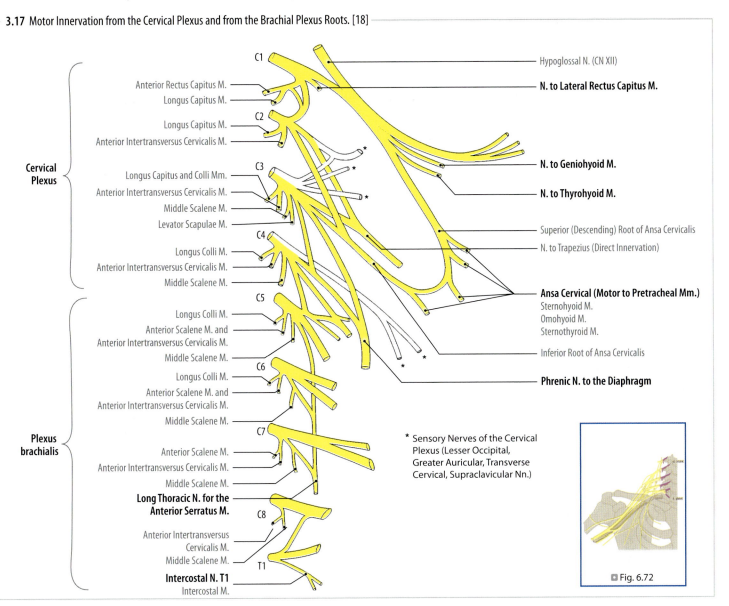

C1
Anterior Rectus Capitus M.
Longus Capitus M.
C2
Longus Capitus M.
Anterior Intertransversus Cervicalis M.
C3
Longus Capitus and Colli Mm.
Anterior Intertransversus Cervicalis M.
Middle Scalene M.
Levator Scapulae M.
C4
Longus Colli M.
Anterior Intertransversus Cervicalis M.
Middle Scalene M.

Cervical Plexus

Hypoglossal N. (CN XII)
N. to Lateral Rectus Capitus M.
N. to Geniohyoid M.
N. to Thyrohyoid M.
Superior (Descending) Root of Ansa Cervicalis
N. to Trapezius (Direct Innervation)
Ansa Cervical (Motor to Pretracheal Mm.)
Sternohyoid M.
Omohyoid M.
Sternothyroid M.
Inferior Root of Ansa Cervicalis
Phrenic N. to the Diaphragm

C5
Longus Colli M.
Anterior Scalene M. and
Anterior Intertransversus Cervicalis M.
Middle Scalene M.
C6
Longus Colli M.
Anterior Scalene M. and
Anterior Intertransversus Cervicalis M.
Middle Scalene M.
C7
Anterior Scalene M.
Anterior Intertransversus Cervicalis M.
Middle Scalene M.
Long Thoracic N. for the Anterior Serratus M.
C8
Anterior Intertransversus Cervicalis M.
Middle Scalene M.
T1
Intercostal N. T1
Intercostal M.

Plexus brachialis

* Sensory Nerves of the Cervical Plexus (Lesser Occipital, Greater Auricular, Transverse Cervical, Supraclavicular Nn.)

◻ Fig. 6.72

3.18 Sensory Supply of the Skin of the Neck. [47]

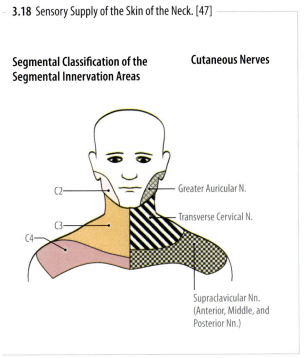

Segmental Classification of the Segmental Innervation Areas

Cutaneous Nerves

C2
C3
C4

Greater Auricular N.
Transverse Cervical N.
Supraclavicular Nn. (Anterior, Middle, and Posterior Nn.)

3.19 Autonomic (Vegetative) Nerve Plexus of the Large Cervical Vessels and the Carotid Body and Sinus of the Right Side. [20]

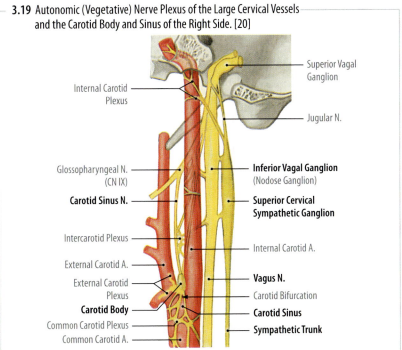

Internal Carotid Plexus
Glossopharyngeal N. (CN IX)
Carotid Sinus N.
Intercarotid Plexus
External Carotid A.
External Carotid Plexus
Carotid Body
Common Carotid Plexus
Common Carotid A.

Superior Vagal Ganglion
Jugular N.
Inferior Vagal Ganglion (Nodose Ganglion)
Superior Cervical Sympathetic Ganglion
Internal Carotid A.
Vagus N.
Carotid Bifurcation
Carotid Sinus
Sympathetic Trunk

Submandibular Triangle

3.20 Submandibular Triangle of the Right Side, Lateral View; Submaxillary Fascial Space; and Muscle Compartment within the Superficial Layer of the Deep Cervical Fascia for the Submandibular Salivary Gland. [20]

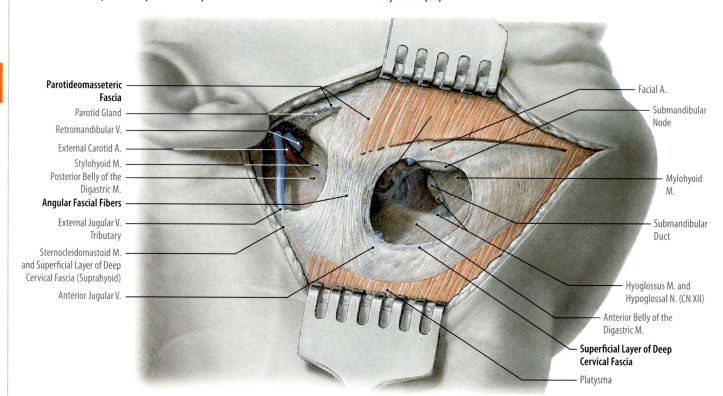

Parotideomasseteric Fascia
Parotid Gland
Retromandibular V.
External Carotid A.
Stylohyoid M.
Posterior Belly of the Digastric M.
Angular Fascial Fibers
External Jugular V. Tributary
Sternocleidomastoid M. and Superficial Layer of Deep Cervical Fascia (Suprahyoid)
Anterior Jugular V.

Facial A.
Submandibular Node
Mylohyoid M.
Submandibular Duct
Hyoglossus M. and Hypoglossal N. (CN XII)
Anterior Belly of the Digastric M.
Superficial Layer of Deep Cervical Fascia
Platysma

The Lower Part of the Parotid Gland has been Removed; the Platysma in the Superficial Fasci was Resected in the area of the Submandibular Triangle.

Mylohyoid M. attachment line (Mylohyoid Line) Slants Anteriorly. The Roots of the Two Last Molars are Below this Line. Abscess of these roots Drains into the Submandibular Triangle in the Submaxillary Fascial Space. The Abscess may Extend Posteriorly into the Lateral Pharyngeal Space. (Peritonsillar Abscess may also extend into the Lateral Pharyngeal Space.) The Symptoms include Difficulty in Swallowing and Deviation/Bulging of the Pharyngeal Wall on the Affected Side.

3.21 Submandibular Triangle. [20]

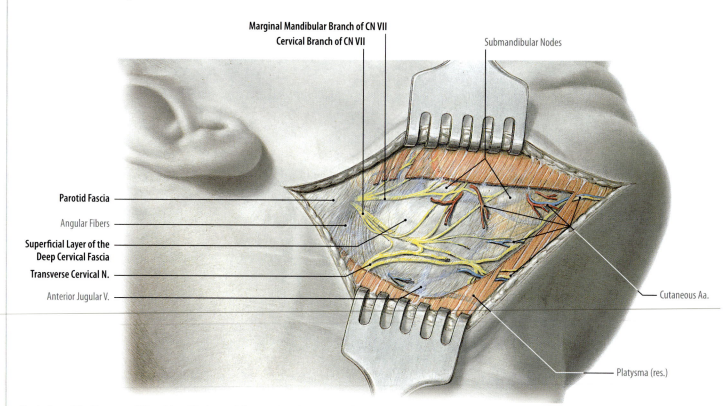

Marginal Mandibular Branch of CN VII
Cervical Branch of CN VII
Submandibular Nodes

Parotid Fascia
Angular Fibers
Superficial Layer of the Deep Cervical Fascia
Transverse Cervical N.
Anterior Jugular V.

Cutaneous Aa.
Platysma (res.)

Illustration of the Nerves and Blood Vessel Pathways following Partial Resection of the Platysma (in the Superficial Fascia).

Submandibular Triangle

3.22 Submandibular Triangle of the Right Side of the Body: Lateral View. [20]

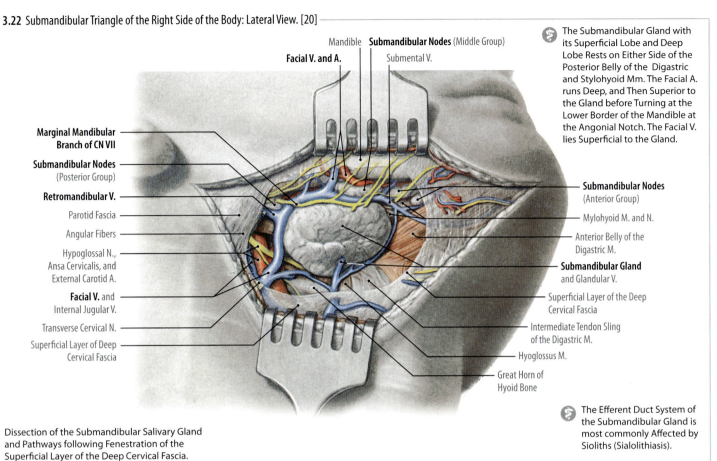

Marginal Mandibular Branch of CN VII

Submandibular Nodes (Posterior Group)

Retromandibular V.

Parotid Fascia

Angular Fibers

Hypoglossal N., Ansa Cervicalis, and External Carotid A.

Facial V. and Internal Jugular V.

Transverse Cervical N.

Superficial Layer of Deep Cervical Fascia

Facial V. and A.

Mandible

Submandibular Nodes (Middle Group)

Submental V.

Submandibular Nodes (Anterior Group)

Mylohyoid M. and N.

Anterior Belly of the Digastric M.

Submandibular Gland and Glandular V.

Superficial Layer of the Deep Cervical Fascia

Intermediate Tendon Sling of the Digastric M.

Hyoglossus M.

Great Horn of Hyoid Bone

The Submandibular Gland with its Superficial Lobe and Deep Lobe Rests on Either Side of the Posterior Belly of the Digastric and Stylohyoid Mm. The Facial A. runs Deep, and Then Superior to the Gland before Turning at the Lower Border of the Mandible at the Angonial Notch. The Facial V. lies Superficial to the Gland.

The Efferent Duct System of the Submandibular Gland is most commonly Affected by Sioliths (Sialolithiasis).

Dissection of the Submandibular Salivary Gland and Pathways following Fenestration of the Superficial Layer of the Deep Cervical Fascia.

3.23 Submandibular Triangle of the Right Side of the Body: Lateral View. [20]

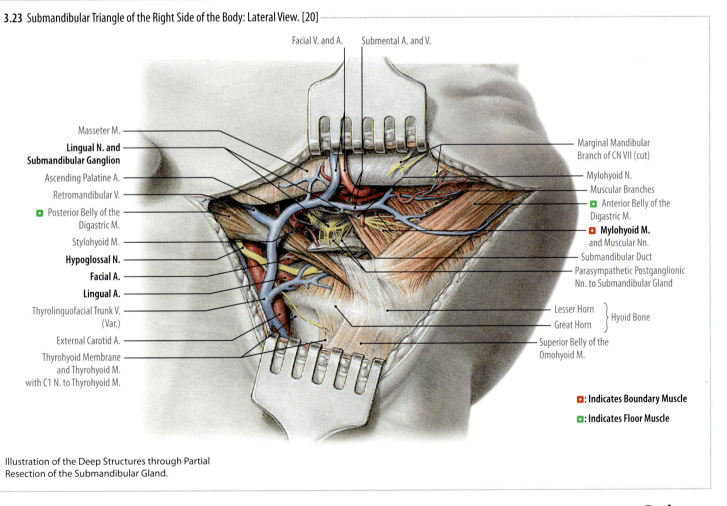

Masseter M.

Lingual N. and Submandibular Ganglion

Ascending Palatine A.

Retromandibular V.

Posterior Belly of the Digastric M.

Stylohyoid M.

Hypoglossal N.

Facial A.

Lingual A.

Thyrolinguofacial Trunk V. (Var.)

External Carotid A.

Thyrohyoid Membrane and Thyrohyoid M. with C1 N. to Thyrohyoid M.

Facial V. and A.

Submental A. and V.

Marginal Mandibular Branch of CN VII (cut)

Mylohyoid N.

Muscular Branches

Anterior Belly of the Digastric M.

Mylohyoid M. and Muscular Nn.

Submandibular Duct

Parasympathetic Postganglionic Nn. to Submandibular Gland

Lesser Horn ⎫ Great Horn ⎬ Hyoid Bone

Superior Belly of the Omohyoid M.

◻: Indicates Boundary Muscle

◻: Indicates Floor Muscle

Illustration of the Deep Structures through Partial Resection of the Submandibular Gland.

Pathways

Superficial Fascial Pathways

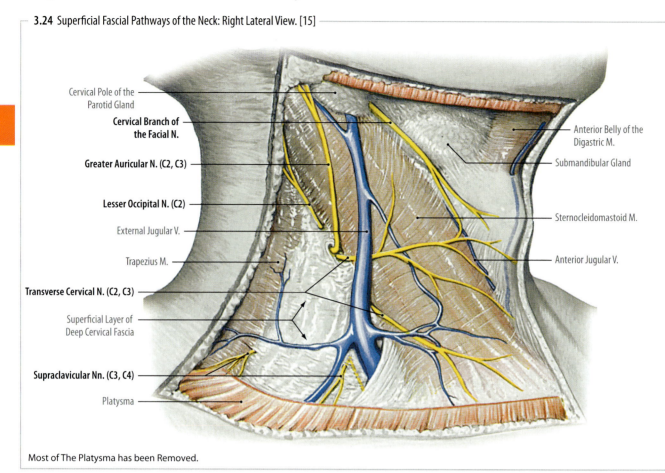

Cervical Pole of the Parotid Gland

Cervical Branch of the Facial N.

Greater Auricular N. (C2, C3)

Lesser Occipital N. (C2)

External Jugular V.

Trapezius M.

Transverse Cervical N. (C2, C3)

Superficial Layer of Deep Cervical Fascia

Supraclavicular Nn. (C3, C4)

Platysma

Anterior Belly of the Digastric M.

Submandibular Gland

Sternocleidomastoid M.

Anterior Jugular V.

Most of The Platysma has been Removed.

3.25 Superficial Pathways in the Right Lateral Cervical Region (Posterior Cervical Triangle). [15]

Erb's Point is the Midposterior Edge of the Sternocleido-mastoid M. This site marks the Emergence of the Cervical Plexus Nn., which is used in Cervical Nerve Block (Regional Anesthesia).

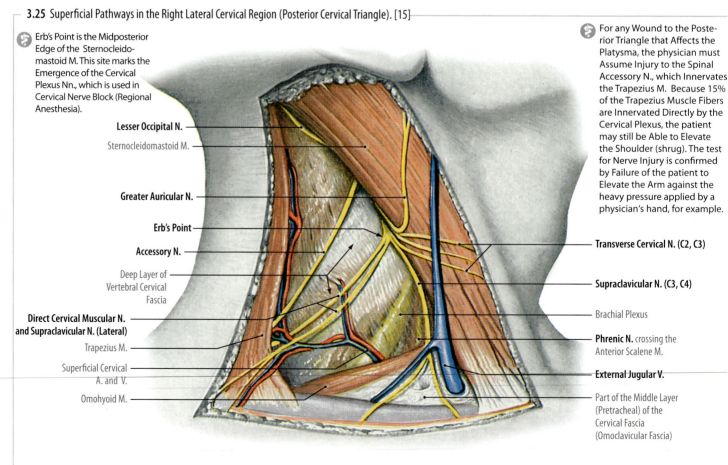

Lesser Occipital N.

Sternocleidomastoid M.

Greater Auricular N.

Erb's Point

Accessory N.

Deep Layer of Vertebral Cervical Fascia

Direct Cervical Muscular N. and Supraclavicular N. (Lateral)

Trapezius M.

Superficial Cervical A. and V.

Omohyoid M.

For any Wound to the Posterior Triangle that Affects the Platysma, the physician must Assume Injury to the Spinal Accessory N., which Innervates the Trapezius M. Because 15% of the Trapezius Muscle Fibers are Innervated Directly by the Cervical Plexus, the patient may still be Able to Elevate the Shoulder (shrug). The test for Nerve Injury is confirmed by Failure of the patient to Elevate the Arm against the heavy pressure applied by a physician's hand, for example.

Transverse Cervical N. (C2, C3)

Supraclavicular N. (C3, C4)

Brachial Plexus

Phrenic N. crossing the Anterior Scalene M.

External Jugular V.

Part of the Middle Layer (Pretracheal) of the Cervical Fascia (Omoclavicular Fascia)

The Superficial Layer of the Cervical Fascia has been Removed.

3.26 Pathways in the Posterior Cervical Triangle of the Right Side of the Body: Lateral View. [15]

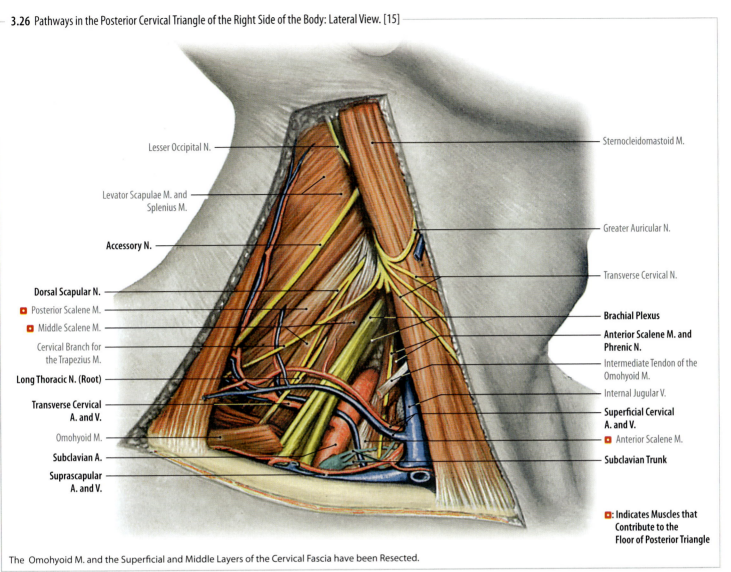

Lesser Occipital N.

Levator Scapulae M. and Splenius M.

Accessory N.

Dorsal Scapular N.

■ Posterior Scalene M.

■ Middle Scalene M.

Cervical Branch for the Trapezius M.

Long Thoracic N. (Root)

Transverse Cervical A. and V.

Omohyoid M.

Subclavian A.

Suprascapular A. and V.

Sternocleidomastoid M.

Greater Auricular N.

Transverse Cervical N.

Brachial Plexus

Anterior Scalene M. and Phrenic N.

Intermediate Tendon of the Omohyoid M.

Internal Jugular V.

Superficial Cervical A. and V.

■ Anterior Scalene M.

Subclavian Trunk

■: Indicates Muscles that Contribute to the Floor of Posterior Triangle

The Omohyoid M. and the Superficial and Middle Layers of the Cervical Fascia have been Resected.

3.27 Scalenus Gap of the Right Side of the Body. [20]

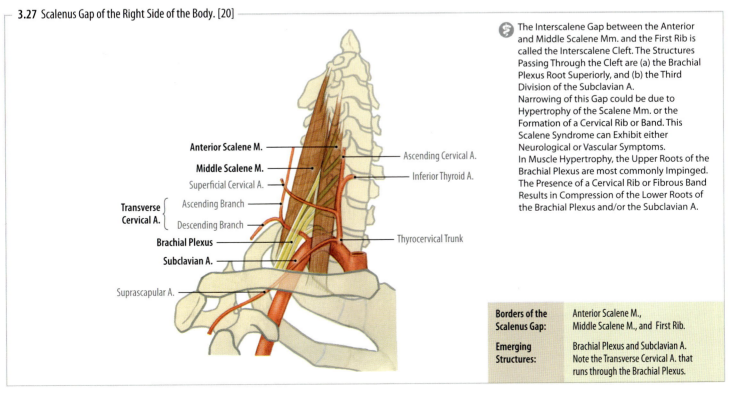

Anterior Scalene M.

Middle Scalene M.

Superficial Cervical A.

Transverse Cervical A. { Ascending Branch / Descending Branch }

Brachial Plexus

Subclavian A.

Suprascapular A.

Ascending Cervical A.

Inferior Thyroid A.

Thyrocervical Trunk

The Interscalene Gap between the Anterior and Middle Scalene Mm. and the First Rib is called the Interscalene Cleft. The Structures Passing Through the Cleft are (a) the Brachial Plexus Root Superiorly, and (b) the Third Division of the Subclavian A.
Narrowing of this Gap could be due to Hypertrophy of the Scalene Mm. or the Formation of a Cervical Rib or Band. This Scalene Syndrome can Exhibit either Neurological or Vascular Symptoms.
In Muscle Hypertrophy, the Upper Roots of the Brachial Plexus are most commonly Impinged. The Presence of a Cervical Rib or Fibrous Band Results in Compression of the Lower Roots of the Brachial Plexus and/or the Subclavian A.

Borders of the Scalenus Gap:	Anterior Scalene M., Middle Scalene M., and First Rib.
Emerging Structures:	Brachial Plexus and Subclavian A. Note the Transverse Cervical A. that runs through the Brachial Plexus.

Pathways

3.28 Pathways and Middle Layer of the Cervical Fascia of the Right Side: Lateral View. [20]

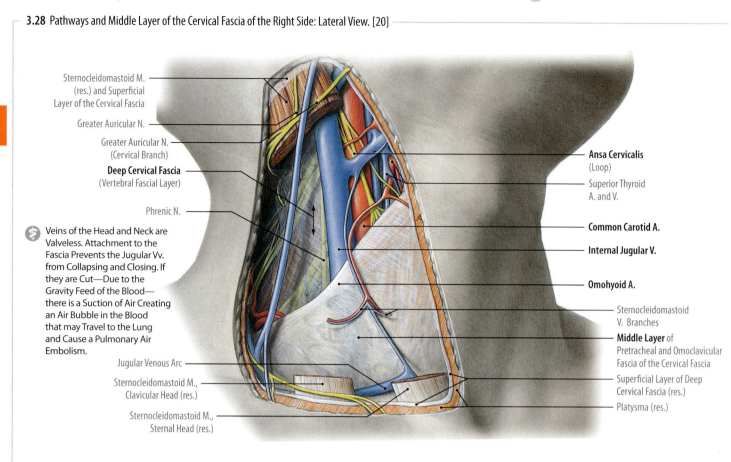

Sternocleidomastoid M. (res.) and Superficial Layer of the Cervical Fascia

Greater Auricular N.

Greater Auricular N. (Cervical Branch)

Deep Cervical Fascia (Vertebral Fascial Layer)

Phrenic N.

Veins of the Head and Neck are Valveless. Attachment to the Fascia Prevents the Jugular Vv. from Collapsing and Closing. If they are Cut—Due to the Gravity Feed of the Blood— there is a Suction of Air Creating an Air Bubble in the Blood that may Travel to the Lung and Cause a Pulmonary Air Embolism.

Jugular Venous Arc

Sternocleidomastoid M., Clavicular Head (res.)

Sternocleidomastoid M., Sternal Head (res.)

Ansa Cervicalis (Loop)

Superior Thyroid A. and V.

Common Carotid A.

Internal Jugular V.

Omohyoid A.

Sternocleidomastoid V. Branches

Middle Layer of Pretracheal and Omoclavicular Fascia of the Cervical Fascia

Superficial Layer of Deep Cervical Fascia (res.)

Platysma (res.)

3.29 Carotid Triangle of the Right Side of the Body: Lateral View. [20]

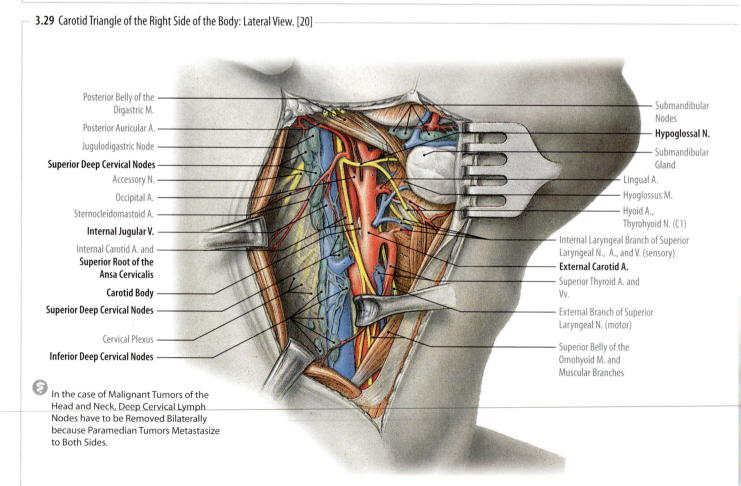

Posterior Belly of the Digastric M.

Posterior Auricular A.

Jugulodigastric Node

Superior Deep Cervical Nodes

Accessory N.

Occipital A.

Sternocleidomastoid A.

Internal Jugular V.

Internal Carotid A. and **Superior Root of the Ansa Cervicalis**

Carotid Body

Superior Deep Cervical Nodes

Cervical Plexus

Inferior Deep Cervical Nodes

Submandibular Nodes

Hypoglossal N.

Submandibular Gland

Lingual A.

Hyoglossus M.

Hyoid A., Thyrohyoid N. (C1)

Internal Laryngeal Branch of Superior Laryngeal N., A., and V. (sensory)

External Carotid A.

Superior Thyroid A. and Vv.

External Branch of Superior Laryngeal N. (motor)

Superior Belly of the Omohyoid M. and Muscular Branches

In the case of Malignant Tumors of the Head and Neck, Deep Cervical Lymph Nodes have to be Removed Bilaterally because Paramedian Tumors Metastasize to Both Sides.

Anterior Cervical Triangle

3.30 Anterior Cervical Region (Right and Left Anterior Cervical Triangles): Frontal View. [20]

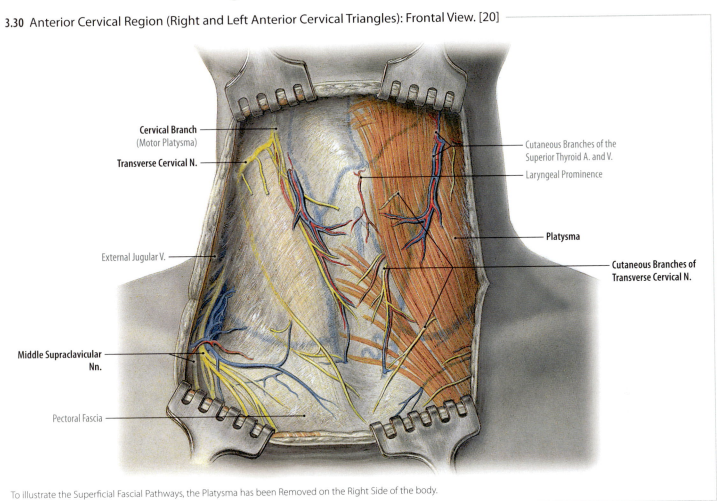

Cervical Branch
(Motor Platysma)

Transverse Cervical N.

Cutaneous Branches of the
Superior Thyroid A. and V.

Laryngeal Prominence

External Jugular V.

Platysma

Cutaneous Branches of
Transverse Cervical N.

Middle Supraclavicular
Nn.

Pectoral Fascia

To illustrate the Superficial Fascial Pathways, the Platysma has been Removed on the Right Side of the body.

3.31 Anterior Cervical Region: Infrahyoid Muscles and Pathways. [20]

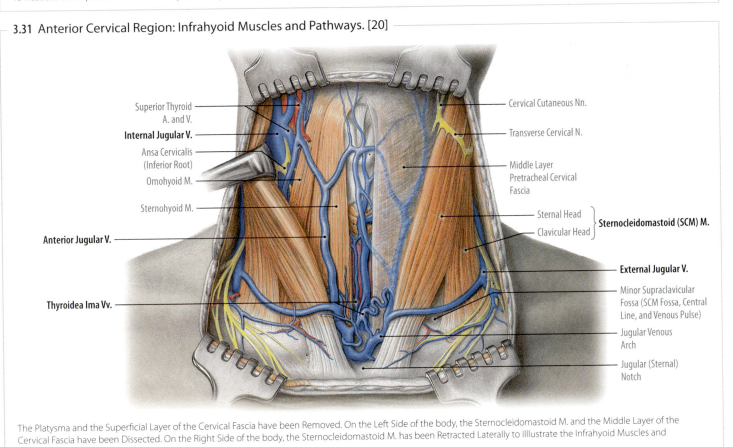

Superior Thyroid
A. and V.

Internal Jugular V.

Ansa Cervicalis
(Inferior Root)

Omohyoid M.

Sternohyoid M.

Anterior Jugular V.

Thyroidea Ima Vv.

Cervical Cutaneous Nn.

Transverse Cervical N.

Middle Layer
Pretracheal Cervical
Fascia

Sternal Head
Clavicular Head

Sternocleidomastoid (SCM) M.

External Jugular V.

Minor Supraclavicular
Fossa (SCM Fossa, Central
Line, and Venous Pulse)

Jugular Venous
Arch

Jugular (Sternal)
Notch

The Platysma and the Superficial Layer of the Cervical Fascia have been Removed. On the Left Side of the body, the Sternocleidomastoid M. and the Middle Layer of the Cervical Fascia have been Dissected. On the Right Side of the body, the Sternocleidomastoid M. has been Retracted Laterally to illlustrate the Infrahyoid Muscles and Pathways.

Pathways

3.32 Infrahyoid Muscles and Their Nerve Supply and the Structures of the Carotid Sheath. [20]

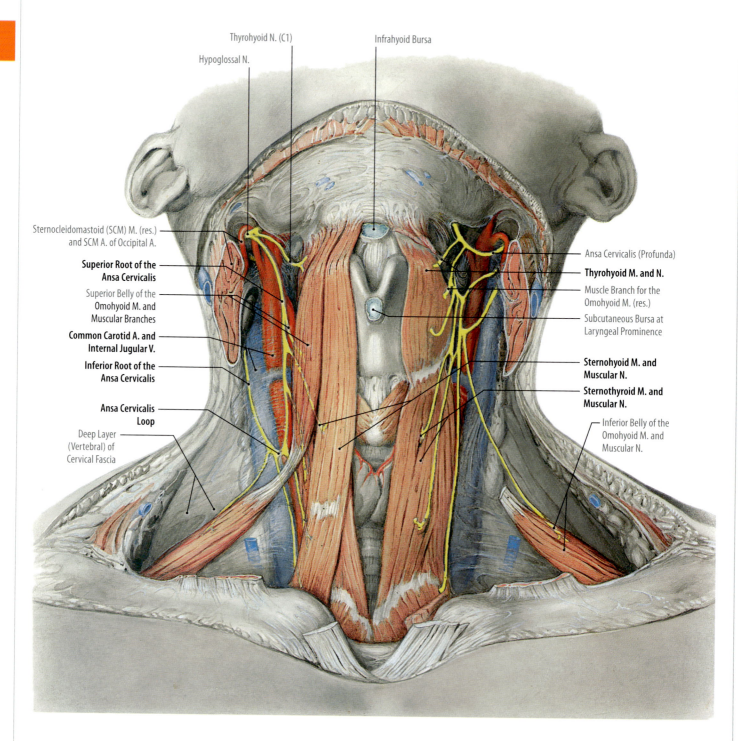

Thyrohyoid N. (C1)

Infrahyoid Bursa

Hypoglossal N.

Sternocleidomastoid (SCM) M. (res.)
and SCM A. of Occipital A.

**Superior Root of the
Ansa Cervicalis**

Superior Belly of the
Omohyoid M. and
Muscular Branches

**Common Carotid A. and
Internal Jugular V.**

**Inferior Root of the
Ansa Cervicalis**

**Ansa Cervicalis
Loop**

Deep Layer
(Vertebral) of
Cervical Fascia

Ansa Cervicalis (Profunda)

Thyrohyoid M. and N.

Muscle Branch for the
Omohyoid M. (res.)

Subcutaneous Bursa at
Laryngeal Prominence

**Sternohyoid M. and
Muscular N.**

**Sternothyroid M. and
Muscular N.**

Inferior Belly of the
Omohyoid M. and
Muscular N.

The Sternocleidomastoid Mm.
have been Removed. On the Left
Side of the body, the Sternohyoid
M. and the Upper Belly of the
Omohyoid M. have been Resected.

Thyroid Gland

3.33a,b Thyroid and Parathyroid Glands. [a 20, b 48]

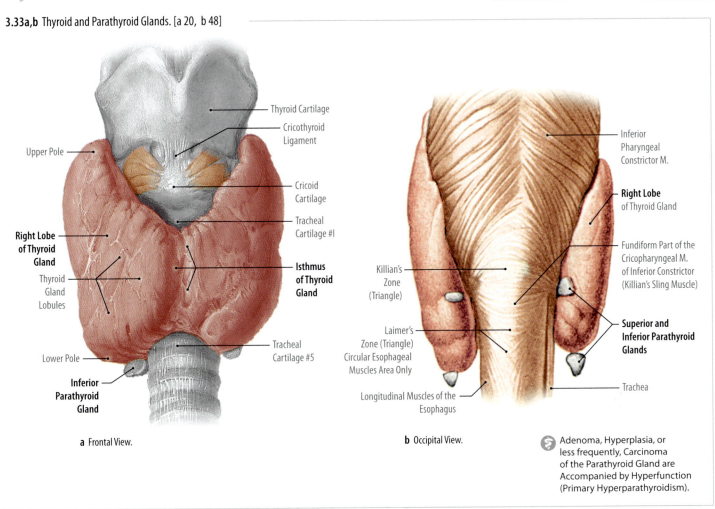

Thyroid Cartilage

Cricothyroid Ligament

Upper Pole

Cricoid Cartilage

Tracheal Cartilage #1

Right Lobe of Thyroid Gland

Isthmus of Thyroid Gland

Thyroid Gland Lobules

Lower Pole

Tracheal Cartilage #5

Inferior Parathyroid Gland

a Frontal View.

Inferior Pharyngeal Constrictor M.

Right Lobe of Thyroid Gland

Fundiform Part of the Cricopharyngeal M. of Inferior Constrictor (Killian's Sling Muscle)

Killian's Zone (Triangle)

Superior and Inferior Parathyroid Glands

Laimer's Zone (Triangle) Circular Esophageal Muscles Area Only

Longitudinal Muscles of the Esophagus

Trachea

b Occipital View.

Adenoma, Hyperplasia, or less frequently, Carcinoma of the Parathyroid Gland are Accompanied by Hyperfunction (Primary Hyperparathyroidism).

3.34 Scintigram: Anterior View. [49]

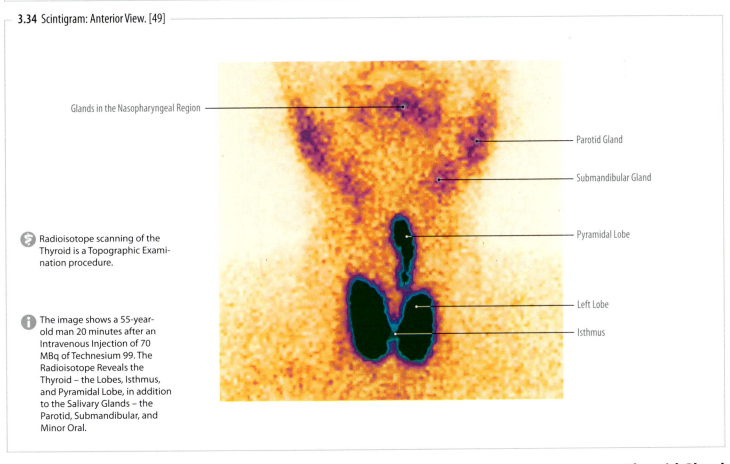

Glands in the Nasopharyngeal Region

Radioisotope scanning of the Thyroid is a Topographic Examination procedure.

The image shows a 55-year-old man 20 minutes after an Intravenous Injection of 70 MBq of Technesium 99. The Radioisotope Reveals the Thyroid – the Lobes, Isthmus, and Pyramidal Lobe, in addition to the Salivary Glands – the Parotid, Submandibular, and Minor Oral.

Parotid Gland

Submandibular Gland

Pyramidal Lobe

Left Lobe

Isthmus

Thyroid Gland: Pathways

3.35 Arteries of the Thyroid Gland: Frontal View. Branches on the Deep Side are Illustrated as Translucent. [20]

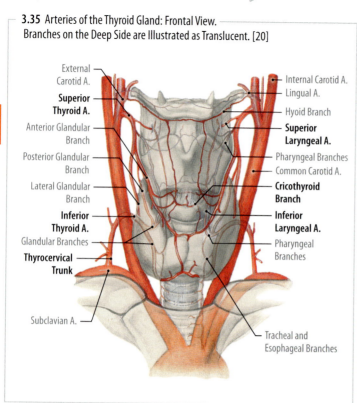

External Carotid A.
Superior Thyroid A.
Anterior Glandular Branch
Posterior Glandular Branch
Lateral Glandular Branch
Inferior Thyroid A.
Glandular Branches
Thyrocervical Trunk
Subclavian A.

Internal Carotid A.
Lingual A.
Hyoid Branch
Superior Laryngeal A.
Pharyngeal Branches
Common Carotid A.
Cricothyroid Branch
Inferior Laryngeal A.
Pharyngeal Branches
Tracheal and Esophageal Branches

3.36 Veins of the Thyroid Gland: Frontal View. Branches on the Deep Side are Illustrated as Translucent. [20]

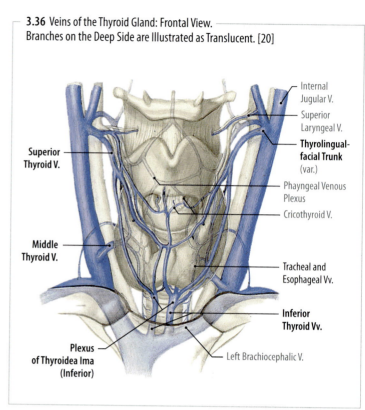

Superior Thyroid V.
Middle Thyroid V.
Plexus of Thyroidea Ima (Inferior)

Internal Jugular V.
Superior Laryngeal V.
Thyrolingual-facial Trunk (var.)
Phayngeal Venous Plexus
Cricothyroid V.
Tracheal and Esophageal Vv.
Inferior Thyroid Vv.
Left Brachiocephalic V.

3.37 Thyroid Gland and its Pathways: Frontal View. [20]

In Emergency Cricothyroidotomy, the best approach is Through the Cricothyroid Ligament and Membrane.
Tracheostomy can Utilize Either an Upper or Lower Approach. The Lower Approach necessitates Transaction of the Thyroid Isthmus and Anastomotic Superior Thyroid Vessels. This may Cause Aspiration of Blood—Bleeding should be Controlled.

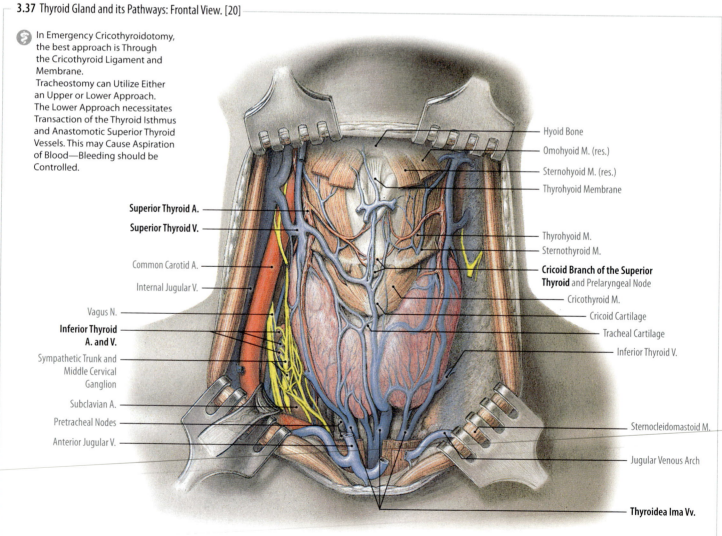

Superior Thyroid A.
Superior Thyroid V.
Common Carotid A.
Internal Jugular V.
Vagus N.
Inferior Thyroid A. and V.
Sympathetic Trunk and Middle Cervical Ganglion
Subclavian A.
Pretracheal Nodes
Anterior Jugular V.

Hyoid Bone
Omohyoid M. (res.)
Sternohyoid M. (res.)
Thyrohyoid Membrane
Thyrohyoid M.
Sternothyroid M.
Cricoid Branch of the Superior Thyroid and Prelaryngeal Node
Cricothyroid M.
Cricoid Cartilage
Tracheal Cartilage
Inferior Thyroid V.
Sternocleidomastoid M.
Jugular Venous Arch
Thyroidea Ima Vv.

Thyroid Gland: Topography · Sonogram

3.38 Transverse Section through the Neck at the Level of the Thyroid Gland: Cranial View. [20]

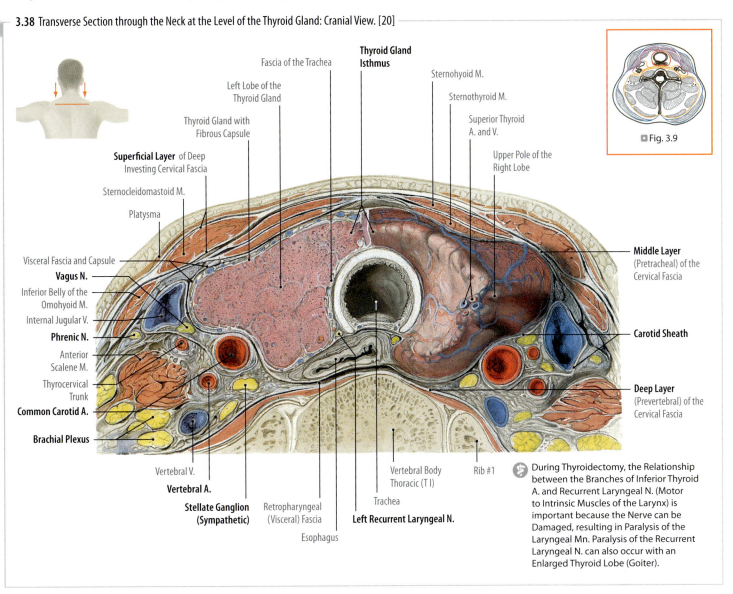

Fascia of the Trachea

Thyroid Gland Isthmus

Left Lobe of the Thyroid Gland

Sternohyoid M.

Sternothyroid M.

Thyroid Gland with Fibrous Capsule

Superior Thyroid A. and V.

Superficial Layer of Deep Investing Cervical Fascia

Upper Pole of the Right Lobe

Sternocleidomastoid M.

Platysma

Visceral Fascia and Capsule

Middle Layer (Pretracheal) of the Cervical Fascia

Vagus N.

Inferior Belly of the Omohyoid M.

Internal Jugular V.

Phrenic N.

Carotid Sheath

Anterior Scalene M.

Thyrocervical Trunk

Deep Layer (Prevertebral) of the Cervical Fascia

Common Carotid A.

Brachial Plexus

Vertebral V.

Vertebral A.

Stellate Ganglion (Sympathetic)

Retropharyngeal (Visceral) Fascia

Esophagus

Vertebral Body Thoracic (T I)

Trachea

Left Recurrent Laryngeal N.

Rib #1

☞ During Thyroidectomy, the Relationship between the Branches of Inferior Thyroid A. and Recurrent Laryngeal N. (Motor to Intrinsic Muscles of the Larynx) is important because the Nerve can be Damaged, resulting in Paralysis of the Laryngeal Mn. Paralysis of the Recurrent Laryngeal N. can also occur with an Enlarged Thyroid Lobe (Goiter).

☐ Fig. 3.9

3.39 Sonogram, Transversal Section at the Level of the Isthmus of the Thyroid Gland. [50]

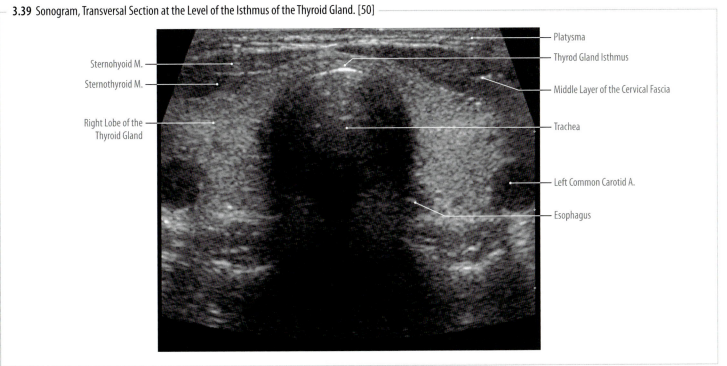

Sternohyoid M.

Sternothyroid M.

Right Lobe of the Thyroid Gland

Platysma

Thyrod Gland Isthmus

Middle Layer of the Cervical Fascia

Trachea

Left Common Carotid A.

Esophagus

Thyroid Gland

Laryngeal Skeleton

3.40a–d Laryngeal Skeleton (Cartilages and Articulations of the Larynx) and Hyoid Bone. [20]

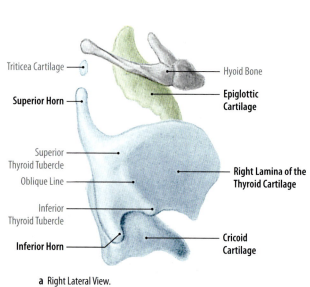

Triticea Cartilage
Hyoid Bone
Superior Horn
Epiglottic Cartilage
Superior Thyroid Tubercle
Oblique Line
Right Lamina of the Thyroid Cartilage
Inferior Thyroid Tubercle
Inferior Horn
Cricoid Cartilage

a Right Lateral View.

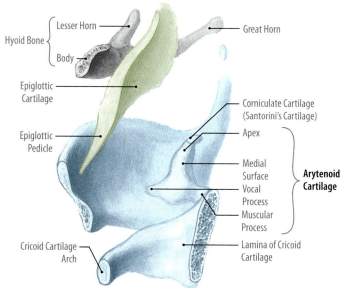

Hyoid Bone
Lesser Horn
Body
Great Horn
Epiglottic Cartilage
Epiglottic Pedicle
Cricoid Cartilage Arch
Corniculate Cartilage (Santorini's Cartilage)
Apex
Medial Surface
Vocal Process
Muscular Process
Arytenoid Cartilage
Lamina of Cricoid Cartilage

b Median Sagittal Section, Right Half of the Larynx, Interior View.

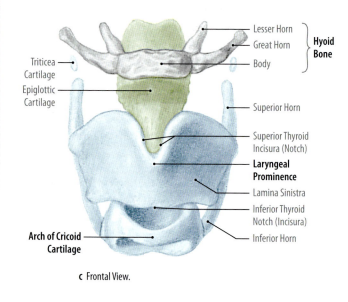

Triticea Cartilage
Epiglottic Cartilage
Lesser Horn
Great Horn
Body
Hyoid Bone
Superior Horn
Superior Thyroid Incisura (Notch)
Laryngeal Prominence
Lamina Sinistra
Inferior Thyroid Notch (Incisura)
Inferior Horn
Arch of Cricoid Cartilage

c Frontal View.

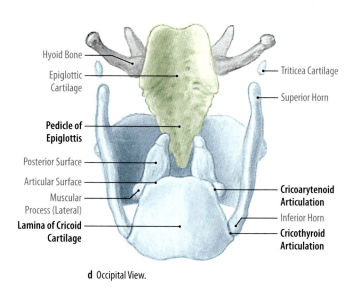

Hyoid Bone
Epiglottic Cartilage
Pedicle of Epiglottis
Posterior Surface
Articular Surface
Muscular Process (Lateral)
Lamina of Cricoid Cartilage
Triticea Cartilage
Superior Horn
Cricoarytenoid Articulation
Inferior Horn
Cricothyroid Articulation

d Occipital View.

3.41 Bony Laryngeal Skeleton of a 67-Year-Old Man: Occipital View. [6]

In 20- to 30-year-old patients, there is Increased Ossification of the Cartilage of the Skeleton of the Larynx due to Increased Mineralization. External Trauma may cause Fractures, resulting in Dystopia (Obstruction of Airway) and Edema requiring Tracheostomy.

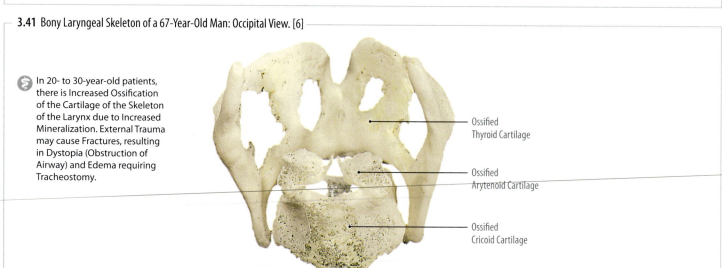

Ossified Thyroid Cartilage
Ossified Arytenoid Cartilage
Ossified Cricoid Cartilage

3.42a–d Joints and Ligament System of the Larynx. [20]

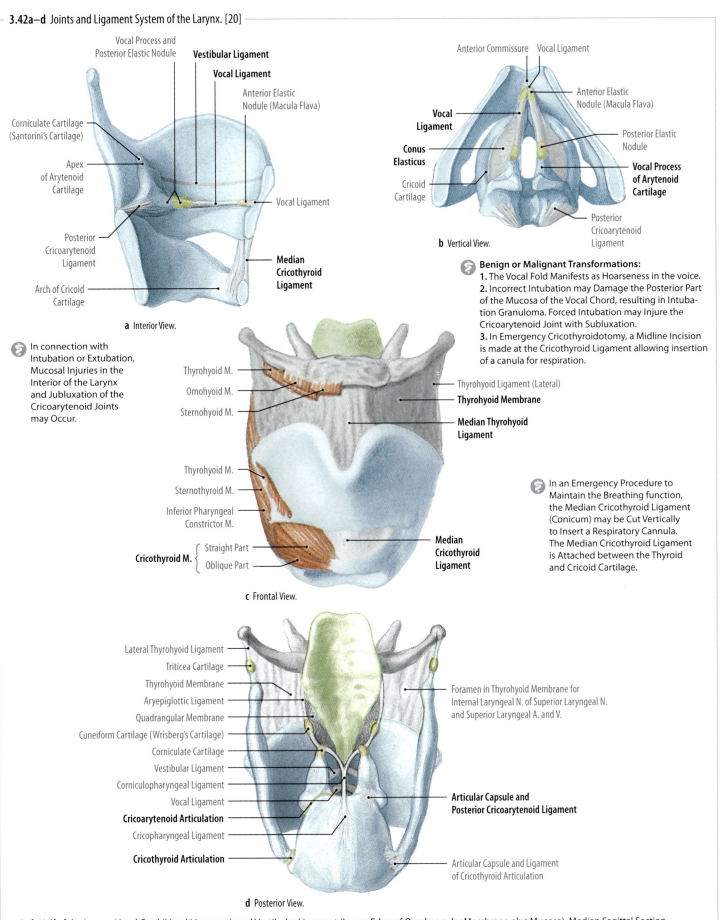

Vocal Process and
Posterior Elastic Nodule

Vestibular Ligament

Vocal Ligament

Anterior Elastic
Nodule (Macula Flava)

Corniculate Cartilage
(Santorini's Cartilage)

Apex
of Arytenoid
Cartilage

Vocal Ligament

Posterior
Cricoarytenoid
Ligament

Arch of Cricoid
Cartilage

**Median
Cricothyroid
Ligament**

a Interior View.

Anterior Commissure   Vocal Ligament

Anterior Elastic
Nodule (Macula Flava)

**Vocal
Ligament**

**Conus
Elasticus**

Cricoid
Cartilage

Posterior Elastic
Nodule

**Vocal Process
of Arytenoid
Cartilage**

Posterior
Cricoarytenoid
Ligament

b Vertical View.

Benign or Malignant Transformations:
1. The Vocal Fold Manifests as Hoarseness in the voice.
2. Incorrect Intubation may Damage the Posterior Part
of the Mucosa of the Vocal Chord, resulting in Intubation Granuloma. Forced Intubation may Injure the
Cricoarytenoid Joint with Subluxation.
3. In Emergency Cricothyroidotomy, a Midline Incision
is made at the Cricothyroid Ligament allowing insertion
of a canula for respiration.

In connection with
Intubation or Extubation,
Mucosal Injuries in the
Interior of the Larynx
and Jubluxation of the
Cricoarytenoid Joints
may Occur.

Thyrohyoid M.

Omohyoid M.

Sternohyoid M.

Thyrohyoid Ligament (Lateral)

Thyrohyoid Membrane

**Median Thyrohyoid
Ligament**

Thyrohyoid M.

Sternothyroid M.

Inferior Pharyngeal
Constrictor M.

Cricothyroid M. { Straight Part / Oblique Part

**Median
Cricothyroid
Ligament**

In an Emergency Procedure to
Maintain the Breathing function,
the Median Cricothyroid Ligament
(Conicum) may be Cut Vertically
to Insert a Respiratory Cannula.
The Median Cricothyroid Ligament
is Attached between the Thyroid
and Cricoid Cartilage.

c Frontal View.

Lateral Thyrohyoid Ligament

Triticea Cartilage

Thyrohyoid Membrane

Aryepiglottic Ligament

Quadrangular Membrane

Cuneiform Cartilage (Wrisberg's Cartilage)

Corniculate Cartilage

Vestibular Ligament

Corniculopharyngeal Ligament

Vocal Ligament

Cricoarytenoid Articulation

Cricopharyngeal Ligament

Cricothyroid Articulation

Foramen in Thyrohyoid Membrane for
Internal Laryngeal N. of Superior Laryngeal N.
and Superior Laryngeal A. and V.

**Articular Capsule and
Posterior Cricoarytenoid Ligament**

Articular Capsule and Ligament
of Cricothyroid Articulation

d Posterior View.

a Left Half of the Larynx, Vocal Cord (Vocal Ligament), and Vestibular Ligament (Lower Edge of Quadrangular Membrane plus Mucosa), Median Sagittal Section.
b Vocal Ligament (Upper Edge of the Conus Elasticus plus Mucosa) and Conus Elasticus.
c The Cricothyroid M. is illustrated for the Right Side of the body.

Laryngeal Muscles

3.43a–d Laryngeal Muscles. [b 6, a c d 20]

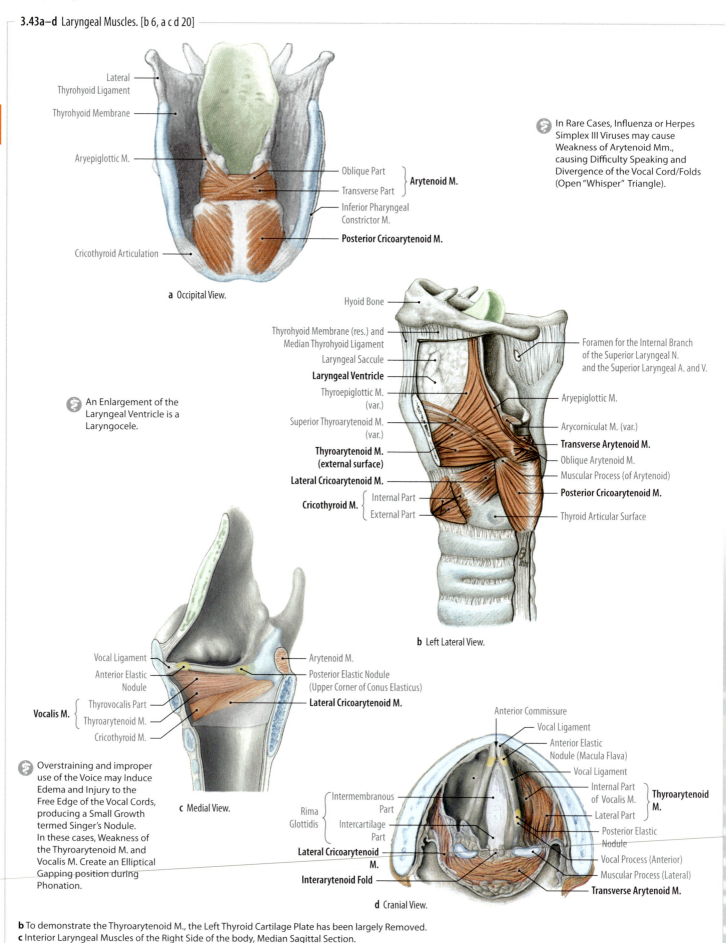

Lateral Thyrohyoid Ligament

Thyrohyoid Membrane

3

Aryepiglottic M.

Cricothyroid Articulation

Oblique Part
Transverse Part **Arytenoid M.**

Inferior Pharyngeal Constrictor M.

Posterior Cricoarytenoid M.

a Occipital View.

In Rare Cases, Influenza or Herpes Simplex III Viruses may cause Weakness of Arytenoid Mm., causing Difficulty Speaking and Divergence of the Vocal Cord/Folds (Open "Whisper" Triangle).

Hyoid Bone

Thyrohyoid Membrane (res.) and Median Thyrohyoid Ligament

Laryngeal Saccule

Laryngeal Ventricle

Thyroepiglottic M. (var.)

Superior Thyroarytenoid M. (var.)

Thyroarytenoid M. (external surface)

Lateral Cricoarytenoid M.

Cricothyroid M. { Internal Part
External Part

Foramen for the Internal Branch of the Superior Laryngeal N. and the Superior Laryngeal A. and V.

Aryepiglottic M.

Arycorniculat M. (var.)

Transverse Arytenoid M.

Oblique Arytenoid M.

Muscular Process (of Arytenoid)

Posterior Cricoarytenoid M.

Thyroid Articular Surface

An Enlargement of the Laryngeal Ventricle is a Laryngocele.

b Left Lateral View.

Vocal Ligament

Anterior Elastic Nodule

Vocalis M. { Thyrovocalis Part
Thyroarytenoid M.
Cricothyroid M.

Arytenoid M.

Posterior Elastic Nodule (Upper Corner of Conus Elasticus)

Lateral Cricoarytenoid M.

Overstraining and improper use of the Voice may Induce Edema and Injury to the Free Edge of the Vocal Cords, producing a Small Growth termed Singer's Nodule. In these cases, Weakness of the Thyroarytenoid M. and Vocalis M. Create an Elliptical Gapping position during Phonation.

c Medial View.

Rima Glottidis {

Intermembranous Part

Intercartilage Part

Lateral Cricoarytenoid M.

Interarytenoid Fold

Anterior Commissure

Vocal Ligament

Anterior Elastic Nodule (Macula Flava)

Vocal Ligament

Internal Part of Vocalis M.

Lateral Part

Thyroarytenoid M.

Posterior Elastic Nodule

Vocal Process (Anterior)

Muscular Process (Lateral)

Transverse Arytenoid M.

d Cranial View.

b To demonstrate the Thyroarytenoid M., the Left Thyroid Cartilage Plate has been largely Removed.
c Interior Laryngeal Muscles of the Right Side of the body, Median Sagittal Section.
d Horizontal Section through the Larynx above the Vocal Folds. On the Left Side of the body, the Thyroarytenoid M. has been Removed.

Function, Histology, Layers of the Larynx

3.44 Schematic Illustration of the Effect of the Transverse Arytenoid Mm. (Adductor), Lateral Cricoarytenoid (Adductor), and Posterior Cricoarytenoid (Abductor) on the Rima Glottidis. [31]

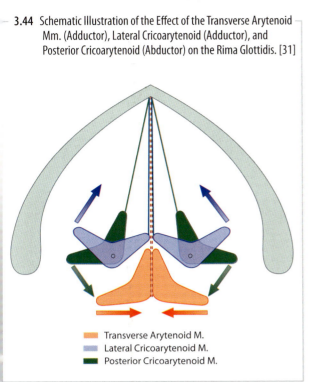

- ■ Transverse Arytenoid M.
- ■ Lateral Cricoarytenoid M.
- ■ Posterior Cricoarytenoid M.

3.45 Histology of Frontal Section through the Larynx of a 29-Year-Old Man. [81]

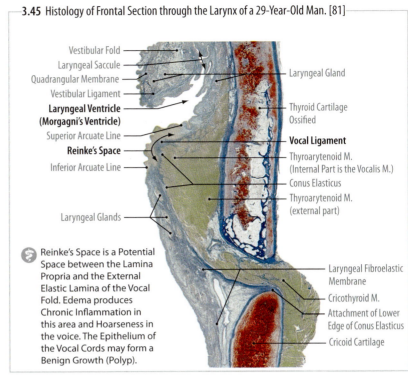

Vestibular Fold
Laryngeal Saccule
Quadrangular Membrane
Vestibular Ligament
Laryngeal Ventricle (Morgagni's Ventricle)
Superior Arcuate Line
Reinke's Space
Inferior Arcuate Line
Laryngeal Glands

Laryngeal Gland
Thyroid Cartilage Ossified
Vocal Ligament
Thyroarytenoid M. (Internal Part is the Vocalis M.)
Conus Elasticus
Thyroarytenoid M. (external part)
Laryngeal Fibroelastic Membrane
Cricothyroid M.
Attachment of Lower Edge of Conus Elasticus
Cricoid Cartilage

Reinke's Space is a Potential Space between the Lamina Propria and the External Elastic Lamina of the Vocal Fold. Edema produces Chronic Inflammation in this area and Hoarseness in the voice. The Epithelium of the Vocal Cords may form a Benign Growth (Polyp).

3.46a,b Magnifying Endoscopic Pictures of the Larynx, 90° Optics. [24]

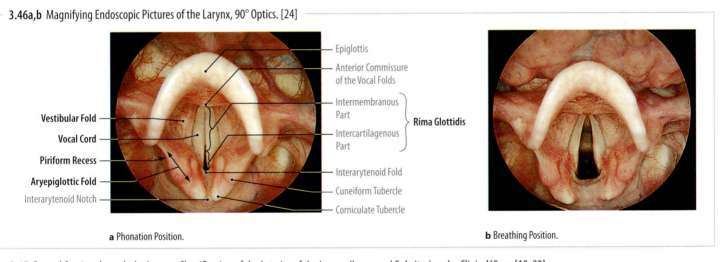

Vestibular Fold
Vocal Cord
Piriform Recess
Aryepiglottic Fold
Interarytenoid Notch

Epiglottis
Anterior Commissure of the Vocal Folds
Intermembranous Part
Intercartilagenous Part
} Rima Glottidis
Interarytenoid Fold
Cuneiform Tubercle
Corniculate Tubercle

a Phonation Position.   **b** Breathing Position.

3.47 Frontal Section through the Larynx. Classification of the Interior of the Larynx (Laryngeal Subsites) under Clinical View. [18, 20]

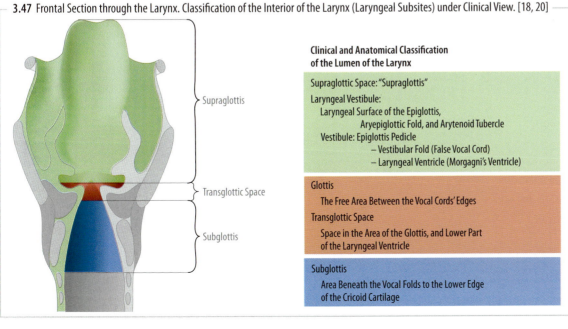

Supraglottis
Transglottic Space
Subglottis

Clinical and Anatomical Classification of the Lumen of the Larynx

Supraglottic Space: "Supraglottis"
Laryngeal Vestibule:
Laryngeal Surface of the Epiglottis, Aryepiglottic Fold, and Arytenoid Tubercle
Vestibule: Epiglottis Pedicle
— Vestibular Fold (False Vocal Cord)
— Laryngeal Ventricle (Morgagni's Ventricle)

Glottis
The Free Area Between the Vocal Cords' Edges
Transglottic Space
Space in the Area of the Glottis, and Lower Part of the Laryngeal Ventricle

Subglottis
Area Beneath the Vocal Folds to the Lower Edge of the Cricoid Cartilage

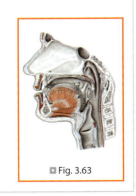

⬚ Fig. 3.63

Larynx

Larynx: Pathways

3.48 Arterial Supply (Right Side of the Body) and Nerve Supply (Left Side of the Body) of the Larynx: Frontal View. [20]

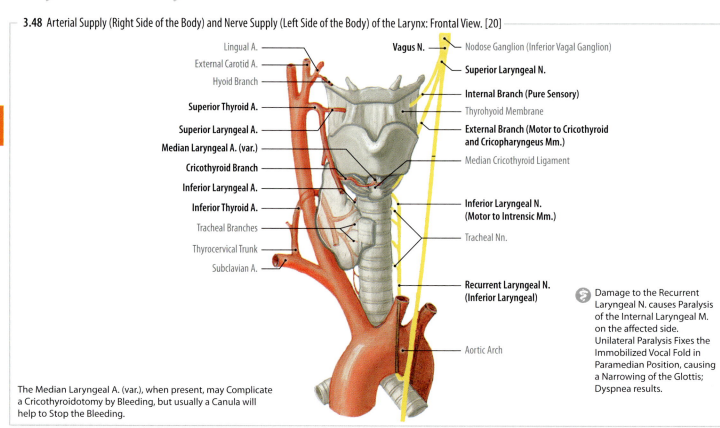

Lingual A.
External Carotid A.
Hyoid Branch
Superior Thyroid A.
Superior Laryngeal A.
Median Laryngeal A. (var.)
Cricothyroid Branch
Inferior Laryngeal A.
Inferior Thyroid A.
Tracheal Branches
Thyrocervical Trunk
Subclavian A.

Vagus N.
Nodose Ganglion (Inferior Vagal Ganglion)
Superior Laryngeal N.
Internal Branch (Pure Sensory)
Thyrohyoid Membrane
External Branch (Motor to Cricothyroid and Cricopharyngeus Mm.)
Median Cricothyroid Ligament
Inferior Laryngeal N. (Motor to Intrensic Mm.)
Tracheal Nn.
Recurrent Laryngeal N. (Inferior Laryngeal)
Aortic Arch

Damage to the Recurrent Laryngeal N. causes Paralysis of the Internal Laryngeal M. on the affected side. Unilateral Paralysis Fixes the Immobilized Vocal Fold in Paramedian Position, causing a Narrowing of the Glottis; Dyspnea results.

The Median Laryngeal A. (var.), when present, may Complicate a Cricothyroidotomy by Bleeding, but usually a Canula will help to Stop the Bleeding.

3.49 Anterior Cervical Region, Pathways of the Larynx and Thyroid Gland: Frontal View. [20]

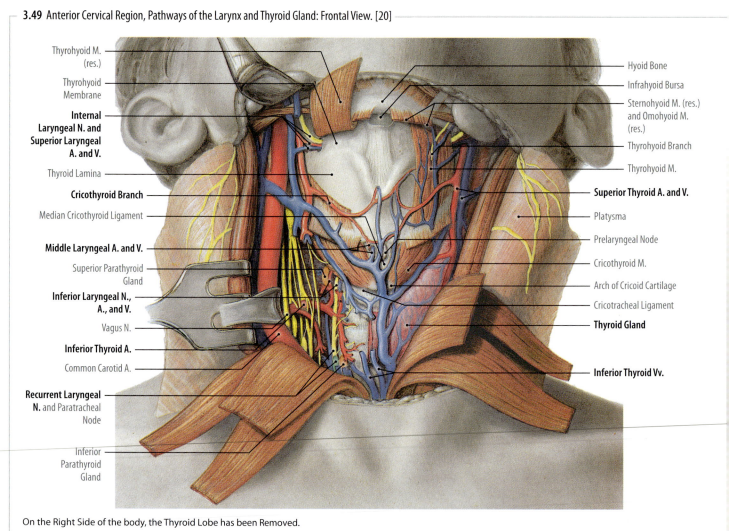

Thyrohyoid M. (res.)
Thyrohyoid Membrane
Internal Laryngeal N. and Superior Laryngeal A. and V.
Thyroid Lamina
Cricothyroid Branch
Median Cricothyroid Ligament
Middle Laryngeal A. and V.
Superior Parathyroid Gland
Inferior Laryngeal N., A., and V.
Vagus N.
Inferior Thyroid A.
Common Carotid A.
Recurrent Laryngeal N. and Paratracheal Node
Inferior Parathyroid Gland

Hyoid Bone
Infrahyoid Bursa
Sternohyoid M. (res.) and Omohyoid M. (res.)
Thyrohyoid Branch
Thyrohyoid M.
Superior Thyroid A. and V.
Platysma
Prelaryngeal Node
Cricothyroid M.
Arch of Cricoid Cartilage
Cricotracheal Ligament
Thyroid Gland
Inferior Thyroid Vv.

On the Right Side of the body, the Thyroid Lobe has been Removed.

3.50 Blood and Nerve Supply of the Larynx, Pharynx, and Thyroid Gland: Occipital View. [20]

ℹ️ The Right Recurrent Laryngeal N. Loops around the Right Subclavian A. The Left Recurrent Laryngeal N. Loops around the Arch of the Aorta and Ligamentum Arteriosum in the Thoracic Cavity.

The Superior Parathyroid Gland is commonly present in its Normal Position Above the Inferior Thyroid Artery on the Posterior Edge of the Thyroid Gland and Close to the Recurrent Laryngeal N. The Inferior Parathyroid is more Likely to Vary in its Position Below the Inferior Thyroid Artery to the Superior Mediastinum.

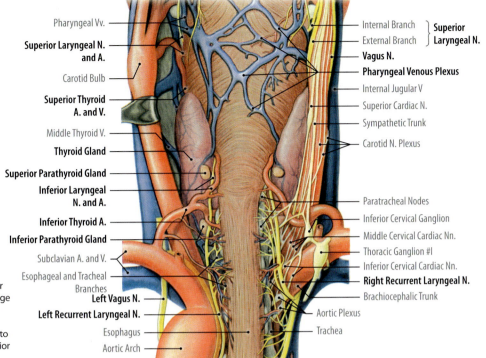

Pharyngeal Vv.
Superior Laryngeal N. and A.
Carotid Bulb
Superior Thyroid A. and V.
Middle Thyroid V.
Thyroid Gland
Superior Parathyroid Gland
Inferior Laryngeal N. and A.
Inferior Thyroid A.
Inferior Parathyroid Gland
Subclavian A. and V.
Esophageal and Tracheal Branches
Left Vagus N.
Left Recurrent Laryngeal N.
Esophagus
Aortic Arch

Internal Branch } Superior
External Branch } Laryngeal N.
Vagus N.
Pharyngeal Venous Plexus
Internal Jugular V
Superior Cardiac N.
Sympathetic Trunk
Carotid N. Plexus
Paratracheal Nodes
Inferior Cervical Ganglion
Middle Cervical Cardiac Nn.
Thoracic Ganglion #I
Inferior Cervical Cardiac Nn.
Right Recurrent Laryngeal N.
Brachiocephalic Trunk
Aortic Plexus
Trachea

3.51 Root of the Tongue and Larynx: Occipital View. [20]

ⓢ The Superior Laryngeal N. has Two Branches:
1. Internal Laryngeal N. – Purely Sensory above the Vocal Cord
2. External Laryngeal N.– Motor to the Cricothyroid M. and Cricopharyngeus M.

ⓢ Lingual Branches carry General Sensation (pain, temperature, touch, and pressure) to the Posterior One Third of the Tongue in addition to the Special Sensation of Taste.

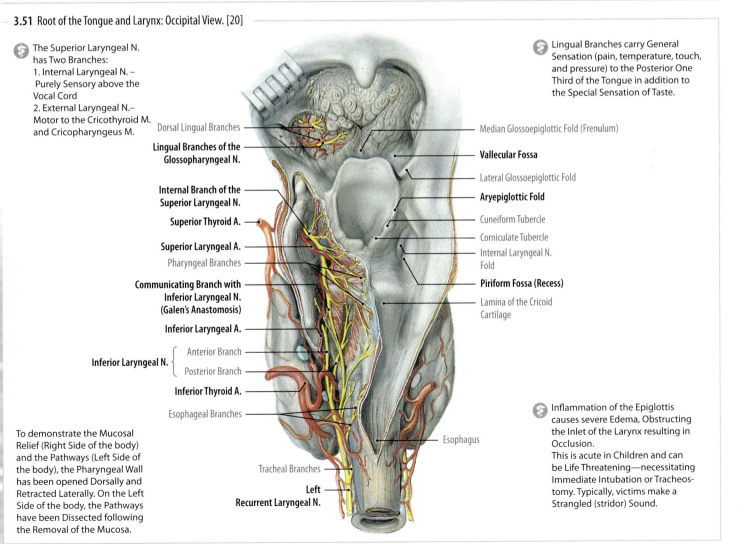

Dorsal Lingual Branches
Lingual Branches of the Glossopharyngeal N.
Internal Branch of the Superior Laryngeal N.
Superior Thyroid A.
Superior Laryngeal A.
Pharyngeal Branches
Communicating Branch with Inferior Laryngeal N. (Galen's Anastomosis)
Inferior Laryngeal A.
Inferior Laryngeal N. { Anterior Branch / Posterior Branch }
Inferior Thyroid A.
Esophageal Branches
Tracheal Branches
Left Recurrent Laryngeal N.

Median Glossoepiglottic Fold (Frenulum)
Vallecular Fossa
Lateral Glossoepiglottic Fold
Aryepiglottic Fold
Cuneiform Tubercle
Corniculate Tubercle
Internal Laryngeal N. Fold
Piriform Fossa (Recess)
Lamina of the Cricoid Cartilage
Esophagus

ⓢ Inflammation of the Epiglottis causes severe Edema, Obstructing the Inlet of the Larynx resulting in Occlusion.
This is acute in Children and can be Life Threatening—necessitating Immediate Intubation or Tracheostomy. Typically, victims make a Strangled (stridor) Sound.

To demonstrate the Mucosal Relief (Right Side of the body) and the Pathways (Left Side of the body), the Pharyngeal Wall has been opened Dorsally and Retracted Laterally. On the Left Side of the body, the Pathways have been Dissected following the Removal of the Mucosa.

Muscles of the Pharynx

3.52 Pharyngeal Muscles: Occipital View. [48]

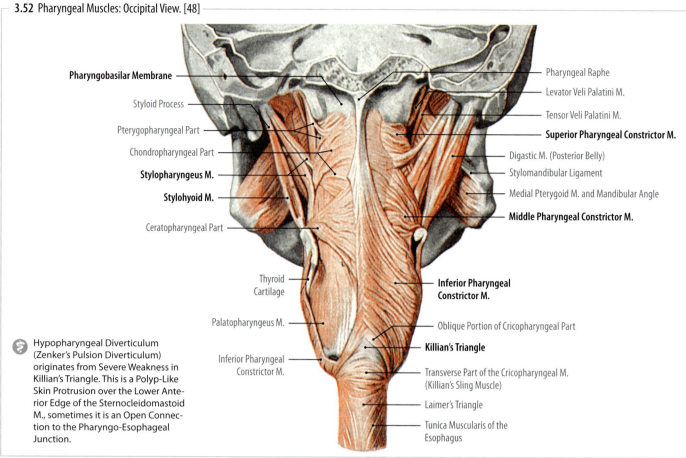

- Pharyngobasilar Membrane
- Styloid Process
- Pterygopharyngeal Part
- Chondropharyngeal Part
- **Stylopharyngeus M.**
- **Stylohyoid M.**
- Ceratopharyngeal Part
- Thyroid Cartilage
- Palatopharyngeus M.
- Inferior Pharyngeal Constrictor M.
- Pharyngeal Raphe
- Levator Veli Palatini M.
- Tensor Veli Palatini M.
- **Superior Pharyngeal Constrictor M.**
- Digastic M. (Posterior Belly)
- Stylomandibular Ligament
- Medial Pterygoid M. and Mandibular Angle
- **Middle Pharyngeal Constrictor M.**
- **Inferior Pharyngeal Constrictor M.**
- Oblique Portion of Cricopharyngeal Part
- **Killian's Triangle**
- Transverse Part of the Cricopharyngeal M. (Killian's Sling Muscle)
- Laimer's Triangle
- Tunica Muscularis of the Esophagus

Hypopharyngeal Diverticulum (Zenker's Pulsion Diverticulum) originates from Severe Weakness in Killian's Triangle. This is a Polyp-Like Skin Protrusion over the Lower Anterior Edge of the Sternocleidomastoid M., sometimes it is an Open Connection to the Pharyngo-Esophageal Junction.

3.53 a Pharyngeal Muscles of the Left Side [18]. **b** Insertions of the Constrictor of Isthmus of Fauces and Pharyngeal Mm.

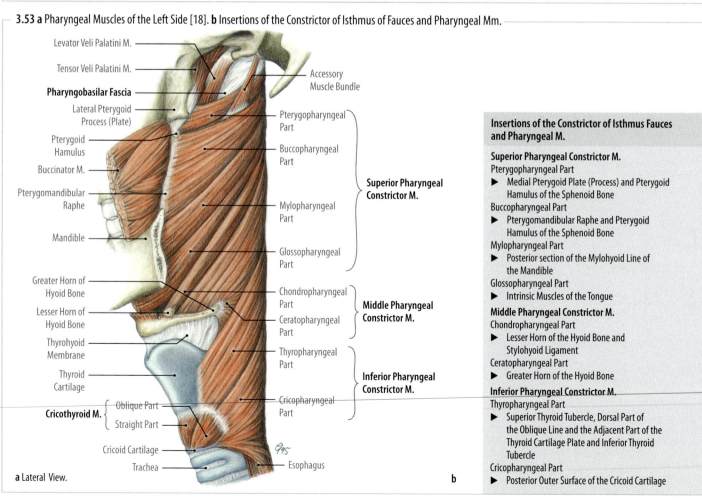

- Levator Veli Palatini M.
- Tensor Veli Palatini M.
- **Pharyngobasilar Fascia**
- Lateral Pterygoid Process (Plate)
- Pterygoid Hamulus
- Buccinator M.
- Pterygomandibular Raphe
- Mandible
- Greater Horn of Hyoid Bone
- Lesser Horn of Hyoid Bone
- Thyrohyoid Membrane
- Thyroid Cartilage
- **Cricothyroid M.** { Oblique Part / Straight Part }
- Cricoid Cartilage
- Trachea
- Accessory Muscle Bundle
- Pterygopharyngeal Part
- Buccopharyngeal Part
- Mylopharyngeal Part
- Glossopharyngeal Part
- Chondropharyngeal Part
- Ceratopharyngeal Part
- Thyropharyngeal Part
- Cricopharyngeal Part
- Esophagus
- **Superior Pharyngeal Constrictor M.**
- **Middle Pharyngeal Constrictor M.**
- **Inferior Pharyngeal Constrictor M.**

a Lateral View.

b

Insertions of the Constrictor of Isthmus Fauces and Pharyngeal M.

Superior Pharyngeal Constrictor M.
Pterygopharyngeal Part
► Medial Pterygoid Plate (Process) and Pterygoid Hamulus of the Sphenoid Bone
Buccopharyngeal Part
► Pterygomandibular Raphe and Pterygoid Hamulus of the Sphenoid Bone
Mylopharyngeal Part
► Posterior section of the Mylohyoid Line of the Mandible
Glossopharyngeal Part
► Intrinsic Muscles of the Tongue

Middle Pharyngeal Constrictor M.
Chondropharyngeal Part
► Lesser Horn of the Hyoid Bone and Stylohyoid Ligament
Ceratopharyngeal Part
► Greater Horn of the Hyoid Bone

Inferior Pharyngeal Constrictor M.
Thyropharyngeal Part
► Superior Thyroid Tubercle, Dorsal Part of the Oblique Line and the Adjacent Part of the Thyroid Cartilage Plate and Inferior Thyroid Tubercle
Cricopharyngeal Part
► Posterior Outer Surface of the Cricoid Cartilage

3.54 Pharynx: Occipital View. [18]

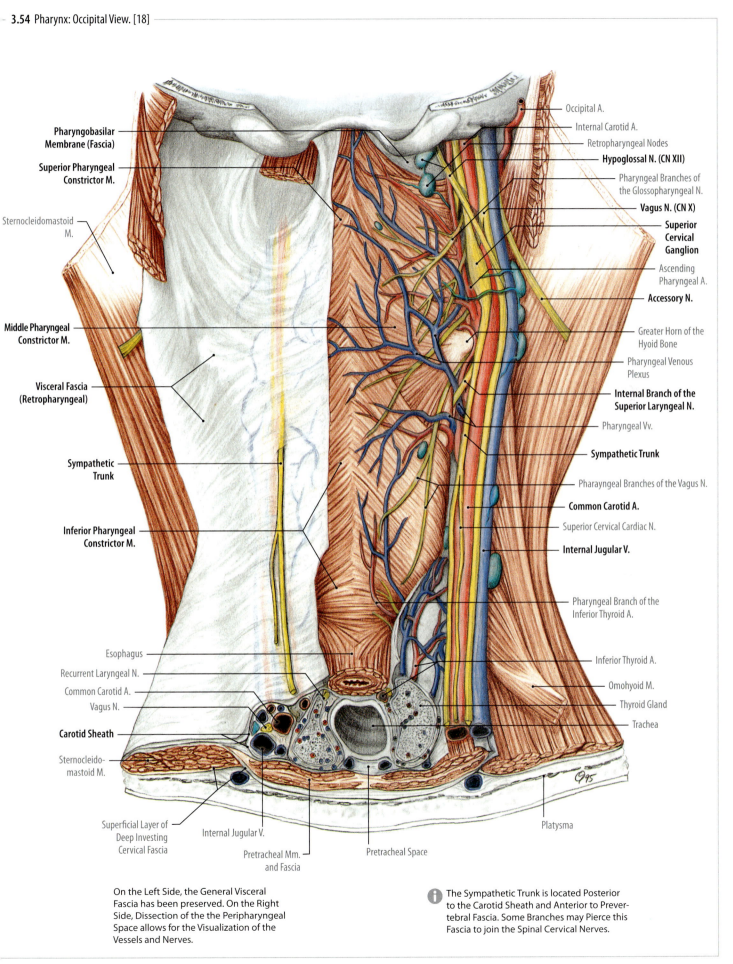

Pharyngobasilar Membrane (Fascia)

Superior Pharyngeal Constrictor M.

Sternocleidomastoid M.

Middle Pharyngeal Constrictor M.

Visceral Fascia (Retropharyngeal)

Sympathetic Trunk

Inferior Pharyngeal Constrictor M.

Esophagus

Recurrent Laryngeal N.

Common Carotid A.

Vagus N.

Carotid Sheath

Sternocleido-mastoid M.

Superficial Layer of Deep Investing Cervical Fascia

Internal Jugular V.

Pretracheal Mm. and Fascia

Pretracheal Space

Occipital A.

Internal Carotid A.

Retropharyngeal Nodes

Hypoglossal N. (CN XII)

Pharyngeal Branches of the Glossopharyngeal N.

Vagus N. (CN X)

Superior Cervical Ganglion

Ascending Pharyngeal A.

Accessory N.

Greater Horn of the Hyoid Bone

Pharyngeal Venous Plexus

Internal Branch of the Superior Laryngeal N.

Pharyngeal Vv.

Sympathetic Trunk

Pharayngeal Branches of the Vagus N.

Common Carotid A.

Superior Cervical Cardiac N.

Internal Jugular V.

Pharyngeal Branch of the Inferior Thyroid A.

Inferior Thyroid A.

Omohyoid M.

Thyroid Gland

Trachea

Platysma

On the Left Side, the General Visceral Fascia has been preserved. On the Right Side, Dissection of the the Peripharyngeal Space allows for the Visualization of the Vessels and Nerves.

ⓘ The Sympathetic Trunk is located Posterior to the Carotid Sheath and Anterior to Prevertebral Fascia. Some Branches may Pierce this Fascia to join the Spinal Cervical Nerves.

Pharynx

3.55 Partial View of the Pharyngeal Wall: Right Side, Occipital View. [18]

Notice the Crossing of the CN XII over the Vagus N. Medially to Laterally, Sheathed Together by the Fascia, which may cause Confusion in a Dissection. The Vagus N. runs Posterior to the Carotid Artery and the Hypoglossal N. Lateral to the Arteries.

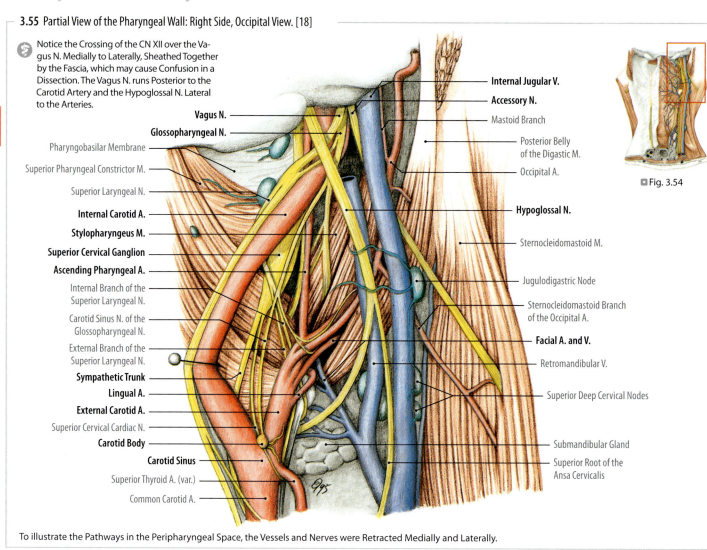

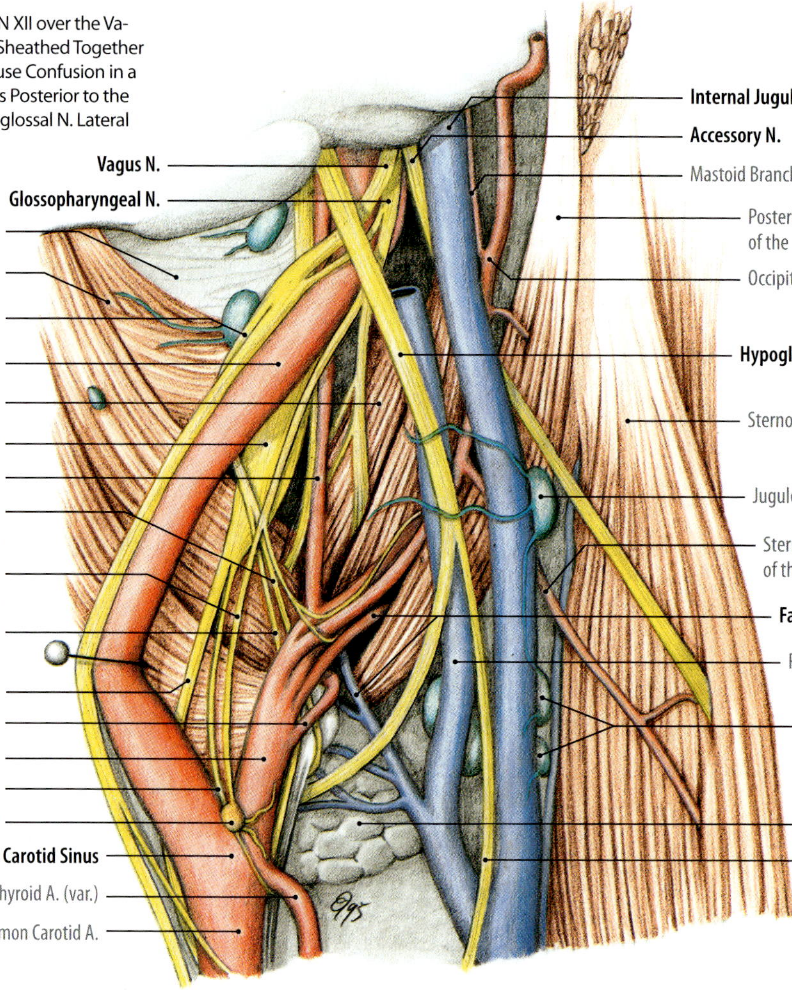
Vagus N.
Glossopharyngeal N.
Pharyngobasilar Membrane
Superior Pharyngeal Constrictor M.
Superior Laryngeal N.
Internal Carotid A.
Stylopharyngeus M.
Superior Cervical Ganglion
Ascending Pharyngeal A.
Internal Branch of the Superior Laryngeal N.
Carotid Sinus N. of the Glossopharyngeal N.
External Branch of the Superior Laryngeal N.
Sympathetic Trunk
Lingual A.
External Carotid A.
Superior Cervical Cardiac N.
Carotid Body
Carotid Sinus
Superior Thyroid A. (var.)
Common Carotid A.
Internal Jugular V.
Accessory N.
Mastoid Branch
Posterior Belly of the Digastic M.
Occipital A.
Hypoglossal N.
Sternocleidomastoid M.
Jugulodigastric Node
Sternocleidomastoid Branch of the Occipital A.
Facial A. and V.
Retromandibular V.
Superior Deep Cervical Nodes
Submandibular Gland
Superior Root of the Ansa Cervicalis

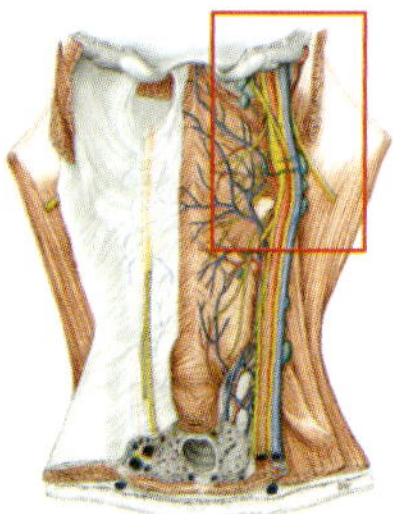

Fig. 3.54

To illustrate the Pathways in the Peripharyngeal Space, the Vessels and Nerves were Retracted Medially and Laterally.

3.56 Sinus-Shaped Formation of the Cervical Part of the Internal Carotid A. on the Posterolateral Pharyngeal Wall (called Dangerous Carotid Sling - ~7% of cases). [6]

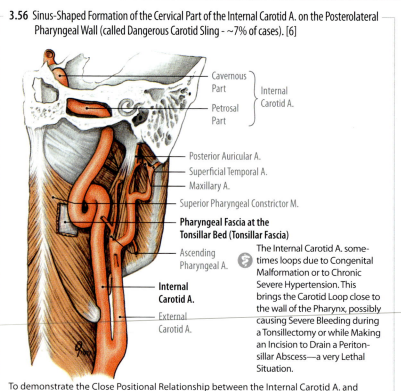

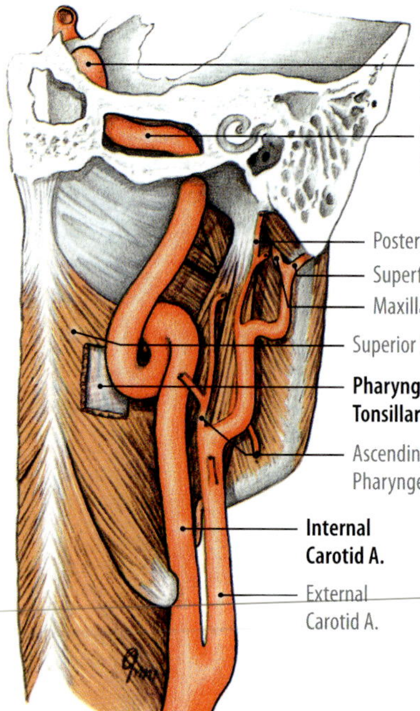
Cavernous Part
Petrosal Part
Internal Carotid A.
Posterior Auricular A.
Superficial Temporal A.
Maxillary A.
Superior Pharyngeal Constrictor M.
Pharyngeal Fascia at the Tonsillar Bed (Tonsillar Fascia)
Ascending Pharyngeal A.
Internal Carotid A.
External Carotid A.

The Internal Carotid A. sometimes loops due to Congenital Malformation or to Chronic Severe Hypertension. This brings the Carotid Loop close to the wall of the Pharynx, possibly causing Severe Bleeding during a Tonsillectomy or while Making an Incision to Drain a Peritonsillar Abscess—a very Lethal Situation.

To demonstrate the Close Positional Relationship between the Internal Carotid A. and the Tonsillar Bed, the Pharyngeal Muscles have been Fenestrated in this area.

3.57a,b Ascending Pharyngeal A.: Variants. [51]

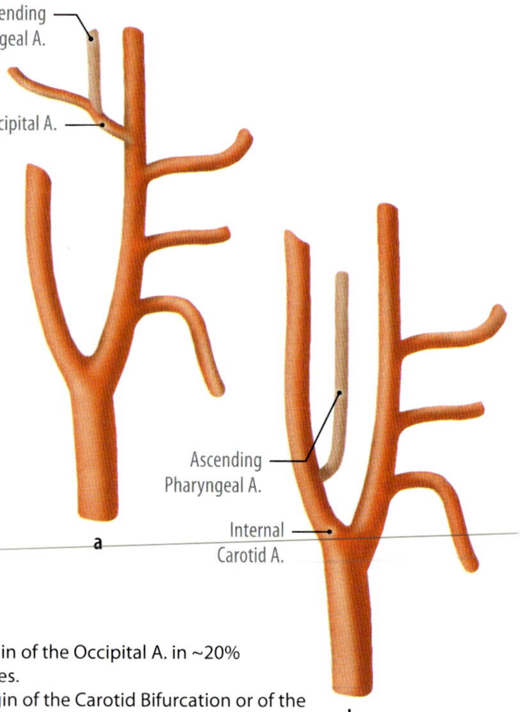
Ascending Pharyngeal A.
Occipital A.
a
Ascending Pharyngeal A.
Internal Carotid A.
b

a Origin of the Occipital A. in ~20% of cases.
b Origin of the Carotid Bifurcation or of the Internal Carotid A. in ~10% of cases.

3.58 Mucosal Surface of the Pharynx and the Inlet to the Larynx: Occipital View. [48]

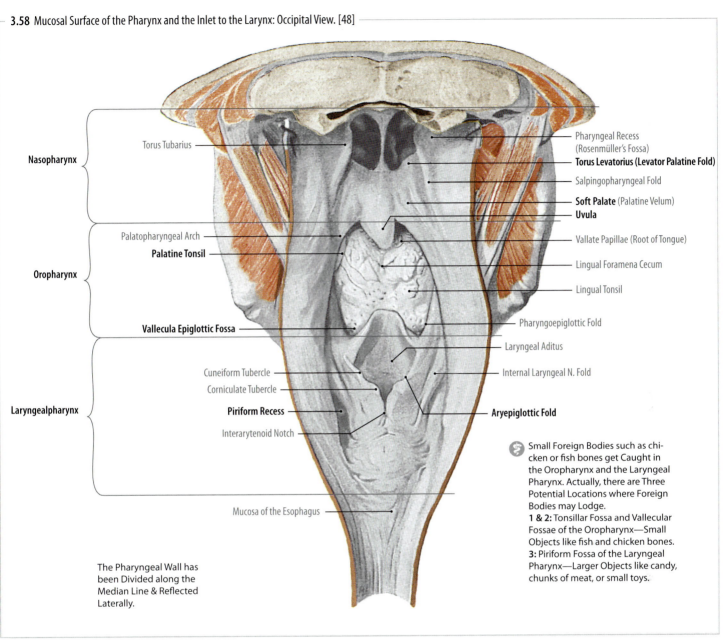

Nasopharynx

Torus Tubarius

Pharyngeal Recess
(Rosenmüller's Fossa)

Torus Levatorius (Levator Palatine Fold)

Salpingopharyngeal Fold

Soft Palate (Palatine Velum)

Uvula

Oropharynx

Palatopharyngeal Arch

Palatine Tonsil

Vallate Papillae (Root of Tongue)

Lingual Foramena Cecum

Lingual Tonsil

Vallecula Epiglottic Fossa

Pharyngoepiglottic Fold

Laryngeal Aditus

Cuneiform Tubercle

Corniculate Tubercle

Piriform Recess

Interarytenoid Notch

Internal Laryngeal N. Fold

Aryepiglottic Fold

Laryngealpharynx

Mucosa of the Esophagus

The Pharyngeal Wall has been Divided along the Median Line & Reflected Laterally.

Small Foreign Bodies such as chicken or fish bones get Caught in the Oropharynx and the Laryngeal Pharynx. Actually, there are Three Potential Locations where Foreign Bodies may Lodge.
1 & 2: Tonsillar Fossa and Vallecular Fossae of the Oropharynx—Small Objects like fish and chicken bones.
3: Piriform Fossa of the Laryngeal Pharynx—Larger Objects like candy, chunks of meat, or small toys.

3.59 Mirror Image of the Nasopharynx. [24]

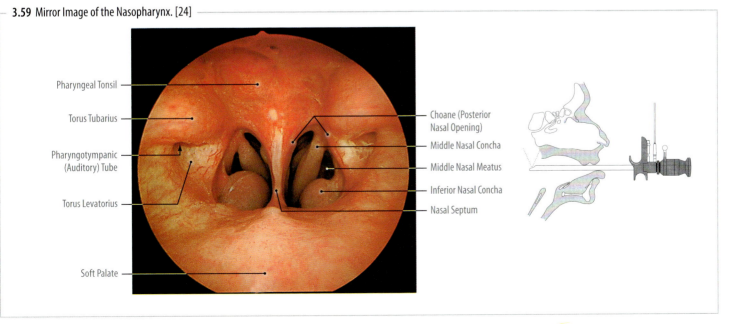

Pharyngeal Tonsil

Torus Tubarius

Pharyngotympanic (Auditory) Tube

Torus Levatorius

Soft Palate

Choane (Posterior Nasal Opening)

Middle Nasal Concha

Middle Nasal Meatus

Inferior Nasal Concha

Nasal Septum

Pharynx

3.60 Muscles of the Soft Palate in Their Relation to the Auditory Tube (Eustachian Tube): Inferior View. [18]

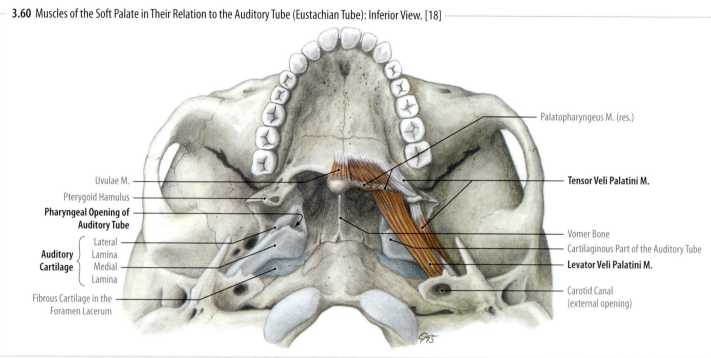

Palatopharyngeus M. (res.)

Uvulae M.

Pterygoid Hamulus

Tensor Veli Palatini M.

Pharyngeal Opening of Auditory Tube

Auditory Cartilage { Lateral Lamina / Medial Lamina }

Vomer Bone

Cartilaginous Part of the Auditory Tube

Levator Veli Palatini M.

Fibrous Cartilage in the Foramen Lacerum

Carotid Canal (external opening)

3.61 Muscles of the Soft Palate in Their Relation to the Auditory Tube: Occipital View. [18]

The Tensor Veli Palatini opens the Auditory Tube by Flattening and Tightening the Soft Palate. This results in a Depression of the Membranous Part of the Auditory Tube, allowing Air to Enter into the Middle Ear. Closure of the Auditory Tube Traps Air in the Middle Ear. This causes Oxygen to be Absorbed by the Tissue of the Mucous Membrane. The Pressure in the Middle Ear is then Lowered, Stimulating the Mucosa to Secrete large amounts of Serous Fluid (Serous Otitis Media).

On the Right Side, the Levator Veli Palatini and Salpingopharyngeus Mm., as well as the Palatoglossus and Palatopharyngeus Mm. have been Resected.

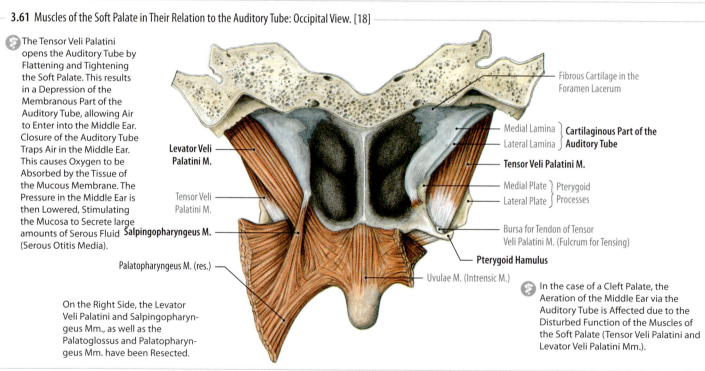

Fibrous Cartilage in the Foramen Lacerum

Levator Veli Palatini M.

Medial Lamina / Lateral Lamina } **Cartilaginous Part of the Auditory Tube**

Tensor Veli Palatini M.

Tensor Veli Palatini M.

Medial Plate } Pterygoid / Lateral Plate } Processes

Salpingopharyngeus M.

Bursa for Tendon of Tensor Veli Palatini M. (Fulcrum for Tensing)

Palatopharyngeus M. (res.)

Pterygoid Hamulus

Uvulae M. (Intrensic M.)

In the case of a Cleft Palate, the Aeration of the Middle Ear via the Auditory Tube is Affected due to the Disturbed Function of the Muscles of the Soft Palate (Tensor Veli Palatini and Levator Veli Palatini Mm.).

3.62a,b Transversal Sections through the Cartilaginous and Membranous Part of the Left Auditory Tube. [52]

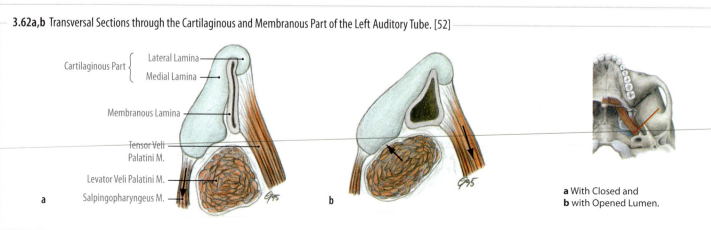

Cartilaginous Part { Lateral Lamina / Medial Lamina }

Membranous Lamina

Tensor Veli Palatini M.

Levator Veli Palatini M.

Salpingopharyngeus M.

a

b

a With Closed and
b with Opened Lumen.

3.63 Nasal and Oral Cavities, Pharynx and Larynx: Median Sagittal Section through Head and Neck, Medial View of the Right Half. [6]

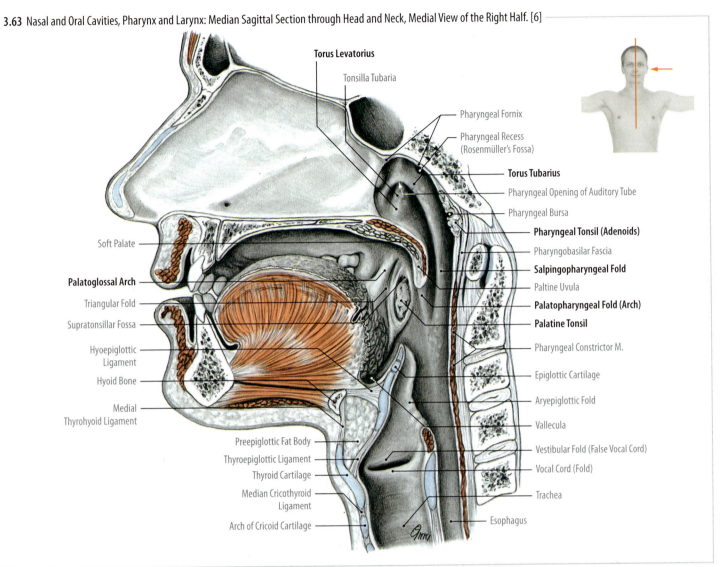

Torus Levatorius

Tonsilla Tubaria

Pharyngeal Fornix

Pharyngeal Recess (Rosenmüller's Fossa)

Torus Tubarius

Pharyngeal Opening of Auditory Tube

Pharyngeal Bursa

Pharyngeal Tonsil (Adenoids)

Pharyngobasilar Fascia

Salpingopharyngeal Fold

Paltine Uvula

Palatopharyngeal Fold (Arch)

Palatine Tonsil

Pharyngeal Constrictor M.

Epiglottic Cartilage

Aryepiglottic Fold

Vallecula

Vestibular Fold (False Vocal Cord)

Vocal Cord (Fold)

Trachea

Esophagus

Soft Palate

Palatoglossal Arch

Triangular Fold

Supratonsillar Fossa

Hyoepiglottic Ligament

Hyoid Bone

Medial Thyrohyoid Ligament

Preepiglottic Fat Body

Thyroepiglottic Ligament

Thyroid Cartilage

Median Cricothyroid Ligament

Arch of Cricoid Cartilage

3.64 The Right Side of the Head and Neck: Median Sagittal Section, Medial View. [6]

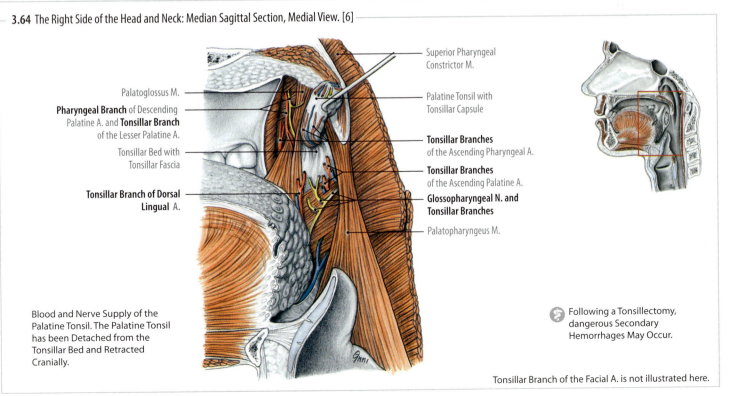

Superior Pharyngeal Constrictor M.

Palatoglossus M.

Pharyngeal Branch of Descending Palatine A. and **Tonsillar Branch** of the Lesser Palatine A.

Tonsillar Bed with Tonsillar Fascia

Tonsillar Branch of Dorsal Lingual A.

Palatine Tonsil with Tonsillar Capsule

Tonsillar Branches of the Ascending Pharyngeal A.

Tonsillar Branches of the Ascending Palatine A.

Glossopharyngeal N. and Tonsillar Branches

Palatopharyngeus M.

Blood and Nerve Supply of the Palatine Tonsil. The Palatine Tonsil has been Detached from the Tonsillar Bed and Retracted Cranially.

Following a Tonsillectomy, dangerous Secondary Hemorrhages May Occur.

Tonsillar Branch of the Facial A. is not illustrated here.

Topography

3.65 Pre- and Paravertebral Structures of the Neck and the Superior Thoracic Aperture: Frontal View. [18]

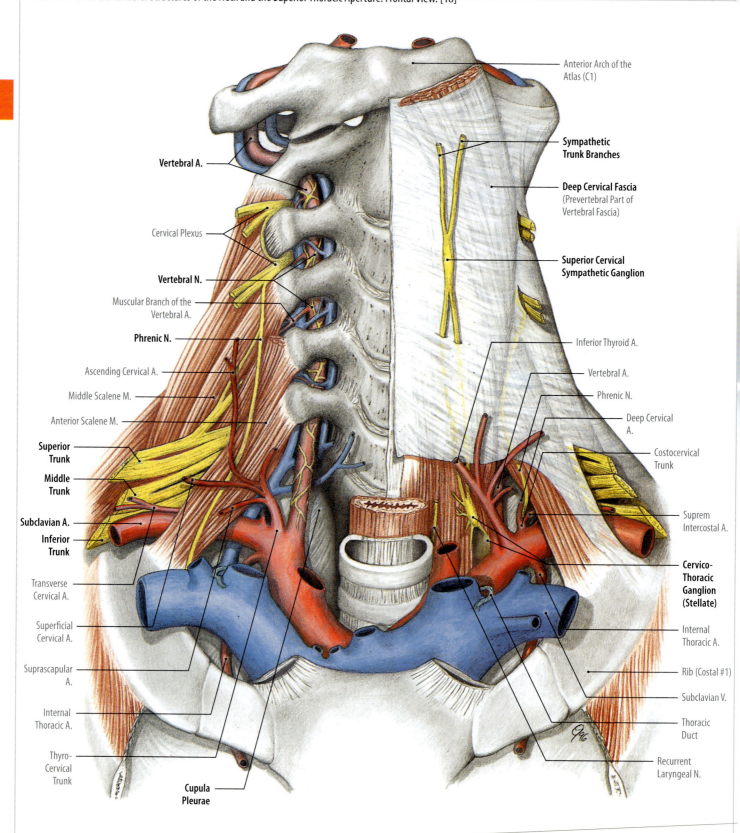

Anterior Arch of the Atlas (C1)

Vertebral A.

Cervical Plexus

Vertebral N.

Muscular Branch of the Vertebral A.

Phrenic N.

Ascending Cervical A.

Middle Scalene M.

Anterior Scalene M.

Superior Trunk

Middle Trunk

Subclavian A.

Inferior Trunk

Transverse Cervical A.

Superficial Cervical A.

Suprascapular A.

Internal Thoracic A.

Thyro-Cervical Trunk

Cupula Pleurae

Sympathetic Trunk Branches

Deep Cervical Fascia (Prevertebral Part of Vertebral Fascia)

Superior Cervical Sympathetic Ganglion

Inferior Thyroid A.

Vertebral A.

Phrenic N.

Deep Cervical A.

Costocervical Trunk

Suprem Intercostal A.

Cervico-Thoracic Ganglion (Stellate)

Internal Thoracic A.

Rib (Costal #1)

Subclavian V.

Thoracic Duct

Recurrent Laryngeal N.

On the Left Side of the body, the Prevertebral Layer of Deep Cervical Fascia has been Preserved in the upper area. Note the passage of the Sympathetic Trunk Branches through the Fascia to Join the Cervical Nerves. On the Right Side of the body, the Prevertebral Muscles have been Removed to illustrate the Vertebral A. and the Cervical and Brachial Plexi.

A Bronchial Carcinoma in the area of the Apex of the Right Lung may Spread to Neighboring Structures: the Lower Parts of the Brachial Plexus, Right Phrenic N., Right Recurrent Laryngeal N., Subclavian A. and V., and Sympathetic Stellate Ganglion (with Horner's Syndrome: Narrow Palpebral Fissure, Miosis, and Enophthalmos).

Transition Neck - Thoracic Cavity

3.66 Transverse Section through the Neck at the Level of the Fourth Cervical Vertebra: Cranial View. [20]

This image illustrates the Floor of the Posterior Triangle of the Neck and the Root of the Neck.

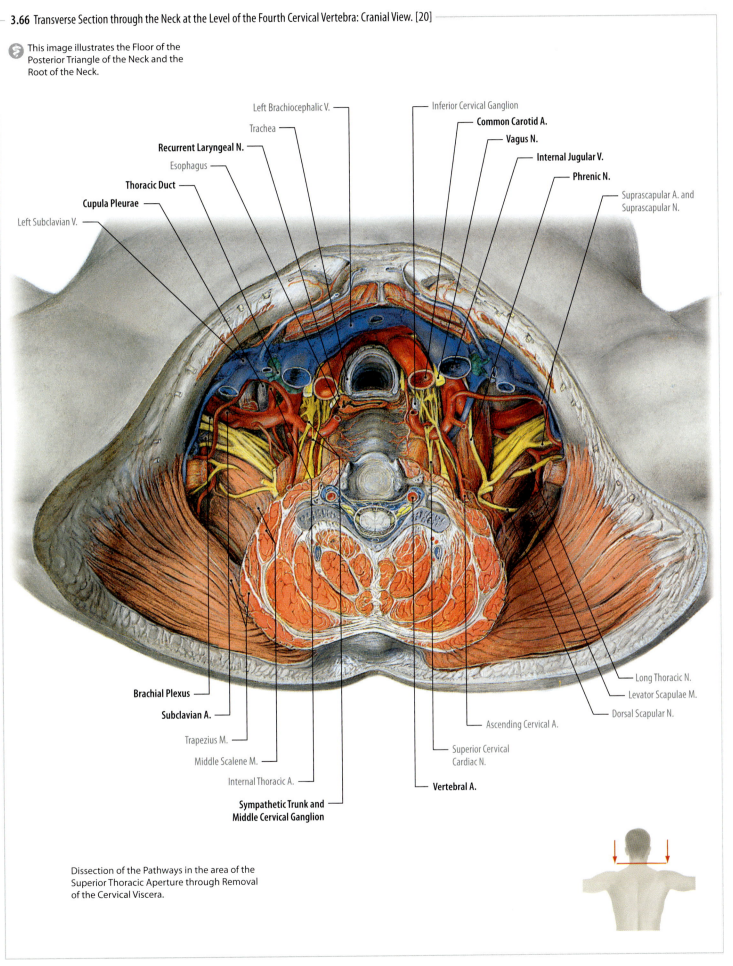

Left Brachiocephalic V.
Trachea
Recurrent Laryngeal N.
Esophagus
Thoracic Duct
Cupula Pleurae
Left Subclavian V.

Inferior Cervical Ganglion
Common Carotid A.
Vagus N.
Internal Jugular V.
Phrenic N.
Suprascapular A. and Suprascapular N.

Long Thoracic N.
Levator Scapulae M.
Dorsal Scapular N.
Ascending Cervical A.

Brachial Plexus
Subclavian A.
Trapezius M.
Middle Scalene M.
Internal Thoracic A.
Sympathetic Trunk and Middle Cervical Ganglion

Superior Cervical Cardiac N.
Vertebral A.

Dissection of the Pathways in the area of the Superior Thoracic Aperture through Removal of the Cervical Viscera.

Topography

Thoracic Duct · Sympathetic Trunk

3.67 Pleural Dome of the Left Side and Neighboring Structures: Frontal View. [15]

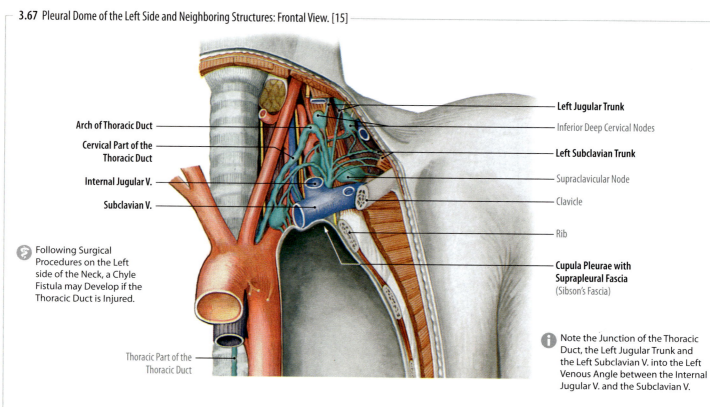

Arch of Thoracic Duct

Cervical Part of the
Thoracic Duct

Internal Jugular V.

Subclavian V.

Left Jugular Trunk

Inferior Deep Cervical Nodes

Left Subclavian Trunk

Supraclavicular Node

Clavicle

Rib

**Cupula Pleurae with
Suprapleural Fascia**
(Sibson's Fascia)

Following Surgical
Procedures on the Left
side of the Neck, a Chyle
Fistula may Develop if the
Thoracic Duct is Injured.

Thoracic Part of the
Thoracic Duct

Note the Junction of the Thoracic
Duct, the Left Jugular Trunk and
the Left Subclavian V. into the Left
Venous Angle between the Internal
Jugular V. and the Subclavian V.

3.68a–c Variants in Course and Confluence of the Thoracic Duct. [53]

3.69 Cervical Part of the Sympathetic Trunk. [20]

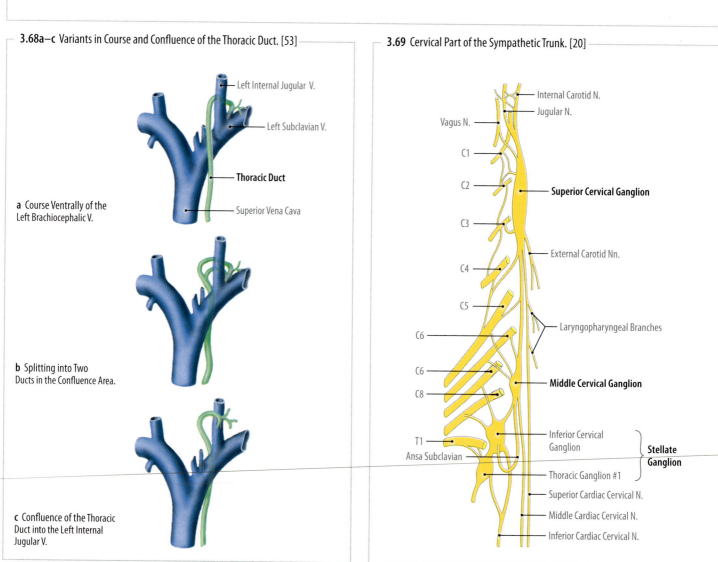

Left Internal Jugular V.

Left Subclavian V.

Thoracic Duct

Superior Vena Cava

a Course Ventrally of the
Left Brachiocephalic V.

b Splitting into Two
Ducts in the Confluence Area.

c Confluence of the Thoracic
Duct into the Left Internal
Jugular V.

Internal Carotid N.

Vagus N.

Jugular N.

C1

C2

C3

C4

C5

C6

C6

C8

T1

Ansa Subclavian

Superior Cervical Ganglion

External Carotid Nn.

Laryngopharyngeal Branches

Middle Cervical Ganglion

Inferior Cervical
Ganglion

Thoracic Ganglion #1

**Stellate
Ganglion**

Superior Cardiac Cervical N.

Middle Cardiac Cervical N.

Inferior Cardiac Cervical N.

3.A Cervical Muscles Belonging to the Muscles of the Head: Origins on the Skull, Right Lateral View.

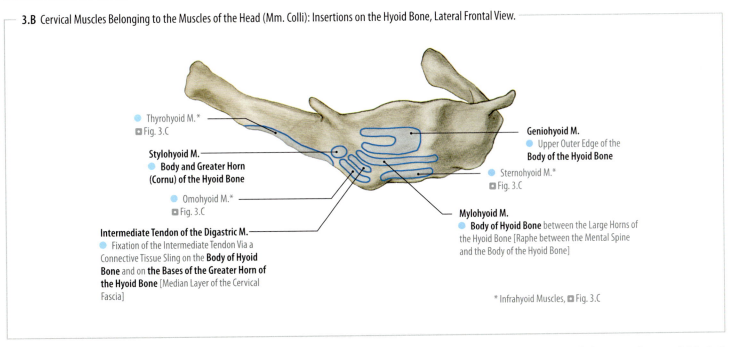

Digastric M.
- Posterior Belly
Mastoid Notch

Stylohyoid M.
- Base and Median Area of the **Styloid Process**

Mylohyoid M.
- Body of the Internal Surface of the Mandible an Oblique Line Anteroinferiorly, the **Mylohyoid Line**

Geniohyoid M. *
- Lower Protuberance of the **Mandible (Inferior Mental Spine)**
* The Geniohyoid M. genetically belongs to the Group Ventrolateral Muscles of the Trunk ▸ Fig. 3.C

Digastric M.
- Anterior Belly
Digastric Fossa of the Mandible

3.B Cervical Muscles Belonging to the Muscles of the Head (Mm. Colli): Insertions on the Hyoid Bone, Lateral Frontal View.

Thyrohyoid M. *
▸ Fig. 3.C

Stylohyoid M.
Body and Greater Horn (Cornu) of the Hyoid Bone

Omohyoid M. *
▸ Fig. 3.C

Intermediate Tendon of the Digastric M.
- Fixation of the Intermediate Tendon Via a Connective Tissue Sling on the **Body of Hyoid Bone** and on the **Bases of the Greater Horn of the Hyoid Bone** [Median Layer of the Cervical Fascia]

Geniohyoid M.
- Upper Outer Edge of the **Body of the Hyoid Bone**

Sternohyoid M. *
▸ Fig. 3.C

Mylohyoid M.
- **Body of Hyoid Bone** between the Large Horns of the Hyoid Bone [Raphe between the Mental Spine and the Body of the Hyoid Bone]

* Infrahyoid Muscles, ▸ Fig. 3.C

3

Function	Innervation	Blood Supply

Digastric M.
With a Fixated Hyoid Bone:
  With Bilateral Activity:
    Lowering of the Mandible (opening the Mouth)
  With Unilateral Activity:
    Ipsilateral movement of the Mandible to the side
    (grinding movement)
 	
With a Fixated Mandible:
  Lifting of the Hyoid Bone and the Larynx
 	
Variants: Occipitohyoid M. (accessory parts of the posterior belly that originate on the Occipital Bone), intersection and expansion of the anterior muscle bellies.
	Anterior Belly:
	Mylohyoid N. a Branch of CN V-3
	Posterior Belly:
	Digastric Branch of the Facial N. (CN VII)
		Occipital A.
		Posterior Auricular A.
		Submental A. of the Facial A.

Mylohyoid M.
With a Fixated Hyoid Bone:
  With Bilateral Activity:
    Lowering of the Mandible
  With Unilateral Activity:
    Ipsilateral movement of the Mandible to the side
 	
With a Fixated Mandible:
  Lifting of the Hyoid Bone (lifting of the floor of the Mouth and pressing the Tongue against the roof of the Mouth)
 	
Variants: Subdivision of the muscle in the insertion area with cavity (Lacuna) formation of the floor of the Mouth.
	Mylohyoid N. (CN V-3)	Submental A. of the Facial A.
		Sublingual A. of the Lingual A.

Geniohyoid M.
With a Fixated Hyoid Bone:
  With Bilateral Activity:
    Lowering of and retracting the Mandible
  With Unilateral Activity:
    Ipsilateral movement of the Mandible to the side
 	
With a Fixated Mandible:
  Movement of the Hyoid Bone forward and upward
	Muscular Branches of Cervical N. C1 traveling with Hypoglossal N. (CN XII)	Sublingual A. of the Lingual A.

Stylohyoid M. Movement of the Hyoid Hone backward and upward	Stylohyoid N. of the Facial N. (CN VII)	Occipital A. Posterior Auricular A.

Infrahyoid Muscles | pp. 149–152

3.C Anterior Cervical Muscles – Pretracheal Muscle: Origins on the Shoulder Girdle and on the Thyroid Cartilage, Insertion on the Thyroid Cartilage and on the Hyoid Bone (Right Side of the Body), Lateral View.

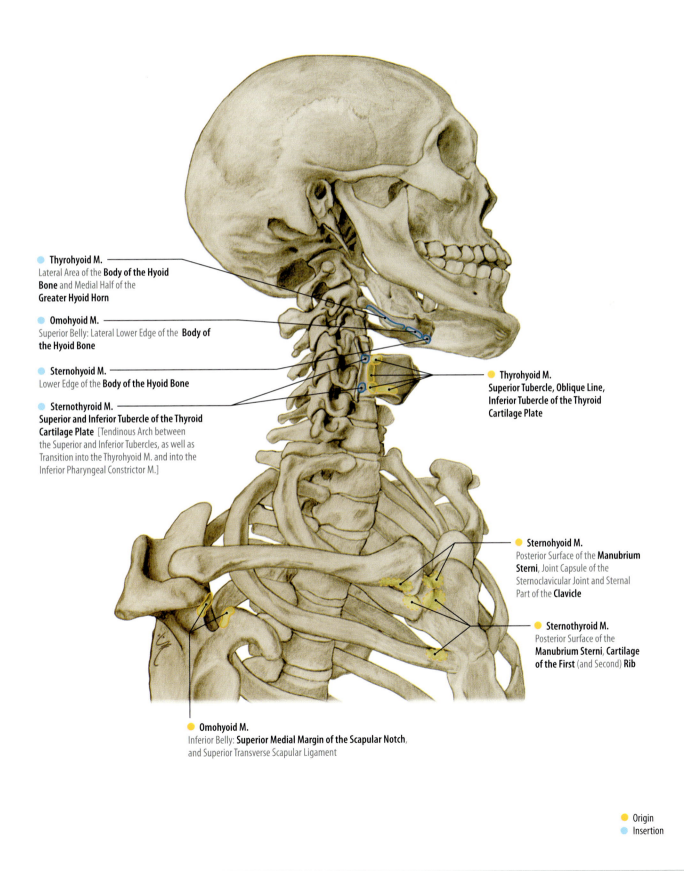

Thyrohyoid M.
Lateral Area of the **Body of the Hyoid Bone** and Medial Half of the **Greater Hyoid Horn**

Omohyoid M.
Superior Belly: Lateral Lower Edge of the **Body of the Hyoid Bone**

Sternohyoid M.
Lower Edge of the **Body of the Hyoid Bone**

Sternothyroid M.
Superior and Inferior Tubercle of the Thyroid Cartilage Plate [Tendinous Arch between the Superior and Inferior Tubercles, as well as Transition into the Thyrohyoid M. and into the Inferior Pharyngeal Constrictor M.]

Thyrohyoid M.
Superior Tubercle, Oblique Line, Inferior Tubercle of the Thyroid Cartilage Plate

Sternohyoid M.
Posterior Surface of the **Manubrium Sterni**, Joint Capsule of the Sternoclavicular Joint and Sternal Part of the **Clavicle**

Sternothyroid M.
Posterior Surface of the **Manubrium Sterni, Cartilage of the First** (and Second) **Rib**

Omohyoid M.
Inferior Belly: **Superior Medial Margin of the Scapular Notch**, and Superior Transverse Scapular Ligament

● Origin
● Insertion

Muscles of the Neck

Function	Innervation	Blood Supply
Sternohyoid M. Pulls the Hyoid Bone in a caudal direction Fixates the Hyoid Bone in connection with isometric contraction for the opening movement of the Jaw and for the grinding movement • *Infrahyoid Bursa*	Ansa Cervicalis C1–C3	Superior Thyroid A. Suprahyoid Branch from the Lingual A.
Sternothyroid M. Pulls the Larynx in a caudal direction Fixates the Larynx in connection with isometric contraction during phonation	Ansa Cervicalis (C1) C2–C3 (C4)	Superior Thyroid A.

Thyrohyoid M.
With a Fixated Hyoid Bone:
    Lifting of the Larynx (deglutition)
With a Fixated Larynx:
    Lowering of the Hyoid Bone,
    Influence of phonation
Variant: Lateral Levator Thyroid Gland M.: Muscle fiber bundles radiating into the Thyroid Capsule.
	Superior Root of the Ansa Cervicalis C1–C2	Superior Thyroid A.

Omohyoid M. Pulls the Hyoid Bone in a caudal direction Fixates the Hyoid Bone in connection with isometric contraction ▣ Sternohyoid M. Tension of the Median Cervical Fascia and furthering of the venous backflow • *Thyrohyoid Bursa*	Superior Belly: Superior Root of the Ansa Cervicalis C1–C2, Inferior Belly: Inferior Root of the Ansa Cervicalis C2–C4	Superior Thyroid A. Transverse Cervical A. Suprascapular A.

• Bursa = Synovial Bursa assigned to a muscle.

3.D Prevertebral Cervical Muscles – Muscles of the Head and Vertebral Joints: Origins (Right Side of the Body) on the Cervical and Thoracic Spine, Insertions (Left Side of the Body) on the Cervical Spine.

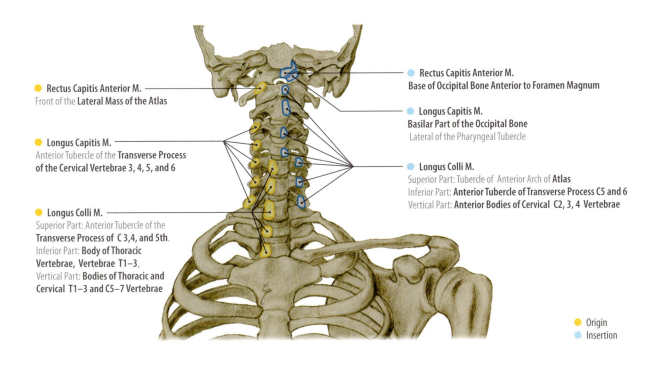

● **Rectus Capitis Anterior M.**
Front of the **Lateral Mass of the Atlas**

● **Longus Capitis M.**
Anterior Tubercle of the **Transverse Process
of the Cervical Vertebrae 3, 4, 5, and 6**

● **Longus Colli M.**
Superior Part: Anterior Tubercle of the
Transverse Process of C 3,4, and 5th.
Inferior Part: **Body of Thoracic
Vertebrae, Vertebrae T1–3,**
Vertical Part: **Bodies of Thoracic and
Cervical T1–3 and C5–7 Vertebrae**

● **Rectus Capitis Anterior M.**
Base of Occipital Bone Anterior to Foramen Magnum

● **Longus Capitis M.**
Basilar Part of the Occipital Bone
Lateral of the Pharyngeal Tubercle

● **Longus Colli M.**
Superior Part: Tubercle of Anterior Arch of **Atlas**
Inferior Part: **Anterior Tubercle of Transverse Process C5 and 6**
Vertical Part: **Anterior Bodies of Cervical C2, 3, 4 Vertebrae**

● Origin
● Insertion

3.E Lateral, Deep Cervical Muscles; Muscles of the Vertebral and Costal Joints: Origins (Right Side of the Body) on the Cervical Spine, Insertions (Left Side of the Body) on the Ribs.

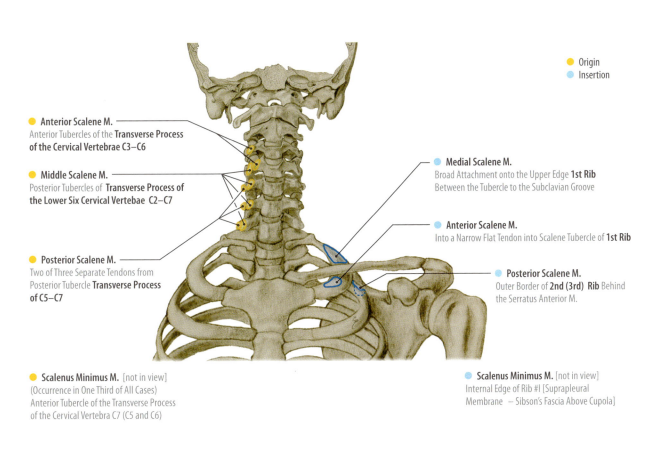

● Origin
● Insertion

● **Anterior Scalene M.**
Anterior Tubercles of the **Transverse Process
of the Cervical Vertebrae C3–C6**

● **Middle Scalene M.**
Posterior Tubercles of **Transverse Process of
the Lower Six Cervical Vertebae C2–C7**

● **Posterior Scalene M.**
Two of Three Separate Tendons from
Posterior Tubercle **Transverse Process
of C5–C7**

● **Medial Scalene M.**
Broad Attachment onto the Upper Edge **1st Rib**
Between the Tubercle to the Subclavian Groove

● **Anterior Scalene M.**
Into a Narrow Flat Tendon into Scalene Tubercle of **1st Rib**

● **Posterior Scalene M.**
Outer Border of **2nd (3rd) Rib** Behind
the Serratus Anterior M.

● **Scalenus Minimus M.** [not in view]
(Occurrence in One Third of All Cases)
Anterior Tubercle of the Transverse Process
of the Cervical Vertebra C7 (C5 and C6)

● **Scalenus Minimus M.** [not in view]
Internal Edge of Rib #I [Suprapleural
Membrane – Sibson's Fascia Above Cupola]

Muscles of the Neck

Function	Innervation	Blood Supply
Rectus Capitis Anterior M. Fine adjustment of the Head in the Joints of the Head Support of lateral inclination	Anterior Branch (Ventral) of the Cervical N. C1	Vertebral A. Ascending Pharyngeal A.

Longus Capitis M.
Bilateral Activity:
    Support of forward inclination
Unilateral Activity:
    Lateral inclination of the Head
	Anterior (Ventral) Branches of the Cervical Nn. C1–3	Ascending Pharyngeal A.
		Vertebral A.
		Ascending Cervical A.

Longus Colli M.
Bilateral Activity:
    Support of forward inclination of the Cervical Spine
Unilateral Activity:
    Lateral inclination and rotation of the Cervical Spine toward the ipsilateral side
	Anterior (Ventral) Branches of the Cervical Nn. C2–C4 (C7)	Ascending Cervical A.
		Vertebral A.
		Deep Cervical A.
		Suprem Intercostal A.

Anterior Scalene M.
With a Fixated Cervical Spine:
    Lifting of the First Rib (support [Accessory Mm.] of inspiration),
    Stabilization of the Upper Thorax Aperture
Unilateral activity:
    Lateral inclination and rotation of the Cervical Spine toward the ipsilateral side
Unilateral activity:
    Forward inclination of the Cervical Spine
	Anterior (Ventral) Branches of the Cervical Nn. (C4) C5–C7	Inferior Thyroid A.
		Ascending Cervical A.
		Vertebral A.
		Deep Cervical A.

Middle Scalene M. Like Anterior Scalene M. (without forward inclination of the Cervical Spine)	Anterior (Ventral) Branches of the Cervical Nn. (C3) C4–C7	Ascending Cervical A. Deep Cervical A. Vertebral A. Transverse Cervical A.

Posterior Scalene M.
With a Fixated Cervical Spine:
    Lifting of Ribs #1 and 2 (support of inspiration)
    Stabilization of the Upper Thorax Aperture
Unilateral Activity:
    Support of lateral inclination and rotation of the Cervical Spine toward the ipsilateral side
	Anterior (Ventral) Branches of the Cervical Nn. C7–C8	Deep Cervical A.
		Transverse Cervical A.
		Suprem Intercostal A.

Scalene Minimus M. (Sibson's Muscle – Scalene Pleuralis M. occurs in one third of cases) Tensing and strengthening the Suprapleural Membrane (Sibson's Fascia) of the Dome of Pleura	Anterior (Ventral) Branch of the Cervical N. C8	Inferior Thyroid A. Ascending Cervical A. Vertebral A.

3.Fa–c Laryngeal Muscles: Origins on the Thyroid and Cricoid Cartilage as well as Insertions on the Thyroid Cartilage, **a,b**. Origins on the Cricoid and Thyroid Cartilage as well as Insertions on the Arytenoid Cartilage, **c**.

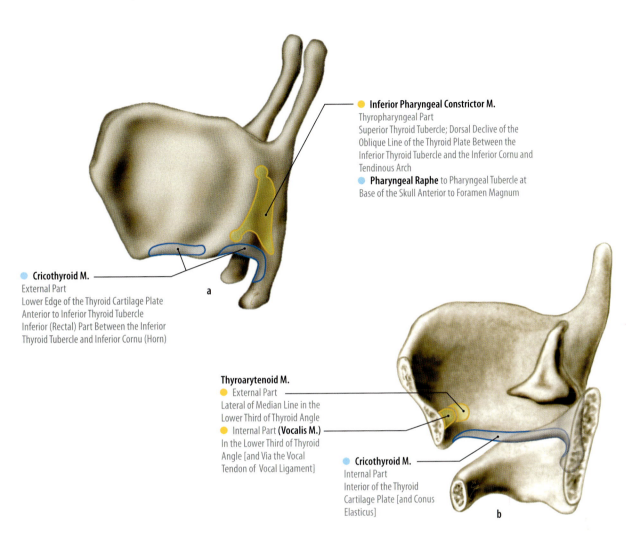

● **Inferior Pharyngeal Constrictor M.**
Thyropharyngeal Part
Superior Thyroid Tubercle; Dorsal Declive of the
Oblique Line of the Thyroid Plate Between the
Inferior Thyroid Tubercle and the Inferior Cornu and
Tendinous Arch
● **Pharyngeal Raphe** to Pharyngeal Tubercle at
Base of the Skull Anterior to Foramen Magnum

● **Cricothyroid M.**
External Part
Lower Edge of the Thyroid Cartilage Plate
Anterior to Inferior Thyroid Tubercle
Inferior (Rectal) Part Between the Inferior
Thyroid Tubercle and Inferior Cornu (Horn)

a

Thyroarytenoid M.
● External Part
Lateral of Median Line in the
Lower Third of Thyroid Angle
● Internal Part (**Vocalis M.**)
In the Lower Third of Thyroid
Angle [and Via the Vocal
Tendon of Vocal Ligament]

● **Cricothyroid M.**
Internal Part
Interior of the Thyroid
Cartilage Plate [and Conus
Elasticus]

b

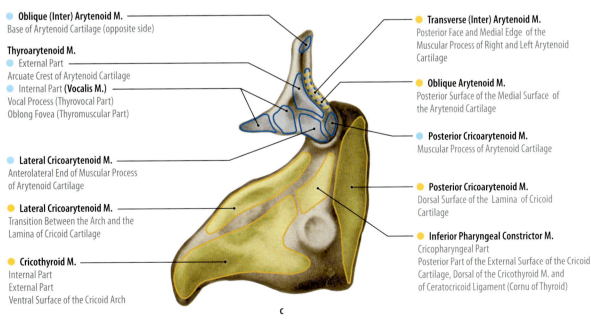

● **Oblique (Inter) Arytenoid M.**
Base of Arytenoid Cartilage (opposite side)

Thyroarytenoid M.
● External Part
Arcuate Crest of Arytenoid Cartilage
● Internal Part (**Vocalis M.**)
Vocal Process (Thyrovocal Part)
Oblong Fovea (Thyromuscular Part)

● **Lateral Cricoarytenoid M.**
Anterolateral End of Muscular Process
of Arytenoid Cartilage

● **Lateral Cricoarytenoid M.**
Transition Between the Arch and the
Lamina of Cricoid Cartilage

● **Cricothyroid M.**
Internal Part
External Part
Ventral Surface of the Cricoid Arch

● **Transverse (Inter) Arytenoid M.**
Posterior Face and Medial Edge of the
Muscular Process of Right and Left Arytenoid
Cartilage

● **Oblique Arytenoid M.**
Posterior Surface of the Medial Surface of
the Arytenoid Cartilage

● **Posterior Cricoarytenoid M.**
Muscular Process of Arytenoid Cartilage

● **Posterior Cricoarytenoid M.**
Dorsal Surface of the Lamina of Cricoid
Cartilage

● **Inferior Pharyngeal Constrictor M.**
Cricopharyngeal Part
Posterior Part of the External Surface of the Cricoid
Cartilage, Dorsal of the Cricothyroid M. and
of Ceratocricoid Ligament (Cornu of Thyroid)

c

Muscles of the Neck

3

Function	Innervation	Blood Supply
External Muscles of the Larynx		
Cricothyroid M. **Internal Part** and **External Part** with straight part and oblique part Tensing (elongating) the Vocal Folds *Variants*: Development of a intermediate part; outright lack of subdivision of the muscle; direct transition of the oblique part into the Thyropharyngeal part of the Inferior Pharyngeal Constrictors M. of the Pharynx; Accessory Muscle fibers between the Thyroid Cartilage and the Trachea (Thyrotrachealis M.)	**Superior Laryngeal N.** – External Branch	Cricothyroid Branch of the Superior Thyroid A.
Inferior Pharyngeal Constrictor M. **Thyropharyngeal Part** Elevates the Larynx during deglutition Tenses the Vocal Folds **Cricopharyngeal Part** Relaxes the Vocal Folds *Variant*: Direct transition of the muscle fibers of the Cricothyroid M. into the Cricopharyngeal part	Superior Laryngeal N. –External Branch – Pharyngeal Plexus	Cricothyroid Branch of the Superior Thyroid A.
Thyrohyoid M. ▣ Infrahyoid Muscles, Fig. 3.C		
Internal Muscles of the Larynx		
Posterior Cricoarytenoid M. Abduction and elevation of the Vocal Process, thereby causing maximum opening of the Rima Glottidis for inspiration Synergistic with the Cricothyroid M. in its function of Vocal Fold elongation (tension) through stabilization of the Arytenoid Cartilage *Variant*: Fibers toward the inferior horn of the Thyroid Cartilage (Ceratocricoid M.)	Inferior Laryngeal N. –Posterior Branch	Superior Laryngeal A. Inferior Laryngeal A.
Transverse Arytenoid M. Merging of the Arytenoid Cartilage, thereby causing occlusion of the Intercartilaginous Part of the Rima Glottidis	Inferior Laryngeal N. –Posterior Branch	Superior Laryngeal A.
Oblique Arytenoid M. Adduction of the Arytenoid Cartilage, thereby causing occlusion of the intercartilaginous part; low-grade outward rotation of the Vocal Process—minimal opening of the intermembranous part *Variants*: Variable intersection mode, development of the Aryepiglottic part (Aryepiglottic M.) as a continuation of the fibers of the Oblique Arytenoid M.; muscular basis of the Aryepiglottic Fold; actively lowers the Epiglottis partially Aberrant muscle fibers to the Corniculate Cartilage	Inferior Laryngeal N. –Posterior Branch	Superior Laryngeal A.
Lateral Cricoarytenoid M. Adduction and slight lowering of the Vocal Process, thereby causing occlusion of the intermembranous part of the Rima Glottidis, opening of the intercartilaginous part (Whisper Triangle)	Inferior Laryngeal N. –Anterior Branch	Inferior Laryngeal A.
Thyroarytenoid M. **External Part** Adduction and lowering of the Vocal Process, thereby occlusion of the intermembranous part of the Rima Glottidis and relaxation and shortening of the Vocal Cord **Thyroepiglottic Part** (Thyroepiglottic M.) Modify the inlet of the Larynx, important for phonation **Internal Part (Vocalis M.)** Thicker attachment posteriorly to the Vocal Ligament at different points Adjusts tension of part of the Vocal Ligament by isometric contraction to tense and shorten part of the Vocal Ligament	Inferior Laryngeal N. –Anterior Branch	Superior Laryngeal A.

Palatine and Pharyngeal Muscles | pp. 176–180

3.G Pharyngeal Muscles, Muscles of the Soft Palate: Origins and Insertions on the External Cranial Base.

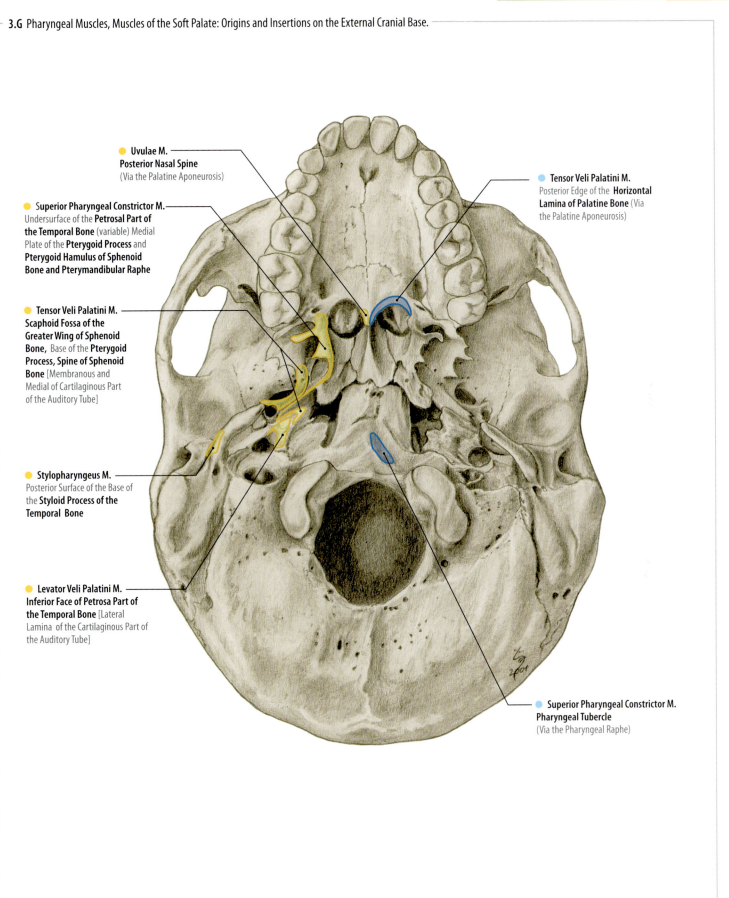

● **Uvulae M.**
Posterior Nasal Spine
(Via the Palatine Aponeurosis)

● **Superior Pharyngeal Constrictor M.**
Undersurface of the **Petrosal Part of
the Temporal Bone** (variable) Medial
Plate of the **Pterygoid Process** and
**Pterygoid Hamulus of Sphenoid
Bone and Pterymandibular Raphe**

● **Tensor Veli Palatini M.**
**Scaphoid Fossa of the
Greater Wing of Sphenoid
Bone,** Base of the **Pterygoid
Process, Spine of Sphenoid
Bone** [Membranous and
Medial of Cartilaginous Part
of the Auditory Tube]

● **Stylopharyngeus M.**
Posterior Surface of the Base of
the **Styloid Process of the
Temporal Bone**

● **Levator Veli Palatini M.**
**Inferior Face of Petrosa Part of
the Temporal Bone** [Lateral
Lamina of the Cartilaginous Part of
the Auditory Tube]

● **Tensor Veli Palatini M.**
Posterior Edge of the **Horizontal
Lamina of Palatine Bone** (Via
the Palatine Aponeurosis)

● **Superior Pharyngeal Constrictor M.**
Pharyngeal Tubercle
(Via the Pharyngeal Raphe)

Muscles of the Neck

3

Function	Innervation	Blood Supply
Tensor Veli Palatini M. Tension of the Palatine Velum (Soft Palate) Lowering or lifting of the Soft Palate to the level of the Pterygoid Hamulus Dilatation of the Auditory Tube	Muscular N. to Tensor Veli Palatini M. of the Mandibular N. (CN V) Pharyngeal Plexus (Glossopharyngeal N. (CN IX) and Vagus N. (CN X))	Descending Palatine A. Pterygoid Canal A. (Vidian Artery) Ascending Palatine A. Ascending Pharyngeal A.
Levator Veli Palatini Lifting of the Soft Palate (Together with the Superior Pharyngeal Constrictor M., occlusion of the Nasopharyngeal Space during deglutition)	Facial N. (CN VII) Pharyngeal Plexus (Glossopharyngeal N. and Vagus N.)	Descending Palatine A. Pterygoid Canal A. (Vidian A.) Ascending Palatine A. Ascending Pharyngeal A.
Uvulae M. Shortening of the Uvula (squeezing of the Palatine Glands)	Pharyngeal Plexus	Lesser Palatine A.
Palatoglossus M. (Muscular basis of the Palatoglossal Arch) Constriction of the Isthmus Fauces and strangulation of the bite (Together with the Transverse Lingular M.) Lowering of the Soft Palate with a fixated Tongue Lifting of the root of the Tongue with a fixated Soft Palate (squeezing of the Palatine Glands)	Glossopharyngeal N. (CN IX)	Descending Palatine A. Ascending Palatine A. Lesser Palatine Aa. Dorsal Lingual Branch of the Lingual A.
Palatopharyngeus M. (Muscular basis of the Palatopharyngeal Arch) Lifting and shortening of the Pharynx Relocation of the Larynx forward and upward Approximation of the Palatopharyngeal Arch Constriction of the Isthmus Fauces	Pharyngeal Plexus Glossopharyngeal N.	Ascending Palatine A. Ascending Pharyngeal A.
Salpingopharyngeus M. (Muscular basis of the Salpingopharyngeal Fold, dissociation of muscle fibers of the Palatopharyngeus M.) Lifting of the Pharynx Dilatation of the Auditory Tube	Pharyngeal Plexus Glossopharyngeal N.	Ascending Palatine A. Ascending Pharyngeal A.
Stylopharyngeus M. Lifting of the Pharynx and of the Larynx Dilatation of the Pharynx	Glossopharyngeal N.	Ascending Pharyngeal A. Ascending Palatine A.
Superior Pharyngeal Constrictor M. Bulging forward of the Pharyngeal Wall (Passavant's Bar) during deglutition	Pharyngeal Plexus (Glossopharyngeal M.)	Ascending Pharyngeal A. Ascending Palatine A. Descending Pharyngeal A.
Middle Pharyngeal Constrictor M. Constriction of the Pharynx	Pharyngeal Plexus (Glossopharyngeal N. and Vagus N.)	Ascending Pharyngeal A. Ascending Palatine A. Descending Pharyngeal A.
Inferior Pharyngeal Constrictor M. Constriction of the Pharynx	Pharyngeal Plexus (Vagus N.) Superior Laryngeal N.	Ascending Pharyngeal A. Ascending Palatine A. Descending Pharyngeal A.

Trunk

Axial Skeleton of the Trunk

4.1 Bones of the Skeleton of the Trunk: Ventral View. [54]

The Jugular Notch is at the Second and Third Vertebra level. The Thoracic Inlet Faces Anteriorly and is Inclined Inferiorly.

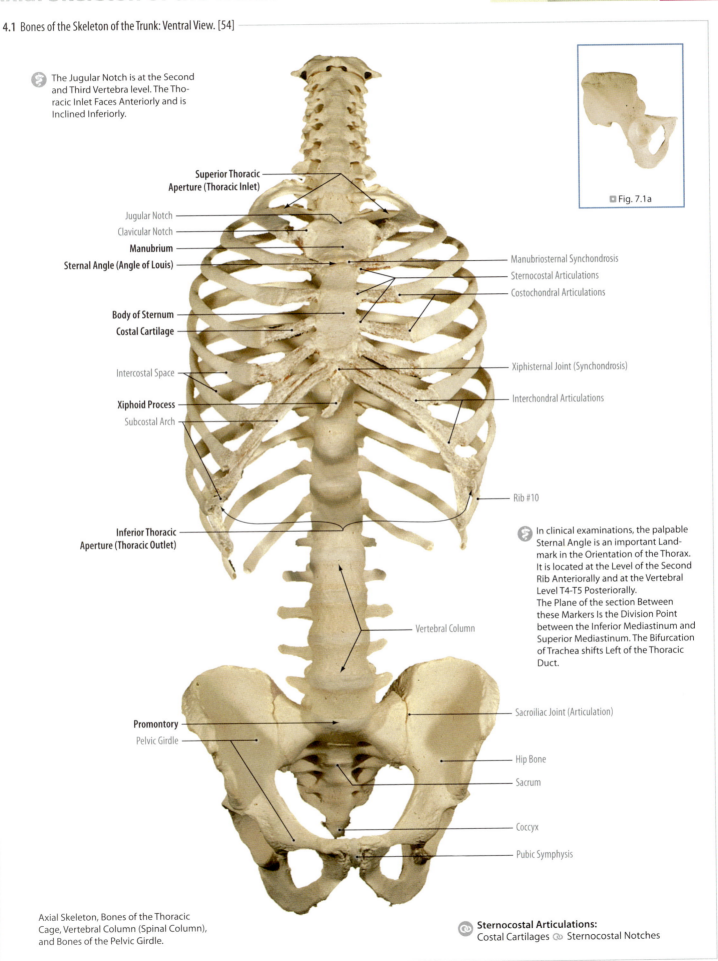

□ Fig. 7.1a

Superior Thoracic Aperture (Thoracic Inlet)

Jugular Notch

Clavicular Notch

Manubrium

Sternal Angle (Angle of Louis)

Body of Sternum

Costal Cartilage

Intercostal Space

Xiphoid Process

Subcostal Arch

Inferior Thoracic Aperture (Thoracic Outlet)

Promontory

Pelvic Girdle

Manubriosternal Synchondrosis

Sternocostal Articulations

Costochondral Articulations

Xiphisternal Joint (Synchondrosis)

Interchondral Articulations

Rib #10

Vertebral Column

Sacroiliac Joint (Articulation)

Hip Bone

Sacrum

Coccyx

Pubic Symphysis

In clinical examinations, the palpable Sternal Angle is an important Landmark in the Orientation of the Thorax. It is located at the Level of the Second Rib Anteriorly and at the Vertebral Level T4-T5 Posteriorly.
The Plane of the section Between these Markers Is the Division Point between the Inferior Mediastinum and Superior Mediastinum. The Bifurcation of Trachea shifts Left of the Thoracic Duct.

Axial Skeleton, Bones of the Thoracic Cage, Vertebral Column (Spinal Column), and Bones of the Pelvic Girdle.

Sternocostal Articulations:
Costal Cartilages ∞ Sternocostal Notches

Skeleton and Joints

4.2 Bones of the Skeleton of the Trunk: Dorsal View. [54]

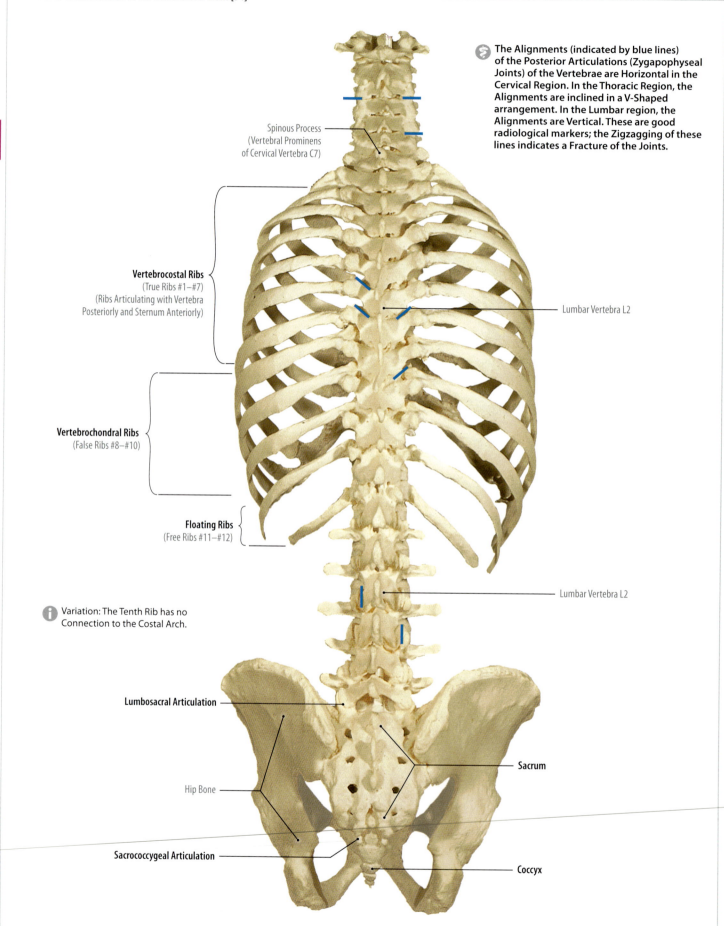

The Alignments (indicated by blue lines) of the Posterior Articulations (Zygapophyseal Joints) of the Vertebrae are Horizontal in the Cervical Region. In the Thoracic Region, the Alignments are inclined in a V-Shaped arrangement. In the Lumbar region, the Alignments are Vertical. These are good radiological markers; the Zigzagging of these lines indicates a Fracture of the Joints.

Spinous Process
(Vertebral Prominens
of Cervical Vertebra C7)

Vertebrocostal Ribs
(True Ribs #1–#7)
(Ribs Articulating with Vertebra
Posteriorly and Sternum Anteriorly)

Lumbar Vertebra L2

Vertebrochondral Ribs
(False Ribs #8–#10)

Floating Ribs
(Free Ribs #11–#12)

Variation: The Tenth Rib has no
Connection to the Costal Arch.

Lumbar Vertebra L2

Lumbosacral Articulation

Hip Bone

Sacrum

Sacrococcygeal Articulation

Coccyx

Ribs

4.3a–d Ribs (Costae) of the Right Side.

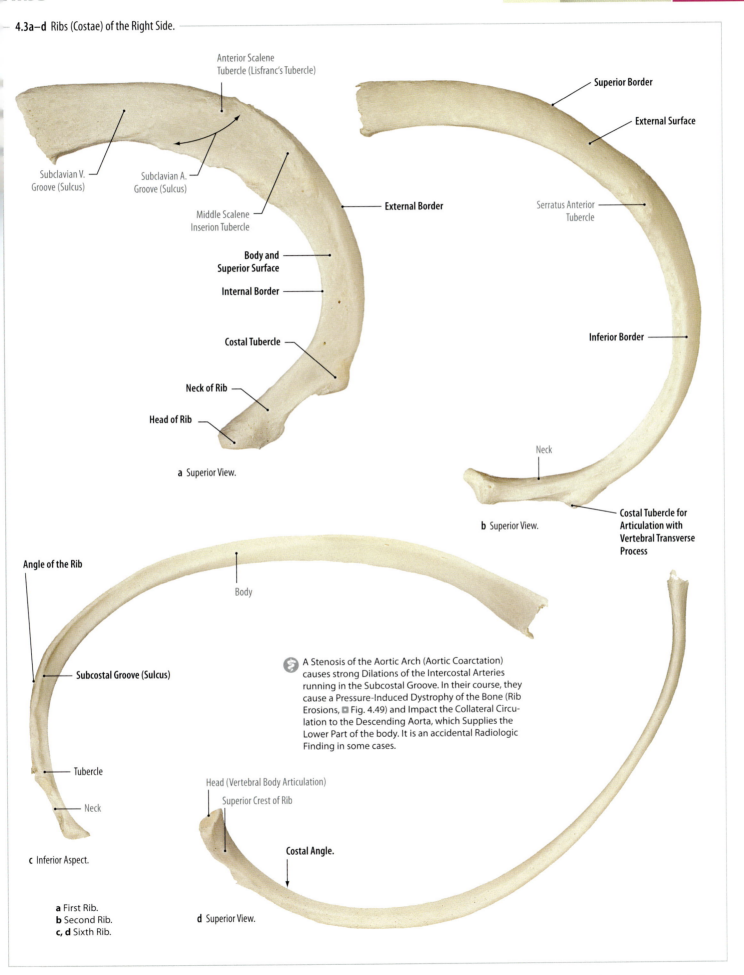

Anterior Scalene
Tubercle (Lisfranc's Tubercle)

Subclavian V.
Groove (Sulcus)

Subclavian A.
Groove (Sulcus)

Middle Scalene
Inserion Tubercle

**Body and
Superior Surface**

Internal Border

External Border

Costal Tubercle

Neck of Rib

Head of Rib

a Superior View.

Superior Border

External Surface

Serratus Anterior
Tubercle

Inferior Border

Neck

**Costal Tubercle for
Articulation with
Vertebral Transverse
Process**

b Superior View.

Angle of the Rib

Body

Subcostal Groove (Sulcus)

Tubercle

Neck

c Inferior Aspect.

Head (Vertebral Body Articulation)

Superior Crest of Rib

Costal Angle.

A Stenosis of the Aortic Arch (Aortic Coarctation) causes strong Dilations of the Intercostal Arteries running in the Subcostal Groove. In their course, they cause a Pressure-Induced Dystrophy of the Bone (Rib Erosions, ◻ Fig. 4.49) and Impact the Collateral Circulation to the Descending Aorta, which Supplies the Lower Part of the body. It is an accidental Radiologic Finding in some cases.

d Superior View.

a First Rib.
b Second Rib.
c, d Sixth Rib.

Spinal Column

4.4a,b Spinal Column (Vertebral Column). [54]

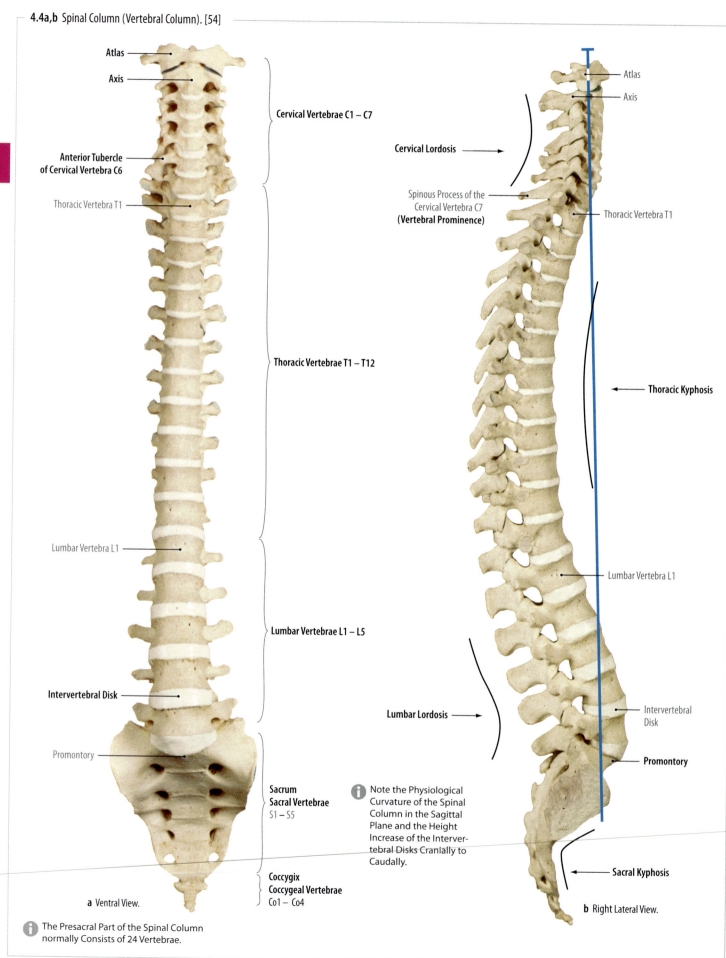

Atlas

Axis

Cervical Vertebrae C1 – C7

Anterior Tubercle
of Cervical Vertebra C6

Thoracic Vertebra T1

Thoracic Vertebrae T1 – T12

Lumbar Vertebra L1

Lumbar Vertebrae L1 – L5

Intervertebral Disk

Promontory

**Sacrum
Sacral Vertebrae
S1 – S5**

**Coccygix
Coccygeal Vertebrae
Co1 – Co4**

a Ventral View.

ⓘ The Presacral Part of the Spinal Column
normally Consists of 24 Vertebrae.

Atlas

Axis

Cervical Lordosis

Spinous Process of the
Cervical Vertebra C7
(Vertebral Prominence)

Thoracic Vertebra T1

Thoracic Kyphosis

Lumbar Vertebra L1

Lumbar Lordosis

Intervertebral
Disk

Promontory

ⓘ Note the Physiological
Curvature of the Spinal
Column in the Sagittal
Plane and the Height
Increase of the Interver-
tebral Disks Cranially to
Caudally.

Sacral Kyphosis

b Right Lateral View.

4.5a,b Cervical Spine (C1 – C7).

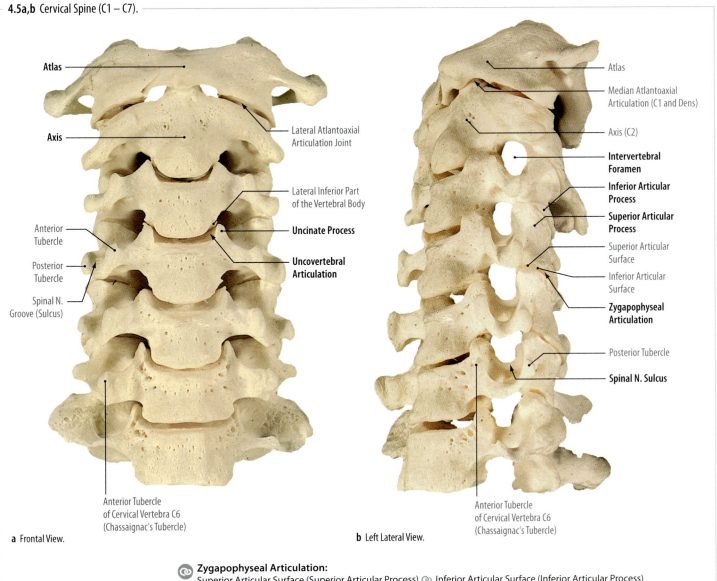

Atlas

Axis

Anterior
Tubercle

Posterior
Tubercle

Spinal N.
Groove (Sulcus)

Lateral Atlantoaxial
Articulation Joint

Lateral Inferior Part
of the Vertebral Body

Uncinate Process

**Uncovertebral
Articulation**

Anterior Tubercle
of Cervical Vertebra C6
(Chassaignac's Tubercle)

a Frontal View.

Atlas

Median Atlantoaxial
Articulation (C1 and Dens)

Axis (C2)

**Intervertebral
Foramen**

**Inferior Articular
Process**

**Superior Articular
Process**

Superior Articular
Surface

Inferior Articular
Surface

**Zygapophyseal
Articulation**

Posterior Tubercle

Spinal N. Sulcus

Anterior Tubercle
of Cervical Vertebra C6
(Chassaignac's Tubercle)

b Left Lateral View.

⊚ Zygapophyseal Articulation:
Superior Articular Surface (Superior Articular Process) ⊚ Inferior Articular Surface (Inferior Articular Process)

Uncovertebral (Hemiarthrosis) Articulation :
Lateral Inferior Part of the Vertebral Body ⊚ Uncinate Process

4.6 Skeletal Parts of the Superior and Inferior Joints of the Head (Atlantooccipital Articulation and Median and Lateral Atlantooccipital Articulation): Frontal View.

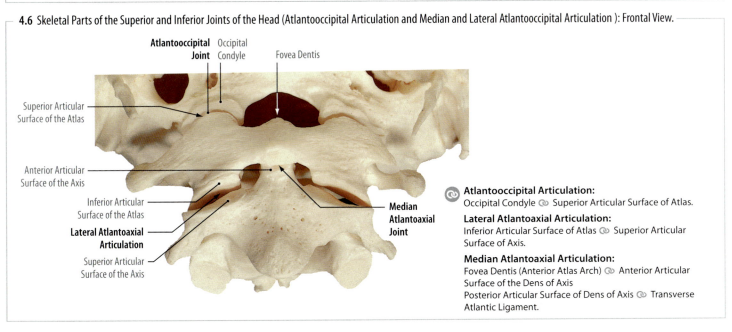

**Atlantooccipital
Joint**

Occipital
Condyle

Fovea Dentis

Superior Articular
Surface of the Atlas

Anterior Articular
Surface of the Axis

Inferior Articular
Surface of the Atlas

**Lateral Atlantoaxial
Articulation**

Superior Articular
Surface of the Axis

**Median
Atlantoaxial
Joint**

⊚ Atlantooccipital Articulation:
Occipital Condyle ⊚ Superior Articular Surface of Atlas.

Lateral Atlantoaxial Articulation:
Inferior Articular Surface of Atlas ⊚ Superior Articular
Surface of Axis.

Median Atlantoaxial Articulation:
Fovea Dentis (Anterior Atlas Arch) ⊚ Anterior Articular
Surface of the Dens of Axis
Posterior Articular Surface of Dens of Axis ⊚ Transverse
Atlantic Ligament.

Skeleton and Joints

4.7a,b Atlas.

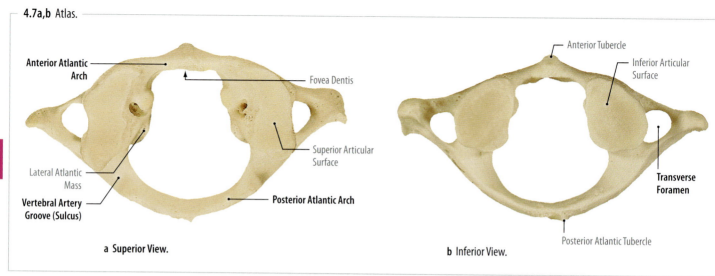

Anterior Atlantic Arch

Fovea Dentis

Superior Articular Surface

Lateral Atlantic Mass

Vertebral Artery Groove (Sulcus)

Posterior Atlantic Arch

a Superior View.

Anterior Tubercle

Inferior Articular Surface

Transverse Foramen

Posterior Atlantic Tubercle

b Inferior View.

4.8a–d Axis.

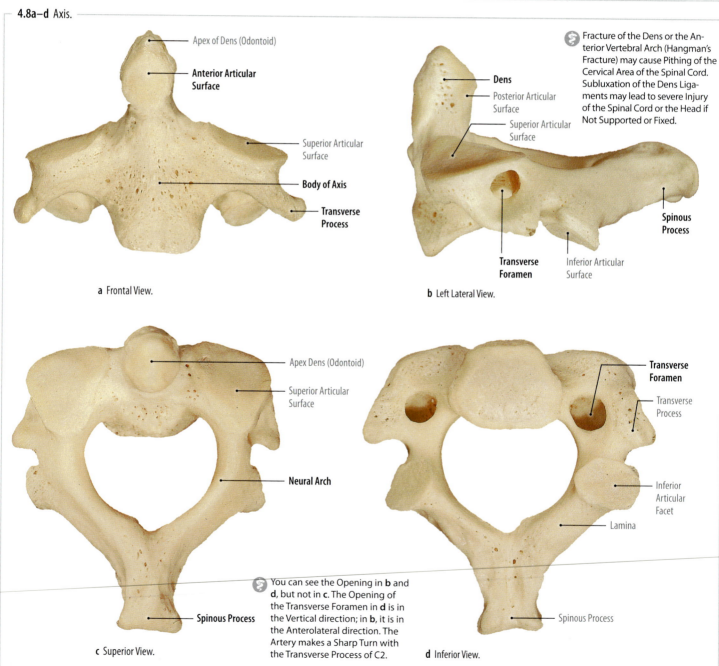

Apex of Dens (Odontoid)

Anterior Articular Surface

Superior Articular Surface

Body of Axis

Transverse Process

a Frontal View.

Dens

Posterior Articular Surface

Superior Articular Surface

Transverse Foramen

Inferior Articular Surface

Spinous Process

Fracture of the Dens or the Anterior Vertebral Arch (Hangman's Fracture) may cause Pithing of the Cervical Area of the Spinal Cord. Subluxation of the Dens Ligaments may lead to severe Injury of the Spinal Cord or the Head if Not Supported or Fixed.

b Left Lateral View.

Apex Dens (Odontoid)

Superior Articular Surface

Neural Arch

Spinous Process

c Superior View.

Transverse Foramen

Transverse Process

Inferior Articular Facet

Lamina

Spinous Process

d Inferior View.

You can see the Opening in **b** and **d**, but not in **c**. The Opening of the Transverse Foramen in **d** is in the Vertical direction; in **b**, it is in the Anterolateral direction. The Artery makes a Sharp Turn with the Transverse Process of C2.

4.9a–c Fourth and Sixth Cervical Vertebrae.

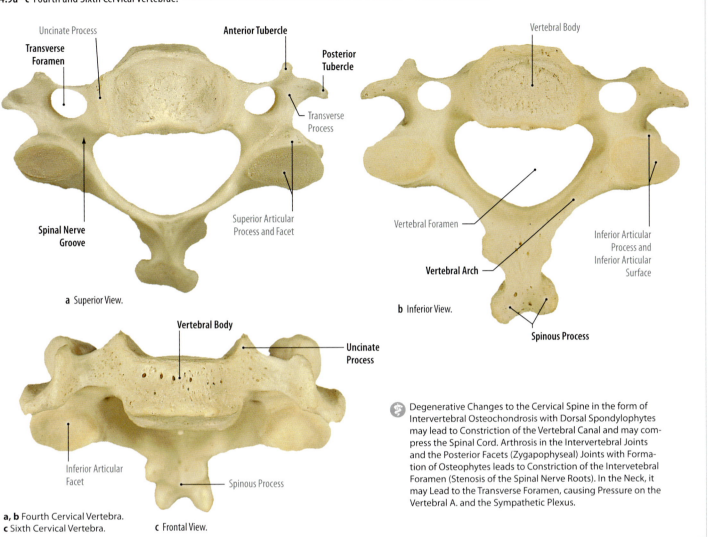

Uncinate Process

Transverse Foramen

Anterior Tubercle

Posterior Tubercle

Transverse Process

Vertebral Body

Spinal Nerve Groove

Superior Articular Process and Facet

Vertebral Foramen

Vertebral Arch

Inferior Articular Process and Inferior Articular Surface

Spinous Process

a Superior View.

b Inferior View.

Vertebral Body

Uncinate Process

Inferior Articular Facet

Spinous Process

a, b Fourth Cervical Vertebra.
c Sixth Cervical Vertebra.

c Frontal View.

Degenerative Changes to the Cervical Spine in the form of Intervertebral Osteochondrosis with Dorsal Spondylophytes may lead to Constriction of the Vertebral Canal and may compress the Spinal Cord. Arthrosis in the Intervertebral Joints and the Posterior Facets (Zygapophyseal) Joints with Formation of Osteophytes leads to Constriction of the Intervetebral Foramen (Stenosis of the Spinal Nerve Roots). In the Neck, it may Lead to the Transverse Foramen, causing Pressure on the Vertebral A. and the Sympathetic Plexus.

4.10 Skeletal Part of a Right Sixth Costovertebral Joint, Joint Areas of the Fifth and Sixth Thoracic Vertebrae: Right Lateral View.

All Superior Articular Surfaces face Posteriorly; all Inferior Articular Surfaces face Anteriorly.

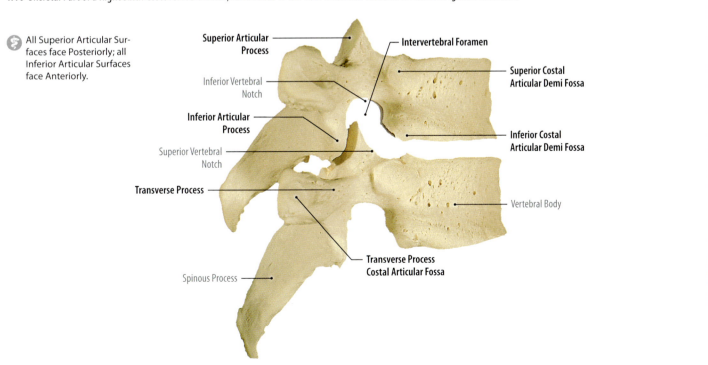

Superior Articular Process

Intervertebral Foramen

Inferior Vertebral Notch

Superior Costal Articular Demi Fossa

Inferior Articular Process

Superior Vertebral Notch

Inferior Costal Articular Demi Fossa

Transverse Process

Vertebral Body

Transverse Process Costal Articular Fossa

Spinous Process

Skeleton and Joints

Costovertebral Joints

4.11a–d Skeletal Part of the Right Lateral Sixth Costovertebral Joint.

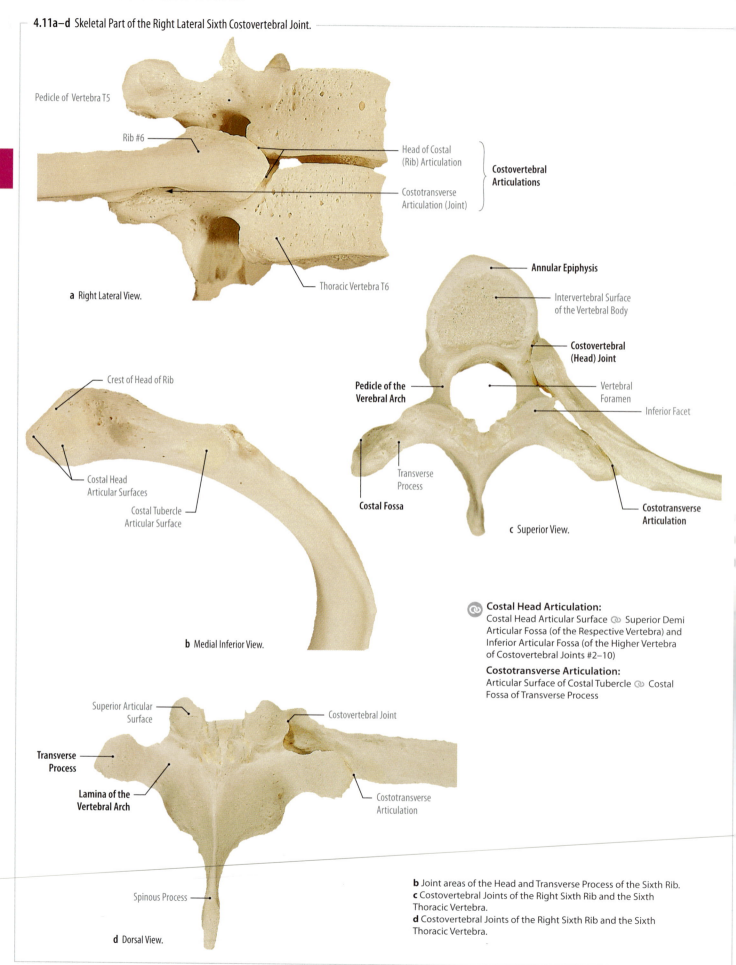

Pedicle of Vertebra T5

Rib #6

Head of Costal (Rib) Articulation

Costotransverse Articulation (Joint)

Costovertebral Articulations

Thoracic Vertebra T6

a Right Lateral View.

Annular Epiphysis

Intervertebral Surface of the Vertebral Body

Costovertebral (Head) Joint

Pedicle of the Verebral Arch

Vertebral Foramen

Inferior Facet

Transverse Process

Costal Fossa

Costotransverse Articulation

c Superior View.

Crest of Head of Rib

Costal Head Articular Surfaces

Costal Tubercle Articular Surface

b Medial Inferior View.

Costal Head Articulation:
Costal Head Articular Surface ◎ Superior Demi Articular Fossa (of the Respective Vertebra) and Inferior Articular Fossa (of the Higher Vertebra of Costovertebral Joints #2–10)

Costotransverse Articulation:
Articular Surface of Costal Tubercle ◎ Costal Fossa of Transverse Process

Superior Articular Surface

Costovertebral Joint

Transverse Process

Lamina of the Vertebral Arch

Costotransverse Articulation

Spinous Process

d Dorsal View.

b Joint areas of the Head and Transverse Process of the Sixth Rib.
c Costovertebral Joints of the Right Sixth Rib and the Sixth Thoracic Vertebra.
d Costovertebral Joints of the Right Sixth Rib and the Sixth Thoracic Vertebra.

Lumbar Spine

4.12a–d Lumbar Spine (Lumbar Vertebrae L1 – L5).

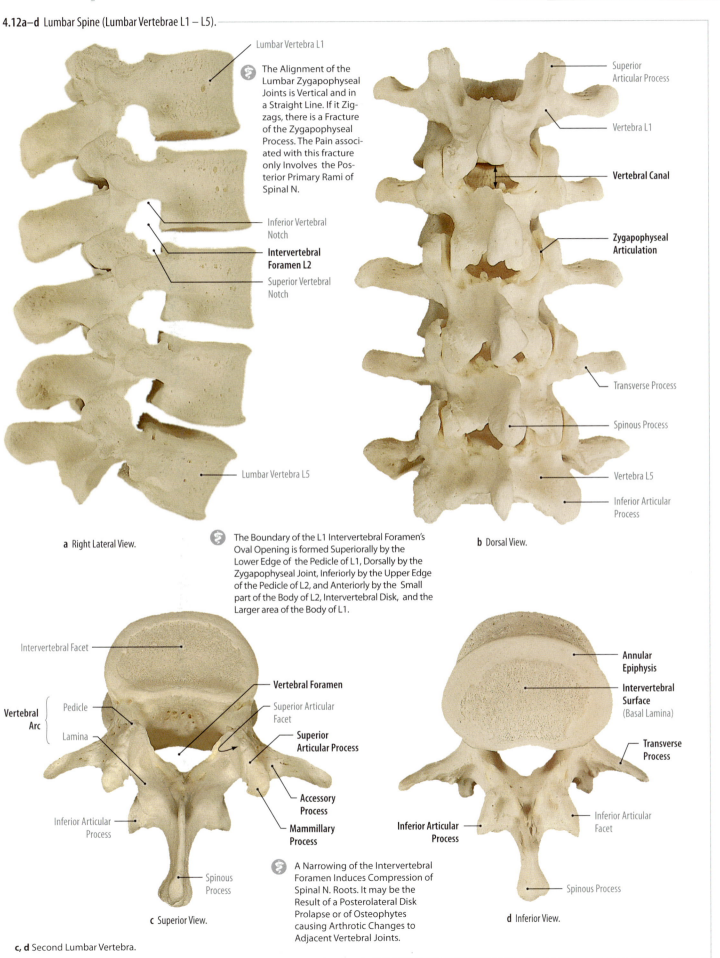

Lumbar Vertebra L1

The Alignment of the Lumbar Zygapophyseal Joints is Vertical and in a Straight Line. If it Zigzags, there is a Fracture of the Zygapophyseal Process. The Pain associated with this fracture only Involves the Posterior Primary Rami of Spinal N.

Inferior Vertebral Notch

Intervertebral Foramen L2

Superior Vertebral Notch

Lumbar Vertebra L5

Superior Articular Process

Vertebra L1

Vertebral Canal

Zygapophyseal Articulation

Transverse Process

Spinous Process

Vertebra L5

Inferior Articular Process

a Right Lateral View.

The Boundary of the L1 Intervertebral Foramen's Oval Opening is formed Superiorally by the Lower Edge of the Pedicle of L1, Dorsally by the Zygapophyseal Joint, Inferiorly by the Upper Edge of the Pedicle of L2, and Anteriorly by the Small part of the Body of L2, Intervertebral Disk, and the Larger area of the Body of L1.

b Dorsal View.

Intervertebral Facet

Vertebral Arc { Pedicle / Lamina

Vertebral Foramen

Superior Articular Facet

Superior Articular Process

Accessory Process

Mammillary Process

Inferior Articular Process

Spinous Process

c Superior View.

A Narrowing of the Intervertebral Foramen Induces Compression of Spinal N. Roots. It may be the Result of a Posterolateral Disk Prolapse or of Osteophytes causing Arthrotic Changes to Adjacent Vertebral Joints.

Annular Epiphysis

Intervertebral Surface (Basal Lamina)

Transverse Process

Inferior Articular Facet

Inferior Articular Process

Spinous Process

d Inferior View.

c, d Second Lumbar Vertebra.

Skeleton and Joints

4.13a,b Sacrum (Sacral Bone) and Coccyx (Coccygeal Bone).

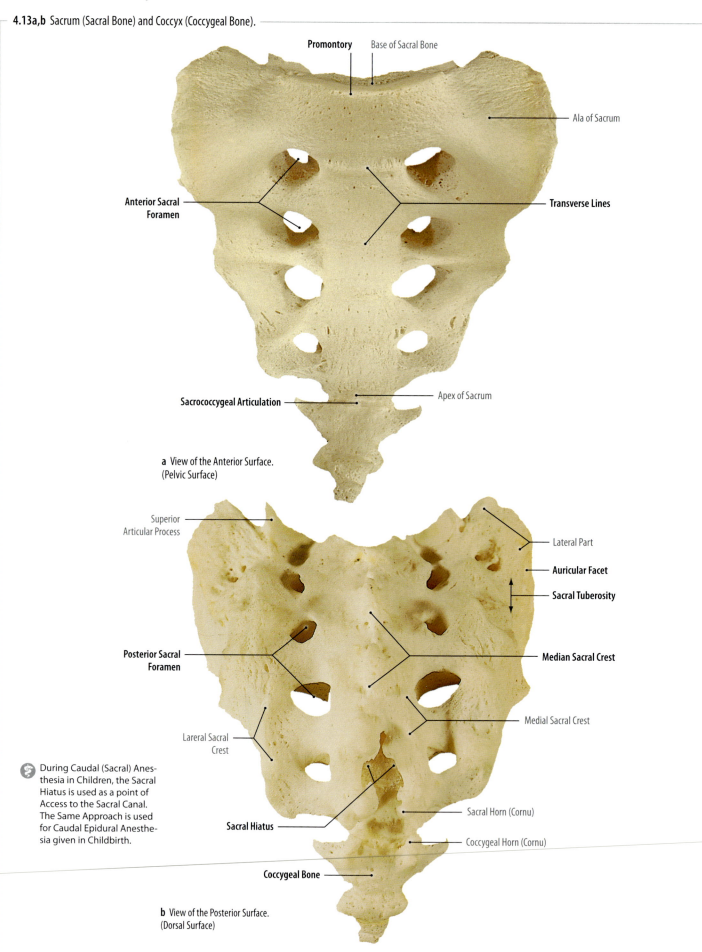

Promontory Base of Sacral Bone

Ala of Sacrum

Anterior Sacral Foramen

Transverse Lines

Sacrococcygeal Articulation Apex of Sacrum

a View of the Anterior Surface.
(Pelvic Surface)

Superior Articular Process

Lateral Part

Auricular Facet

Sacral Tuberosity

Posterior Sacral Foramen

Median Sacral Crest

Medial Sacral Crest

Lareral Sacral Crest

During Caudal (Sacral) Anesthesia in Children, the Sacral Hiatus is used as a point of Access to the Sacral Canal. The Same Approach is used for Caudal Epidural Anesthesia given in Childbirth.

Sacral Horn (Cornu)

Sacral Hiatus

Coccygeal Horn (Cornu)

Coccygeal Bone

b View of the Posterior Surface.
(Dorsal Surface)

Sacrum and Coccyx · Lumbosacral Transition

4.14a,b Sacrum (Sacral Bone).

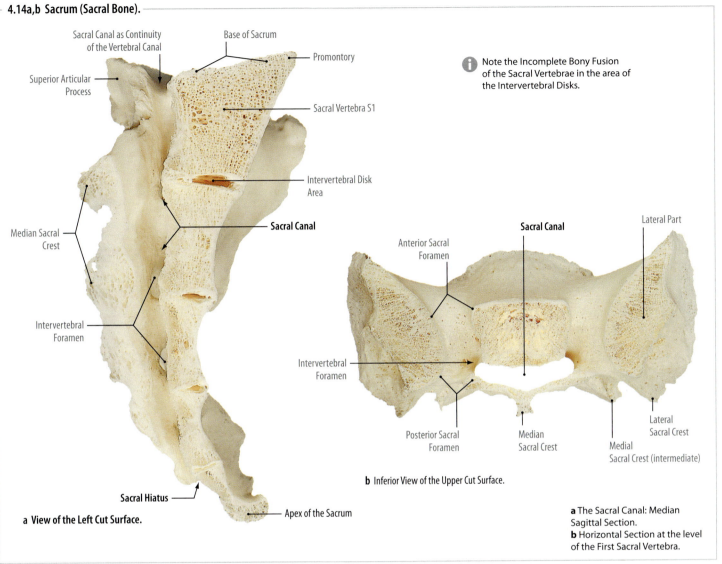

Sacral Canal as Continuity of the Vertebral Canal

Base of Sacrum

Promontory

Superior Articular Process

Sacral Vertebra S1

Intervertebral Disk Area

Median Sacral Crest

Sacral Canal

Intervertebral Foramen

Sacral Hiatus

Apex of the Sacrum

a View of the Left Cut Surface.

ⓘ Note the Incomplete Bony Fusion of the Sacral Vertebrae in the area of the Intervertebral Disks.

Anterior Sacral Foramen

Sacral Canal

Lateral Part

Intervertebral Foramen

Posterior Sacral Foramen

Median Sacral Crest

Medial Sacral Crest (intermediate)

Lateral Sacral Crest

b Inferior View of the Upper Cut Surface.

a The Sacral Canal: Median Sagittal Section.
b Horizontal Section at the level of the First Sacral Vertebra.

4.15 Skeletal Part of the Lumbosacral Joint (Articulation): Left Lateral View.

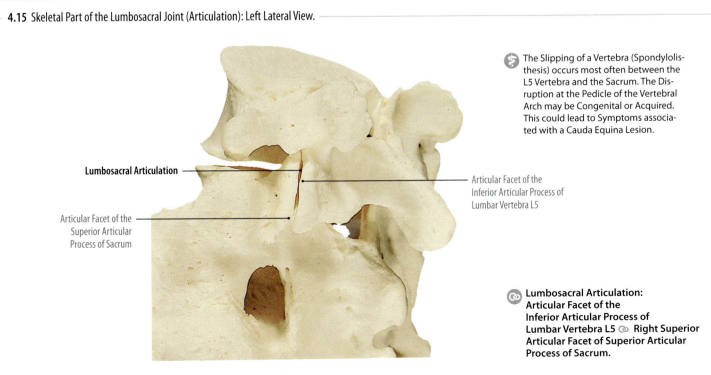

Lumbosacral Articulation

Articular Facet of the Superior Articular Process of Sacrum

The Slipping of a Vertebra (Spondylolisthesis) occurs most often between the L5 Vertebra and the Sacrum. The Disruption at the Pedicle of the Vertebral Arch may be Congenital or Acquired. This could lead to Symptoms associated with a Cauda Equina Lesion.

Articular Facet of the Inferior Articular Process of Lumbar Vertebra L5

Lumbosacral Articulation: Articular Facet of the Inferior Articular Process of Lumbar Vertebra L5 ⟳ Right Superior Articular Facet of Superior Articular Process of Sacrum.

Skeleton and Joints

Ligaments of the Spinal Column

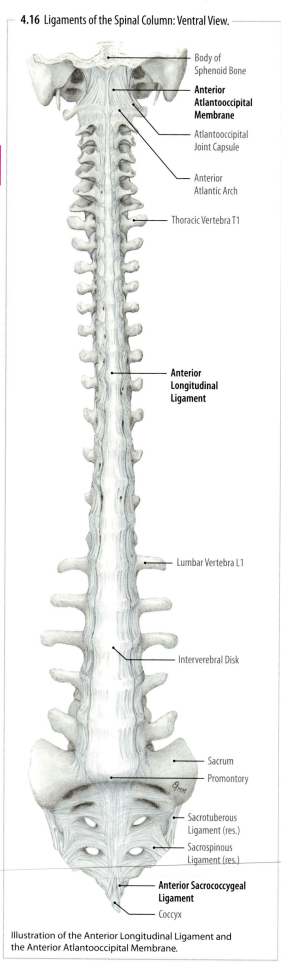

Body of
Sphenoid Bone

**Anterior
Atlantooccipital
Membrane**

Atlantooccipital
Joint Capsule

Anterior
Atlantic Arch

Thoracic Vertebra T1

**Anterior
Longitudinal
Ligament**

Lumbar Vertebra L1

Interverebral Disk

Sacrum

Promontory

Sacrotuberous
Ligament (res.)

Sacrospinous
Ligament (res.)

**Anterior Sacrococcygeal
Ligament**

Coccyx

Illustration of the Anterior Longitudinal Ligament and
the Anterior Atlantooccipital Membrane.

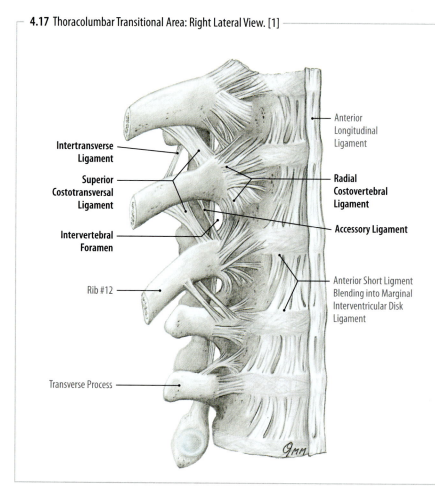

**Intertransverse
Ligament**

**Superior
Costotransversal
Ligament**

**Intervertebral
Foramen**

Rib #12

Transverse Process

Anterior
Longitudinal
Ligament

**Radial
Costovertebral
Ligament**

Accessory Ligament

Anterior Short Ligment
Blending into Marginal
Interventricular Disk
Ligament

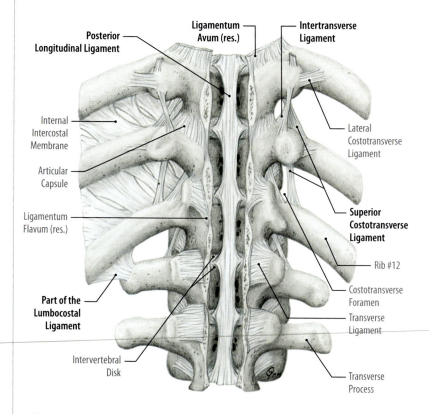

**Posterior
Longitudinal Ligament**

**Ligamentum
Avum (res.)**

**Intertransverse
Ligament**

Internal
Intercostal
Membrane

Articular
Capsule

Ligamentum
Flavum (res.)

**Part of the
Lumbocostal
Ligament**

Intervertebral
Disk

Lateral
Costotransverse
Ligament

**Superior
Costotransverse
Ligament**

Rib #12

Costotransverse
Foramen

Transverse
Ligament

Transverse
Process

To illustrate the Posterior Longitudinal Ligament, the Spinal Canal has been Opened by Removing
the Laminae of the Vertebral Arches.

4.19 Ligaments of the Costovertebral Joints: Dorsal Superior View. [1]

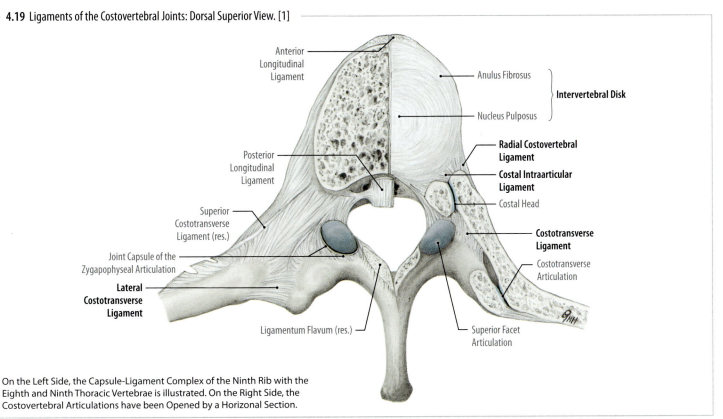

Anterior Longitudinal Ligament

Anulus Fibrosus

Nucleus Pulposus

Intervertebral Disk

Posterior Longitudinal Ligament

Radial Costovertebral Ligament

Costal Intraarticular Ligament

Costal Head

Superior Costotransverse Ligament (res.)

Costotransverse Ligament

Joint Capsule of the Zygapophyseal Articulation

Costotransverse Articulation

Lateral Costotransverse Ligament

Ligamentum Flavum (res.)

Superior Facet Articulation

On the Left Side, the Capsule-Ligament Complex of the Ninth Rib with the Eighth and Ninth Thoracic Vertebrae is illustrated. On the Right Side, the Costovertebral Articulations have been Opened by a Horizonal Section.

4.20 Capitular Articulation of the Rib: Right Lateral View.

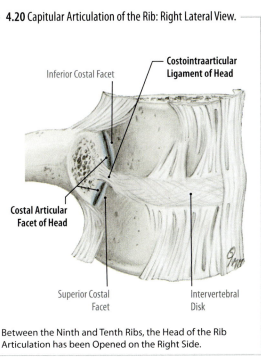

Costointraarticular Ligament of Head

Inferior Costal Facet

Costal Articular Facet of Head

Superior Costal Facet

Intervertebral Disk

Between the Ninth and Tenth Ribs, the Head of the Rib Articulation has been Opened on the Right Side.

4.21 Ligaments of the Spinal Column.

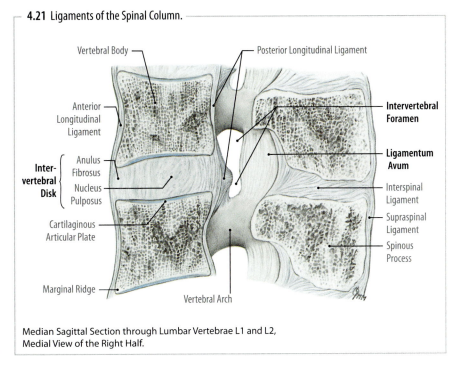

Vertebral Body

Posterior Longitudinal Ligament

Anterior Longitudinal Ligament

Intervertebral Foramen

Inter-vertebral Disk

Anulus Fibrosus

Nucleus Pulposus

Ligamentum Avum

Interspinal Ligament

Cartilaginous Articular Plate

Supraspinal Ligament

Spinous Process

Marginal Ridge

Vertebral Arch

Median Sagittal Section through Lumbar Vertebrae L1 and L2, Medial View of the Right Half.

Left: Primary Costal Synchondrosis, Radiating Sternocostal Ligament, Intraarticular Sternocostal Ligament, Costoclavicular Ligament.
▪ Fig. 6.12.

Center: External Intercostal Membrane, Costoxiphoid Ligament, External Sternal Membrane, Radiating Sternocostal Ligament.
▪ Fig. 4.30.

Right: Internal Sternal Membrane, Radiating Sternocostal Ligament.
▪ Fig. 4.31.

▪ Fig. 6.12

▪ Fig. 4.30

▪ Fig. 4.31

Skeleton and Joints

Ligament System and Joints of the Head

4.22a–c Joints of the Head: Ligament Complex in Various Partial Views. [b 1, c 6]

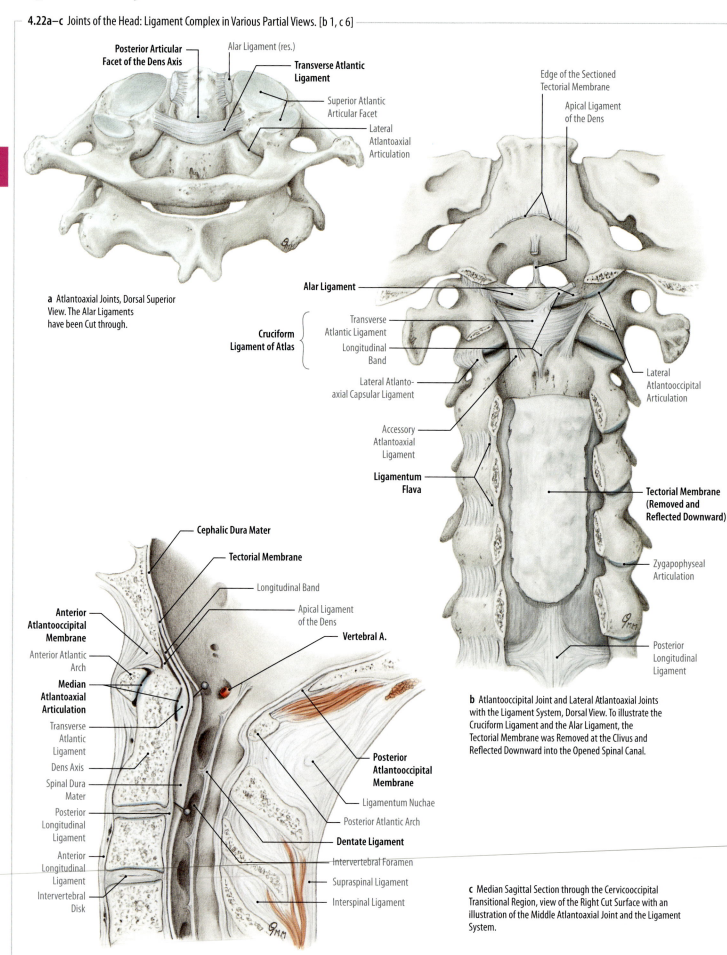

Posterior Articular Facet of the Dens Axis

Alar Ligament (res.)

Transverse Atlantic Ligament

Superior Atlantic Articular Facet

Lateral Atlantoaxial Articulation

a Atlantoaxial Joints, Dorsal Superior View. The Alar Ligaments have been Cut through.

Edge of the Sectioned Tectorial Membrane

Apical Ligament of the Dens

Alar Ligament

Cruciform Ligament of Atlas

Transverse Atlantic Ligament

Longitudinal Band

Lateral Atlanto-axial Capsular Ligament

Accessory Atlantoaxial Ligament

Ligamentum Flava

Lateral Atlantooccipital Articulation

Tectorial Membrane (Removed and Reflected Downward)

Zygapophyseal Articulation

Posterior Longitudinal Ligament

b Atlantooccipital Joint and Lateral Atlantoaxial Joints with the Ligament System, Dorsal View. To illustrate the Cruciform Ligament and the Alar Ligament, the Tectorial Membrane was Removed at the Clivus and Reflected Downward into the Opened Spinal Canal.

Cephalic Dura Mater

Tectorial Membrane

Longitudinal Band

Apical Ligament of the Dens

Vertebral A.

Anterior Atlantooccipital Membrane

Anterior Atlantic Arch

Median Atlantoaxial Articulation

Transverse Atlantic Ligament

Dens Axis

Spinal Dura Mater

Posterior Longitudinal Ligament

Anterior Longitudinal Ligament

Intervertebral Disk

Posterior Atlantooccipital Membrane

Ligamentum Nuchae

Posterior Atlantic Arch

Dentate Ligament

Intervertebral Foramen

Supraspinal Ligament

Interspinal Ligament

c Median Sagittal Section through the Cervicooccipital Transitional Region, view of the Right Cut Surface with an illustration of the Middle Atlantoaxial Joint and the Ligament System.

4.23 Transversal Section through an Intervertebral Disk in the Lumbar Area: Superior View.

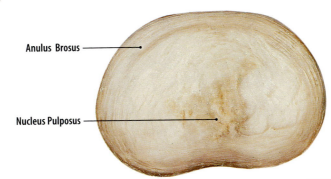

Anulus Brosus

Nucleus Pulposus

 Degeneratively Induced Changes of the Intervertebral Disks occur most often in the area of the Lumbar Spine. An Intervertebral Disk Protrusion or Prolapse causes Displacement of Disk Tissue. Displacement occurs either Posterolaterally into the Intervertebral Foramen (most common) where it Impinges on Spinal N. Roots or Protrudes into the Spinal Canal (◨ Fig. 4.21) Posteromedially where it Impinges on Roots of L3 to S1, causing Spinal Radicular Symptoms (Spinal Radicular Syndrome).

4.24 Frontal Section through the Cervical Spine of a 12-Year-Old Child.

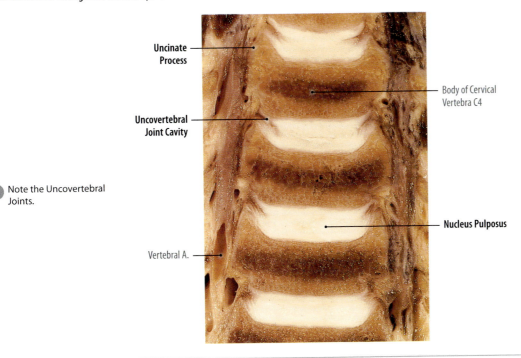

Uncinate Process

Uncovertebral Joint Cavity

Body of Cervical Vertebra C4

ⓘ Note the Uncovertebral Joints.

Nucleus Pulposus

Vertebral A.

4.25 T1-Weighted Magnetic Resonance Imaging (MRI) of the Cervical Spine of a 31-Year-Old Man: Coronary Section in the Area of the Dens Axis. [10]

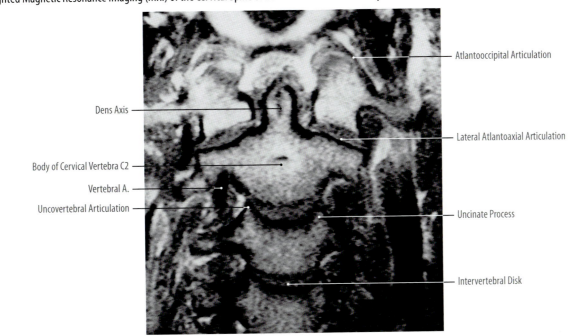

Atlantooccipital Articulation

Dens Axis

Lateral Atlantoaxial Articulation

Body of Cervical Vertebra C2

Vertebral A.

Uncovertebral Articulation

Uncinate Process

Intervertebral Disk

Skeleton and Joints

Thoracic Spine: X-Ray Images

4.26 Cervical Spine of a 23-Year-Old Woman: Lateral Optical Path, Dorsal Extension. [10]

Diagnosis after Whiplash Injury:
If a patient presents with symptoms of Cervical Pain, Spasm, or Stiffness, Examine the Lateral View for Stenosis of the Intervertebral Foramen of the Upper Cervical Vertebrae. If there are Symptoms of Tingling/Paresthesia in the Upper Limb, Examine the Intervetebral Foramen of the Lower Cervical Vertebrae. In the Anterior View, check for:

1. Alignment of C1 and C2
2. No Displacement of Lateral Atlantoaxial Articulation
3. Fracture Line on the Base of the Dens
4. Fracture of the Anterior Arch of C1

Anterior Atlantic Arch

Median Atlantoaxial Articulation

Zygapophyseal Articulation

Spinous Process of Cervical Vertebra C7

4.27 Cervical Spine of a 37-Year-Old Man: Anteroposterior (AP) Projection. [10]

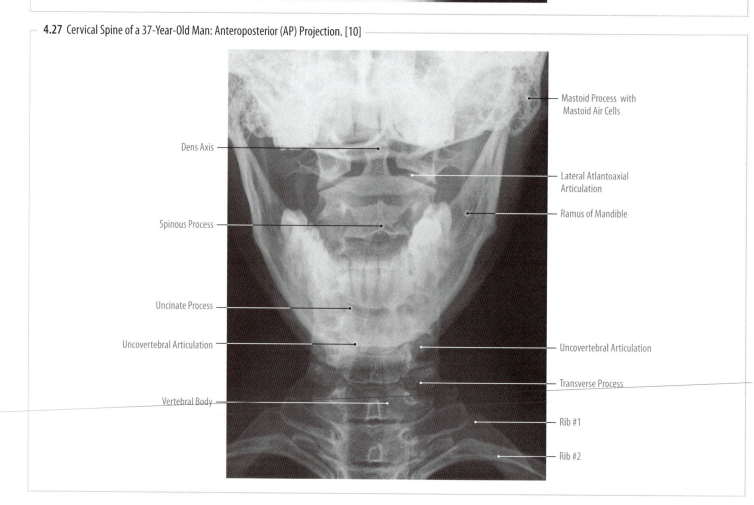

Mastoid Process with Mastoid Air Cells

Dens Axis

Lateral Atlantoaxial Articulation

Ramus of Mandible

Spinous Process

Uncinate Process

Uncovertebral Articulation

Uncovertebral Articulation

Transverse Process

Vertebral Body

Rib #1

Rib #2

4.28 Lower Thoracic Spine and Lumbar Spine of a 25-Year-Old Woman: Anteroposterior (AP) Projection. [10]

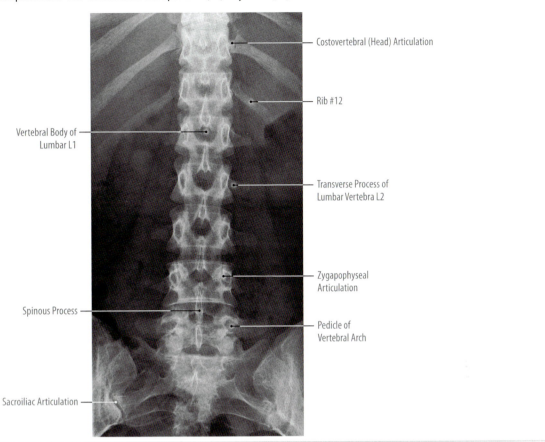

Costovertebral (Head) Articulation

Rib #12

Vertebral Body of
Lumbar L1

Transverse Process of
Lumbar Vertebra L2

Zygapophyseal
Articulation

Spinous Process

Pedicle of
Vertebral Arch

Sacroiliac Articulation

4.29 Lumbar Spine of a 23-Year-Old Woman: Lateral Projection. [10]

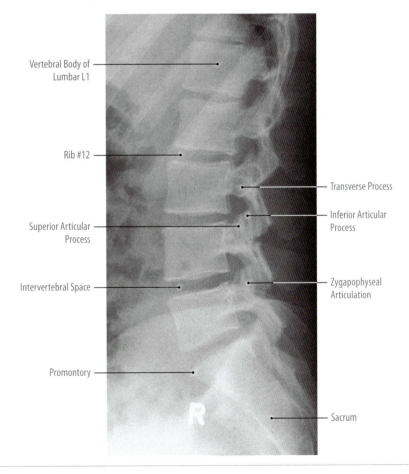

Vertebral Body of
Lumbar L1

Rib #12

Transverse Process

Inferior Articular
Process

Superior Articular
Process

Intervertebral Space

Zygapophyseal
Articulation

Promontory

Sacrum

Skeleton and Joints

Muscles of the Thoracic Wall

4.30 Muscles of the Thoracic Wall: Ventral Dorsal View. [6]

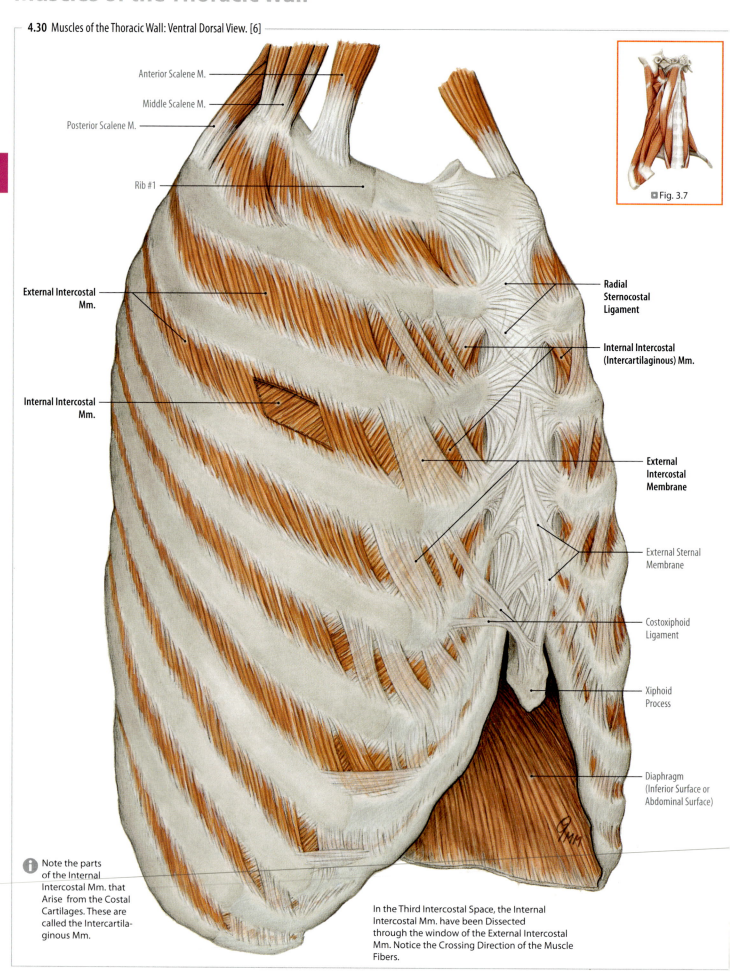

Anterior Scalene M.

Middle Scalene M.

Posterior Scalene M.

Rib #1

External Intercostal Mm.

Internal Intercostal Mm.

Radial Sternocostal Ligament

Internal Intercostal (Intercartilaginous) Mm.

External Intercostal Membrane

External Sternal Membrane

Costoxiphoid Ligament

Xiphoid Process

Diaphragm (Inferior Surface or Abdominal Surface)

□ Fig. 3.7

ⓘ Note the parts of the Internal Intercostal Mm. that Arise from the Costal Cartilages. These are called the Intercartilaginous Mm.

In the Third Intercostal Space, the Internal Intercostal Mm. have been Dissected through the window of the External Intercostal Mm. Notice the Crossing Direction of the Muscle Fibers.

Muscles of the Anterior Thoracic Wall

4.31 Muscles of the Anterior Thoracic Wall: Dorsal View. [8]

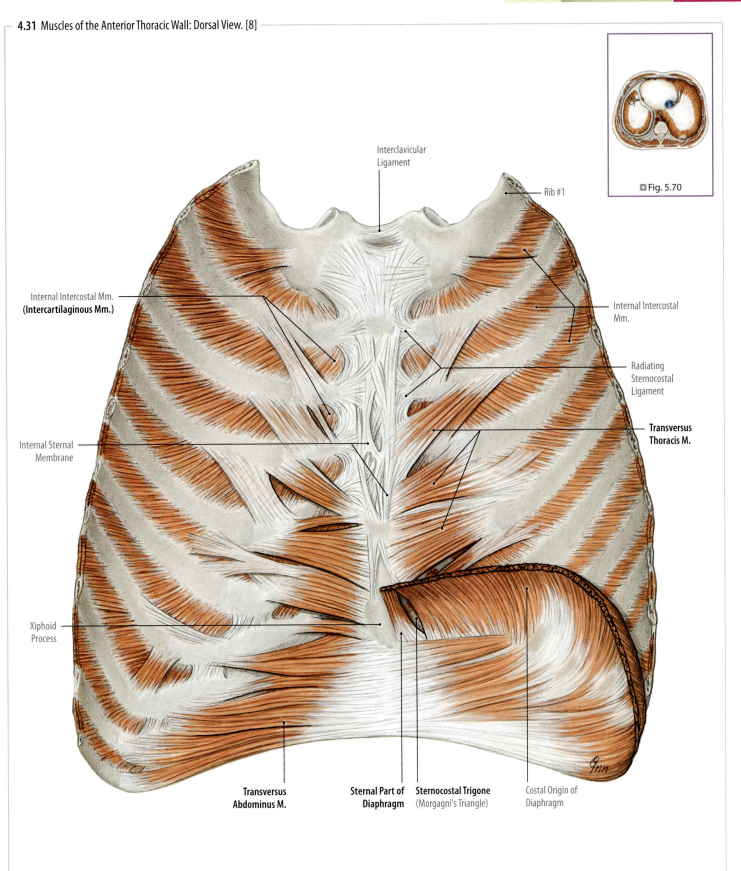

Interclavicular
Ligament

Rib #1

■ Fig. 5.70

Internal Intercostal Mm.
(Intercartilaginous Mm.)

Internal Intercostal
Mm.

Radiating
Sternocostal
Ligament

**Transversus
Thoracis M.**

Internal Sternal
Membrane

Xiphoid
Process

**Transversus
Abdominus M.**

**Sternal Part of
Diaphragm**

Sternocostal Trigone
(Morgagni's Triangle)

Costal Origin of
Diaphragm

Illustration of the Transversus Thoracis M.
On the Left Side, the Diaphragm has been
Removed.

🔄 The Sternocostal Trigone may become a
Hernial Orifice (Herniation of the Greater
Omentum or Small Intestine Retrosternally),
a Diaphragmatic Hernia (Morgagni's Hernia).

Muscles

4.32 Muscles of the Posterior Thoracic Wall and the Lumbar Region. [6]

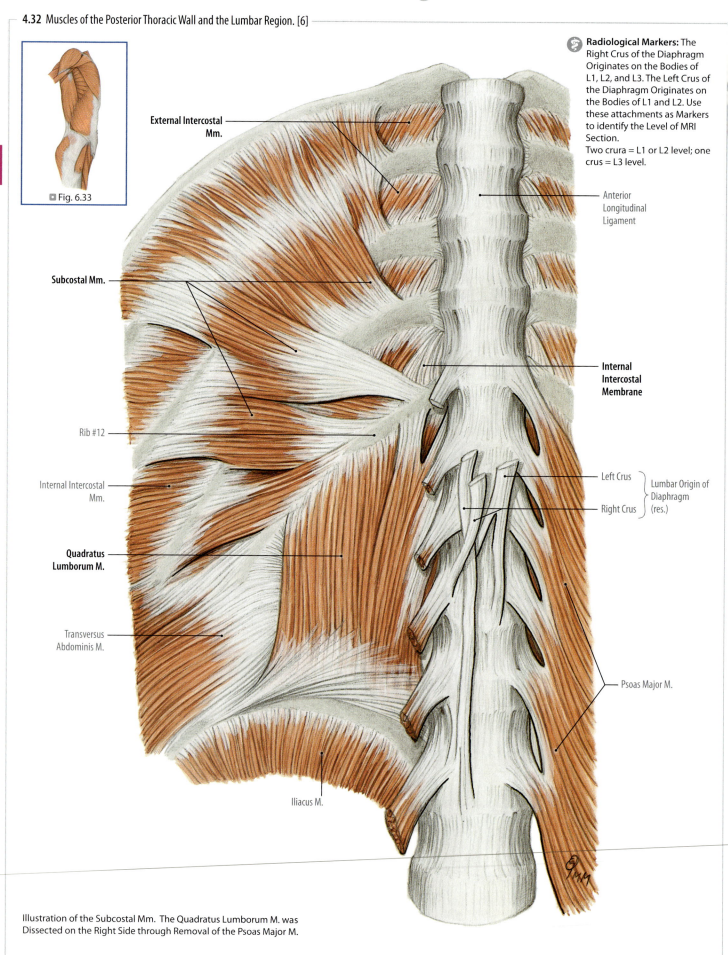

□ Fig. 6.33

Radiological Markers: The Right Crus of the Diaphragm Originates on the Bodies of L1, L2, and L3. The Left Crus of the Diaphragm Originates on the Bodies of L1 and L2. Use these attachments as Markers to identify the Level of MRI Section.
Two crura = L1 or L2 level; one crus = L3 level.

External Intercostal Mm.

Subcostal Mm.

Rib #12

Internal Intercostal Mm.

Quadratus Lumborum M.

Transversus Abdominis M.

Iliacus M.

Anterior Longitudinal Ligament

Internal Intercostal Membrane

Left Crus
Right Crus
Lumbar Origin of Diaphragm (res.)

Psoas Major M.

Illustration of the Subcostal Mm. The Quadratus Lumborum M. was Dissected on the Right Side through Removal of the Psoas Major M.

Muscles of the Thoracic and Abdominal Walls

4.33 Muscles of the Anterior Body Wall. [1]

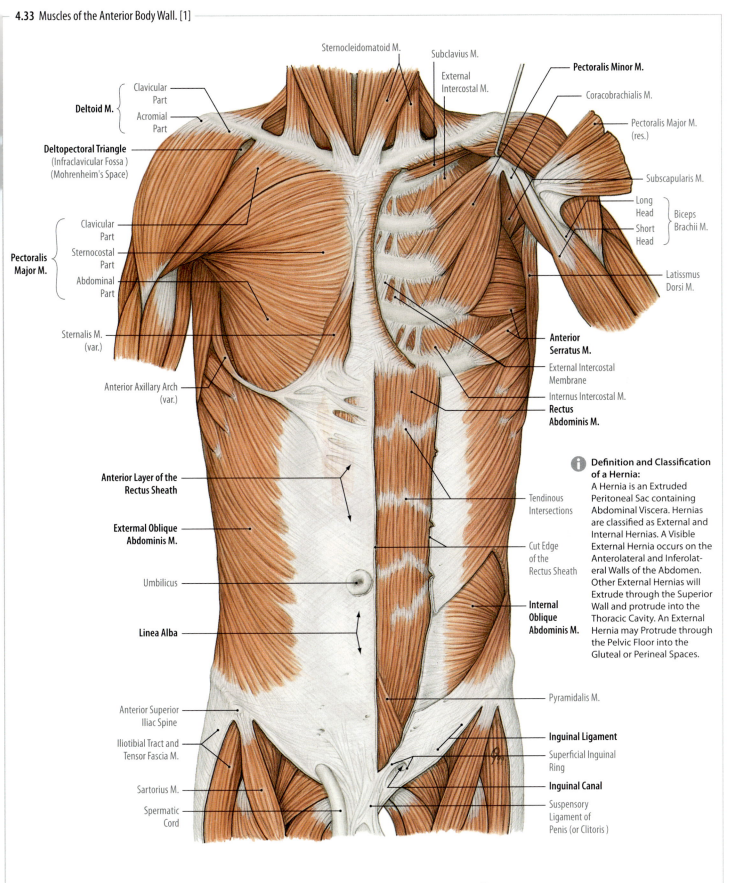

Sternocleidomastoid M.

Subclavius M.

External Intercostal M.

Pectoralis Minor M.

Coracobrachialis M.

Pectoralis Major M. (res.)

Subscapularis M.

Long Head
Short Head } Biceps Brachii M.

Latissimus Dorsi M.

Deltoid M. { Clavicular Part / Acromial Part

Deltopectoral Triangle (Infraclavicular Fossa) (Mohrenheim's Space)

Pectoralis Major M. { Clavicular Part / Sternocostal Part / Abdominal Part

Sternalis M. (var.)

Anterior Axillary Arch (var.)

Anterior Serratus M.

External Intercostal Membrane

Internus Intercostal M.

Rectus Abdominis M.

Anterior Layer of the Rectus Sheath

External Oblique Abdominis M.

Umbilicus

Linea Alba

Tendinous Intersections

Cut Edge of the Rectus Sheath

Internal Oblique Abdominis M.

Anterior Superior Iliac Spine

Iliotibial Tract and Tensor Fascia M.

Sartorius M.

Spermatic Cord

Pyramidalis M.

Inguinal Ligament

Superficial Inguinal Ring

Inguinal Canal

Suspensory Ligament of Penis (or Clitoris)

ⓘ **Definition and Classification of a Hernia:**
A Hernia is an Extruded Peritoneal Sac containing Abdominal Viscera. Hernias are classified as External and Internal Hernias. A Visible External Hernia occurs on the Anterolateral and Inferolateral Walls of the Abdomen. Other External Hernias will Extrude through the Superior Wall and protrude into the Thoracic Cavity. An External Hernia may Protrude through the Pelvic Floor into the Gluteal or Perineal Spaces.

On the Left Side, the Pectoralis Major M. has been Removed; the Rectus Abdominis M. has been Dissected by Removing the Anterior Layer of the Rectus Sheath. In the Lower region of the Abdominal Wall, the Internal Obliquus Abdominis M. can be seen, following Fenestration of the External Obliquus Abdominis M. The Spermatic Cord has been Removed on the Left Side.

ⓘ Note the Variants in the area of the Thoracic Vestigial Remnant of the Sternalis M. (Rectus Thoracic) and the Anterior Axillary Arch.

Muscles of the Abdominal Wall

4.34 Muscles of the Anterior Body Wall. [8]

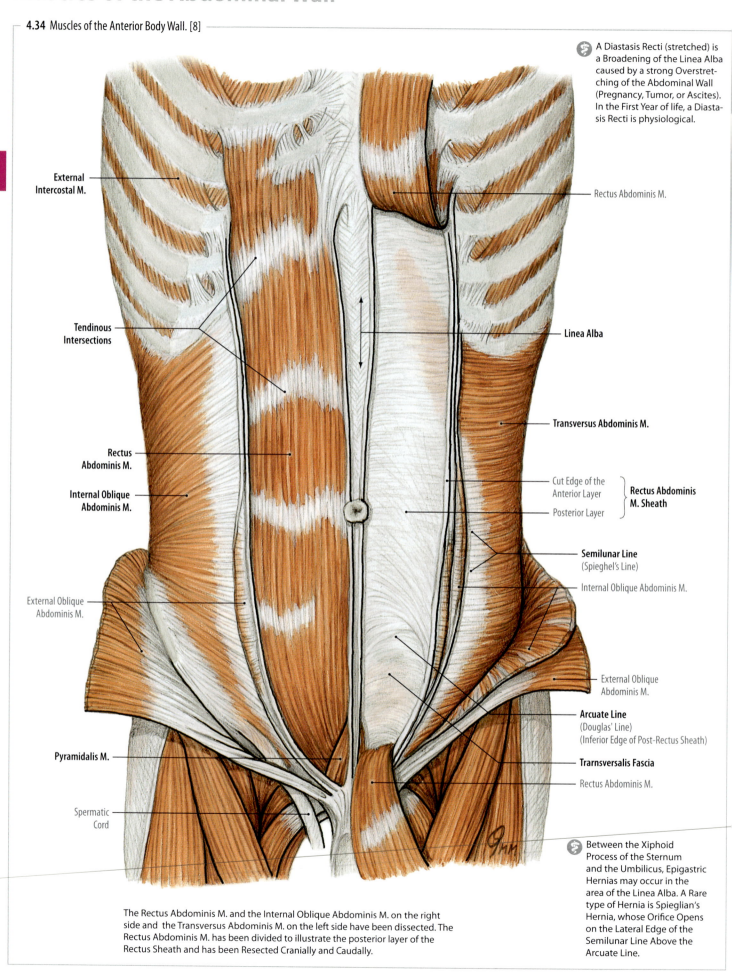

A Diastasis Recti (stretched) is a Broadening of the Linea Alba caused by a strong Overstretching of the Abdominal Wall (Pregnancy, Tumor, or Ascites). In the First Year of life, a Diastasis Recti is physiological.

External Intercostal M.

Rectus Abdominis M.

Tendinous Intersections

Linea Alba

Transversus Abdominis M.

Rectus Abdominis M.

Internal Oblique Abdominis M.

Cut Edge of the Anterior Layer

Posterior Layer

Rectus Abdominis M. Sheath

Semilunar Line (Spieghel's Line)

Internal Oblique Abdominis M.

External Oblique Abdominis M.

External Oblique Abdominis M.

Arcuate Line (Douglas' Line) (Inferior Edge of Post-Rectus Sheath)

Pyramidalis M.

Trarnsversalis Fascia

Rectus Abdominis M.

Spermatic Cord

Between the Xiphoid Process of the Sternum and the Umbilicus, Epigastric Hernias may occur in the area of the Linea Alba. A Rare type of Hernia is Spieglian's Hernia, whose Orifice Opens on the Lateral Edge of the Semilunar Line Above the Arcuate Line.

The Rectus Abdominis M. and the Internal Oblique Abdominis M. on the right side and the Transversus Abdominis M. on the left side have been dissected. The Rectus Abdominis M. has been divided to illustrate the posterior layer of the Rectus Sheath and has been Resected Cranially and Caudally.

Rectus Sheath and Inguinal Region

4.35a,b Cross-Section through the Anterior Area of the Abdominal Wall. [6]

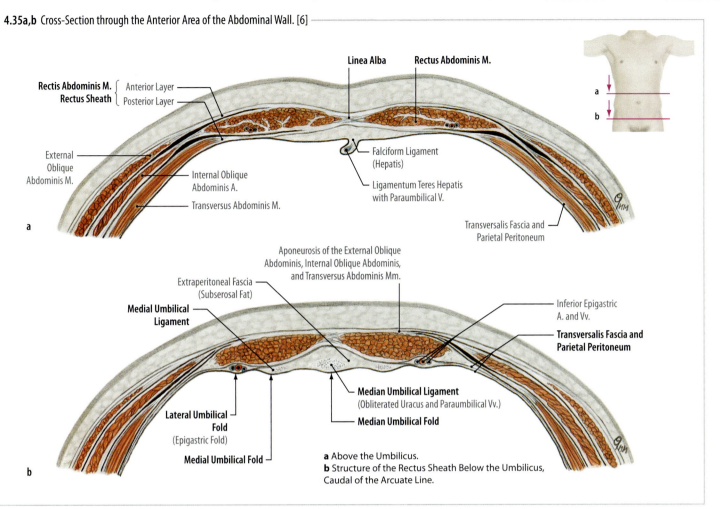

Rectis Abdominis M.
Rectus Sheath { Anterior Layer
Posterior Layer

Linea Alba   **Rectus Abdominis M.**

a
b

External
Oblique
Abdominis M.

Internal Oblique
Abdominis A.

Transversus Abdominis M.

Falciform Ligament
(Hepatis)

Ligamentum Teres Hepatis
with Paraumbilical V.

Transversalis Fascia and
Parietal Peritoneum

a

Aponeurosis of the External Oblique
Abdominis, Internal Oblique Abdominis,
and Transversus Abdominis Mm.

Extraperitoneal Fascia
(Subserosal Fat)

**Medial Umbilical
Ligament**

Inferior Epigastric
A. and Vv.

**Transversalis Fascia and
Parietal Peritoneum**

Median Umbilical Ligament
(Obliterated Uracus and Paraumbilical Vv.)

Median Umbilical Fold

**Lateral Umbilical
Fold**
(Epigastric Fold)

Medial Umbilical Fold

a Above the Umbilicus.
b Structure of the Rectus Sheath Below the Umbilicus,
Caudal of the Arcuate Line.

b

4.36 Anterior Body Wall, Inguinal Region. [6]

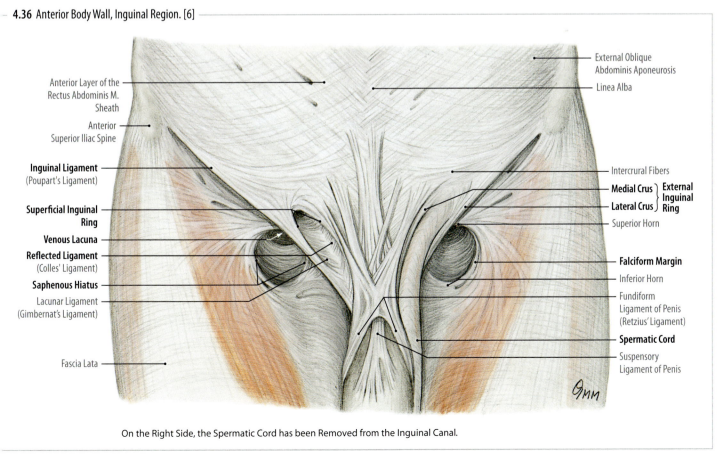

Anterior Layer of the
Rectus Abdominis M.
Sheath

Anterior
Superior Iliac Spine

Inguinal Ligament
(Poupart's Ligament)

**Superficial Inguinal
Ring**

Venous Lacuna

Reflected Ligament
(Colles' Ligament)

Saphenous Hiatus

Lacunar Ligament
(Gimbernat's Ligament)

Fascia Lata

External Oblique
Abdominis Aponeurosis

Linea Alba

Intercrural Fibers

Medial Crus } **External
Inguinal**
Lateral Crus } **Ring**

Superior Horn

Falciform Margin

Inferior Horn

Fundiform
Ligament of Penis
(Retzius' Ligament)

Spermatic Cord

Suspensory
Ligament of Penis

On the Right Side, the Spermatic Cord has been Removed from the Inguinal Canal.

Muscles

Inguinal Region

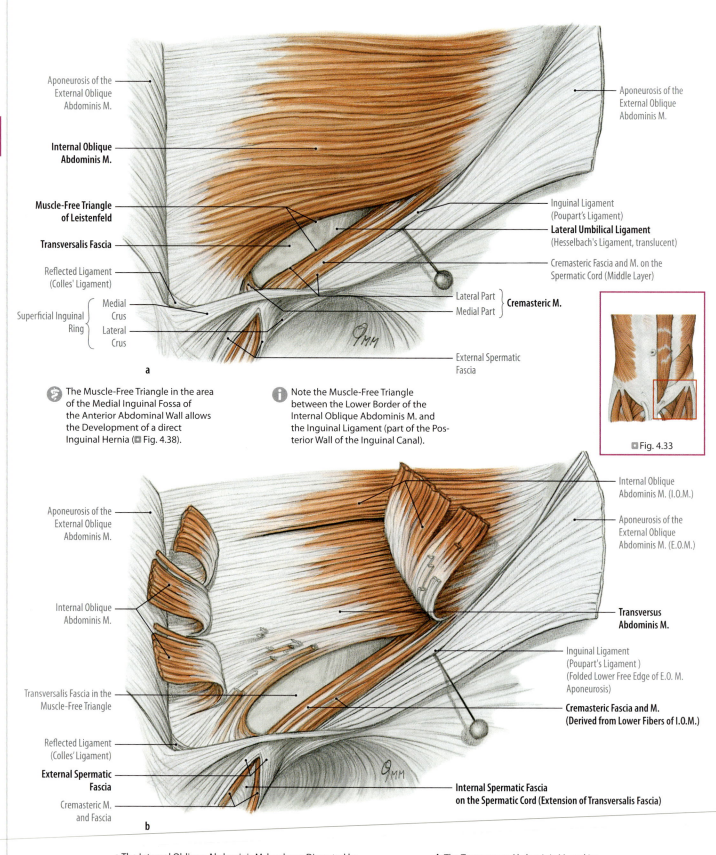

Aponeurosis of the
External Oblique
Abdominis M.

**Internal Oblique
Abdominis M.**

**Muscle-Free Triangle
of Leistenfeld**

Transversalis Fascia

Reflected Ligament
(Colles' Ligament)

Superficial Inguinal
Ring {
  Medial Crus
  Lateral Crus
}

Aponeurosis of the
External Oblique
Abdominis M.

Inguinal Ligament
(Poupart's Ligament)

Lateral Umbilical Ligament
(Hesselbach's Ligament, translucent)

Cremasteric Fascia and M. on the
Spermatic Cord (Middle Layer)

Lateral Part
Medial Part } **Cremasteric M.**

External Spermatic
Fascia

a

The Muscle-Free Triangle in the area
of the Medial Inguinal Fossa of
the Anterior Abdominal Wall allows
the Development of a direct
Inguinal Hernia (◻ Fig. 4.38).

Note the Muscle-Free Triangle
between the Lower Border of the
Internal Oblique Abdominis M. and
the Inguinal Ligament (part of the Posterior Wall of the Inguinal Canal).

◻ Fig. 4.33

Internal Oblique
Abdominis M. (I.O.M.)

Aponeurosis of the
External Oblique
Abdominis M. (E.O.M.)

Aponeurosis of the
External Oblique
Abdominis M.

Internal Oblique
Abdominis M.

**Transversus
Abdominis M.**

Inguinal Ligament
(Poupart's Ligament)
(Folded Lower Free Edge of E.O. M.
Aponeurosis)

**Cremasteric Fascia and M.
(Derived from Lower Fibers of I.O.M.)**

Transversalis Fascia in the
Muscle-Free Triangle

Reflected Ligament
(Colles' Ligament)

**External Spermatic
Fascia**

Cremasteric M.
and Fascia

**Internal Spermatic Fascia
on the Spermatic Cord (Extension of Transversalis Fascia)**

b

a The Internal Oblique Abdominis M. has been Dissected by
Splitting and retracting the Aponeurosis of the External
Oblique Abdominis M. and the Cremaster M. The Cremasteric
Fascia have been Dissected by Splitting the Internal Spermatic
Fascia.

b The Transversus Abdominis M. and its
Aponeurosis have been Dissected by
Removing the External Oblique Abdominis M.
and the Internal Oblique Abdominis M.

4.38 Internal View of Anterior Abdominal Wall in the Area of the Left Inguinal Region: Dorsal View. [6]

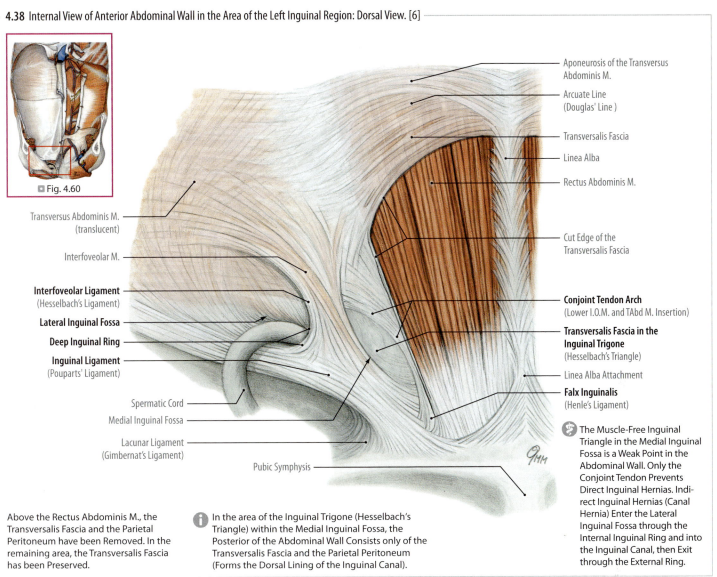

□ Fig. 4.60

Transversus Abdominis M. (translucent)

Interfoveolar M.

Interfoveolar Ligament (Hesselbach's Ligament)

Lateral Inguinal Fossa

Deep Inguinal Ring

Inguinal Ligament (Pouparts' Ligament)

Spermatic Cord

Medial Inguinal Fossa

Lacunar Ligament (Gimbernat's Ligament)

Pubic Symphysis

Aponeurosis of the Transversus Abdominis M.

Arcuate Line (Douglas' Line)

Transversalis Fascia

Linea Alba

Rectus Abdominis M.

Cut Edge of the Transversalis Fascia

Conjoint Tendon Arch (Lower I.O.M. and TAbd M. Insertion)

Transversalis Fascia in the Inguinal Trigone (Hesselbach's Triangle)

Linea Alba Attachment

Falx Inguinalis (Henle's Ligament)

The Muscle-Free Inguinal Triangle in the Medial Inguinal Fossa is a Weak Point in the Abdominal Wall. Only the Conjoint Tendon Prevents Direct Inguinal Hernias. Indirect Inguinal Hernias (Canal Hernia) Enter the Lateral Inguinal Fossa through the Internal Inguinal Ring and into the Inguinal Canal, then Exit through the External Ring.

Above the Rectus Abdominis M., the Transversalis Fascia and the Parietal Peritoneum have been Removed. In the remaining area, the Transversalis Fascia has been Preserved.

ℹ️ In the area of the Inguinal Trigone (Hesselbach's Triangle) within the Medial Inguinal Fossa, the Posterior of the Abdominal Wall Consists only of the Transversalis Fascia and the Parietal Peritoneum (Forms the Dorsal Lining of the Inguinal Canal).

4.39 Tension of the Abdominal Wall through the Muscular Slings of the Anterior Body Wall. [55]

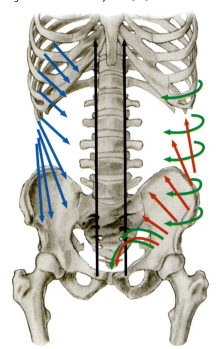

→ The External Oblique Abdominis M. Originates from the Lower Ribs and Fibers and runs Inferiorly and Anteriorly; it Inserts into the Iliac Crest. The Aponeurosis Attaches to the Anterior Superior Iliac Spine, Pubic Tubercle and Symphysis, and to the Midline of the Linea Alba.

→ The Internal Oblique Abdominis M. Originates Inferiorly from the Iliac Crest and the Lateral Half of the Inguinal Ligament and Fibers and runs Superiorly and Anteriorly. It Inserts into the Pubic Tubercle via the Conjoint Tendon, Thoracic Wall, and Linea Alba.

→ The Transversus Abdominis M. Originates from the Lower Ribs, Thoracolumbar Fascia, Iliac Crest, and one third of the Inguinal Ligament. It Inserts into the Conjoint Tendon and Linea Alba. The Muscle Fibers run Horizontally.

→ The Rectus Abdominis M. Originates from the Pubic Crest and the Anterior Ligament of Symphysis. It Inserts into the Anterior Surface of Xiphoid Process and the 5th, 6th, and 7th Costal Cartilages, and are Ensheathed by the Rectus Sheath.

I.O.M. = Internal Oblique Muscle
TAbd M. = Transversus Abdominis Muscle

Muscles

4.40a,b Diaphragm and Muscles of the Posterior Body Wall. [12]

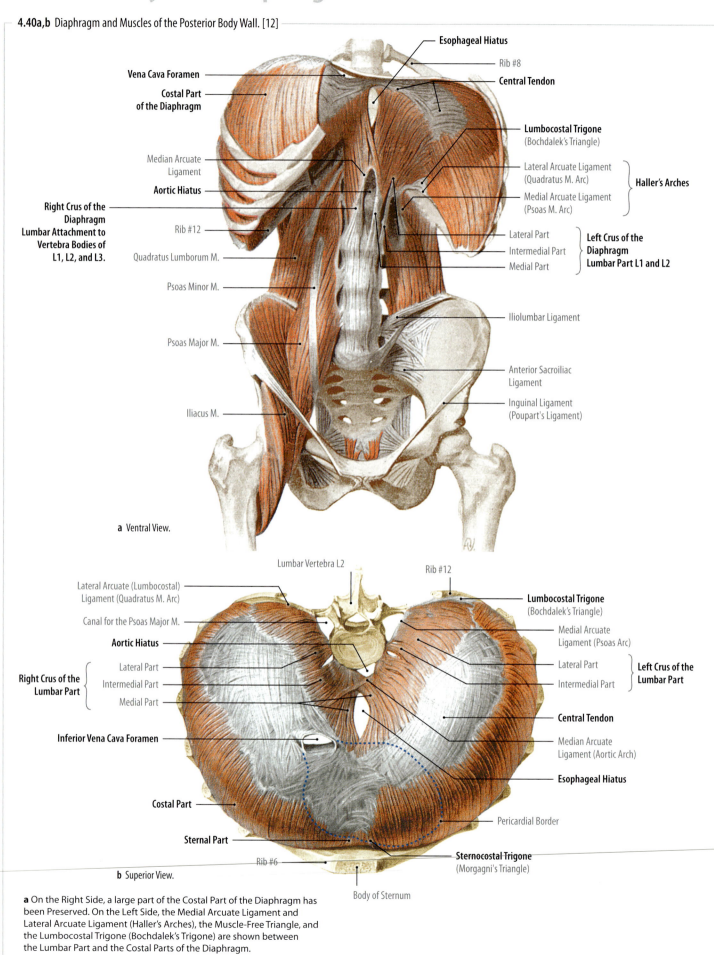

Esophageal Hiatus

Rib #8

Central Tendon

Vena Cava Foramen

Costal Part of the Diaphragm

Lumbocostal Trigone (Bochdalek's Triangle)

Median Arcuate Ligament

Lateral Arcuate Ligament (Quadratus M. Arc)

Medial Arcuate Ligament (Psoas M. Arc)

Haller's Arches

Aortic Hiatus

Right Crus of the Diaphragm Lumbar Attachment to Vertebra Bodies of L1, L2, and L3.

Lateral Part

Intermedial Part

Medial Part

Left Crus of the Diaphragm Lumbar Part L1 and L2

Rib #12

Quadratus Lumborum M.

Psoas Minor M.

Iliolumbar Ligament

Psoas Major M.

Anterior Sacroiliac Ligament

Inguinal Ligament (Poupart's Ligament)

Iliacus M.

a Ventral View.

Lumbar Vertebra L2

Rib #12

Lateral Arcuate (Lumbocostal) Ligament (Quadratus M. Arc)

Lumbocostal Trigone (Bochdalek's Triangle)

Canal for the Psoas Major M.

Medial Arcuate Ligament (Psoas Arc)

Aortic Hiatus

Lateral Part

Intermedial Part

Medial Part

Left Crus of the Lumbar Part

Lateral Part

Intermedial Part

Right Crus of the Lumbar Part

Central Tendon

Inferior Vena Cava Foramen

Median Arcuate Ligament (Aortic Arch)

Esophageal Hiatus

Costal Part

Pericardial Border

Sternal Part

Sternocostal Trigone (Morgagni's Triangle)

Rib #6

Body of Sternum

b Superior View.

a On the Right Side, a large part of the Costal Part of the Diaphragm has been Preserved. On the Left Side, the Medial Arcuate Ligament and Lateral Arcuate Ligament (Haller's Arches), the Muscle-Free Triangle, and the Lumbocostal Trigone (Bochdalek's Trigone) are shown between the Lumbar Part and the Costal Parts of the Diaphragm.

4

Muscles of the Back

4.41 Muscles of the Back: Ventral Origin and True Dorsal Origin, Dorsal View. [12]

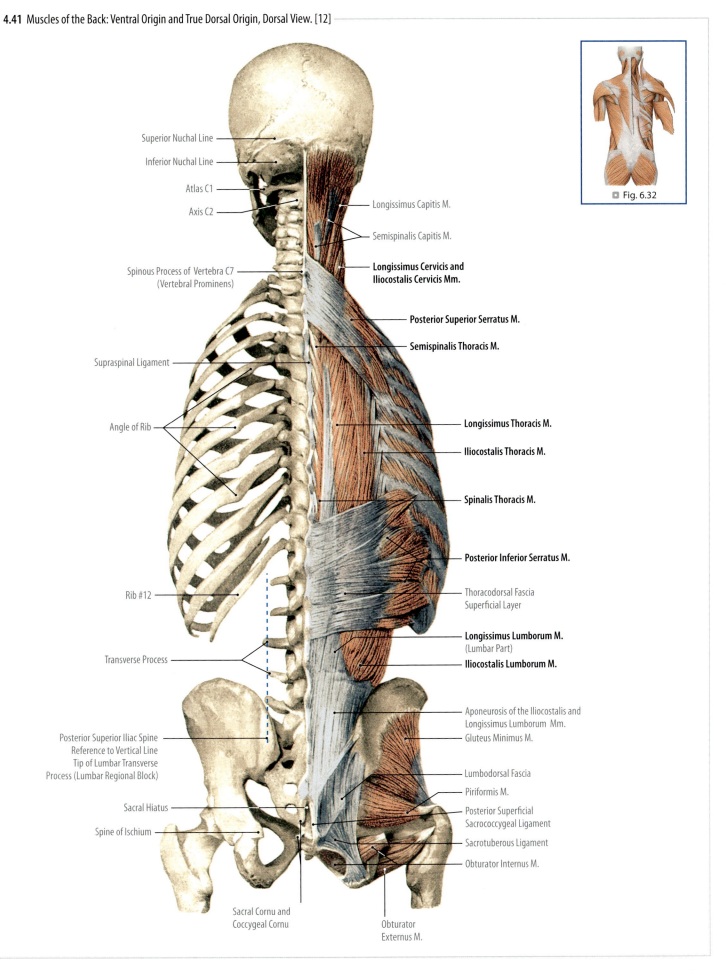

Fig. 6.32

Superior Nuchal Line

Inferior Nuchal Line

Atlas C1

Axis C2

Spinous Process of Vertebra C7
(Vertebral Prominens)

Supraspinal Ligament

Angle of Rib

Rib #12

Transverse Process

Posterior Superior Iliac Spine
Reference to Vertical Line
Tip of Lumbar Transverse
Process (Lumbar Regional Block)

Sacral Hiatus

Spine of Ischium

Sacral Cornu and
Coccygeal Cornu

Longissimus Capitis M.

Semispinalis Capitis M.

**Longissimus Cervicis and
Iliocostalis Cervicis Mm.**

Posterior Superior Serratus M.

Semispinalis Thoracis M.

Longissimus Thoracis M.

Iliocostalis Thoracis M.

Spinalis Thoracis M.

Posterior Inferior Serratus M.

Thoracodorsal Fascia
Superficial Layer

Longissimus Lumborum M.
(Lumbar Part)

Iliocostalis Lumborum M.

Aponeurosis of the Iliocostalis and
Longissimus Lumborum Mm.

Gluteus Minimus M.

Lumbodorsal Fascia

Piriformis M.

Posterior Superficial
Sacrococcygeal Ligament

Sacrotuberous Ligament

Obturator Internus M.

Obturator
Externus M.

Muscles

Muscles of the Back

4.42 Muscles of the Back (Erector Spinae - True Back): Cross-Section. [6]

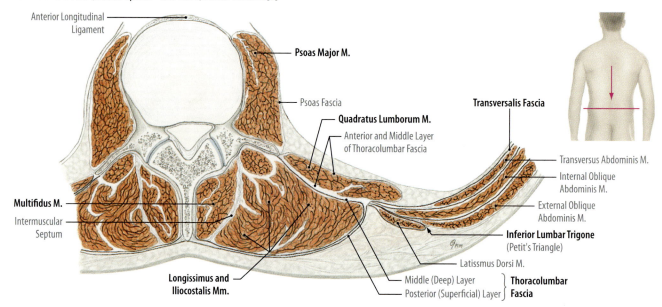

Anterior Longitudinal Ligament

Psoas Major M.

Psoas Fascia

Quadratus Lumborum M.

Anterior and Middle Layer of Thoracolumbar Fascia

Transversalis Fascia

Transversus Abdominis M.

Internal Oblique Abdominis M.

External Oblique Abdominis M.

Inferior Lumbar Trigone (Petit's Triangle)

Multifidus M.

Intermuscular Septum

Latissmus Dorsi M.

Middle (Deep) Layer

Posterior (Superficial) Layer

Thoracolumbar Fascia

Longissimus and Iliocostalis Mm.

Cross-section through the Posterior Body section at the level of the Intervertebral Disk between the Second and Third Lumbar Vertebra. Section of the Medial Tract (Multifidus M.) and the Lateral Tract (Longissimus and Iliocostalis Mm.) of the Erector Spinae Mm. of the Back and of the Anterior, Middle (deep), and Posterior Layers of the Thoracolumbar Fascia.

4.43 Muscles of the Lower Thoracic and Lumbar Regions: Dorsal View. [12]

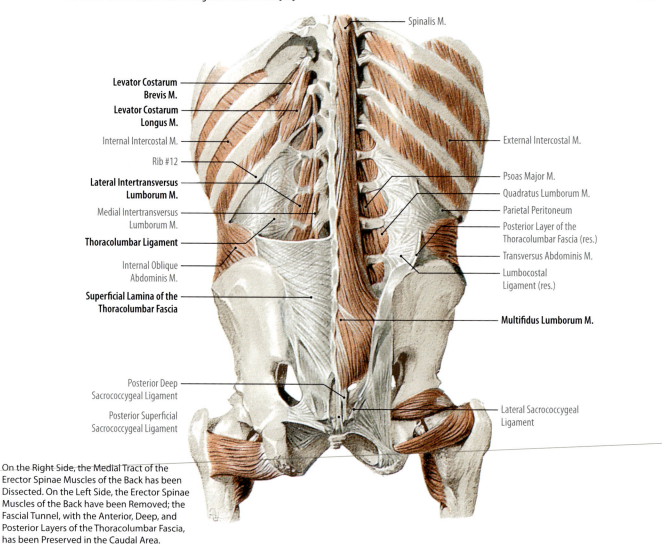

Spinalis M.

Levator Costarum Brevis M.

Levator Costarum Longus M.

Internal Intercostal M.

Rib #12

Lateral Intertransversus Lumborum M.

Medial Intertransversus Lumborum M.

Thoracolumbar Ligament

Internal Oblique Abdominis M.

Superficial Lamina of the Thoracolumbar Fascia

External Intercostal M.

Psoas Major M.

Quadratus Lumborum M.

Parietal Peritoneum

Posterior Layer of the Thoracolumbar Fascia (res.)

Transversus Abdominis M.

Lumbocostal Ligament (res.)

Multifidus Lumborum M.

Posterior Deep Sacrococcygeal Ligament

Posterior Superficial Sacrococcygeal Ligament

Lateral Sacrococcygeal Ligament

On the Right Side, the Medial Tract of the Erector Spinae Muscles of the Back has been Dissected. On the Left Side, the Erector Spinae Muscles of the Back have been Removed; the Fascial Tunnel, with the Anterior, Deep, and Posterior Layers of the Thoracolumbar Fascia, has been Preserved in the Caudal Area.

4.44 Erector Spinae Muscles of the Back: Dorsal View. [8]

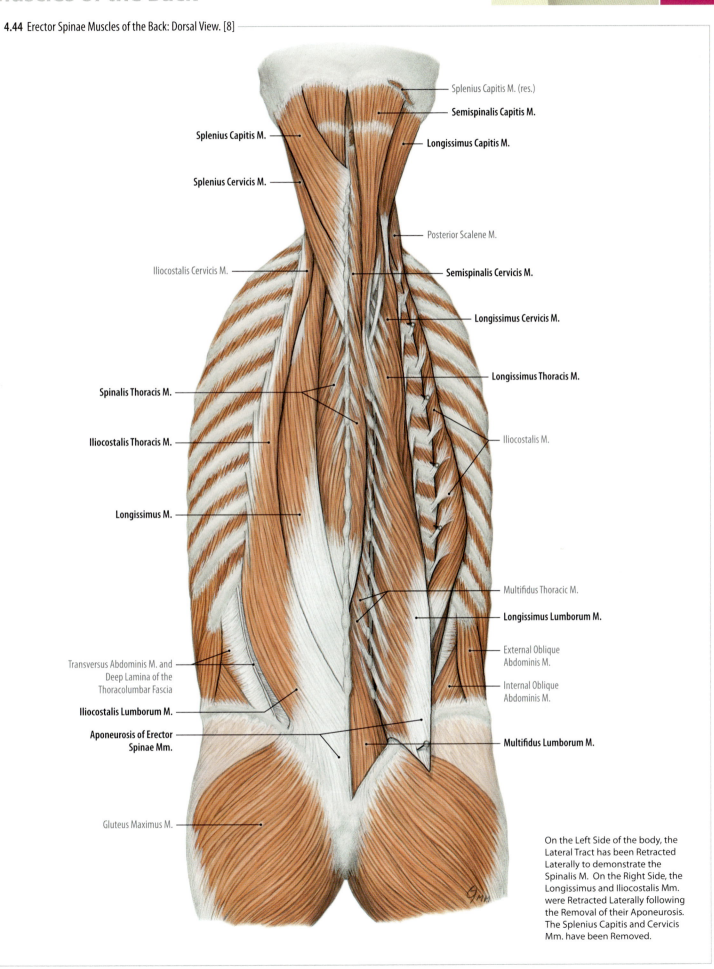

Splenius Capitis M. (res.)

Semispinalis Capitis M.

Splenius Capitis M.

Longissimus Capitis M.

Splenius Cervicis M.

Posterior Scalene M.

Iliocostalis Cervicis M.

Semispinalis Cervicis M.

Longissimus Cervicis M.

Longissimus Thoracis M.

Spinalis Thoracis M.

Iliocostalis M.

Iliocostalis Thoracis M.

Longissimus M.

Multifidus Thoracic M.

Longissimus Lumborum M.

External Oblique
Abdominis M.

Transversus Abdominis M. and
Deep Lamina of the
Thoracolumbar Fascia

Internal Oblique
Abdominis M.

Iliocostalis Lumborum M.

**Aponeurosis of Erector
Spinae Mm.**

Multifidus Lumborum M.

Gluteus Maximus M.

On the Left Side of the body, the
Lateral Tract has been Retracted
Laterally to demonstrate the
Spinalis M. On the Right Side, the
Longissimus and Iliocostalis Mm.
were Retracted Laterally following
the Removal of their Aponeurosis.
The Splenius Capitis and Cervicis
Mm. have been Removed.

Muscles

4.45a–c Erector Spinae Muscles of the Back: Illustration of Individual Muscles. [12]

4.46 Erector Spinae Muscles of the Back of the Right Side of the Body in the Thoracolumbar Transitional Area: Dorsal View. [12]

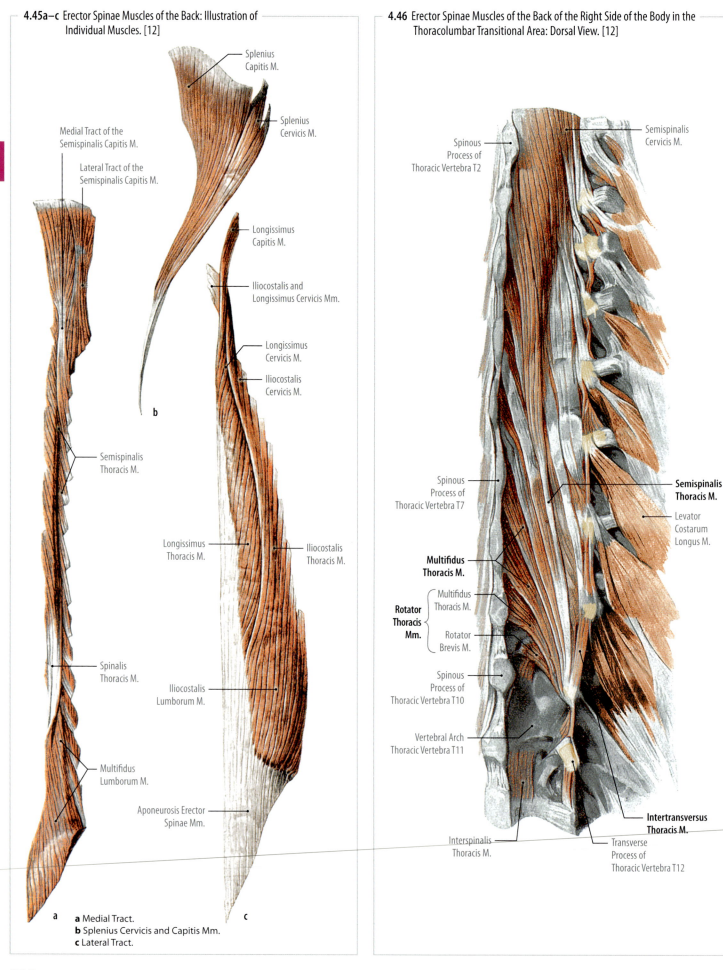

Splenius Capitis M.

Splenius Cervicis M.

Medial Tract of the Semispinalis Capitis M.

Lateral Tract of the Semispinalis Capitis M.

Longissimus Capitis M.

Iliocostalis and Longissimus Cervicis Mm.

Longissimus Cervicis M.

Iliocostalis Cervicis M.

b

Semispinalis Thoracis M.

Longissimus Thoracis M.

Iliocostalis Thoracis M.

Spinalis Thoracis M.

Iliocostalis Lumborum M.

Multifidus Lumborum M.

Aponeurosis Erector Spinae Mm.

a

a Medial Tract.
b Splenius Cervicis and Capitis Mm.
c Lateral Tract.

c

Spinous Process of Thoracic Vertebra T2

Semispinalis Cervicis M.

Spinous Process of Thoracic Vertebra T7

Semispinalis Thoracis M.

Levator Costarum Longus M.

Multifidus Thoracis M.

Multifidus Thoracis M.

Rotator Thoracis Mm.

Rotator Brevis M.

Spinous Process of Thoracic Vertebra T10

Vertebral Arch Thoracic Vertebra T11

Intertransversus Thoracis M.

Interspinalis Thoracis M.

Transverse Process of Thoracic Vertebra T12

Muscles of the Back: Function

4.47a–c Range of Movement in the Vertebral Joints and Operating Muscles.

Range of Movement of the Vertebral Joints

—— Extension (Leaning Backward) of the Body
  Iliocostalis M.
  Longissimus M.
  Splenius M.
  Spinalis M.
  Semispinalis M.
  Multifidus M.
  Trapezius M.
  Levatores Costarum Mm.

—— Flexion (Leaning Forward) of the Body
  Rectus Abdominis M.
  External Oblique Abdominis M.
  Internal Oblique Abdominis M.
  Psoas Major M.

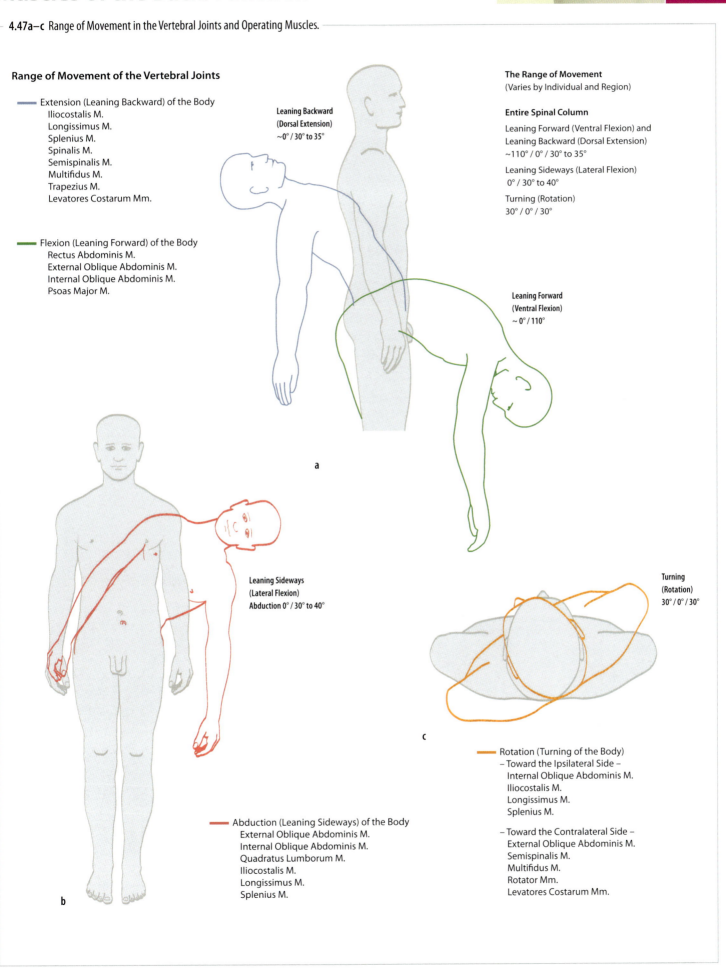

Leaning Backward
(Dorsal Extension)
~0° / 30° to 35°

Leaning Forward
(Ventral Flexion)
~ 0° / 110°

The Range of Movement
(Varies by Individual and Region)

Entire Spinal Column

Leaning Forward (Ventral Flexion) and
Leaning Backward (Dorsal Extension)
~110° / 0° / 30° to 35°

Leaning Sideways (Lateral Flexion)
 0° / 30° to 40°

Turning (Rotation)
30° / 0° / 30°

a

Leaning Sideways
(Lateral Flexion)
Abduction 0° / 30° to 40°

Turning
(Rotation)
30° / 0° / 30°

c

—— Rotation (Turning of the Body)
– Toward the Ipsilateral Side –
  Internal Oblique Abdominis M.
  Iliocostalis M.
  Longissimus M.
  Splenius M.

– Toward the Contralateral Side –
  External Oblique Abdominis M.
  Semispinalis M.
  Multifidus M.
  Rotator Mm.
  Levatores Costarum Mm.

—— Abduction (Leaning Sideways) of the Body
  External Oblique Abdominis M.
  Internal Oblique Abdominis M.
  Quadratus Lumborum M.
  Iliocostalis M.
  Longissimus M.
  Splenius M.

b

Muscles

Muscles of the Back and Neck

4.48 Erector Spinae Muscles of the Back of the Cervical Region and Muscles of the Back of the Neck: Dorsal View. [6]

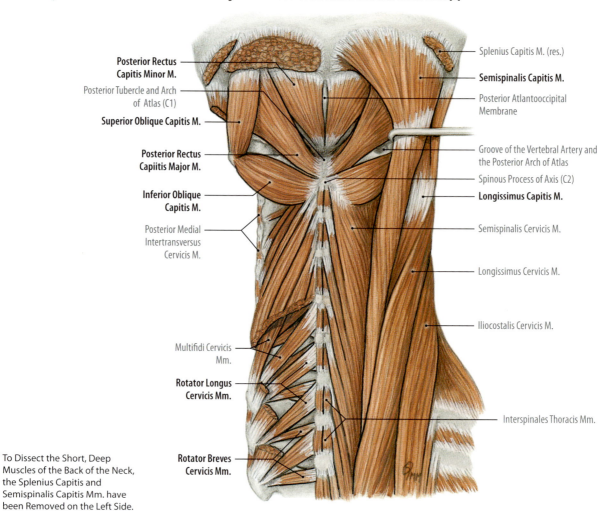

Posterior Rectus Capitis Minor M.

Posterior Tubercle and Arch of Atlas (C1)

Superior Oblique Capitis M.

Posterior Rectus Capiitis Major M.

Inferior Oblique Capitis M.

Posterior Medial Intertransversus Cervicis M.

Multifidi Cervicis Mm.

Rotator Longus Cervicis Mm.

Rotator Breves Cervicis Mm.

Splenius Capitis M. (res.)

Semispinalis Capitis M.

Posterior Atlantooccipital Membrane

Groove of the Vertebral Artery and the Posterior Arch of Atlas

Spinous Process of Axis (C2)

Longissimus Capitis M.

Semispinalis Cervicis M.

Longissimus Cervicis M.

Iliocostalis Cervicis M.

Interspinales Thoracis Mm.

To Dissect the Short, Deep Muscles of the Back of the Neck, the Splenius Capitis and Semispinalis Capitis Mm. have been Removed on the Left Side.

4.49 Arterial Blood Supply of the Body Wall in the Area of the Thorax from the Thoracic Aorta and from the Internal Thoracic (Mammary) Aa. [23]

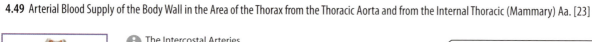

□ Fig. 5.2

ⓘ The Intercostal Arteries Build Anastomoses between the Thoracic Internal Artery and the Thoracic Aorta.

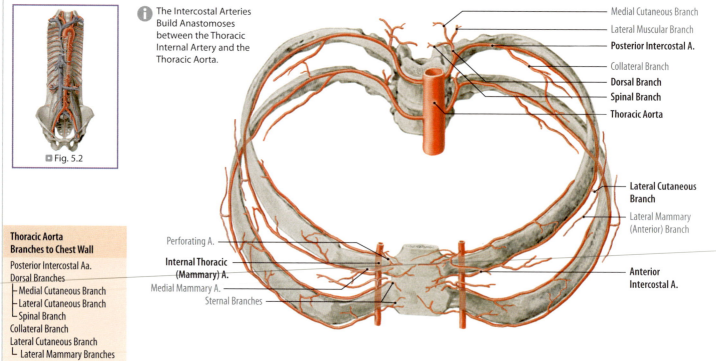

Medial Cutaneous Branch

Lateral Muscular Branch

Posterior Intercostal A.

Collateral Branch

Dorsal Branch

Spinal Branch

Thoracic Aorta

Lateral Cutaneous Branch

Lateral Mammary (Anterior) Branch

Anterior Intercostal A.

Perforating A.

Internal Thoracic (Mammary) A.

Medial Mammary A.

Sternal Branches

Thoracic Aorta Branches to Chest Wall

Posterior Intercostal Aa.
Dorsal Branches
└ Medial Cutaneous Branch
└ Lateral Cutaneous Branch
└ Spinal Branch
Collateral Branch
Lateral Cutaneous Branch
└ Lateral Mammary Branches

218

Anterior Body Wall: Arteries

4.50 Arteries of the Anterior Body Wall: Ventral View. [13]

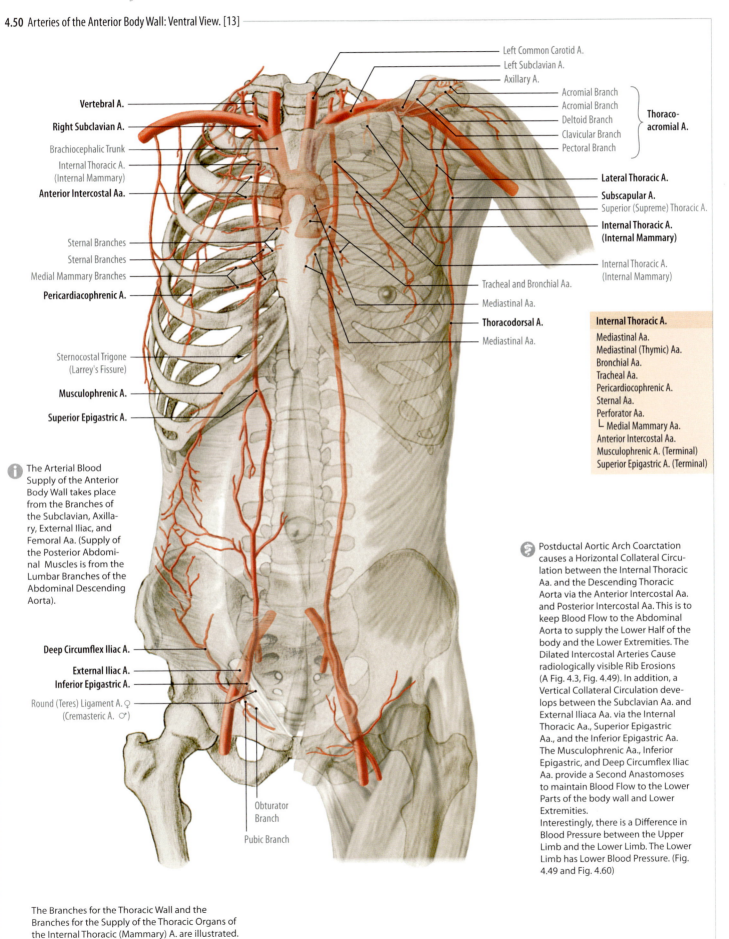

Left Common Carotid A.
Left Subclavian A.
Axillary A.
Acromial Branch
Acromial Branch
Deltoid Branch
Clavicular Branch
Pectoral Branch
} **Thoraco-acromial A.**

Vertebral A.

Right Subclavian A.

Brachiocephalic Trunk

Internal Thoracic A.
(Internal Mammary)

Anterior Intercostal Aa.

Lateral Thoracic A.

Subscapular A.

Superior (Supreme) Thoracic A.

**Internal Thoracic A.
(Internal Mammary)**

Internal Thoracic A.
(Internal Mammary)

Sternal Branches

Sternal Branches

Medial Mammary Branches

Pericardiacophrenic A.

Tracheal and Bronchial Aa.

Mediastinal Aa.

Thoracodorsal A.

Mediastinal Aa.

Sternocostal Trigone
(Larrey's Fissure)

Musculophrenic A.

Superior Epigastric A.

Internal Thoracic A.

Mediastinal Aa.
Mediastinal (Thymic) Aa.
Bronchial Aa.
Tracheal Aa.
Pericardiocophrenic A.
Sternal Aa.
Perforator Aa.
└ Medial Mammary Aa.
Anterior Intercostal Aa.
Musculophrenic A. (Terminal)
Superior Epigastric A. (Terminal)

ⓘ The Arterial Blood Supply of the Anterior Body Wall takes place from the Branches of the Subclavian, Axillary, External Iliac, and Femoral Aa. (Supply of the Posterior Abdominal Muscles is from the Lumbar Branches of the Abdominal Descending Aorta).

Deep Circumflex Iliac A.

External Iliac A.

Inferior Epigastric A.

Round (Teres) Ligament A. ♀
(Cremasteric A. ♂)

Obturator Branch

Pubic Branch

ⓢ Postductal Aortic Arch Coarctation causes a Horizontal Collateral Circulation between the Internal Thoracic Aa. and the Descending Thoracic Aorta via the Anterior Intercostal Aa. and Posterior Intercostal Aa. This is to keep Blood Flow to the Abdominal Aorta to supply the Lower Half of the body and the Lower Extremities. The Dilated Intercostal Arteries Cause radiologically visible Rib Erosions (A Fig. 4.3, Fig. 4.49). In addition, a Vertical Collateral Circulation develops between the Subclavian Aa. and External Iliaca Aa. via the Internal Thoracic Aa., Superior Epigastric Aa., and the Inferior Epigastric Aa. The Musculophrenic Aa., Inferior Epigastric, and Deep Circumflex Iliac Aa. provide a Second Anastomoses to maintain Blood Flow to the Lower Parts of the body wall and Lower Extremities.
Interestingly, there is a Difference in Blood Pressure between the Upper Limb and the Lower Limb. The Lower Limb has Lower Blood Pressure. (Fig. 4.49 and Fig. 4.60)

The Branches for the Thoracic Wall and the Branches for the Supply of the Thoracic Organs of the Internal Thoracic (Mammary) A. are illustrated.

Pathways and Topography

Body Wall: Veins

4.51a,b Veins of the Body Wall: Ventral View. [13]

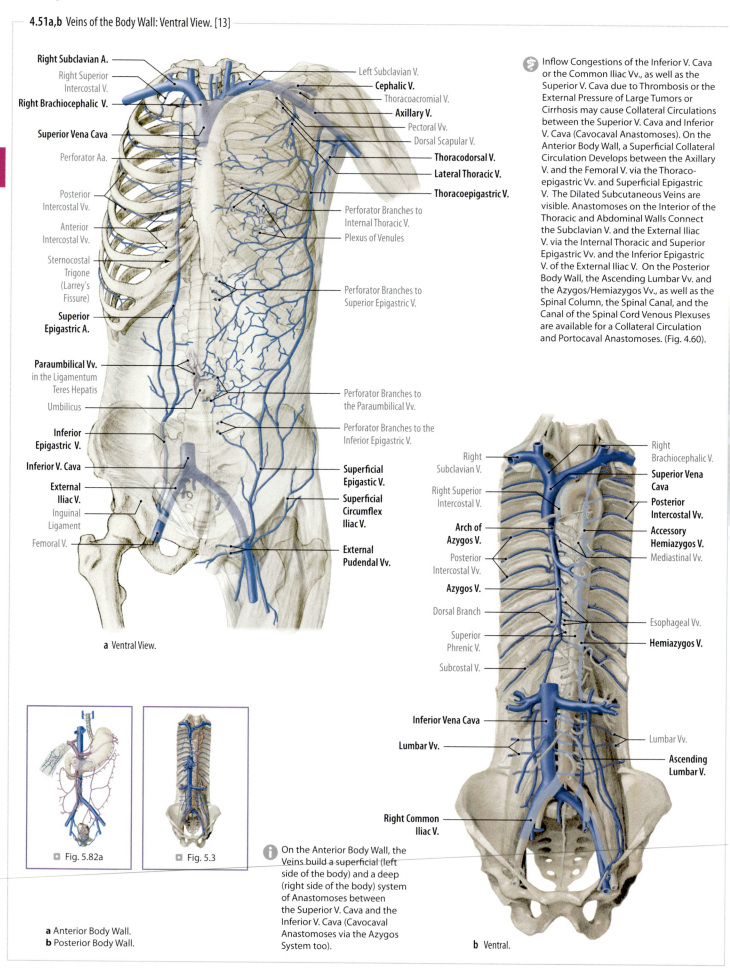

Right Subclavian A.
Right Superior Intercostal V.
Right Brachiocephalic V.
Superior Vena Cava
Perforator Aa.
Posterior Intercostal Vv.
Anterior Intercostal Vv.
Sternocostal Trigone (Larrey's Fissure)
Superior Epigastric A.
Paraumbilical Vv. in the Ligamentum Teres Hepatis
Umbilicus
Inferior Epigastric V.
Inferior V. Cava
External Iliac V.
Inguinal Ligament
Femoral V.

Left Subclavian V.
Cephalic V.
Thoracoacromial V.
Axillary V.
Pectoral Vv.
Dorsal Scapular V.
Thoracodorsal V.
Lateral Thoracic V.
Thoracoepigastric V.
Perforator Branches to Internal Thoracic V.
Plexus of Venules
Perforator Branches to Superior Epigastric V.
Perforator Branches to the Paraumbilical Vv.
Perforator Branches to the Inferior Epigastric V.
Superficial Epigastic V.
Superficial Circumflex Iliac V.
External Pudendal Vv.

a Ventral View.

Inflow Congestions of the Inferior V. Cava or the Common Iliac Vv., as well as the Superior V. Cava due to Thrombosis or the External Pressure of Large Tumors or Cirrhosis may cause Collateral Circulations between the Superior V. Cava and Inferior V. Cava (Cavocaval Anastomoses). On the Anterior Body Wall, a Superficial Collateral Circulation Develops between the Axillary V. and the Femoral V. via the Thoraco-epigastric Vv. and Superficial Epigastric V. The Dilated Subcutaneous Veins are visible. Anastomoses on the Interior of the Thoracic and Abdominal Walls Connect the Subclavian V. and the External Iliac V. via the Internal Thoracic and Superior Epigastric Vv. and the Inferior Epigastric V. of the External Iliac V. On the Posterior Body Wall, the Ascending Lumbar Vv. and the Azygos/Hemiazygos Vv., as well as the Spinal Column, the Spinal Canal, and the Canal of the Spinal Cord Venous Plexuses are available for a Collateral Circulation and Portocaval Anastomoses. (Fig. 4.60).

Right Subclavian V.
Right Superior Intercostal V.
Arch of Azygos V.
Posterior Intercostal Vv.
Azygos V.
Dorsal Branch
Superior Phrenic V.
Subcostal V.
Inferior Vena Cava
Lumbar Vv.
Right Common Iliac V.

Right Brachiocephalic V.
Superior Vena Cava
Posterior Intercostal Vv.
Accessory Hemiazygos V.
Mediastinal Vv.
Esophageal Vv.
Hemiazygos V.
Lumbar Vv.
Ascending Lumbar V.

☐ Fig. 5.82a

☐ Fig. 5.3

On the Anterior Body Wall, the Veins build a superficial (left side of the body) and a deep (right side of the body) system of Anastomoses between the Superior V. Cava and the Inferior V. Cava (Cavocaval Anastomoses via the Azygos System too).

a Anterior Body Wall.
b Posterior Body Wall.

b Ventral.

4

Body Wall: Lymphatic System

4.52a–c Superficial Lymph Channels and Regional Lymph Nodes. [a, b 61; c 15]

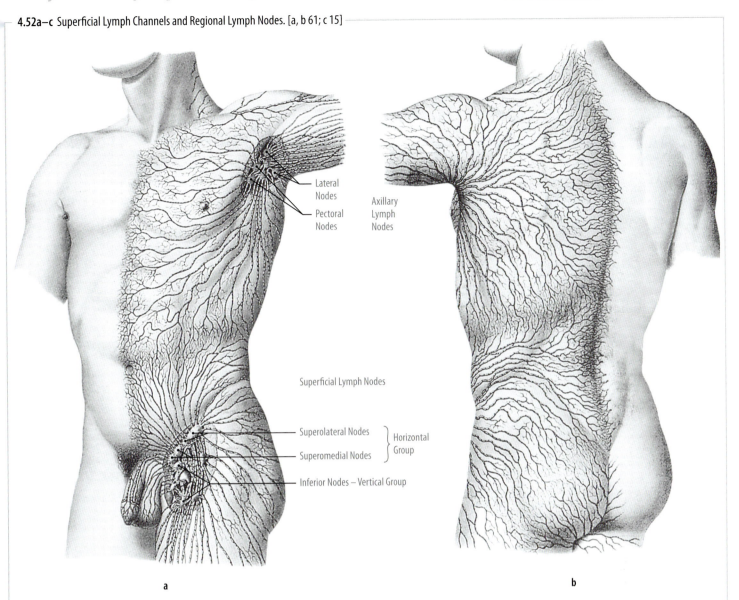

Lateral
Nodes

Pectoral
Nodes

Axillary
Lymph
Nodes

Superficial Lymph Nodes

Superolateral Nodes ⎫ Horizontal
                    ⎬ Group
Superomedial Nodes ⎭

Inferior Nodes – Vertical Group

a   b

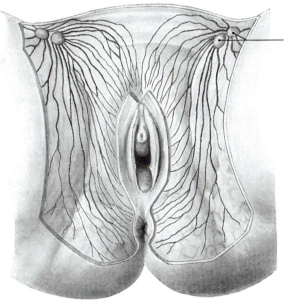

Superomedial Nodes of the
Superficial Inguinal Nodes

The Inguinal Lymph Nodes are grouped in a T-shape with Three distinct Areas of Drainage. The Medial Horizontal Part Drains the Medial Thigh and Perineum (Anal Area, External Genitalia including the Outer Part of the Urethra in Men and the Vagina in Women). The Lateral Horizontal Part Drains the Lower Abdomen, the Gluteal Region, and some of the Lumbar Area. The Inferior Part Drains the Lower Limbs Below the Mid-thigh.

The Inguinal Lymph Nodes are of importance because they are Indicators for Inflammatory Disease and Metastatic Tumors in the nonvisible Genital Area. In women, the area of the Tubal Angle of the Uterus Drains (small amount) via the Lymphatics of the Ligamentum Teres Uteri in the Medial Inguinal Nodes (Metastatic Invasion Dissemination).

a Anterior Body Wall.
b Posterior Body Wall.
c Anal Area, Perineal Area, and Female Exterior Genitals.

c

Pathways and Topography

Anterior Body Wall: Sensory Supply

4.53a–c Nerve Supply. [a 65; c 57, 63, 66]

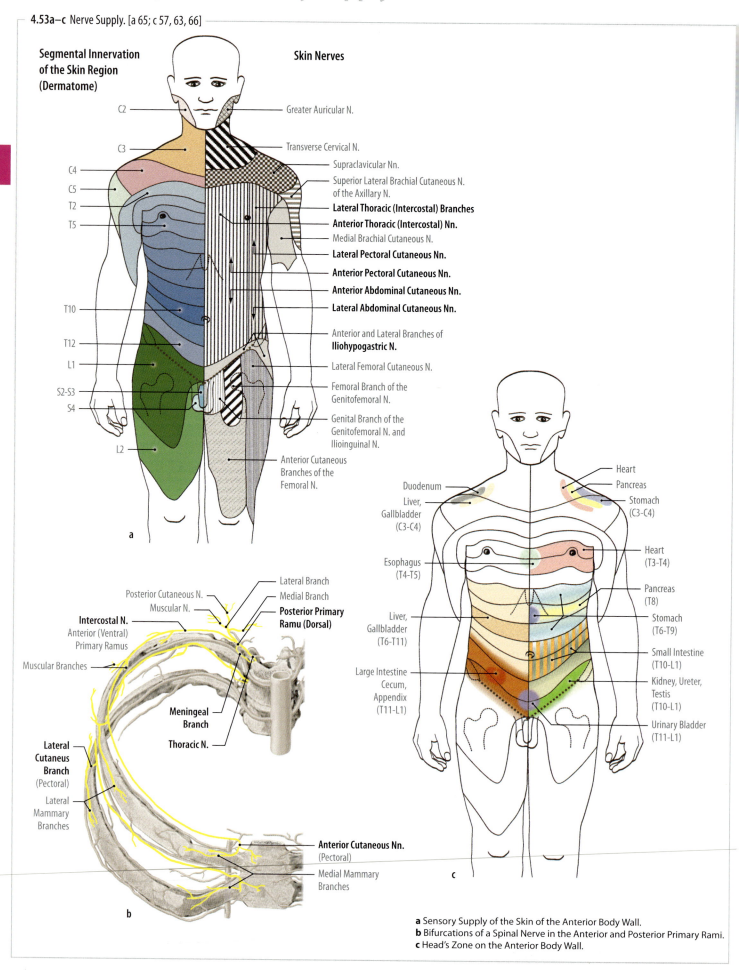

Segmental Innervation of the Skin Region (Dermatome)

- C2
- C3
- C4
- C5
- T2
- T5
- T10
- T12
- L1
- S2-S3
- S4
- L2

a

Skin Nerves

- Greater Auricular N.
- Transverse Cervical N.
- Supraclavicular Nn.
- Superior Lateral Brachial Cutaneous N. of the Axillary N.
- **Lateral Thoracic (Intercostal) Branches**
- **Anterior Thoracic (Intercostal) Nn.**
- Medial Brachial Cutaneous N.
- **Lateral Pectoral Cutaneous Nn.**
- **Anterior Pectoral Cutaneous Nn.**
- **Anterior Abdominal Cutaneous Nn.**
- **Lateral Abdominal Cutaneous Nn.**
- Anterior and Lateral Branches of **Iliohypogastric N.**
- Lateral Femoral Cutaneous N.
- Femoral Branch of the Genitofemoral N.
- Genital Branch of the Genitofemoral N. and Ilioinguinal N.
- Anterior Cutaneous Branches of the Femoral N.

b

- Posterior Cutaneous N.
- Muscular N.
- **Intercostal N.**
- Anterior (Ventral) Primary Ramus
- Muscular Branches
- **Lateral Cutaneus Branch** (Pectoral)
- Lateral Mammary Branches
- Lateral Branch
- Medial Branch
- **Posterior Primary Ramu (Dorsal)**
- **Meningeal Branch**
- **Thoracic N.**
- **Anterior Cutaneous Nn.** (Pectoral)
- Medial Mammary Branches

c

- Duodenum
- Liver, Gallbladder (C3-C4)
- Esophagus (T4-T5)
- Liver, Gallbladder (T6-T11)
- Large Intestine Cecum, Appendix (T11-L1)
- Heart
- Pancreas
- Stomach (C3-C4)
- Heart (T3-T4)
- Pancreas (T8)
- Stomach (T6-T9)
- Small Intestine (T10-L1)
- Kidney, Ureter, Testis (T10-L1)
- Urinary Bladder (T11-L1)

a Sensory Supply of the Skin of the Anterior Body Wall.
b Bifurcations of a Spinal Nerve in the Anterior and Posterior Primary Rami.
c Head's Zone on the Anterior Body Wall.

Subclavian Triangle and Space

4.54 Thoracic and Shoulder Regions in the Area of Mohrenheim's Fossa (Deltopectoral Fossa): Right Side, Ventral View. [56]

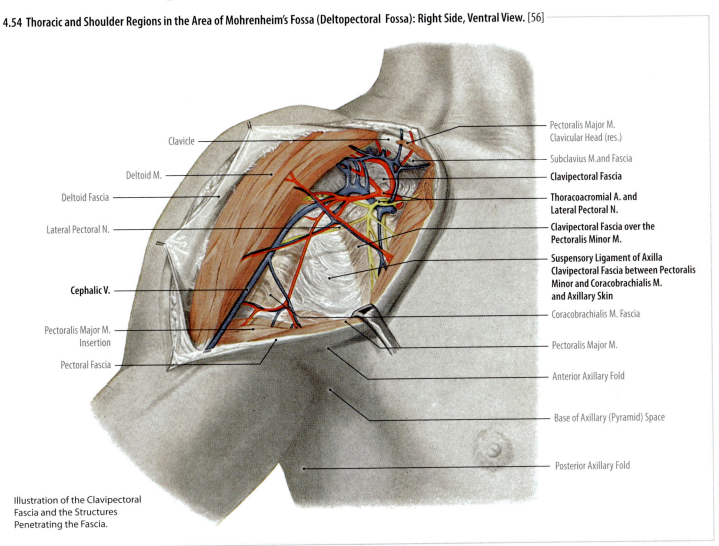

Clavicle

Deltoid M.

Deltoid Fascia

Lateral Pectoral N.

Cephalic V.

Pectoralis Major M. Insertion

Pectoral Fascia

Pectoralis Major M. Clavicular Head (res.)

Subclavius M.and Fascia

Clavipectoral Fascia

Thoracoacromial A. and Lateral Pectoral N.

Clavipectoral Fascia over the Pectoralis Minor M.

Suspensory Ligament of Axilla Clavipectoral Fascia between Pectoralis Minor and Coracobrachialis M. and Axillary Skin

Coracobrachialis M. Fascia

Pectoralis Major M.

Anterior Axillary Fold

Base of Axillary (Pyramid) Space

Posterior Axillary Fold

Illustration of the Clavipectoral Fascia and the Structures Penetrating the Fascia.

4.55 Mohrenheim's (Subclavicular or Deltopectoral) Fossa: Right Side, Ventral View. [6]

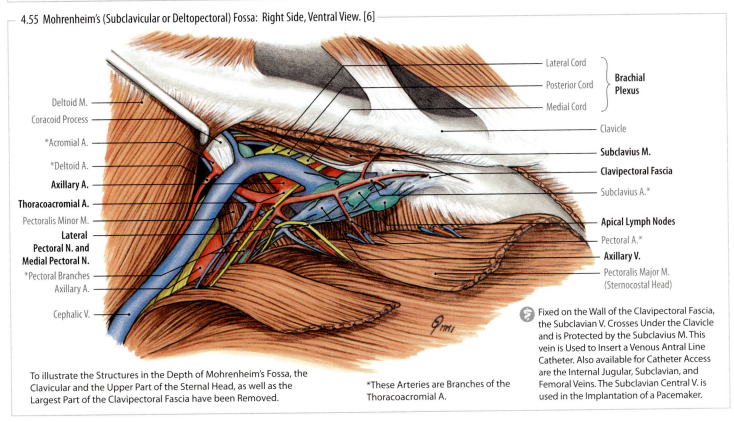

Deltoid M.

Coracoid Process

*Acromial A.

*Deltoid A.

Axillary A.

Thoracoacromial A.

Pectoralis Minor M.

Lateral Pectoral N. and Medial Pectoral N.

*Pectoral Branches

Axillary A.

Cephalic V.

Lateral Cord

Posterior Cord

Medial Cord

Brachial Plexus

Clavicle

Subclavius M.

Clavipectoral Fascia

Subclavius A.*

Apical Lymph Nodes

Pectoral A.*

Axillary V.

Pectoralis Major M. (Sternocostal Head)

To illustrate the Structures in the Depth of Mohrenheim's Fossa, the Clavicular and the Upper Part of the Sternal Head, as well as the Largest Part of the Clavipectoral Fascia have been Removed.

*These Arteries are Branches of the Thoracoacromial A.

Fixed on the Wall of the Clavipectoral Fascia, the Subclavian V. Crosses Under the Clavicle and is Protected by the Subclavius M. This vein is Used to Insert a Venous Antral Line Catheter. Also available for Catheter Access are the Internal Jugular, Subclavian, and Femoral Veins. The Subclavian Central V. is used in the Implantation of a Pacemaker.

Pathways and Topography

4.56a–c Mammary Gland. [a 2, 67; b 67, 68; c 62]

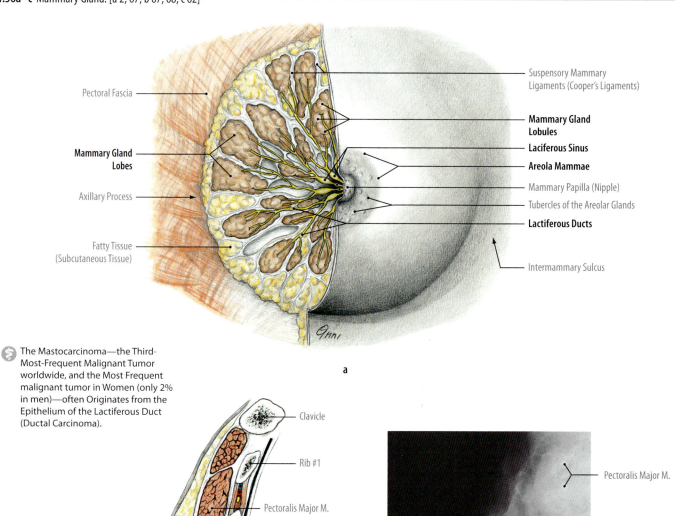

Pectoral Fascia

Mammary Gland Lobes

Axillary Process

Fatty Tissue (Subcutaneous Tissue)

Suspensory Mammary Ligaments (Cooper's Ligaments)

Mammary Gland Lobules

Laciferous Sinus

Areola Mammae

Mammary Papilla (Nipple)

Tubercles of the Areolar Glands

Lactiferous Ducts

Intermammary Sulcus

a

The Mastocarcinoma—the Third-Most-Frequent Malignant Tumor worldwide, and the Most Frequent malignant tumor in Women (only 2% in men)—often Originates from the Epithelium of the Lactiferous Duct (Ductal Carcinoma).

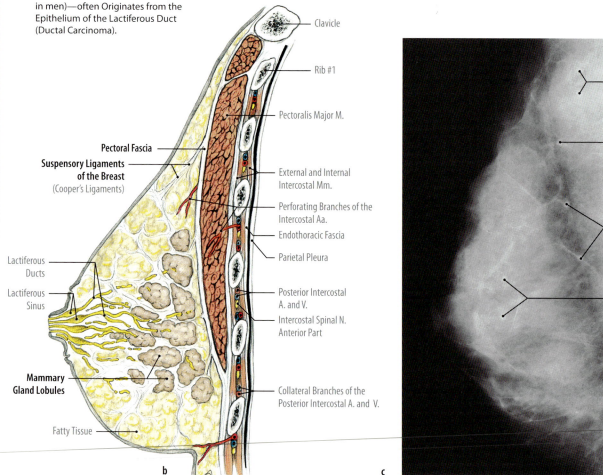

Clavicle

Rib #1

Pectoralis Major M.

Pectoral Fascia

Suspensory Ligaments of the Breast (Cooper's Ligaments)

External and Internal Intercostal Mm.

Perforating Branches of the Intercostal Aa.

Endothoracic Fascia

Parietal Pleura

Lactiferous Ducts

Lactiferous Sinus

Posterior Intercostal A. and V.

Intercostal Spinal N. Anterior Part

Mammary Gland Lobules

Collateral Branches of the Posterior Intercostal A. and V.

Fatty Tissue

Pectoralis Major M.

Pectoralis Fascia (Deep)

Suspensory Ligaments (Cooper's Ligaments)

Glandular Tissue

b

c

a Right Mammary Gland of a woman Before Menopause. Glandular and Fatty Tissue and the Efferent Duct System have been Dissected in the Lateral Half.
b Sagittal Section through the Mammary Gland and the Anterior Thoracic Wall near a woman's nipple.
c X-ray Image of the Right Mammary Gland of a 39-year-old woman: Lateral Projection.

4.57a,b Blood Supply (a) and Lymph Nodes (b) of the Mammary Gland.

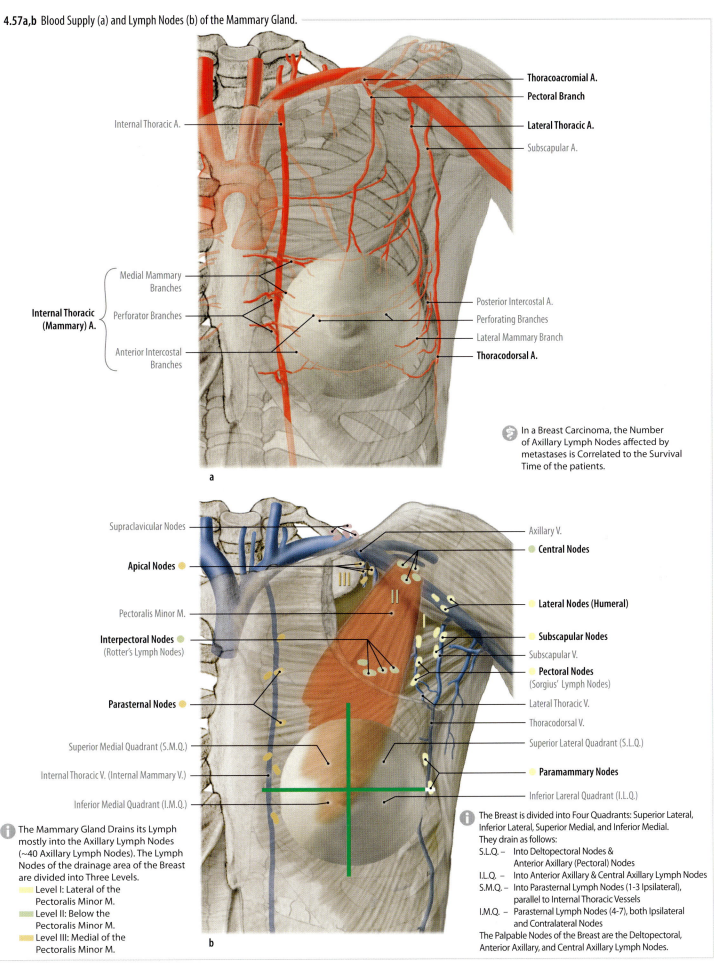

Thoracoacromial A.

Pectoral Branch

Lateral Thoracic A.

Subscapular A.

Internal Thoracic A.

Medial Mammary Branches

Perforator Branches

Internal Thoracic (Mammary) A.

Anterior Intercostal Branches

Posterior Intercostal A.

Perforating Branches

Lateral Mammary Branch

Thoracodorsal A.

a

In a Breast Carcinoma, the Number of Axillary Lymph Nodes affected by metastases is Correlated to the Survival Time of the patients.

Supraclavicular Nodes

Apical Nodes

Pectoralis Minor M.

Interpectoral Nodes
(Rotter's Lymph Nodes)

Parasternal Nodes

Superior Medial Quadrant (S.M.Q.)

Internal Thoracic V. (Internal Mammary V.)

Inferior Medial Quadrant (I.M.Q.)

Axillary V.

Central Nodes

III

II

Lateral Nodes (Humeral)

Subscapular Nodes

Subscapular V.

Pectoral Nodes
(Sorgius' Lymph Nodes)

Lateral Thoracic V.

Thoracodorsal V.

Superior Lateral Quadrant (S.L.Q.)

Paramammary Nodes

Inferior Lateral Quadrant (I.L.Q.)

The Mammary Gland Drains its Lymph mostly into the Axillary Lymph Nodes (~40 Axillary Lymph Nodes). The Lymph Nodes of the drainage area of the Breast are divided into Three Levels.
  Level I: Lateral of the Pectoralis Minor M.
  Level II: Below the Pectoralis Minor M.
  Level III: Medial of the Pectoralis Minor M.

The Breast is divided into Four Quadrants: Superior Lateral, Inferior Lateral, Superior Medial, and Inferior Medial. They drain as follows:
S.L.Q. –   Into Deltopectoral Nodes & Anterior Axillary (Pectoral) Nodes
I.L.Q. –   Into Anterior Axillary & Central Axillary Lymph Nodes
S.M.Q. –   Into Parasternal Lymph Nodes (1-3 Ipsilateral), parallel to Internal Thoracic Vessels
I.M.Q. –   Parasternal Lymph Nodes (4-7), both Ipsilateral and Contralateral Nodes
The Palpable Nodes of the Breast are the Deltopectoral, Anterior Axillary, and Central Axillary Lymph Nodes.

b

Pathways and Topography

4.58 Anterior Body Wall of a Woman: Topography and Pathways, Ventral View. [8]

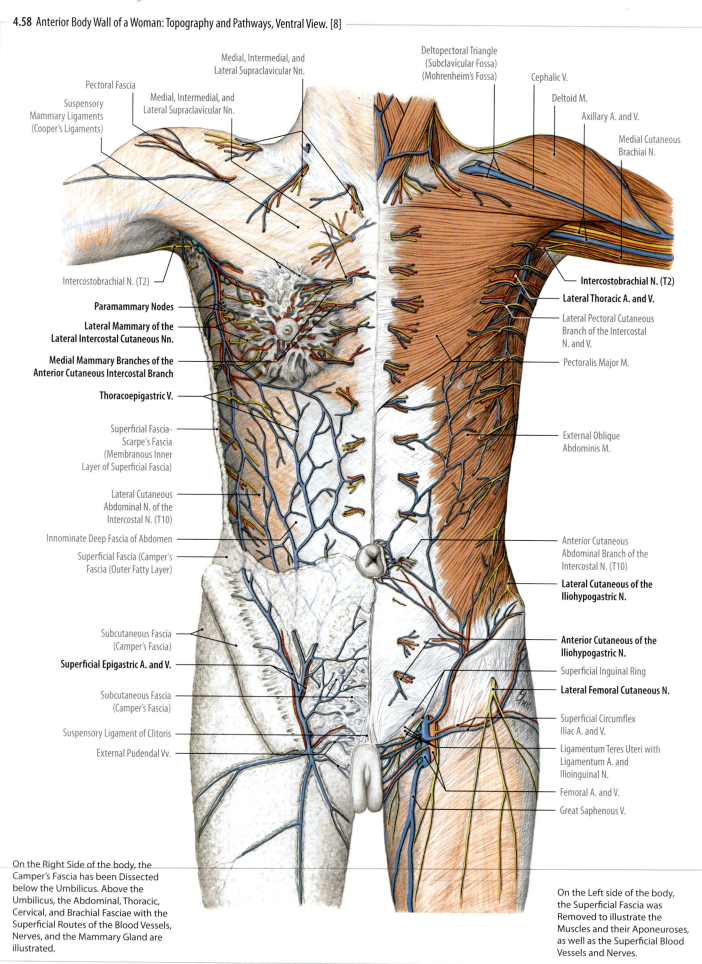

Deltopectoral Triangle
(Subclavicular Fossa)
(Mohrenheim's Fossa)

Cephalic V.

Deltoid M.

Axillary A. and V.

Medial Cutaneous
Brachiai N.

Medial, Intermedial, and
Lateral Supraclavicular Nn.

Pectoral Fascia

Medial, Intermedial, and
Lateral Supraclavicular Nn.

Suspensory
Mammary Ligaments
(Cooper's Ligaments)

Intercostobrachial N. (T2)

Paramammary Nodes

**Lateral Mammary of the
Lateral Intercostal Cutaneous Nn.**

**Medial Mammary Branches of the
Anterior Cutaneous Intercostal Branch**

Thoracoepigastric V.

Superficial Fascia-
Scarpe's Fascia
(Membranous Inner
Layer of Superficial Fascia)

Lateral Cutaneous
Abdominal N. of the
Intercostal N. (T10)

Innominate Deep Fascia of Abdomen

Superficial Fascia (Camper's
Fascia (Outer Fatty Layer)

Subcutaneous Fascia
(Camper's Fascia)

Superficial Epigastric A. and V.

Subcutaneous Fascia
(Camper's Fascia)

Suspensory Ligament of Clitoris

External Pudendal Vv.

Intercostobrachial N. (T2)

Lateral Thoracic A. and V.

Lateral Pectoral Cutaneous
Branch of the Intercostal
N. and V.

Pectoralis Major M.

External Oblique
Abdominis M.

Anterior Cutaneous
Abdominal Branch of the
Intercostal N. (T10)

**Lateral Cutaneous of the
Iliohypogastric N.**

**Anterior Cutaneous of the
Iliohypogastric N.**

Superficial Inguinal Ring

Lateral Femoral Cutaneous N.

Superficial Circumflex
Iliac A. and V.

Ligamentum Teres Uteri with
Ligamentum A. and
Ilioinguinal N.

Femoral A. and V.

Great Saphenous V.

On the Right Side of the body, the
Camper's Fascia has been Dissected
below the Umbilicus. Above the
Umbilicus, the Abdominal, Thoracic,
Cervical, and Brachial Fasciae with the
Superficial Routes of the Blood Vessels,
Nerves, and the Mammary Gland are
illustrated.

On the Left side of the body,
the Superficial Fascia was
Removed to illustrate the
Muscles and their Aponeuroses,
as well as the Superficial Blood
Vessels and Nerves.

4.59 Anterior Body Wall of a Woman: Topography and Pathways, Ventral View. [8]

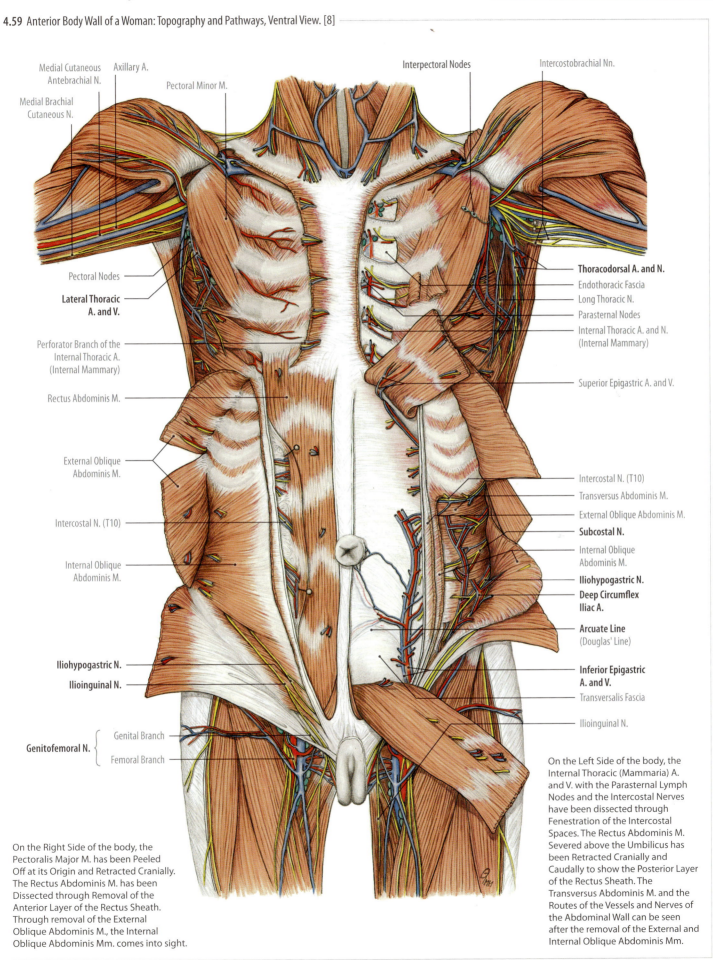

Medial Cutaneous Antebrachial N.

Medial Brachial Cutaneous N.

Axillary A.

Pectoral Minor M.

Interpectoral Nodes

Intercostobrachial Nn.

Pectoral Nodes

Lateral Thoracic A. and V.

Perforator Branch of the Internal Thoracic A. (Internal Mammary)

Rectus Abdominis M.

External Oblique Abdominis M.

Intercostal N. (T10)

Internal Oblique Abdominis M.

Iliohypogastric N.

Ilioinguinal N.

Genitofemoral N. { Genital Branch
Femoral Branch }

Thoracodorsal A. and N.
Endothoracic Fascia
Long Thoracic N.
Parasternal Nodes
Internal Thoracic A. and N. (Internal Mammary)

Superior Epigastric A. and V.

Intercostal N. (T10)
Transversus Abdominis M.
External Oblique Abdominis M.
Subcostal N.
Internal Oblique Abdominis M.
Iliohypogastric N.
Deep Circumflex Iliac A.
Arcuate Line (Douglas' Line)
Inferior Epigastric A. and V.
Transversalis Fascia
Ilioinguinal N.

On the Right Side of the body, the Pectoralis Major M. has been Peeled Off at its Origin and Retracted Cranially. The Rectus Abdominis M. has been Dissected through Removal of the Anterior Layer of the Rectus Sheath. Through removal of the External Oblique Abdominis M., the Internal Oblique Abdominis Mm. comes into sight.

On the Left Side of the body, the Internal Thoracic (Mammaria) A. and V. with the Parasternal Lymph Nodes and the Intercostal Nerves have been dissected through Fenestration of the Intercostal Spaces. The Rectus Abdominis M. Severed above the Umbilicus has been Retracted Cranially and Caudally to show the Posterior Layer of the Rectus Sheath. The Transversus Abdominis M. and the Routes of the Vessels and Nerves of the Abdominal Wall can be seen after the removal of the External and Internal Oblique Abdominis Mm.

Pathways and Topography

4.60 Interior of the Anterior Body Wall, Dorsal View. [1]

Portal Hypertension (Hepatocirrhosis) may lead to a Dilation of the Superficial Veins of the Anterior Body Wall, the Paraumbilcal Veins for the Portocaval Anastomoses, which results in the Spidery Venous Enlargement in the Umbilical Area, the so-called Caput Medusae (Fig. 4.58). Caput Medusae is Induced in Anastomosis of the Inferior Epigastric Vv. with the Superior Epigastric Vv. in cases of Inferior Vena Cava Thrombosis. It is also a Factor in cases of Congenital Absence of the Hepatic Portion of Inferior Vena Cava. In the latter case, the Azygos Venous System has the Highest Rule in Bypass of Venous Blood from the Lower Body to the Superior Vena Cava.

To surgically Revascularize the Heart in the case of a high-grade Coronary Stenosis, the Internal Thoracic (Mammary) A. is suitable as a Bypass. This Artery is also part of the main Collateral Circulation with a Stenosis of the Aortic Arch Coarctation. (Fig. 4.50).

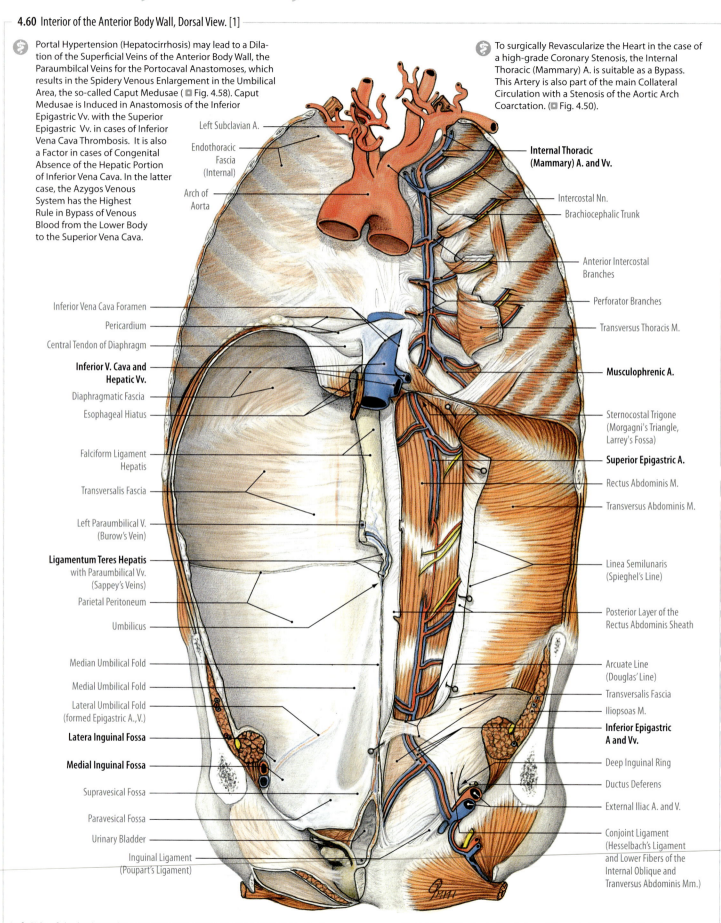

Left Subclavian A.

Endothoracic Fascia (Internal)

Arch of Aorta

Inferior Vena Cava Foramen

Pericardium

Central Tendon of Diaphragm

Inferior V. Cava and Hepatic Vv.

Diaphragmatic Fascia

Esophageal Hiatus

Falciform Ligament Hepatis

Transversalis Fascia

Left Paraumbilical V. (Burow's Vein)

Ligamentum Teres Hepatis with Paraumbilical Vv. (Sappey's Veins)

Parietal Peritoneum

Umbilicus

Median Umbilical Fold

Medial Umbilical Fold

Lateral Umbilical Fold (formed Epigastric A., V.)

Latera Inguinal Fossa

Medial Inguinal Fossa

Supravesical Fossa

Paravesical Fossa

Urinary Bladder

Inguinal Ligament (Poupart's Ligament)

Internal Thoracic (Mammary) A. and Vv.

Intercostal Nn.

Brachiocephalic Trunk

Anterior Intercostal Branches

Perforator Branches

Transversus Thoracis M.

Musculophrenic A.

Sternocostal Trigone (Morgagni's Triangle, Larrey's Fossa)

Superior Epigastric A.

Rectus Abdominis M.

Transversus Abdominis M.

Linea Semilunaris (Spieghel's Line)

Posterior Layer of the Rectus Abdominis Sheath

Arcuate Line (Douglas' Line)

Transversalis Fascia

Iliopsoas M.

Inferior Epigastric A and Vv.

Deep Inguinal Ring

Ductus Deferens

External Iliac A. and V.

Conjoint Ligament (Hesselbach's Ligament and Lower Fibers of the Internal Oblique and Transversus Abdominis Mm.)

Left Side of the body: In the Lower Section of the Abdominal Wall, the Peritoneum has been Preserved. In the Upper Section of the Abdominal Wall and at the Thoracic Wall, the Transversalis Fascia and the Internal Thoracic Fascia have been Dissected.

Right Side of the body: The Internal Thoracic (Mammary) Vessels, Superior and Inferior Epigastric Vessels are shown following Removal of the Transversus Thoracis M. and the Opening of the Rectus Sheath.

Umbilical Area

4.61 Horizontal Section through the Abdominal Wall of an Adult in the Area of the Umbilicus. [15]

Umbilical Hernias in a Newborn child develop near the not yet developed Umbilical Papilla. In the Adult, Umbilical Hernias develop due to Dissociation of the Connective Tissue of the Umbilical Papilla following Overstretching of the Abdominal Wall (Pregnancy, Adiposis, Ascites).

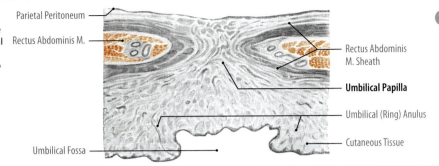

Parietal Peritoneum

Rectus Abdominis M.

Rectus Abdominis M. Sheath

Umbilical Papilla

Umbilical (Ring) Anulus

Cutaneous Tissue

Umbilical Fossa

The Umbilical Ring is the Hernial Orifice for Umbilical Hernias. The Congenital Umbilical Hernia in a newborn (Omphalocele) is a Reduction Deformity based on the Persistence of the Physiological Herniation of the Intestine during the Embryonic Develpment Period.

4.62 Horizontal Section through the Trunk at the Level of the Fifth Lumbar Vertebra: Superior View of the Pelvic Organs. [15]

The Descent of the Testis should be Completed at the time of Birth. If the Testis has Not Descended, you should observe the child and Expect the Testis to Descend within the First Year of life. If it does not, it is called Cryptorchidism or Retention of the Testis. The Testicle may Lie at the Posterior Body Wall (Abdominal Testis), in the Inguinal Canal (Inguinal Testis), or as an Ectopic Testical Outside of the Embryonic Testical (Testis) Descending Path Near the Inguinal Canal or Scrotum.

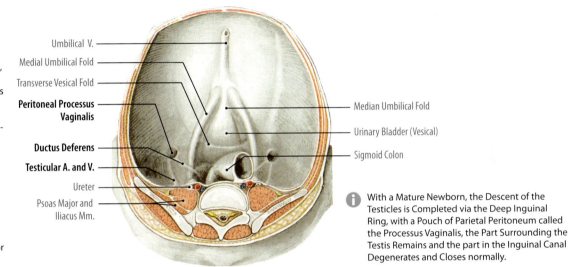

Umbilical V.

Medial Umbilical Fold

Transverse Vesical Fold

Peritoneal Processus Vaginalis

Ductus Deferens

Testicular A. and V.

Ureter

Psoas Major and Iliacus Mm.

Median Umbilical Fold

Urinary Bladder (Vesical)

Sigmoid Colon

With a Mature Newborn, the Descent of the Testicles is Completed via the Deep Inguinal Ring, with a Pouch of Parietal Peritoneum called the Processus Vaginalis, the Part Surrounding the Testis Remains and the part in the Inguinal Canal Degenerates and Closes normally.

4.63 Partial Interior View of the Back of the Anterior Abdominal Wall. [15]

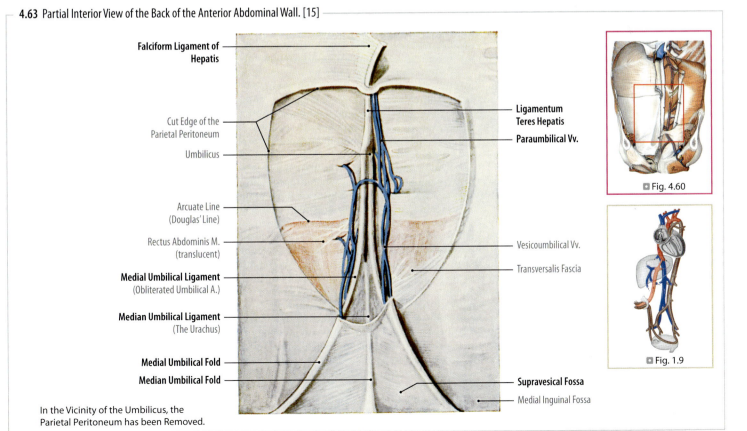

Falciform Ligament of Hepatis

Cut Edge of the Parietal Peritoneum

Umbilicus

Arcuate Line (Douglas' Line)

Rectus Abdominis M. (translucent)

Medial Umbilical Ligament (Obliterated Umbilical A.)

Median Umbilical Ligament (The Urachus)

Medial Umbilical Fold

Median Umbilical Fold

Ligamentum Teres Hepatis

Paraumbilical Vv.

□ Fig. 4.60

Vesicoumbilical Vv.

Transversalis Fascia

□ Fig. 1.9

Supravesical Fossa

Medial Inguinal Fossa

In the Vicinity of the Umbilicus, the Parietal Peritoneum has been Removed.

Pathways and Topography

Inguinal Fossa and Vascular Groove

4.64 Back of the Anterior Abdominal Wall of the Right Side of the Body: Interior View. [57]

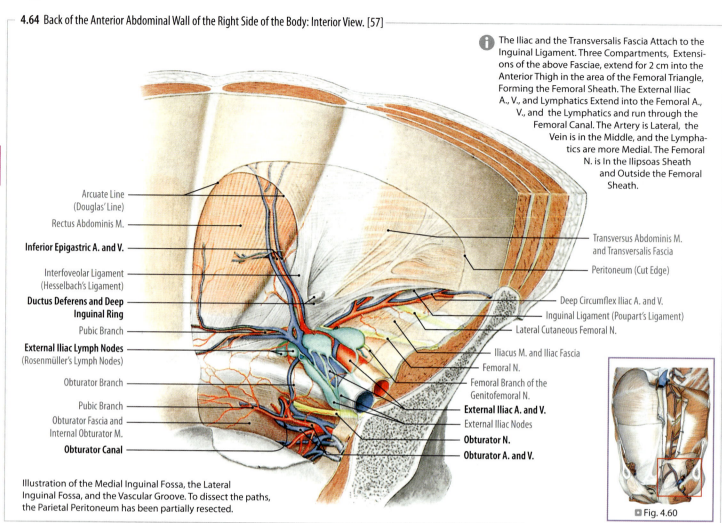

The Iliac and the Transversalis Fascia Attach to the Inguinal Ligament. Three Compartments, Extensions of the above Fasciae, extend for 2 cm into the Anterior Thigh in the area of the Femoral Triangle, Forming the Femoral Sheath. The External Iliac A., V., and Lymphatics Extend into the Femoral A., V., and the Lymphatics and run through the Femoral Canal. The Artery is Lateral, the Vein is in the Middle, and the Lymphatics are more Medial. The Femoral N. is In the Ilipsoas Sheath and Outside the Femoral Sheath.

Arcuate Line (Douglas' Line)

Rectus Abdominis M.

Inferior Epigastric A. and V.

Interfoveolar Ligament (Hesselbach's Ligament)

Ductus Deferens and Deep Inguinal Ring

Pubic Branch

External Iliac Lymph Nodes (Rosenmüller's Lymph Nodes)

Obturator Branch

Pubic Branch

Obturator Fascia and Internal Obturator M.

Obturator Canal

Transversus Abdominis M. and Transversalis Fascia

Peritoneum (Cut Edge)

Deep Circumflex Iliac A. and V.

Inguinal Ligament (Poupart's Ligament)

Lateral Cutaneous Femoral N.

Iliacus M. and Iliac Fascia

Femoral N.

Femoral Branch of the Genitofemoral N.

External Iliac A. and V.

External Iliac Nodes

Obturator N.

Obturator A. and V.

Illustration of the Medial Inguinal Fossa, the Lateral Inguinal Fossa, and the Vascular Groove. To dissect the paths, the Parietal Peritoneum has been partially resected.

☐ Fig. 4.60

4.65 Interior View of the Inguinal Region and the Vascular Groove of the Right Side of the Body. [46]

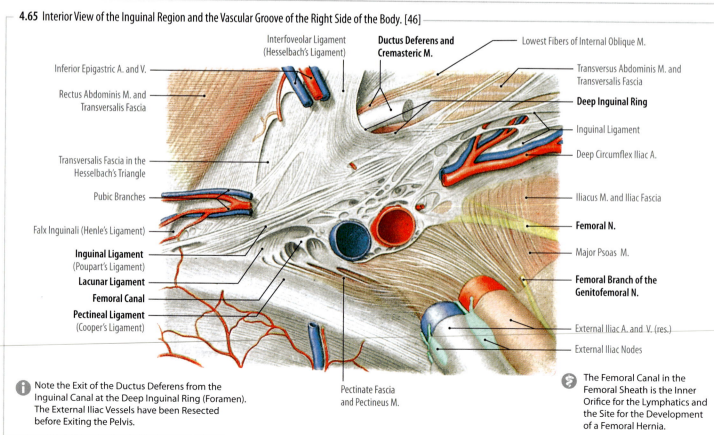

Interfoveolar Ligament (Hesselbach's Ligament)

Ductus Deferens and Cremasteric M.

Lowest Fibers of Internal Oblique M.

Inferior Epigastric A. and V.

Rectus Abdominis M. and Transversalis Fascia

Transversus Abdominis M. and Transversalis Fascia

Deep Inguinal Ring

Inguinal Ligament

Deep Circumflex Iliac A.

Transversalis Fascia in the Hesselbach's Triangle

Iliacus M. and Iliac Fascia

Pubic Branches

Femoral N.

Falx Inguinali (Henle's Ligament)

Major Psoas M.

Inguinal Ligament (Poupart's Ligament)

Femoral Branch of the Genitofemoral N.

Lacunar Ligament

Femoral Canal

Pectineal Ligament (Cooper's Ligament)

External Iliac A. and V. (res.)

External Iliac Nodes

Note the Exit of the Ductus Deferens from the Inguinal Canal at the Deep Inguinal Ring (Foramen). The External Iliac Vessels have been Resected before Exiting the Pelvis.

Pectinate Fascia and Pectineus M.

The Femoral Canal in the Femoral Sheath is the Inner Orifice for the Lymphatics and the Site for the Development of a Femoral Hernia.

Inguinal Canal

4.66 Ligament Structures in the Area of Inguinal Region.

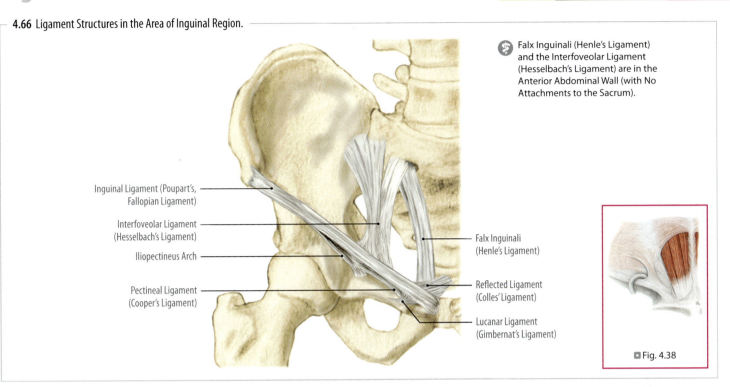

Inguinal Ligament (Poupart's, Fallopian Ligament)

Interfoveolar Ligament (Hesselbach's Ligament)

Iliopectineus Arch

Pectineal Ligament (Cooper's Ligament)

Falx Inguinali (Henle's Ligament)

Reflected Ligament (Colles' Ligament)

Lucanar Ligament (Gimbernat's Ligament)

Falx Inguinali (Henle's Ligament) and the Interfoveolar Ligament (Hesselbach's Ligament) are in the Anterior Abdominal Wall (with No Attachments to the Sacrum).

▶Fig. 4.38

4.67 Sagittal Sections through the Inguinal Canal of the Right Side of the Body of a Newborn. [57]

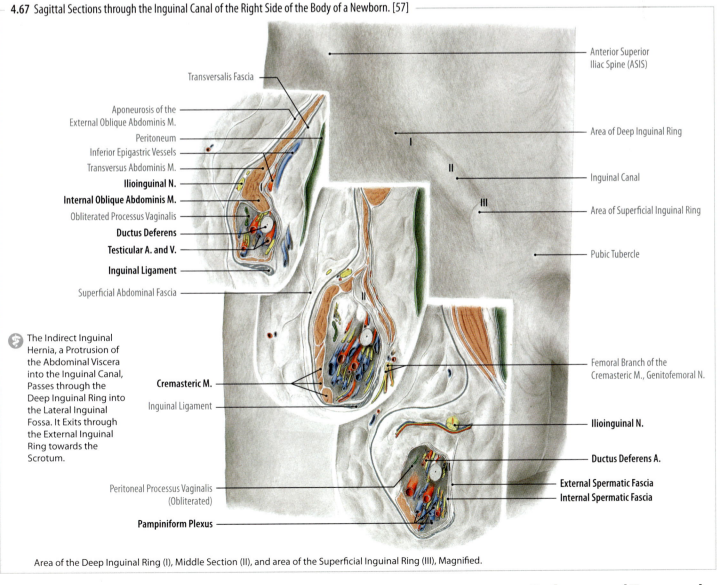

Transversalis Fascia

Aponeurosis of the External Oblique Abdominis M.

Peritoneum

Inferior Epigastric Vessels

Transversus Abdominis M.

Ilioinguinal N.

Internal Oblique Abdominis M.

Obliterated Processus Vaginalis

Ductus Deferens

Testicular A. and V.

Inguinal Ligament

Superficial Abdominal Fascia

Anterior Superior Iliac Spine (ASIS)

Area of Deep Inguinal Ring

Inguinal Canal

Area of Superficial Inguinal Ring

Pubic Tubercle

The Indirect Inguinal Hernia, a Protrusion of the Abdominal Viscera into the Inguinal Canal, Passes through the Deep Inguinal Ring into the Lateral Inguinal Fossa. It Exits through the External Inguinal Ring towards the Scrotum.

Cremasteric M.

Inguinal Ligament

Femoral Branch of the Cremasteric M., Genitofemoral N.

Ilioinguinal N.

Ductus Deferens A.

External Spermatic Fascia
Internal Spermatic Fascia

Peritoneal Processus Vaginalis (Obliterated)

Pampiniform Plexus

Area of the Deep Inguinal Ring (I), Middle Section (II), and area of the Superficial Inguinal Ring (III), Magnified.

Pathways and Topography

4.68 Testicular Fascia: Ventral View. [6]

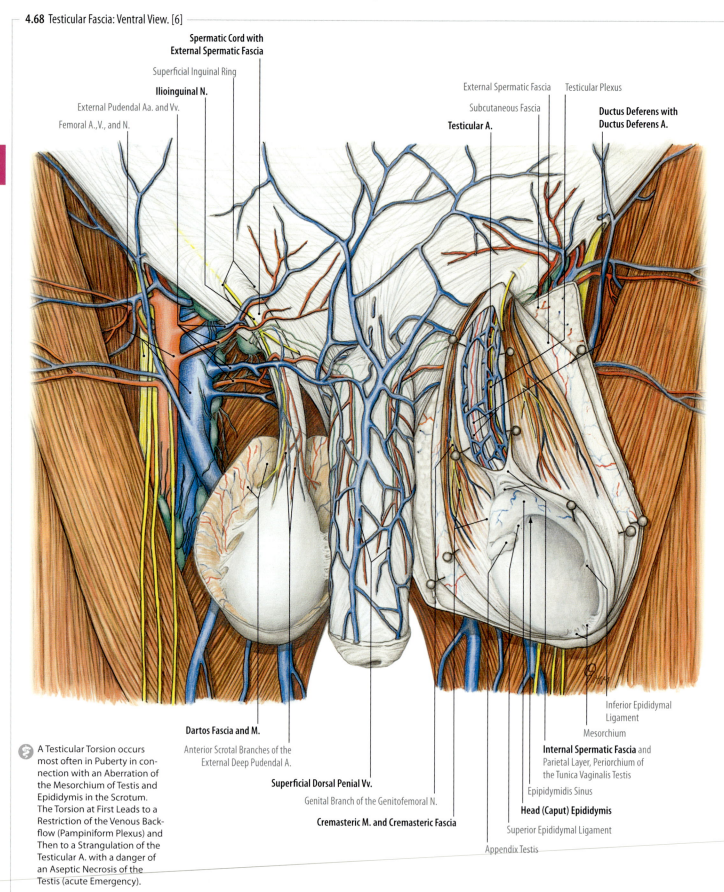

Spermatic Cord with
External Spermatic Fascia

Superficial Inguinal Ring

Ilioinguinal N.

External Pudendal Aa. and Vv.

Femoral A.,V., and N.

External Spermatic Fascia

Subcutaneous Fascia

Testicular A.

Testicular Plexus

**Ductus Deferens with
Ductus Deferens A.**

Inferior Epididymal
Ligament

Mesorchium

Internal Spermatic Fascia and
Parietal Layer, Periorchium of
the Tunica Vaginalis Testis

Epipidymidis Sinus

Head (Caput) Epididymis

Superior Epididymal Ligament

Appendix Testis

Dartos Fascia and M.

Anterior Scrotal Branches of the
External Deep Pudendal A.

Superficial Dorsal Penial Vv.

Genital Branch of the Genitofemoral N.

Cremasteric M. and Cremasteric Fascia

A Testicular Torsion occurs most often in Puberty in connection with an Aberration of the Mesorchium of Testis and Epididymis in the Scrotum. The Torsion at First Leads to a Restriction of the Venous Backflow (Pampiniform Plexus) and Then to a Strangulation of the Testicular A. with a danger of an Aseptic Necrosis of the Testis (acute Emergency).

Right Side of the body: The Skin of the Scrotum has been Removed, a part of the Tunica Dartos has been Preserved. Illustration of the Spermatic Cord and the Testis with the External Spermatic Fascia of the Tunica Vaginalis Testis.

Left Sde of the body: The Subcutaneous and the Tunica Dartos, as well as the Covering of the Spermatic Cord and the Testis have been Divided and Retracted to the Side. The Contents of the Spermatic Cord, the Testis, and the Epididymis can be seen.

4.69 Fascia of the Spermatic Cord, the Left Testis, and the Penis: Ventral View. [6]

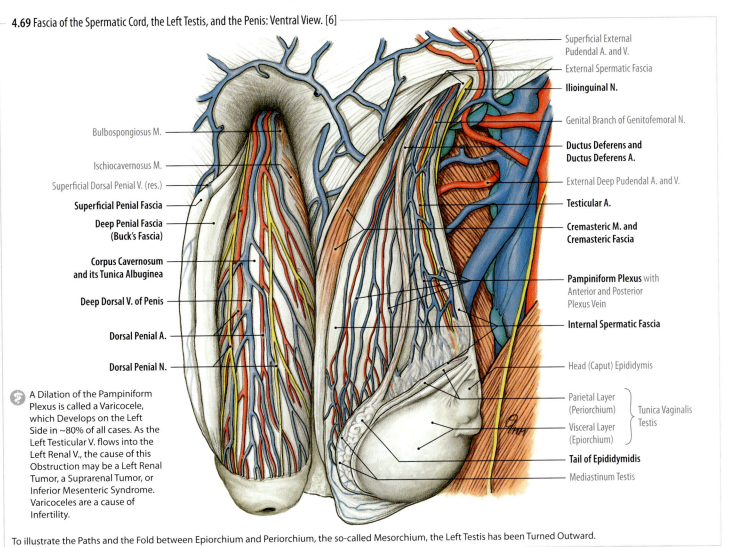

Superficial External Pudendal A. and V.

External Spermatic Fascia

Ilioinguinal N.

Genital Branch of Genitofemoral N.

Ductus Deferens and Ductus Deferens A.

External Deep Pudendal A. and V.

Testicular A.

Cremasteric M. and Cremasteric Fascia

Pampiniform Plexus with Anterior and Posterior Plexus Vein

Internal Spermatic Fascia

Head (Caput) Epididymis

Parietal Layer (Periorchium) ⎫
                               ⎬ Tunica Vaginalis Testis
Visceral Layer (Epiorchium)   ⎭

Tail of Epididymidis

Mediastinum Testis

Bulbospongiosus M.

Ischiocavernosus M.

Superficial Dorsal Penial V. (res.)

Superficial Penial Fascia

Deep Penial Fascia (Buck's Fascia)

Corpus Cavernosum and its Tunica Albuginea

Deep Dorsal V. of Penis

Dorsal Penial A.

Dorsal Penial N.

A Dilation of the Pampiniform Plexus is called a Varicocele, which Develops on the Left Side in ~80% of all cases. As the Left Testicular V. flows into the Left Renal V., the cause of this Obstruction may be a Left Renal Tumor, a Suprarenal Tumor, or Inferior Mesenteric Syndrome. Varicoceles are a cause of Infertility.

To illustrate the Paths and the Fold between Epiorchium and Periorchium, the so-called Mesorchium, the Left Testis has been Turned Outward.

4.70 Schematic Illustration of the Structure of the Abdominal Wall and the Fascia of the Spermatic Cord and the Testis. [15]

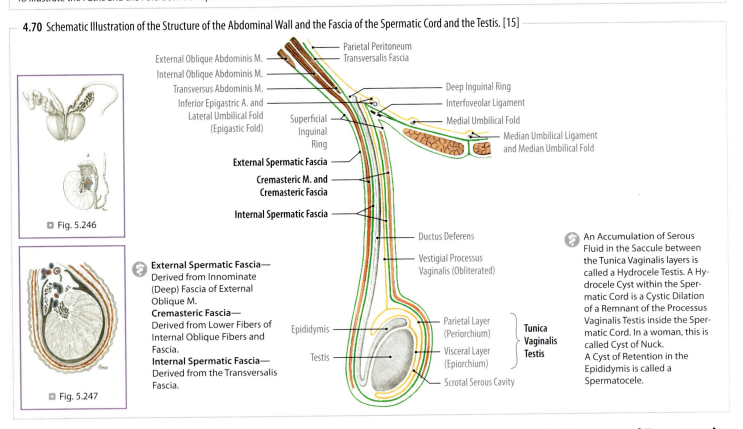

☐ Fig. 5.246

☐ Fig. 5.247

Parietal Peritoneum
Transversalis Fascia

External Oblique Abdominis M.
Internal Oblique Abdominis M.
Transversus Abdominis M.
Inferior Epigastric A. and Lateral Umbilical Fold (Epigastic Fold)

Superficial Inguinal Ring

Deep Inguinal Ring
Interfoveolar Ligament
Medial Umbilical Fold

Median Umbilical Ligament and Median Umbilical Fold

External Spermatic Fascia

Cremasteric M. and Cremasteric Fascia

Internal Spermatic Fascia

Ductus Deferens

Vestigial Processus Vaginalis (Obliterated)

External Spermatic Fascia— Derived from Innominate (Deep) Fascia of External Oblique M.
Cremasteric Fascia— Derived from Lower Fibers of Internal Oblique Fibers and Fascia.
Internal Spermatic Fascia— Derived from the Transversalis Fascia.

Epididymis

Testis

Parietal Layer (Periorchium) ⎫
                               ⎬ Tunica Vaginalis Testis
Visceral Layer (Epiorchium)   ⎭

Scrotal Serous Cavity

An Accumulation of Serous Fluid in the Saccule between the Tunica Vaginalis layers is called a Hydrocele Testis. A Hydrocele Cyst within the Spermatic Cord is a Cystic Dilation of a Remnant of the Processus Vaginalis Testis inside the Spermatic Cord. In a woman, this is called Cyst of Nuck.
A Cyst of Retention in the Epididymis is called a Spermatocele.

Pathways and Topography

Blood Supply of the Spinal Column

4.71 Blood Supply of the Spinal Column: Cross-Section in the Thoracic Area, Superior View. [58, 64]

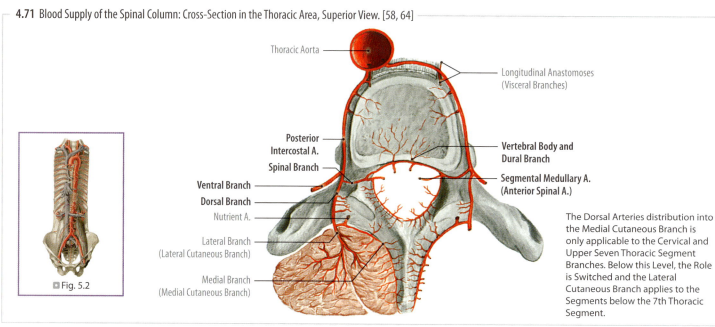

Thoracic Aorta

Longitudinal Anastomoses
(Visceral Branches)

Posterior
Intercostal A.

Vertebral Body and
Dural Branch

Spinal Branch

Segmental Medullary A.
(Anterior Spinal A.)

Ventral Branch

Dorsal Branch

Nutrient A.

Lateral Branch
(Lateral Cutaneous Branch)

Medial Branch
(Medial Cutaneous Branch)

□ Fig. 5.2

The Dorsal Arteries distribution into the Medial Cutaneous Branch is only applicable to the Cervical and Upper Seven Thoracic Segment Branches. Below this Level, the Role is Switched and the Lateral Cutaneous Branch applies to the Segments below the 7th Thoracic Segment.

4.72 Posterior Body Wall: Sensory Supply of the Skin and Segmental Innervation. [65]

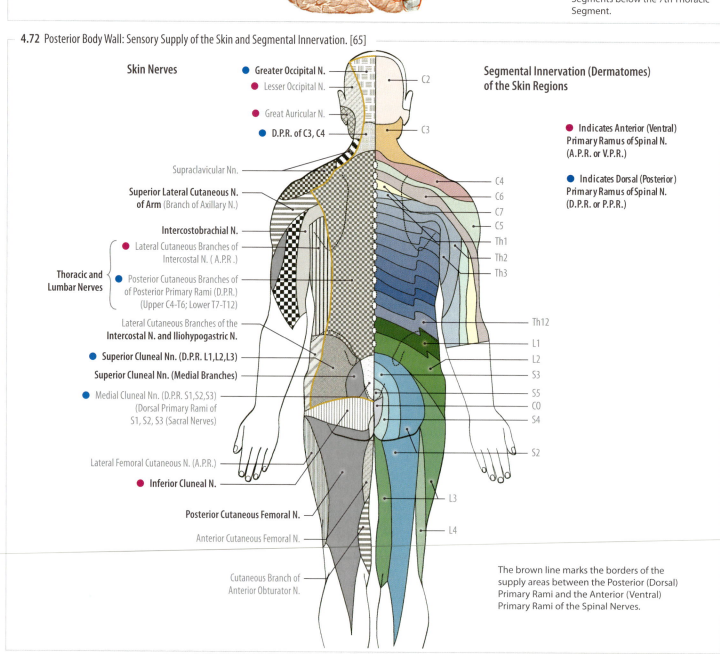

Skin Nerves

- Greater Occipital N.
- Lesser Occipital N.
- Great Auricular N.
- D.P.R. of C3, C4

Supraclavicular Nn.

Superior Lateral Cutaneous N. of Arm (Branch of Axillary N.)

Intercostobrachial N.

Thoracic and Lumbar Nerves
- Lateral Cutaneous Branches of Intercostal N. (A.P.R .)
- Posterior Cutaneous Branches of of Posterior Primary Rami (D.P.R.) (Upper C4-T6; Lower T7-T12)

Lateral Cutaneous Branches of the **Intercostal N. and Iliohypogastric N.**

- **Superior Cluneal Nn. (D.P.R. L1,L2,L3)**
- **Superior Cluneal Nn. (Medial Branches)**
- Medial Cluneal Nn. (D.P.R. S1,S2,S3) (Dorsal Primary Rami of S1, S2, S3 (Sacral Nerves)

Lateral Femoral Cutaneous N. (A.P.R.)

- **Inferior Cluneal N.**

Posterior Cutaneous Femoral N.

Anterior Cutaneous Femoral N.

Cutaneous Branch of Anterior Obturator N.

Segmental Innervation (Dermatomes) of the Skin Regions

- Indicates Anterior (Ventral) Primary Ramus of Spinal N. (A.P.R. or V.P.R.)
- Indicates Dorsal (Posterior) Primary Ramus of Spinal N. (D.P.R. or P.P.R.)

C2
C3
C4
C6
C7
C5
Th1
Th2
Th3
Th12
L1
L2
S3
S5
C0
S4
S2
L3
L4

The brown line marks the borders of the supply areas between the Posterior (Dorsal) Primary Rami and the Anterior (Ventral) Primary Rami of the Spinal Nerves.

Posterior Body Wall: Sensory Supply

4.73 Skin Branches of the Posterior Body Wall, the Occipital Region, and the Gluteal Area. [13]

● Indicates Anterior (Ventral) Primary Ramus of Spinal N. (A.P.R. or V.P.R.)

● Indicates Dorsal (Posterior) Primary Ramus of Spinal N. (D.P.R. or P.P.R.)

ⓘ The Skin on the Back is supplied by Sensory Fibers from the Posterior (Dorsal) Rami of the Spinal Nerves to the Scapular Line (◻ Fig. 4.72). In the Superior Section, the Medial Branches are Cutaneous; in the Lower Section, the Lateral Branches are Cutaneous. Skin Branches of the Posterior (Dorsal) Rami: No Cutaneous N. from C1; Greater Occipital N. is from C2; 3rd Occipital Nerve is from C3. Cutaneous Nerves below T7 are from the Lateral Branches of the Dorsal Rami. The Posterior (Dorsal) Branches are the Superior Cluneal Nn. from the Dorsal Lumbar L1-L3; Medial Cluneal Nn. from the Medial Sacral Nn. S1-S3.

Semispinalis Capitis M. (Folded Upward)

Suboccipital N.

● Dorsal Ramus of the Cervical N. C2

Spinous Process of Cervical Vertebra C7

Intertransverse Ligament

Spinalis Thoracic M.

Medial Branches of the Posterior Rami (P.P.R. N.)

● Thoracic Nn.

Lateral Branches of the Posterior Rami (D.P.R. N.)

Iliocastalis M.

Longissimus M.

◻ Fig. 7.99

Gluteus Maximus

● **Greater Occipital N. (D.P.R. C2)**

● Lesser Occipital N.

● Great Auricular N.

● Great Auricular N.

Trapezius M.

● **Posterior Cutaneous Nn. of the Medial Branches (P.P.R.) of T1-T6**

Deltoid M.

● **Posterior Cutaneous Nn. of the Lateral Branches of T7–T12**

Latissmus Dorsi M.

Spinous Process of Thoracic Vertebra T12

Thoracolumbar Fascia

● **Superior Cluneal Nn.**

● Medial Cluneal Nn.

Coccygeal Nn.

4.74 Occipital Region and Posterior Cervical Region (Nuchal Area): Dorsal View. [6]

4

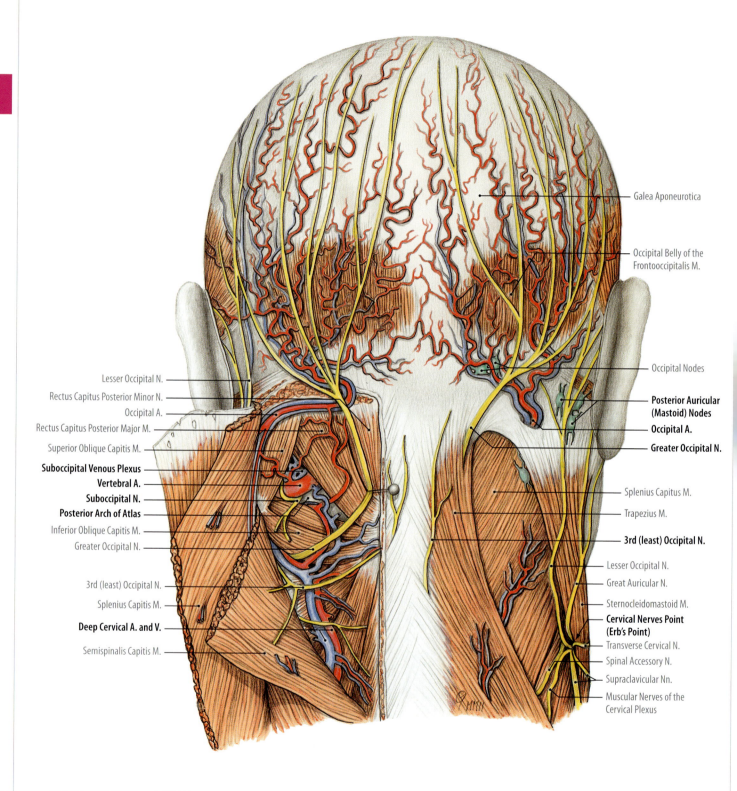

Galea Aponeurotica

Occipital Belly of the Frontooccipitalis M.

Occipital Nodes

Lesser Occipital N.

Rectus Capitus Posterior Minor N.

Occipital A.

Rectus Capitus Posterior Major M.

Superior Oblique Capitis M.

Suboccipital Venous Plexus

Vertebral A.

Suboccipital N.

Posterior Arch of Atlas

Inferior Oblique Capitis M.

Greater Occipital N.

3rd (least) Occipital N.

Splenius Capitis M.

Deep Cervical A. and V.

Semispinalis Capitis M.

Posterior Auricular (Mastoid) Nodes

Occipital A.

Greater Occipital N.

Splenius Capitus M.

Trapezius M.

3rd (least) Occipital N.

Lesser Occipital N.

Great Auricular N.

Sternocleidomastoid M.

Cervical Nerves Point (Erb's Point)

Transverse Cervical N.

Spinal Accessory N.

Supraclavicular Nn.

Muscular Nerves of the Cervical Plexus

Illustration of the Superficial Structures on the Right Side. To Dissect the Deep Structures in the Suboccipital (Vertebral) Triangle, the Trapezius, Sternocleidomastoid, Splenius Capitis, and Semispinalis Capitis Mm. have been removed and Retracted Laterally on the Left Side.

Superficial Back Region: Distribution

4.75 Superficial Back Area of the Right Side: Dorsal View. [15]

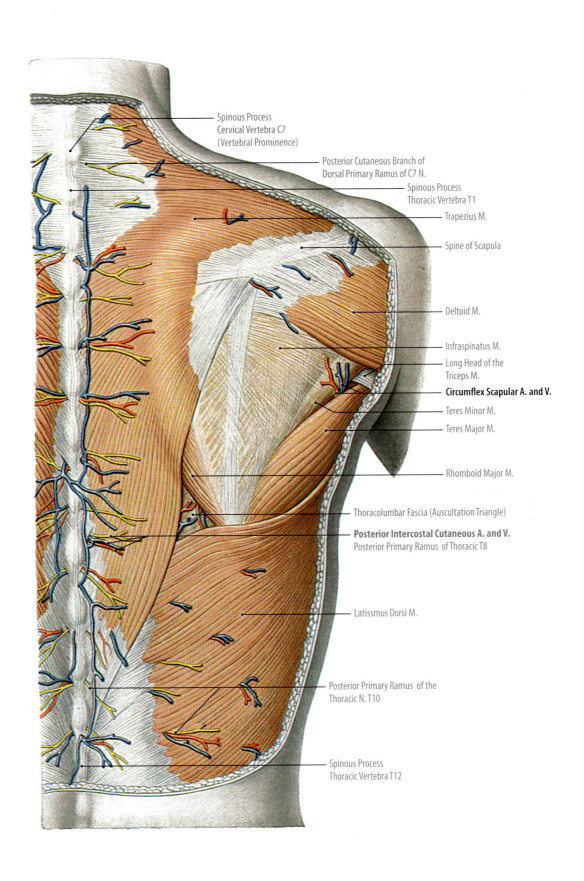

Spinous Process
Cervical Vertebra C7
(Vertebral Prominence)

Posterior Cutaneous Branch of
Dorsal Primary Ramus of C7 N.

Spinous Process
Thoracic Vertebra T1

Trapezius M.

Spine of Scapula

Deltoid M.

Infraspinatus M.

Long Head of the
Triceps M.

Circumflex Scapular A. and V.

Teres Minor M.

Teres Major M.

Rhomboid Major M.

Thoracolumbar Fascia (Auscultation Triangle)

Posterior Intercostal Cutaneous A. and V.
Posterior Primary Ramus of Thoracic T8

Latissmus Dorsi M.

Posterior Primary Ramus of the
Thoracic N. T10

Spinous Process
Thoracic Vertebra T12

Pathways and Topography

Shoulder Blade and Loin Areas: Pathways

4.76 Dorsal Body Wall: Scapula Area, Dorsal Aspect. [15]

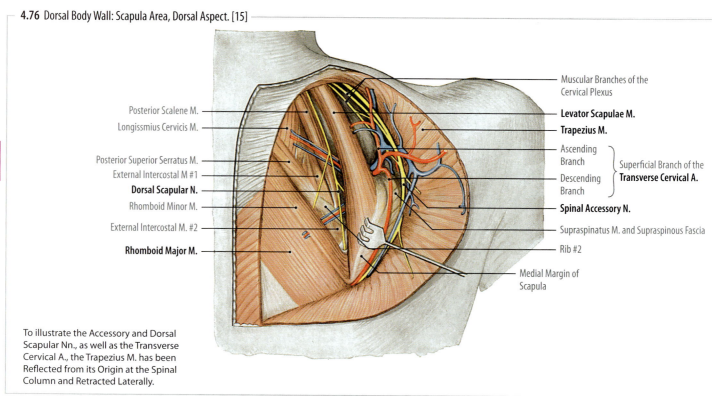

Posterior Scalene M.
Longissimus Cervicis M.

Posterior Superior Serratus M.
External Intercostal M #1
Dorsal Scapular N.
Rhomboid Minor M.
External Intercostal M. #2
Rhomboid Major M.

Muscular Branches of the Cervical Plexus
Levator Scapulae M.
Trapezius M.
Ascending Branch
Descending Branch
Superficial Branch of the **Transverse Cervical A.**
Spinal Accessory N.
Supraspinatus M. and Supraspinous Fascia
Rib #2
Medial Margin of Scapula

To illustrate the Accessory and Dorsal Scapular Nn., as well as the Transverse Cervical A., the Trapezius M. has been Reflected from its Origin at the Spinal Column and Retracted Laterally.

4.77 Dorsal Body Wall: Superficial and Deep Lumbar Area. [15]

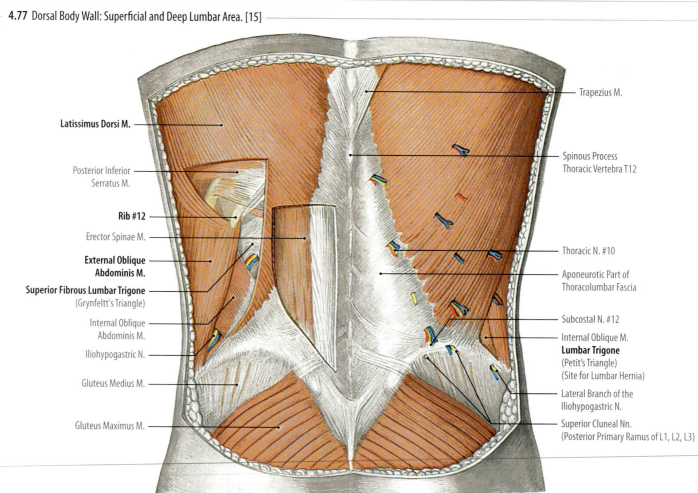

Latissimus Dorsi M.

Posterior Inferior Serratus M.

Rib #12
Erector Spinae M.

External Oblique Abdominis M.

Superior Fibrous Lumbar Trigone (Grynfeltt's Triangle)

Internal Oblique Abdominis M.

Iliohypogastric N.

Gluteus Medius M.

Gluteus Maximus M.

Trapezius M.

Spinous Process Thoracic Vertebra T12

Thoracic N. #10

Aponeurotic Part of Thoracolumbar Fascia

Subcostal N. #12

Internal Oblique M.
Lumbar Trigone (Petit's Triangle) (Site for Lumbar Hernia)

Lateral Branch of the Iliohypogastric N.

Superior Cluneal Nn. (Posterior Primary Ramus of L1, L2, L3)

On the Left Side, parts of the Thoracolumbar Fascia and the Latissimus Dorsi M. have been Removed to Dissect the Superior Fibrous Lumbar Trigone (Grynfeltt's Triangle).

The Inferior Lumbar Trigone (Petit's Triangle) and the Superior Fibrous Lumbar Trigone (Grynfeltt's Triangle) may become the Site of a Hernial Orifice for Petit's and for Grynfeltt's Lumbar Hernias.

4.78 Spinal Cord and Structure of the Spinal Nerves. [79]

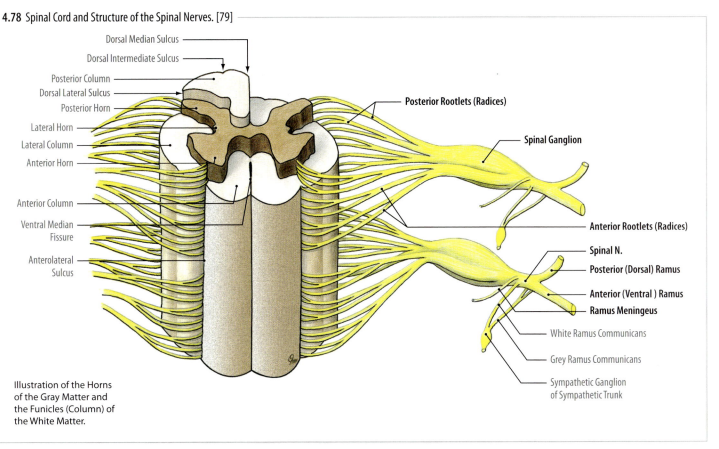

Dorsal Median Sulcus
Dorsal Intermediate Sulcus
Posterior Column
Dorsal Lateral Sulcus
Posterior Horn
Lateral Horn
Lateral Column
Anterior Horn
Anterior Column
Ventral Median Fissure
Anterolateral Sulcus

Posterior Rootlets (Radices)

Spinal Ganglion

Anterior Rootlets (Radices)

Spinal N.
Posterior (Dorsal) Ramus
Anterior (Ventral) Ramus
Ramus Meningeus
White Ramus Communicans
Grey Ramus Communicans
Sympathetic Ganglion of Sympathetic Trunk

Illustration of the Horns of the Gray Matter and the Funicles (Column) of the White Matter.

4.79a–c Cross-Sections through the Spinal Cord. [54]

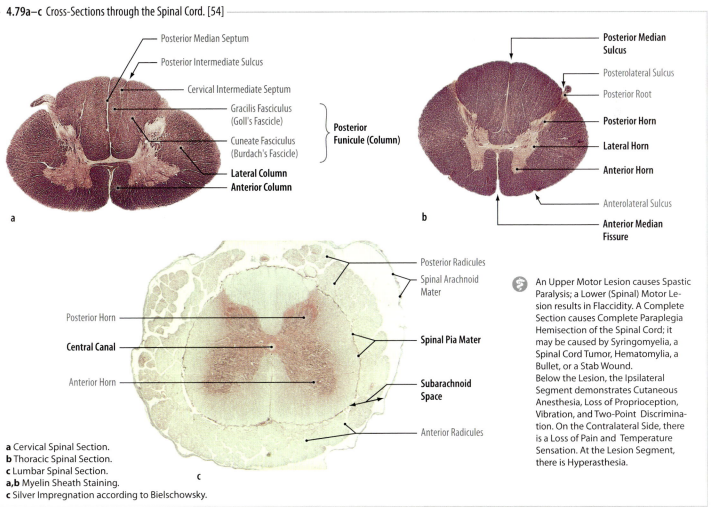

Posterior Median Septum
Posterior Intermediate Sulcus
Cervical Intermediate Septum
Gracilis Fasciculus (Goll's Fascicle)
Cuneate Fasciculus (Burdach's Fascicle)
Posterior Funicule (Column)
Lateral Column
Anterior Column

a

Posterior Median Sulcus
Posterolateral Sulcus
Posterior Root
Posterior Horn
Lateral Horn
Anterior Horn
Anterolateral Sulcus
Anterior Median Fissure

b

Posterior Horn
Central Canal
Anterior Horn

Posterior Radicules
Spinal Arachnoid Mater
Spinal Pia Mater
Subarachnoid Space
Anterior Radicules

An Upper Motor Lesion causes Spastic Paralysis; a Lower (Spinal) Motor Lesion results in Flaccidity. A Complete Section causes Complete Paraplegia Hemisection of the Spinal Cord; it may be caused by Syringomylia, a Spinal Cord Tumor, Hematomylia, a Bullet, or a Stab Wound.
Below the Lesion, the Ipsilateral Segment demonstrates Cutaneous Anesthesia, Loss of Proprioception, Vibration, and Two-Point Discrimination. On the Contralateral Side, there is a Loss of Pain and Temperature Sensation. At the Lesion Segment, there is Hyperasthesia.

a Cervical Spinal Section.
b Thoracic Spinal Section.
c Lumbar Spinal Section.
a,b Myelin Sheath Staining.
c Silver Impregnation according to Bielschowsky.

c

Spinal Cord and Spinal Nerves

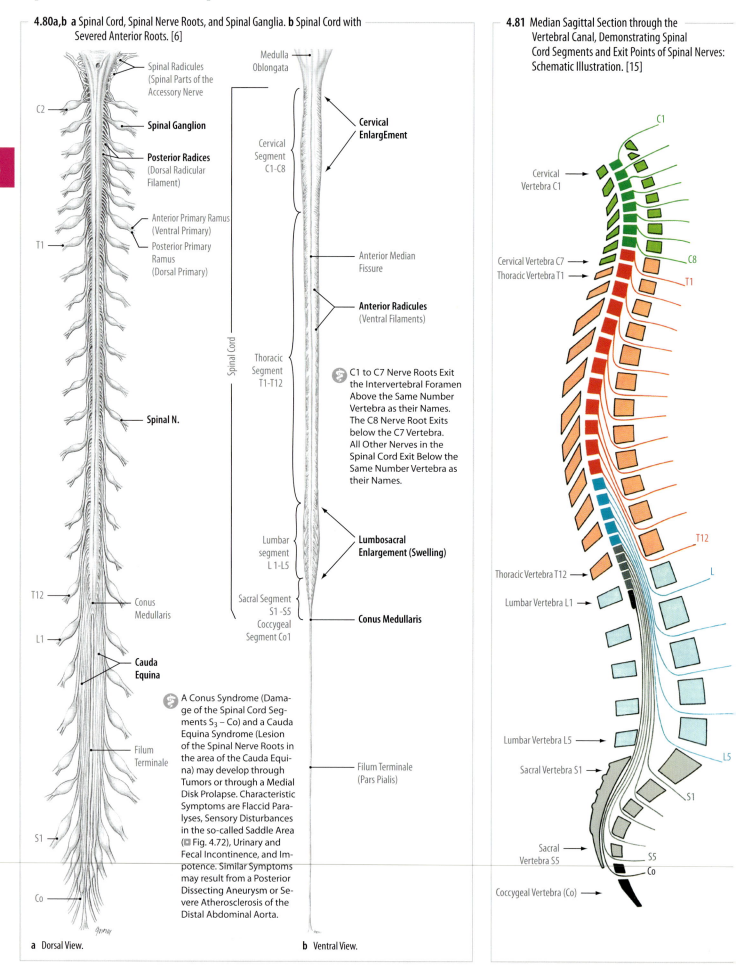

4.80a,b a Spinal Cord, Spinal Nerve Roots, and Spinal Ganglia. **b** Spinal Cord with Severed Anterior Roots. [6]

4.81 Median Sagittal Section through the Vertebral Canal, Demonstrating Spinal Cord Segments and Exit Points of Spinal Nerves: Schematic Illustration. [15]

Spinal Radicules (Spinal Parts of the Accessory Nerve

C2

Spinal Ganglion

Posterior Radices (Dorsal Radicular Filament)

Anterior Primary Ramus (Ventral Primary)

Posterior Primary Ramus (Dorsal Primary)

T1

Spinal N.

T12

L1

Cauda Equina

Filum Terminale

S1

Co

Medulla Oblongata

Cervical Segment C1-C8

Spinal Cord

Thoracic Segment T1-T12

Lumbar segment L 1-L5

Sacral Segment S1 -S5 Coccygeal Segment Co1

Conus Medullaris

Filum Terminale (Pars Pialis)

Cervical EnlargEment

Anterior Median Fissure

Anterior Radicules (Ventral Filaments)

C1 to C7 Nerve Roots Exit the Intervertebral Foramen Above the Same Number Vertebra as their Names. The C8 Nerve Root Exits below the C7 Vertebra. All Other Nerves in the Spinal Cord Exit Below the Same Number Vertebra as their Names.

Lumbosacral Enlargement (Swelling)

Conus Medullaris

A Conus Syndrome (Damage of the Spinal Cord Segments S₃ – Co) and a Cauda Equina Syndrome (Lesion of the Spinal Nerve Roots in the area of the Cauda Equina) may develop through Tumors or through a Medial Disk Prolapse. Characteristic Symptoms are Flaccid Paralyses, Sensory Disturbances in the so-called Saddle Area (◻ Fig. 4.72), Urinary and Fecal Incontinence, and Impotence. Similar Symptoms may result from a Posterior Dissecting Aneurysm or Severe Atherosclerosis of the Distal Abdominal Aorta.

C1

Cervical Vertebra C1

Cervical Vertebra C7

Thoracic Vertebra T1

C8

T1

Thoracic Vertebra T12

Lumbar Vertebra L1

T12

L

Lumbar Vertebra L5

Sacral Vertebra S1

L5

S1

Sacral Vertebra S5

S5

Co

Coccygeal Vertebra (Co)

a Dorsal View.

b Ventral View.

4.82 Spinal Cord in Situ: Dorsal View. [8]

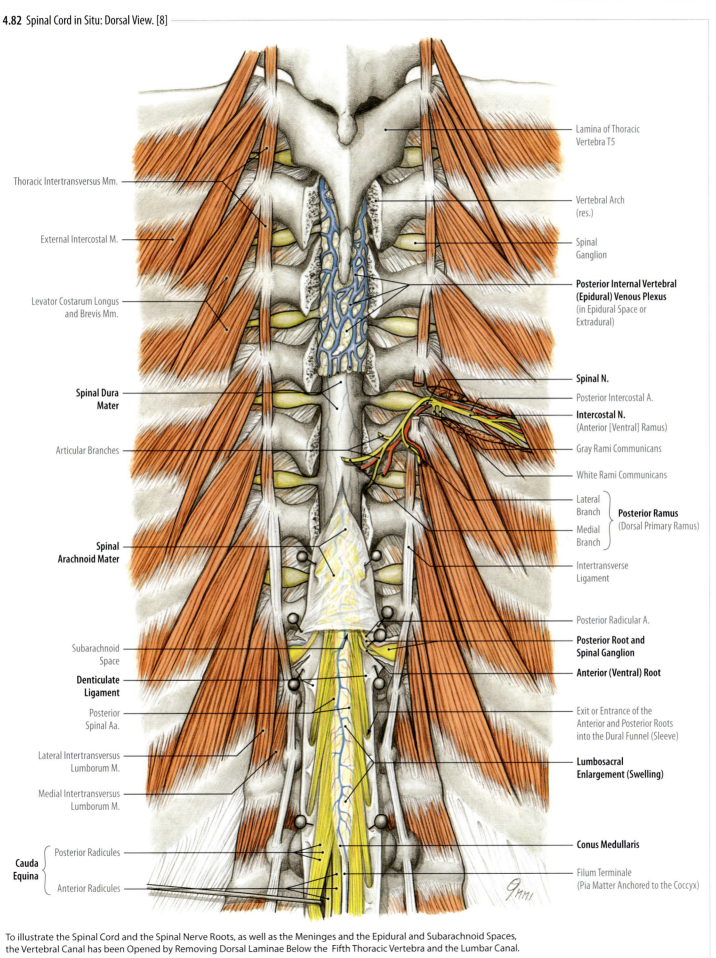

Lamina of Thoracic
Vertebra T5

Thoracic Intertransversus Mm.

External Intercostal M.

Levator Costarum Longus
and Brevis Mm.

Vertebral Arch
(res.)

Spinal
Ganglion

**Posterior Internal Vertebral
(Epidural) Venous Plexus**
(in Epidural Space or
Extradural)

**Spinal Dura
Mater**

Spinal N.

Posterior Intercostal A.

Intercostal N.
(Anterior [Ventral] Ramus)

Articular Branches

Gray Rami Communicans

White Rami Communicans

Lateral
Branch
Posterior Ramus
(Dorsal Primary Ramus)
Medial
Branch

**Spinal
Arachnoid Mater**

Intertransverse
Ligament

Posterior Radicular A.

**Posterior Root and
Spinal Ganglion**

Subarachnoid
Space

Anterior (Ventral) Root

**Denticulate
Ligament**

Exit or Entrance of the
Anterior and Posterior Roots
into the Dural Funnel (Sleeve)

Posterior
Spinal Aa.

**Lumbosacral
Enlargement (Swelling)**

Lateral Intertransversus
Lumborum M.

Medial Intertransversus
Lumborum M.

Conus Medullaris

Cauda
Equina
Posterior Radicules

Filum Terminale
(Pia Matter Anchored to the Coccyx)

Anterior Radicules

To illustrate the Spinal Cord and the Spinal Nerve Roots, as well as the Meninges and the Epidural and Subarachnoid Spaces,
the Vertebral Canal has been Opened by Removing Dorsal Laminae Below the Fifth Thoracic Vertebra and the Lumbar Canal.

Spinal Cord

Spinal Cord in Situ

4.83 Spinal Cord In Situ: Cervical Area, Superior View. [6]

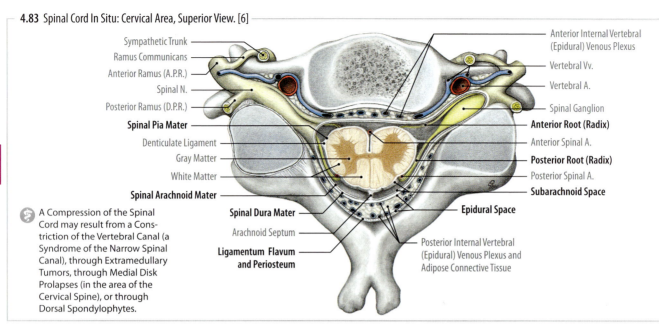

Sympathetic Trunk
Ramus Communicans
Anterior Ramus (A.P.R.)
Spinal N.
Posterior Ramus (D.P.R.)
Spinal Pia Mater
Denticulate Ligament
Gray Matter
White Matter
Spinal Arachnoid Mater
Spinal Dura Mater
Arachnoid Septum
Ligamentum Flavum and Periosteum

Anterior Internal Vertebral (Epidural) Venous Plexus
Vertebral Vv.
Vertebral A.
Spinal Ganglion
Anterior Root (Radix)
Anterior Spinal A.
Posterior Root (Radix)
Posterior Spinal A.
Subarachnoid Space
Epidural Space
Posterior Internal Vertebral (Epidural) Venous Plexus and Adipose Connective Tissue

A Compression of the Spinal Cord may result from a Constriction of the Vertebral Canal (a Syndrome of the Narrow Spinal Canal), through Extramedullary Tumors, through Medial Disk Prolapses (in the area of the Cervical Spine), or through Dorsal Spondylophytes.

4.84 Lumbar Vertebral Canal and Sacral Canal, Opened from View. [15]

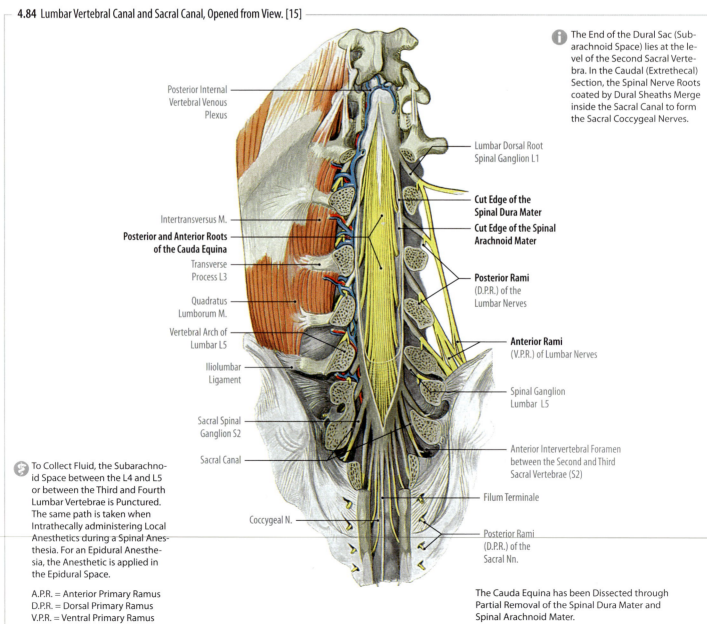

The End of the Dural Sac (Subarachnoid Space) lies at the level of the Second Sacral Vertebra. In the Caudal (Extrethecal) Section, the Spinal Nerve Roots coated by Dural Sheaths Merge inside the Sacral Canal to form the Sacral Coccygeal Nerves.

Posterior Internal Vertebral Venous Plexus
Intertransversus M.
Posterior and Anterior Roots of the Cauda Equina
Transverse Process L3
Quadratus Lumborum M.
Vertebral Arch of Lumbar L5
Iliolumbar Ligament
Sacral Spinal Ganglion S2
Sacral Canal
Coccygeal N.

Lumbar Dorsal Root Spinal Ganglion L1
Cut Edge of the Spinal Dura Mater
Cut Edge of the Spinal Arachnoid Mater
Posterior Rami (D.P.R.) of the Lumbar Nerves
Anterior Rami (V.P.R.) of Lumbar Nerves
Spinal Ganglion Lumbar L5
Anterior Intervertebral Foramen between the Second and Third Sacral Vertebrae (S2)
Filum Terminale
Posterior Rami (D.P.R.) of the Sacral Nn.

To Collect Fluid, the Subarachnoid Space between the L4 and L5 or between the Third and Fourth Lumbar Vertebrae is Punctured. The same path is taken when Intrathecally administering Local Anesthetics during a Spinal Anesthesia. For an Epidural Anesthesia, the Anesthetic is applied in the Epidural Space.

A.P.R. = Anterior Primary Ramus
D.P.R. = Dorsal Primary Ramus
V.P.R. = Ventral Primary Ramus

The Cauda Equina has been Dissected through Partial Removal of the Spinal Dura Mater and Spinal Arachnoid Mater.

Spinal Cord: Blood Supply

4.85a–c Blood Supply of the Spinal Cord: Semi-Schematic Illustration. [79, 63]

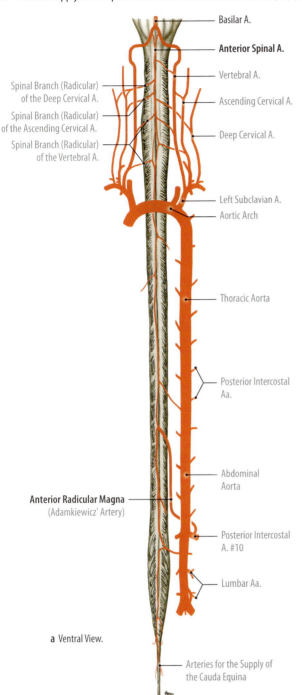

Basilar A.

Anterior Spinal A.

Vertebral A.

Ascending Cervical A.

Deep Cervical A.

Spinal Branch (Radicular) of the Deep Cervical A.

Spinal Branch (Radicular) of the Ascending Cervical A.

Spinal Branch (Radicular) of the Vertebral A.

Left Subclavian A.

Aortic Arch

Thoracic Aorta

Posterior Intercostal Aa.

Abdominal Aorta

Anterior Radicular Magna (Adamkiewicz' Artery)

Posterior Intercostal A. #10

Lumbar Aa.

a Ventral View.

Arteries for the Supply of the Cauda Equina

Anterior Spinal V.

Deep Cervical V.

Vertebral V.

Internal Jugular V. (res.)

Subclavian V.

Superior Vena Cava

Accessory Hemiazygos V.

Azygos V.

Hemiazygos V.

Ascending Lumbar V.

b Ventral View.

a Arterial Supply: Posterior Spinal (Posterolateral) Aa., Anterior Spinal A., as well as the Anterior and Posterior Radicular Aa. from the Vertebral A., Ascending Cervical, Deep Cervical, Supreme Intercostal, Posterior Intercostal, and Lumbar Aa.
b Venous Drainage.
c Cross-Section through the Spinal Cord. Arterial Supply of the Left side, Venous Drainage on the Right Side.

ⓘ Note the Supply Areas from the Anterior Spinal A. and the Posterior Spinal A.

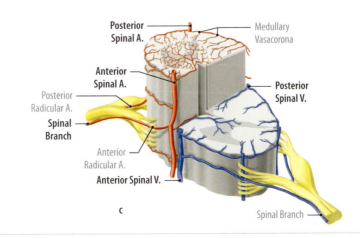

Posterior Spinal A.

Medullary Vasacorona

Anterior Spinal A.

Posterior Radicular A.

Posterior Spinal V.

Spinal Branch

Anterior Radicular A.

Anterior Spinal V.

Spinal Branch

c

Damage to the Great Radicular A. causes an Ischemia and Functional Loss of the Spinal Cord Section supplied by it.
Anterior Spinal A. Syndrome due to Thrombosis results in Damage to the Anterior and Lateral Column of the Spinal Column on That Side. Patients present with:
• Flaccid Paralysis at the level of the Affected Segment and Spasticity Below the Lesion
• Sensory Loss of Pain and Temperature Sensation (Lateral Column)
• Preserved Proprioception and Vibration Below the Affected Segment (Posterior Column)

Spinal Cord

Vertebral Column and Vertebral Canal: Veins

4.86a–c Veins of the Spinal Cord and the Vertebral Canal. [a–c 58, 59; c 13]

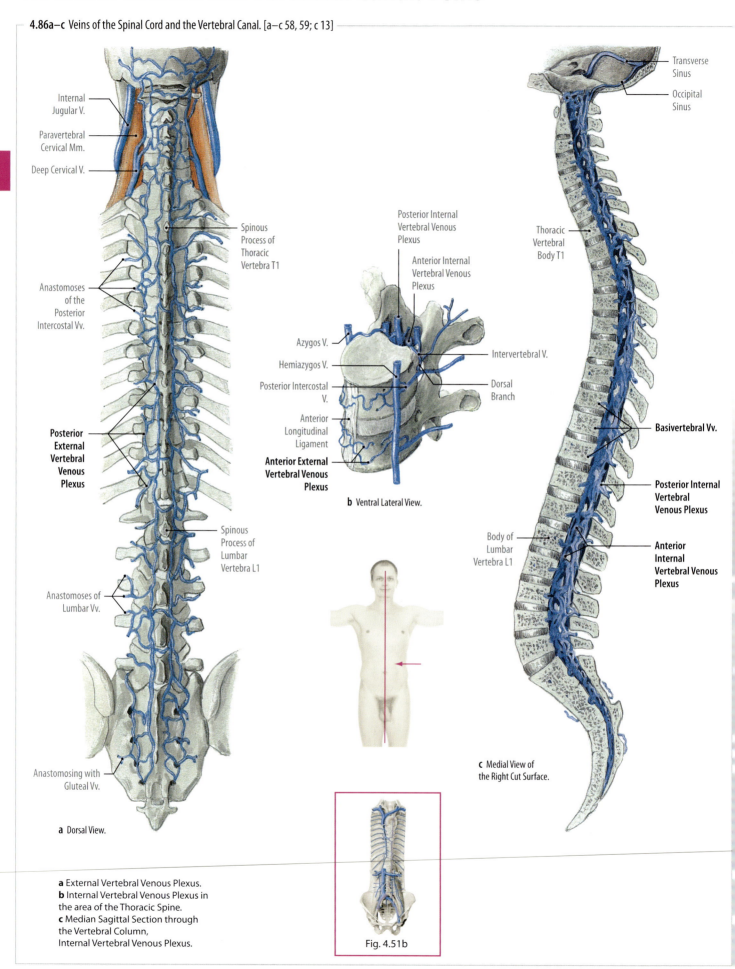

Internal Jugular V.

Paravertebral Cervical Mm.

Deep Cervical V.

Spinous Process of Thoracic Vertebra T1

Anastomoses of the Posterior Intercostal Vv.

Posterior External Vertebral Venous Plexus

Spinous Process of Lumbar Vertebra L1

Anastomoses of Lumbar Vv.

Anastomosing with Gluteal Vv.

a Dorsal View.

Posterior Internal Vertebral Venous Plexus

Anterior Internal Vertebral Venous Plexus

Azygos V.

Hemiazygos V.

Posterior Intercostal V.

Anterior Longitudinal Ligament

Anterior External Vertebral Venous Plexus

Intervertebral V.

Dorsal Branch

b Ventral Lateral View.

Transverse Sinus

Occipital Sinus

Thoracic Vertebral Body T1

Basivertebral Vv.

Posterior Internal Vertebral Venous Plexus

Body of Lumbar Vertebra L1

Anterior Internal Vertebral Venous Plexus

c Medial View of the Right Cut Surface.

Fig. 4.51b

a External Vertebral Venous Plexus.
b Internal Vertebral Venous Plexus in the area of the Thoracic Spine.
c Median Sagittal Section through the Vertebral Column, Internal Vertebral Venous Plexus.

Spinal Cord and Vertebral Canal: Imaging

4.87 Median Sagittal Section through the Vertebral Canal of a 15-Year-Old Boy. [60]

Medulla Oblongata

Posterior Cerebellomedullary Cistern

Spinal Cord

Subarachnoid Space (Leptomeningeal)

Lumbar Vertebra L1

Conus Medullaris

Magnetic Resonance Transfer (MRT) T2-weibthd exposure.

4.88 Lumbar Myelography of a 60-Year-Old Woman in Anteroposterior (AP) Projection. [60]

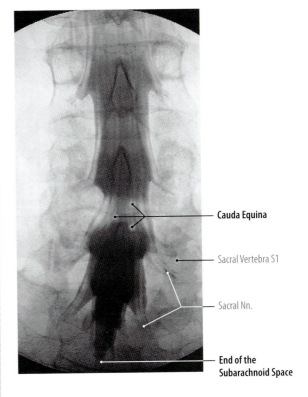

Cauda Equina

Sacral Vertebra S1

Sacral Nn.

End of the Subarachnoid Space

ⓘ Note the Transgression of the Contrast Medium into the Endoneural Spaces of the Lumbar and Sacral Nerves Coated by the Perineurium (Extension of the Cerebrospinal Fluid).

4.89 Axial Computed Tomography (CT) Scan at the Level of the Fourth Lumbar Vertebra L4 of a 60-Year-Old Woman. [60]

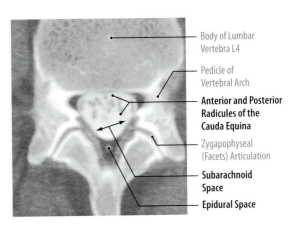

Body of Lumbar Vertebra L4

Pedicle of Vertebral Arch

Anterior and Posterior Radicules of the Cauda Equina

Zygapophyseal (Facets) Articulation

Subarachnoid Space

Epidural Space

Postmyelo-CT following the insertion of a contrast medium into the Subarachnoid Space, illustration of the Cauda Equina.

Spinal Cord

4.A Interior of the Thoracic Skeleton: Origin (Left Side of the Body), Insertion (Right Side of the Body), Dorsal View.

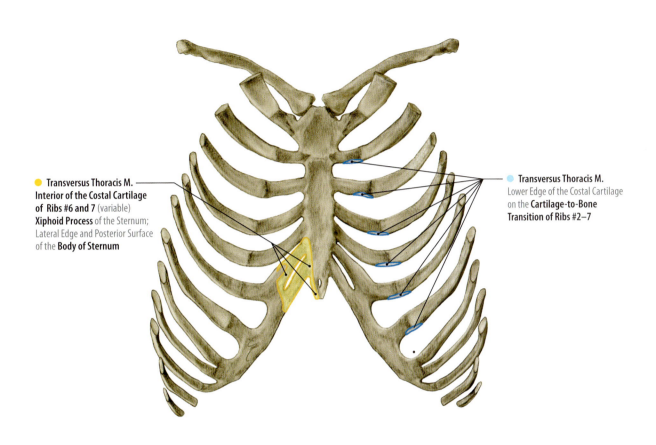

● **Transversus Thoracis M.**
Interior of the Costal Cartilage of Ribs #6 and 7 (variable) **Xiphoid Process** of the Sternum; Lateral Edge and Posterior Surface of the **Body of Sternum**

● **Transversus Thoracis M.**
Lower Edge of the Costal Cartilage on the **Cartilage-to-Bone Transition of Ribs #2–7**

4.B Origins and Insertions on the Thoracic Skeletal Muscles: Ventral View.

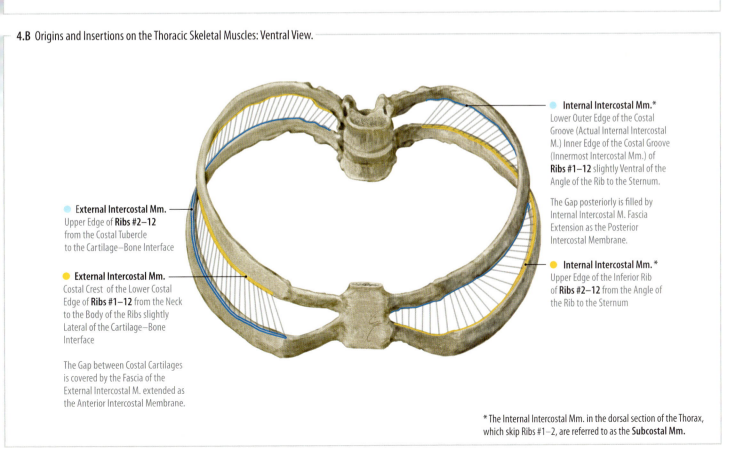

● **External Intercostal Mm.**
Upper Edge of **Ribs #2–12** from the Costal Tubercle to the Cartilage–Bone Interface

● **External Intercostal Mm.**
Costal Crest of the Lower Costal Edge of **Ribs #1–12** from the Neck to the Body of the Ribs slightly Lateral of the Cartilage–Bone Interface

The Gap between Costal Cartilages is covered by the Fascia of the External Intercostal M. extended as the Anterior Intercostal Membrane.

● **Internal Intercostal Mm.***
Lower Outer Edge of the Costal Groove (Actual Internal Intercostal M.) Inner Edge of the Costal Groove (Innermost Intercostal Mm.) of **Ribs #1–12** slightly Ventral of the Angle of the Rib to the Sternum.

The Gap posteriorly is filled by Internal Intercostal M. Fascia Extension as the Posterior Intercostal Membrane.

● **Internal Intercostal Mm.***
Upper Edge of the Inferior Rib of **Ribs #2–12** from the Angle of the Rib to the Sternum

* The Internal Intercostal Mm. in the dorsal section of the Thorax, which skip Ribs #1–2, are referred to as the **Subcostal Mm.**

Muscles of the Trunk • MA-4:1

Function	Innervation	Blood Supply
Intercostal Muscles		
External Intercostal Mm. Lifting of the Ribs (support of inspiration)	Intercostal Nn. T1–T11	Intercostal Branches of the Internal Thoracic A. Musculophrenic A.

Internal Intercostal Mm.
Splitting of the Internal Intercostal Mm. through the pathways
into the actual Internal Intercostal Mm.
and the Intercostales Intimi (Innermost Intercostal Mm.)
Median and Posterior Part:
   Lowering of the Ribs (support of expiration)
Anterior Part (Intercartilaginous Part):
   Lifting of the Ribs (support of inspiration)
Joint Function:
Tension of the Intercostal Spaces
	Intercostal Nn.
	T1–T11
		Posterior Intercostal Aa.
		split into two branches.
		The Suprem Intercostal A.
		from the Costocervical Trunk of
		Subclavian A. supplies the upper three of four
		Intercostal Spaces. The rest of the Intercostal
		Spaces are supplied by the Descending Thoracic
		Aorta.

Subcostal Mm. Lowering of the Ribs (support of expiration)	Intercostal Nn. T4–T11	Posterior Intercostal Aa. of the Thoracic Aorta
Transversus Thoracis M. Lowering of the Ribs (support of expiration)	Intercostal Nn. T2–T6	Anterior Intercostal Aa. of the Internal Thoracic A. and Musculophrenic A.

4

4.Ca Abdominal Muscles: Origins (Right Side of the Body), Insertions (Left Side of the Body) on the Skeleton of Trunk, Ventral View.

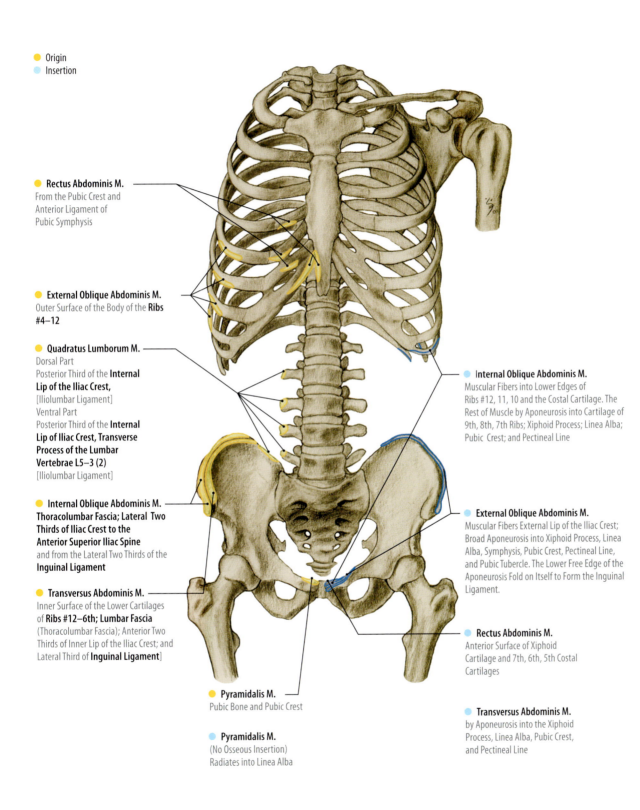

● Origin
● Insertion

● **Rectus Abdominis M.**
From the Pubic Crest and
Anterior Ligament of
Pubic Symphysis

● **External Oblique Abdominis M.**
Outer Surface of the Body of the **Ribs**
#4–12

● **Quadratus Lumborum M.**
Dorsal Part
Posterior Third of the **Internal**
Lip of the Iliac Crest,
[Iliolumbar Ligament]
Ventral Part
Posterior Third of the **Internal**
Lip of Iliac Crest, Transverse
Process of the Lumbar
Vertebrae L5–3 (2)
[Iliolumbar Ligament]

● **Internal Oblique Abdominis M.**
Thoracolumbar Fascia; Lateral Two
Thirds of Iliac Crest to the
Anterior Superior Iliac Spine
and from the Lateral Two Thirds of the
Inguinal Ligament

● **Transversus Abdominis M.**
Inner Surface of the Lower Cartilages
of Ribs **#12–6th; Lumbar Fascia**
(Thoracolumbar Fascia); Anterior Two
Thirds of Inner Lip of the Iliac Crest; and
Lateral Third of **Inguinal Ligament**]

● **Pyramidalis M.**
Pubic Bone and Pubic Crest

● **Pyramidalis M.**
(No Osseous Insertion)
Radiates into Linea Alba

● **Internal Oblique Abdominis M.**
Muscular Fibers into Lower Edges of
Ribs #12, 11, 10 and the Costal Cartilage. The
Rest of Muscle by Aponeurosis into Cartilage of
9th, 8th, 7th Ribs; Xiphoid Process; Linea Alba;
Pubic Crest; and Pectineal Line

● **External Oblique Abdominis M.**
Muscular Fibers External Lip of the Iliac Crest;
Broad Aponeurosis into Xiphoid Process, Linea
Alba, Symphysis, Pubic Crest, Pectineal Line,
and Pubic Tubercle. The Lower Free Edge of the
Aponeurosis Fold on Itself to Form the Inguinal
Ligament.

● **Rectus Abdominis M.**
Anterior Surface of Xiphoid
Cartilage and 7th, 6th, 5th Costal
Cartilages

● **Transversus Abdominis M.**
by Aponeurosis into the Xiphoid
Process, Linea Alba, Pubic Crest,
and Pectineal Line

Muscles of the Trunk

4

Function	Innervation	Blood Supply
Lateral and Anterior Abdominal Muscles		

External Oblique Abdominis M.
Unilateral Activity:
    Sideward inclination of the Trunk and rotation of the Trunk to the contralateral side, together with the Internal Oblique Abdominis M. of the opposite side
Bilateral Activity:
    Forward inclination of the Trunk (support of expiration and of the abdominal press), tension of the Abdominal Wall, participation in the Arcuate Tendon construction
    ▫ Rectus Abdominis M.
	Intercostal Nn. T8 –T12 Iliohypogastric and Ilioinguinal Nn. L1 Variable T5–12, L1	Anterior Intercostal Aa. of the Internal Thoracic A. Superior Epigastric A. Lateral Thoracic A. Inferior Epigastric A. Deep Circumflex Iliac A.

Internal Oblique Abdominis M.
Unilateral Activity:
    Sideward inclination of the Trunk and rotation of the Trunk to the ipsilateral side, together with the External Oblique Abdominis M. of the opposite side
Bilateral Activity:
    Forward inclination of the Trunk
    Lowering of the Ribs (support of expiration and the abdominal press, tension of the Abdominal Wall, participation in the Arcuate Tendon construction)
    ▫ Rectus Abdominis M.
	Intercostal Nn. T8 –T 12, Iliohypogastric, Ilioinguinal Nn. (and Genitofemoral) (T8) T9–12, L1 (L2)	Musculophrenic A. Superior Epigastric A. Posterior Intercostal Aa. Deep Circumflex Iliac A.

Transversus Abdominis M. ▫ Fig. 4.Cb Tension of the Abdominal Wall Abdominal press (support of expiration)	Intercostal Nn. T5–12 (variable), Iliohypogastric, Ilioinguinal, and Genitofemoral Nn. (T5–6) T7–12, L1–L2	Musculophrenic A. Superior Epigastric A. Posterior Intercostal Aa. Deep Circumflex Iliac A.
Rectus Abdominis M. Forward inclination of the Trunk Tension of the Abdominal Wall Development of the "Tendon" within the Arcuate Tendon construction of the Spinal Column Tilting the Pelvis in a ventral direction	Intercostal Nn. (T6) T7– T12 (variable) Iliohypogastric N. (Ilioinguinal N.) (T5) T6–12, L1 (L2)	Superior Epigastric A. Inferior Epigastric A.

4.Cb Abdominal Muscles, Muscles of the Vertebral and Costal Joints: Origins (Right Side of the Body), Insertions (Left Side of the Body), on the Skeleton of the Trunk, Dorsal View.

- Origin
- Insertion

External Oblique Abdominis M.
Outer Surface of Ribs #4 (5)–12

Internal Oblique Abdominis M.
Lower Edge of Ribs #(9) 10 , 11, and 12 and Costal Cartilages 7, 8, 9th. The major part form Aponeurosis (Contribute to Formation of Rectal Sheath), Linea Alba, Xiphoid, Pubic Crest, and Pectineal Line.

Quadratus Lumborum M.
● Dorsal Part
Transverse Process of Lumbar Vertebrae L1–2 (4)
● Ventral Part
Medial Half of Rib #12

Transversus Abdominis M.
Inner Surface of Lower Cartilages of Ribs #12–6; Thoracolumbar (Lumbar) Fascia and Anterior Two Third of the Internal Lip of Iliac Crest and the Lateral One Third of the Inguinal Ligament (▣ Fig. 4.Ca)

Quadratus Lumborum M.
● Dorsal Part
Posterior Third of the Internal Lip of the Iliac Crest [Iliolumbar (Fascia) Ligament]
● Ventral Part
Transverse Processes of Lumbar Vertebrae L (2) L3–L5 [Iliolumbar Ligament] (▣ Fig. 4.Ca)

External Oblique Abdominis M.
External Lip of the Iliac Crest, Broad Aponeurosis to Xiphoid, Linea Alba, Pubic Crest, Symphysis, and Pectineal Line. Inguinal Ligament is Folded at Lower Edge and Forms Rectus Sheath (▣ Fig. 4.Ca).

Transversus Abdominis M.
Aponeurosis Extends to the Xiphoid Cartilage Linea Alba, to Pubic Crest and Pectineal Line. Fuses with Other at the Semilunar Line on the Outer Edge of Rectus M. to Form the Posterior Wall of the Rectus Sheath Down to the Level of Arcuate Line.

Muscles of the Trunk

Function	Innervation	Blood Supply
Cremaster M. Separation from the lower fibers of the Internal Oblique Abdominis M. Descend to Testis and loop back up to Pubic Tubercle Lifting of the Testis	Genital Branch of the Genitofemoral N. L1–L2	Cremasteric A.
Pyramidalis M. May function as a tensor for the Linea Alba.	Subcostal N. T 12 Muscular Nn. of the Lumbar Plexus T12, L1–L3	Inferior Epigastric A.
Deep Posterior Abdominal Muscles		
Quadratus Lumborum M. Unilateral Activity: 　Sideward inclination of the Trunk Bilateral Activity: 　Lowering of the 12 pair of Ribs Isometric Contraction: 　Fixation of the 12 pair of Ribs for the contraction of the Diaphragm in connection with inspiration (accessory muscles of respiration)	Intercostal N. T12 Iliohypogastric N. T12–L1	Subcostal A. Dorsal Branches of the Lumbar Aa. Lumbar Branch of the Iliolumbar A.

4

Diaphragm | pp. 212, 290–291

4.Da Cervical Muscles that Migrated into the Thorax, the Diaphragm: Origins on the Thoracic Skeleton, Dorsal View of the Interior of the Thoracic Skeleton.

Muscles of the Trunk

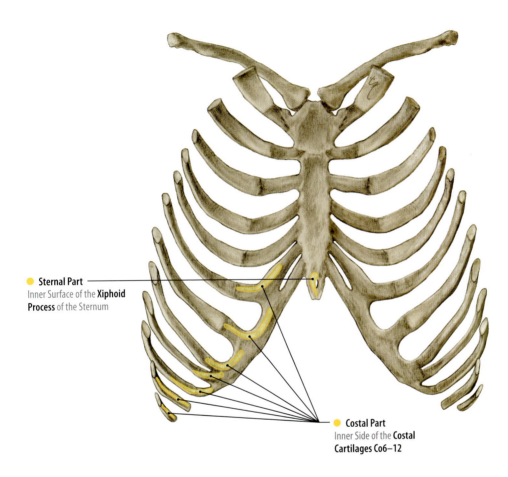

● **Sternal Part**
Inner Surface of the **Xiphoid Process** of the Sternum

● **Costal Part**
Inner Side of the **Costal Cartilages Co6–12**

● Origin
● Insertion

● **The Diaphragm does not have an insertion on the skeleton:** All muscle fibers converge from the periphery to the center of the Diaphragm at the **Central Tendon.**

4.Db Origins on the Lumbar Spine and on the Medial and Lateral Arcuate Ligament: Ventral View.

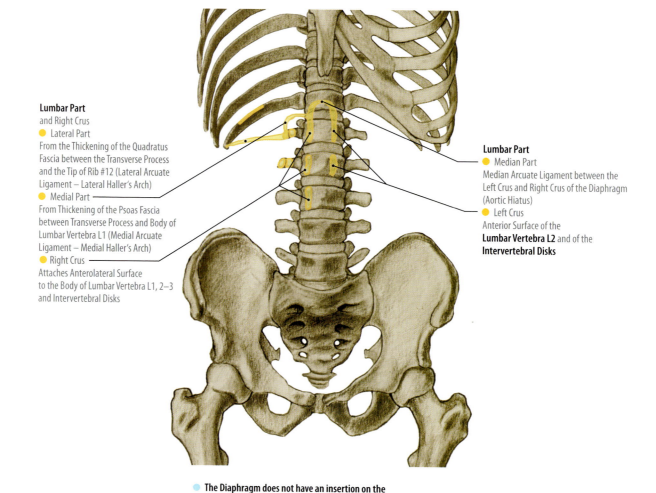

Lumbar Part
and Right Crus
● **Lateral Part**
From the Thickening of the Quadratus
Fascia between the Transverse Process
and the Tip of Rib #12 (Lateral Arcuate
Ligament – Lateral Haller's Arch)
● **Medial Part**
From Thickening of the Psoas Fascia
between Transverse Process and Body of
Lumbar Vertebra L1 (Medial Arcuate
Ligament – Medial Haller's Arch)
● **Right Crus**
Attaches Anterolateral Surface
to the Body of Lumbar Vertebra L1, 2–3
and Intervertebral Disks

Lumbar Part
● **Median Part**
Median Arcuate Ligament between the
Left Crus and Right Crus of the Diaphragm
(Aortic Hiatus)
● **Left Crus**
Anterior Surface of the
Lumbar Vertebra L2 and of the
Intervertebral Disks

● **The Diaphragm does not have an insertion on the
skeleton:** All muscle fibers converge on the **Central Tendon.**

Function	Innervation	Blood Supply
Inspiration through leveling of the diaphragmatic domes	Phrenic N. C3, C4 (C5)	Pericardiacophrenic A. Musculophrenic A. from the Internal Thoracic (Mammary) A. Superior Phrenic A. from the Thoracic Aorta Inferior Phrenic A. from the Abdominal Aorta

4.E Muscles of the Head and Vertebral Joints as well as Muscles of the Costal Joints: Origin (Left Side of the Body), Insertion (Right Side of the Body), Dorsal View.

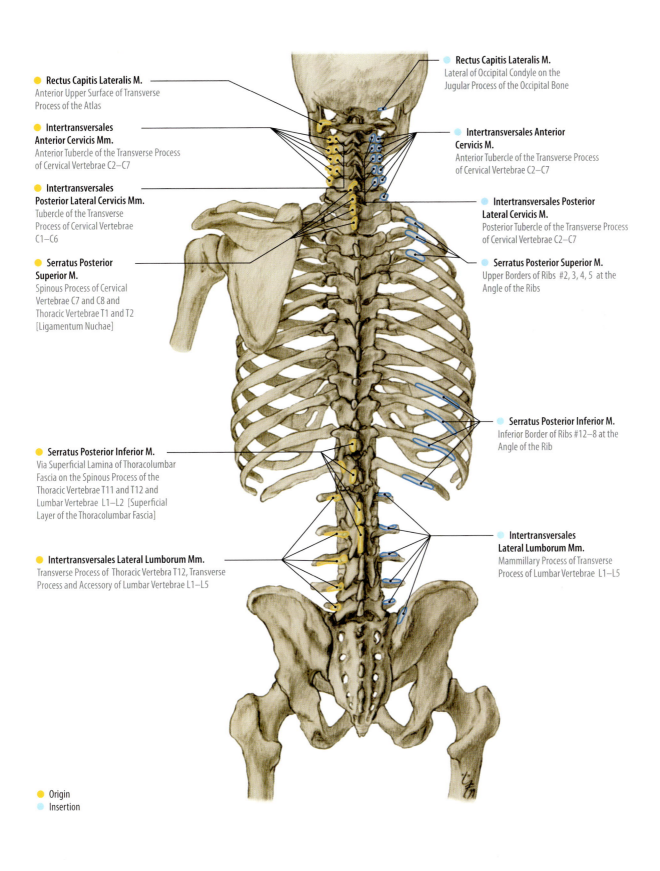

● **Rectus Capitis Lateralis M.**
Anterior Upper Surface of Transverse
Process of the Atlas

● **Intertransversales
Anterior Cervicis Mm.**
Anterior Tubercle of the Transverse Process
of Cervical Vertebrae C2–C7

● **Intertransversales
Posterior Lateral Cervicis Mm.**
Tubercle of the Transverse
Process of Cervical Vertebrae
C1–C6

● **Serratus Posterior
Superior M.**
Spinous Process of Cervical
Vertebrae C7 and C8 and
Thoracic Vertebrae T1 and T2
[Ligamentum Nuchae]

● **Serratus Posterior Inferior M.**
Via Superficial Lamina of Thoracolumbar
Fascia on the Spinous Process of the
Thoracic Vertebrae T11 and T12 and
Lumbar Vertebrae L1–L2 [Superficial
Layer of the Thoracolumbar Fascia]

● **Intertransversales Lateral Lumborum Mm.**
Transverse Process of Thoracic Vertebra T12, Transverse
Process and Accessory of Lumbar Vertebrae L1–L5

● **Rectus Capitis Lateralis M.**
Lateral of Occipital Condyle on the
Jugular Process of the Occipital Bone

● **Intertransversales Anterior
Cervicis M.**
Anterior Tubercle of the Transverse Process
of Cervical Vertebrae C2–C7

● **Intertransversales Posterior
Lateral Cervicis M.**
Posterior Tubercle of the Transverse Process
of Cervical Vertebrae C2–C7

● **Serratus Posterior Superior M.**
Upper Borders of Ribs #2, 3, 4, 5 at the
Angle of the Ribs

● **Serratus Posterior Inferior M.**
Inferior Border of Ribs #12–8 at the
Angle of the Rib

● **Intertransversales
Lateral Lumborum Mm.**
Mammillary Process of Transverse
Process of Lumbar Vertebrae L1–L5

● Origin
● Insertion

Muscles of the Trunk

4

Function	Innervation	Blood Supply
Group of the Short Muscles of the Head Joints		
Rectus Capitis Lateralis M. Ipsilateral sideward inclination in the Head Joints	Anterior (ventral) Rami of the Cervical Nn. C1 and C2	Vertebral A. Occipital A.
Group of the Muscles of the Intertransversal System		
Intertransversales Anterior Cervicis Mm. Support of the sideward inclination and extension of the Cervical Spine Stabilization of the Cervical Spine	Anterior (ventral) Rami of the Cervical Nn.	Vertebral A.
Intertransversales Posterior Laterales Cervicis ◫ Intertransversales Anterior Cervicis Mm.	Anterior (ventral) Rami of the Cervical Nn.	Vertebral A.
Intertransversales Lateral Lumborum Mm. Support of the sideward inclination of the Lumbar Spine Stabilization of the Lumbar Spine	Anterior (ventral) Rami [variable also Posterior (dorsal) Rami] of the Lumbar Nn.	Lumbar Aa.
Group of the Spinocostales		
Serratus Posterior Superior M. Lifting of the Upper Ribs (support of inspiration)	Intercostal Nn. T2–T4 Cervical N. CN 8	Posterior Intercostal Aa. Deep Cervical A.
Serratus Posterior Inferior M. Dilatation of the Inferior Thorax Aperture Stabilization of the Lower Ribs for the contraction of the Costal Part of the Diaphragm (support of inspiration)	Intercostal Nn. T9,10, and T12	Posterior Intercostal A.

The Levator Costarum Mm. are primarily innervated from dorsal and partially from Intercostal (Ventral Spinal Nerve) Branches,
◫ Autochthonous Muscles of the Back.

4.Fa Spinal and Transversospinal Systems. Muscles of the Back, Medial Tract (Proper Dorsal Mm. – Erector Spinae M.): Courses, Origins, and Insertions (Muscles of the Head and Vertebral Joints), Dorsal View.

● **Spinalis Capitis M.**
(inconstant)
Spinous Process of Thoracic Vertebrae T1–2 (3) and of Cervical Vertebrae C (5) 6-7

● **Spinalis Cervicis M.**
Spinous Process of Thoracic Vertebrae T1– 2 (3) and of Cervical Vertebrae C (5) 6–7

● **Spinalis Thoracis M.**
Spinous Process of Thoracic Vertebrae T11–12 and of Lumbar Vertebrae L1–2 (3)

● **Interspinales Cervicis Mm.**
Lower Edge of the Spinous Process of Cervical Vertebrae C2–7

● **Interspinales Thoracis M.**
(inconstant)
Lower Edge of Spinous Process of Thoracic Vertebral T1 (2) and T11 (T12)

● **Interspinales Lumborum M.**
Lower Edge of Spinosus Process of Lumbar Vertebrae L1–L5

● **Rotator Breves Thoracis M.**
Root of Transverse Process of Thoracic Vertebra Below T1–T12

● **Rotator Longi Cervicis M.**
(inconstant)
Transverse Process of Cervical Vertebrae C4– C7

● **Rotator Longi Thoracis M.**
Transverse Process of Thoracic Vertebrae T1–T12

● **Rotator Longi Lumborum M.**
(inconstant)
Mamillary Process of Lumbar Vertebrae L1–L5

● **Spinalis Capitis M.** (inconstant)
External Occipital Protuberance

● **Spinalis Cervicis M.**
Spinous Process of Cervical Vertebrae C2–C6

● **Spinalis Thoracis M.**
Spinous Process of Thoracic Vertebrae T2–T8

● **Interspinales Cervicis M.**
Upper Edge of the Spinous Process of Cervical Vertebrae C3–C7 and of Thoracic Vertebra T1

● **Interspinales Thoracis M.**
(inconstant)
Upper Edge of Spinous Process of Thoracic Vertebrae T2 (3), T12 and of Lumbar Vertebra L1

● **Interspinales Lumborum M.**
Upper Edge of the Spinous Process of Lumbar Vertebrae L2–L5 and Variable on the Upper Area of Iliac Crest and Median Sacral Area

● **Rotator Breves Thoracis M.**
Base of the Spinous Process of Cervical Vetebrae C7 and of Thoracic Vertebrae T1–T10

● **Rotator Longi Cervicis M.**
(inconstant)
Spinous Process of Cervical Vertebrae C2–C5

● **Rotator Longi Thoracis M.**
Spinous Process of Cervical Vertebrae C6–C7 and of Thoracic Vertebrae T1–T10

● **Rotator Longi Lumborum M.**
(inconstant)
Spinous Process of Thoracic Vertebrae T11–T12 and Lumbar Vertebrae L1– L3

● Origin
● Insertion

Muscles of the Trunk

4.Fb Transversospinal System. Muscles of the Back – Medial Tract (Proper Dorsal Mm. – Erector Spinae M.): Courses, Origins, and Insertions (Muscles of the Head and Vertebral Joints), Dorsal View.

4

● **Semispinalis Capitis M.**
Transverse Process of Thoracic Vertebrae T1–T6 (7) and **Cervical Vertebra** C7

● **Semispinalis Cervicis M.**
Transverse Process of Thoracic Vertebrae T(1) 2–T5 (6)

● **Semispinalis Thoracis M.**
Transverse Process of Thoracic Vertebrae T6–T10 (12)

● **Multifidus Cervicis M.**
Articular Process of Cervical Vertebrae C5–C7

● **Multifidus Thoracis M.**
Transverse Process of Thoracic Vertebrae T1–T12

● **Multifidus Lumborum M.**
Dorsal Surface of the Sacrum Bone, **Iliac Crest**, Iliac Tuberosity, Mamillary Process of **Lumbar Vertebrae** L1–5 [Posterior Sacroiliac Ligament Tendon of Longissimus Lumborum M.]

● **Semispinalis Capitis M.**
Medial Area of **Occipital Squamous** Bone between the Superior and Inferior Nuchal Lines

● **Semispinalis Cervicis M.**
Spinous Process of Cervical Vertebrae C2–C5 (6)

● **Semispinalis Thoracis M.**
Spinous Process of Cervical Vertebrae C6–C7 and of Thoracic Vertebrae T1–T5 (6)

● **Multifidus Cervicis M.**
Spinous Process of Cervical Vertebrae C2–C5

● **Multifidus Thoracis M.**
Spinous Process of Cervical Vertebrae C6–C7 and of the Thoracic Vertebrae T1–T10

● **Multifidus Lumborum M.**
Spinous Process of Thoracic Vertebrae T11–12 **and of Lumbar Vertebrae** L1–5

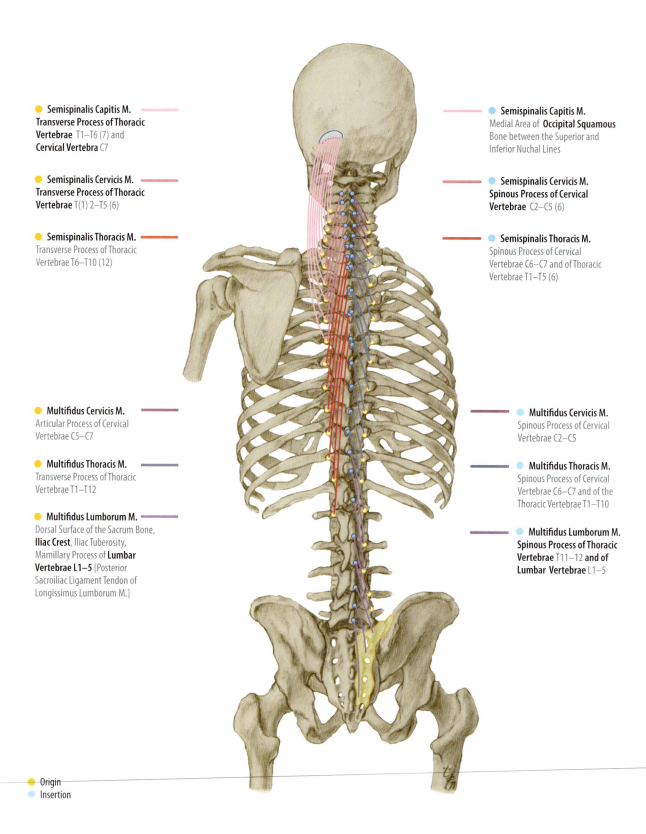

● Origin
● Insertion

Muscles of the Back: Medial Tract | pp. 213–218

4.G Transversospinal System. Muscles of the Back – Medial Tract (Proper Dorsal Mm. – Erector Spinae M.): Courses, Origins, and Insertions (Thoracic Muscles of the Vertebral Joints).

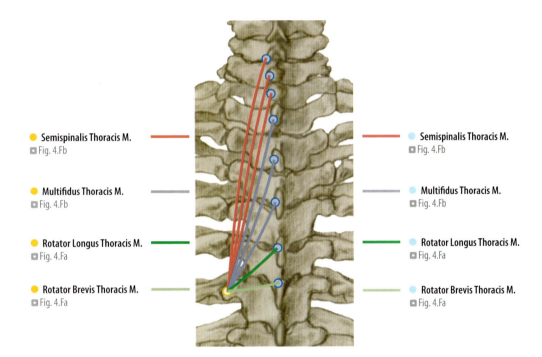

● Semispinalis Thoracis M.
▣ Fig. 4.Fb

● Multifidus Thoracis M.
▣ Fig. 4.Fb

● Rotator Longus Thoracis M.
▣ Fig. 4.Fa

● Rotator Brevis Thoracis M.
▣ Fig. 4.Fa

● Semispinalis Thoracis M.
▣ Fig. 4.Fb

● Multifidus Thoracis M.
▣ Fig. 4.Fb

● Rotator Longus Thoracis M.
▣ Fig. 4.Fa

● Rotator Brevis Thoracis M.
▣ Fig. 4.Fa

The Superficial Layer That Mainly Crosses Laterally Is Called the Transversocostal Group:

Splenius Capitus, Splenius Cervicis, Sacrospinalis (Iliocostalis, Longissimus, Spinalis)

Divisions of the Erector Spinae Muscles of the Back Sacrospinalis Group:

Lateral Column Iliocostalis	Intermediate Column Longissimus	Medial Column Spinalis
I. Lumborum	L. Thoracic	S. Thoracic
I. Thoracic	L. Cervicis	S. Cervicis
I. Cervicis	L. Capitus	S. Capitis

Deep Muscles of the Back:

Semispinalis	Rotators	Interspinalis
Multifidus		Intertransversaris

● Origin
● Insertion

4

Function	Innervation	Blood Supply
Medial Tract		
Spinal System		

Spinalis Capitis Mm.
    Cervicis Mm.
    Thoracis Mm.
Unilateral Activity:
    Support of the sideward inclination of the Spinal Column
    to the ipsilateral side
Bilateral Activity:
    Backward inclination of the Spinal Column
	Medial Branches
	of the Posterior Rami
	(dorsal) of the Spinal Nn.
	(C2–T10)
		Vertebral A.
		Deep Cervical A.
		Dorsal Branches of the Posterior
		Intercostal Aa.
		Dorsal Branches of the Lumbar Aa.

Interspinales Cervicis Mm.
    Thoracis Mm.
    Lumborum Mm.
Stabilization and fine adjustment of the movement segments
Support of backward inclination
	Medial Branches of the Posterior
	(dorsal) Rami of the Spinal Nn.
	of the respective segments
		Vertebral A.
		Deep Cervical A.
		Dorsal Branches of the Posterior
		Intercostal Aa.
		Dorsal Branches of the Lumbar Aa.

Transversospinal System		

Rotator Breves and Longi M.
Unilateral Activity:
    Support of the rotation of the Spinal Column in the Thoracic Area
    (Cervicolumbar Area) to the contralateral side
Stabilization of the movement segments
	Medial Branches of the Posterior
	(dorsal) Rami of the Spinal Nn. of
	the respective segments
		Vertebral A.
		Deep Cervical A.
		Dorsal Branches of the Posterior
		Intercostal Aa.
		Dorsal Branches of the Lumbar Aa.

Multifidus Cervicis M.
    Thoracis M.
    Lumborum M.
Unilateral Activity:
    Rotation of the Spinal Column to the contralateral side
    and support of sideward inclination
Bilateral Activity:
    Backward inclination of the Spinal Column
Tension and stabilization of the Spinal Column
▣ Semispinalis M.
	Medial Branches of the Posterior
	(dorsal) Rami of the Spinal Nn.
	(C3–L5)
		Vertebral A.
		Deep Cervical A.
		Dorsal Branches of the Posterior
		Intercostal Aa.
		Dorsal Branches of the Lumbar Aa.

Semispinalis Capitis M.
    Cervicis M.
    Thoracis M.
Unilateral Activity:
    Rotation of the Head and the Cervical and Thoracic Spines to the
    contralateral side and inclination of the Head and the Cervical
    and Thoracic Spines to the ipsilateral side
Bilateral Activity:
    Backward inclination of the Head and of the Spinal Column
Tension and stabilization of the Thoracic and Cervical Spines
("Tendon" in the reversed Arcuate Tendon construction)
	Medial Rami of the Posterior
	(dorsal) Rami of the Spinal Nn.
	(C1–T6)
		Vertebral A.
		Deep Cervical A.
		Dorsal Branches of the Posterior
		Intercostal Aa.
		Dorsal Branches of the Lumbar Aa.

4.H Spinotransversal System. Muscles of the Back – Lateral Tract (Proper Dorsal Mm. – Erector Spinae M.): Courses and Origins
(Muscles of the Head – Vertebral Joints as well as Muscles of the Costal Joints).

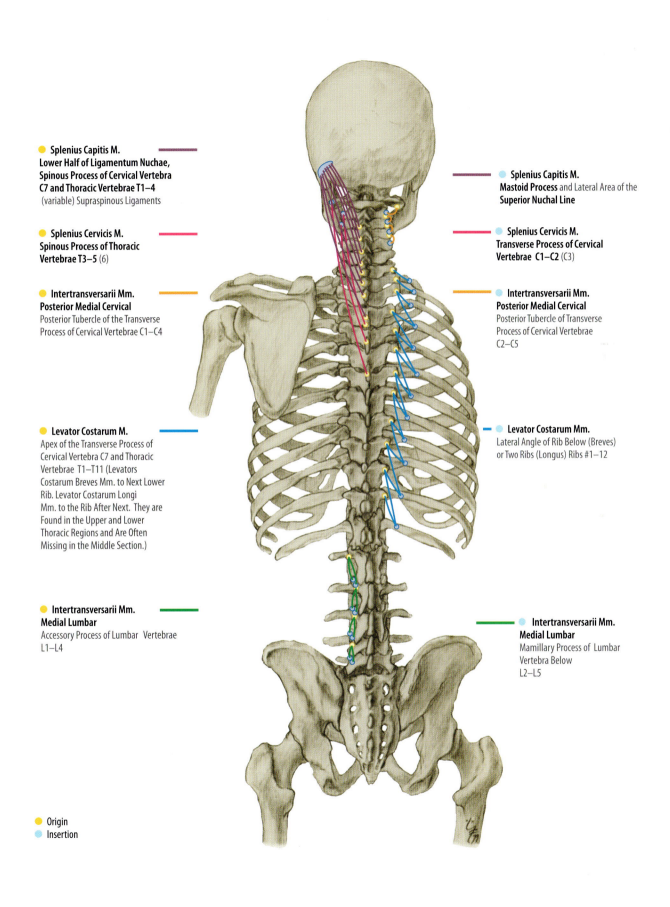

● **Splenius Capitis M.**
Lower Half of Ligamentum Nuchae,
Spinous Process of Cervical Vertebra
C7 and Thoracic Vertebrae T1–4
(variable) Supraspinous Ligaments

● **Splenius Cervicis M.**
Spinous Process of Thoracic
Vertebrae T3–5 (6)

● **Intertransversarii Mm.**
Posterior Medial Cervical
Posterior Tubercle of the Transverse
Process of Cervical Vertebrae C1–C4

● **Levator Costarum M.**
Apex of the Transverse Process of
Cervical Vertebra C7 and Thoracic
Vertebrae T1–T11 (Levators
Costarum Breves Mm. to Next Lower
Rib. Levator Costarum Longi
Mm. to the Rib After Next. They are
Found in the Upper and Lower
Thoracic Regions and Are Often
Missing in the Middle Section.)

● **Intertransversarii Mm.**
Medial Lumbar
Accessory Process of Lumbar Vertebrae
L1–L4

● **Splenius Capitis M.**
Mastoid Process and Lateral Area of the
Superior Nuchal Line

● **Splenius Cervicis M.**
Transverse Process of Cervical
Vertebrae C1–C2 (C3)

● **Intertransversarii Mm.**
Posterior Medial Cervical
Posterior Tubercle of Transverse
Process of Cervical Vertebrae
C2–C5

● **Levator Costarum Mm.**
Lateral Angle of Rib Below (Breves)
or Two Ribs (Longus) Ribs #1–12

● **Intertransversarii Mm.**
Medial Lumbar
Mamillary Process of Lumbar
Vertebra Below
L2–L5

● Origin
● Insertion

Muscles of the Trunk

4

Function	Innervation	Blood Supply
Spinotransversal System		
Splenius Capitis M. **Cervicis M.** Bilateral Activity: Backward inclination of the Head and the Cervical Spine Unilateral Activity: Inclination and rotation of the Head and Cervical Spine to the ipsilateral side Tension of the Cervical Spine ("Tendon" in the reversed Arcuate Tendon construction)	Lateral Branches (C1) C2–C5 (C6) of the Posterior (dorsal) Rami of the Spinal Nn.	Occipital A. Deep Cervical A. Vertebral A.
Intertransversal System		
Intertransversarii Posterior Medial Cervicis Mm. (Function unknown)	Lateral Branches (C1) C2–C5 (C6) of the Posterior (dorsal) Rami of the Spinal Nn.	Deep Cervical A. Vertebral A.
Intertransversarii Medial Lumborum Mm. Stabilization of the respective movement segments Support of sideward inclination and backward inclination of the Cervical and Lumbar Spines	Lateral Branches of the Posterior (dorsal) Rami of the Spinal Nn. of the respective segments	Vertebral A. Deep Cervical A. Dorsal Branches of the Lumbar Aa.
Levatores Costarum Breves Mm. **Longi Mm.** Ambilateral Activity: Support of backward inclination of the Spinal Column and of the lifting of the Ribs (inspiration) Unilateral Activity: Rotation of the Spinal Column to the contralateral side and sideward inclination to the ipsilateral side	Lateral Branches C7–T10 (T11) of the Posterior (dorsal) Rami and variable the Anterior (ventral) Rami of the Spinal Nerves	Dorsal Branches of the Posterior Intercostal Aa.

4.I Sacrospinal System. Muscles of the Back – Lateral Tract (Proper Dorsal Mm. – Erector Spinae M.): Courses, Origins, and Insertions (Muscles of the Head – Vertebral Joints as well as Muscles of the Costal Joints).

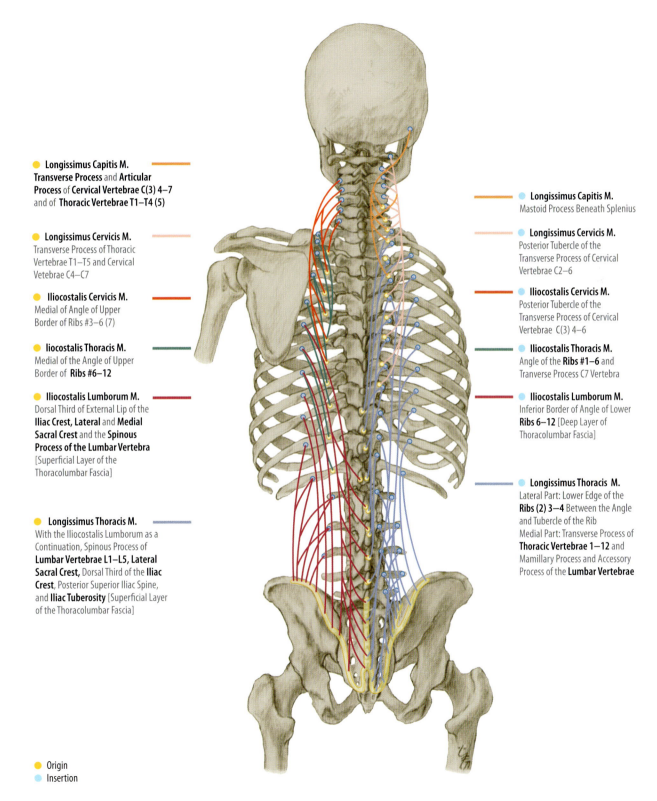

● **Longissimus Capitis M.**
Transverse Process and **Articular Process** of **Cervical Vertebrae C(3) 4–7** and of **Thoracic Vertebrae T1–T4 (5)**

● **Longissimus Cervicis M.**
Transverse Process of Thoracic Vertebrae T1–T5 and Cervical Vetebrae C4–C7

● **Iliocostalis Cervicis M.**
Medial of Angle of Upper Border of Ribs #3–6 (7)

● **Iiocostalis Thoracis M.**
Medial of the Angle of Upper Border of **Ribs #6–12**

● **Iliocostalis Lumborum M.**
Dorsal Third of External Lip of the **Iliac Crest, Lateral** and **Medial Sacral Crest** and the **Spinous Process of the Lumbar Vertebra** [Superficial Layer of the Thoracolumbar Fascia]

● **Longissimus Thoracis M.**
With the Iliocostalis Lumborum as a Continuation, Spinous Process of **Lumbar Vertebrae L1–L5, Lateral Sacral Crest,** Dorsal Third of the **Iliac Crest**, Posterior Superior Iliac Spine, and **Iliac Tuberosity** [Superficial Layer of the Thoracolumbar Fascia]

● **Longissimus Capitis M.**
Mastoid Process Beneath Splenius

● **Longissimus Cervicis M.**
Posterior Tubercle of the Transverse Process of Cervical Vertebrae C2–6

● **Iliocostalis Cervicis M.**
Posterior Tubercle of the Transverse Process of Cervical Vertebrae C(3) 4–6

● **Iliocostalis Thoracis M.**
Angle of the **Ribs #1–6** and Tranverse Process C7 Vertebra

● **Iliocostalis Lumborum M.**
Inferior Border of Angle of Lower Ribs 6–12 [Deep Layer of Thoracolumbar Fascia]

● **Longissimus Thoracis M.**
Lateral Part: Lower Edge of the **Ribs (2) 3–4** Between the Angle and Tubercle of the Rib
Medial Part: Transverse Process of **Thoracic Vertebra 1–12** and Mamillary Process and Accessory Process of the **Lumbar Vertebrae**

● Origin
● Insertion

Muscles of the Trunk

4

Function	Innervation	Blood Supply
Lateral Tract		
Sacrospinal System		
Longissimus Capitis M. 　　　　**Cervicis M.** 　　　　**Thoracis M.** Unilateral Activity: 　　Sideward inclination and rotation of the Head and 　　Spinal Column to the ipsilateral side Bilateral Activity: 　　Backward inclination of the Head and Spinal Column Tension of the Spinal Column	Lateral Branches of the Posterior (dorsal) Rami of the Spinal Nn. (C8–L1)	Occipital A. Vertebral A. Deep Cervical A. Dorsal Branches of the Posterior Intercostal Aa. Dorsal Branches of the Lumbar Aa.
Iliocostalis Cervicis M. 　　　　**Thoracis M.** 　　　　**Lumborum M.** Unilateral Activity: 　　Sideward inclination and rotation of the spinal column 　　　to the ipsilateral side 　　Support of inspiration Bilateral Activity: 　　Backward inclination (straightening up-stretching) 　　　of the Spinal Column Tension of the Spinal Column	Lateral Branches of the Posterior (dorsal) Rami of the Spinal Nn. (C8–L1)	Occipital A. Vertebral A. Deep Cervical A. Dorsal Branches of the Posterior Intercostal Aa. Dorsal Branches of the Lumbar Aa.

4.J Muscles of the Back, Short Deep Muscles of the Back of the Neck, Suboccipital Mm. (Muscles of the Head Joints): Origins (Left Side of the Body), Insertions (Right Side of the Body), Occipital View.

● **Oblique Capitis Superior M.**
Posterior Tubercle of the **Transverse Process of the Atlas**

● **Rectus Capitis Posterior Minor M.**
Posterior Tubercle of the **Posterior Arch of the Atlas**

● **Rectus Capitis Posterior Major M.**
Spinous Process of the Axis

● **Oblique Capitis Inferior M.**
Spinous Process of the Axis

● **Rectus Capitis Posterior Minor M.**
Internal Third of the **Inferior Nuchal Line**

● **Oblique Capitis Superior M.**
Lateral Part of the **Inferior Lateral Nuchal Line**

● **Rectus Capitis Posterior Major M.**
Median Third of the **Inferior Nuchal Line**

● **Oblique Capitis Inferior M.**
Posterior Tubercle of the **Transverse Process of the Atlas**

● Origin
● Insertion

Muscles of the Trunk

Function	Innervation	Blood Supply
Rectus Capitis Posterior Minor M. Fine adjustment of the Head in the Atlantooccipital Joint Bilateral Activity: Backward inclination of the Head	Medial Branch of the Posterior (dorsal) Rami of the Cervical C1 N. (Suboccipital N.)	Vertebral A. Deep Cervical A. Occipital A.

Rectus Capitis Posterior Major M.
Fine adjustment of the Head in the Atlantooccipital Joint
Unilateral Activity:
    Slight rotation of the Head to the ipsilateral side
Bilateral Activity:
    Slight backward inclination of the Head
	Medial Branch of the Posterior (dorsal) Rami of the Cervical C1 N. (Suboccipital) and and of the Cervical C2 N.	Vertebral A.
		Deep Cervical A.
		Occipital A.

Oblique Capitis Superior M.
Fine adjustment of the Head in the Head Joints
Unilateral Activity:
    Slight sideward inclination to the ipsilateral side
Bilateral Activity:
    Backward inclination of the Head
	Lateral Branch of the Posterior (dorsal) Rami of the Cervical C1 N. (Suboccipital N.) and of the Cervical C2 N.	Vertebral A.
		Deep Cervical A.
		Occipital A.

Oblique Capitis Inferior M. Fine adjustment of the Head in the Head Joints Unilateral Activity: Support of the rotation of the Head to the ipsilateral side	Medial Branch of the Posterior (dorsal) Rami of the Cervical C1 N. (Suboccipital N.) and of the Cervical C2 N.	Vertebral A. Deep Cervical A. Occipital A.

4

Thoracic, Abdominal, and Pelvic Spaces

5.1 Paramedian Sagittal Section through the Torso of a Man: Medial View of the Left Cut Surface. [69]

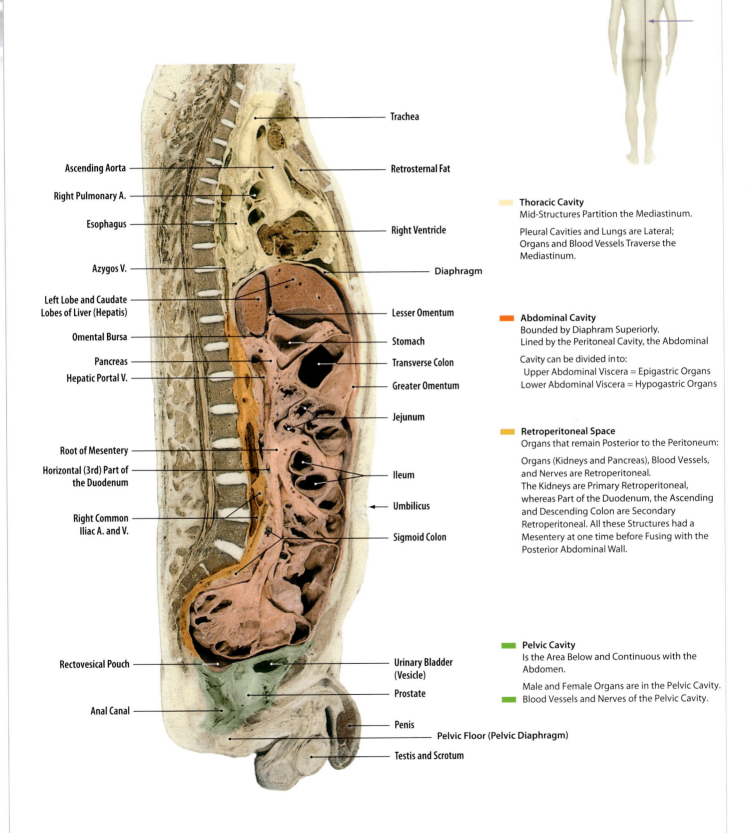

Trachea

Retrosternal Fat

Ascending Aorta

Right Pulmonary A.

Esophagus

Right Ventricle

Azygos V.

Diaphragm

Left Lobe and Caudate
Lobes of Liver (Hepatis)

Lesser Omentum

Omental Bursa

Stomach

Pancreas

Transverse Colon

Hepatic Portal V.

Greater Omentum

Jejunum

Root of Mesentery

Horizontal (3rd) Part of
the Duodenum

Ileum

Umbilicus

Right Common
Iliac A. and V.

Sigmoid Colon

Rectovesical Pouch

Urinary Bladder
(Vesicle)

Prostate

Anal Canal

Penis

Pelvic Floor (Pelvic Diaphragm)

Testis and Scrotum

Thoracic Cavity
Mid-Structures Partition the Mediastinum.

Pleural Cavities and Lungs are Lateral;
Organs and Blood Vessels Traverse the
Mediastinum.

Abdominal Cavity
Bounded by Diaphram Superiorly.
Lined by the Peritoneal Cavity, the Abdominal

Cavity can be divided into:
 Upper Abdominal Viscera = Epigastric Organs
Lower Abdominal Viscera = Hypogastric Organs

Retroperitoneal Space
Organs that remain Posterior to the Peritoneum:

Organs (Kidneys and Pancreas), Blood Vessels,
and Nerves are Retroperitoneal.
The Kidneys are Primary Retroperitoneal,
whereas Part of the Duodenum, the Ascending
and Descending Colon are Secondary
Retroperitoneal. All these Structures had a
Mesentery at one time before Fusing with the
Posterior Abdominal Wall.

Pelvic Cavity
Is the Area Below and Continuous with the
Abdomen.

Male and Female Organs are in the Pelvic Cavity.
Blood Vessels and Nerves of the Pelvic Cavity.

Overview

Aorta and Its Branches

5.2 Branches of the Aorta in the Thoracic and Abdominal Cavities: Ventral View. [13]

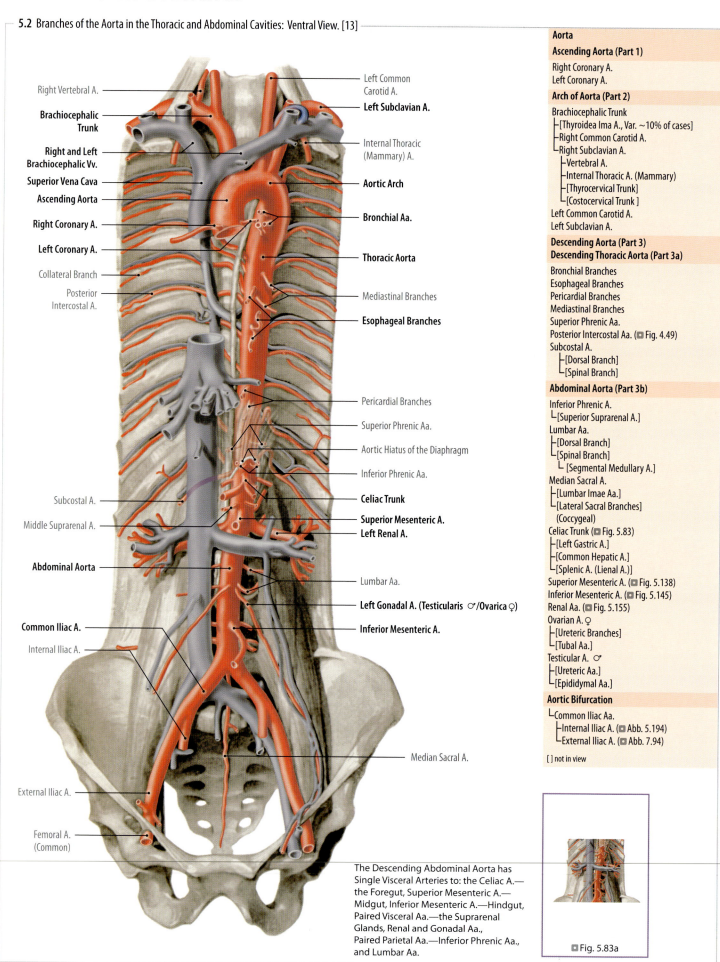

Right Vertebral A.

Brachiocephalic Trunk

Right and Left Brachiocephalic Vv.

Superior Vena Cava

Ascending Aorta

Right Coronary A.

Left Coronary A.

Collateral Branch

Posterior Intercostal A.

Subcostal A.

Middle Suprarenal A.

Abdominal Aorta

Common Iliac A.

Internal Iliac A.

External Iliac A.

Femoral A. (Common)

Left Common Carotid A.

Left Subclavian A.

Internal Thoracic (Mammary) A.

Aortic Arch

Bronchial Aa.

Thoracic Aorta

Mediastinal Branches

Esophageal Branches

Pericardial Branches

Superior Phrenic Aa.

Aortic Hiatus of the Diaphragm

Inferior Phrenic Aa.

Celiac Trunk

Superior Mesenteric A.

Left Renal A.

Lumbar Aa.

Left Gonadal A. (Testicularis ♂/Ovarica ♀)

Inferior Mesenteric A.

Median Sacral A.

The Descending Abdominal Aorta has Single Visceral Arteries to: the Celiac A.—the Foregut, Superior Mesenteric A.—Midgut, Inferior Mesenteric A.—Hindgut, Paired Visceral Aa.—the Suprarenal Glands, Renal and Gonadal Aa., Paired Parietal Aa.—Inferior Phrenic Aa., and Lumbar Aa.

Aorta
Ascending Aorta (Part 1)
Right Coronary A.
Left Coronary A.

Arch of Aorta (Part 2)
Brachiocephalic Trunk
├[Thyroidea Ima A., Var. ~10% of cases]
├Right Common Carotid A.
└Right Subclavian A.
  ├Vertebral A.
  ├Internal Thoracic A. (Mammary)
  ├[Thyrocervical Trunk]
  └[Costocervical Trunk]
Left Common Carotid A.
Left Subclavian A.

Descending Aorta (Part 3)
Descending Thoracic Aorta (Part 3a)
Bronchial Branches
Esophageal Branches
Pericardial Branches
Mediastinal Branches
Superior Phrenic Aa.
Posterior Intercostal Aa. (▣ Fig. 4.49)
Subcostal A.
  ├[Dorsal Branch]
  └[Spinal Branch]

Abdominal Aorta (Part 3b)
Inferior Phrenic A.
└[Superior Suprarenal A.]
Lumbar Aa.
├[Dorsal Branch]
└[Spinal Branch]
  └ [Segmental Medullary A.]
Median Sacral A.
├[Lumbar Imae Aa.]
├[Lateral Sacral Branches]
  (Coccygeal)
Celiac Trunk (▣ Fig. 5.83)
├[Left Gastric A.]
├[Common Hepatic A.]
└[Splenic A. (Lienal A.)]
Superior Mesenteric A. (▣ Fig. 5.138)
Inferior Mesenteric A. (▣ Fig. 5.145)
Renal Aa. (▣ Fig. 5.155)
Ovarian A. ♀
├[Ureteric Branches]
└[Tubal Aa.]
Testicular A. ♂
├[Ureteric Aa.]
└[Epididymal Aa.]

Aortic Bifurcation
└Common Iliac Aa.
├Internal Iliac A. (▣ Abb. 5.194)
└External Iliac A. (▣ Abb. 7.94)

[ ] not in view

▣ Fig. 5.83a

5.3 Veins of the Thoracic and Abdominal Cavities: Ventral View (Veins of the Body Wall ▶ Fig. 4.51a; Portal Circulation ▶ Fig. 5.82a). [13]

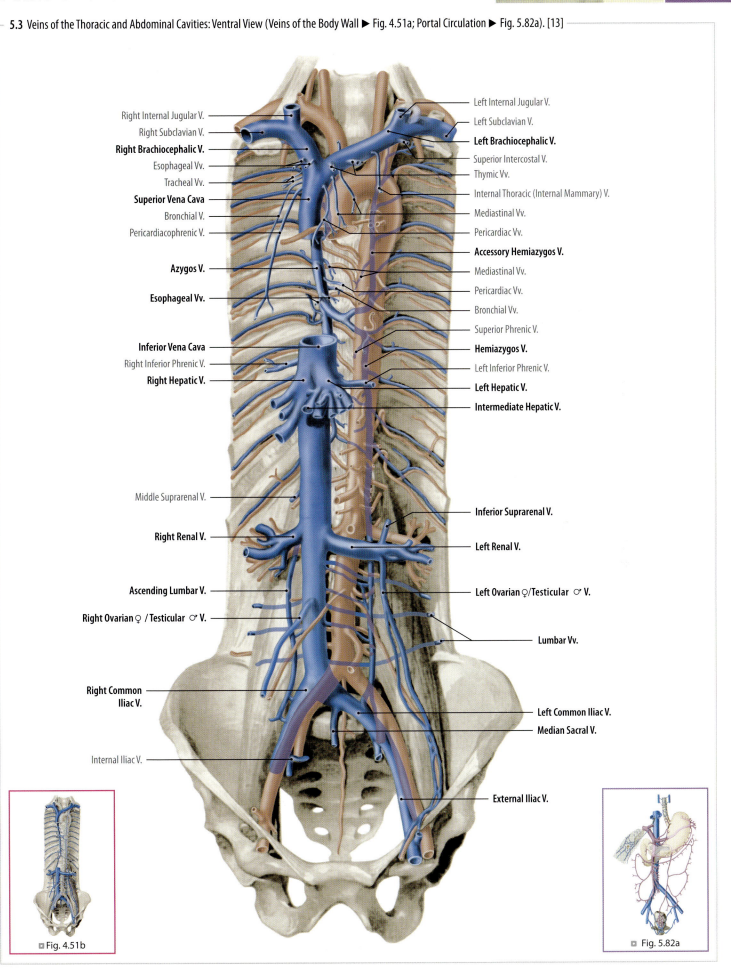

Right Internal Jugular V.
Right Subclavian V.
Right Brachiocephalic V.
Esophageal Vv.
Tracheal Vv.
Superior Vena Cava
Bronchial V.
Pericardiacophrenic V.
Azygos V.
Esophageal Vv.
Inferior Vena Cava
Right Inferior Phrenic V.
Right Hepatic V.
Middle Suprarenal V.
Right Renal V.
Ascending Lumbar V.
Right Ovarian ♀ / Testicular ♂ V.
Right Common Iliac V.
Internal Iliac V.

Left Internal Jugular V.
Left Subclavian V.
Left Brachiocephalic V.
Superior Intercostal V.
Thymic Vv.
Internal Thoracic (Internal Mammary) V.
Mediastinal Vv.
Pericardiac Vv.
Accessory Hemiazygos V.
Mediastinal Vv.
Pericardiac Vv.
Bronchial Vv.
Superior Phrenic V.
Hemiazygos V.
Left Inferior Phrenic V.
Left Hepatic V.
Intermediate Hepatic V.
Inferior Suprarenal V.
Left Renal V.
Left Ovarian ♀/Testicular ♂ V.
Lumbar Vv.
Left Common Iliac V.
Median Sacral V.
External Iliac V.

◻ Fig. 4.51b

◻ Fig. 5.82a

Overview

Sympathetic and Parasympathetic Autonomic Nerve Supply

5.4 Sympathetic and Parasympathetic Supply of the Organs of the Head, Neck, and Trunk. [34]

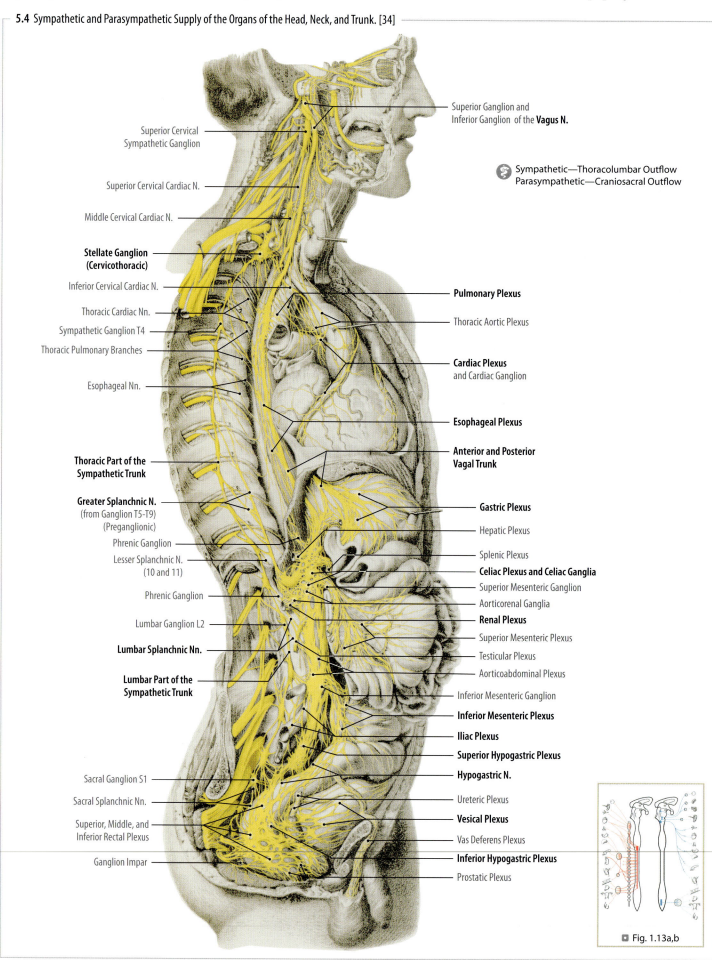

Superior Ganglion and
Inferior Ganglion of the **Vagus N.**

Sympathetic—Thoracolumbar Outflow
Parasympathetic—Craniosacral Outflow

Superior Cervical
Sympathetic Ganglion

Superior Cervical Cardiac N.

Middle Cervical Cardiac N.

**Stellate Ganglion
(Cervicothoracic)**

Inferior Cervical Cardiac N.

Thoracic Cardiac Nn.

Sympathetic Ganglion T4

Thoracic Pulmonary Branches

Esophageal Nn.

**Thoracic Part of the
Sympathetic Trunk**

Greater Splanchnic N.
(from Ganglion T5–T9)
(Preganglionic)

Phrenic Ganglion

Lesser Splanchnic N.
(10 and 11)

Phrenic Ganglion

Lumbar Ganglion L2

Lumbar Splanchnic Nn.

**Lumbar Part of the
Sympathetic Trunk**

Sacral Ganglion S1

Sacral Splanchnic Nn.

Superior, Middle, and
Inferior Rectal Plexus

Ganglion Impar

Pulmonary Plexus

Thoracic Aortic Plexus

Cardiac Plexus
and Cardiac Ganglion

Esophageal Plexus

**Anterior and Posterior
Vagal Trunk**

Gastric Plexus

Hepatic Plexus

Splenic Plexus

Celiac Plexus and Celiac Ganglia

Superior Mesenteric Ganglion

Aorticorenal Ganglia

Renal Plexus

Superior Mesenteric Plexus

Testicular Plexus

Aorticoabdominal Plexus

Inferior Mesenteric Ganglion

Inferior Mesenteric Plexus

Iliac Plexus

Superior Hypogastric Plexus

Hypogastric N.

Ureteric Plexus

Vesical Plexus

Vas Deferens Plexus

Inferior Hypogastric Plexus

Prostatic Plexus

□ Fig. 1.13a,b

5.5 Classification of the Mediastinum: Sagittal Section through the Thorax. [23]

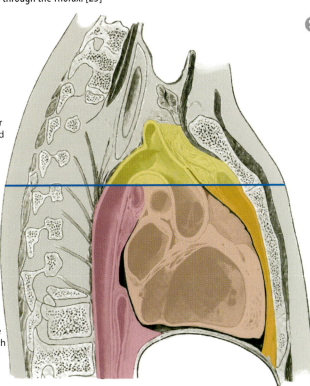

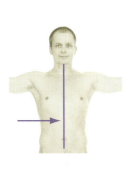

Superior Mediastinum

▮ The Area above the Dividing Plane and Posterior to the Manubrium, with Thymus, Aortic Arch and Branches, Brachiocephalic Vv., Superior V. Cava Formation, Trachea, Esophagus, Vagi Nn., Phrenic Nn., and Ductus (Ligamentum) Arteriosus

Inferior Mediastinum

▮ Anterior Mediastinum:
Space between the Sternum and Pericardium

▮ Middle Mediastinum:
Space occupied by the Pericardium with Phrenic Nn., Pericardiacophrenic Blood Vessels, Heart, and Roots of the Great Vessels

▮ Posterior Mediastinum:
Space between the Dorsal Pericardium Surface and the Diaphragm and the Spinal Column with the Esophagus, Vagi Nn., Descending Aorta, Thoracic Duct, Hemiazygos and Azygos Vv., and Splanchnic Nn.

🔄 Tumors of the Mediastinum have Various types of Tissues of Origin. According to their Location, they are classified as Tumors in the Superior Mediastinum (e.g., Thyroid Tumors, Thymus Tumors, Dermoids, or Sarcomas); Tumors in the Middle-Inferior Mediastinum (e.g., Lymph Node Metastases, Pericardial Cysts, Bronchogenic Cysts, Teratomas); Tumors in the Posterior Mediastinum (e.g., Esophageal Tumors or Neurogenic Tumors).

5.6a,b Pleura and Pleural Recesses. [15]

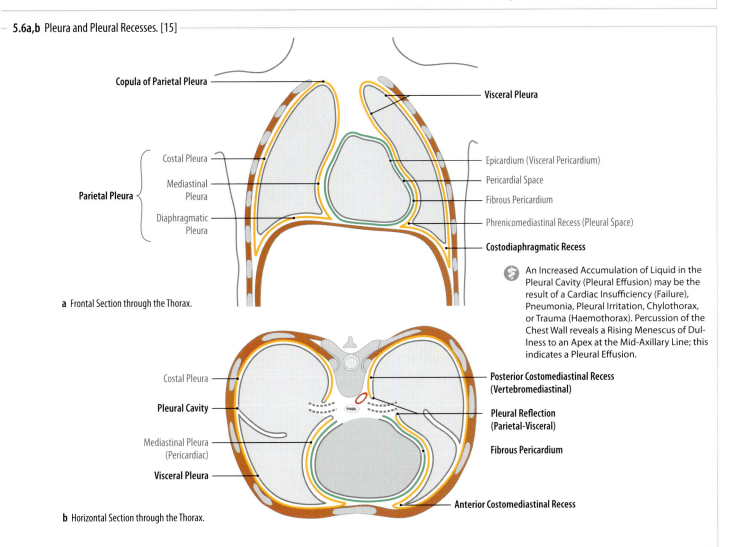

Copula of Parietal Pleura

Visceral Pleura

Costal Pleura

Parietal Pleura {
Mediastinal Pleura

Diaphragmatic Pleura

Epicardium (Visceral Pericardium)

Pericardial Space

Fibrous Pericardium

Phrenicomediastinal Recess (Pleural Space)

Costodiaphragmatic Recess

a Frontal Section through the Thorax.

🔄 An Increased Accumulation of Liquid in the Pleural Cavity (Pleural Effusion) may be the result of a Cardiac Insufficiency (Failure), Pneumonia, Pleural Irritation, Chylothorax, or Trauma (Haemothorax). Percussion of the Chest Wall reveals a Rising Menescus of Dullness to an Apex at the Mid-Axillary Line; this indicates a Pleural Effusion.

Costal Pleura

Pleural Cavity

Mediastinal Pleura (Pericardiac)

Visceral Pleura

Posterior Costomediastinal Recess (Vertebromediastinal)

Pleural Reflection (Parietal-Visceral)

Fibrous Pericardium

Anterior Costomediastinal Recess

b Horizontal Section through the Thorax.

Thoracic Cavity

5.7 Thorax: Ventral View. [1]

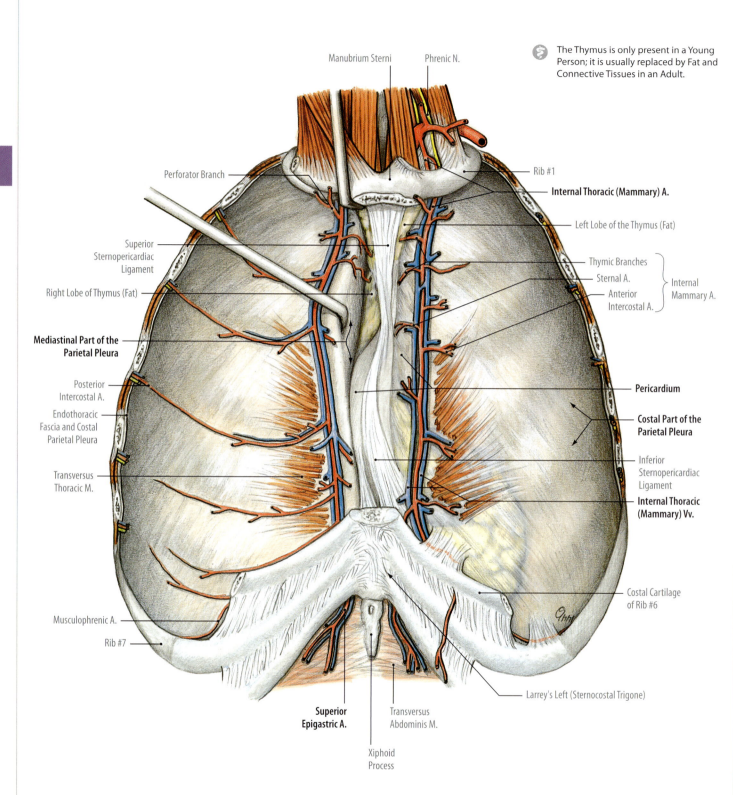

The Thymus is only present in a Young Person; it is usually replaced by Fat and Connective Tissues in an Adult.

Manubrium Sterni

Phrenic N.

Perforator Branch

Superior Sternopericardiac Ligament

Right Lobe of Thymus (Fat)

Mediastinal Part of the Parietal Pleura

Posterior Intercostal A.

Endothoracic Fascia and Costal Parietal Pleura

Transversus Thoracic M.

Musculophrenic A.

Rib #7

Superior Epigastric A.

Transversus Abdominis M.

Xiphoid Process

Rib #1

Internal Thoracic (Mammary) A.

Left Lobe of the Thymus (Fat)

Thymic Branches

Sternal A.

Anterior Intercostal A.

Internal Mammary A.

Pericardium

Costal Part of the Parietal Pleura

Inferior Sternopericardiac Ligament

Internal Thoracic (Mammary) Vv.

Costal Cartilage of Rib #6

Larrey's Left (Sternocostal Trigone)

Illustration of the Parietal Pleura with the Internal Thoracic (Mammary) Vessels and the Mediastinum through Partial Removal of the Anterior Thoracic Wall.

The Internal Thoracic (Mammary) Aa. are used as a Bypass in Surgical Revascularization Procedures ("Bypass Surgery") for the Treatment of the Constriction of Coronary Arteries.
Thymomas are the most Common Tumors in the Superior Mediastinum. Other Masses could develop in the Retrosternal Struma, the Descending Retrosternal Thyroid, and/or the Parathyroid Glands.

5.8 Thorax: Ventral View. [1]

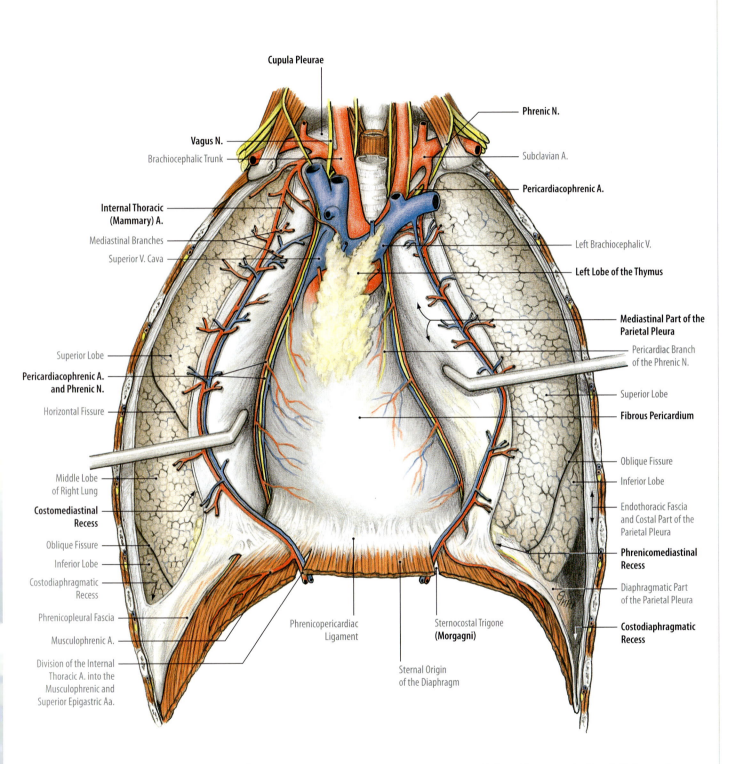

Cupula Pleurae

Vagus N.
Brachiocephalic Trunk

Phrenic N.

Subclavian A.

Pericardiacophrenic A.

Internal Thoracic
(Mammary) A.

Mediastinal Branches
Superior V. Cava

Left Brachiocephalic V.

Left Lobe of the Thymus

Mediastinal Part of the
Parietal Pleura

Superior Lobe

Pericardiac Branch
of the Phrenic N.

Pericardiacophrenic A.
and Phrenic N.

Superior Lobe

Horizontal Fissure

Fibrous Pericardium

Oblique Fissure
Inferior Lobe

Middle Lobe
of Right Lung

Endothoracic Fascia
and Costal Part of the
Parietal Pleura

Costomediastinal
Recess

Phrenicomediastinal
Recess

Oblique Fissure
Inferior Lobe
Costodiaphragmatic
Recess

Diaphragmatic Part
of the Parietal Pleura

Phrenicopleural Fascia

Costodiaphragmatic
Recess

Musculophrenic A.

Phrenicopericardiac
Ligament

Sternocostal Trigone
(Morgagni)

Division of the Internal
Thoracic A. into the
Musculophrenic and
Superior Epigastric Aa.

Sternal Origin
of the Diaphragm

To illustrate the Pericardium and the Adjacent Pathways, the Pleural Cavities with the Lungs have been Resected Laterally.

A Puncture of the Pericardial Cavity is made on the Left Side between the Xiphoid Process and the Costal Arch (Larrey's Point) at the Bare Area. To Drain the Pleural Cavity, a patient with a Pleural Effusion (Thoracocentesis) would have the Needle Inserted While he or she is Seated to Avoid Injury of the Intercostal Vessels. The Needle must Pass Over the Upper Edge of Ribs #4–#6, at the Middle Axilllary Line to Prevent Piercing the Diaphragm.

Unilateral Damage to the Phrenic N. due to a Surgical Injury, a Traumatic Birth with Upper Brachial Plexus Paresis (Erb Paralysis ☐ Fig. 6.73b), or Pressure during a Scalene Block (☐ Fig. 6.73a) – leads to a Paralysis of the Half of the Diaphragm with a Diaphragmatic Elevation. A Bilateral Failure of the Phrenic Nn. is accompanied by severe Respiratory Disorders.

Thoracic Cavity

Lung and Pleura Reflections

5.9 a Lung and Pleura Reflections. **b** Topographic Relationship between Thoracic and Epigastric Organs. [a,b 15]

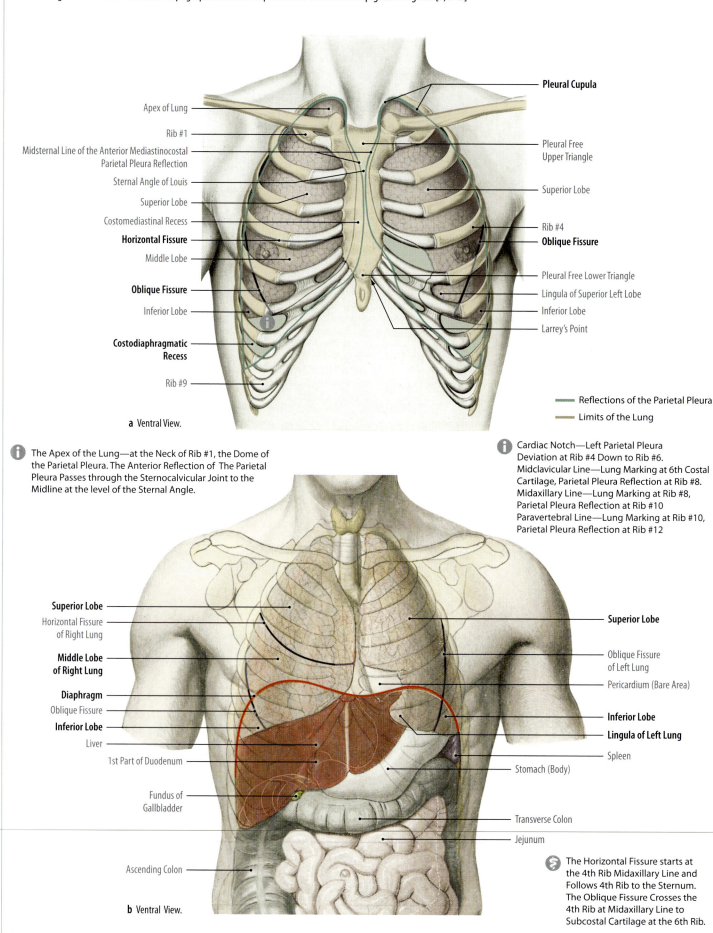

Pleural Cupula

Apex of Lung

Rib #1

Midsternal Line of the Anterior Mediastinocostal
Parietal Pleura Reflection

Pleural Free
Upper Triangle

Sternal Angle of Louis

Superior Lobe

Superior Lobe

Costomediastinal Recess

Rib #4

Horizontal Fissure

Oblique Fissure

Middle Lobe

Pleural Free Lower Triangle

Oblique Fissure

Lingula of Superior Left Lobe

Inferior Lobe

Inferior Lobe

Larrey's Point

**Costodiaphragmatic
Recess**

Rib #9

a Ventral View.

— Reflections of the Parietal Pleura

— Limits of the Lung

ⓘ The Apex of the Lung—at the Neck of Rib #1, the Dome of
the Parietal Pleura. The Anterior Reflection of The Parietal
Pleura Passes through the Sternocalvicular Joint to the
Midline at the level of the Sternal Angle.

ⓘ Cardiac Notch—Left Parietal Pleura
Deviation at Rib #4 Down to Rib #6.
Midclavicular Line—Lung Marking at 6th Costal
Cartilage, Parietal Pleura Reflection at Rib #8.
Midaxillary Line—Lung Marking at Rib #8,
Parietal Pleura Reflection at Rib #10
Paravertebral Line—Lung Marking at Rib #10,
Parietal Pleura Reflection at Rib #12

Superior Lobe

Horizontal Fissure
of Right Lung

Superior Lobe

**Middle Lobe
of Right Lung**

Oblique Fissure
of Left Lung

Pericardium (Bare Area)

Diaphragm

Oblique Fissure

Inferior Lobe

Inferior Lobe

Liver

Lingula of Left Lung

1st Part of Duodenum

Spleen

Stomach (Body)

Fundus of
Gallbladder

Transverse Colon

Jejunum

Ascending Colon

↻ The Horizontal Fissure starts at
the 4th Rib Midaxillary Line and
Follows 4th Rib to the Sternum.
The Oblique Fissure Crosses the
4th Rib at Midaxillary Line to
Subcostal Cartilage at the 6th Rib.

b Ventral View.

Lung and Pleura Reflections

5.10 a Lung and Pleura Reflections. **b** Topographic Relationship between Thoracic and Abdominal Organs. [a,b 15]

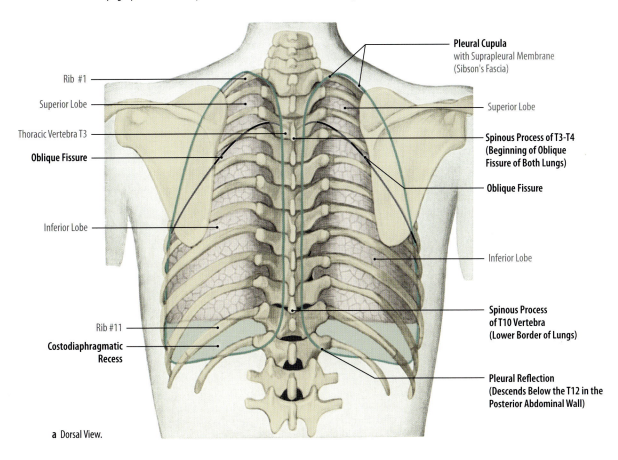

Rib #1

Superior Lobe

Thoracic Vertebra T3

Oblique Fissure

Inferior Lobe

Rib #11

Costodiaphragmatic Recess

Pleural Cupula
with Suprapleural Membrane
(Sibson's Fascia)

Superior Lobe

Spinous Process of T3-T4
(Beginning of Oblique
Fissure of Both Lungs)

Oblique Fissure

Inferior Lobe

**Spinous Process
of T10 Vertebra**
(Lower Border of Lungs)

Pleural Reflection
(Descends Below the T12 in the
Posterior Abdominal Wall)

a Dorsal View.

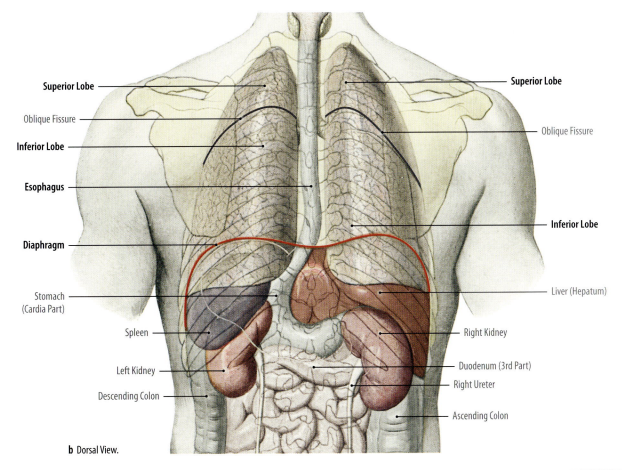

Superior Lobe

Oblique Fissure

Inferior Lobe

Esophagus

Diaphragm

Stomach
(Cardia Part)

Spleen

Left Kidney

Descending Colon

Superior Lobe

Oblique Fissure

Inferior Lobe

Liver (Hepatum)

Right Kidney

Duodenum (3rd Part)

Right Ureter

Ascending Colon

b Dorsal View.

Thoracic Cavity

Lobes of the Lungs and Bronchopulmonary Segments

5.11a,b Lung and Pleura Borders. [15]

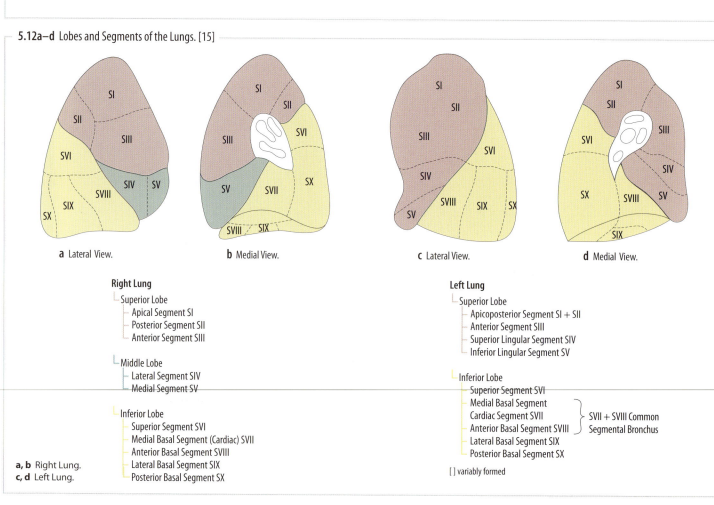

Rib #1

Superior Lobe

Rib #4

Horizontal Fissure

Middle Lobe

Oblique Fissure

Inferior Lobe

Rib #7

Costodiaphragmatic Recess

Rib #10

a Right Lateral View.

Cupula of Pleura and Suprapleural Membrane (Sibson's Fascia)

Rib #1

Superior Lobe

Oblique Fissure

Inferior Lobe

Costodiaphragmatic Recess

Reflection Line of the Costal to Diaphragmatic Parietal Pleura

Rib #10

b Left Lateral View.

5.12a–d Lobes and Segments of the Lungs. [15]

a Lateral View.

b Medial View.

c Lateral View.

d Medial View.

Right Lung

└ Superior Lobe
 ├ Apical Segment SI
 ├ Posterior Segment SII
 └ Anterior Segment SIII

└ Middle Lobe
 ├ Lateral Segment SIV
 └ Medial Segment SV

└ Inferior Lobe
 ├ Superior Segment SVI
 ├ Medial Basal Segment (Cardiac) SVII
 ├ Anterior Basal Segment SVIII
 ├ Lateral Basal Segment SIX
 └ Posterior Basal Segment SX

a, b Right Lung.
c, d Left Lung.

Left Lung

└ Superior Lobe
 ├ Apicoposterior Segment SI + SII
 ├ Anterior Segment SIII
 ├ Superior Lingular Segment SIV
 └ Inferior Lingular Segment SV

└ Inferior Lobe
 ├ Superior Segment SVI
 ├ Medial Basal Segment
 ├ Cardiac Segment SVII   } SVII + SVIII Common
 ├ Anterior Basal Segment SVIII } Segmental Bronchus
 ├ Lateral Basal Segment SIX
 └ Posterior Basal Segment SX

[ ] variably formed

258

5

5.13a,b Right and Left Lung and Hili of the Lung. [48]

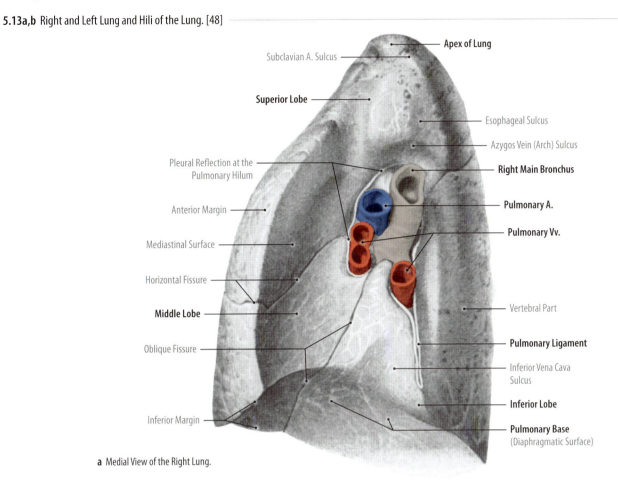

Apex of Lung

Subclavian A. Sulcus

Superior Lobe

Esophageal Sulcus

Azygos Vein (Arch) Sulcus

Pleural Reflection at the
Pulmonary Hilum

Right Main Bronchus

Anterior Margin

Pulmonary A.

Mediastinal Surface

Pulmonary Vv.

Horizontal Fissure

Middle Lobe

Vertebral Part

Oblique Fissure

Pulmonary Ligament

Inferior Vena Cava
Sulcus

Inferior Lobe

Inferior Margin

Pulmonary Base
(Diaphragmatic Surface)

a Medial View of the Right Lung.

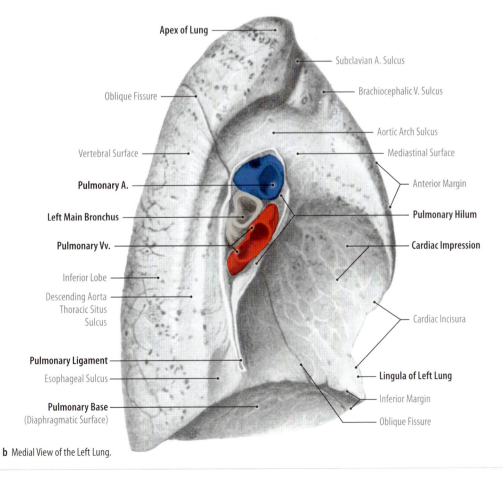

Apex of Lung

Subclavian A. Sulcus

Oblique Fissure

Brachiocephalic V. Sulcus

Vertebral Surface

Aortic Arch Sulcus

Mediastinal Surface

Pulmonary A.

Anterior Margin

Left Main Bronchus

Pulmonary Hilum

Pulmonary Vv.

Cardiac Impression

Inferior Lobe

Descending Aorta
Thoracic Situs
Sulcus

Cardiac Incisura

Pulmonary Ligament

Esophageal Sulcus

Lingula of Left Lung

Inferior Margin

Pulmonary Base
(Diaphragmatic Surface)

Oblique Fissure

b Medial View of the Left Lung.

Thoracic Cavity

Larynx, Trachea, and Bronchial Tree

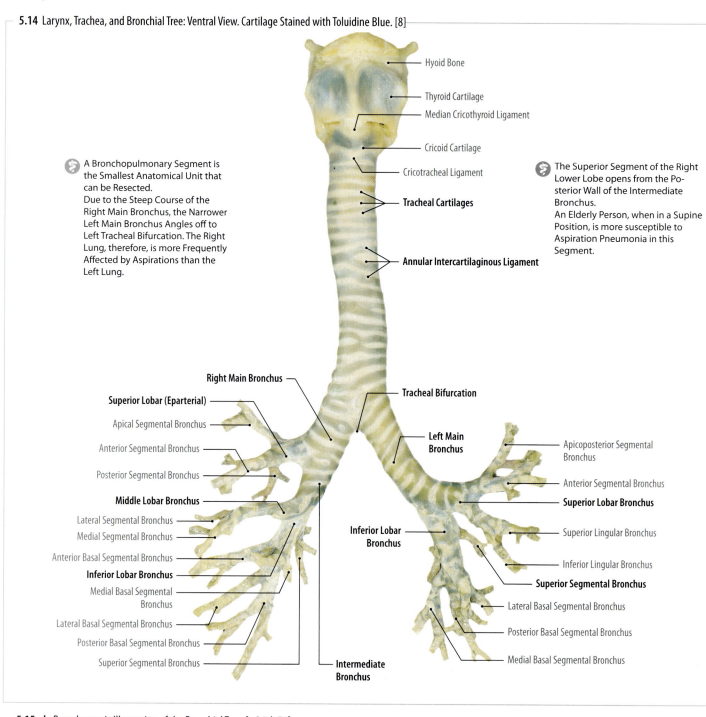

5.14 Larynx, Trachea, and Bronchial Tree: Ventral View. Cartilage Stained with Toluidine Blue. [8]

A Bronchopulmonary Segment is the Smallest Anatomical Unit that can be Resected.
Due to the Steep Course of the Right Main Bronchus, the Narrower Left Main Bronchus Angles off to Left Tracheal Bifurcation. The Right Lung, therefore, is more Frequently Affected by Aspirations than the Left Lung.

The Superior Segment of the Right Lower Lobe opens from the Posterior Wall of the Intermediate Bronchus.
An Elderly Person, when in a Supine Position, is more susceptible to Aspiration Pneumonia in this Segment.

Hyoid Bone

Thyroid Cartilage

Median Cricothyroid Ligament

Cricoid Cartilage

Cricotracheal Ligament

Tracheal Cartilages

Annular Intercartilaginous Ligament

Right Main Bronchus

Superior Lobar (Eparterial)

Apical Segmental Bronchus

Anterior Segmental Bronchus

Posterior Segmental Bronchus

Middle Lobar Bronchus

Lateral Segmental Bronchus

Medial Segmental Bronchus

Anterior Basal Segmental Bronchus

Inferior Lobar Bronchus

Medial Basal Segmental Bronchus

Lateral Basal Segmental Bronchus

Posterior Basal Segmental Bronchus

Superior Segmental Bronchus

Tracheal Bifurcation

Left Main Bronchus

Apicoposterior Segmental Bronchus

Anterior Segmental Bronchus

Superior Lobar Bronchus

Superior Lingular Bronchus

Inferior Lobar Bronchus

Inferior Lingular Bronchus

Superior Segmental Bronchus

Lateral Basal Segmental Bronchus

Posterior Basal Segmental Bronchus

Medial Basal Segmental Bronchus

Intermediate Bronchus

5.15a,b Bronchoscopic Illustration of the Bronchial Tree. [a 24, b 71]

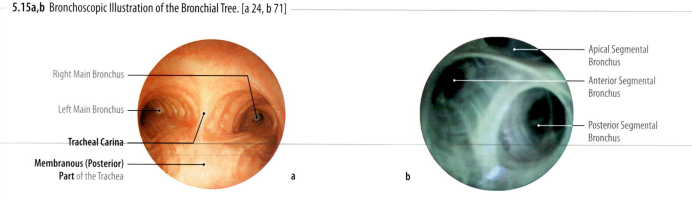

Right Main Bronchus

Left Main Bronchus

Tracheal Carina

Membranous (Posterior) Part of the Trachea

Apical Segmental Bronchus

Anterior Segmental Bronchus

Posterior Segmental Bronchus

a Tracheal Bifurcation with the Right and Left Main Bronchus.
b Fluorescent Bronchoscopy: View from the Superior Lobe Bronchus of the Lung into the Segmental Bronchi.
The continual blue staining is a sign of an Intact Ciliated Epithelium Covering the Bronchi.

Vessels of the Lung and Bronchial Tree

5.16 Pulmonary Arteries, Pulmonary Trunk with Branches, and Tracheobronchial Tree: Ventral View. [72]

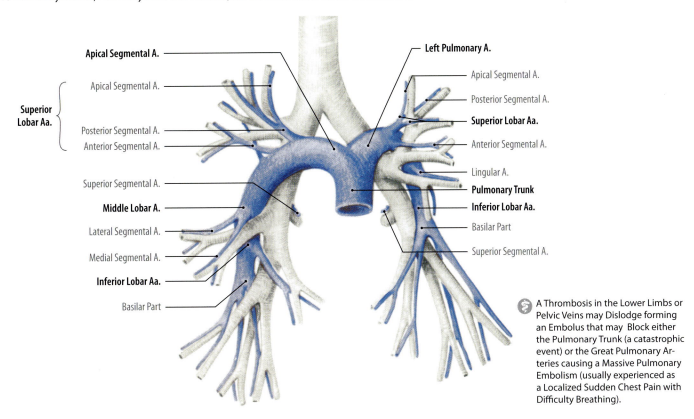

Apical Segmental A.

Superior Lobar Aa.
- Apical Segmental A.
- Posterior Segmental A.
- Anterior Segmental A.

Superior Segmental A.

Middle Lobar A.

Lateral Segmental A.

Medial Segmental A.

Inferior Lobar Aa.

Basilar Part

Left Pulmonary A.

Apical Segmental A.

Posterior Segmental A.

Superior Lobar Aa.

Anterior Segmental A.

Lingular A.

Pulmonary Trunk

Inferior Lobar Aa.

Basilar Part

Superior Segmental A.

A Thrombosis in the Lower Limbs or Pelvic Veins may Dislodge forming an Embolus that may Block either the Pulmonary Trunk (a catastrophic event) or the Great Pulmonary Arteries causing a Massive Pulmonary Embolism (usually experienced as a Localized Sudden Chest Pain with Difficulty Breathing).

5.17 Corrosion Preparation of the Lung. [6]

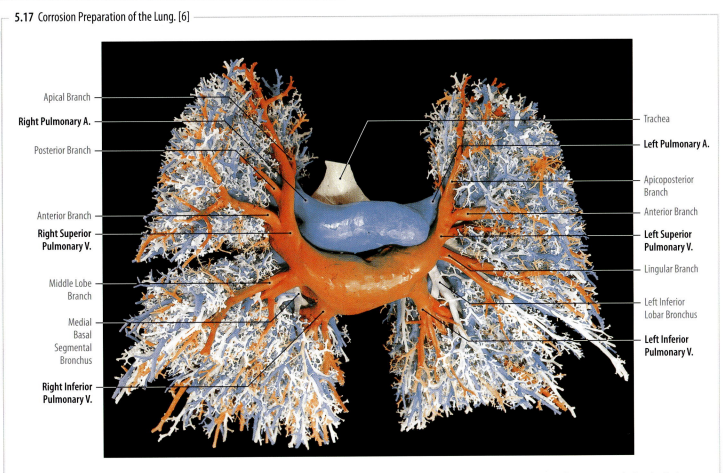

Apical Branch

Right Pulmonary A.

Posterior Branch

Anterior Branch

Right Superior Pulmonary V.

Middle Lobe Branch

Medial Basal Segmental Bronchus

Right Inferior Pulmonary V.

Trachea

Left Pulmonary A.

Apicoposterior Branch

Anterior Branch

Left Superior Pulmonary V.

Lingular Branch

Left Inferior Lobar Bronchus

Left Inferior Pulmonary V.

Illustration of the Pulmonary Arteries (blue), the Pulmonary Veins (red), and the Tracheobronchial Tree (white): Ventral view. Following the Injection of a Synthetic Agent, the Pulmonary Arteries in the area of the Pulmonary Trunk Bifurcation and the Pulmonary Veins in the area of the Left Auricle have been Connected to Each Other.

Thoracic Cavity

5.18a,b a Pulmonary Surface with Preserved Pulmonary Pleura. **b** Partial View of a Section from the Right Superior Lobe of the Lung. [6]

The Bronchopulmonary Segment is a Pyramidal Structure of the Lung, with the Base Facing the Visceral Surface and the Apex in the Center of the Lobe. After ~14–6 divisions, the Terminal Bronchioles give rise to a Number of Respiratory Bronchioles. Each Respiratory Bronchiole is Divided into a number of Alveolar Sacs.

Intersegmental Septum

(Interbronchial) Nodes

Lobule

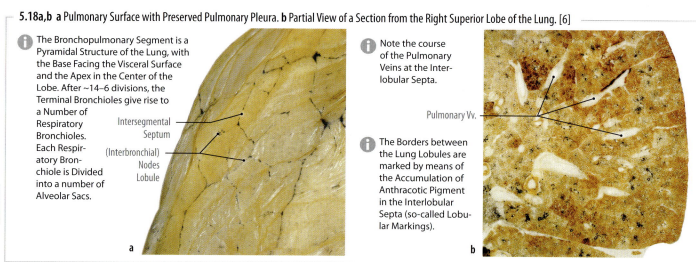

a

Note the course of the Pulmonary Veins at the Interlobular Septa.

Pulmonary Vv.

The Borders between the Lung Lobules are marked by means of the Accumulation of Anthracotic Pigment in the Interlobular Septa (so-called Lobular Markings).

b

5.19 Corrosion Preparation of the Bronchial Tree and the Alveoli. [1]

Lobular Bronchi

Terminal Bronchiole

Alveolar Sac

Lobule

5.20 Lymph Nodes and Lymph Outlet of the Lung. [15]

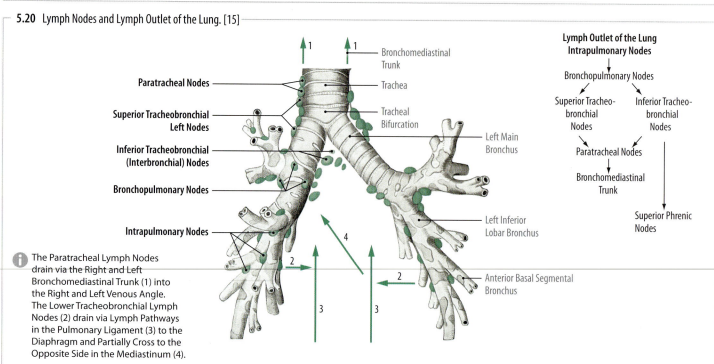

Paratracheal Nodes

Superior Tracheobronchial Left Nodes

Inferior Tracheobronchial (Interbronchial) Nodes

Bronchopulmonary Nodes

Intrapulmonary Nodes

Bronchomediastinal Trunk

Trachea

Tracheal Bifurcation

Left Main Bronchus

Left Inferior Lobar Bronchus

Anterior Basal Segmental Bronchus

Lymph Outlet of the Lung Intrapulmonary Nodes

Bronchopulmonary Nodes

Superior Tracheobronchial Nodes

Inferior Tracheobronchial Nodes

Paratracheal Nodes

Bronchomediastinal Trunk

Superior Phrenic Nodes

The Paratracheal Lymph Nodes drain via the Right and Left Bronchomediastinal Trunk (1) into the Right and Left Venous Angle. The Lower Tracheobronchial Lymph Nodes (2) drain via Lymph Pathways in the Pulmonary Ligament (3) to the Diaphragm and Partially Cross to the Opposite Side in the Mediastinum (4).

Lung: Systemic, Pulmonary Vessels

5.21 Bronchial Tree and Pulmonary Alveoli with Pulmonary Vessels and Systemic Vessels. [48]

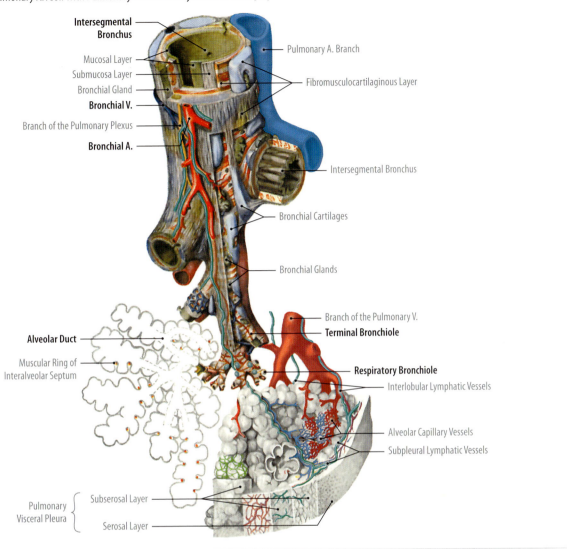

Intersegmental Bronchus

Mucosal Layer
Submucosa Layer
Bronchial Gland
Bronchial V.
Branch of the Pulmonary Plexus
Bronchial A.

Pulmonary A. Branch
Fibromusculocartilaginous Layer
Intersegmental Bronchus
Bronchial Cartilages
Bronchial Glands
Branch of the Pulmonary V.
Terminal Bronchiole

Alveolar Duct
Muscular Ring of Interalveolar Septum

Respiratory Bronchiole
Interlobular Lymphatic Vessels
Alveolar Capillary Vessels
Subpleural Lymphatic Vessels

Pulmonary Visceral Pleura { Subserosal Layer
Serosal Layer

5.22 Bronchial Arteries, Trachea, Main Bronchi, and Aorta: Dorsal View. [6]

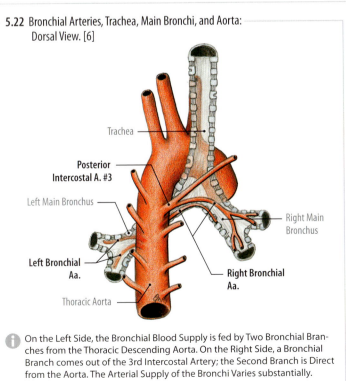

Trachea
Posterior Intercostal A. #3
Left Main Bronchus
Right Main Bronchus
Left Bronchial Aa.
Right Bronchial Aa.
Thoracic Aorta

ⓘ On the Left Side, the Bronchial Blood Supply is fed by Two Bronchial Branches from the Thoracic Descending Aorta. On the Right Side, a Bronchial Branch comes out of the 3rd Intercostal Artery; the Second Branch is Direct from the Aorta. The Arterial Supply of the Bronchi Varies substantially.

5.23 Bronchial Veins of the Right Side: Ventral View. [6]

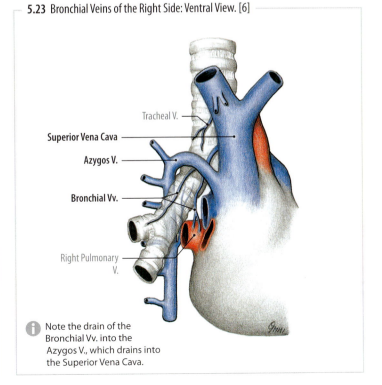

Tracheal V.
Superior Vena Cava
Azygos V.
Bronchial Vv.
Right Pulmonary V.

ⓘ Note the drain of the Bronchial Vv. into the Azygos V., which drains into the Superior Vena Cava.

Thoracic Cavity

5.24 Hilum of the Lung of the Right Side: Ventral View. [15]

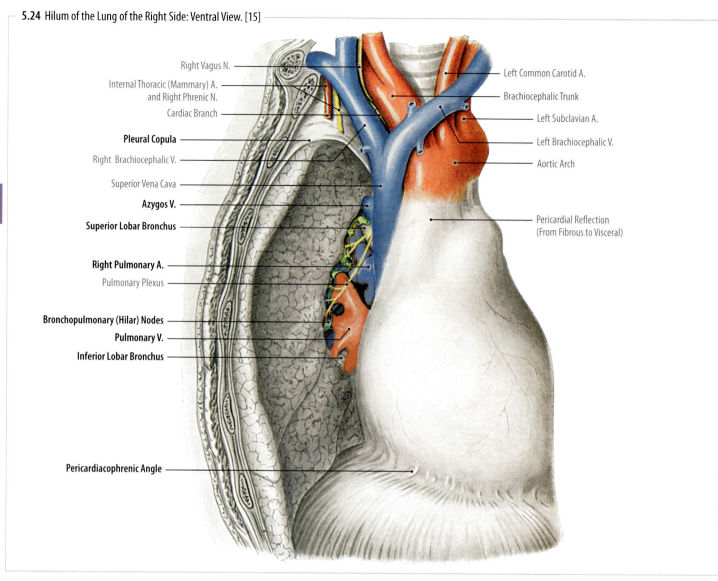

Right Vagus N.

Internal Thoracic (Mammary) A. and Right Phrenic N.

Cardiac Branch

Pleural Copula

Right Brachiocephalic V.

Superior Vena Cava

Azygos V.

Superior Lobar Bronchus

Right Pulmonary A.

Pulmonary Plexus

Bronchopulmonary (Hilar) Nodes

Pulmonary V.

Inferior Lobar Bronchus

Pericardiacophrenic Angle

Left Common Carotid A.

Brachiocephalic Trunk

Left Subclavian A.

Left Brachiocephalic V.

Aortic Arch

Pericardial Reflection (From Fibrous to Visceral)

5.25 Right Lung: Ventral View. [15]

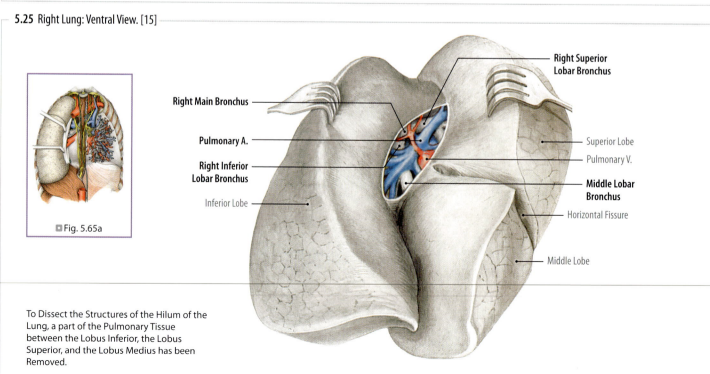

☐ Fig. 5.65a

Right Main Bronchus

Pulmonary A.

Right Inferior Lobar Bronchus

Inferior Lobe

Right Superior Lobar Bronchus

Superior Lobe

Pulmonary V.

Middle Lobar Bronchus

Horizontal Fissure

Middle Lobe

To Dissect the Structures of the Hilum of the Lung, a part of the Pulmonary Tissue between the Lobus Inferior, the Lobus Superior, and the Lobus Medius has been Removed.

Left Hilum of the Lung

5.26 Hilum of the Lung of the Left Side: Ventral View. [15]

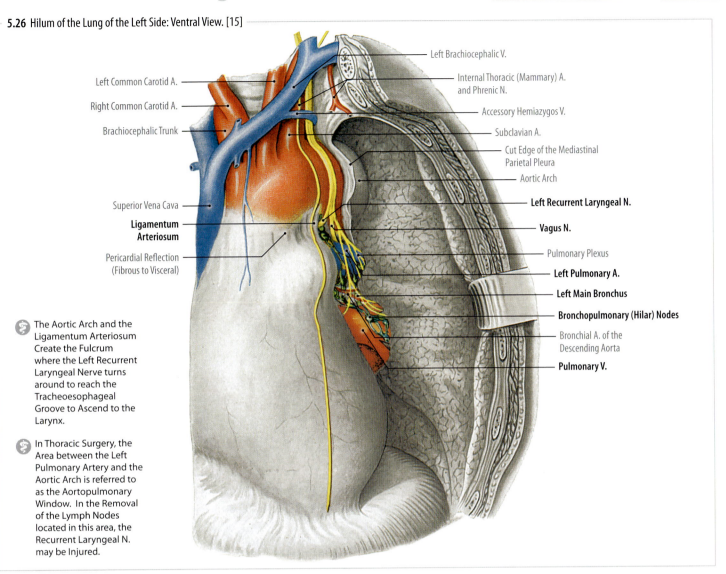

Left Common Carotid A.

Right Common Carotid A.

Brachiocephalic Trunk

Superior Vena Cava

Ligamentum Arteriosum

Pericardial Reflection (Fibrous to Visceral)

Left Brachiocephalic V.

Internal Thoracic (Mammary) A. and Phrenic N.

Accessory Hemiazygos V.

Subclavian A.

Cut Edge of the Mediastinal Parietal Pleura

Aortic Arch

Left Recurrent Laryngeal N.

Vagus N.

Pulmonary Plexus

Left Pulmonary A.

Left Main Bronchus

Bronchopulmonary (Hilar) Nodes

Bronchial A. of the Descending Aorta

Pulmonary V.

The Aortic Arch and the Ligamentum Arteriosum Create the Fulcrum where the Left Recurrent Laryngeal Nerve turns around to reach the Tracheoesophageal Groove to Ascend to the Larynx.

In Thoracic Surgery, the Area between the Left Pulmonary Artery and the Aortic Arch is referred to as the Aortopulmonary Window. In the Removal of the Lymph Nodes located in this area, the Recurrent Laryngeal N. may be Injured.

5.27 Left Lung: Ventral View. [15]

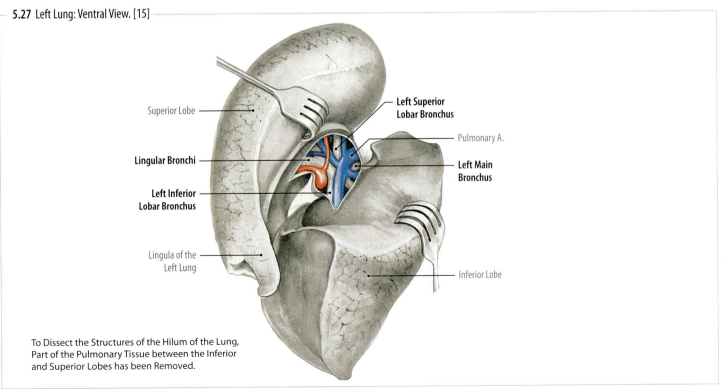

Superior Lobe

Lingular Bronchi

Left Inferior Lobar Bronchus

Lingula of the Left Lung

Left Superior Lobar Bronchus

Pulmonary A.

Left Main Bronchus

Inferior Lobe

To Dissect the Structures of the Hilum of the Lung, Part of the Pulmonary Tissue between the Inferior and Superior Lobes has been Removed.

Thoracic Cavity

Thorax: Topography

5.28 Horizontal Section through the Thorax at the Level of the Seventh Thoracic Vertebra: Cranial View, Section of the Lower Mediastinum. [15]

A Mitral Stenosis causes a Constriction that results in Stasis and Enlargment of the Left Atrium. The Enlargment of the Posterior Heart Impinges on the Posterior Mediastinum, Compressing the Esophagus. This causes Difficulty in Swallowing (Dysphagia), which may be a Symptom of Mitral Stenosis.

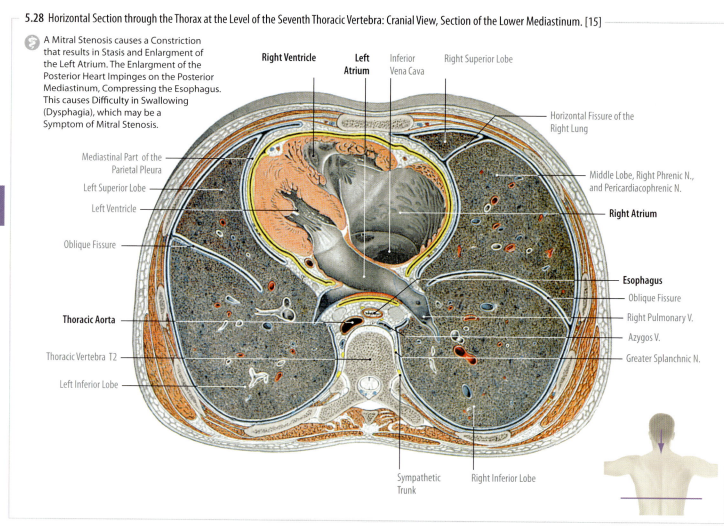

Right Ventricle
Left Atrium
Inferior Vena Cava
Right Superior Lobe

Mediastinal Part of the Parietal Pleura
Left Superior Lobe
Left Ventricle
Oblique Fissure
Thoracic Aorta
Thoracic Vertebra T2
Left Inferior Lobe

Horizontal Fissure of the Right Lung
Middle Lobe, Right Phrenic N., and Pericardiacophrenic N.
Right Atrium
Esophagus
Oblique Fissure
Right Pulmonary V.
Azygos V.
Greater Splanchnic N.

Sympathetic Trunk
Right Inferior Lobe

5.29 Computed Tomography (CT) Following the Addition of a Contrast Medium: Transversal Section through the Thorax of a 49-Year-Old Man at the Level of the Fifth Thoracic Vertebra. [73]

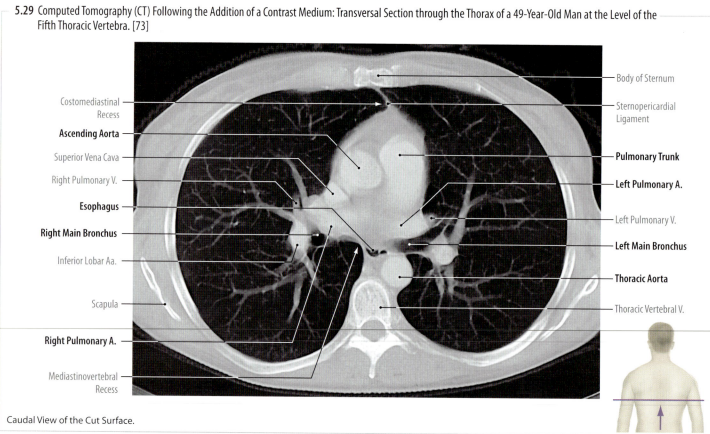

Costomediastinal Recess
Ascending Aorta
Superior Vena Cava
Right Pulmonary V.
Esophagus
Right Main Bronchus
Inferior Lobar Aa.
Scapula
Right Pulmonary A.
Mediastinovertebral Recess

Body of Sternum
Sternopericardial Ligament
Pulmonary Trunk
Left Pulmonary A.
Left Pulmonary V.
Left Main Bronchus
Thoracic Aorta
Thoracic Vertebral V.

Caudal View of the Cut Surface.

266

5.30 Thoracic Cavity: Ventral View. [15]

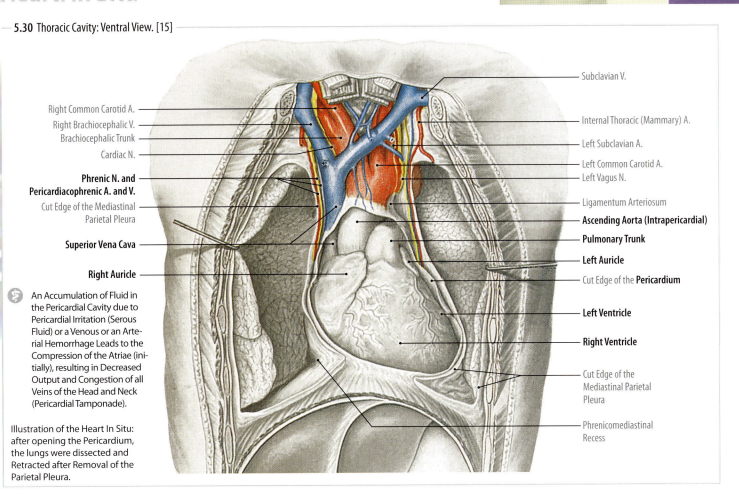

Right Common Carotid A.

Right Brachiocephalic V.

Brachiocephalic Trunk

Cardiac N.

**Phrenic N. and
Pericardiacophrenic A. and V.**

Cut Edge of the Mediastinal
Parietal Pleura

Superior Vena Cava

Right Auricle

Subclavian V.

Internal Thoracic (Mammary) A.

Left Subclavian A.

Left Common Carotid A.

Left Vagus N.

Ligamentum Arteriosum

Ascending Aorta (Intrapericardial)

Pulmonary Trunk

Left Auricle

Cut Edge of the **Pericardium**

Left Ventricle

Right Ventricle

Cut Edge of the
Mediastinal Parietal
Pleura

Phrenicomediastinal
Recess

An Accumulation of Fluid in the Pericardial Cavity due to Pericardial Irritation (Serous Fluid) or a Venous or an Arterial Hemorrhage Leads to the Compression of the Atriae (initially), resulting in Decreased Output and Congestion of all Veins of the Head and Neck (Pericardial Tamponade).

Illustration of the Heart In Situ: after opening the Pericardium, the lungs were dissected and Retracted after Removal of the Parietal Pleura.

5.31 Thoracic Cavity: Ventral View. [15]

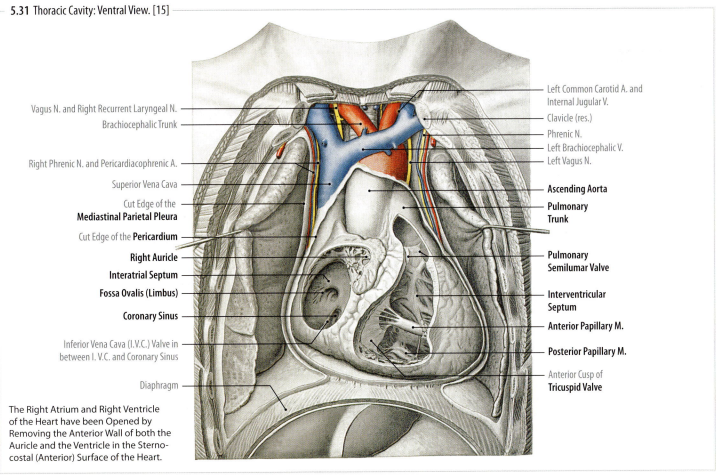

Vagus N. and Right Recurrent Laryngeal N.

Brachiocephalic Trunk

Right Phrenic N. and Pericardiacophrenic A.

Superior Vena Cava

Cut Edge of the
Mediastinal Parietal Pleura

Cut Edge of the **Pericardium**

Right Auricle

Interatrial Septum

Fossa Ovalis (Limbus)

Coronary Sinus

Inferior Vena Cava (I.V.C.) Valve in
between I.V.C. and Coronary Sinus

Diaphragm

Left Common Carotid A. and
Internal Jugular V.

Clavicle (res.)

Phrenic N.

Left Brachiocephalic V.

Left Vagus N.

Ascending Aorta

**Pulmonary
Trunk**

**Pulmonary
Semilumar Valve**

**Interventricular
Septum**

Anterior Papillary M.

Posterior Papillary M.

Anterior Cusp of
Tricuspid Valve

The Right Atrium and Right Ventricle of the Heart have been Opened by Removing the Anterior Wall of both the Auricle and the Ventricle in the Sternocostal (Anterior) Surface of the Heart.

5.32 Projection of the Cardiac Valves and Their Auscultation Points on the Anterior Thoracic Wall. [15]

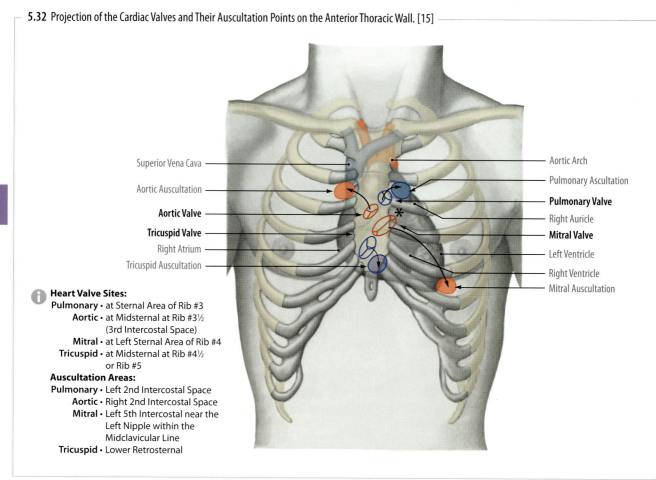

Superior Vena Cava

Aortic Auscultation

Aortic Valve

Tricuspid Valve

Right Atrium

Tricuspid Auscultation

Aortic Arch

Pulmonary Asccultation

Pulmonary Valve

Right Auricle

Mitral Valve

Left Ventricle

Right Ventricle

Mitral Auscultation

ⓘ Heart Valve Sites:
Pulmonary · at Sternal Area of Rib #3
Aortic · at Midsternal at Rib #3½
(3rd Intercostal Space)
Mitral · at Left Sternal Area of Rib #4
Tricuspid · at Midsternal at Rib #4½
or Rib #5
Auscultation Areas:
Pulmonary · Left 2nd Intercostal Space
Aortic · Right 2nd Intercostal Space
Mitral · Left 5th Intercostal near the
Left Nipple within the
Midclavicular Line
Tricuspid · Lower Retrosternal

5.33 X-Ray Image of the Thorax of a 35-Year-Old Man in Anteroposterior Projection (Radiation). [10]

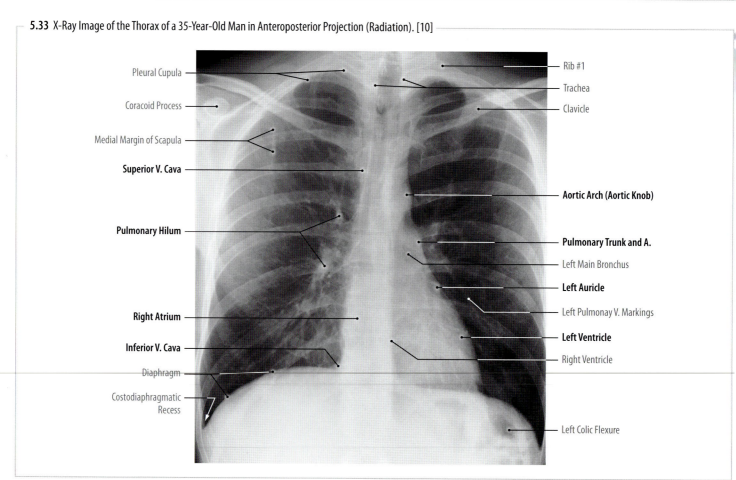

Pleural Cupula

Coracoid Process

Medial Margin of Scapula

Superior V. Cava

Pulmonary Hilum

Right Atrium

Inferior V. Cava

Diaphragm

Costodiaphragmatic
Recess

Rib #1

Trachea

Clavicle

Aortic Arch (Aortic Knob)

Pulmonary Trunk and A.

Left Main Bronchus

Left Auricle

Left Pulmonay V. Markings

Left Ventricle

Right Ventricle

Left Colic Flexure

Heart and Pericardium

5.34a,b Pericardium and Heart with Afferent and Efferent Vessels. [a 15, b 48]

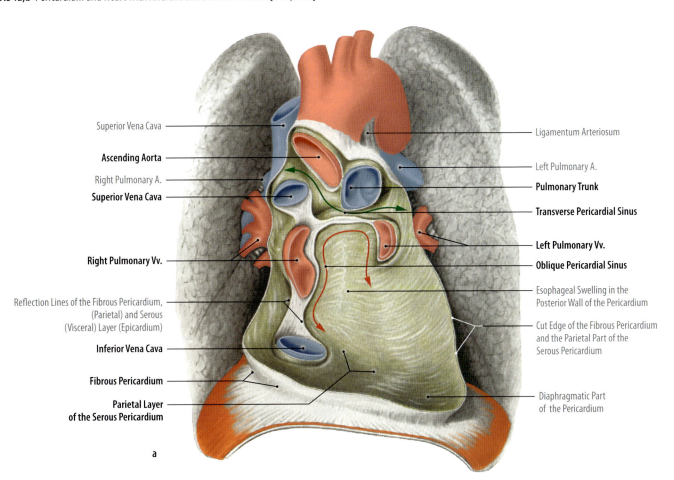

Superior Vena Cava

Ascending Aorta

Right Pulmonary A.

Superior Vena Cava

Right Pulmonary Vv.

Reflection Lines of the Fibrous Pericardium, (Parietal) and Serous (Visceral) Layer (Epicardium)

Inferior Vena Cava

Fibrous Pericardium

Parietal Layer of the Serous Pericardium

Ligamentum Arteriosum

Left Pulmonary A.

Pulmonary Trunk

Transverse Pericardial Sinus

Left Pulmonary Vv.

Oblique Pericardial Sinus

Esophageal Swelling in the Posterior Wall of the Pericardium

Cut Edge of the Fibrous Pericardium and the Parietal Part of the Serous Pericardium

Diaphragmatic Part of the Pericardium

a

ℹ Note the Transfer Points of the Parietal Layer into the Visceral Layer of the Serous Pericardium (Epicardium) in an "h" shaped reflection to form the Transverse and Oblique Pericardial Sinuses within the Pericardial Cavity.

A Pericarditis may occur as a concomitant symptom of other diseases or conditions, e.g., Tuberculosis, a Myocardial Infarction, Renal Failure (Uremic Pericarditis), Rheumatic or Viral Infections, Inflammations or Tumors of the Lung or Kidney that may reach the Pericardium. In the case of a Constrictive Pericarditis (Armored Heart), the Calcification of Fibrous Pericardium causes a Constriction of the Heart and an Obstruction of the Filling of Atriae and Ventricles. Fainting is a frequent occurrence with Increased Demand on the Heart.

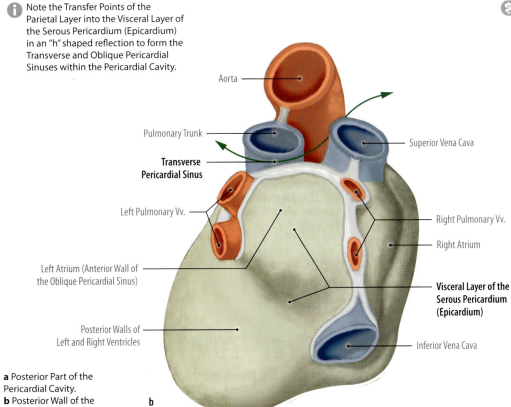

Aorta

Pulmonary Trunk

Transverse Pericardial Sinus

Left Pulmonary Vv.

Left Atrium (Anterior Wall of the Oblique Pericardial Sinus)

Posterior Walls of Left and Right Ventricles

Superior Vena Cava

Right Pulmonary Vv.

Right Atrium

Visceral Layer of the Serous Pericardium (Epicardium)

Inferior Vena Cava

a Posterior Part of the Pericardial Cavity.
b Posterior Wall of the Heart Resected from the Pericardial Cavity.

b

Thoracic Cavity

5.35a,b Coronary Arteries (Right and Left Coronary Aa.).

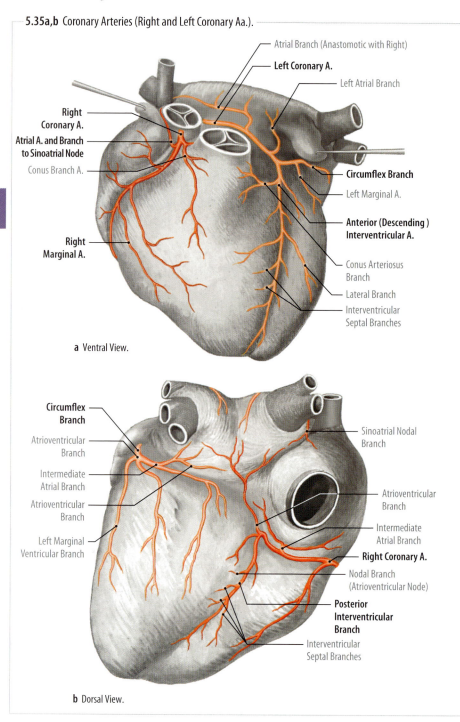

Atrial Branch (Anastomotic with Right)

Left Coronary A.

Left Atrial Branch

Right Coronary A.

Atrial A. and Branch to Sinoatrial Node

Conus Branch A.

Circumflex Branch

Left Marginal A.

Anterior (Descending) Interventricular A.

Conus Arteriosus Branch

Lateral Branch

Interventricular Septal Branches

Right Marginal A.

a Ventral View.

Circumflex Branch

Atrioventricular Branch

Intermediate Atrial Branch

Atrioventricular Branch

Left Marginal Ventricular Branch

Sinoatrial Nodal Branch

Atrioventricular Branch

Intermediate Atrial Branch

Right Coronary A.

Nodal Branch (Atrioventricular Node)

Posterior Interventricular Branch

Interventricular Septal Branches

b Dorsal View.

Branch Sequence of the Right and Left Coronary Arteries with the Abbreviations used in Clinical Settings.

Right Coronary A. RCA
Atrioventricular Branches
[Conus Arteriosus Branch]
Atrial Branches
[Sinoatrial Nodal Branch]
Right Marginal A.   RMA
Right Posterolateral Branch   RPLB
Intermediate Atrial Branch
Posterior Interventricular A.   RIVP
└ Interventricular Septal Branches
Atrioventricular Nodal Branch

Left Coronary A. LCA
Atrial Branches from Main Artery
├ Atrial Anastomotic A.
└ Left Atrial A. (SA Nodal Artery [var.])
Anterior Interventricular (Descending) A. LAD
├ Conus Arteriosus Branch
├ Lateral Branch LD (Diagonal Branches)
└ Interventricular Septal Branches
Circumflex Branch   LCX
├ Atrioventricular Branch
├ Left Marginal Ventricular Branch
│ or Posterolateral Branches   PLB
├ Intermediate Atrial Branch
├ Posterior Left Ventricular Branch
├ Left Atrial Branch
└ Atrioventricular Branch

ℹ In ~60% of cases, the Right Coronary A. originates from Right Aortic Sinus (Valsalva's Sinus) of the Right Anterior Semilunar Valve and the Left Coronary A. originates from Anterior Left Aortic Sinus (Valsalva's Sinus) of the Left Anterior Semilunar Valve (vars.) ◘ Fig. 5.43.

🔁 Coronary Heart Disease is among the most Common Causes of Death in the Western world. The Constriction of the Coronary Arteries by Atheromatous Plaque typically is Located in the initial sections of the Coronary Arteries.
An Acute Occlusion of the Anterior Interventricular A. (LAD) causes an Anterior Myocardial Infarction.

5.36a–c Cross-Section through the Ventricles. [15, 83]

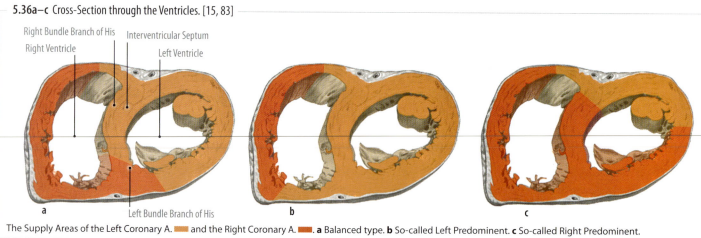

Right Bundle Branch of His

Right Ventricle

Interventricular Septum

Left Ventricle

a

Left Bundle Branch of His

b

c

The Supply Areas of the Left Coronary A. ▬ and the Right Coronary A. ▬ . **a** Balanced type. **b** So-called Left Predominent. **c** So-called Right Predominent.

5.37a,b Coronary Arteries, Types of Supply: Dorsal View.

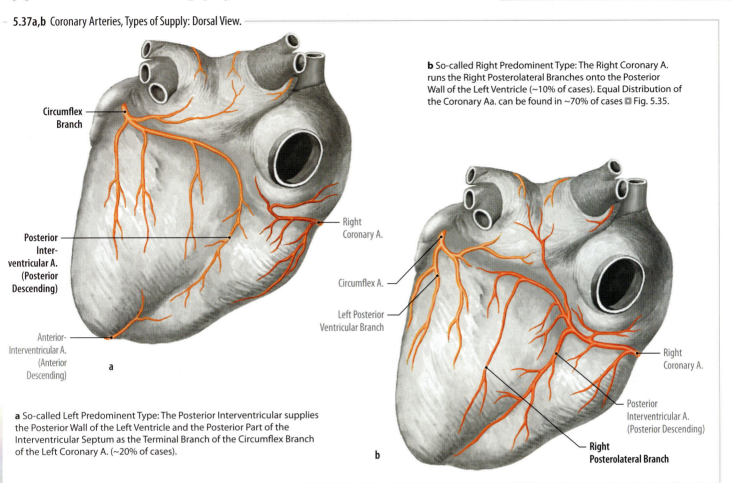

b So-called Right Predominent Type: The Right Coronary A. runs the Right Posterolateral Branches onto the Posterior Wall of the Left Ventricle (~10% of cases). Equal Distribution of the Coronary Aa. can be found in ~70% of cases ☐ Fig. 5.35.

Circumflex Branch

Posterior Interventricular A. (Posterior Descending)

Anterior-Interventricular A. (Anterior Descending)

a

Right Coronary A.

Circumflex A.

Left Posterior Ventricular Branch

Right Coronary A.

Posterior Interventricular A. (Posterior Descending)

Right Posterolateral Branch

b

a So-called Left Predominent Type: The Posterior Interventricular supplies the Posterior Wall of the Left Ventricle and the Posterior Part of the Interventricular Septum as the Terminal Branch of the Circumflex Branch of the Left Coronary A. (~20% of cases).

5.38a,b Cardiac Veins.

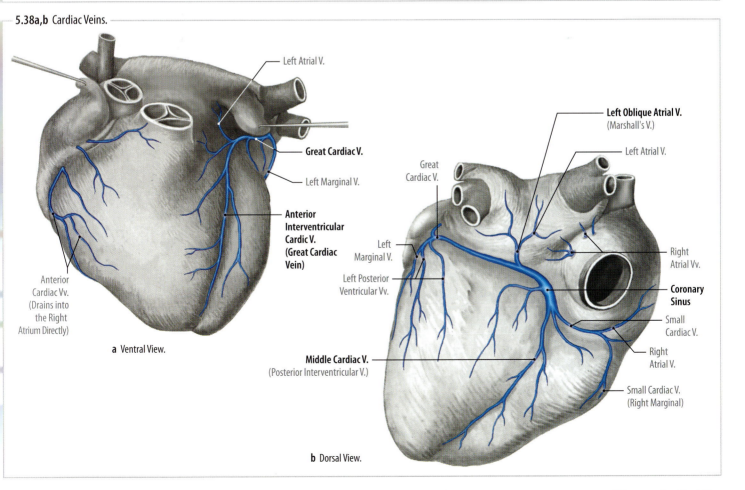

Left Atrial V.

Great Cardiac V.

Left Marginal V.

Anterior Interventricular Cardic V. (Great Cardiac Vein)

Anterior Cardiac Vv. (Drains into the Right Atrium Directly)

a Ventral View.

Left Oblique Atrial V. (Marshall's V.)

Left Atrial V.

Great Cardiac V.

Left Marginal V.

Left Posterior Ventricular Vv.

Right Atrial Vv.

Coronary Sinus

Small Cardiac V.

Right Atrial V.

Middle Cardiac V. (Posterior Interventricular V.)

Small Cardiac V. (Right Marginal)

b Dorsal View.

Thoracic Cavity

Heart

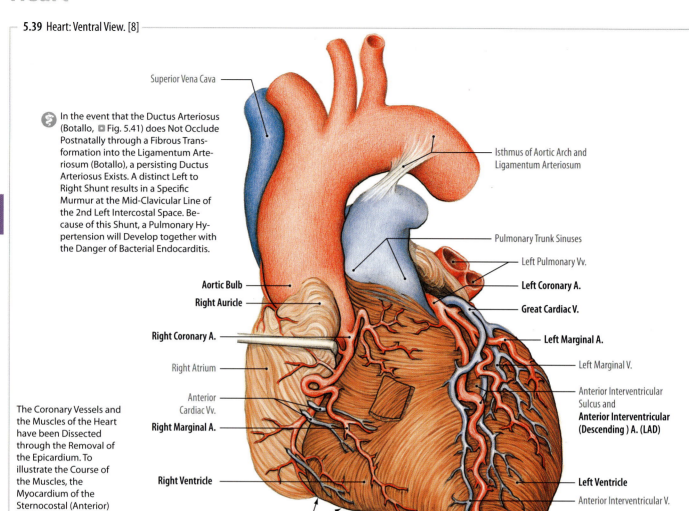

In the event that the Ductus Arteriosus (Botallo, ☐ Fig. 5.41) does Not Occlude Postnatally through a Fibrous Transformation into the Ligamentum Arteriosum (Botallo), a persisting Ductus Arteriosus Exists. A distinct Left to Right Shunt results in a Specific Murmur at the Mid-Clavicular Line of the 2nd Left Intercostal Space. Because of this Shunt, a Pulmonary Hypertension will Develop together with the Danger of Bacterial Endocarditis.

The Coronary Vessels and the Muscles of the Heart have been Dissected through the Removal of the Epicardium. To illustrate the Course of the Muscles, the Myocardium of the Sternocostal (Anterior) Surface has been Fenestrated in the area of the Right Ventricle.

Superior Vena Cava

Isthmus of Aortic Arch and Ligamentum Arteriosum

Pulmonary Trunk Sinuses

Left Pulmonary Vv.

Aortic Bulb

Left Coronary A.

Right Auricle

Great Cardiac V.

Right Coronary A.

Left Marginal A.

Right Atrium

Left Marginal V.

Anterior Cardiac Vv.

Anterior Interventricular Sulcus and **Anterior Interventricular (Descending) A. (LAD)**

Right Marginal A.

Right Ventricle

Left Ventricle

Anterior Interventricular V.

Right Inferior Margin

Apex of the Heart

Apical Incisura (Notch)

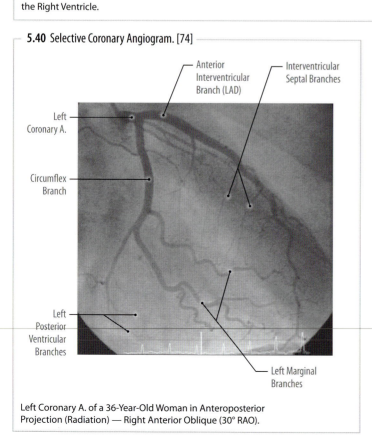

Anterior Interventricular Branch (LAD)

Interventricular Septal Branches

Left Coronary A.

Circumflex Branch

Left Posterior Ventricular Branches

Left Marginal Branches

Left Coronary A. of a 36-Year-Old Woman in Anteroposterior Projection (Radiation) — Right Anterior Oblique (30° RAO).

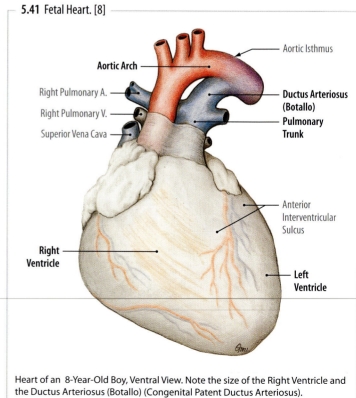

Aortic Isthmus

Aortic Arch

Right Pulmonary A.

Ductus Arteriosus (Botallo)

Right Pulmonary V.

Pulmonary Trunk

Superior Vena Cava

Anterior Interventricular Sulcus

Right Ventricle

Left Ventricle

Heart of an 8-Year-Old Boy, Ventral View. Note the size of the Right Ventricle and the Ductus Arteriosus (Botallo) (Congenital Patent Ductus Arteriosus).

5.42 Heart: Dorsal View. [8]

With a Right Predominent Type (☐ Fig. 5.37b), an Acute Occlusion of the Right Coronary Artery leads to a Posterior Myocardial Infarction. With a Left Predominent Type, a Posterior Myocardial Infarction develops through an Acute Occlusion of the Posterior Interventricular Artery as the Terminal Branch of the Circumflex A. (☐ Fig. 5.37a). The Atrioventricular Nodal Branch may be Affected, necessitating the Implantation of a Pacemaker in the Lower Part of the Interventricular Septum in the Right Ventricle to Drive Both Ventricles. Through the Implantation of a Pacemaker Probe into the Coronary Sinus, the Left Ventricle may be Stimulated Electrically.

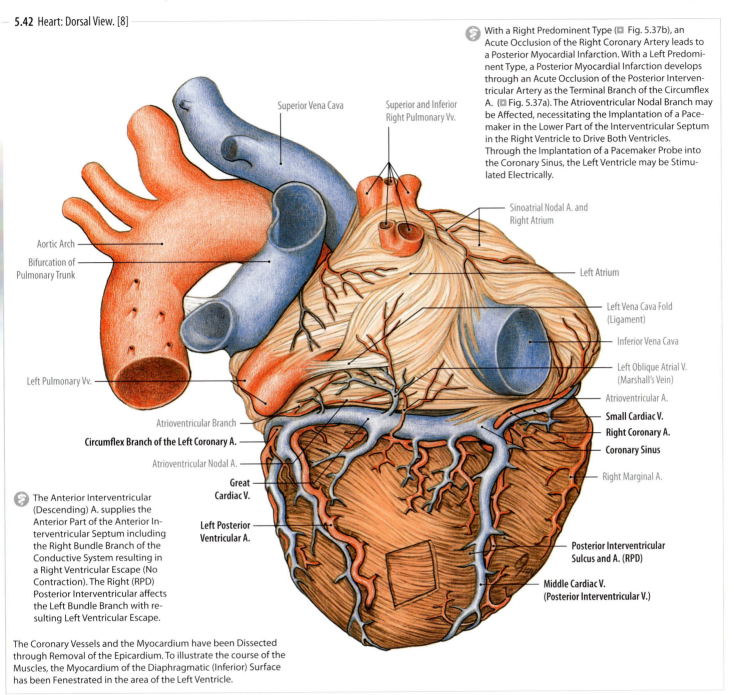

Superior Vena Cava

Superior and Inferior
Right Pulmonary Vv.

Sinoatrial Nodal A. and
Right Atrium

Aortic Arch

Bifurcation of
Pulmonary Trunk

Left Atrium

Left Vena Cava Fold
(Ligament)

Inferior Vena Cava

Left Pulmonary Vv.

Left Oblique Atrial V.
(Marshall's Vein)

Atrioventricular A.

Atrioventricular Branch

Small Cardiac V.

Circumflex Branch of the Left Coronary A.

Right Coronary A.

Atrioventricular Nodal A.

Coronary Sinus

**Great
Cardiac V.**

Right Marginal A.

**Left Posterior
Ventricular A.**

**Posterior Interventricular
Sulcus and A. (RPD)**

**Middle Cardiac V.
(Posterior Interventricular V.)**

The Anterior Interventricular (Descending) A. supplies the Anterior Part of the Anterior Interventricular Septum including the Right Bundle Branch of the Conductive System resulting in a Right Ventricular Escape (No Contraction). The Right (RPD) Posterior Interventricular affects the Left Bundle Branch with resulting Left Ventricular Escape.

The Coronary Vessels and the Myocardium have been Dissected through Removal of the Epicardium. To illustrate the course of the Muscles, the Myocardium of the Diaphragmatic (Inferior) Surface has been Fenestrated in the area of the Left Ventricle.

5.43a,b Variants of Coronary Arteries. [83]

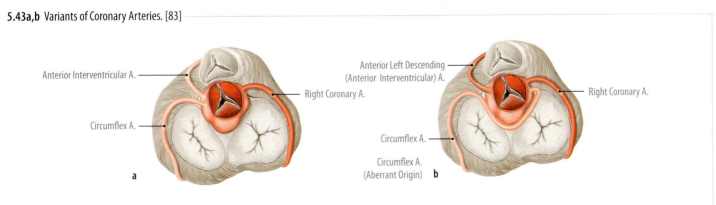

Anterior Interventricular A.

Anterior Left Descending
(Anterior Interventricular) A.

Right Coronary A.

Right Coronary A.

Circumflex A.

Circumflex A.

Circumflex A.
(Aberrant Origin)

a   b

a Accessory · Coronary Arteries, Independent Outlets of the Anterior Interventricular A., and the Circumflex A. from the Left Anterior Aortic Sinus (Left Anterior Semilunar Valve).
b An Aberrant Origin of the Circumflex A. from the Aortic Sinus of the Right (Coronary) Semilunar Valve and the Right Coronary A., which runs to the Myocardium in the area of the Pulmonary Trunk, the so-called Conus Artery.

Thoracic Cavity

Coronary Vessels, Cardiac Valves

5.44 Heart: Superior Ventral View. [8]

An Acquired Aortic Valve Stenosis commonly Develops due to Degenerative Changes of the Valve caused by Bacterial Colonies on the Semilunar Cusps, which become Calcified and Fibrotic. This Reduces the Aperture Opening, thus increasing the Resistance of the Left Ventricle. This leads to Increased Systolic Left Ventricular Pressure, and a Concentric Hypertrophy of the Wall of the Left Ventricle Develops. Thus, the Myocardium Requires More Oxygen. An Aortic Valve Insufficiency leads to Volume Loading of the Left Ventricle; a Regurgitation (backup) may Ensue Later.

Note the Extension of the Cardiac Muscles onto the Pulmonary Vv. and the Pulmonary Trunk.

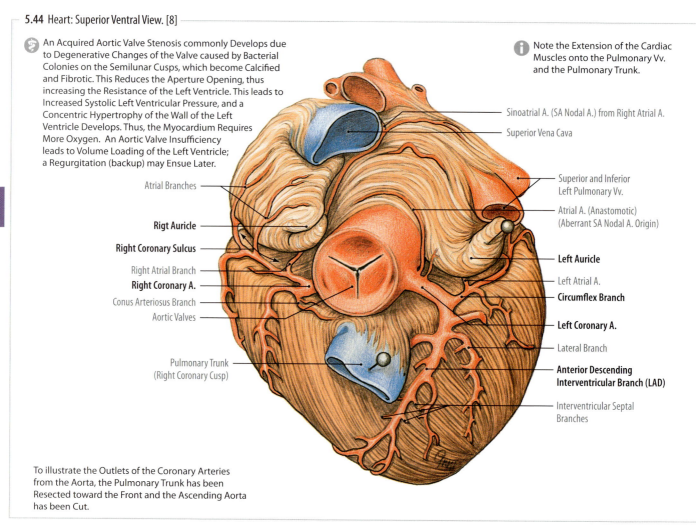

- Atrial Branches
- **Rigt Auricle**
- **Right Coronary Sulcus**
- Right Atrial Branch
- **Right Coronary A.**
- Conus Arteriosus Branch
- Aortic Valves
- Pulmonary Trunk (Right Coronary Cusp)

- Sinoatrial A. (SA Nodal A.) from Right Atrial A.
- Superior Vena Cava
- Superior and Inferior Left Pulmonary Vv.
- Atrial A. (Anastomotic) (Aberrant SA Nodal A. Origin)
- **Left Auricle**
- Left Atrial A.
- **Circumflex Branch**
- **Left Coronary A.**
- Lateral Branch
- **Anterior Descending Interventricular Branch (LAD)**
- Interventricular Septal Branches

To illustrate the Outlets of the Coronary Arteries from the Aorta, the Pulmonary Trunk has been Resected toward the Front and the Ascending Aorta has been Cut.

5.45 Heart and Cardiac Valves: Superior Dorsal View. [6]

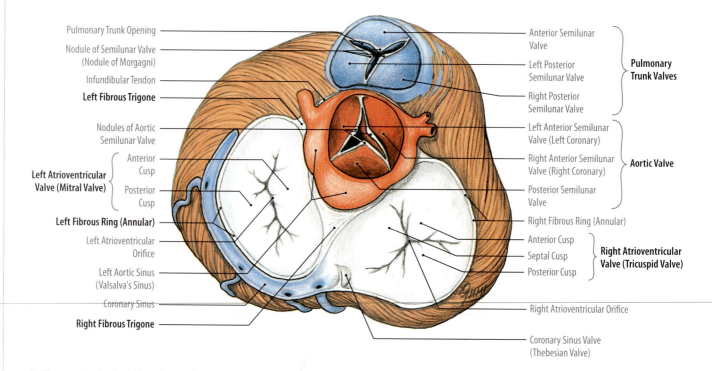

- Pulmonary Trunk Opening
- Nodule of Semilunar Valve (Nodule of Morgagni)
- Infundibular Tendon
- **Left Fibrous Trigone**
- Nodules of Aortic Semilunar Valve
- **Left Atrioventricular Valve (Mitral Valve)** — Anterior Cusp / Posterior Cusp
- **Left Fibrous Ring (Annular)**
- Left Atrioventricular Orifice
- Left Aortic Sinus (Valsalva's Sinus)
- Coronary Sinus
- **Right Fibrous Trigone**

- Anterior Semilunar Valve
- Left Posterior Semilunar Valve
- Right Posterior Semilunar Valve
- **Pulmonary Trunk Valves**
- Left Anterior Semilunar Valve (Left Coronary)
- Right Anterior Semilunar Valve (Right Coronary)
- Posterior Semilunar Valve
- **Aortic Valve**
- Right Fibrous Ring (Annular)
- Anterior Cusp
- Septal Cusp
- Posterior Cusp
- **Right Atrioventricular Valve (Tricuspid Valve)**
- Right Atrioventricular Orifice
- Coronary Sinus Valve (Thebesian Valve)

To illustrate the Cardiac Valves, the Cardiac Skeleton with the Right and Left Fibrous Trigone, the Fibrous Rings, and the Atria have been Removed.

5.46 Corrosion Preparation of the Heart and the Blood Vessels: Ventral View. [76]

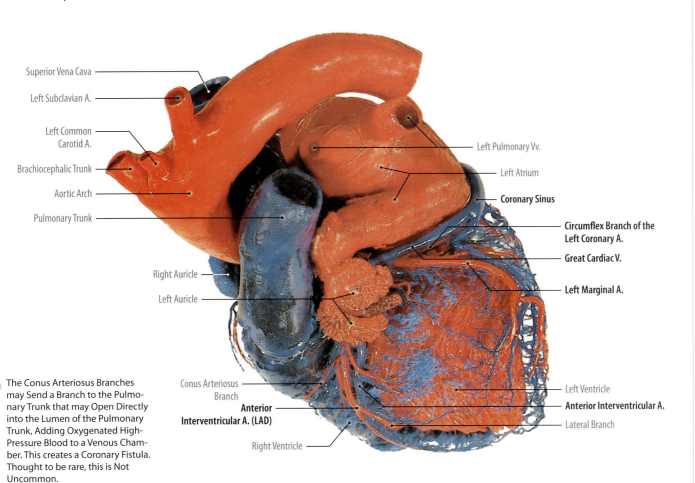

Superior Vena Cava

Left Subclavian A.

Left Common Carotid A.

Brachiocephalic Trunk

Aortic Arch

Pulmonary Trunk

Left Pulmonary Vv.

Left Atrium

Coronary Sinus

Circumflex Branch of the Left Coronary A.

Great Cardiac V.

Left Marginal A.

Right Auricle

Left Auricle

Conus Arteriosus Branch

Anterior Interventricular A. (LAD)

Right Ventricle

Left Ventricle

Anterior Interventricular A.

Lateral Branch

ℹ The Conus Arteriosus Branches may Send a Branch to the Pulmonary Trunk that may Open Directly into the Lumen of the Pulmonary Trunk, Adding Oxygenated High-Pressure Blood to a Venous Chamber. This creates a Coronary Fistula. Thought to be rare, this is Not Uncommon.

5.47 Heart and Vessels: Transversal Plane. [75]

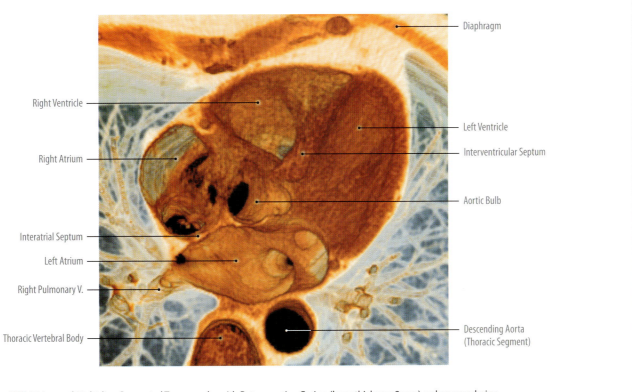

Right Ventricle

Right Atrium

Interatrial Septum

Left Atrium

Right Pulmonary V.

Thoracic Vertebral Body

Diaphragm

Left Ventricle

Interventricular Septum

Aortic Bulb

Descending Aorta (Thoracic Segment)

Electrocardiogram- (ECG-) Triggered Multislice Computed Tomography with Retrospective Gating (layer thickness 2 mm), volume rendering.

Thoracic Cavity

Heart: Imaging

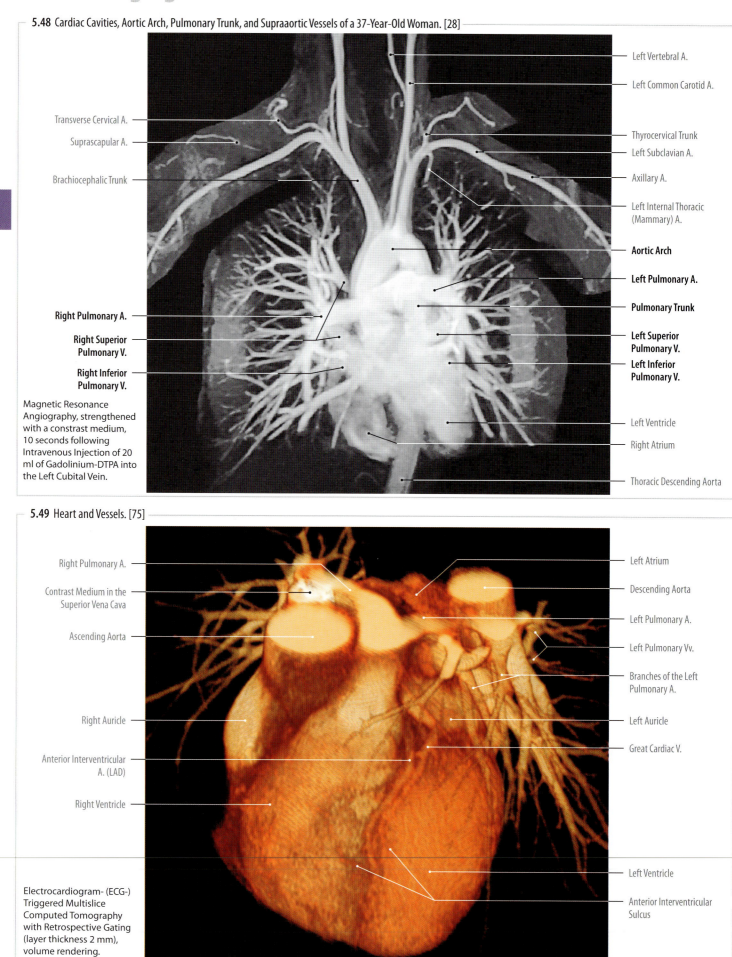

5.48 Cardiac Cavities, Aortic Arch, Pulmonary Trunk, and Supraaortic Vessels of a 37-Year-Old Woman. [28]

Transverse Cervical A.

Suprascapular A.

Brachiocephalic Trunk

Right Pulmonary A.

Right Superior Pulmonary V.

Right Inferior Pulmonary V.

Left Vertebral A.

Left Common Carotid A.

Thyrocervical Trunk

Left Subclavian A.

Axillary A.

Left Internal Thoracic (Mammary) A.

Aortic Arch

Left Pulmonary A.

Pulmonary Trunk

Left Superior Pulmonary V.

Left Inferior Pulmonary V.

Left Ventricle

Right Atrium

Thoracic Descending Aorta

Magnetic Resonance Angiography, strengthened with a constrast medium, 10 seconds following Intravenous Injection of 20 ml of Gadolinium-DTPA into the Left Cubital Vein.

5.49 Heart and Vessels. [75]

Right Pulmonary A.

Contrast Medium in the Superior Vena Cava

Ascending Aorta

Right Auricle

Anterior Interventricular A. (LAD)

Right Ventricle

Left Atrium

Descending Aorta

Left Pulmonary A.

Left Pulmonary Vv.

Branches of the Left Pulmonary A.

Left Auricle

Great Cardiac V.

Left Ventricle

Anterior Interventricular Sulcus

Electrocardiogram- (ECG-) Triggered Multislice Computed Tomography with Retrospective Gating (layer thickness 2 mm), volume rendering.

Interior of the Heart

5.50a,b Frontal Section through the Middle Section of a Vertically Positioned Heart. [48]

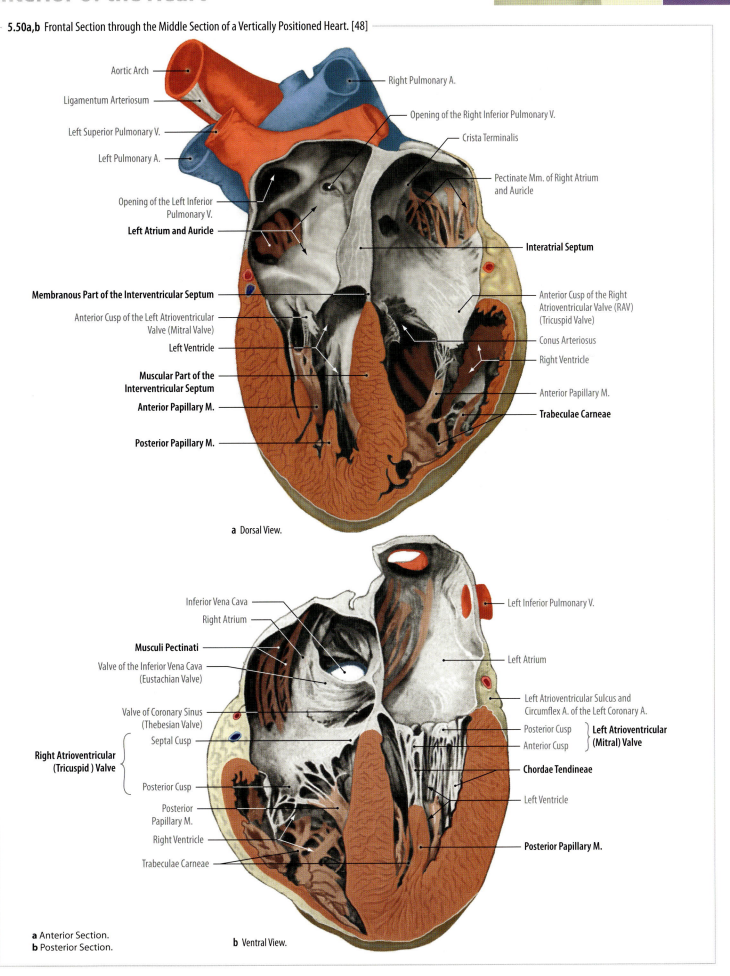

Aortic Arch

Ligamentum Arteriosum

Left Superior Pulmonary V.

Left Pulmonary A.

Opening of the Left Inferior Pulmonary V.

Left Atrium and Auricle

Membranous Part of the Interventricular Septum

Anterior Cusp of the Left Atrioventricular Valve (Mitral Valve)

Left Ventricle

Muscular Part of the Interventricular Septum

Anterior Papillary M.

Posterior Papillary M.

Right Pulmonary A.

Opening of the Right Inferior Pulmonary V.

Crista Terminalis

Pectinate Mm. of Right Atrium and Auricle

Interatrial Septum

Anterior Cusp of the Right Atrioventricular Valve (RAV) (Tricuspid Valve)

Conus Arteriosus

Right Ventricle

Anterior Papillary M.

Trabeculae Carneae

a Dorsal View.

Inferior Vena Cava

Right Atrium

Musculi Pectinati

Valve of the Inferior Vena Cava (Eustachian Valve)

Valve of Coronary Sinus (Thebesian Valve)

Septal Cusp

Right Atrioventricular (Tricuspid) Valve

Posterior Cusp

Posterior Papillary M.

Right Ventricle

Trabeculae Carneae

Left Inferior Pulmonary V.

Left Atrium

Left Atrioventricular Sulcus and Circumflex A. of the Left Coronary A.

Posterior Cusp

Anterior Cusp

Left Atrioventricular (Mitral) Valve

Chordae Tendineae

Left Ventricle

Posterior Papillary M.

a Anterior Section.
b Posterior Section.

b Ventral View.

Thoracic Cavity

Interior of the Heart

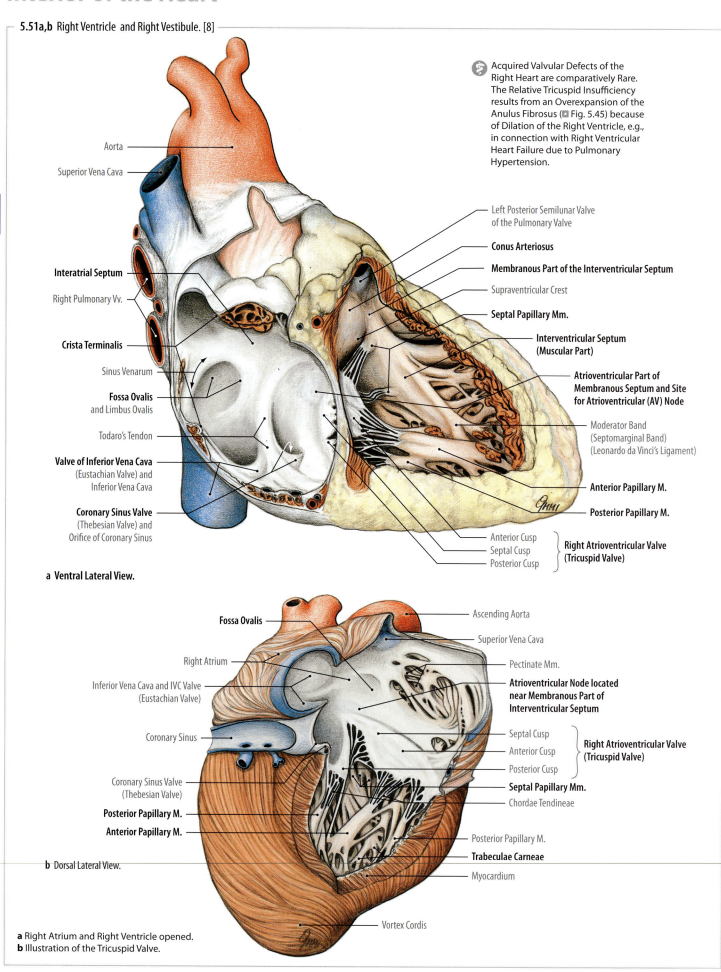

Acquired Valvular Defects of the Right Heart are comparatively Rare. The Relative Tricuspid Insufficiency results from an Overexpansion of the Anulus Fibrosus (■ Fig. 5.45) because of Dilation of the Right Ventricle, e.g., in connection with Right Ventricular Heart Failure due to Pulmonary Hypertension.

Aorta

Superior Vena Cava

Left Posterior Semilunar Valve of the Pulmonary Valve

Conus Arteriosus

Interatrial Septum

Membranous Part of the Interventricular Septum

Supraventricular Crest

Right Pulmonary Vv.

Septal Papillary Mm.

Crista Terminalis

Interventricular Septum (Muscular Part)

Sinus Venarum

Fossa Ovalis and Limbus Ovalis

Atrioventricular Part of Membranous Septum and Site for Atrioventricular (AV) Node

Todaro's Tendon

Moderator Band (Septomarginal Band) (Leonardo da Vinci's Ligament)

Valve of Inferior Vena Cava (Eustachian Valve) and Inferior Vena Cava

Anterior Papillary M.

Coronary Sinus Valve (Thebesian Valve) and Orifice of Coronary Sinus

Posterior Papillary M.

Anterior Cusp
Septal Cusp
Posterior Cusp

Right Atrioventricular Valve (Tricuspid Valve)

a Ventral Lateral View.

Ascending Aorta

Fossa Ovalis

Superior Vena Cava

Right Atrium

Pectinate Mm.

Inferior Vena Cava and IVC Valve (Eustachian Valve)

Atrioventricular Node located near Membranous Part of Interventricular Septum

Coronary Sinus

Septal Cusp
Anterior Cusp
Posterior Cusp

Right Atrioventricular Valve (Tricuspid Valve)

Coronary Sinus Valve (Thebesian Valve)

Septal Papillary Mm.

Chordae Tendineae

Posterior Papillary M.

Anterior Papillary M.

Posterior Papillary M.

Trabeculae Carneae

b Dorsal Lateral View.

Myocardium

Vortex Cordis

a Right Atrium and Right Ventricle opened.
b Illustration of the Tricuspid Valve.

Interior of the Heart

5.52a,b Left Ventricle and Left Atrium. [6]

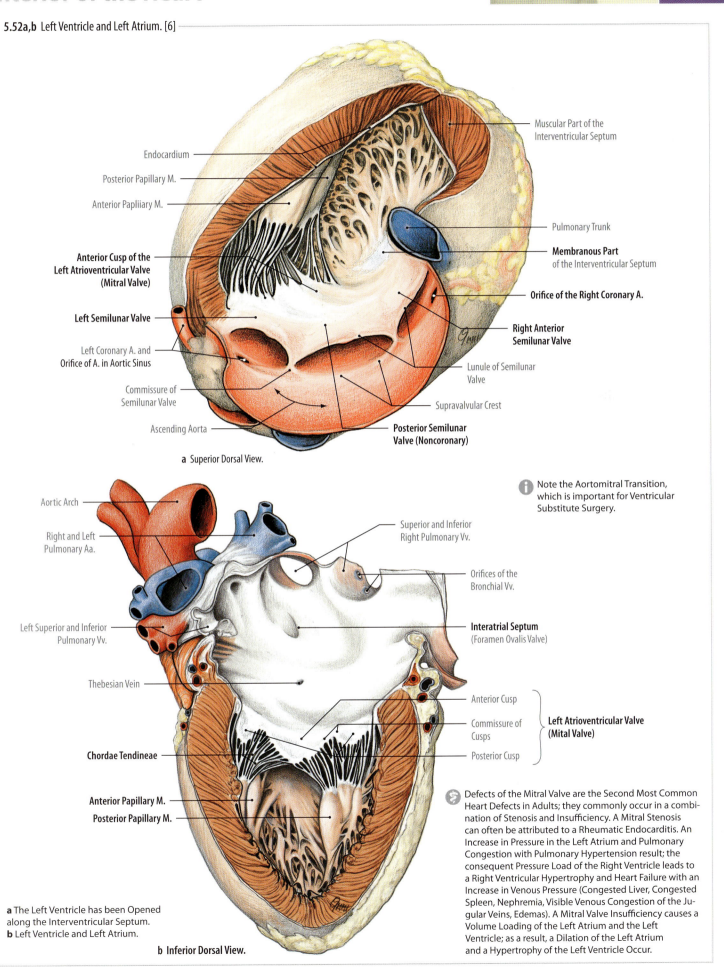

Muscular Part of the Interventricular Septum

Endocardium

Posterior Papillary M.

Anterior Papiliary M.

Pulmonary Trunk

Membranous Part of the Interventricular Septum

Anterior Cusp of the Left Atrioventricular Valve (Mitral Valve)

Orifice of the Right Coronary A.

Left Semilunar Valve

Right Anterior Semilunar Valve

Left Coronary A. and Orifice of A. in Aortic Sinus

Lunule of Semilunar Valve

Commissure of Semilunar Valve

Ascending Aorta

Supravalvular Crest

Posterior Semilunar Valve (Noncoronary)

a Superior Dorsal View.

Note the Aortomitral Transition, which is important for Ventricular Substitute Surgery.

Aortic Arch

Right and Left Pulmonary Aa.

Superior and Inferior Right Pulmonary Vv.

Orifices of the Bronchial Vv.

Left Superior and Inferior Pulmonary Vv.

Interatrial Septum (Foramen Ovalis Valve)

Thebesian Vein

Anterior Cusp

Commissure of Cusps

Left Atrioventricular Valve (Mital Valve)

Chordae Tendineae

Posterior Cusp

Anterior Papillary M.
Posterior Papillary M.

Defects of the Mitral Valve are the Second Most Common Heart Defects in Adults; they commonly occur in a combination of Stenosis and Insufficiency. A Mitral Stenosis can often be attributed to a Rheumatic Endocarditis. An Increase in Pressure in the Left Atrium and Pulmonary Congestion with Pulmonary Hypertension result; the consequent Pressure Load of the Right Ventricle leads to a Right Ventricular Hypertrophy and Heart Failure with an Increase in Venous Pressure (Congested Liver, Congested Spleen, Nephremia, Visible Venous Congestion of the Jugular Veins, Edemas). A Mitral Valve Insufficiency causes a Volume Loading of the Left Atrium and the Left Ventricle; as a result, a Dilation of the Left Atrium and a Hypertrophy of the Left Ventricle Occur.

a The Left Ventricle has been Opened along the Interventricular Septum.
b Left Ventricle and Left Atrium.

b Inferior Dorsal View.

Thoracic Cavity

5.53 Innervation of the Heart and the Lungs: Ventral View. [23, 34]

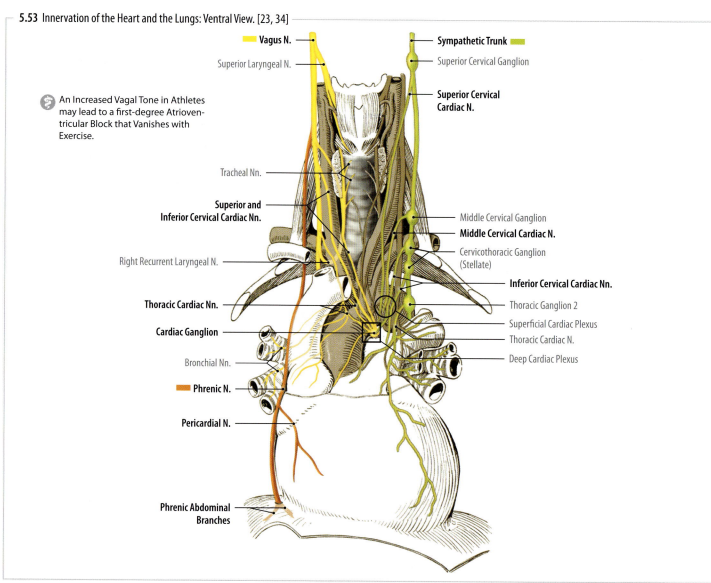

An Increased Vagal Tone in Athletes may lead to a first-degree Atrioventricular Block that Vanishes with Exercise.

Vagus N.

Superior Laryngeal N.

Tracheal Nn.

Superior and Inferior Cervical Cardiac Nn.

Right Recurrent Laryngeal N.

Thoracic Cardiac Nn.

Cardiac Ganglion

Bronchial Nn.

Phrenic N.

Pericardial N.

Phrenic Abdominal Branches

Sympathetic Trunk

Superior Cervical Ganglion

Superior Cervical Cardiac N.

Middle Cervical Ganglion

Middle Cervical Cardiac N.

Cervicothoracic Ganglion (Stellate)

Inferior Cervical Cardiac Nn.

Thoracic Ganglion 2

Superficial Cardiac Plexus

Thoracic Cardiac N.

Deep Cardiac Plexus

5.54 Conduction System of the Heart: Superior Dorsal View. [83]

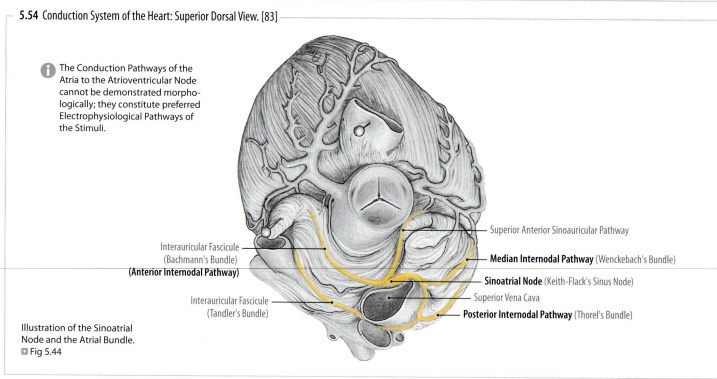

The Conduction Pathways of the Atria to the Atrioventricular Node cannot be demonstrated morphologically; they constitute preferred Electrophysiological Pathways of the Stimuli.

Interauricular Fascicule (Bachmann's Bundle)

(Anterior Internodal Pathway)

Interauricular Fascicule (Tandler's Bundle)

Superior Anterior Sinoauricular Pathway

Median Internodal Pathway (Wenckebach's Bundle)

Sinoatrial Node (Keith-Flack's Sinus Node)

Superior Vena Cava

Posterior Internodal Pathway (Thorel's Bundle)

Illustration of the Sinoatrial Node and the Atrial Bundle.
Fig 5.44

5

5.55a,b Conduction System of the Heart. [83]

The Cardiac Cycle is controlled by the Sinoatrial Node (Pacemaker) of the Heart. The Atrial Muscle sends Impulses to the Atrioventricular (AV) Node then to the Bundle of His, which splits into the Right and Left Bundle Branches of the Conductive System of the heart. Heart Rhythm Irregularity, Arrhythmia, can originate in either the Atria or AV Node. If it originates in the Atria, it is Supraventricular Tachycardia (SVT). If it originates in the AV Node, it is Ventricular Tachycardia (VT).

Excitation Changes may Originate from the Sinoatrial Node (Normotopic Excitation Changes) or Develop Outside of the Sinoatrial Node from either the Atria or the AV Node (Heterotopic Excitation– Supraventricular or Ventricular if it does not involve the above). For example, a Sinoatrial Block (SA Block) with Delayed Conduction or Total Conduction Disruption from the Sinoatrial Node to the Atrial Muscles can occur. In an Atrioventricular Block (AV Block), the blocking may be Located Above (Type 1) or Within and Below (Type 2) the Bundle of His. One speaks of Intraventricular Blockings (Bundle Branch Block) if the blocking is located Below the Bundle of His to either the Right or Left Bundle.

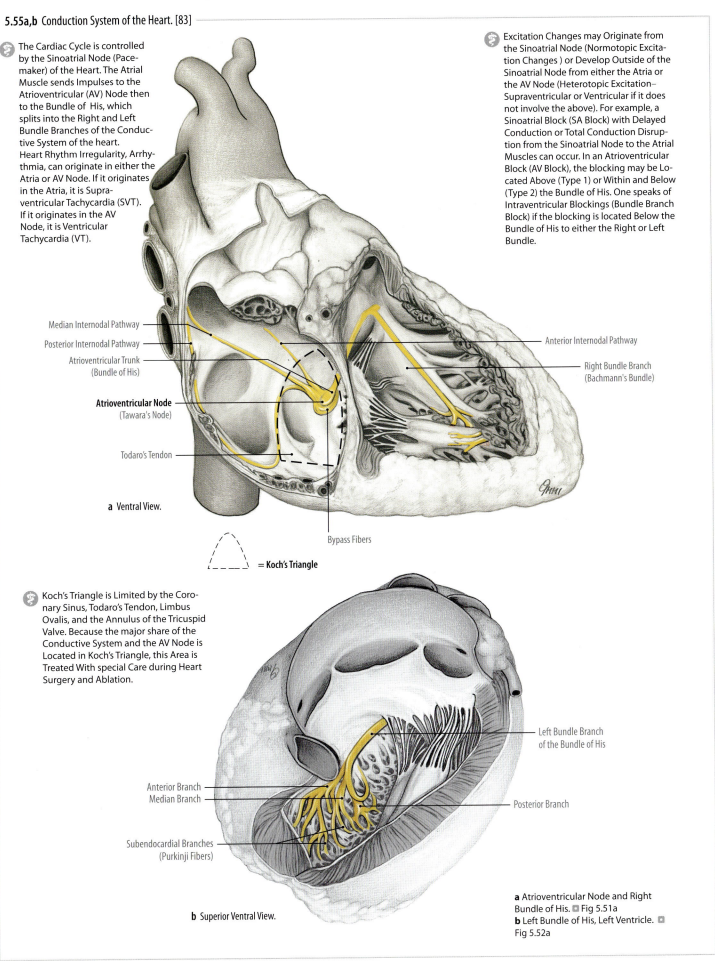

Median Internodal Pathway

Posterior Internodal Pathway

Atrioventricular Trunk (Bundle of His)

Atrioventricular Node (Tawara's Node)

Todaro's Tendon

Anterior Internodal Pathway

Right Bundle Branch (Bachmann's Bundle)

a Ventral View.

Bypass Fibers

= **Koch's Triangle**

Koch's Triangle is Limited by the Coronary Sinus, Todaro's Tendon, Limbus Ovalis, and the Annulus of the Tricuspid Valve. Because the major share of the Conductive System and the AV Node is Located in Koch's Triangle, this Area is Treated With special Care during Heart Surgery and Ablation.

Left Bundle Branch of the Bundle of His

Anterior Branch
Median Branch

Posterior Branch

Subendocardial Branches (Purkinji Fibers)

b Superior Ventral View.

a Atrioventricular Node and Right Bundle of His. ◻ Fig 5.51a
b Left Bundle of His, Left Ventricle. ◻ Fig 5.52a

Thoracic Cavity

5.56 Right Pleural Cavity with Parietal Pleura and Organ Profile of the Mediastinum: Right Lateral View. [15]

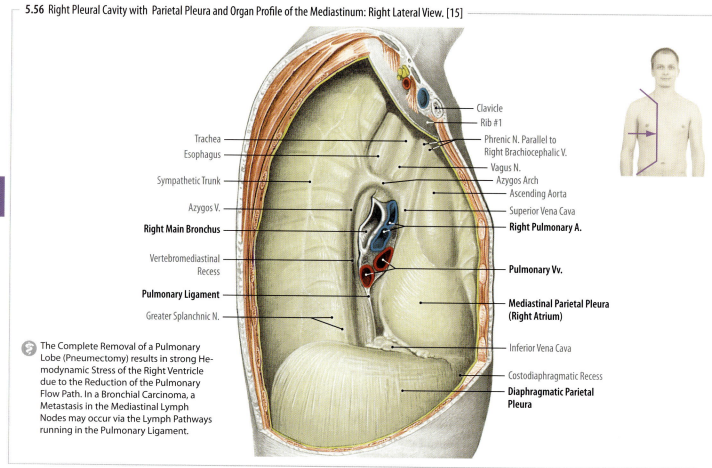

Clavicle
Rib #1
Trachea
Esophagus
Phrenic N. Parallel to Right Brachiocephalic V.
Vagus N.
Sympathetic Trunk
Azygos Arch
Ascending Aorta
Azygos V.
Superior Vena Cava
Right Main Bronchus
Right Pulmonary A.
Vertebromediastinal Recess
Pulmonary Vv.
Pulmonary Ligament
Mediastinal Parietal Pleura (Right Atrium)
Greater Splanchnic N.
Inferior Vena Cava
Costodiaphragmatic Recess
Diaphragmatic Parietal Pleura

The Complete Removal of a Pulmonary Lobe (Pneumectomy) results in strong Hemodynamic Stress of the Right Ventricle due to the Reduction of the Pulmonary Flow Path. In a Bronchial Carcinoma, a Metastasis in the Mediastinal Lymph Nodes may occur via the Lymph Pathways running in the Pulmonary Ligament.

5.57 Left Pleural Cavity with Parietal Pleura and Organ Profile of the Mediastinum: Left Lateral View. [15]

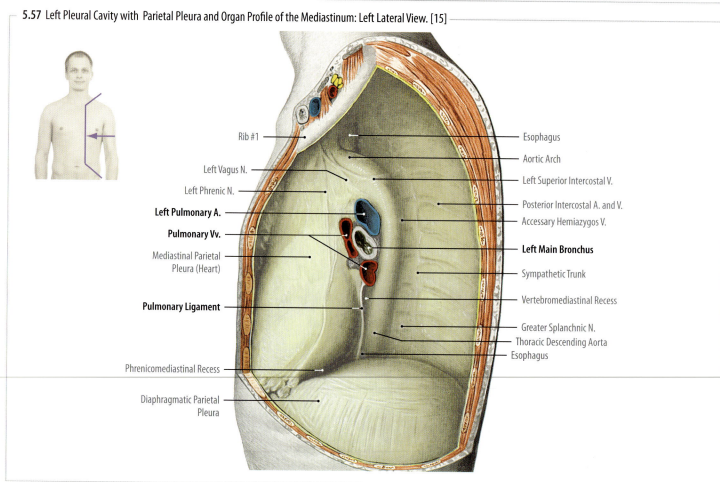

Rib #1
Esophagus
Aortic Arch
Left Vagus N.
Left Superior Intercostal V.
Left Phrenic N.
Left Pulmonary A.
Posterior Intercostal A. and V.
Accessary Hemiazygos V.
Pulmonary Vv.
Left Main Bronchus
Mediastinal Parietal Pleura (Heart)
Sympathetic Trunk
Vertebromediastinal Recess
Pulmonary Ligament
Greater Splanchnic N.
Thoracic Descending Aorta
Esophagus
Phrenicomediastinal Recess
Diaphragmatic Parietal Pleura

5.58 Pathways of the Interior Thoracic Wall and the Organs of the Mediastinum: Right Side, Right Lateral View. [15]

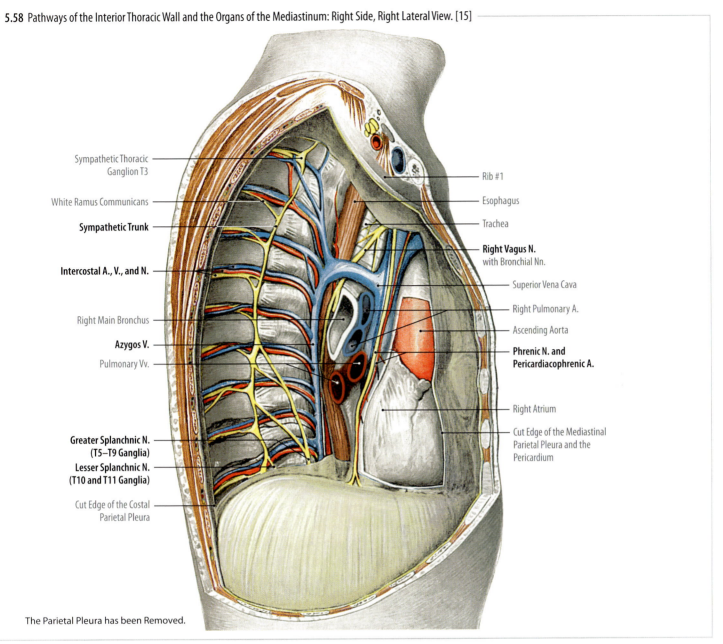

Sympathetic Thoracic Ganglion T3

White Ramus Communicans

Sympathetic Trunk

Intercostal A., V., and N.

Right Main Bronchus

Azygos V.

Pulmonary Vv.

Greater Splanchnic N. (T5–T9 Ganglia)

Lesser Splanchnic N. (T10 and T11 Ganglia)

Cut Edge of the Costal Parietal Pleura

Rib #1

Esophagus

Trachea

Right Vagus N. with Bronchial Nn.

Superior Vena Cava

Right Pulmonary A.

Ascending Aorta

Phrenic N. and Pericardiacophrenic A.

Right Atrium

Cut Edge of the Mediastinal Parietal Pleura and the Pericardium

The Parietal Pleura has been Removed.

5.59 Illustration of the Segmental (Red) and Suprasegmental (Green) Sympathetic Fibers. [77]

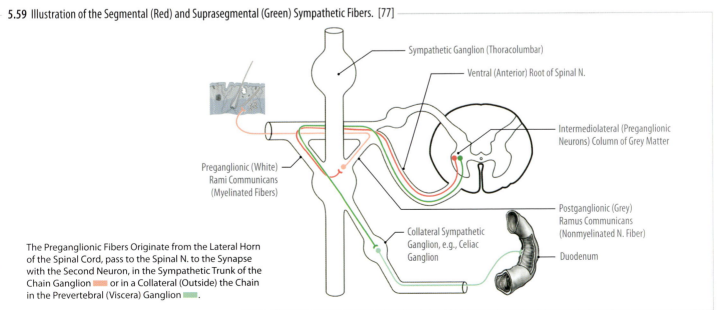

Sympathetic Ganglion (Thoracolumbar)

Ventral (Anterior) Root of Spinal N.

Intermediolateral (Preganglionic Neurons) Column of Grey Matter

Preganglionic (White) Rami Communicans (Myelinated Fibers)

Collateral Sympathetic Ganglion, e.g., Celiac Ganglion

Postganglionic (Grey) Ramus Communicans (Nonmyelinated N. Fiber)

Duodenum

The Preganglionic Fibers Originate from the Lateral Horn of the Spinal Cord, pass to the Spinal N. to the Synapse with the Second Neuron, in the Sympathetic Trunk of the Chain Ganglion ▬ or in a Collateral (Outside) the Chain in the Prevertebral (Viscera) Ganglion ▬ .

Thoracic Cavity

5.60 Pathways of the Interior Thoracic Wall and Organs of the Mediastinum: Left Lateral View. [15]

In cases of Bronchial Carcinoma and an Aneurysm in the area of the Aortic Arch or (less commonly) of the Brachiocephalic Trunk, Damage to the Recurrent Laryngeal N. and a Paralysis of the Interior Laryngeal Mm. may occur. A typical symptom would be a Hoarse Voice.

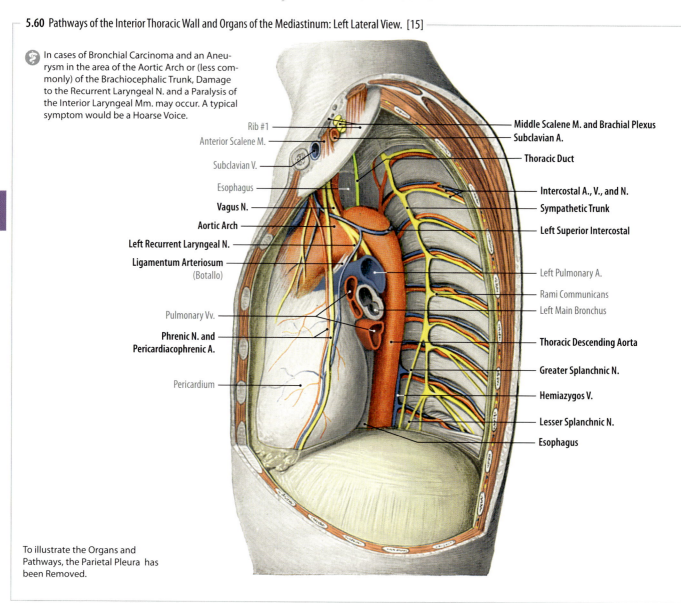

Rib #1
Anterior Scalene M.
Subclavian V.
Esophagus
Vagus N.
Aortic Arch
Left Recurrent Laryngeal N.
Ligamentum Arteriosum
(Botallo)
Pulmonary Vv.
Phrenic N. and
Pericardiacophrenic A.
Pericardium

Middle Scalene M. and Brachial Plexus
Subclavian A.
Thoracic Duct
Intercostal A., V., and N.
Sympathetic Trunk
Left Superior Intercostal
Left Pulmonary A.
Rami Communicans
Left Main Bronchus
Thoracic Descending Aorta
Greater Splanchnic N.
Hemiazygos V.
Lesser Splanchnic N.
Esophagus

To illustrate the Organs and Pathways, the Parietal Pleura has been Removed.

5.61a–c Azygos V. and Hemiazygos V. (◻ Fig. 5.3), Variants. [a 48; b, c 17]

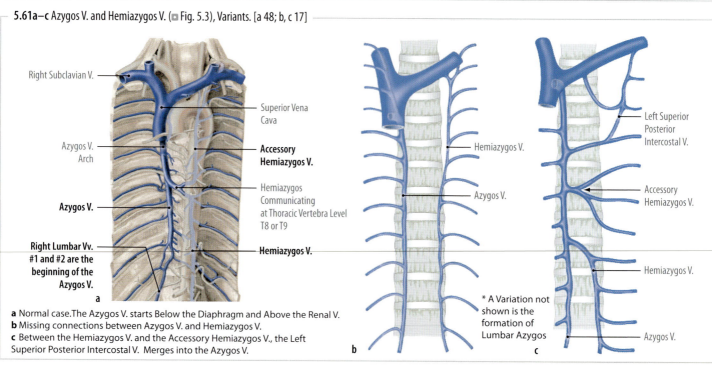

Right Subclavian V.
Azygos V. Arch
Azygos V.
Right Lumbar Vv. #1 and #2 are the beginning of the Azygos V.

Superior Vena Cava
Accessory Hemiazygos V.
Hemiazygos Communicating at Thoracic Vertebra Level T8 or T9
Hemiazygos V.

Left Superior Posterior Intercostal V.
Hemiazygos V.
Azygos V.
Accessory Hemiazygos V.
Hemiazygos V.
Azygos V.

a

* A Variation not shown is the formation of Lumbar Azygos

b   c

a Normal case. The Azygos V. starts Below the Diaphragm and Above the Renal V.
b Missing connections between Azygos V. and Hemiazygos V.
c Between the Hemiazygos V. and the Accessory Hemiazygos V., the Left Superior Posterior Intercostal V. Merges into the Azygos V.

Organs of the Posterior Mediastinum

5.62 a Organs of the Posterior Mediastinum: Ventral View. To Illustrate the Course of the Thoracic Duct, Part of the Esophagus Has Been Resected.
  b Variant Course of the Thoracic Duct. [a 15, b 17]

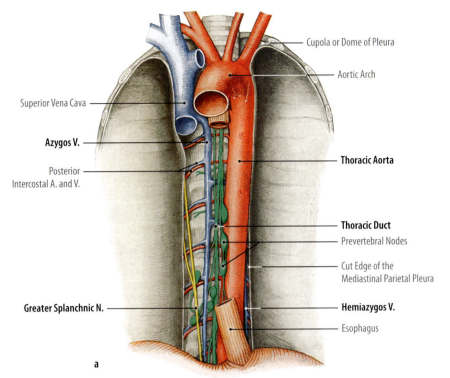

Cupola or Dome of Pleura

Aortic Arch

Superior Vena Cava

Azygos V.

Posterior
Intercostal A. and V.

Thoracic Aorta

Thoracic Duct
Prevertebral Nodes

Cut Edge of the
Mediastinal Parietal Pleura

Greater Splanchnic N.

Hemiazygos V.

Esophagus

Left
Venous Angle

ⓘ The Thoracic Duct
turns Left at the
T4–T5 Vertebra (due
to Tracheal Bifur-
cation), then turns
Superiorly and runs in
the Groove between
the Esophagus and
the Vertebral Bodies
to Drain at the Jugular
V. Junction.

First Lumbar Vertebra

a

b In ~30–40% of all cases, the Thoracic Duct
runs on the Left Edge of the Spinal Column.

Ⓢ Damage to the Thoracic Duct Causes
Lymph to Leak into the Pleural Thoracic Cavity (Chylothorax).

5.63 Organs of the Posterior Mediastinum: Dorsal View. [15]

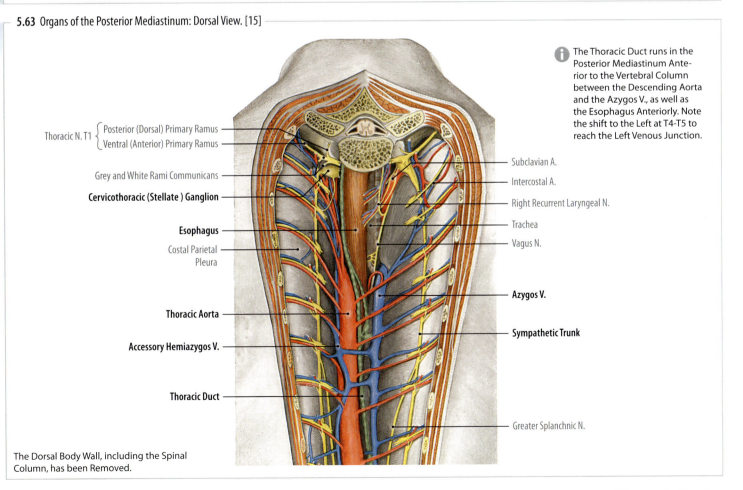

ⓘ The Thoracic Duct runs in the
Posterior Mediastinum Anterior to the Vertebral Column
between the Descending Aorta
and the Azygos V., as well as
the Esophagus Anteriorly. Note
the shift to the Left at T4–T5 to
reach the Left Venous Junction.

Thoracic N. T1 { Posterior (Dorsal) Primary Ramus
                 Ventral (Anterior) Primary Ramus

Grey and White Rami Communicans

Cervicothoracic (Stellate) Ganglion

Esophagus

Costal Parietal
Pleura

Thoracic Aorta

Accessory Hemiazygos V.

Thoracic Duct

Subclavian A.

Intercostal A.

Right Recurrent Laryngeal N.

Trachea

Vagus N.

Azygos V.

Sympathetic Trunk

Greater Splanchnic N.

The Dorsal Body Wall, including the Spinal
Column, has been Removed.

Thoracic Cavity

5.64 Pleural Cavities and Posterior Mediastinum: Dorsal View (Compare Fig. 5.164). [1]

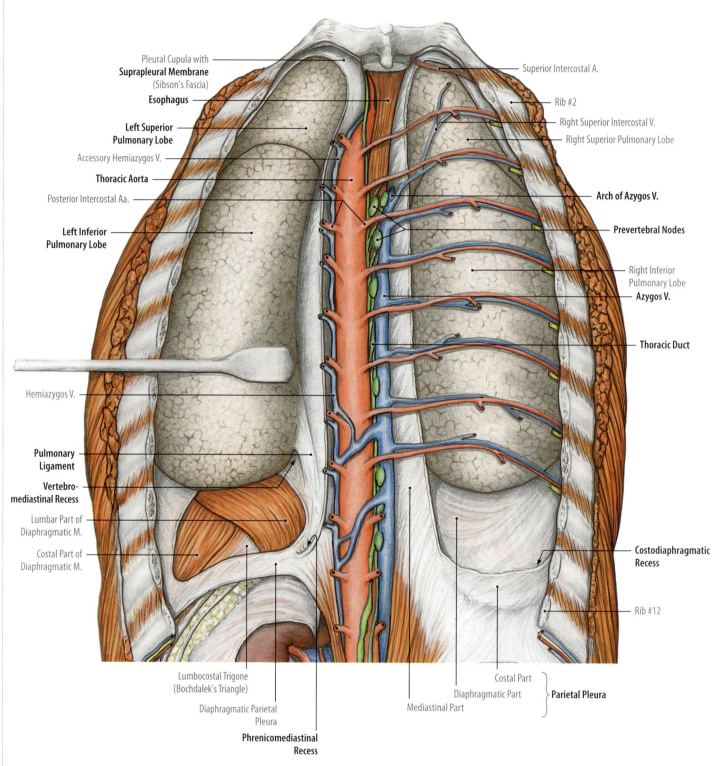

Pleural Cupula with
Suprapleural Membrane
(Sibson's Fascia)

Esophagus

**Left Superior
Pulmonary Lobe**

Accessory Hemiazygos V.

Thoracic Aorta

Posterior Intercostal Aa.

**Left Inferior
Pulmonary Lobe**

Hemiazygos V.

**Pulmonary
Ligament**

**Vertebro-
mediastinal Recess**

Lumbar Part of
Diaphragmatic M.

Costal Part of
Diaphragmatic M.

Superior Intercostal A.

Rib #2

Right Superior Intercostal V.

Right Superior Pulmonary Lobe

Arch of Azygos V.

Prevertebral Nodes

Right Inferior
Pulmonary Lobe

Azygos V.

Thoracic Duct

**Costodiaphragmatic
Recess**

Rib #12

Lumbocostal Trigone
(Bochdalek's Triangle)

Diaphragmatic Parietal
Pleura

**Phrenicomediastinal
Recess**

Costal Part

Diaphragmatic Part   } **Parietal Pleura**

Mediastinal Part

An Emergency Drainage of the Pleural Cavity, e.g., to remove a life-threatening Increase in Intrapleural Pressure (Tension Pneumothorax), is carried out in the 2nd Intercostal Space in the Area Anterior to the Mid-Clavicular Line. For a Hydroythorax, the Drainage is done at the 4th–5th Intercostal Space at the Mid-Axillary Line. Following a Skin Incision, the Muscle Fibers of the Serratus Anterior M. and Intercostales Mm. are Bluntly Split Apart with a pair of scissors, or if necessary, with a finger, and a Drain is Inserted into the Pleural Cavity. The Catheter is placed in a Container Under 10 cm of Water to Prevent Air Sucking Through and Creating Negative Pressure.

The Dorsal Body Wall and the
Spinal Column have been Removed.

5.65a,b Lung, Hilum of the Lung, and Mediastinum: Dorsal View. [1]

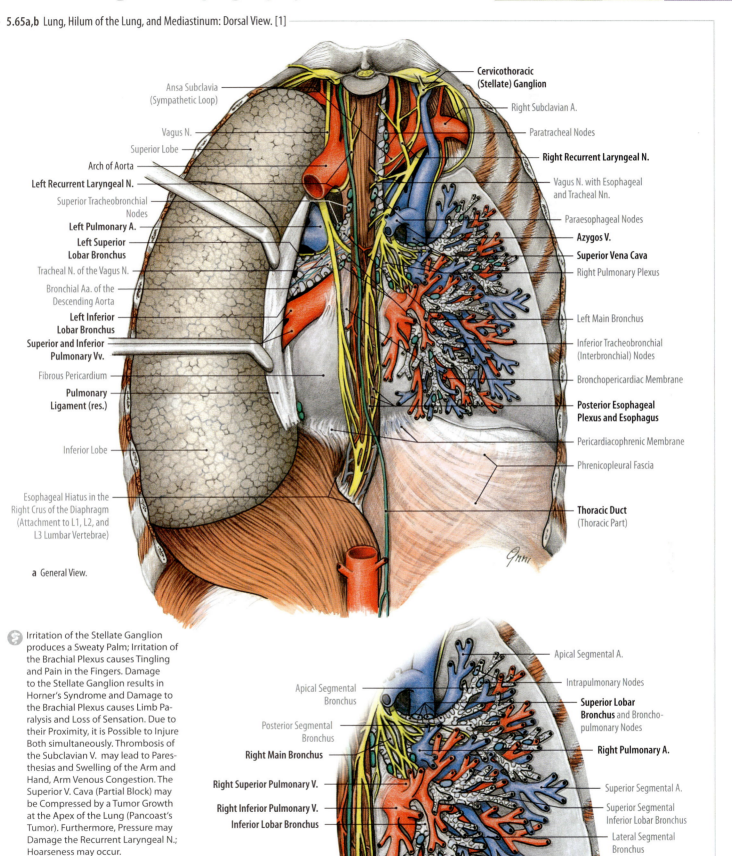

Ansa Subclavia (Sympathetic Loop)

Vagus N.

Superior Lobe

Arch of Aorta

Left Recurrent Laryngeal N.

Superior Tracheobronchial Nodes

Left Pulmonary A.

Left Superior Lobar Bronchus

Tracheal N. of the Vagus N.

Bronchial Aa. of the Descending Aorta

Left Inferior Lobar Bronchus

Superior and Inferior Pulmonary Vv.

Fibrous Pericardium

Pulmonary Ligament (res.)

Inferior Lobe

Esophageal Hiatus in the Right Crus of the Diaphragm (Attachment to L1, L2, and L3 Lumbar Vertebrae)

Cervicothoracic (Stellate) Ganglion

Right Subclavian A.

Paratracheal Nodes

Right Recurrent Laryngeal N.

Vagus N. with Esophageal and Tracheal Nn.

Paraesophageal Nodes

Azygos V.

Superior Vena Cava

Right Pulmonary Plexus

Left Main Bronchus

Inferior Tracheobronchial (Interbronchial) Nodes

Bronchopericardiac Membrane

Posterior Esophageal Plexus and Esophagus

Pericardiacophrenic Membrane

Phrenicopleural Fascia

Thoracic Duct (Thoracic Part)

a General View.

Irritation of the Stellate Ganglion produces a Sweaty Palm; Irritation of the Brachial Plexus causes Tingling and Pain in the Fingers. Damage to the Stellate Ganglion results in Horner's Syndrome and Damage to the Brachial Plexus causes Limb Paralysis and Loss of Sensation. Due to their Proximity, it is Possible to Injure Both simultaneously. Thrombosis of the Subclavian V. may lead to Paresthesias and Swelling of the Arm and Hand, Arm Venous Congestion. The Superior V. Cava (Partial Block) may be Compressed by a Tumor Growth at the Apex of the Lung (Pancoast's Tumor). Furthermore, Pressure may Damage the Recurrent Laryngeal N.; Hoarseness may occur.

a On the Left Side, the Lung and part of the Parietal Pleura have been Preserved. On the Right Side, the Bronchi, Pulmonary Arteries, and Pulmonary Veins have been Dissected.

Apical Segmental Bronchus

Posterior Segmental Bronchus

Right Main Bronchus

Right Superior Pulmonary V.

Right Inferior Pulmonary V.

Inferior Lobar Bronchus

Posterior Basal Segmental Bronchus

Inferior Basal Segmental A.

Apical Segmental A.

Intrapulmonary Nodes

Superior Lobar Bronchus and Bronchopulmonary Nodes

Right Pulmonary A.

Superior Segmental A.

Superior Segmental Inferior Lobar Bronchus

Lateral Segmental Bronchus

Lateral Basal Segmental A.

b Section.

Thoracic Cavity

5.66 Left Pleural Dome: Left Inferior View. [8]

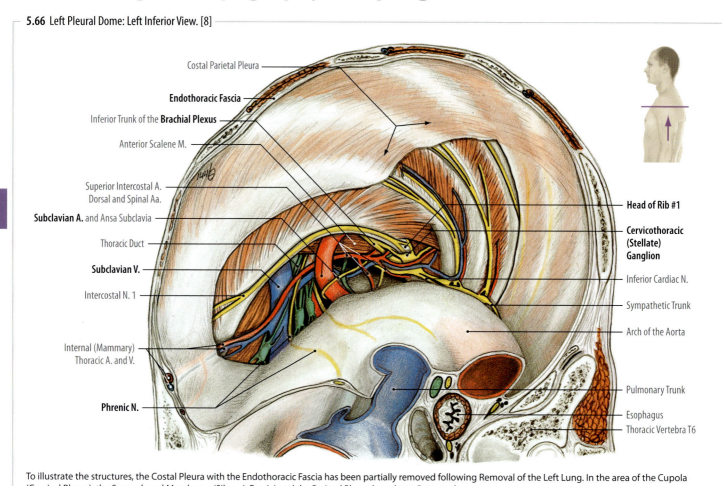

Costal Parietal Pleura

Endothoracic Fascia

Inferior Trunk of the **Brachial Plexus**

Anterior Scalene M.

Superior Intercostal A.
Dorsal and Spinal Aa.

Subclavian A. and Ansa Subclavia

Thoracic Duct

Subclavian V.

Intercostal N. 1

Internal (Mammary)
Thoracic A. and V.

Phrenic N.

Head of Rib #1

**Cervicothoracic
(Stellate)
Ganglion**

Inferior Cardiac N.

Sympathetic Trunk

Arch of the Aorta

Pulmonary Trunk

Esophagus

Thoracic Vertebra T6

To illustrate the structures, the Costal Pleura with the Endothoracic Fascia has been partially removed following Removal of the Left Lung. In the area of the Cupola (Cervical Pleura), the Suprapleural Membrane (Sibson's Fascia) and the Parietal Pleura have been Removed.

5.67 Posterior Mediastinum with Esophagus and Hili of the Lung: Ventral View. [15]

Due to the Close Topographic Relationship of the Aortic Arch and the Bronchial Tree, Widespread Aneurysms of the Aortic Arch Push on the Left Main Bronchus, which becomes a Visible Tugging of the Larynx with Each Pulse (Oliver-Cardarell Sign).

Hoarseness may be a Symptom of an Aneurysm in the area of the Aortic Arch following Compression of the Left Recurrent Laryngeal N.

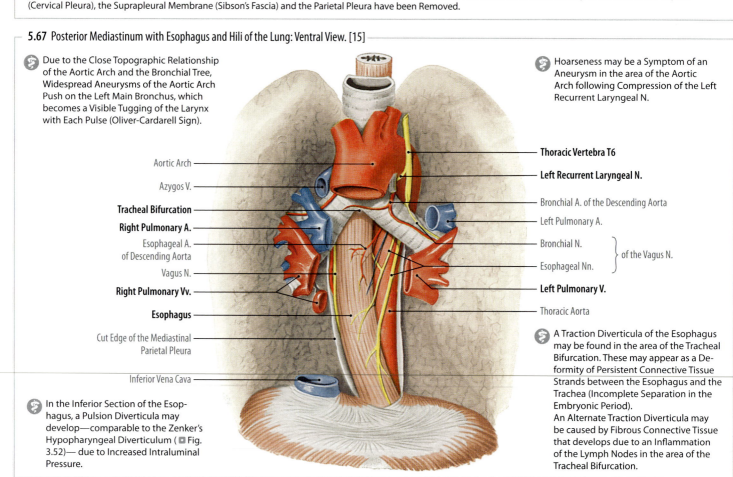

Aortic Arch

Azygos V.

Tracheal Bifurcation

Right Pulmonary A.

Esophageal A.
of Descending Aorta

Vagus N.

Right Pulmonary Vv.

Esophagus

Cut Edge of the Mediastinal
Parietal Pleura

Inferior Vena Cava

Thoracic Vertebra T6

Left Recurrent Laryngeal N.

Bronchial A. of the Descending Aorta

Left Pulmonary A.

Bronchial N.

Esophageal Nn.

} of the Vagus N.

Left Pulmonary V.

Thoracic Aorta

In the Inferior Section of the Esophagus, a Pulsion Diverticula may develop—comparable to the Zenker's Hypopharyngeal Diverticulum (Fig. 3.52)— due to Increased Intraluminal Pressure.

A Traction Diverticula of the Esophagus may be found in the area of the Tracheal Bifurcation. These may appear as a Deformity of Persistent Connective Tissue Strands between the Esophagus and the Trachea (Incomplete Separation in the Embryonic Period).
An Alternate Traction Diverticula may be caused by Fibrous Connective Tissue that develops due to an Inflammation of the Lymph Nodes in the area of the Tracheal Bifurcation.

Esophagus

5.68 Esophagus, Blood Supply, Lymphatic and Esophageal Sphincters: Ventral View. [57]

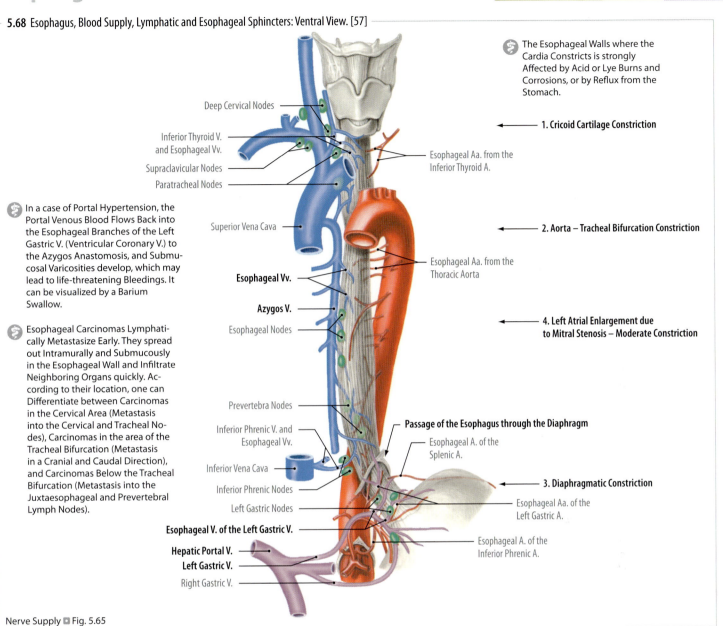

The Esophageal Walls where the Cardia Constricts is strongly Affected by Acid or Lye Burns and Corrosions, or by Reflux from the Stomach.

In a case of Portal Hypertension, the Portal Venous Blood Flows Back into the Esophageal Branches of the Left Gastric V. (Ventricular Coronary V.) to the Azygos Anastomosis, and Submucosal Varicosities develop, which may lead to life-threatening Bleedings. It can be visualized by a Barium Swallow.

Esophageal Carcinomas Lymphatically Metastasize Early. They spread out Intramurally and Submucously in the Esophageal Wall and Infiltrate Neighboring Organs quickly. According to their location, one can Differentiate between Carcinomas in the Cervical Area (Metastasis into the Cervical and Tracheal Nodes), Carcinomas in the area of the Tracheal Bifurcation (Metastasis in a Cranial and Caudal Direction), and Carcinomas Below the Tracheal Bifurcation (Metastasis into the Juxtaesophageal and Prevertebral Lymph Nodes).

Deep Cervical Nodes

Inferior Thyroid V. and Esophageal Vv.

Supraclavicular Nodes

Paratracheal Nodes

Esophageal Aa. from the Inferior Thyroid A.

Superior Vena Cava

1. Cricoid Cartilage Constriction

Esophageal Aa. from the Thoracic Aorta

Esophageal Vv.

Azygos V.

Esophageal Nodes

2. Aorta – Tracheal Bifurcation Constriction

4. Left Atrial Enlargement due to Mitral Stenosis – Moderate Constriction

Prevertebra Nodes

Inferior Phrenic V. and Esophageal Vv.

Inferior Vena Cava

Inferior Phrenic Nodes

Left Gastric Nodes

Esophageal V. of the Left Gastric V.

Hepatic Portal V.

Left Gastric V.

Right Gastric V.

Passage of the Esophagus through the Diaphragm

Esophageal A. of the Splenic A.

3. Diaphragmatic Constriction

Esophageal Aa. of the Left Gastric A.

Esophageal A. of the Inferior Phrenic A.

Nerve Supply ◻ Fig. 5.65

5.69 Course of the Esophagus through the Esophageal Hiatus of the Diaphragm. [57]

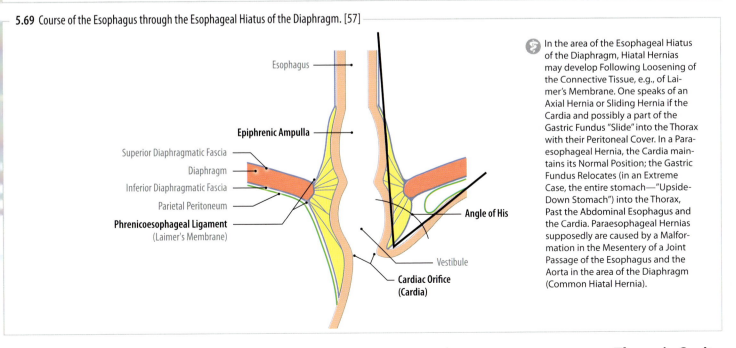

Esophagus

Epiphrenic Ampulla

Superior Diaphragmatic Fascia

Diaphragm

Inferior Diaphragmatic Fascia

Parietal Peritoneum

Phrenicoesophageal Ligament
(Laimer's Membrane)

Angle of His

Vestibule

Cardiac Orifice
(Cardia)

In the area of the Esophageal Hiatus of the Diaphragm, Hiatal Hernias may develop Following Loosening of the Connective Tissue, e.g., of Laimer's Membrane. One speaks of an Axial Hernia or Sliding Hernia if the Cardia and possibly a part of the Gastric Fundus "Slide" into the Thorax with their Peritoneal Cover. In a Paraesophageal Hernia, the Cardia maintains its Normal Position; the Gastric Fundus Relocates (in an Extreme Case, the entire stomach—"Upside-Down Stomach") into the Thorax, Past the Abdominal Esophagus and the Cardia. Paraesophageal Hernias supposedly are caused by a Malformation in the Mesentery of a Joint Passage of the Esophagus and the Aorta in the area of the Diaphragm (Common Hiatal Hernia).

Thoracic Cavity

Diaphragm

5.70 Diaphragm and Structures Passing Through the Diaphragm: Superior View. [18]

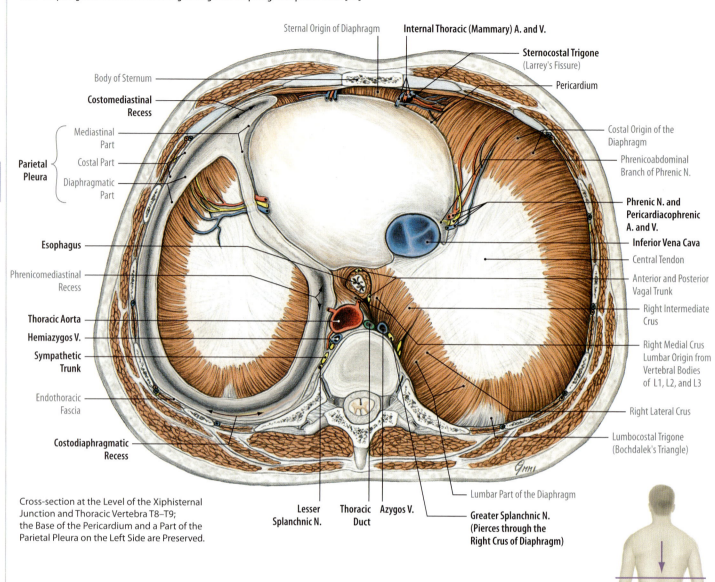

Sternal Origin of Diaphragm

Internal Thoracic (Mammary) A. and V.

Sternocostal Trigone
(Larrey's Fissure)

Body of Sternum

Pericardium

Costomediastinal Recess

Costal Origin of the Diaphragm

Mediastinal Part

Phrenicoabdominal Branch of Phrenic N.

Parietal Pleura

Costal Part

Diaphragmatic Part

Phrenic N. and Pericardiacophrenic A. and V.

Esophagus

Inferior Vena Cava

Central Tendon

Phrenicomediastinal Recess

Anterior and Posterior Vagal Trunk

Right Intermediate Crus

Thoracic Aorta

Hemiazygos V.

Right Medial Crus Lumbar Origin from Vertebral Bodies of L1, L2, and L3

Sympathetic Trunk

Endothoracic Fascia

Right Lateral Crus

Costodiaphragmatic Recess

Lumbocostal Trigone (Bochdalek's Triangle)

Lumbar Part of the Diaphragm

Cross-section at the Level of the Xiphisternal Junction and Thoracic Vertebra T8–T9; the Base of the Pericardium and a Part of the Parietal Pleura on the Left Side are Preserved.

Lesser Splanchnic N.   **Thoracic Duct**   **Azygos V.**

Greater Splanchnic N. (Pierces through the Right Crus of Diaphragm)

Structures Passing Through the Diaphragm and Their Respective Points of Passage	
Points of Passage	**Structures Passing Through**
Sternocostal Trigone (Larrey's Fissure)	Superior Epigastric of Internal Thoracic A. and V.
In the Central Tendon Foramen Vena Cava	Inferior Vena Cava Right Phrenicoabdominal N. (Phrenic N.)
Esophageal Hiatus in the Right Medial Crus	Esophagus, Vagal Nn., Esophageal Vv., Phrenicoabdominal N. of the Left Phrenic N. (Variable through the Central Tendon or through the Lumbar Origin of the Diaphragm)
Aortic Hiatus between the Right and Left Crus Median of the Lumbar Origin	Aorta, Thoracic Duct Azygos V. (Right Side) Hemiazygos V. (Left Side)
Gaps through the Medial (right and left) Crus of the Lumbar Origin	Greater Splanchnic N., Lesser Splanchnic N., and Least Splanchnic N.
Gap under Medial Arcuate Ligament	Sympathetic Trunk

▢ Fig. 4.40b   ▢ Fig. 5.71

5.71 Diaphragm with Structures Passing Through It: Inferior View (Abdominal). [57]

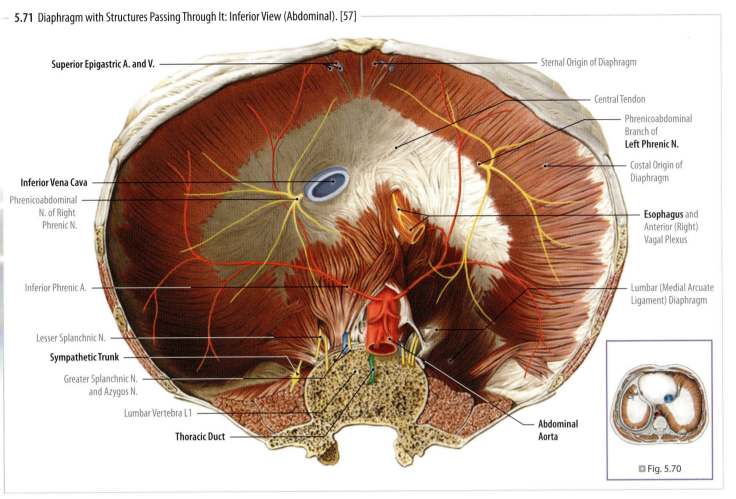

Superior Epigastric A. and V.

Sternal Origin of Diaphragm

Central Tendon

Phrenicoabdominal Branch of **Left Phrenic N.**

Inferior Vena Cava

Costal Origin of Diaphragm

Phrenicoabdominal N. of Right Phrenic N.

Esophagus and Anterior (Right) Vagal Plexus

Inferior Phrenic A.

Lumbar (Medial Arcuate Ligament) Diaphragm

Lesser Splanchnic N.

Sympathetic Trunk

Greater Splanchnic N. and Azygos N.

Lumbar Vertebra L1

Abdominal Aorta

Thoracic Duct

□ Fig. 5.70

5.72 Position of the Epigastric Organs and Their Projection onto the Anterior Abdominal Wall. [57]

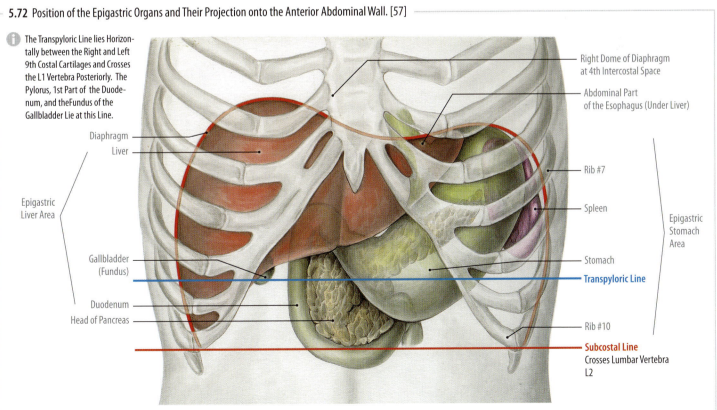

ⓘ The Transpyloric Line lies Horizontally between the Right and Left 9th Costal Cartilages and Crosses the L1 Vertebra Posteriorly. The Pylorus, 1st Part of the Duodenum, and the Fundus of the Gallbladder Lie at this Line.

Right Dome of Diaphragm at 4th Intercostal Space

Abdominal Part of the Esophagus (Under Liver)

Diaphragm

Liver

Rib #7

Spleen

Epigastric Liver Area

Epigastric Stomach Area

Gallbladder (Fundus)

Stomach

Transpyloric Line

Duodenum

Head of Pancreas

Rib #10

Subcostal Line Crosses Lumbar Vertebra L2

ⓘ The Upper Abdomen Extends Superiorly into the Thoracic Area to the Inferior Surface of the Diaphragm at the Vertebra level T8–T9 and the Lower Edge of Rib #10 (Subcostal Line). The Subcostal Line is between the 10 Costal Cartilages and It Crosses the L2 Vertebra Body and the Upper Edge of the Third Part of the Duodenum. The area encompasses what is called the Epigastric Area.

Abdominal Cavity

5.73 Parietal Peritoneum and Visceral Peritoneum (Framed in Red). [23, 80]

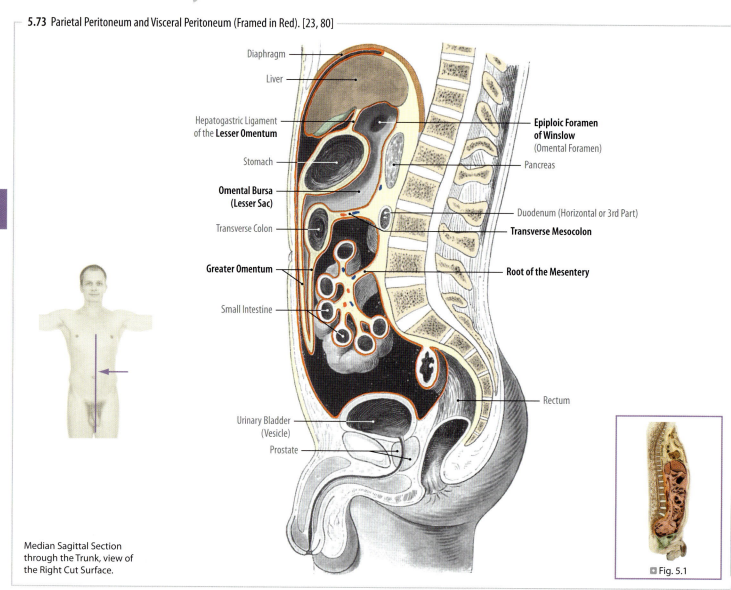

Diaphragm

Liver

Hepatogastric Ligament of the **Lesser Omentum**

Stomach

Omental Bursa (Lesser Sac)

Transverse Colon

Greater Omentum

Small Intestine

Epiploic Foramen of Winslow (Omental Foramen)

Pancreas

Duodenum (Horizontal or 3rd Part)

Transverse Mesocolon

Root of the Mesentery

Rectum

Urinary Bladder (Vesicle)

Prostate

Median Sagittal Section through the Trunk, view of the Right Cut Surface.

▣ Fig. 5.1

5.74 Parietal Peritoneum and Visceral Peritoneum (Framed in Red). [15]

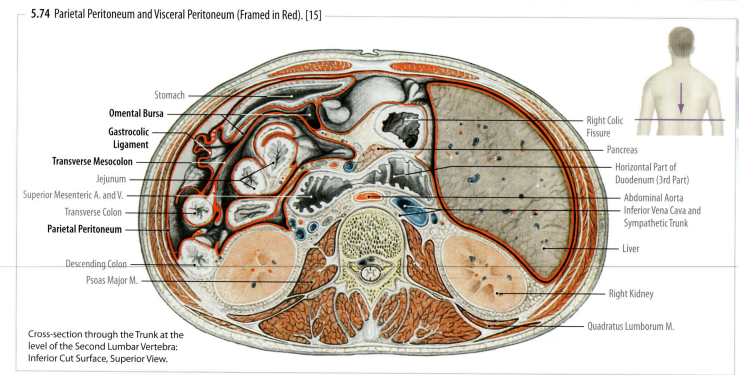

Stomach

Omental Bursa

Gastrocolic Ligament

Transverse Mesocolon

Jejunum

Superior Mesenteric A. and V.

Transverse Colon

Parietal Peritoneum

Descending Colon

Psoas Major M.

Right Colic Fissure

Pancreas

Horizontal Part of Duodenum (3rd Part)

Abdominal Aorta

Inferior Vena Cava and Sympathetic Trunk

Liver

Right Kidney

Quadratus Lumborum M.

Cross-section through the Trunk at the level of the Second Lumbar Vertebra: Inferior Cut Surface, Superior View.

5.75a,b Liver. [57]

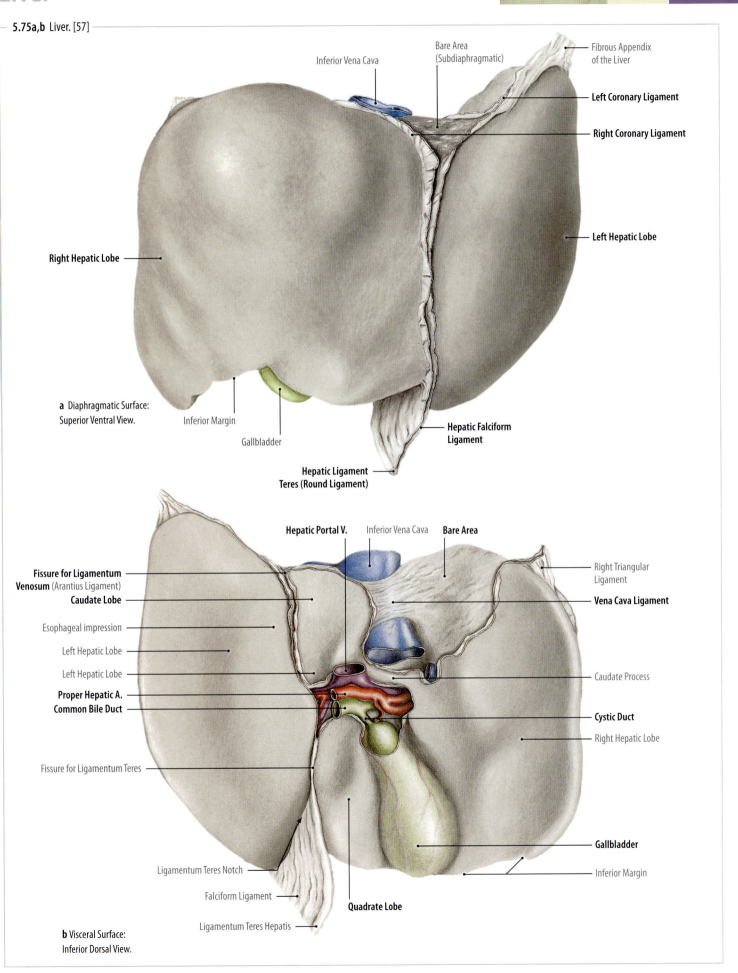

Inferior Vena Cava

Bare Area
(Subdiaphragmatic)

Fibrous Appendix
of the Liver

Left Coronary Ligament

Right Coronary Ligament

Left Hepatic Lobe

Right Hepatic Lobe

a Diaphragmatic Surface:
Superior Ventral View.

Inferior Margin

Gallbladder

Hepatic Falciform Ligament

Hepatic Ligament Teres (Round Ligament)

Hepatic Portal V.   Inferior Vena Cava   **Bare Area**

Right Triangular
Ligament

Fissure for Ligamentum Venosum (Arantius Ligament)

Caudate Lobe

Vena Cava Ligament

Esophageal impression

Left Hepatic Lobe

Left Hepatic Lobe

Caudate Process

Proper Hepatic A.
Common Bile Duct

Cystic Duct

Right Hepatic Lobe

Fissure for Ligamentum Teres

Gallbladder

Inferior Margin

Ligamentum Teres Notch

Falciform Ligament

Quadrate Lobe

Ligamentum Teres Hepatis

b Visceral Surface:
Inferior Dorsal View.

Abdominal Cavity

Liver: Topography · Vessels, Bile Ducts

5.76 Topographical Relationship of the Liver to Neighboring Organs, Border Fissures. [2, 57]

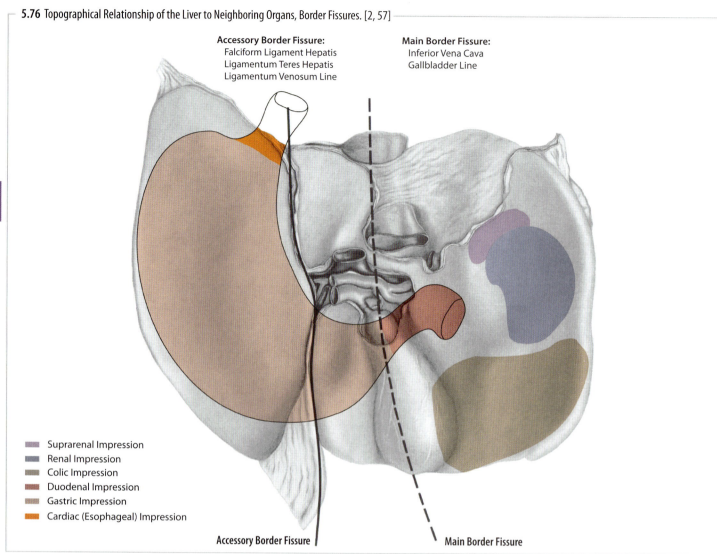

Accessory Border Fissure:
Falciform Ligament Hepatis
Ligamentum Teres Hepatis
Ligamentum Venosum Line

Main Border Fissure:
Inferior Vena Cava
Gallbladder Line

Suprarenal Impression
Renal Impression
Colic Impression
Duodenal Impression
Gastric Impression
Cardiac (Esophageal) Impression

Accessory Border Fissure

Main Border Fissure

5.77 Liver, Diaphragmatic Surface: Superior Ventral View. [57]

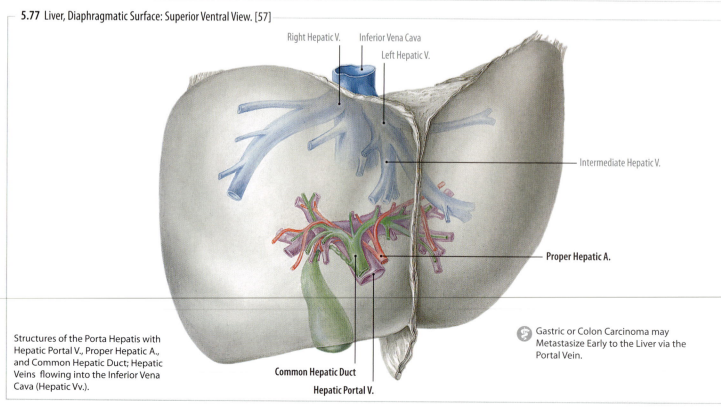

Right Hepatic V.

Inferior Vena Cava

Left Hepatic V.

Intermediate Hepatic V.

Proper Hepatic A.

Common Hepatic Duct

Hepatic Portal V.

Structures of the Porta Hepatis with
Hepatic Portal V., Proper Hepatic A.,
and Common Hepatic Duct; Hepatic
Veins flowing into the Inferior Vena
Cava (Hepatic Vv.).

Gastric or Colon Carcinoma may
Metastasize Early to the Liver via the
Portal Vein.

5.78 Vessels and Bile Ducts of the Liver: Visceral Surface, Dorsal View. [88]

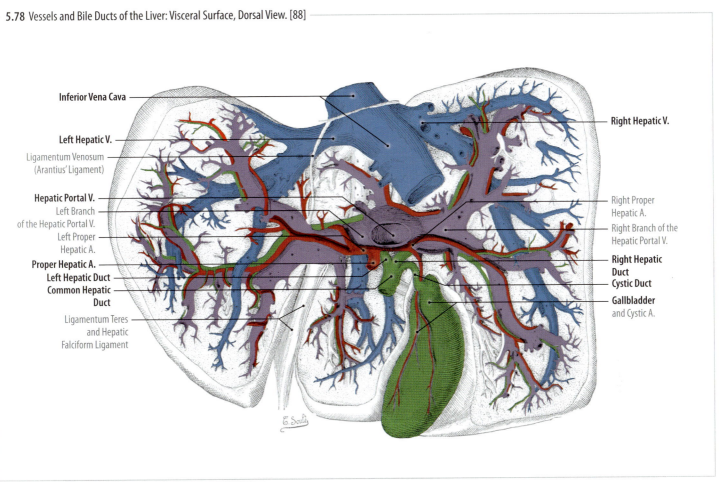

Inferior Vena Cava

Left Hepatic V.

Ligamentum Venosum
(Arantius' Ligament)

Hepatic Portal V.
Left Branch
of the Hepatic Portal V.
Left Proper
Hepatic A.
Proper Hepatic A.
Left Hepatic Duct
Common Hepatic
Duct
Ligamentum Teres
and Hepatic
Falciform Ligament

Right Hepatic V.

Right Proper
Hepatic A.
Right Branch of the
Hepatic Portal V.
Right Hepatic
Duct
Cystic Duct
Gallbladder
and Cystic A.

5.79 Blood Supply of Liver and Stomach, Structures in the Hepatoduodenal Ligament and the Porta Hepatis: Ventral View. [15]

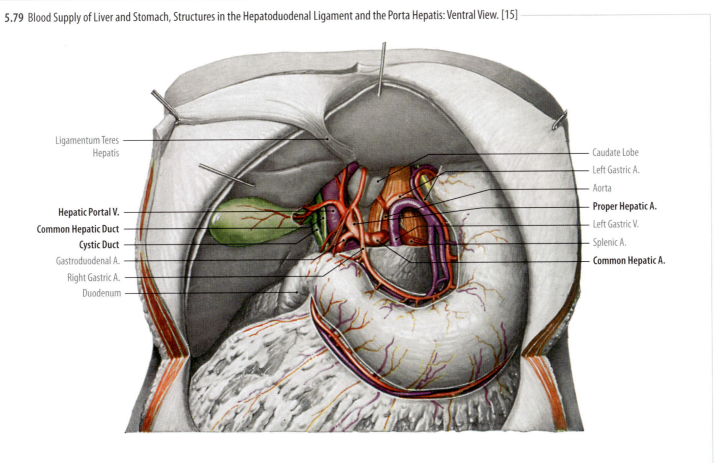

Ligamentum Teres
Hepatis

Hepatic Portal V.
Common Hepatic Duct
Cystic Duct
Gastroduodenal A.
Right Gastric A.
Duodenum

Caudate Lobe
Left Gastric A.
Aorta
Proper Hepatic A.
Left Gastric V.
Splenic A.
Common Hepatic A.

Abdominal Cavity

5.80 Liver, Segmentation (Portal Vein Segments): Ventral View. [57]

The Segmentation of the Liver permits the Partial Resection of Hepatic Tissue while Protecting the Supply of the Remaining Segments of the Liver.

A Right Ventricular Heart Failure leads to a Congested Liver due to the Backflow of the Blood of the Vena Cava and the Hepatic Vv. Edema in the Ankles is a visible symptom.

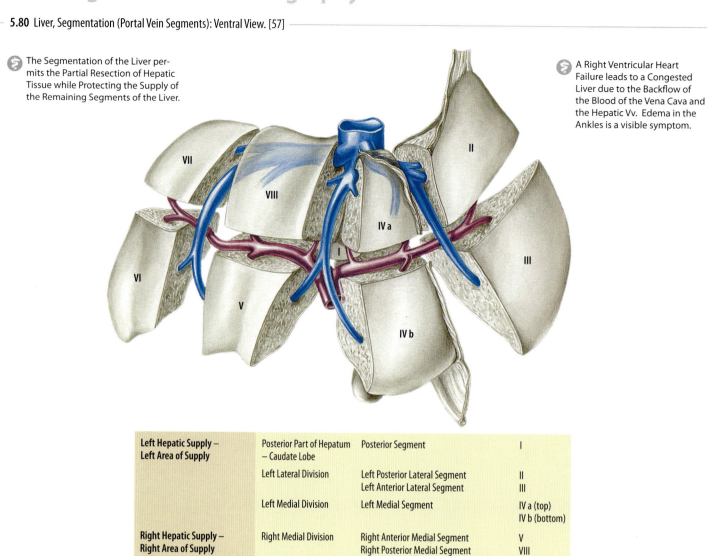

Left Hepatic Supply – Left Area of Supply	Posterior Part of Hepatum – Caudate Lobe	Posterior Segment	I
	Left Lateral Division	Left Posterior Lateral Segment	II
		Left Anterior Lateral Segment	III
	Left Medial Division	Left Medial Segment	IV a (top) IV b (bottom)
Right Hepatic Supply – Right Area of Supply	Right Medial Division	Right Anterior Medial Segment	V
		Right Posterior Medial Segment	VIII
	Right Lateral Division	Right Anterior Lateral Segment	VI
		Right Posterior Lateral Segment	VII

5.81 Transjugular Portography of a 60-Year-Old Woman. [28]

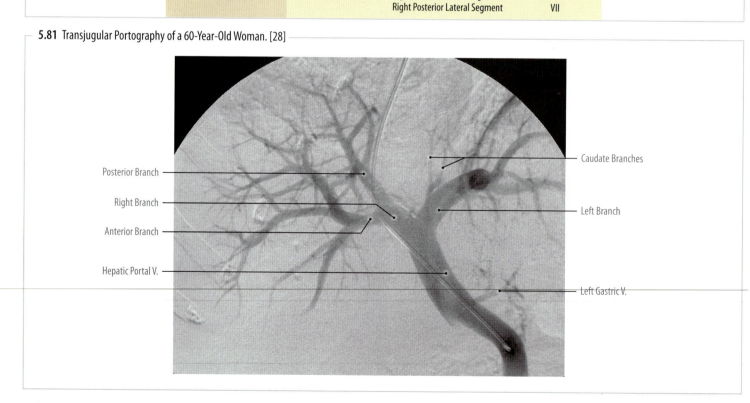

Posterior Branch

Right Branch

Anterior Branch

Hepatic Portal V.

Caudate Branches

Left Branch

Left Gastric V.

Portal Circulation

5.82a,b Portal Circulation and Portocaval Anastomoses. [a 48]

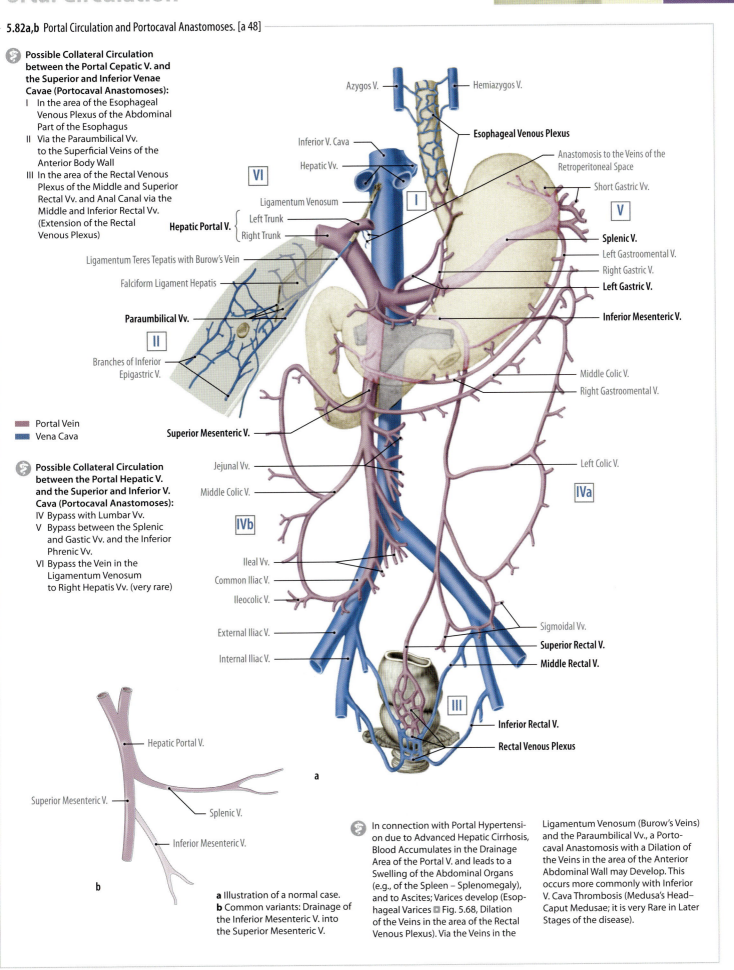

Possible Collateral Circulation between the Portal Cepatic V. and the Superior and Inferior Venae Cavae (Portocaval Anastomoses):

I   In the area of the Esophageal Venous Plexus of the Abdominal Part of the Esophagus

II Via the Paraumbilical Vv. to the Superficial Veins of the Anterior Body Wall

III In the area of the Rectal Venous Plexus of the Middle and Superior Rectal Vv. and Anal Canal via the Middle and Inferior Rectal Vv. (Extension of the Rectal Venous Plexus)

Possible Collateral Circulation between the Portal Hepatic V. and the Superior and Inferior V. Cava (Portocaval Anastomoses):

IV Bypass with Lumbar Vv.

V   Bypass between the Splenic and Gastic Vv. and the Inferior Phrenic Vv.

VI Bypass the Vein in the Ligamentum Venosum to Right Hepatis Vv. (very rare)

Portal Vein
Vena Cava

Azygos V. — Hemiazygos V.

Esophageal Venous Plexus

Inferior V. Cava

Hepatic Vv.

Anastomosis to the Veins of the Retroperitoneal Space

Short Gastric Vv.

Ligamentum Venosum

Hepatic Portal V. { Left Trunk / Right Trunk }

Splenic V.

Left Gastroomental V.

Right Gastric V.

Left Gastric V.

Ligamentum Teres Tepatis with Burow's Vein

Falciform Ligament Hepatis

Inferior Mesenteric V.

Paraumbilical Vv.

Branches of Inferior Epigastric V.

Middle Colic V.

Right Gastroomental V.

Superior Mesenteric V.

Jejunal Vv.

Left Colic V.

Middle Colic V.

Ileal Vv.

Common Iliac V.

Ileocolic V.

External Iliac V.

Internal Iliac V.

Sigmoidal Vv.

Superior Rectal V.

Middle Rectal V.

Inferior Rectal V.

Rectal Venous Plexus

a

Hepatic Portal V.

Superior Mesenteric V.

Splenic V.

Inferior Mesenteric V.

b

a Illustration of a normal case.
b Common variants: Drainage of the Inferior Mesenteric V. into the Superior Mesenteric V.

In connection with Portal Hypertension due to Advanced Hepatic Cirrhosis, Blood Accumulates in the Drainage Area of the Portal V. and leads to a Swelling of the Abdominal Organs (e.g., of the Spleen – Splenomegaly), and to Ascites; Varices develop (Esophageal Varices ◘ Fig. 5.68, Dilation of the Veins in the area of the Rectal Venous Plexus). Via the Veins in the Ligamentum Venosum (Burow's Veins) and the Paraumbilical Vv., a Portocaval Anastomosis with a Dilation of the Veins in the area of the Anterior Abdominal Wall may Develop. This occurs more commonly with Inferior V. Cava Thrombosis (Medusa's Head– Caput Medusae; it is very Rare in Later Stages of the disease).

Abdominal Cavity

5.83a–d Visceral Arteries from the Abdominal Aorta: Ventral View. [a 15; b–d 51]

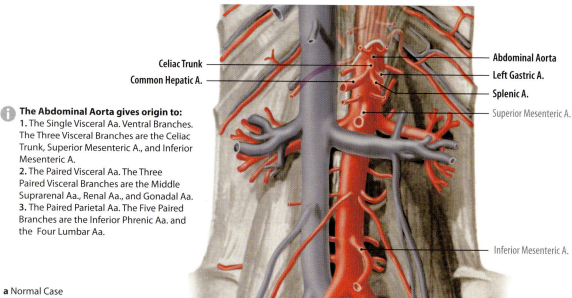

Celiac Trunk

Common Hepatic A.

Abdominal Aorta

Left Gastric A.

Splenic A.

Superior Mesenteric A.

Inferior Mesenteric A.

ⓘ **The Abdominal Aorta gives origin to:**
1. The Single Visceral Aa. Ventral Branches. The Three Visceral Branches are the Celiac Trunk, Superior Mesenteric A., and Inferior Mesenteric A.
2. The Paired Visceral Aa. The Three Paired Visceral Branches are the Middle Suprarenal Aa., Renal Aa., and Gonadal Aa.
3. The Paired Parietal Aa. The Five Paired Branches are the Inferior Phrenic Aa. and the Four Lumbar Aa.

a Normal Case
b–d Variants

a

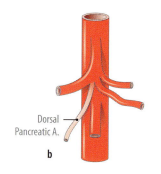

Dorsal Pancreatic A.

b

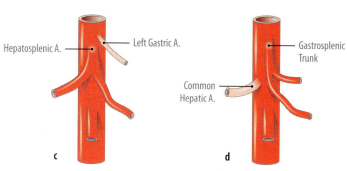

Hepatosplenic A.

Left Gastric A.

c

Gastrosplenic Trunk

Common Hepatic A.

d

Abdominal Aorta
Celiac Trunk ├ Left Gastric A. ├ Common Hepatic A. └ Splenic A. Superior Mesenteric A. Inferior Mesenteric A.

a In ~70% of all cases, the Common Hepatic, Left Gastric, and Splenic Aa. originate from the Celiac Trunk.
b Origin of the Dorsal Pancreatic A. as the 4th Branch from the Celiac Trunk in ~10% of all cases.

c Origin of the Left Gastric A. from the Abdominal Aorta in ~ 5% of all cases. The Celiac Trunk in this case becomes a Hepatosplenic Trunk.
d Origin of the Common Hepatic A. from the Abdominal Aorta in only 3–6% of all cases. The Left Gastric A. and Splenic A. form a Gastrosplenic Trunk.

5.84 Arterial Digital Subtraction Angiography of the Celiac Trunk. [28]

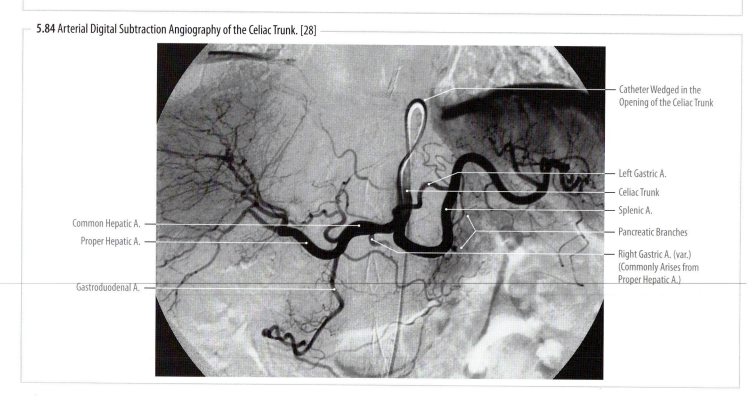

Catheter Wedged in the Opening of the Celiac Trunk

Left Gastric A.

Celiac Trunk

Splenic A.

Pancreatic Branches

Right Gastric A. (var.) (Commonly Arises from Proper Hepatic A.)

Common Hepatic A.

Proper Hepatic A.

Gastroduodenal A.

Hepatic Arteries

5.85 Intrahepatic Branching of the Proper Hepatic A.: Ventral View. [57]

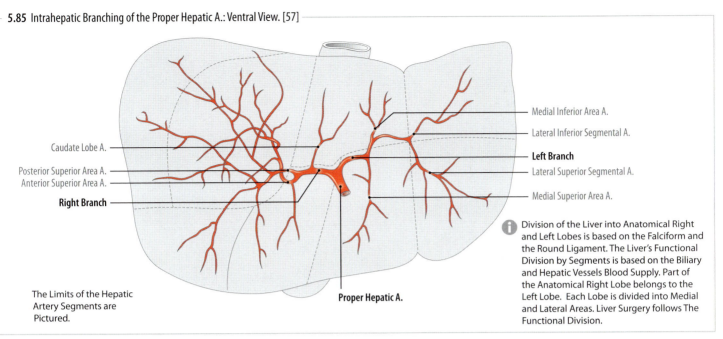

Caudate Lobe A.

Posterior Superior Area A.
Anterior Superior Area A.

Right Branch

Medial Inferior Area A.

Lateral Inferior Segmental A.

Left Branch

Lateral Superior Segmental A.

Medial Superior Area A.

Proper Hepatic A.

The Limits of the Hepatic Artery Segments are Pictured.

ℹ️ Division of the Liver into Anatomical Right and Left Lobes is based on the Falciform and the Round Ligament. The Liver's Functional Division by Segments is based on the Biliary and Hepatic Vessels Blood Supply. Part of the Anatomical Right Lobe belongs to the Left Lobe. Each Lobe is divided into Medial and Lateral Areas. Liver Surgery follows The Functional Division.

5.86a–c Arteries of the Liver, Variants. [a 57, c 28]

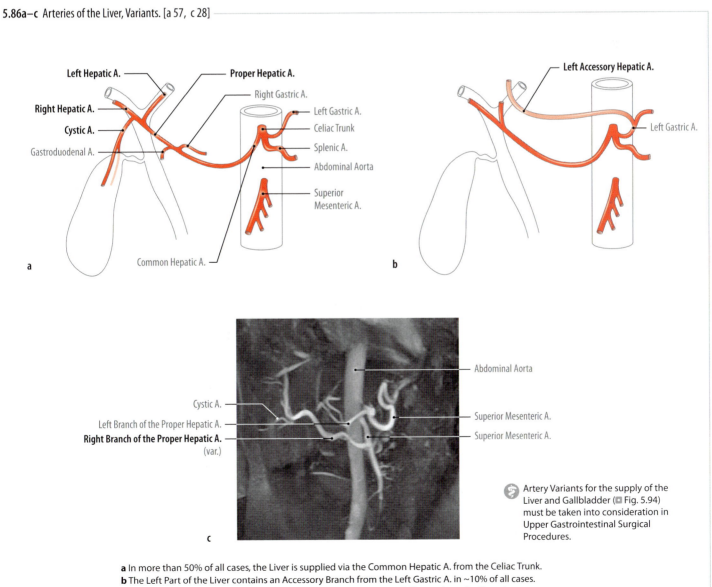

Left Hepatic A.

Proper Hepatic A.

Right Gastric A.

Right Hepatic A.

Left Gastric A.

Cystic A.

Celiac Trunk

Gastroduodenal A.

Splenic A.

Abdominal Aorta

Superior Mesenteric A.

Common Hepatic A.

a

Left Accessory Hepatic A.

Left Gastric A.

b

Abdominal Aorta

Cystic A.

Left Branch of the Proper Hepatic A.

Right Branch of the Proper Hepatic A.
(var.)

Superior Mesenteric A.

Superior Mesenteric A.

c

🔄 Artery Variants for the supply of the Liver and Gallbladder (◻ Fig. 5.94) must be taken into consideration in Upper Gastrointestinal Surgical Procedures.

a In more than 50% of all cases, the Liver is supplied via the Common Hepatic A. from the Celiac Trunk.
b The Left Part of the Liver contains an Accessory Branch from the Left Gastric A. in ~10% of all cases.
c The Right Hepatic A. of the Proper Hepatic A. originates in ~10% of all cases from the Superior Mesenteric A. (Magnetic Resonance Imaging/Angiography of the Celiac Trunk and the Superior Mesenteric A.).

5.87a–c Hepatic Veins: Ventral View. [a–c 57]

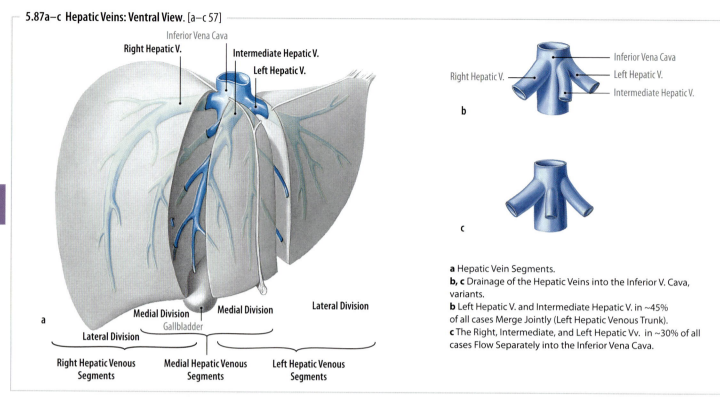

Inferior Vena Cava

Right Hepatic V.

Intermediate Hepatic V.

Left Hepatic V.

Right Hepatic V.

Inferior Vena Cava

Left Hepatic V.

Intermediate Hepatic V.

b

c

a

Medial Division

Gallbladder

Medial Division

Lateral Division

Lateral Division

Right Hepatic Venous Segments

Medial Hepatic Venous Segments

Left Hepatic Venous Segments

a Hepatic Vein Segments.
b, c Drainage of the Hepatic Veins into the Inferior V. Cava, variants.
b Left Hepatic V. and Intermediate Hepatic V. in ~45% of all cases Merge Jointly (Left Hepatic Venous Trunk).
c The Right, Intermediate, and Left Hepatic Vv. in ~30% of all cases Flow Separately into the Inferior Vena Cava.

5.88 Corrosion Preparation of the Abdominal Organs, Illustration of the Arteries (Red), the Veins (Blue), and the Portal Vein (Gray). [1]

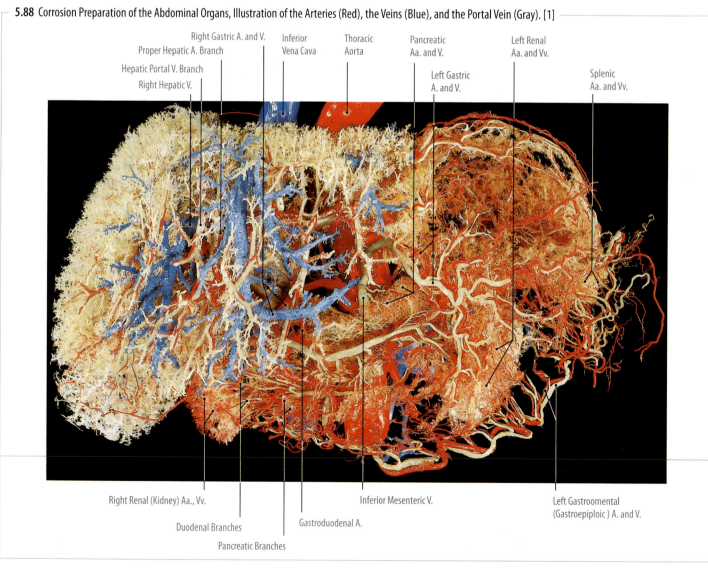

Right Gastric A. and V.

Proper Hepatic A. Branch

Hepatic Portal V. Branch

Right Hepatic V.

Inferior Vena Cava

Thoracic Aorta

Pancreatic Aa. and V.

Left Gastric A. and V.

Left Renal Aa. and Vv.

Splenic Aa. and Vv.

Right Renal (Kidney) Aa., Vv.

Duodenal Branches

Pancreatic Branches

Gastroduodenal A.

Inferior Mesenteric V.

Left Gastroomental (Gastroepiploic) A. and V.

5.89 Bile Ducts, Intrahepatic Branching: Ventral View. [57]

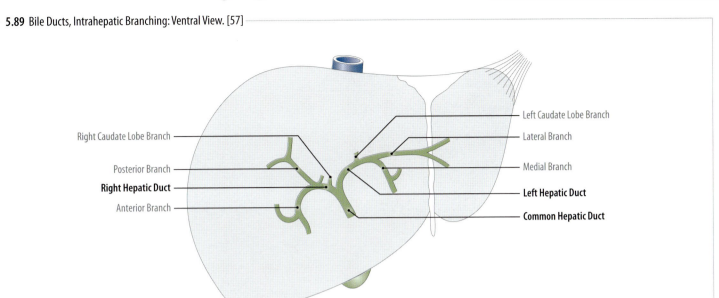

Right Caudate Lobe Branch

Posterior Branch

Right Hepatic Duct

Anterior Branch

Left Caudate Lobe Branch

Lateral Branch

Medial Branch

Left Hepatic Duct

Common Hepatic Duct

5.90a,b Imaging Procedures to Illustrate the Liver and Bile Ducts. [a 84, b 82]

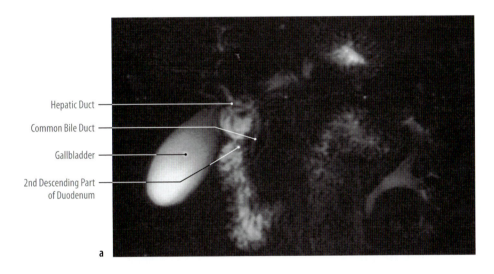

Hepatic Duct

Common Bile Duct

Gallbladder

2nd Descending Part of Duodenum

a

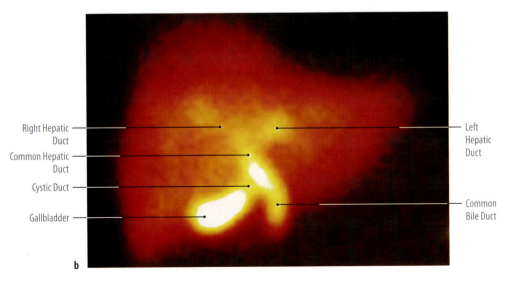

Right Hepatic Duct

Common Hepatic Duct

Cystic Duct

Gallbladder

Left Hepatic Duct

Common Bile Duct

b

a Magnetic Resonance Tomography following Reconstruction of the Intra- and Extrahepatic Bile Duct System. Illustration of the Gallbladder and the Duodenum.
b Liver Function Scintigraphy with 100 MßQ TC-99m-marked BrIDA. Static Detail Scintigram of the Liver after ~20 minutes of Tracer distribution homogeneous in the Liver Parenchyma shows Excretion into the Gallbladder and illustrates the large Intra- and Extrahepatic Bile Ducts.

Abdominal Cavity

Extrahepatic Biliary Ducts

5.91 Structures of the Porta Hepatis, Gallbladder (Removed from the Bed of the Liver), and Extrahepatic Bile Ducts: Dorsal View. [57]

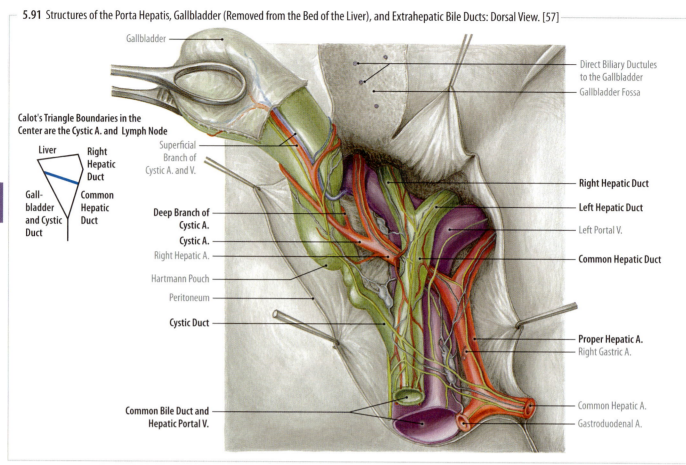

Gallbladder

Direct Biliary Ductules to the Gallbladder

Gallbladder Fossa

Calot's Triangle Boundaries in the Center are the Cystic A. and Lymph Node

Liver

Right Hepatic Duct

Gall-bladder and Cystic Duct

Common Hepatic Duct

Superficial Branch of Cystic A. and V.

Right Hepatic Duct

Left Hepatic Duct

Left Portal V.

Deep Branch of Cystic A.

Cystic A.

Right Hepatic A.

Common Hepatic Duct

Hartmann Pouch

Peritoneum

Cystic Duct

Proper Hepatic A.

Right Gastric A.

Common Bile Duct and Hepatic Portal V.

Common Hepatic A.

Gastroduodenal A.

5.92 **a** Gallbladder and Extrahepatic Bile Ducts (Partially Opened), Bile Duct and Pancreatic Duct in the Duodenum. **b,c** Bile Ducts, Variants. [a 6; b,c 57]

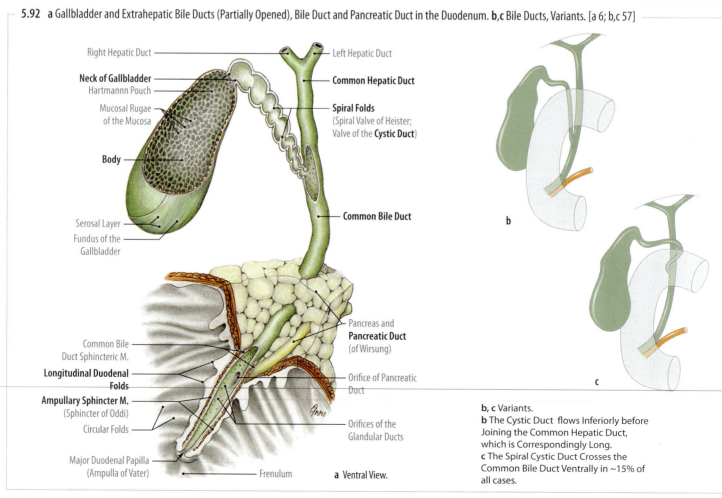

Right Hepatic Duct

Left Hepatic Duct

Neck of Gallbladder

Hartmannn Pouch

Common Hepatic Duct

Mucosal Rugae of the Mucosa

Spiral Folds
(Spiral Valve of Heister; Valve of the **Cystic Duct**)

Body

Common Bile Duct

b

Serosal Layer

Fundus of the Gallbladder

Common Bile Duct Sphincteric M.

Longitudinal Duodenal Folds

Pancreas and **Pancreatic Duct** (of Wirsung)

Orifice of Pancreatic Duct

Ampullary Sphincter M.
(Sphincter of Oddi)

Circular Folds

Orifices of the Glandular Ducts

Major Duodenal Papilla (Ampulla of Vater)

Frenulum

a Ventral View.

c

b, c Variants.
b The Cystic Duct flows Inferiorly before Joining the Common Hepatic Duct, which is Correspondingly Long.
c The Spiral Cystic Duct Crosses the Common Bile Duct Ventrally in ~15% of all cases.

Porta Hepatis: Topography

5.93 Structures of the Porta Hepatis: Ventral View. [57]

In a Cholecystectomy, the Cystic Duct and Cystic A. must be carefully Marked before their Ligature. The Gallbladder is Subserously Peeled Out of the Liver Bed and Put Down (☐ Fig. 5.91).

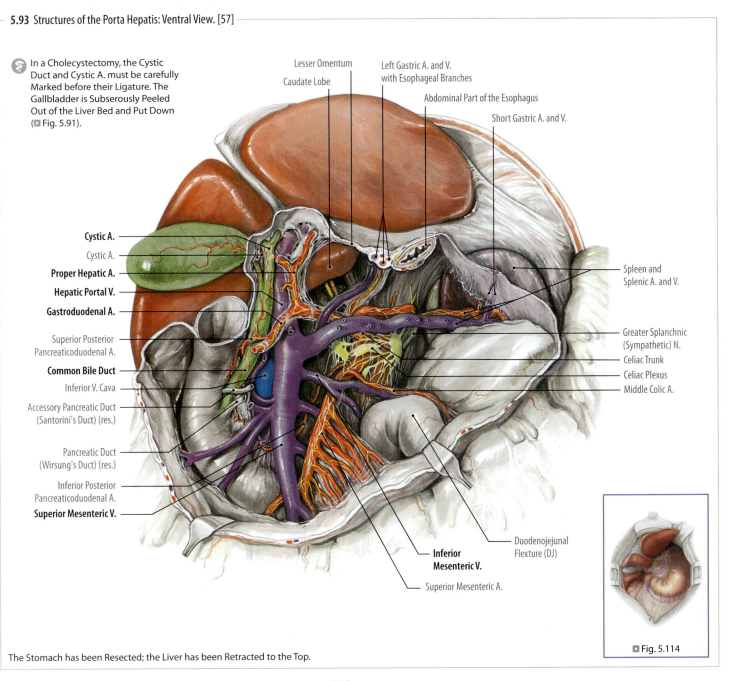

Lesser Omentum

Caudate Lobe

Left Gastric A. and V. with Esophageal Branches

Abdominal Part of the Esophagus

Short Gastric A. and V.

Cystic A.

Cystic A.

Proper Hepatic A.

Hepatic Portal V.

Gastroduodenal A.

Superior Posterior Pancreaticoduodenal A.

Common Bile Duct

Inferior V. Cava

Accessory Pancreatic Duct (Santorini's Duct) (res.)

Pancreatic Duct (Wirsung's Duct) (res.)

Inferior Posterior Pancreaticoduodenal A.

Superior Mesenteric V.

Spleen and Splenic A. and V.

Greater Splanchnic (Sympathetic) N.

Celiac Trunk

Celiac Plexus

Middle Colic A.

Duodenojejunal Flexture (DJ)

Inferior Mesenteric V.

Superior Mesenteric A.

☐ Fig. 5.114

The Stomach has been Resected; the Liver has been Retracted to the Top.

5.94a,b Variants of the Course of the Right Hepatic A. of the Proper Hepatic A. [57]

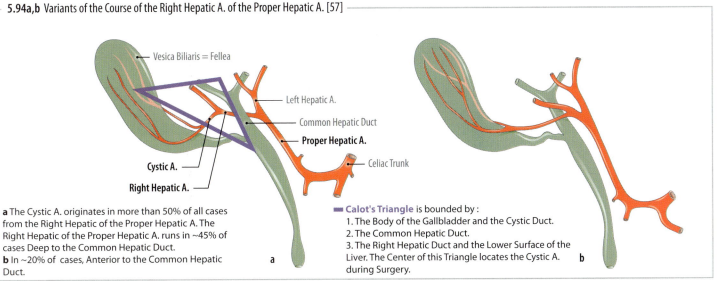

Vesica Biliaris = Fellea

Left Hepatic A.

Common Hepatic Duct

Proper Hepatic A.

Celiac Trunk

Cystic A.

Right Hepatic A.

a The Cystic A. originates in more than 50% of all cases from the Right Hepatic of the Proper Hepatic A. The Right Hepatic of the Proper Hepatic A. runs in ~45% of cases Deep to the Common Hepatic Duct.
b In ~20% of cases, Anterior to the Common Hepatic Duct.

■ **Calot's Triangle** is bounded by :
1. The Body of the Gallbladder and the Cystic Duct.
2. The Common Hepatic Duct.
3. The Right Hepatic Duct and the Lower Surface of the Liver. The Center of this Triangle locates the Cystic A. during Surgery.

a

b

Abdominal Cavity

Pancreas, Duodenum

5.95 Duodenum and Pancreas: Ventral View. [6]

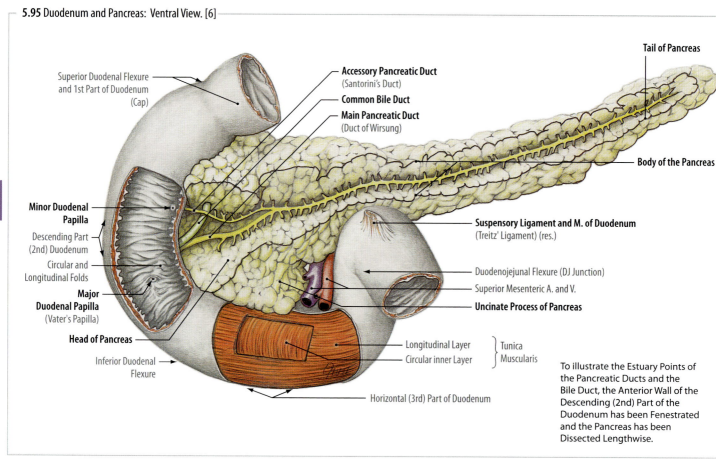

Superior Duodenal Flexure
and 1st Part of Duodenum
(Cap)

Accessory Pancreatic Duct
(Santorini's Duct)

Common Bile Duct

Main Pancreatic Duct
(Duct of Wirsung)

Tail of Pancreas

Body of the Pancreas

Minor Duodenal Papilla

Descending Part
(2nd) Duodenum

Circular and
Longitudinal Folds

Major Duodenal Papilla
(Vater's Papilla)

Head of Pancreas

Inferior Duodenal
Flexure

Suspensory Ligament and M. of Duodenum
(Treitz' Ligament) (res.)

Duodenojejunal Flexure (DJ Junction)

Superior Mesenteric A. and V.

Uncinate Process of Pancreas

Longitudinal Layer

Circular inner Layer

Tunica Muscularis

Horizontal (3rd) Part of Duodenum

To illustrate the Estuary Points of
the Pancreatic Ducts and the
Bile Duct, the Anterior Wall of the
Descending (2nd) Part of the
Duodenum has been Fenestrated
and the Pancreas has been
Dissected Lengthwise.

5.96 Pancreas, Gallbladder, and Duodenum: Dorsal View. [48]

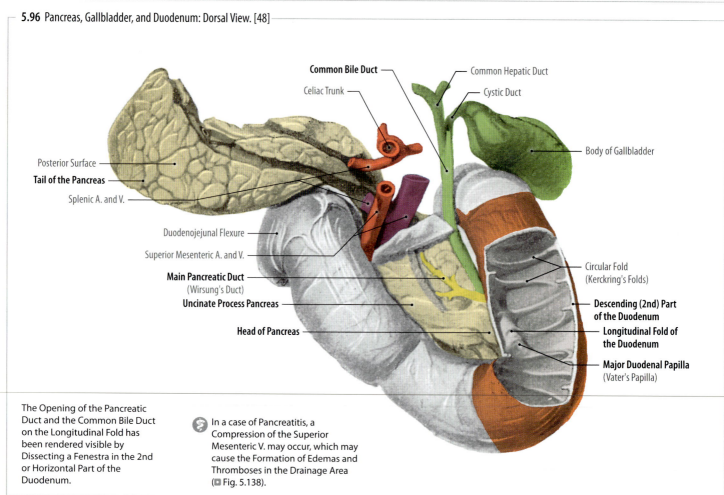

Common Bile Duct

Celiac Trunk

Common Hepatic Duct

Cystic Duct

Posterior Surface

Tail of the Pancreas

Splenic A. and V.

Duodenojejunal Flexure

Superior Mesenteric A. and V.

Main Pancreatic Duct
(Wirsung's Duct)

Uncinate Process Pancreas

Head of Pancreas

Body of Gallbladder

Circular Fold
(Kerckring's Folds)

**Descending (2nd) Part
of the Duodenum**

**Longitudinal Fold of
the Duodenum**

Major Duodenal Papilla
(Vater's Papilla)

The Opening of the Pancreatic
Duct and the Common Bile Duct
on the Longitudinal Fold has
been rendered visible by
Dissecting a Fenestra in the 2nd
or Horizontal Part of the
Duodenum.

In a case of Pancreatitis, a
Compression of the Superior
Mesenteric V. may occur, which may
cause the Formation of Edemas and
Thromboses in the Drainage Area
(☐ Fig. 5.138).

5.97a,b Opening Variants of the Pancreatic Ducts. [57]

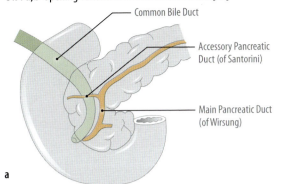

— Common Bile Duct

— Accessory Pancreatic Duct (of Santorini)

— Main Pancreatic Duct (of Wirsung)

a

Pancreatic Carcinoma is most commonly found in the Head of the Pancreas. It is usually an Adenocarcinoma, which originates from the Epithelium Duct (Ductal Carcinoma). Painless Jaundice may be an initial Symptom if there is Compression of the Common Bile Duct (◻ Fig. 5.95, 5.92), which runs in the Pancreatic Tissue through the Tumor.

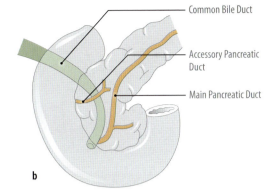

— Common Bile Duct

— Accessory Pancreatic Duct

— Main Pancreatic Duct

b

a The Accessory Pancreatic Duct (Duct of Santorini) connects with the the Main Pancreatic (of Wirsung) Duct in ~30% of cases.

b The Main Pancreatic Duct and Accessory Pancreatic Duct Discharge Independently and are Not Anastomostic in ~10% of cases.

5.98a,b Orifices of the Common Bile Duct and Pancreatic Duct, Variants. [15]

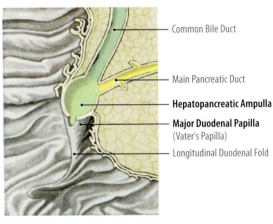

— Common Bile Duct

— Main Pancreatic Duct

Hepatopancreatic Ampulla

Major Duodenal Papilla (Vater's Papilla)

— Longitudinal Duodenal Fold

a

— Common Bile Duct

— Pancreatic Duct

b

a The Common Bile Duct and Pancreatic Duct flow into the Joint Hepatopancreatic Ampulla.
b Both Ducts are separated by a Septum in the Orlfice Area and Secrete Separately via the Major Duodenal Papilla.

5.99 Secretion and Necrosis Originating from a Ruptured Pancreas: Sagittal Section, Schematic. [85, 86]

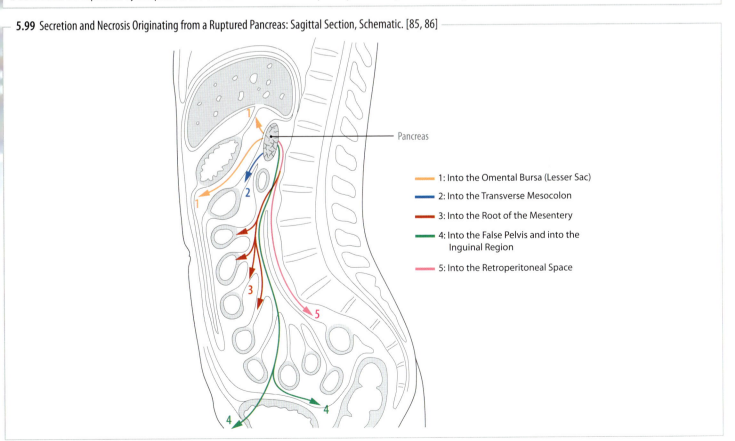

— Pancreas

— 1: Into the Omental Bursa (Lesser Sac)

— 2: Into the Transverse Mesocolon

— 3: Into the Root of the Mesentery

— 4: Into the False Pelvis and into the Inguinal Region

— 5: Into the Retroperitoneal Space

Abdominal Cavity

5.100 Arteries of the Duodenum and the Head of the Pancreas: Ventral View. [57]

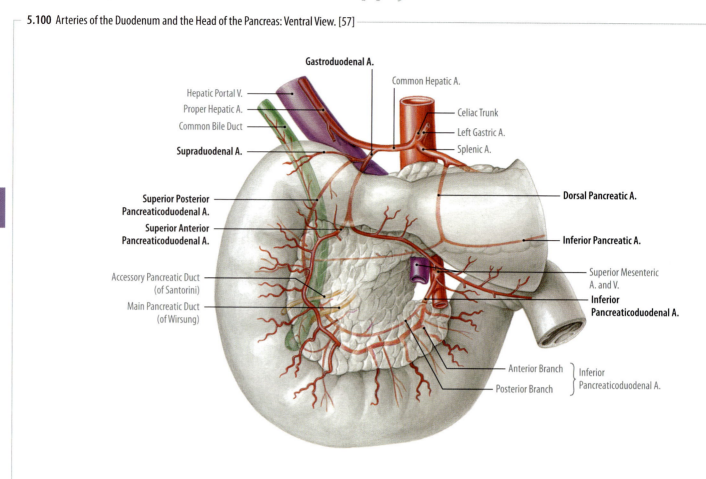

Gastroduodenal A.

Hepatic Portal V.
Proper Hepatic A.
Common Bile Duct

Common Hepatic A.

Supraduodenal A.

Celiac Trunk
Left Gastric A.
Splenic A.

Superior Posterior Pancreaticoduodenal A.

Superior Anterior Pancreaticoduodenal A.

Dorsal Pancreatic A.

Inferior Pancreatic A.

Accessory Pancreatic Duct (of Santorini)

Main Pancreatic Duct (of Wirsung)

Superior Mesenteric A. and V.

Inferior Pancreaticoduodenal A.

Anterior Branch
Posterior Branch
} Inferior Pancreaticoduodenal A.

5.101 Arterial Supply of the Pancreas and the Duodenum: Ventral View. [57]

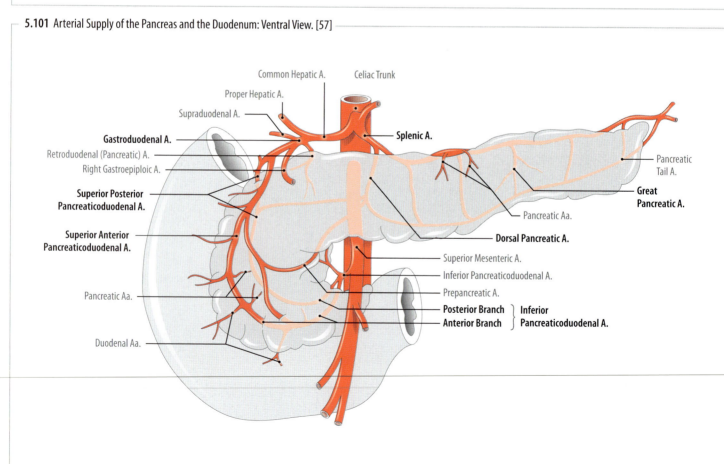

Common Hepatic A.
Proper Hepatic A.
Supraduodenal A.

Celiac Trunk

Gastroduodenal A.
Retroduodenal (Pancreatic) A.
Right Gastroepiploic A.

Splenic A.

Pancreatic Tail A.

Superior Posterior Pancreaticoduodenal A.

Superior Anterior Pancreaticoduodenal A.

Pancreatic Aa.

Great Pancreatic A.

Dorsal Pancreatic A.

Superior Mesenteric A.
Inferior Pancreaticoduodenal A.
Prepancreatic A.

Pancreatic Aa.

Posterior Branch
Anterior Branch
} **Inferior Pancreaticoduodenal A.**

Duodenal Aa.

5.102 Venous Drain of the Pancreas and the Duodenum: Ventral View. [57]

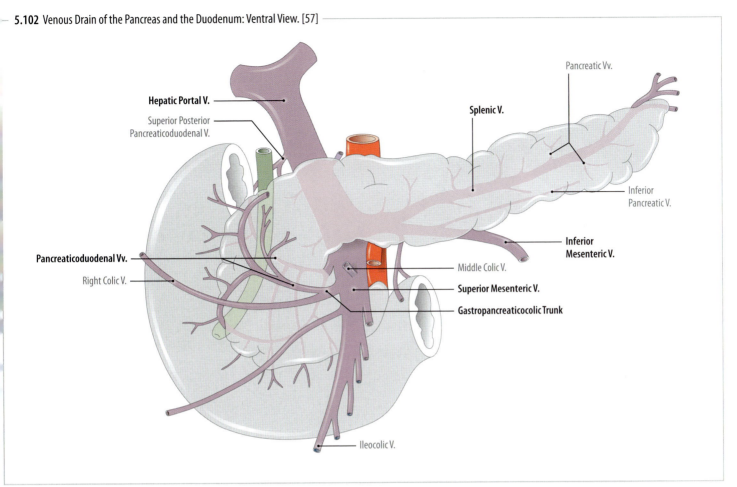

5.103 Lymph Outlet from the Pancreas and the Duodenum, Regional and Accessory Lymph Nodes: Ventral View. [57]

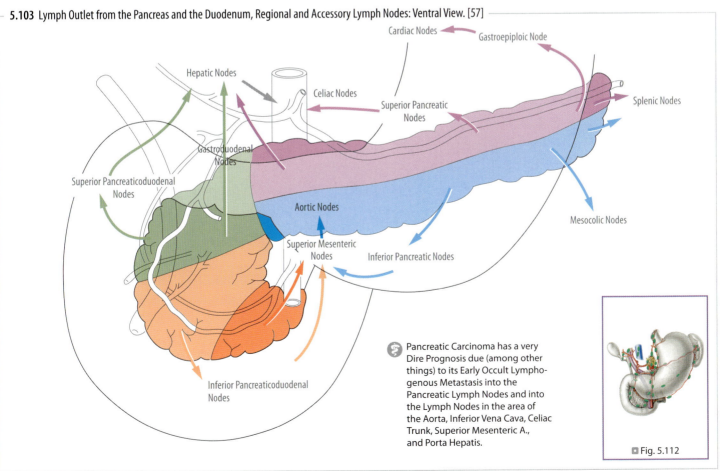

Pancreatic Carcinoma has a very Dire Prognosis due (among other things) to its Early Occult Lymphogenous Metastasis into the Pancreatic Lymph Nodes and into the Lymph Nodes in the area of the Aorta, Inferior Vena Cava, Celiac Trunk, Superior Mesenteric A., and Porta Hepatis.

Fig. 5.112

Abdominal Cavity

5.104 Normal Pancreatogram with Illustration of the Pancreatic Duct
(Duct of Wirsung) and the Accessory Pancreatic Duct
(Duct of Santorini)– Marked by Arrows. [85] Compare Fig. 5.95

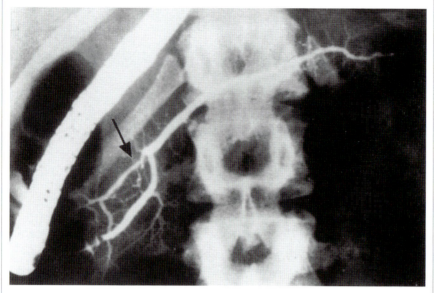

5.105 Endoscopic Picture of the Major Duodenal
Papilla (Vater's Papilla). [87] Side-View
Endoscope

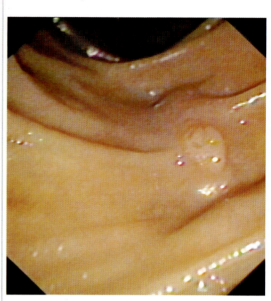

5.106a,b Spleen. [6]

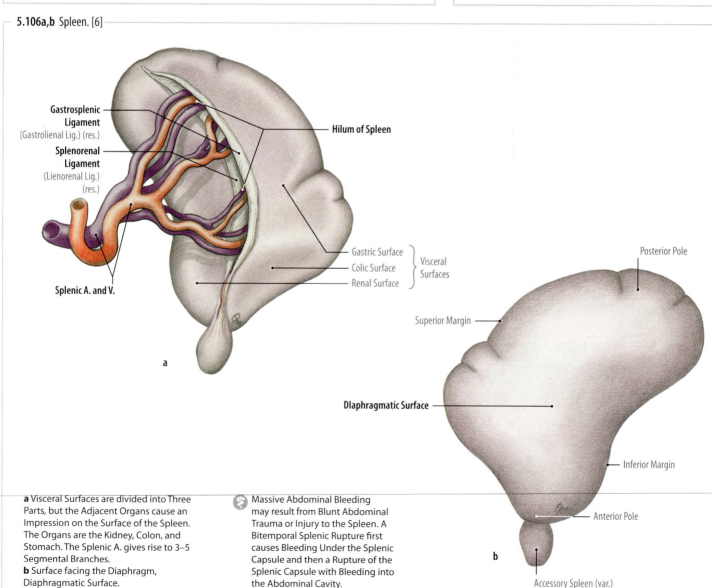

Gastrosplenic
Ligament
(Gastrolienal Lig.) (res.)

Splenorenal
Ligament
(Lienorenal Lig.)
(res.)

Hilum of Spleen

Splenic A. and V.

Gastric Surface
Colic Surface — Visceral Surfaces
Renal Surface

a

Posterior Pole

Superior Margin

Diaphragmatic Surface

Inferior Margin

Anterior Pole

b

Accessory Spleen (var.)

a Visceral Surfaces are divided into Three
Parts, but the Adjacent Organs cause an
Impression on the Surface of the Spleen.
The Organs are the Kidney, Colon, and
Stomach. The Splenic A. gives rise to 3–5
Segmental Branches.
b Surface facing the Diaphragm,
Diaphragmatic Surface.

Massive Abdominal Bleeding
may result from Blunt Abdominal
Trauma or Injury to the Spleen. A
Bitemporal Splenic Rupture first
causes Bleeding Under the Splenic
Capsule and then a Rupture of the
Splenic Capsule with Bleeding into
the Abdominal Cavity.

Spleen

5.107 Spleen, Hilum of the Spleen, and Splenic (Lienal) Recess of the Omental Bursa (Lesser Sac): Ventral View. [57]

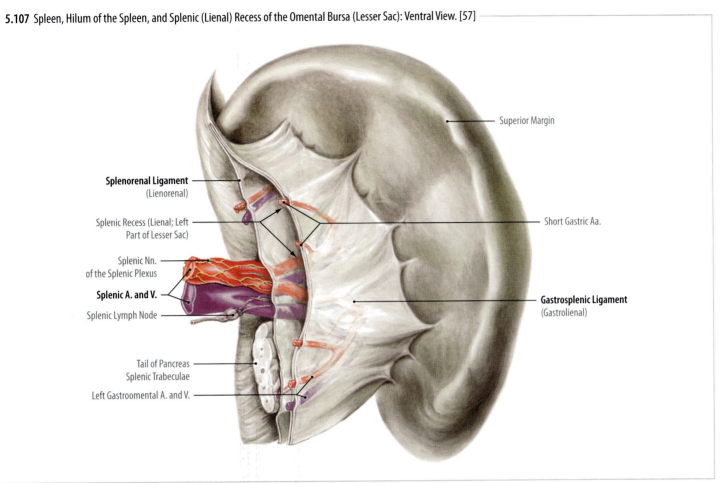

Splenorenal Ligament
(Lienorenal)

Splenic Recess (Lienal; Left
Part of Lesser Sac)

Splenic Nn.
of the Splenic Plexus

Splenic A. and V.

Splenic Lymph Node

Tail of Pancreas
Splenic Trabeculae

Left Gastroomental A. and V.

Superior Margin

Short Gastric Aa.

Gastrosplenic Ligament
(Gastrolienal)

5.108 Horizontal Section through the Spleen at the Level of the Hilum, Section of the Splenic (Lienal) Recess of the Omental Bursa: Superior View of the
Inferior Cut Surface. The Peritoneum is Outlined in Green. [57]

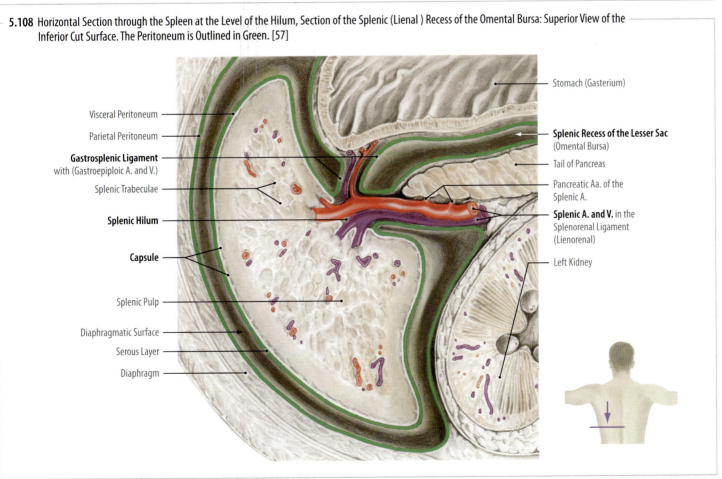

Visceral Peritoneum

Parietal Peritoneum

Gastrosplenic Ligament
with (Gastroepiploic A. and V.)

Splenic Trabeculae

Splenic Hilum

Capsule

Splenic Pulp

Diaphragmatic Surface

Serous Layer

Diaphragm

Stomach (Gasterium)

Splenic Recess of the Lesser Sac
(Omental Bursa)

Tail of Pancreas

Pancreatic Aa. of the
Splenic A.

Splenic A. and V. in the
Splenorenal Ligament
(Lienorenal)

Left Kidney

Abdominal Cavity

Stomach

5.109a,b Stomach: Ventral View. [2, 31, 68]

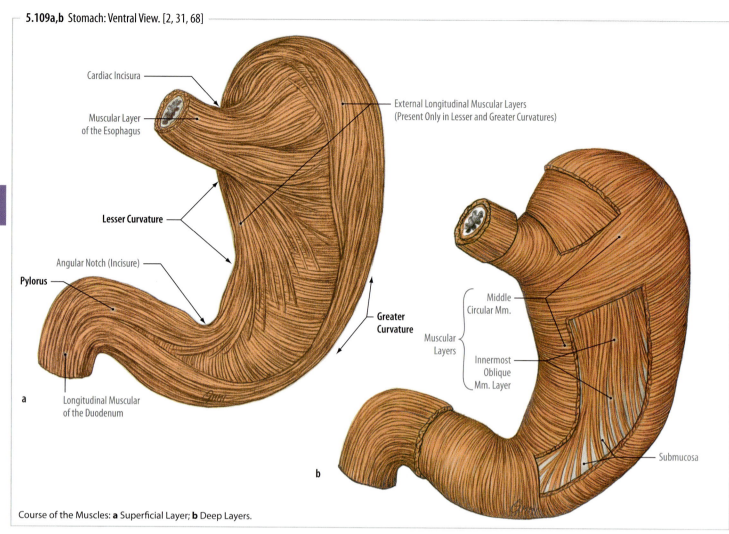

Cardiac Incisura

Muscular Layer of the Esophagus

External Longitudinal Muscular Layers (Present Only in Lesser and Greater Curvatures)

Lesser Curvature

Angular Notch (Incisure)

Pylorus

Greater Curvature

Middle Circular Mm.

Muscular Layers

Innermost Oblique Mm. Layer

a

Longitudinal Muscular of the Duodenum

b

Submucosa

Course of the Muscles: **a** Superficial Layer; **b** Deep Layers.

5.110 Sections of an Opened Stomach and Mucosal Relief. [57]

A Gastric Ulcer occurs most commonly on the Lesser Curvature in the Transitional Area between the Pyloric Antrum and the Body of the Stomach. Ulcers on the Greater Curvature are an ominous sign of a possible Carcinoma.
A Gastric Ulcer is a Disease of the Mucous Membrane in which the Mucosal Defect spreads beyond the Muscularis Mucosae into the Submucosa. If the Muscularis is also Penetrated, an Acute Perforation into the Abdominal Cavity or a Penetration into the Neighboring Organs (e.g., the Pancreas) may result. If the Defect of the Mucous Membrane does Not Penetrate the Muscularis Mucosae, there will be No Associated Perforation of the Stomach at this stage.

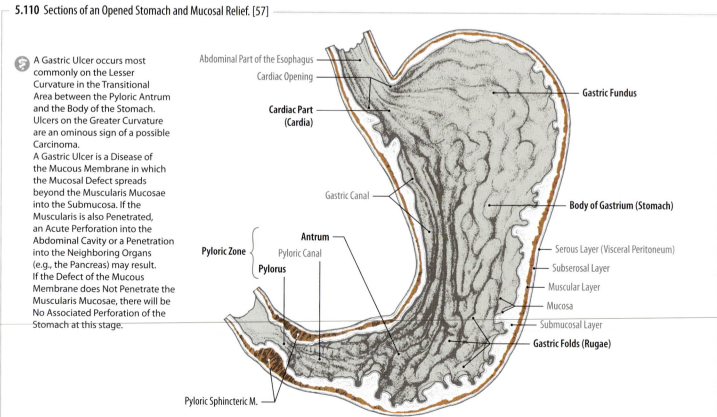

Abdominal Part of the Esophagus

Cardiac Opening

Cardiac Part (Cardia)

Gastric Canal

Pyloric Zone

Antrum

Pyloric Canal

Pylorus

Pyloric Sphincteric M.

Gastric Fundus

Body of Gastrium (Stomach)

Serous Layer (Visceral Peritoneum)

Subserosal Layer

Muscular Layer

Mucosa

Submucosal Layer

Gastric Folds (Rugae)

Stomach: Vascular Supply

5.111a,b Arteries from the Celiac Trunk for the Supply of the Stomach and the Neighboring Organs. [57]

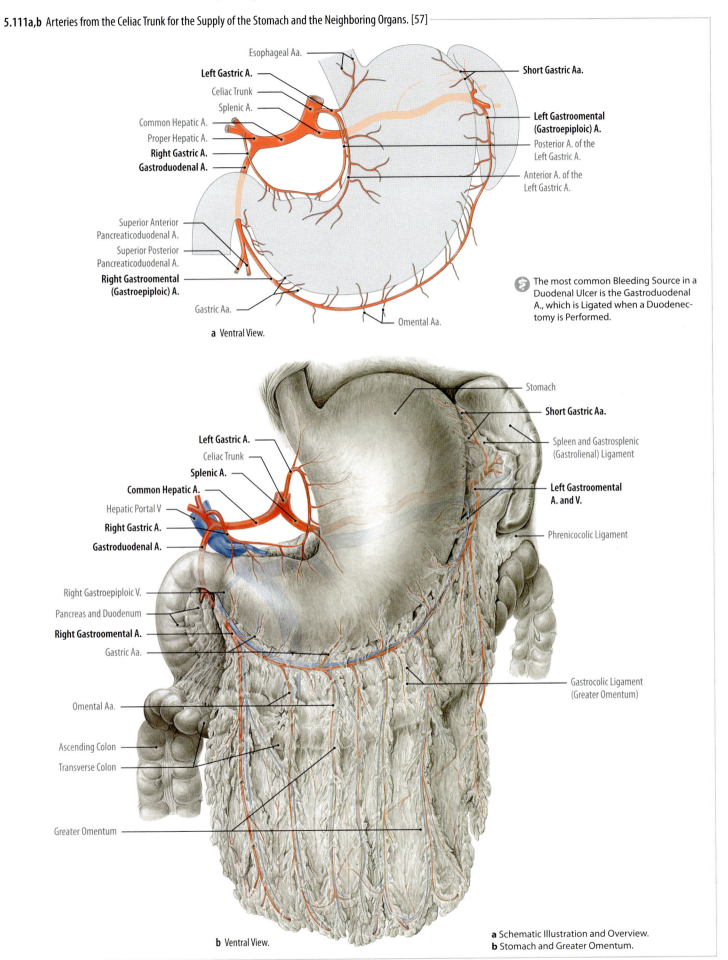

Esophageal Aa.

Left Gastric A.

Celiac Trunk

Splenic A.

Common Hepatic A.

Proper Hepatic A.

Right Gastric A.

Gastroduodenal A.

Short Gastric Aa.

Left Gastroomental (Gastroepiploic) A.

Posterior A. of the Left Gastric A.

Anterior A. of the Left Gastric A.

Superior Anterior Pancreaticoduodenal A.

Superior Posterior Pancreaticoduodenal A.

Right Gastroomental (Gastroepiploic) A.

Gastric Aa.

Omental Aa.

The most common Bleeding Source in a Duodenal Ulcer is the Gastroduodenal A., which is Ligated when a Duodenectomy is Performed.

a Ventral View.

Stomach

Short Gastric Aa.

Spleen and Gastrosplenic (Gastrolienal) Ligament

Left Gastroomental A. and V.

Phrenicocolic Ligament

Left Gastric A.

Celiac Trunk

Splenic A.

Common Hepatic A.

Hepatic Portal V

Right Gastric A.

Gastroduodenal A.

Right Gastroepiploic V.

Pancreas and Duodenum

Right Gastroomental A.

Gastric Aa.

Omental Aa.

Ascending Colon

Transverse Colon

Greater Omentum

Gastrocolic Ligament (Greater Omentum)

b Ventral View.

a Schematic Illustration and Overview.
b Stomach and Greater Omentum.

Abdominal Cavity

5.112 Regional and Central Lymph Nodes of the Stomach and the Adjacent Epigastric Organs: Ventral View. [57]

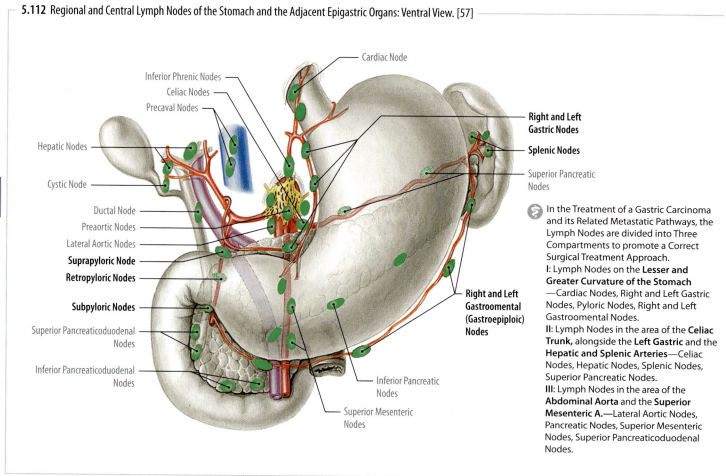

Cardiac Node

Inferior Phrenic Nodes
Celiac Nodes
Precaval Nodes

Hepatic Nodes

Cystic Node

Ductal Node
Preaortic Nodes
Lateral Aortic Nodes
Suprapyloric Node
Retropyloric Nodes

Subpyloric Nodes

Superior Pancreaticoduodenal Nodes

Inferior Pancreaticoduodenal Nodes

Right and Left Gastric Nodes

Splenic Nodes

Superior Pancreatic Nodes

Right and Left Gastroomental (Gastroepiploic) Nodes

Inferior Pancreatic Nodes

Superior Mesenteric Nodes

In the Treatment of a Gastric Carcinoma and its Related Metastatic Pathways, the Lymph Nodes are divided into Three Compartments to promote a Correct Surgical Treatment Approach.
I: Lymph Nodes on the **Lesser and Greater Curvature of the Stomach** —Cardiac Nodes, Right and Left Gastric Nodes, Pyloric Nodes, Right and Left Gastroomental Nodes.
II: Lymph Nodes in the area of the **Celiac Trunk,** alongside the **Left Gastric** and the **Hepatic and Splenic Arteries**—Celiac Nodes, Hepatic Nodes, Splenic Nodes, Superior Pancreatic Nodes.
III: Lymph Nodes in the area of the **Abdominal Aorta** and the **Superior Mesenteric A.**—Lateral Aortic Nodes, Pancreatic Nodes, Superior Mesenteric Nodes, Superior Pancreaticoduodenal Nodes.

5.113 Parasympathetic Innervation of the Stomach: Ventral View. [2]

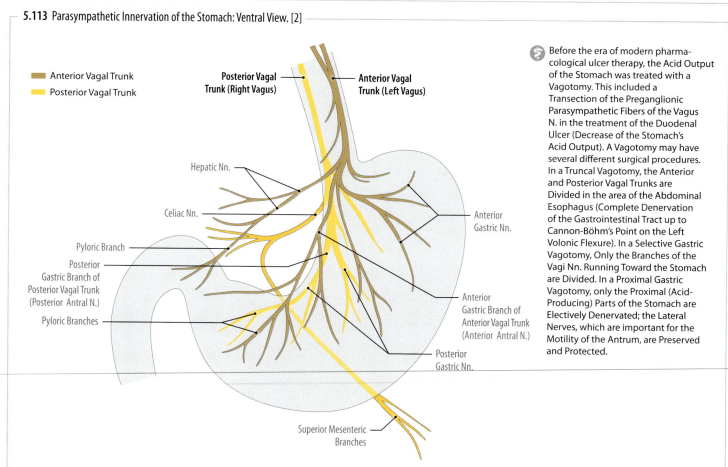

Anterior Vagal Trunk
Posterior Vagal Trunk

Posterior Vagal Trunk (Right Vagus)
Anterior Vagal Trunk (Left Vagus)

Hepatic Nn.

Celiac Nn.

Pyloric Branch

Posterior Gastric Branch of Posterior Vagal Trunk (Posterior Antral N.)

Pyloric Branches

Anterior Gastric Nn.

Anterior Gastric Branch of Anterior Vagal Trunk (Anterior Antral N.)

Posterior Gastric Nn.

Superior Mesenteric Branches

Before the era of modern pharmacological ulcer therapy, the Acid Output of the Stomach was treated with a Vagotomy. This included a Transection of the Preganglionic Parasympathetic Fibers of the Vagus N. in the treatment of the Duodenal Ulcer (Decrease of the Stomach's Acid Output). A Vagotomy may have several different surgical procedures. In a Truncal Vagotomy, the Anterior and Posterior Vagal Trunks are Divided in the area of the Abdominal Esophagus (Complete Denervation of the Gastrointestinal Tract up to Cannon-Böhm's Point on the Left Volonic Flexure). In a Selective Gastric Vagotomy, Only the Branches of the Vagi Nn. Running Toward the Stomach are Divided. In a Proximal Gastric Vagotomy, only the Proximal (Acid-Producing) Parts of the Stomach are Electively Denervated; the Lateral Nerves, which are important for the Motility of the Antrum, are Preserved and Protected.

5.114 Epigastric Area: Ventral View. [57]

Anterior Wall of Lesser Sac:
1- Lesser Omentum
2- Hepatoduodenal Ligament
3- Stomach
3- Greater Omentum (Gastrocolic Ligament)

Right Lateral Wall of Lesser Sac:
1- Epiploic Foramen of Winslow
2- Second Part of Duodenum

Inferior Wall of Lesser Sac:
1- Greater Omentum
2- Transverse Colon
3- Transverse Mesocolon

Left Lateral Wall of Lesser Sac:
1- Gastrosplenic (Gastrolienal) Ligament
2- Hilum of the Spleen
3- Splenorenal (Lieneorenal) Ligament

Boundaries of the Epiploic Foramen:
1- Superior - Caudate Lobe of Liver
2- Anterior- Hepatoduodenal Ligament
3- Inferior- Second Part of Duodenum
4- Posterior- Parietal Peritoneum
          Covering Inferior Vena Cava

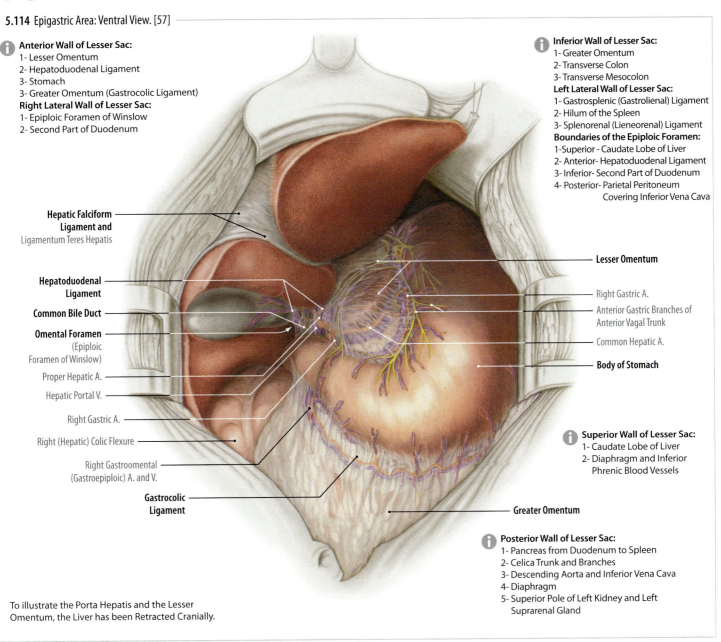

Hepatic Falciform Ligament and
Ligamentum Teres Hepatis

Hepatoduodenal Ligament

Common Bile Duct

Omental Foramen
(Epiploic Foramen of Winslow)

Proper Hepatic A.

Hepatic Portal V.

Right Gastric A.

Right (Hepatic) Colic Flexure

Right Gastroomental (Gastroepiploic) A. and V.

Gastrocolic Ligament

Lesser Omentum

Right Gastric A.

Anterior Gastric Branches of Anterior Vagal Trunk

Common Hepatic A.

Body of Stomach

Superior Wall of Lesser Sac:
1- Caudate Lobe of Liver
2- Diaphragm and Inferior Phrenic Blood Vessels

Greater Omentum

Posterior Wall of Lesser Sac:
1- Pancreas from Duodenum to Spleen
2- Celica Trunk and Branches
3- Descending Aorta and Inferior Vena Cava
4- Diaphragm
5- Superior Pole of Left Kidney and Left Suprarenal Gland

To illustrate the Porta Hepatis and the Lesser Omentum, the Liver has been Retracted Cranially.

5.115 Epigastric Organs and Upper Part of the Colon: Ventral View. [57]

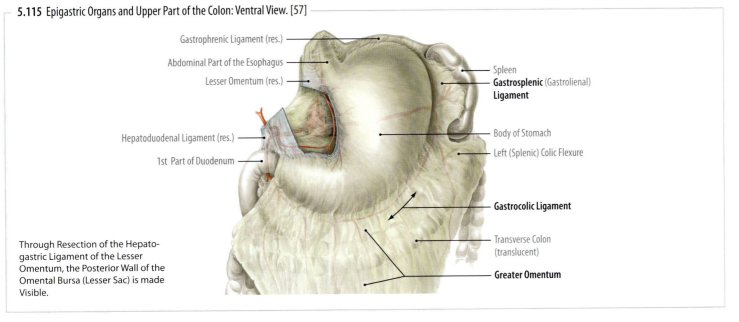

Gastrophrenic Ligament (res.)

Abdominal Part of the Esophagus

Lesser Omentum (res.)

Hepatoduodenal Ligament (res.)

1st Part of Duodenum

Spleen

Gastrosplenic (Gastrolienal) **Ligament**

Body of Stomach

Left (Splenic) Colic Flexure

Gastrocolic Ligament

Transverse Colon (translucent)

Greater Omentum

Through Resection of the Hepato-gastric Ligament of the Lesser Omentum, the Posterior Wall of the Omental Bursa (Lesser Sac) is made Visible.

Abdominal Cavity

5.116 Omental Bursa: Retrogastric Section, Ventral View. [57]

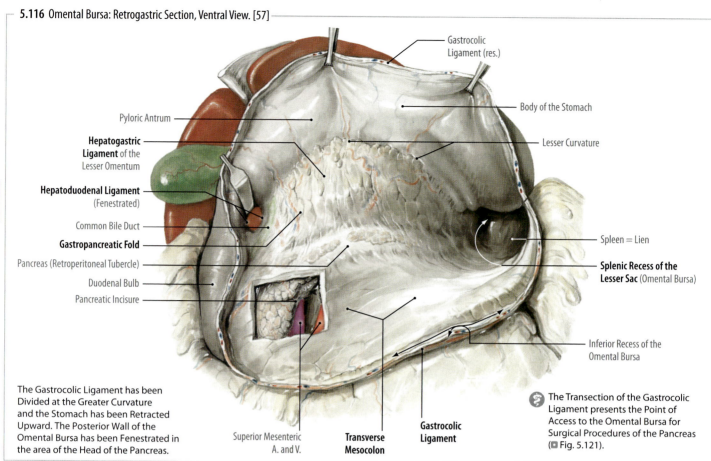

Gastrocolic Ligament (res.)

Pyloric Antrum

Body of the Stomach

Hepatogastric Ligament of the Lesser Omentum

Lesser Curvature

Hepatoduodenal Ligament (Fenestrated)

Common Bile Duct

Gastropancreatic Fold

Spleen = Lien

Pancreas (Retroperitoneal Tubercle)

Splenic Recess of the Lesser Sac (Omental Bursa)

Duodenal Bulb

Pancreatic Incisure

Inferior Recess of the Omental Bursa

Superior Mesenteric A. and V.

Transverse Mesocolon

Gastrocolic Ligament

The Gastrocolic Ligament has been Divided at the Greater Curvature and the Stomach has been Retracted Upward. The Posterior Wall of the Omental Bursa has been Fenestrated in the area of the Head of the Pancreas.

The Transection of the Gastrocolic Ligament presents the Point of Access to the Omental Bursa for Surgical Procedures of the Pancreas (☐ Fig. 5.121).

5.117 Posterior Wall of the Omental Bursa: Ventral View. [57]

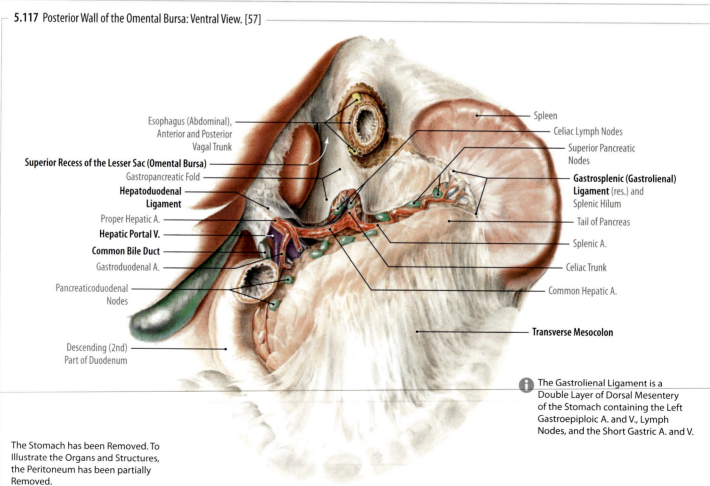

Esophagus (Abdominal), Anterior and Posterior Vagal Trunk

Spleen

Celiac Lymph Nodes

Superior Pancreatic Nodes

Superior Recess of the Lesser Sac (Omental Bursa)

Gastropancreatic Fold

Gastrosplenic (Gastrolienal) Ligament (res.) and Splenic Hilum

Hepatoduodenal Ligament

Proper Hepatic A.

Tail of Pancreas

Hepatic Portal V.

Splenic A.

Common Bile Duct

Gastroduodenal A.

Celiac Trunk

Pancreaticoduodenal Nodes

Common Hepatic A.

Transverse Mesocolon

Descending (2nd) Part of Duodenum

The Stomach has been Removed. To Illustrate the Organs and Structures, the Peritoneum has been partially Removed.

The Gastrolienal Ligament is a Double Layer of Dorsal Mesentery of the Stomach containing the Left Gastroepiploic A. and V., Lymph Nodes, and the Short Gastric A. and V.

Epigastric Area, Omental Bursa

5.118 Epigastric Organs and Omental Bursa: Ventral View. [57]

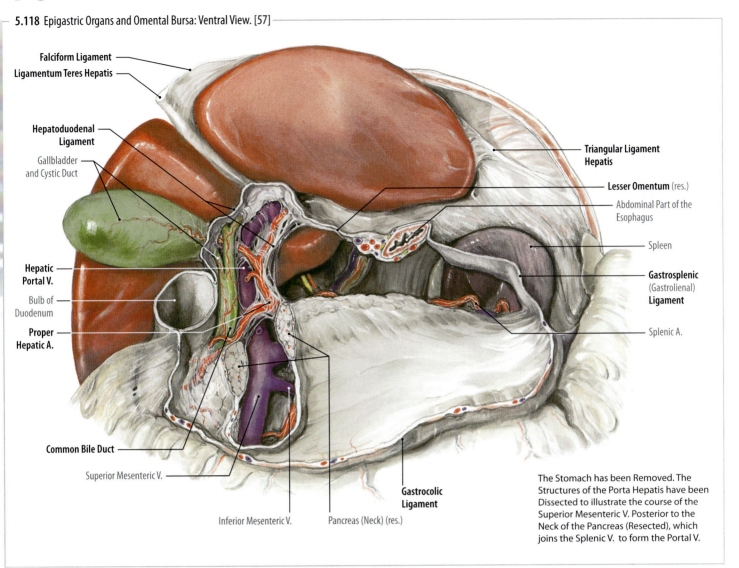

Falciform Ligament
Ligamentum Teres Hepatis

Hepatoduodenal Ligament

Gallbladder and Cystic Duct

Hepatic Portal V.

Bulb of Duodenum

Proper Hepatic A.

Common Bile Duct

Superior Mesenteric V.

Inferior Mesenteric V.

Pancreas (Neck) (res.)

Gastrocolic Ligament

Triangular Ligament Hepatis

Lesser Omentum (res.)

Abdominal Part of the Esophagus

Spleen

Gastrosplenic (Gastrolienal) **Ligament**

Splenic A.

The Stomach has been Removed. The Structures of the Porta Hepatis have been Dissected to illustrate the course of the Superior Mesenteric V. Posterior to the Neck of the Pancreas (Resected), which joins the Splenic V. to form the Portal V.

5.119 Posterior Wall of the Omental Bursa: Ventral View. [15]

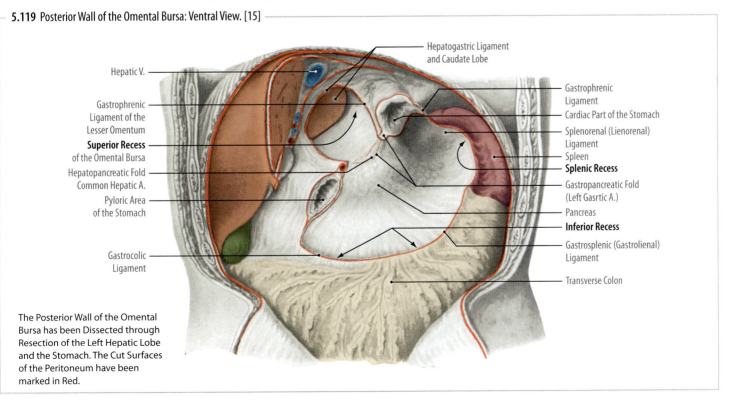

Hepatic V.

Gastrophrenic Ligament of the Lesser Omentum

Superior Recess of the Omental Bursa

Hepatopancreatic Fold Common Hepatic A.

Pyloric Area of the Stomach

Gastrocolic Ligament

Hepatogastric Ligament and Caudate Lobe

Gastrophrenic Ligament

Cardiac Part of the Stomach

Splenorenal (Lienorenal) Ligament

Spleen

Splenic Recess

Gastropancreatic Fold (Left Gasrtic A.)

Pancreas

Inferior Recess

Gastrosplenic (Gastrolienal) Ligament

Transverse Colon

The Posterior Wall of the Omental Bursa has been Dissected through Resection of the Left Hepatic Lobe and the Stomach. The Cut Surfaces of the Peritoneum have been marked in Red.

Abdominal Cavity

Omental Bursa

5.120 Sagittal Section through the Median Area of the Omental Bursa and the Neighboring Organs: Anterolateral View of the Right Cut Surface. [57]

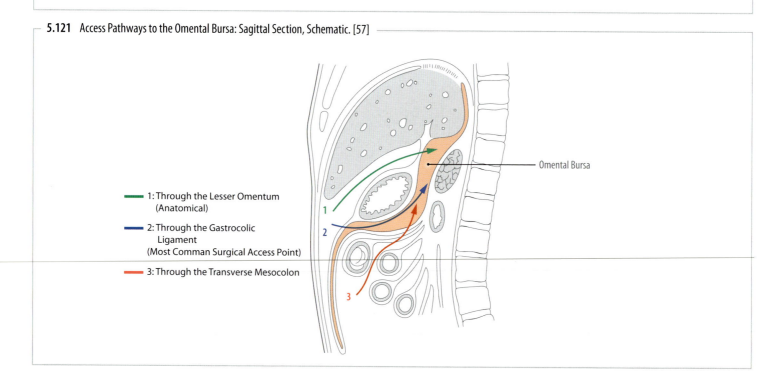

Hepatic Falciform Ligament (res.)
and Ligamentum Teres Hepatis (res.)
(Round Ligament of Liver)

Proper Hepatic A.

Hepatoduodenal Ligament
of the Lesser Omentum

Superior Part of the Duodenum

Right Gastroepiploic A. and V.

Right Colic Flexure

Omental Branches

**Hepatogastric Ligament
of the Lesser Omentum**

Omental Bursa

Stomach

Splenic A. and V.

Pancreas

Gastrocolic Ligament

Inferior Recess of the Omental Bursa

Transverse Mesocolon

Transverse Colon

Inferior Recess of the
Omental Bursa (Lesser Sac)

**Dorsal Layer of the
Greater Omentum**

**Ventral Layer of the
Greater Omentum**

Inflammations in the Abdominal Cavity cause Adhesions of the Greater Omentum with the Viscera in the Area of the Inflammation and Isolate the Area from the Rest of the Peritoneal Cavity.

5.121 Access Pathways to the Omental Bursa: Sagittal Section, Schematic. [57]

Omental Bursa

1: Through the Lesser Omentum
(Anatomical)

2: Through the Gastrocolic
Ligament
(Most Comman Surgical Access Point)

3: Through the Transverse Mesocolon

316

Epigastric Cavity

5.122 Epigastric Organs and Right Kidney: Dorsal View. [15]

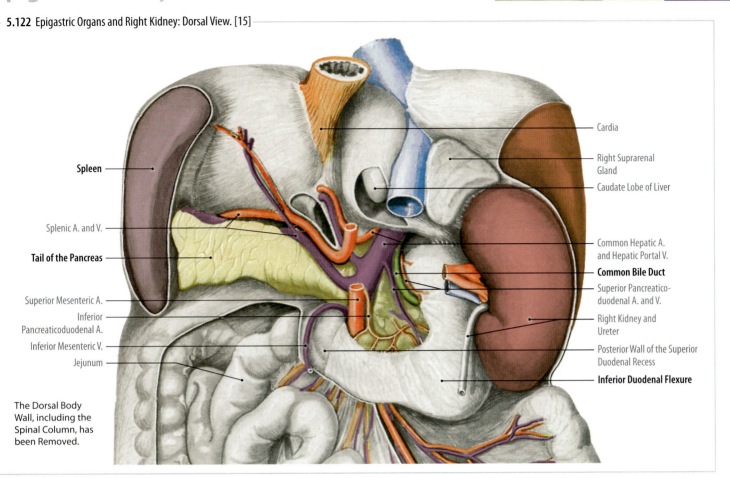

- Spleen
- Splenic A. and V.
- **Tail of the Pancreas**
- Superior Mesenteric A.
- Inferior Pancreaticoduodenal A.
- Inferior Mesenteric V.
- Jejunum

- Cardia
- Right Suprarenal Gland
- Caudate Lobe of Liver
- Common Hepatic A. and Hepatic Portal V.
- **Common Bile Duct**
- Superior Pancreatico-duodenal A. and V.
- Right Kidney and Ureter
- Posterior Wall of the Superior Duodenal Recess
- **Inferior Duodenal Flexure**

The Dorsal Body Wall, including the Spinal Column, has been Removed.

5.123 Epigastric Organs: Ventral View. [15]

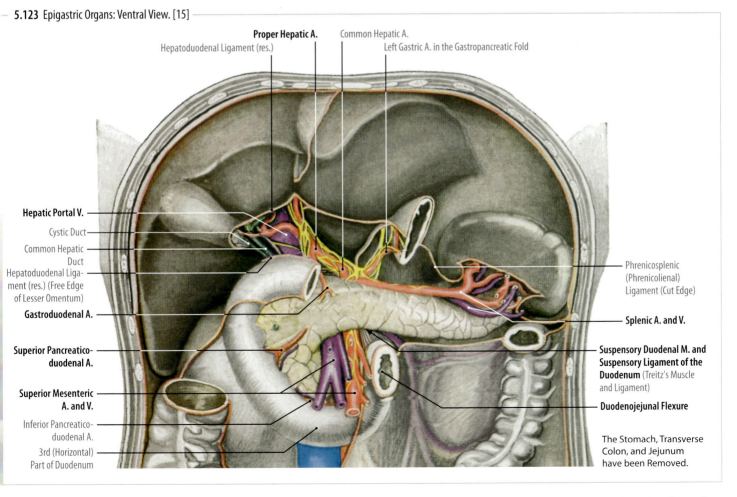

- Hepatoduodenal Ligament (res.)
- **Proper Hepatic A.**
- Common Hepatic A.
- Left Gastric A. in the Gastropancreatic Fold

- **Hepatic Portal V.**
- Cystic Duct
- Common Hepatic Duct
- Hepatoduodenal Ligament (res.) (Free Edge of Lesser Omentum)
- **Gastroduodenal A.**
- **Superior Pancreatico-duodenal A.**
- **Superior Mesenteric A. and V.**
- Inferior Pancreatico-duodenal A.
- 3rd (Horizontal) Part of Duodenum

- Phrenicosplenic (Phrenicolienal) Ligament (Cut Edge)
- **Splenic A. and V.**
- **Suspensory Duodenal M. and Suspensory Ligament of the Duodenum** (Treitz's Muscle and Ligament)
- **Duodenojejunal Flexure**

The Stomach, Transverse Colon, and Jejunum have been Removed.

Abdominal Cavity

5.124 Illustration of the Epigastric Organs: Contrast Medium-Based Multislice Computed Tomography (Layer Thickness 1.3 mm), Volume Rendering [75].

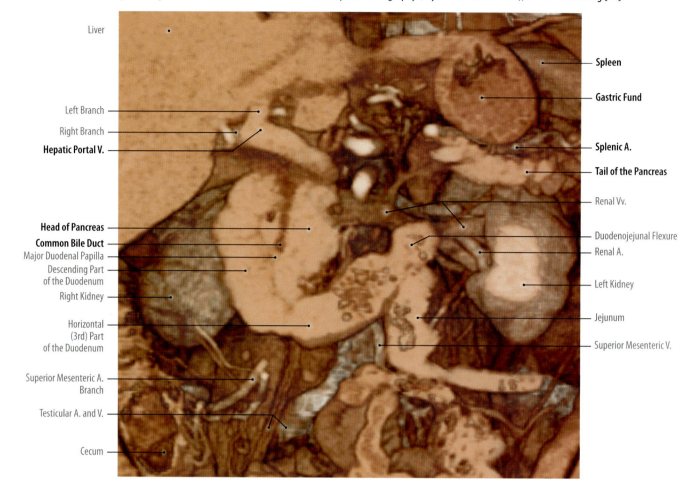

Liver

Left Branch

Right Branch

Hepatic Portal V.

Head of Pancreas

Common Bile Duct

Major Duodenal Papilla

Descending Part of the Duodenum

Right Kidney

Horizontal (3rd) Part of the Duodenum

Superior Mesenteric A. Branch

Testicular A. and V.

Cecum

Spleen

Gastric Fund

Splenic A.

Tail of the Pancreas

Renal Vv.

Duodenojejunal Flexure

Renal A.

Left Kidney

Jejunum

Superior Mesenteric V.

5.125 MRI of the Epigastric Organs Following Intravenous and Administration of a Contrast Medium in a 51-Year-Old Man: Transverse Section at the Level of Thoracic Vertebra T12. [28]

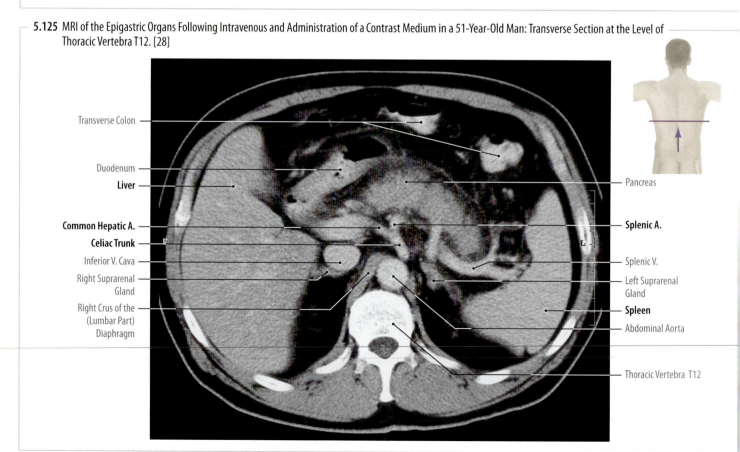

Transverse Colon

Duodenum

Liver

Common Hepatic A.

Celiac Trunk

Inferior V. Cava

Right Suprarenal Gland

Right Crus of the (Lumbar Part) Diaphragm

Pancreas

Splenic A.

Splenic V.

Left Suprarenal Gland

Spleen

Abdominal Aorta

Thoracic Vertebra T12

Epigastric Organs: Imaging

5.126a,b Sonographic Illustration of the Epigastric Organs. [50]

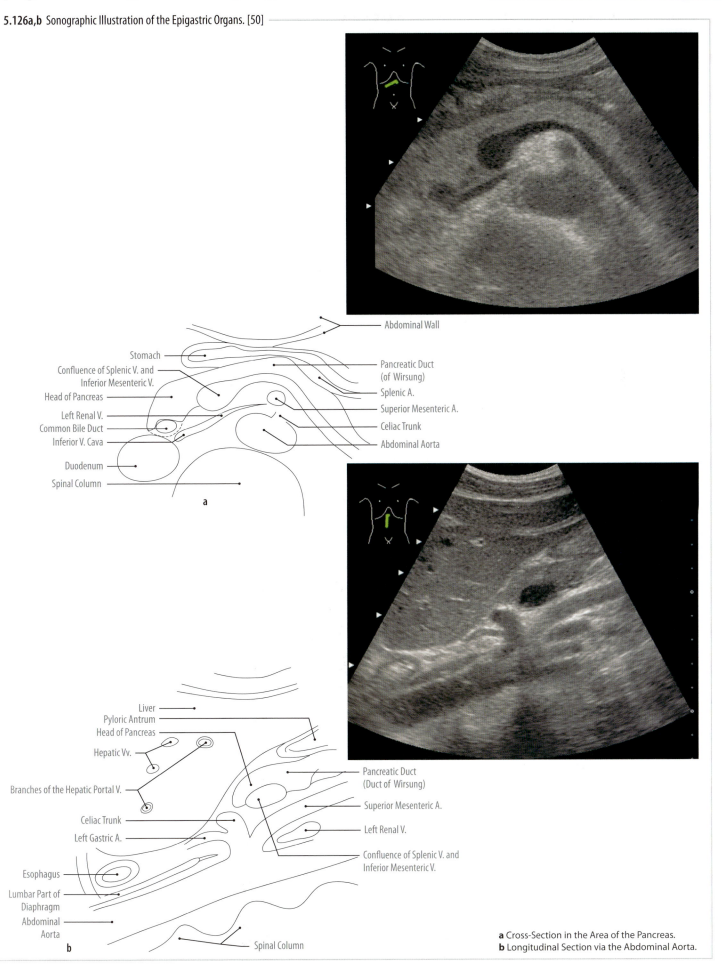

Abdominal Wall

Stomach

Confluence of Splenic V. and
Inferior Mesenteric V.

Head of Pancreas

Left Renal V.

Common Bile Duct

Inferior V. Cava

Duodenum

Spinal Column

Pancreatic Duct
(of Wirsung)

Splenic A.

Superior Mesenteric A.

Celiac Trunk

Abdominal Aorta

a

Liver

Pyloric Antrum

Head of Pancreas

Hepatic Vv.

Branches of the Hepatic Portal V.

Celiac Trunk

Left Gastric A.

Esophagus

Lumbar Part of
Diaphragm

Abdominal
Aorta

b

Spinal Column

Pancreatic Duct
(Duct of Wirsung)

Superior Mesenteric A.

Left Renal V.

Confluence of Splenic V. and
Inferior Mesenteric V.

a Cross-Section in the Area of the Pancreas.
b Longitudinal Section via the Abdominal Aorta.

Abdominal Cavity

5.127 Abdominal Viscera: Ventral View. [6]

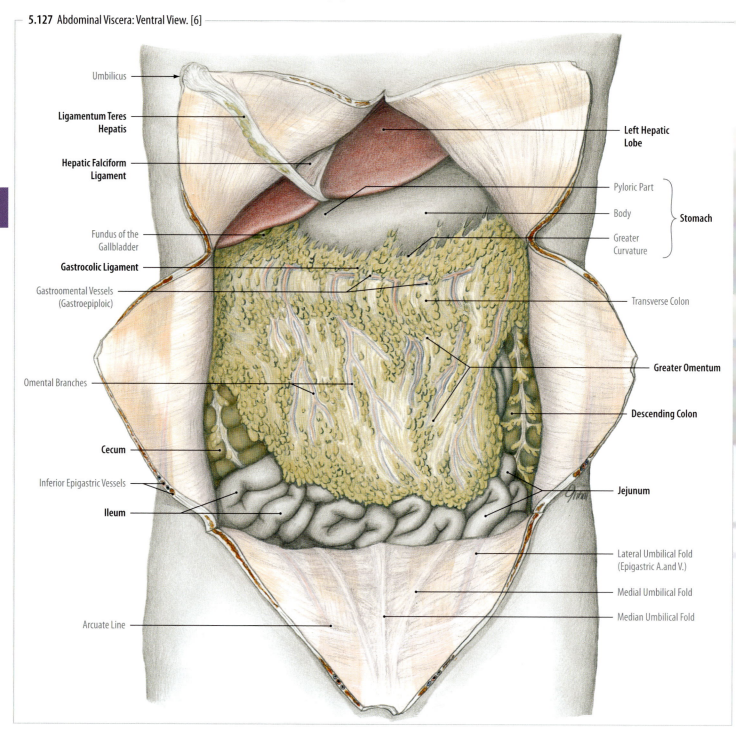

Umbilicus

Ligamentum Teres Hepatis

Hepatic Falciform Ligament

Fundus of the Gallbladder

Gastrocolic Ligament

Gastroomental Vessels (Gastroepiploic)

Omental Branches

Cecum

Inferior Epigastric Vessels

Ileum

Arcuate Line

Left Hepatic Lobe

Pyloric Part

Body

Stomach

Greater Curvature

Transverse Colon

Greater Omentum

Descending Colon

Jejunum

Lateral Umbilical Fold (Epigastric A. and V.)

Medial Umbilical Fold

Median Umbilical Fold

5.128 Positional Variation of the Cecum and the Appendix (Vermiform Appendix). [67]

Localization of McBurney's Point and the Lanz Point: The Lanz Point lies on the Right Third Point of the Connecting Line of the two Anterior Superior Iliac Spines (Interspinal Line). McBurney's Point lies at the Transition from the Lateral to the Middle Third Point on the Connecting Line between the Right Anterior Superior Iliac Spine and the Umbilicus (Monro's Line).

The Midgut rotates 270 degrees to bring the Cecum and Appendix into the Right Lower Quadrant of the Abdomen—first, 90 degrees intraabdominally before Eventration of the Gut, and then 180 degrees when the Gut returns to the Abdominal Cavity.

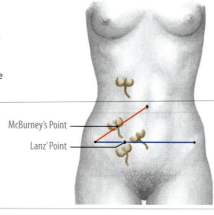

McBurney's Point

Lanz' Point

Positional Variation of the Cecum and the Appendix are caused by Disturbances of the "Intestinal Rotation" in the Embryonic Period (Malrotation); they must be considered in a Differential Diagnosis of Appendicitis. The Main symptoms of Acute Appendicitis are Pressure Pain in the area of McBurney's Point, Muscular Rigidity in the area of the Abdominal Wall, Signs of Infection, Pain due to the Sudden Loosening of the Impressed Abdominal Wall on the Left Side (Contralateral Loosening Pain), Pain due to Rectal Palpation of the Douglas' Space (Not Present in the Retrocecal Position of the Vermiform Appendix ◘ Fig. 5.130 d).

5.129 Hypogastric Organs, Small Intestine and Large Intestine: Ventral View. [6]

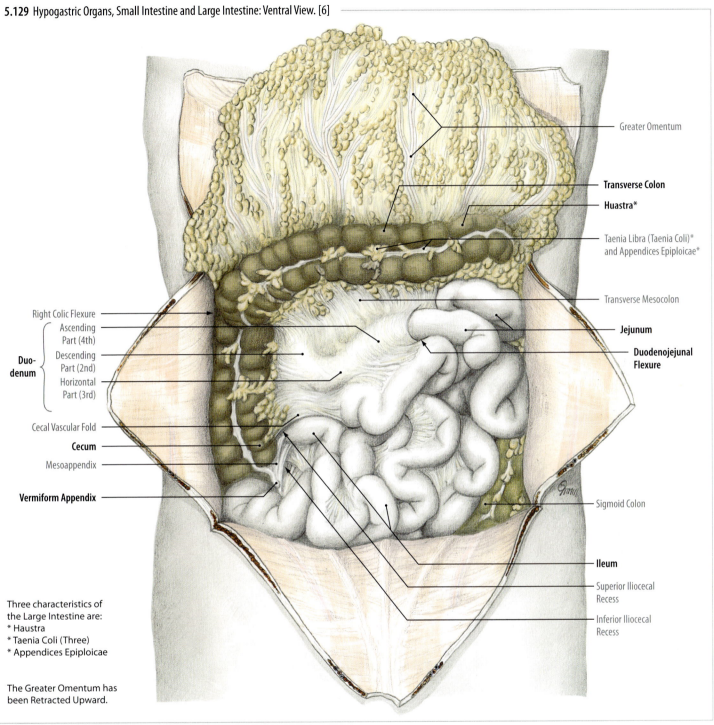

Greater Omentum

Transverse Colon

Huastra*

Taenia Libra (Taenia Coli)*
and Appendices Epiploicae*

Transverse Mesocolon

Right Colic Flexure

Jejunum

Ascending
Part (4th)

**Duodenojejunal
Flexure**

**Duo-
denum**

Descending
Part (2nd)

Horizontal
Part (3rd)

Cecal Vascular Fold

Cecum

Mesoappendix

Sigmoid Colon

Vermiform Appendix

Ileum

Superior Iliocecal
Recess

Three characteristics of
the Large Intestine are:
* Haustra
* Taenia Coli (Three)
* Appendices Epiploicae

Inferior Iliocecal
Recess

The Greater Omentum has
been Retracted Upward.

5.130a–d Position of the Appendix (Vermiform Appendix), Variation. [15]

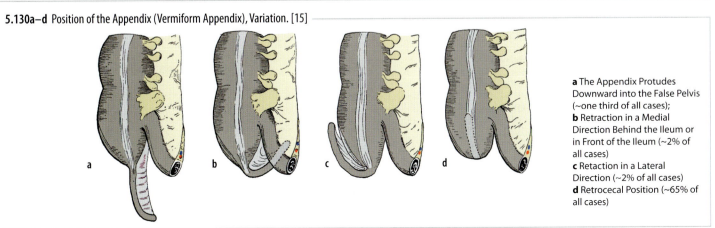

a The Appendix Protudes
Downward into the False Pelvis
(~one third of all cases);
b Retraction in a Medial
Direction Behind the Ileum or
in Front of the Ileum (~2% of
all cases)
c Retaction in a Lateral
Direction (~2% of all cases)
d Retrocecal Position (~65% of
all cases)

a   b   c   d

Abdominal Cavity

5.131 Convolution of the Small Intestine with Root of Mesentery and Large Intestine: Ventral View. [6]

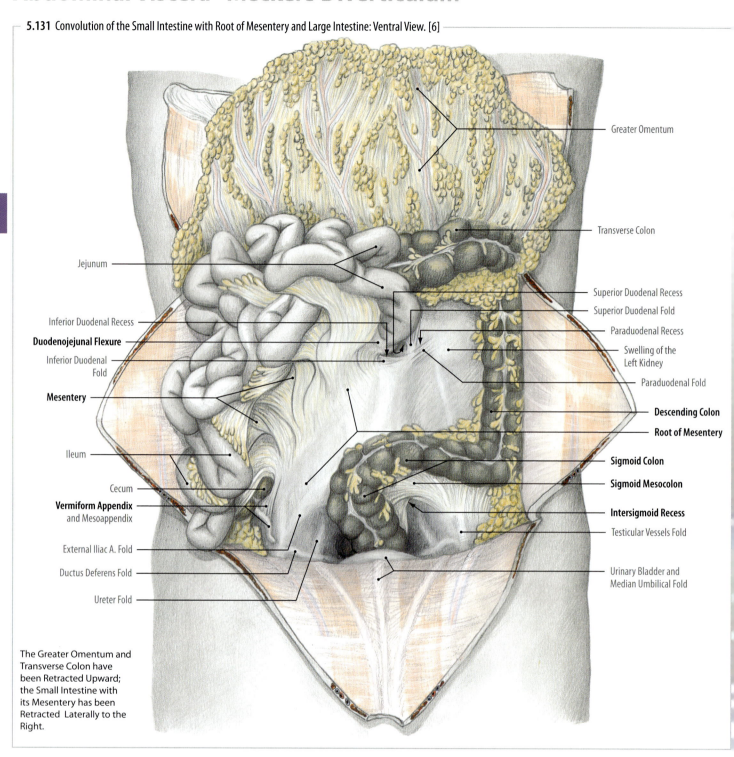

Greater Omentum

Transverse Colon

Jejunum

Superior Duodenal Recess

Superior Duodenal Fold

Inferior Duodenal Recess

Paraduodenal Recess

Duodenojejunal Flexure

Swelling of the
Left Kidney

Inferior Duodenal
Fold

Paraduodenal Fold

Mesentery

Descending Colon

Root of Mesentery

Ileum

Sigmoid Colon

Cecum

Sigmoid Mesocolon

Vermiform Appendix
and Mesoappendix

Intersigmoid Recess

Testicular Vessels Fold

External Iliac A. Fold

Ductus Deferens Fold

Urinary Bladder and
Median Umbilical Fold

Ureter Fold

The Greater Omentum and
Transverse Colon have
been Retracted Upward;
the Small Intestine with
its Mesentery has been
Retracted Laterally to the
Right.

5.132 Part of the Ileum with Large Meckel's Diverticulum. [6]

In ~2–4% of cases, a Meckel's Diverticulum in
the Area of the Ileum occurs. It may lie between
20–100 cm before the Ileocecal Valve; its Length
is very Variable. A Meckel's Diverticulum may be
Inflamed and Simulate Appendicitis. If the Connection between the Meckel's Diverticulum and
the Umbilicus is Preserved, there is Danger of a
Twisting of the Small Intestine (Volvulus) and
Strangulation. If a Meckel's Diverticulum Contains Gastric Mucosa or Pancreatic Tissue, Ulcers
may Develop, which may Cause Bleeding and a
Perforation of a Meckel's Diverticulum.

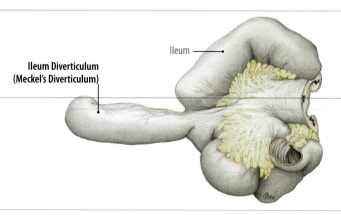

Ileum

**Ileum Diverticulum
(Meckel's Diverticulum)**

5.133a–c Abdominal Cavity, Recess, and Folds in the Area of the Hypogastric Organs. [a,b 57, 15]

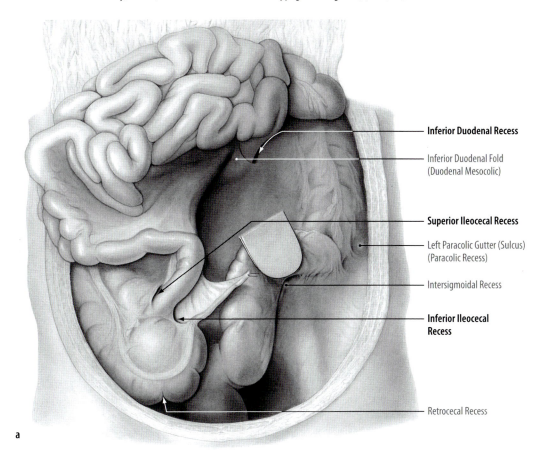

In the event of a Wide Recess in the Area of the Duodenojejunal Flexure, an Internal Hernia may Develop (e.g., Treitz's Hernia).

Inferior Duodenal Recess

Inferior Duodenal Fold (Duodenal Mesocolic)

Superior Ileocecal Recess

Left Paracolic Gutter (Sulcus) (Paracolic Recess)

Intersigmoidal Recess

Inferior Ileocecal Recess

Retrocecal Recess

a

Recesses

– Superior Duodenal
– Inferior Duodenal (Paraduodenal ▪Fig. 5.131)
– Retroduodenal
– Intersigmoid
– Superior Ileocecal
– Inferior Ileocecal
– Retrocecal
Cecal Folds
Paracolic Gutters (Sulci, Recesses)

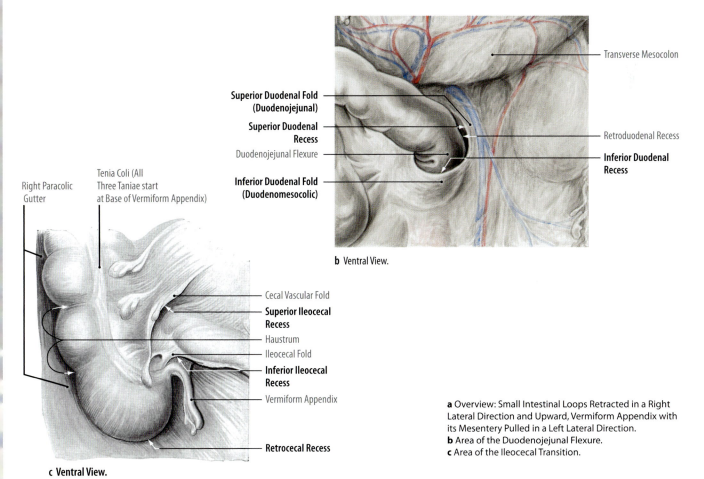

Transverse Mesocolon

Superior Duodenal Fold (Duodenojejunal)

Superior Duodenal Recess

Duodenojejunal Flexure

Inferior Duodenal Fold (Duodenomesocolic)

Retroduodenal Recess

Inferior Duodenal Recess

b Ventral View.

Right Paracolic Gutter

Tenia Coli (All Three Taniae start at Base of Vermiform Appendix)

Cecal Vascular Fold

Superior Ileocecal Recess

Haustrum

Ileocecal Fold

Inferior Ileocecal Recess

Vermiform Appendix

Retrocecal Recess

c Ventral View.

a Overview: Small Intestinal Loops Retracted in a Right Lateral Direction and Upward, Vermiform Appendix with its Mesentery Pulled in a Left Lateral Direction.
b Area of the Duodenojejunal Flexure.
c Area of the Ileocecal Transition.

Abdominal Cavity

5.134a–c Mucosal Layer of the Small Intestine . [a 87; b,c 6]

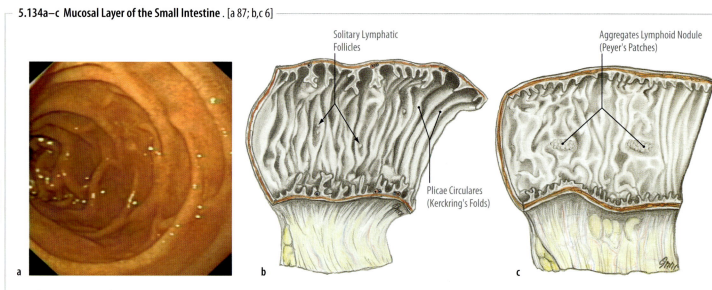

Solitary Lymphatic Follicles

Aggregates Lymphoid Nodule (Peyer's Patches)

Plicae Circulares (Kerckring's Folds)

a · b · c

a Endoscopic Image of the Mucous Membrane of the Duodenum. **b** Mucous Membrane of the Jejunum. **c** Mucous Membrane of the Ileum.

5.135a,b Colon and Transition Between Ileum and Cecum. [6]

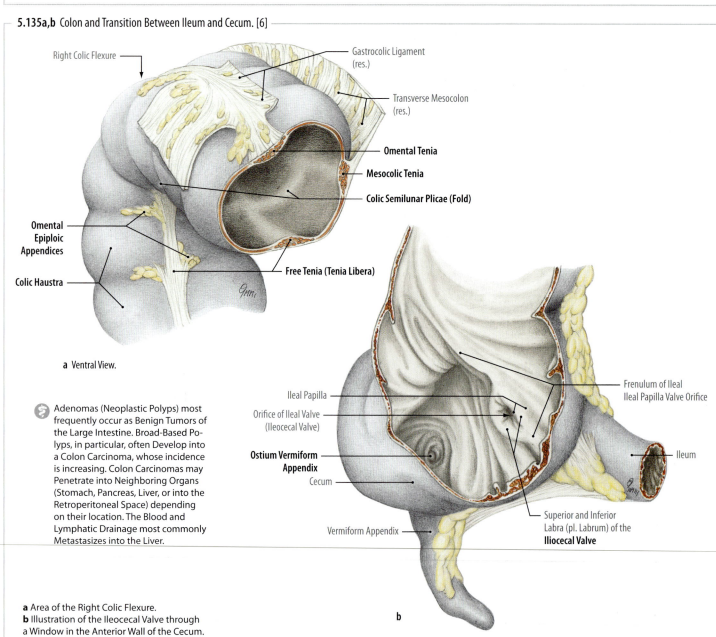

Right Colic Flexure

Gastrocolic Ligament (res.)

Transverse Mesocolon (res.)

Omental Tenia

Mesocolic Tenia

Colic Semilunar Plicae (Fold)

Omental Epiploic Appendices

Colic Haustra

Free Tenia (Tenia Libera)

a Ventral View.

Adenomas (Neoplastic Polyps) most frequently occur as Benign Tumors of the Large Intestine. Broad-Based Polyps, in particular, often Develop into a Colon Carcinoma, whose incidence is increasing. Colon Carcinomas may Penetrate into Neighboring Organs (Stomach, Pancreas, Liver, or into the Retroperitoneal Space) depending on their location. The Blood and Lymphatic Drainage most commonly Metastasizes into the Liver.

Ileal Papilla

Orifice of Ileal Valve (Ileocecal Valve)

Ostium Vermiform Appendix

Cecum

Vermiform Appendix

Frenulum of Ileal Ileal Papilla Valve Orifice

Ileum

Superior and Inferior Labra (pl. Labrum) of the **Iliocecal Valve**

a Area of the Right Colic Flexure.
b Illustration of the Ileocecal Valve through a Window in the Anterior Wall of the Cecum.

b

5.136a,b X-Ray Image of the Intestine. [89]

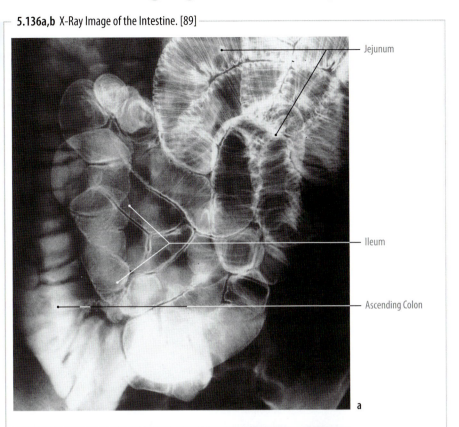

Jejunum

Ileum

Ascending Colon

a

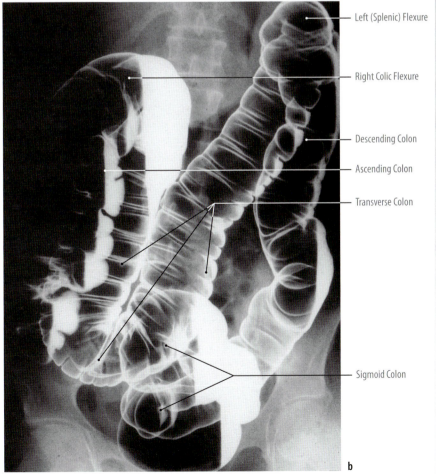

Left (Splenic) Flexure

Right Colic Flexure

Descending Colon

Ascending Colon

Transverse Colon

Sigmoid Colon

b

a Survey Radiogram of the Small Intestine of a Patient taken while Lying Down (technology according to Sellink). Note the Circular Plicae (Kerckring's Folds) in the Jejunum and the Decrease of the Number of Folds, as well as the Height of the Folds in the Area of the Ileum. **b** Survey Radiogram of the Colon (Patient is Lying Down on the Left Side.). V-Form of a Transverse Colon (~25–30% of all cases).

5.137a–c Form of the Colon, Variants. [57]

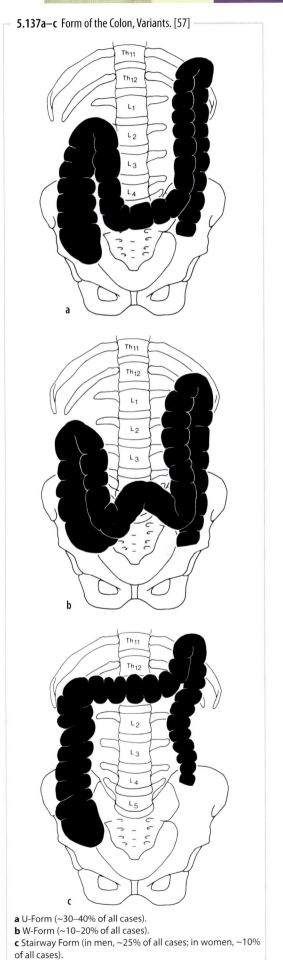

a

b

c

a U-Form (~30–40% of all cases).
b W-Form (~10–20% of all cases).
c Stairway Form (in men, ~25% of all cases; in women, ~10% of all cases).

Abdominal Cavity

5.138 Distribution of the Superior Mesenteric A. and the V.: Ventral View. [15]

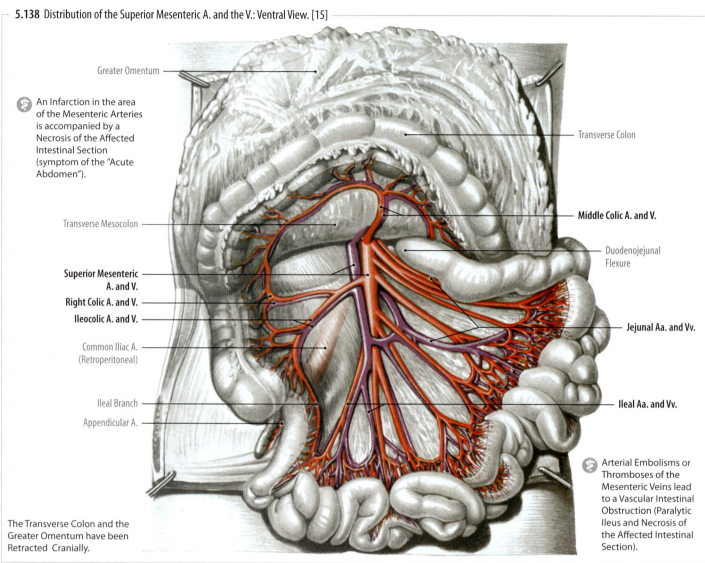

Greater Omentum

An Infarction in the area of the Mesenteric Arteries is accompanied by a Necrosis of the Affected Intestinal Section (symptom of the "Acute Abdomen").

5

Transverse Colon

Transverse Mesocolon

Middle Colic A. and V.

Duodenojejunal Flexure

Superior Mesenteric A. and V.

Right Colic A. and V.

Ileocolic A. and V.

Jejunal Aa. and Vv.

Common Iliac A. (Retroperitoneal)

Ileal Branch

Ileal Aa. and Vv.

Appendicular A.

Arterial Embolisms or Thromboses of the Mesenteric Veins lead to a Vascular Intestinal Obstruction (Paralytic Ileus and Necrosis of the Affected Intestinal Section).

The Transverse Colon and the Greater Omentum have been Retracted Cranially.

5.139a–c Blood Supply of the Small Intestine. [a 15; b,c 2]

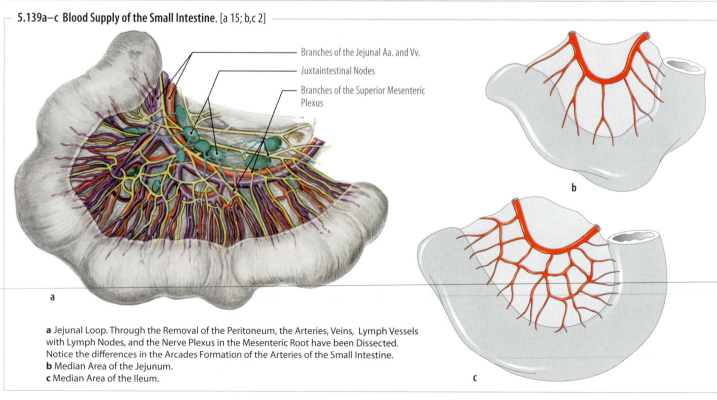

Branches of the Jejunal Aa. and Vv.

Juxtaintestinal Nodes

Branches of the Superior Mesenteric Plexus

b

a

c

a Jejunal Loop. Through the Removal of the Peritoneum, the Arteries, Veins, Lymph Vessels with Lymph Nodes, and the Nerve Plexus in the Mesenteric Root have been Dissected. Notice the differences in the Arcades Formation of the Arteries of the Small Intestine.
b Median Area of the Jejunum.
c Median Area of the Ileum.

Superior Mesenteric A.

5.140 Selective Intraarterial Digital Subtraction Angiography of the Superior Mesenteric A. Supply Area. [73]

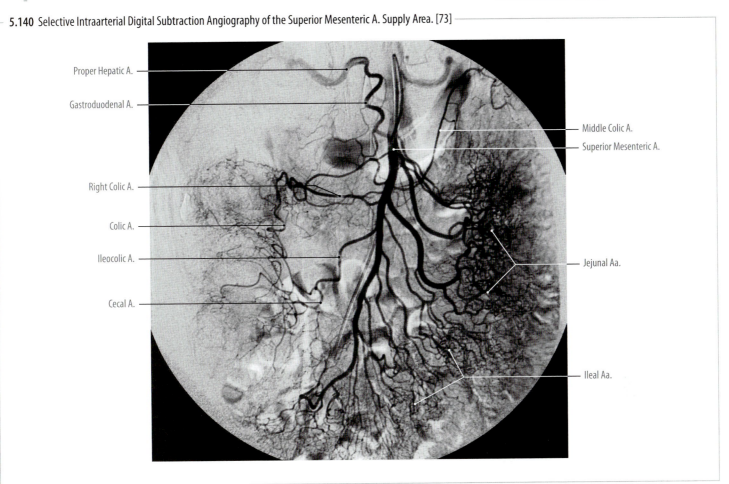

Proper Hepatic A.

Gastroduodenal A.

Right Colic A.

Colic A.

Ileocolic A.

Cecal A.

Middle Colic A.

Superior Mesenteric A.

Jejunal Aa.

Ileal Aa.

5.141 Electrocardiogram- (ECG-) Triggered Multislice Computed Tomography with Retrospective Gating (Layer Thickness 1.3 mm), Volume Rendering. Illustration of the Epigastric and Hypogastric Organs and Their Vessels. [75]

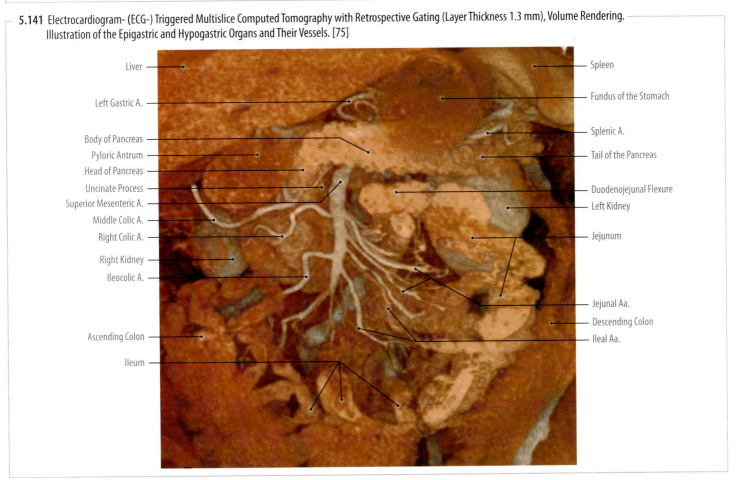

Liver

Left Gastric A.

Body of Pancreas

Pyloric Antrum

Head of Pancreas

Uncinate Process

Superior Mesenteric A.

Middle Colic A.

Right Colic A.

Right Kidney

Ileocolic A.

Ascending Colon

Ileum

Spleen

Fundus of the Stomach

Splenic A.

Tail of the Pancreas

Duodenojejunal Flexure

Left Kidney

Jejunum

Jejunal Aa.

Descending Colon

Ileal Aa.

Abdominal Cavity

5.142 Arterial Supply of the Large Intestine: Ventral View. [57, 90]

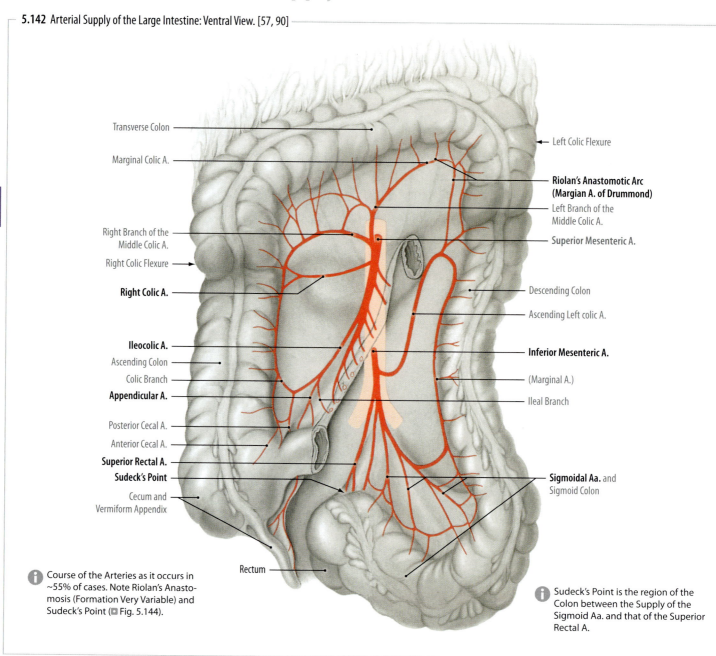

Transverse Colon

Marginal Colic A.

Right Branch of the Middle Colic A.

Right Colic Flexure

Right Colic A.

Ileocolic A.

Ascending Colon

Colic Branch

Appendicular A.

Posterior Cecal A.

Anterior Cecal A.

Superior Rectal A.

Sudeck's Point

Cecum and Vermiform Appendix

Rectum

Left Colic Flexure

Riolan's Anastomotic Arc (Margian A. of Drummond)

Left Branch of the Middle Colic A.

Superior Mesenteric A.

Descending Colon

Ascending Left colic A.

Inferior Mesenteric A.

(Marginal A.)

Ileal Branch

Sigmoidal Aa. and Sigmoid Colon

ℹ️ Course of the Arteries as it occurs in ~55% of cases. Note Riolan's Anastomosis (Formation Very Variable) and Sudeck's Point (◻ Fig. 5.144).

ℹ️ Sudeck's Point is the region of the Colon between the Supply of the Sigmoid Aa. and that of the Superior Rectal A.

5.143 Arterial Supply of the Intestine in the Ileocecal Transition Area, Blood Supply of the Vermiform Appendix. [57]

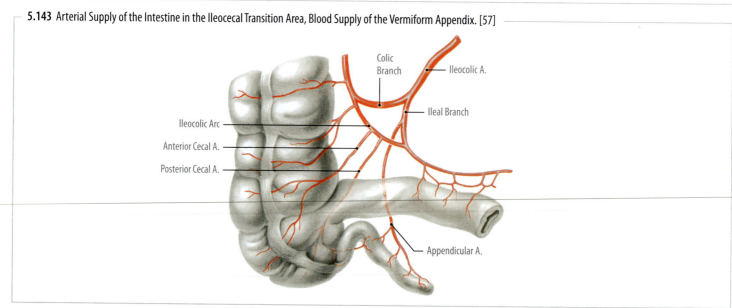

Colic Branch

Ileocolic A.

Ileal Branch

Ileocolic Arc

Anterior Cecal A.

Posterior Cecal A.

Appendicular A.

5.144a–c Anastomoses between the Arteries of the Abdominal Cavity.

The Anastomoses between the Arteries of the Abdominal Viscera have a practical Clinical Significance in Surgical Procedures. These Collateral Circulations are Important in Vascular Stenoses and in cases of Obliteration.
Sudeck's Point marks the Sigmorectal Area where Anastomosis between the Arcade of the Distal Segmoidal A. and the Superior Rectal A. occurs. In the event of a Ligature of the Superior Rectal A. Cranially, the Blood Supply of the Rectum is Ensured.
If the Anastomoses with the Middle
Rectal A. of the Intestinal Wall are Insufficient, A Ligation Caudal of Sudeck's Point may lead to Circulatory Disorders of the Rectum.

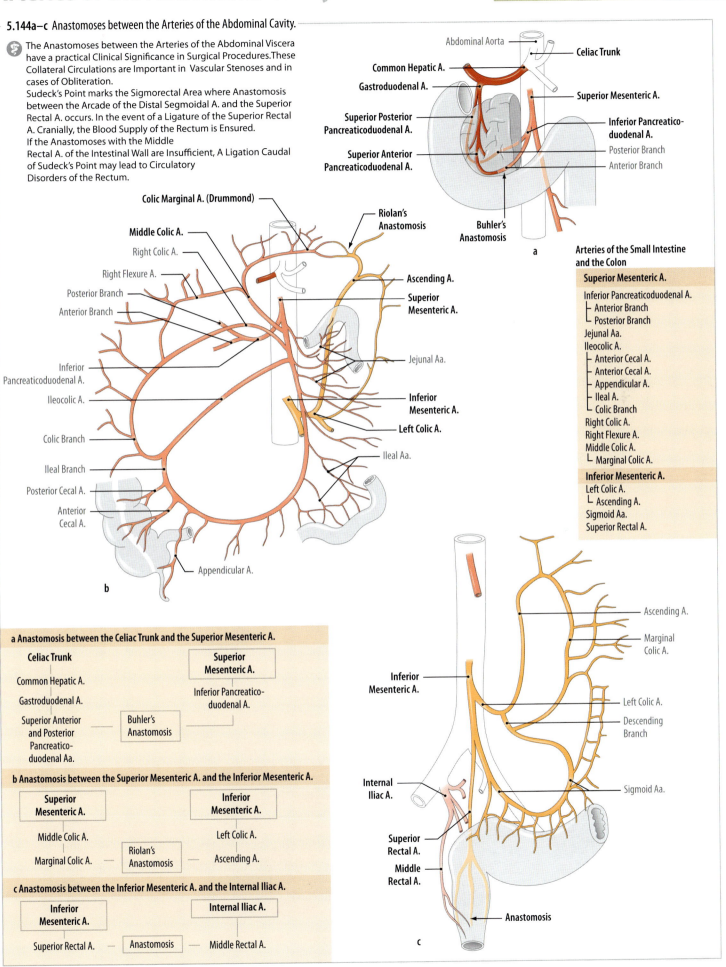

Arteries of the Small Intestine and the Colon

Superior Mesenteric A.

Inferior Pancreaticoduodenal A.
 ├ Anterior Branch
 └ Posterior Branch
Jejunal Aa.
Ileocolic A.
 ├ Anterior Cecal A.
 ├ Anterior Cecal A.
 ├ Appendicular A.
 ├ Ileal A.
 └ Colic Branch
Right Colic A.
Right Flexure A.
Middle Colic A.
 └ Marginal Colic A.

Inferior Mesenteric A.

Left Colic A.
 └ Ascending A.
Sigmoid Aa.
Superior Rectal A.

a Anastomosis between the Celiac Trunk and the Superior Mesenteric A.

b Anastomosis between the Superior Mesenteric A. and the Inferior Mesenteric A.

c Anastomosis between the Inferior Mesenteric A. and the Internal Iliac A.

Abdominal Cavity

5.145 Area of Supply of the Inferior Mesenteric A.: Ventral View. [57]

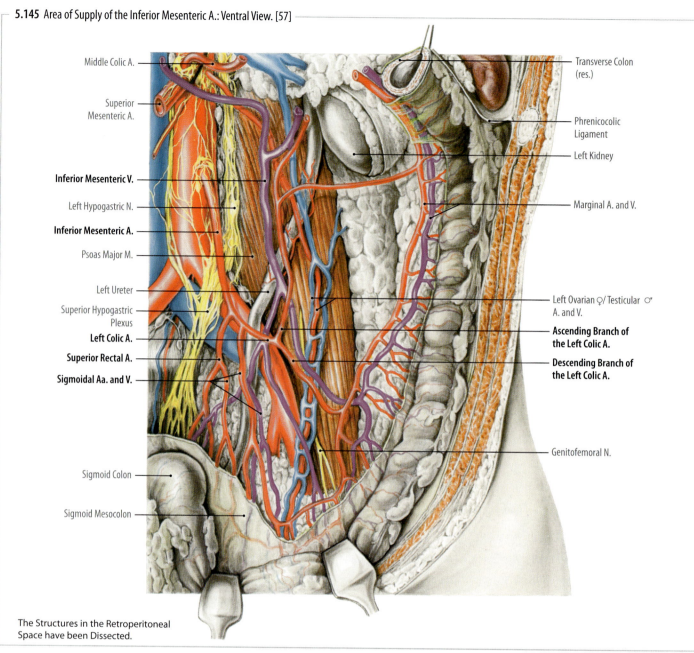

Middle Colic A.

Superior Mesenteric A.

Inferior Mesenteric V.

Left Hypogastric N.

Inferior Mesenteric A.

Psoas Major M.

Left Ureter

Superior Hypogastric Plexus

Left Colic A.

Superior Rectal A.

Sigmoidal Aa. and V.

Sigmoid Colon

Sigmoid Mesocolon

Transverse Colon (res.)

Phrenicocolic Ligament

Left Kidney

Marginal A. and V.

Left Ovarian ♀/ Testicular ♂ A. and V.

Ascending Branch of the Left Colic A.

Descending Branch of the Left Colic A.

Genitofemoral N.

The Structures in the Retroperitoneal Space have been Dissected.

5.146 Blood Supply of the Cecum and the Vermiform Appendix: Ventral View. [57]

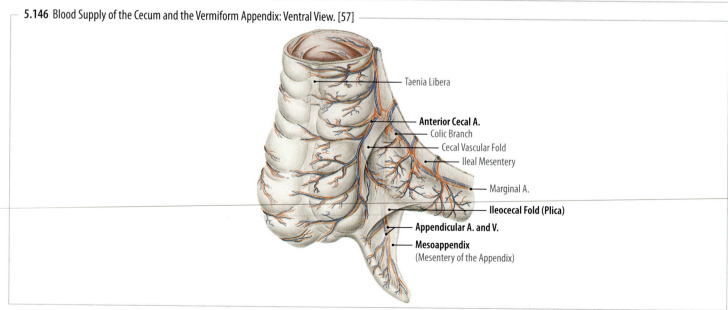

Taenia Libera

Anterior Cecal A.
Colic Branch
Cecal Vascular Fold
Ileal Mesentery

Marginal A.

Ileocecal Fold (Plica)

Appendicular A. and V.

Mesoappendix
(Mesentery of the Appendix)

5.147 Regional Lymph Nodes and Lymph Drain of the Intestine. [57]

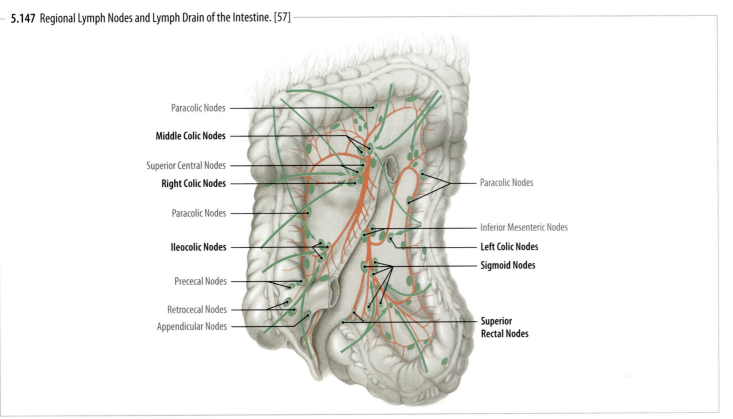

Paracolic Nodes
Middle Colic Nodes
Superior Central Nodes
Right Colic Nodes
Paracolic Nodes
Ileocolic Nodes
Prececal Nodes
Retrocecal Nodes
Appendicular Nodes

Paracolic Nodes
Inferior Mesenteric Nodes
Left Colic Nodes
Sigmoid Nodes
Superior Rectal Nodes

5.148 Dorsal Wall of the Abdominal Cavity. [15]

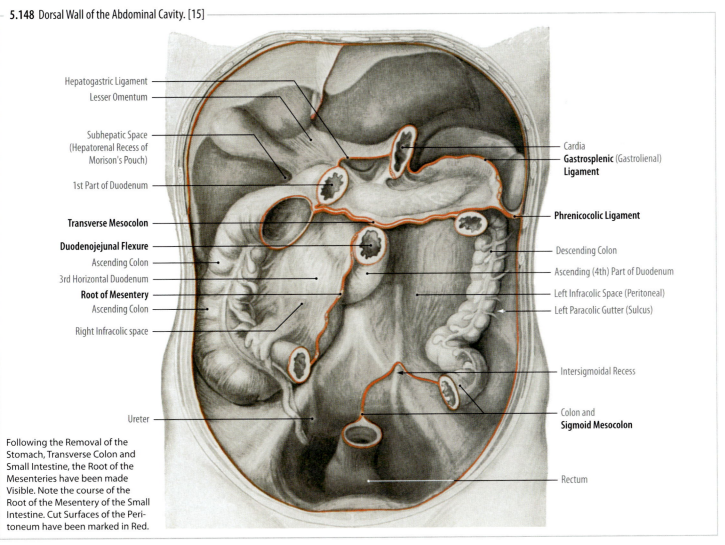

Hepatogastric Ligament
Lesser Omentum
Subhepatic Space (Hepatorenal Recess of Morison's Pouch)
1st Part of Duodenum
Transverse Mesocolon
Duodenojejunal Flexure
Ascending Colon
3rd Horizontal Duodenum
Root of Mesentery
Ascending Colon
Right Infracolic space
Ureter

Cardia
Gastrosplenic (Gastrolienal) **Ligament**
Phrenicocolic Ligament
Descending Colon
Ascending (4th) Part of Duodenum
Left Infracolic Space (Peritoneal)
Left Paracolic Gutter (Sulcus)
Intersigmoidal Recess
Colon and **Sigmoid Mesocolon**
Rectum

Following the Removal of the Stomach, Transverse Colon and Small Intestine, the Root of the Mesenteries have been made Visible. Note the course of the Root of the Mesentery of the Small Intestine. Cut Surfaces of the Peritoneum have been marked in Red.

5.149 Posterior Abdominal Wall: Ventral View. [48]

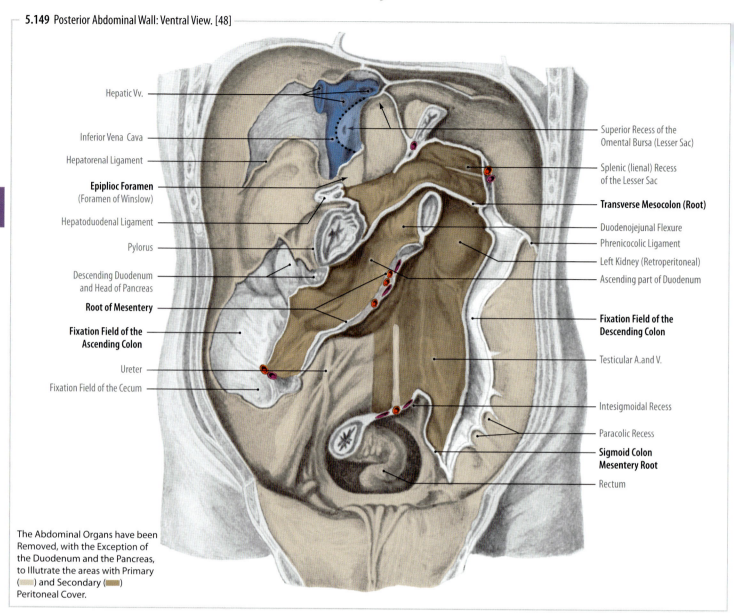

Hepatic Vv.

Inferior Vena Cava

Hepatorenal Ligament

Epiplioc Foramen
(Foramen of Winslow)

Hepatoduodenal Ligament

Pylorus

Descending Duodenum
and Head of Pancreas

Root of Mesentery

**Fixation Field of the
Ascending Colon**

Ureter

Fixation Field of the Cecum

Superior Recess of the
Omental Bursa (Lesser Sac)

Splenic (lienal) Recess
of the Lesser Sac

Transverse Mesocolon (Root)

Duodenojejunal Flexure

Phrenicocolic Ligament

Left Kidney (Retroperitoneal)

Ascending part of Duodenum

**Fixation Field of the
Descending Colon**

Testicular A. and V.

Intesigmoidal Recess

Paracolic Recess

**Sigmoid Colon
Mesentery Root**

Rectum

The Abdominal Organs have been
Removed, with the Exception of
the Duodenum and the Pancreas,
to Illutrate the areas with Primary
(▭) and Secondary (▭)
Peritoneal Cover.

5.150 Posterior Abdominal Wall Following Removal of the Abdominal Organs, Recesses in the Area of the Abdominal Cavity: Ventral View. [57]

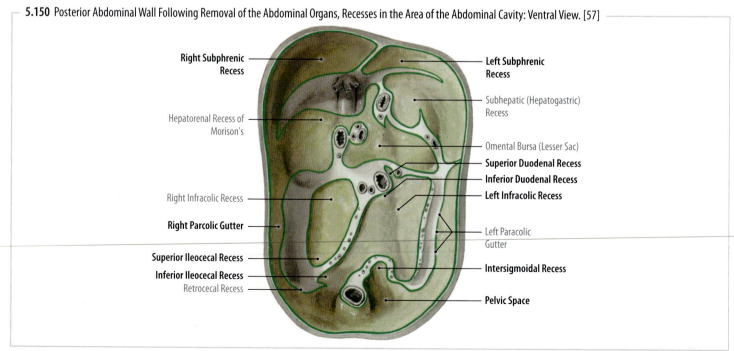

**Right Subphrenic
Recess**

Hepatorenal Recess of
Morison's

Right Infracolic Recess

Right Parcolic Gutter

Superior Ileocecal Recess

Inferior Ileocecal Recess

Retrocecal Recess

**Left Subphrenic
Recess**

Subhepatic (Hepatogastric)
Recess

Omental Bursa (Lesser Sac)

Superior Duodenal Recess

Inferior Duodenal Recess

Left Infracolic Recess

Left Paracolic
Gutter

Intersigmoidal Recess

Pelvic Space

5.151 Organs and Pathways of the Retroperitoneal Space: Ventral View. [57]

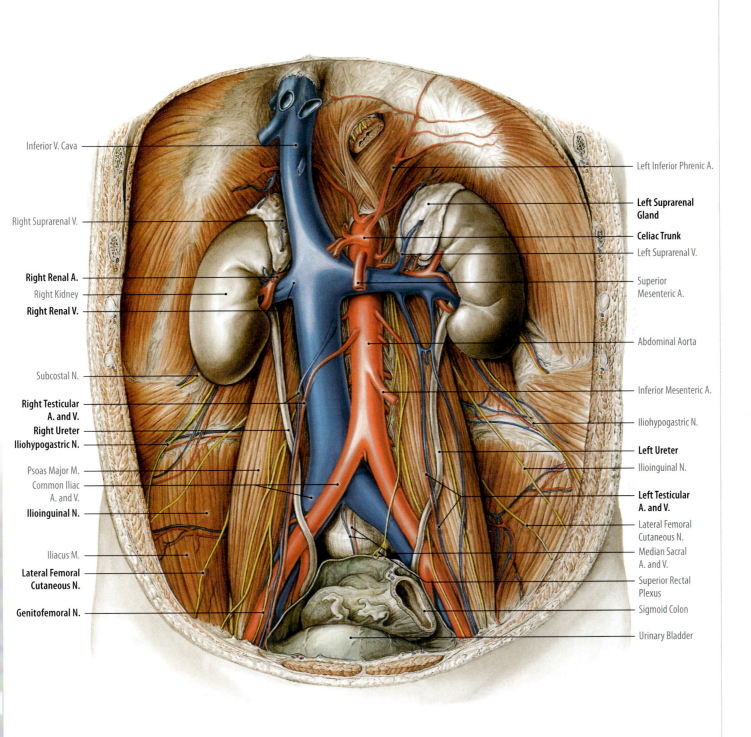

Inferior V. Cava

Left Inferior Phrenic A.

Left Suprarenal Gland

Celiac Trunk

Left Suprarenal V.

Right Suprarenal V.

Right Renal A.

Right Kidney

Right Renal V.

Superior Mesenteric A.

Abdominal Aorta

Subcostal N.

Inferior Mesenteric A.

Right Testicular A. and V.

Right Ureter

Iliohypogastric N.

Iliohypogastric N.

Left Ureter

Ilioinguinal N.

Psoas Major M.

Common Iliac A. and V.

Ilioinguinal N.

Left Testicular A. and V.

Lateral Femoral Cutaneous N.

Median Sacral A. and V.

Iliacus M.

Lateral Femoral Cutaneous N.

Superior Rectal Plexus

Sigmoid Colon

Genitofemoral N.

Urinary Bladder

The Parietal Peritoneum and the Extraperitoneal Fat, as well as the Transversalis Fascia and Muscles have been Removed.

ℹ Note the Crossing of the Ureter through the Gonadal Vessel ♂/or ♀ and Entering the Pelvis by Crossing Over the Common Iliac V. Bifurcation at Sacroiliac Joint.

🔄 **Ureteral Narrowings:**
1. Narrowing: At the Transition from the Renal Pelvis to the Ureter
2. Narrowing: Crossing through the Ovarian /Testicular A. and V.
3. Narrowing: In the area of the Crossing to the Iliac Vessels
4. Narrowing: At the Orifice into the Urinary Bladder

Kidney: Peritoneal Cover · Neighboring Organs

5.152 Parietal Peritoneum and Fixation Surfaces of the Abdominal Organs via the Left Kidney: Ventral View. [57]

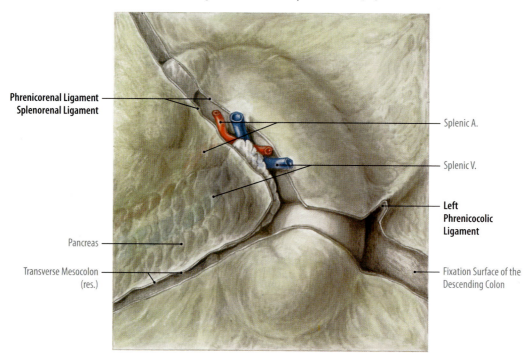

Phrenicorenal Ligament
Splenorenal Ligament

Splenic A.

Splenic V.

Left Phrenicocolic Ligament

Pancreas

Transverse Mesocolon (res.)

Fixation Surface of the Descending Colon

5.153a,b Peritoneal Cover of the Kidneys: Ventral View. [15, 2]

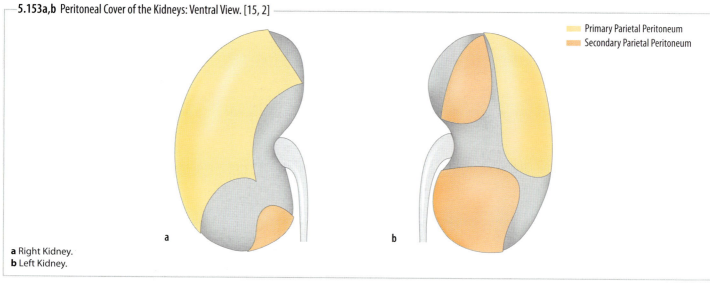

■ Primary Parietal Peritoneum
■ Secondary Parietal Peritoneum

a

b

a Right Kidney.
b Left Kidney.

5.154a,b Contact Fields of the Kidneys and the Adrenal Glands through the Neighboring Organs: Ventral View. [2]

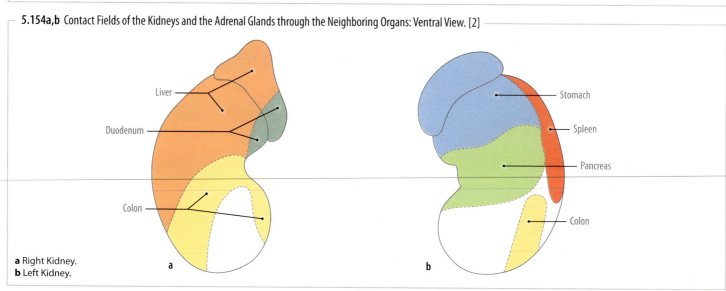

Liver

Duodenum

Colon

Stomach

Spleen

Pancreas

Colon

a Right Kidney.
b Left Kidney.

a

b

Kidneys and Renal Vessels

5.155a,b Kidneys (Right and Left) and Renal Vessels. [6]

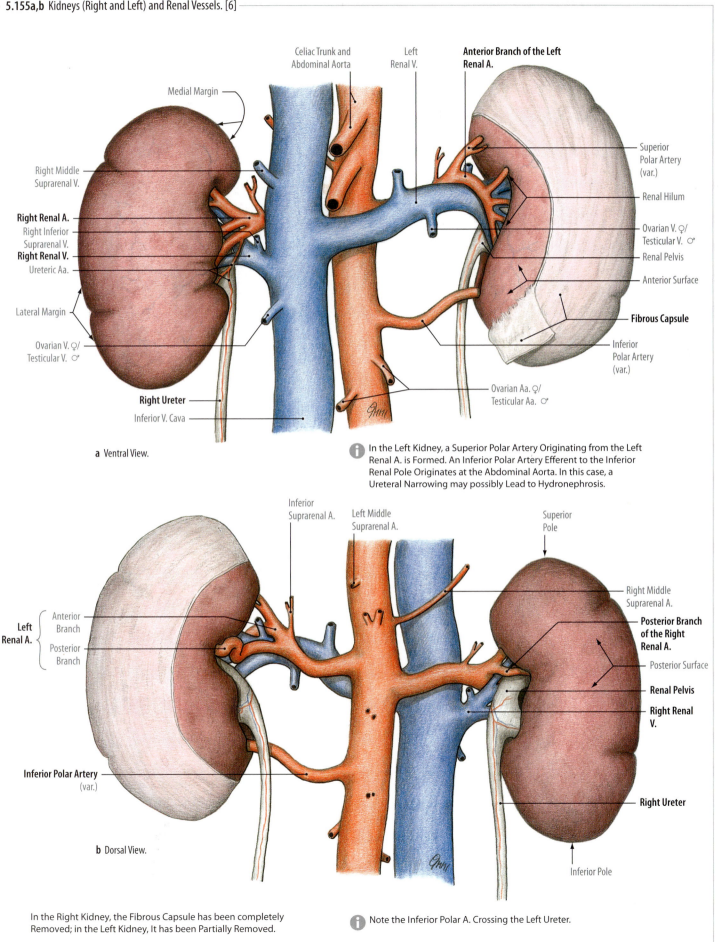

Medial Margin

Celiac Trunk and Abdominal Aorta

Left Renal V.

Anterior Branch of the Left Renal A.

Right Middle Suprarenal V.

Superior Polar Artery (var.)

Renal Hilum

Right Renal A.

Right Inferior Suprarenal V.

Right Renal V.

Ureteric Aa.

Ovarian V. ♀/ Testicular V. ♂

Renal Pelvis

Anterior Surface

Lateral Margin

Fibrous Capsule

Ovarian V. ♀/ Testicular V. ♂

Inferior Polar Artery (var.)

Right Ureter

Inferior V. Cava

Ovarian Aa. ♀/ Testicular Aa. ♂

a Ventral View.

ⓘ In the Left Kidney, a Superior Polar Artery Originating from the Left Renal A. is Formed. An Inferior Polar Artery Efferent to the Inferior Renal Pole Originates at the Abdominal Aorta. In this case, a Ureteral Narrowing may possibly Lead to Hydronephrosis.

Inferior Suprarenal A.

Left Middle Suprarenal A.

Superior Pole

Right Middle Suprarenal A.

Left Renal A.

Anterior Branch

Posterior Branch

Posterior Branch of the Right Renal A.

Posterior Surface

Renal Pelvis

Right Renal V.

Inferior Polar Artery (var.)

Right Ureter

b Dorsal View.

Inferior Pole

In the Right Kidney, the Fibrous Capsule has been completely Removed; in the Left Kidney, It has been Partially Removed.

ⓘ Note the Inferior Polar A. Crossing the Left Ureter.

Retroperitoneal Space

5.156 Median Logitudinal Section through a Left Kidney with a Section of the Renal Calices and the Renal Pelvis. [8]

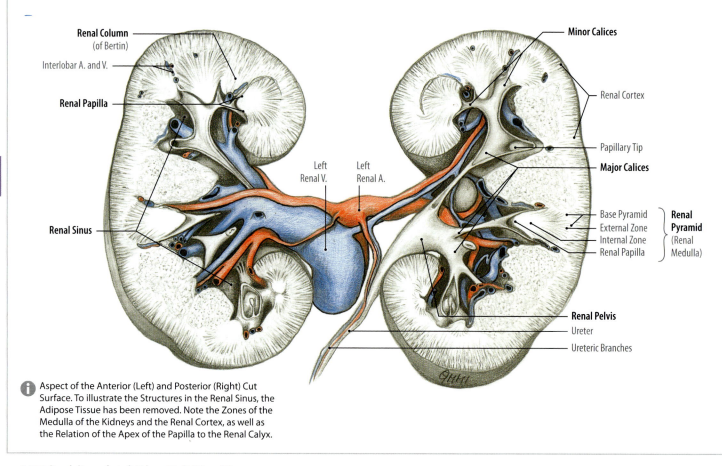

Renal Column
(of Bertin)

Interlobar A. and V.

Renal Papilla

Left
Renal V.

Left
Renal A.

Renal Sinus

Minor Calices

Renal Cortex

Papillary Tip

Major Calices

Base Pyramid ⎱ **Renal**
External Zone ⎰ **Pyramid**
Internal Zone   (Renal
Renal Papilla   Medulla)

Renal Pelvis

Ureter

Ureteric Branches

ⓘ Aspect of the Anterior (Left) and Posterior (Right) Cut
Surface. To illustrate the Structures in the Renal Sinus, the
Adipose Tissue has been removed. Note the Zones of the
Medulla of the Kidneys and the Renal Cortex, as well as
the Relation of the Apex of the Papilla to the Renal Calyx.

5.157 Renal Sinus of a Left Kidney: Medial View. [8]

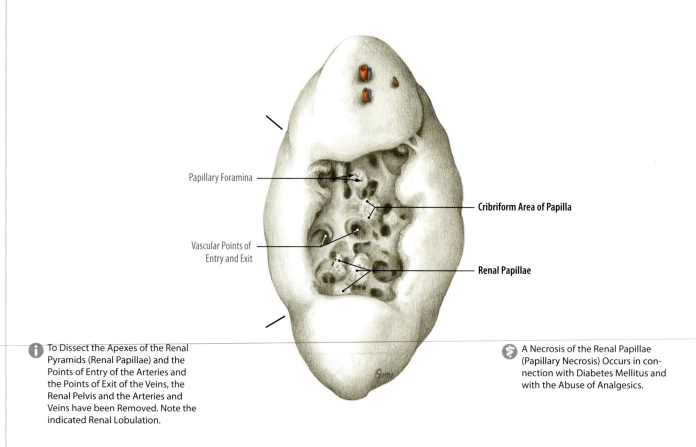

Papillary Foramina

Vascular Points of
Entry and Exit

Cribriform Area of Papilla

Renal Papillae

ⓘ To Dissect the Apexes of the Renal
Pyramids (Renal Papillae) and the
Points of Entry of the Arteries and
the Points of Exit of the Veins, the
Renal Pelvis and the Arteries and
Veins have been Removed. Note the
indicated Renal Lobulation.

Ⓢ A Necrosis of the Renal Papillae
(Papillary Necrosis) Occurs in connection with Diabetes Mellitus and
with the Abuse of Analgesics.

5.158 a Right Adrenal Gland (Right Suprarenal Gland), and **b** Left Adrenal Gland (Left Suprarenal Gland): Ventral View. [6]

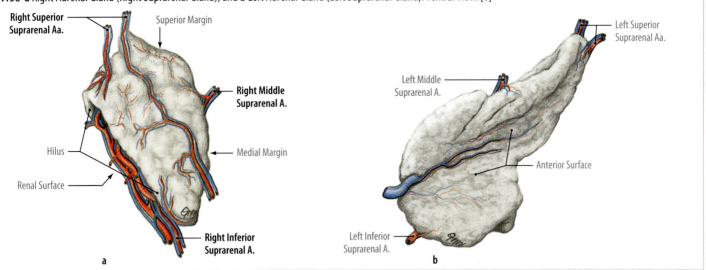

Right Superior Suprarenal Aa.

Superior Margin

Right Middle Suprarenal A.

Hilus

Medial Margin

Renal Surface

Right Inferior Suprarenal A.

a

Left Superior Suprarenal Aa.

Left Middle Suprarenal A.

Anterior Surface

Left Inferior Suprarenal A.

b

5.159 Left Adrenal Gland (Suprarenal Gland) and Left Kidney of a Male Fetus (37 Weeks): Ventral View, Magnification × 2. [8]

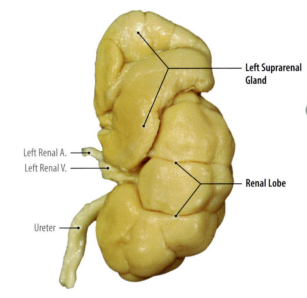

ⓘ Note the Renal Lobing and the Large Adrenal Gland in comparison to an Adult's.

Left Suprarenal Gland

Left Renal A.
Left Renal V.

Renal Lobe

Ureter

ⓘ **Origin of Suprarenal Aa.:**
Superior Suprarenal A. · A Branch of the Inferior Phrenic A.
Middle Suprarenal A. · A Branch of the Abdominal Aorta
Inferior Suprarenal A. · A Branch of the Renal A.

5.160a,b Renal Pelvis (According to Cast Preparations).

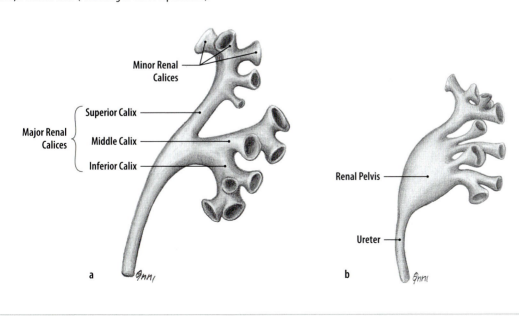

Minor Renal Calices

Major Renal Calices
Superior Calix

Middle Calix

Inferior Calix

a

Renal Pelvis

Ureter

b

a Dendritic Type.
b Ampullary Type.

Kidney, Urinary Tracts: Variations

5.161a–c Kidney and Efferent Urinary Tracts, Variants. [a,b 1, c 92]

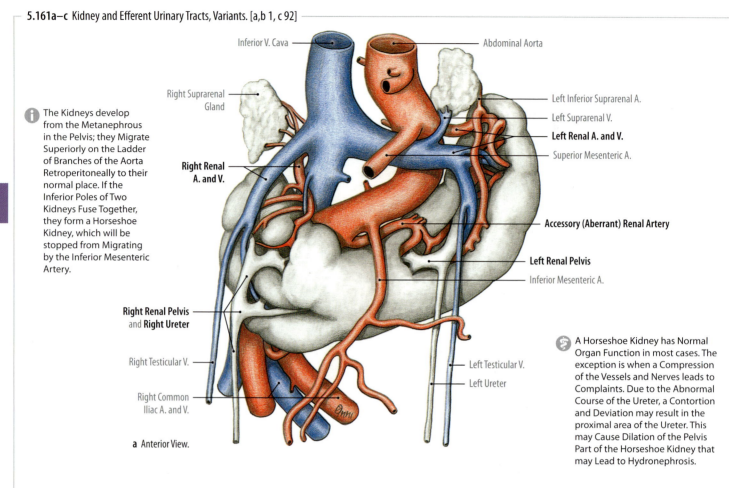

ⓘ The Kidneys develop from the Metanephrous in the Pelvis; they Migrate Superiorly on the Ladder of Branches of the Aorta Retroperitoneally to their normal place. If the Inferior Poles of Two Kidneys Fuse Together, they form a Horseshoe Kidney, which will be stopped from Migrating by the Inferior Mesenteric Artery.

Inferior V. Cava — Abdominal Aorta

Right Suprarenal Gland — Left Inferior Suprarenal A.

— Left Suprarenal V.

Right Renal A. and V. — **Left Renal A. and V.**

— Superior Mesenteric A.

Accessory (Aberrant) Renal Artery

Left Renal Pelvis

Inferior Mesenteric A.

Right Renal Pelvis and **Right Ureter**

Right Testicular V. — Left Testicular V.

— Left Ureter

Right Common Iliac A. and V.

a Anterior View.

ⓢ A Horseshoe Kidney has Normal Organ Function in most cases. The exception is when a Compression of the Vessels and Nerves leads to Complaints. Due to the Abnormal Course of the Ureter, a Contortion and Deviation may result in the proximal area of the Ureter. This may Cause Dilation of the Pelvis Part of the Horseshoe Kidney that may Lead to Hydronephrosis.

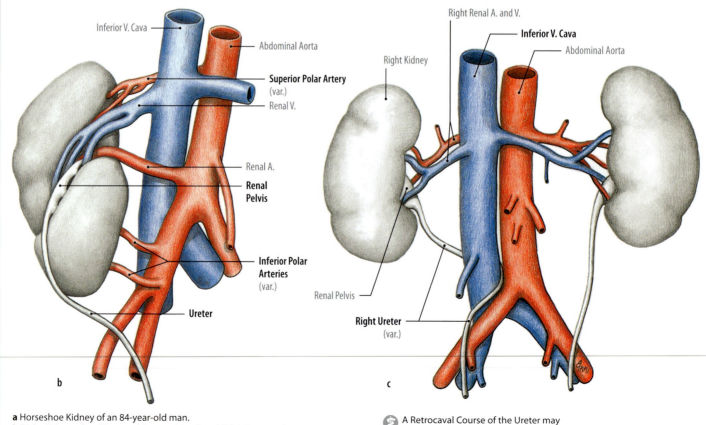

Inferior V. Cava — Abdominal Aorta

Superior Polar Artery (var.)

Renal V.

Renal A.

Renal Pelvis

Inferior Polar Arteries (var.)

Ureter

b

Right Renal A. and V.

Inferior V. Cava — Abdominal Aorta

Right Kidney

Renal Pelvis

Right Ureter (var.)

c

a Horseshoe Kidney of an 84-year-old man.
b Right Kidney of an 82-year-old man with a Renal Pelvis Retracted Ventrally and Three Accessory Renal Arteries.
c Retrocaval Course of the Right Ureter.

ⓢ A Retrocaval Course of the Ureter may Lead to a Urinary Obstruction and, consequently, to a Megaureter (Hydroureter) and to Hydronephrosis of the Kidney.

Variations of the Kidney: Imaging

5.162a,b Kidney and Urinary Tracts, Variations. [a 95, b 96]

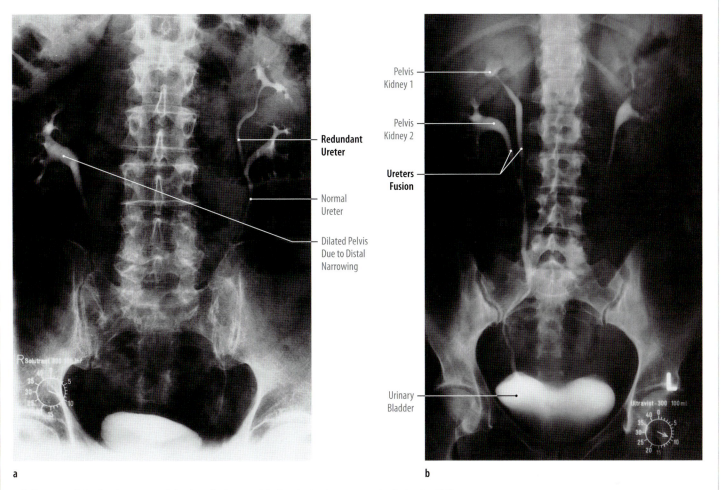

Redundant Ureter

Normal Ureter

Dilated Pelvis Due to Distal Narrowing

Pelvis Kidney 1

Pelvis Kidney 2

Ureters Fusion

Urinary Bladder

a   b

a, b Urograms following Intravenous Injection of a Contrast Medium in the Anteroposterior Projection (AP).
a Duplicate Ureter on the Left Side, 64-year-old man.
b Ureter fusion (Bidureter).

5.163 Topographical Relations of the Kidneys to the Ribs, to the Lower Limit of the Parietal Pleura, and to the Nerves of the Lumbar Plexus: Dorsal View [70]

Pain originating from the area of the Renal Bed is felt in the Lumbar Region via the Inferior Intercostal (Subcostal) N. and via the Iliohypogastric N. It is also transmitted (Referred Pain) into the Hypogastric and Inguinal Regions (◻ Fig. 5.174).

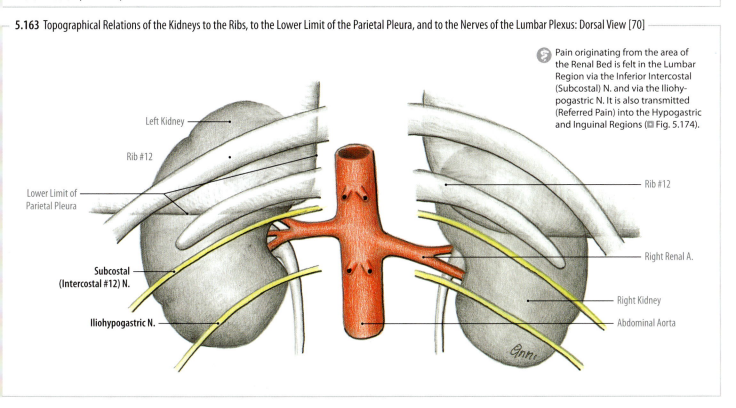

Left Kidney

Rib #12

Lower Limit of Parietal Pleura

Subcostal (Intercostal #12) N.

Iliohypogastric N.

Rib #12

Right Renal A.

Right Kidney

Abdominal Aorta

Retroperitoneal Space

Kidney: Topography

5.164 Organs of the Retroperitoneal Space, Adipose Capsule of the Kidney: Dorsal View. [1]

A Floating Kidney (Nephroptosis, i.e., "Wandering Kidney") Drops to the Brim of the Pelvis due to a severe loss of Perirenaladipose Tissue and Pararenal Fat in a very short time. A Deviation of the Ureter and the Blood Vessels may Obstruct the Urinary Flow from this Kidney and Promote Atrophy.

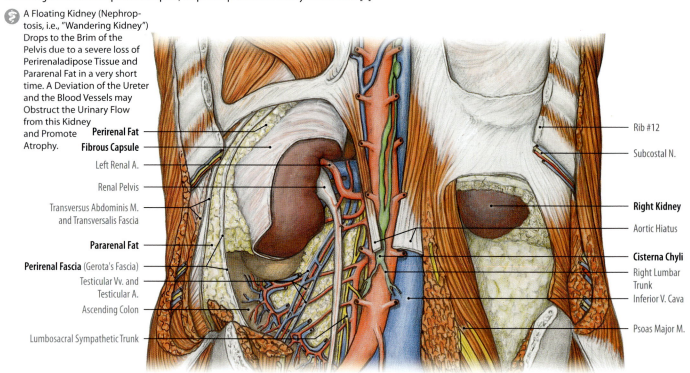

- **Perirenal Fat**
- **Fibrous Capsule**
- Left Renal A.
- Renal Pelvis
- Transversus Abdominis M. and Transversalis Fascia
- **Pararenal Fat**
- **Perirenal Fascia** (Gerota's Fascia)
- Testicular Vv. and Testicular A.
- Ascending Colon
- Lumbosacral Sympathetic Trunk
- Rib #12
- Subcostal N.
- **Right Kidney**
- Aortic Hiatus
- **Cisterna Chyli**
- Right Lumbar Trunk
- Inferior V. Cava
- Psoas Major M.

To Dissect the Organs, the Body Wall and the Dorsal Part of the Pelvis have been Removed.

5.165 Cross-Section through the Torso at the Level of the Intervertebral Disk between the First and Second Lumbar Vertebrae: Cranial View. [69]

Following Blunt Trauma, Damage to the Kidney or Renal Vessels may cause Bleeding into the Perirenal Space. Retroperitoneal Space Bleeding is the result of a Joint Injury to the Perirenal Fascia (Gerota's Fascia) causing Retroperitoneal Hematoma.

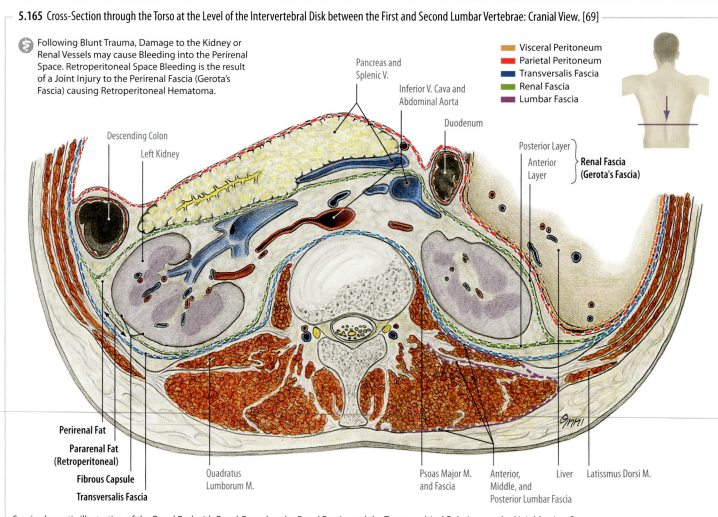

- Visceral Peritoneum
- Parietal Peritoneum
- Transversalis Fascia
- Renal Fascia
- Lumbar Fascia

- Pancreas and Splenic V.
- Inferior V. Cava and Abdominal Aorta
- Duodenum
- Descending Colon
- Left Kidney
- Posterior Layer
- Anterior Layer
- **Renal Fascia (Gerota's Fascia)**
- **Perirenal Fat**
- **Pararenal Fat (Retroperitoneal)**
- **Fibrous Capsule**
- **Transversalis Fascia**
- Quadratus Lumborum M.
- Psoas Major M. and Fascia
- Anterior, Middle, and Posterior Lumbar Fascia
- Liver
- Latissmus Dorsi M.

Semi-schematic illustration of the Renal Bed with Renal Capsules, the Renal Fascia, and the Topographical Relations to the Neighboring Organs.

340

5.166 Arteries of the Kidney and the Adrenal Gland: Ventral View. [2]

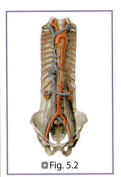
☐ Fig. 5.2

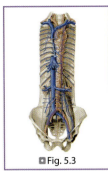
☐ Fig. 5.3

Arteries of the Kidney and Adrenal Gland

Abdominal Aorta

Inferior Phrenic A.
└ Superior Suprarenal Aa.
Middle Suprarenal A.
Renal A.
├ Capsular Aa.
├ Inferior Suprarenal A.
├ Anterior Branch
│ ├[Superior Segmental A.]
│ ├[Anterior Superior Segmental A.]
│ ├[Anterior Inferior Segmental A.]
│ └[Inferior Segmental A.]
├ Posterior Branch
│ └[Posterior Segmental A.]
├ Ureteric Aa.
└ [Intrarenal Aa.]
Ovarian A. ♀/Testicular A. ♂
└ Ureteric Aa.

[ ] not in view

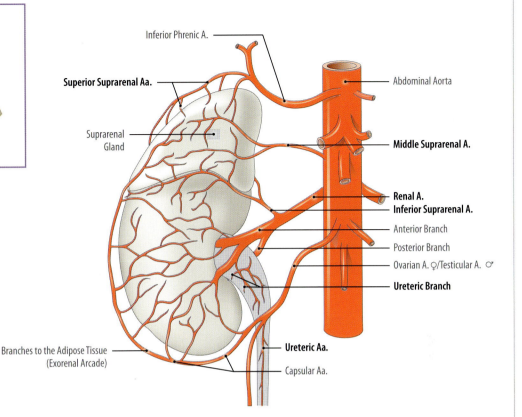

Inferior Phrenic A.

Superior Suprarenal Aa.

Suprarenal Gland

Abdominal Aorta

Middle Suprarenal A.

Renal A.
Inferior Suprarenal A.
Anterior Branch
Posterior Branch
Ovarian A. ♀/Testicular A. ♂
Ureteric Branch

Ureteric Aa.
Capsular Aa.

Branches to the Adipose Tissue (Exorenal Arcade)

ℹ In ~60% of cases, the Renal A. Divides into an Anterior Main Branch, which Branches out into Four Segmental Arteries and into a Posterior Main Branch that Supplies One Segment. The Arteries of the Adrenal Gland in~One Third of all cases Originate from Three Different Sources (Inferior Phrenic A., Adominal Aorta, Renal A.). The Arteries in the area of the Renal Bed form a Vascular Ring (Exorenal Arcade) with the Suprarenal Aa., the Renal Aa., and the Testicular 0/Ovarian R Aa. via the Capsular Branches in the Surrounding Capsular Tissue.

5.167a,b Right Kidney: Renal Segments and Segmental Arteries. [2]

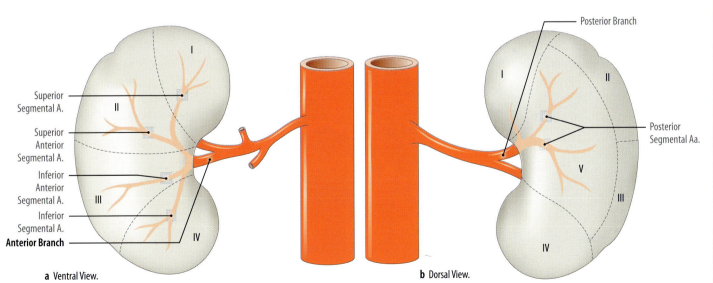

Posterior Branch

Superior Segmental A.

Superior Anterior Segmental A.

Inferior Anterior Segmental A.

Inferior Segmental A.

Anterior Branch

Posterior Segmental Aa.

a Ventral View.

b Dorsal View.

I: Superior Segment
II: Superior Anterior Segment
III: Inferior Anterior Segment
IV: Inferior Segment
V: Posterior Segment

⚡ The Cause of Renal Circulatory Disorders may be a Renal Artery Stenosis at the Efferent Area of the Renal Aa. from the Aorta. A Renal Infarction can most often be Attributed to an Embolism due to Left Ventricular Cardiac Disease. Partial Renal Resections are preferably Conducted with Segmental A. In Mind.

Renal and Adrenal Vessels: Variations

5.168a,b Gonadal Arteries (Ovarian Aa. ♀/ Testicular Aa. ♂), Variations Using The Testicular Aa. as an Example [51, 92]

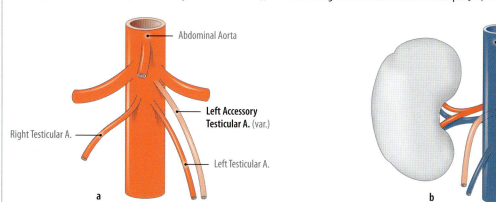

a Two Testicular Aa. develop on the Left Side in ~8% of the population. (On the right side, Development-Double Gonadal Arteries occur in ~4%. A Duplication of the Gonadal Arteries on the Right and Left Side occurs in ~2%).
b The Right Testicular A. runs Behind the Inferior V. Cava and Intersects with the Right Renal V. (in ~20%).

ℹ️ The Testicular ♂/ Ovarian ♀ Aa. in ~80% of the population, Originate Below the Renal Aa. from the Abdominal Aorta (Fig. 5.155a, 5.2).

5.169a,b Renal Arteries and Renal Veins, Variations: Dorsal View. [93]

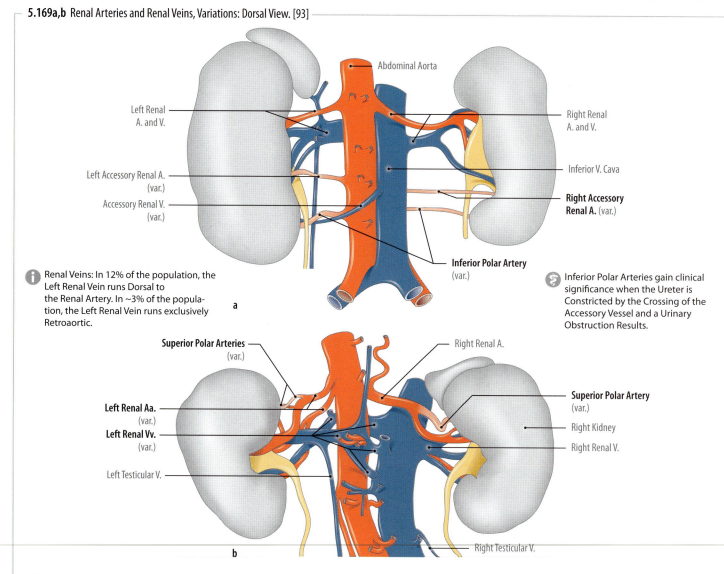

ℹ️ Renal Veins: In 12% of the population, the Left Renal Vein runs Dorsal to the Renal Artery. In ~3% of the population, the Left Renal Vein runs exclusively Retroaortic.

🔬 Inferior Polar Arteries gain clinical significance when the Ureter is Constricted by the Crossing of the Accessory Vessel and a Urinary Obstruction Results.

a From the Left Inferior Renal Pole, an Accessory Renal Vein runs Dorsally of the Abdominal Aorta to the Inferior V. Cava. In the Hilum of the Kidney, Accessory Renal Arteries Enter on the Right and on the Left Sides; Inferior Polar Arteries have Developed on Both Sides (in ~1%).

b The Renal Veins of the Left Side Build a Ring around the Abdominal Aorta (~9% of all cases); the Dorsal Veins Build a Plexus; the Left Testicular V. Flows into the Dorsal Venous Portion. On the Left Side, Two Renal Arteries have Developed (~10% of all cases). On the Right and on the Left Sides, Superior Polar Arteries Originate from the Renal Aa. (~13% of all cases).

Kidney: Imaging

5.170a–c Kidneys, Urinary Tracts, and Renal Vessels: Imaging. [a,b 75, c 10]

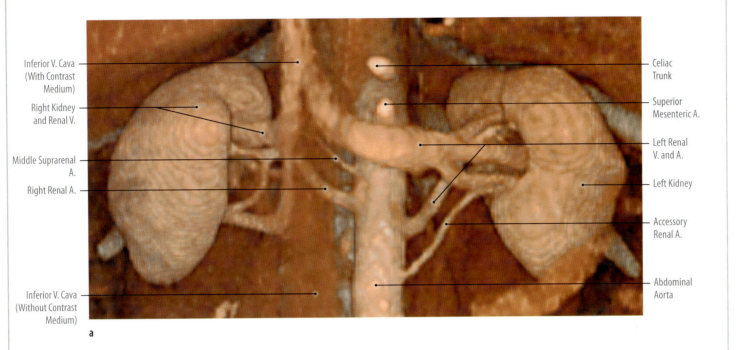

Inferior V. Cava (With Contrast Medium)

Right Kidney and Renal V.

Middle Suprarenal A.

Right Renal A.

Inferior V. Cava (Without Contrast Medium)

Celiac Trunk

Superior Mesenteric A.

Left Renal V. and A.

Left Kidney

Accessory Renal A.

Abdominal Aorta

a

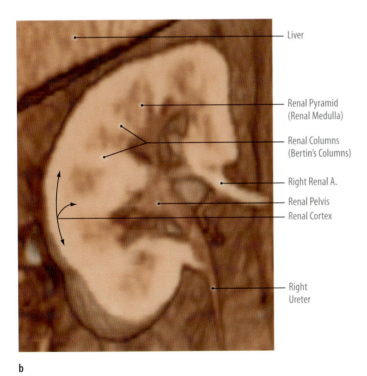

Liver

Renal Pyramid (Renal Medulla)

Renal Columns (Bertin's Columns)

Right Renal A.

Renal Pelvis

Renal Cortex

Right Ureter

b

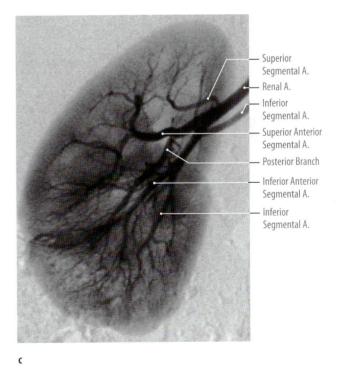

Superior Segmental A.

Renal A.

Inferior Segmental A.

Superior Anterior Segmental A.

Posterior Branch

Inferior Anterior Segmental A.

Inferior Segmental A.

c

a Illustration of the Kidneys and the Renal Vessels of a 50-year-old man.
b Illustration of the Renal Pelvis, the Renal Pyramids, and the Renal Columns of Bertin.

a, b Multislice Computed Tomography with Retrospective Gating (layer thickness 3 mm), volume rendering, following Contrast Medium Injection.

c Arteriogram of the Right Kidney of a 54-year-old woman.

Retroperitoneal Space

5.171 Preserved Left Vena Cava (Left Inferior V. Cava, Variation): Ventral View. [92]

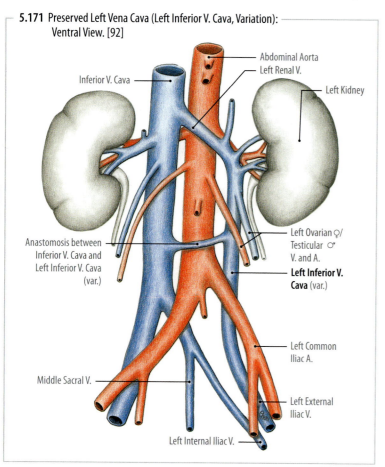

- Abdominal Aorta
- Left Renal V.
- Inferior V. Cava
- Left Kidney
- Anastomosis between Inferior V. Cava and Left Inferior V. Cava (var.)
- Left Ovarian ♀/ Testicular ♂ V. and A.
- **Left Inferior V. Cava** (var.)
- Left Common Iliac A.
- Middle Sacral V.
- Left External Iliac V.
- Left Internal Iliac V.

5.172 Cisterna Chyli: Ventral Aspect. [15]

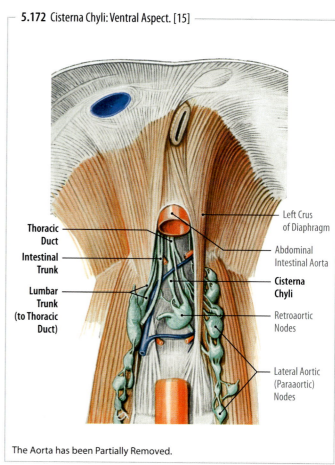

- **Thoracic Duct**
- **Intestinal Trunk**
- **Lumbar Trunk (to Thoracic Duct)**
- Left Crus of Diaphragm
- Abdominal Intestinal Aorta
- **Cisterna Chyli**
- Retroaortic Nodes
- Lateral Aortic (Paraaortic) Nodes

The Aorta has been Partially Removed.

5.173 Lymph Nodes of the Retroperitoneal Space and the Adjacent Upper Pelvic Cavity. [91]

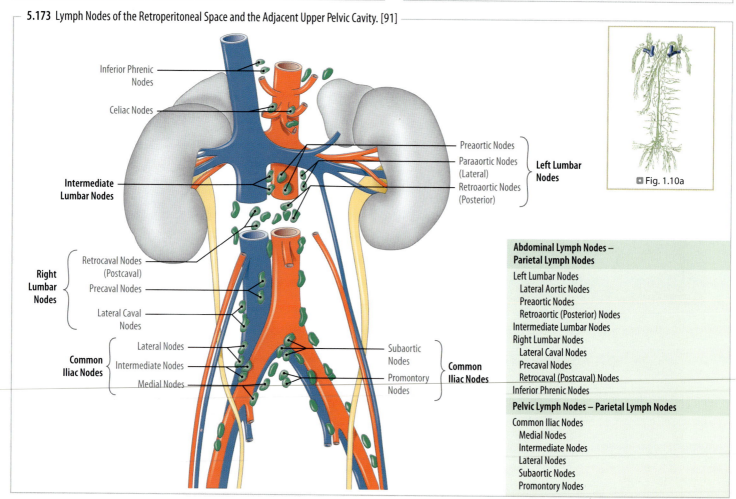

- Inferior Phrenic Nodes
- Celiac Nodes
- **Intermediate Lumbar Nodes**
- **Right Lumbar Nodes**
  - Retrocaval Nodes (Postcaval)
  - Precaval Nodes
  - Lateral Caval Nodes
- **Common Iliac Nodes**
  - Lateral Nodes
  - Intermediate Nodes
  - Medial Nodes
- Preaortic Nodes
- Paraaortic Nodes (Lateral)
- Retroaortic Nodes (Posterior) — **Left Lumbar Nodes**
- Subaortic Nodes
- Promontory Nodes — **Common Iliac Nodes**

☐ Fig. 1.10a

Abdominal Lymph Nodes – Parietal Lymph Nodes

Left Lumbar Nodes
  Lateral Aortic Nodes
  Preaortic Nodes
  Retroaortic (Posterior) Nodes
Intermediate Lumbar Nodes
Right Lumbar Nodes
  Lateral Caval Nodes
  Precaval Nodes
  Retrocaval (Postcaval) Nodes
Inferior Phrenic Nodes

Pelvic Lymph Nodes – Parietal Lymph Nodes

Common Iliac Nodes
  Medial Nodes
  Intermediate Nodes
  Lateral Nodes
  Subaortic Nodes
  Promontory Nodes

Lumbar Plexus, Autonomic Nerve Plexus

5.174 Lumbar Plexus: Ventral View. [15]

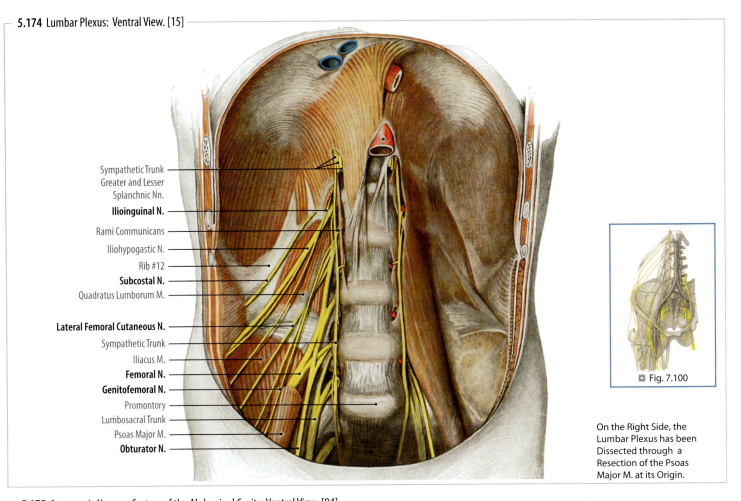

Sympathetic Trunk
Greater and Lesser
Splanchnic Nn.
Ilioinguinal N.
Rami Communicans
Iliohypogastic N.
Rib #12
Subcostal N.
Quadratus Lumborum M.
Lateral Femoral Cutaneous N.
Sympathetic Trunk
Iliacus M.
Femoral N.
Genitofemoral N.
Promontory
Lumbosacral Trunk
Psoas Major M.
Obturator N.

☐ Fig. 7.100

On the Right Side, the
Lumbar Plexus has been
Dissected through a
Resection of the Psoas
Major M. at its Origin.

5.175 Autonomic Nervous System of the Abdominal Cavity: Ventral View. [94]

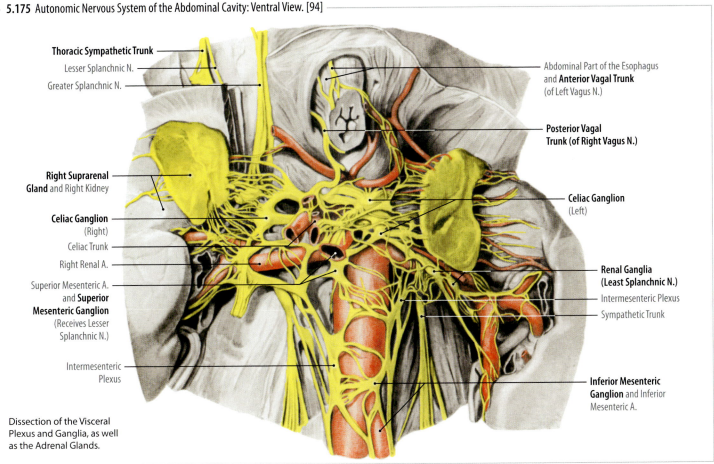

Thoracic Sympathetic Trunk
Lesser Splanchnic N.
Greater Splanchnic N.

Abdominal Part of the Esophagus
and **Anterior Vagal Trunk**
(of Left Vagus N.)

**Posterior Vagal
Trunk (of Right Vagus N.)**

**Right Suprarenal
Gland** and Right Kidney

Celiac Ganglion
(Right)
Celiac Trunk
Right Renal A.
Superior Mesenteric A.
and **Superior
Mesenteric Ganglion**
(Receives Lesser
Splanchnic N.)

Intermesenteric
Plexus

Celiac Ganglion
(Left)

**Renal Ganglia
(Least Splanchnic N.)**
Intermesenteric Plexus
Sympathetic Trunk

**Inferior Mesenteric
Ganglion** and Inferior
Mesenteric A.

Dissection of the Visceral
Plexus and Ganglia, as well
as the Adrenal Glands.

Retroperitoneal Space

5.176a,b The Pelvic Form: Sex Differences in Women and Men.

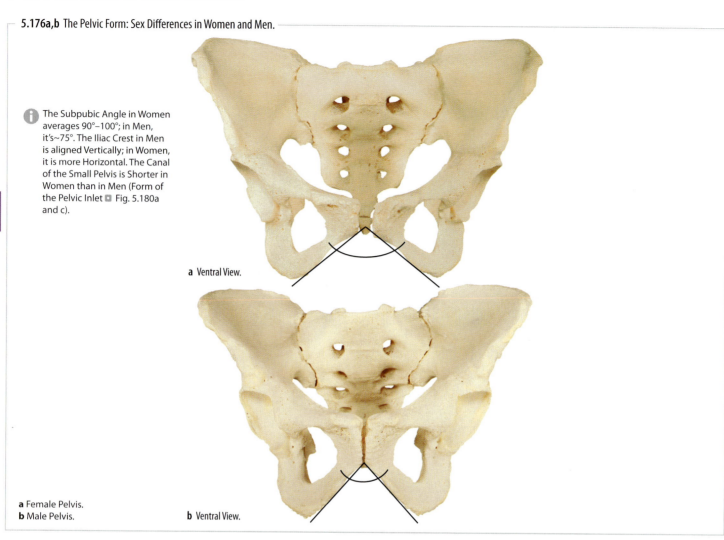

ℹ The Subpubic Angle in Women averages 90°–100°; in Men, it's~75°. The Iliac Crest in Men is aligned Vertically; in Women, it is more Horizontal. The Canal of the Small Pelvis is Shorter in Women than in Men (Form of the Pelvic Inlet ▢ Fig. 5.180a and c).

a Ventral View.

a Female Pelvis.
b Male Pelvis.

b Ventral View.

5.177 X-Ray Image of the Pelvis of a 30-Year-Old Woman in Anteroposterior Projection (Radiation). [10]

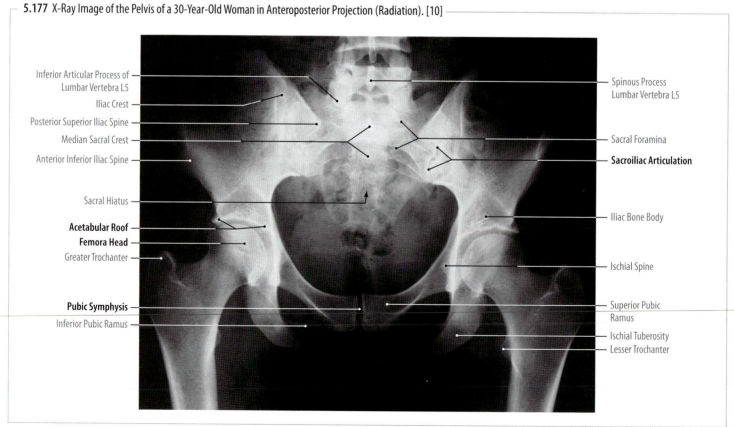

Inferior Articular Process of Lumbar Vertebra L5
Iliac Crest
Posterior Superior Iliac Spine
Median Sacral Crest
Anterior Inferior Iliac Spine
Sacral Hiatus
Acetabular Roof
Femora Head
Greater Trochanter
Pubic Symphysis
Inferior Pubic Ramus

Spinous Process Lumbar Vertebra L5
Sacral Foramina
Sacroiliac Articulation
Iliac Bone Body
Ischial Spine
Superior Pubic Ramus
Ischial Tuberosity
Lesser Trochanter

Exterior Diameters of the Pelvis

5.178a,b Exterior Diameters of the Pelvis According to Michaelis' Specifications.

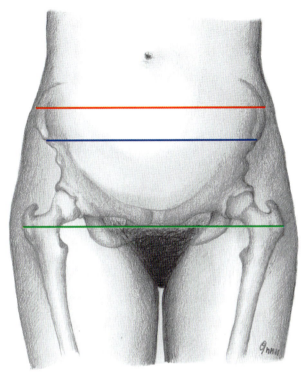

a

b

— Intercrest Distance (28–29 cm)

— Interspinous Distance (25–26 cm)

— Intertrochanteric Distance (31–32 cm)

ℹ From the Exterior Diameters of the Pelvis, the Form of the Small Pelvis (Bony Birth Canal) can be Determined. The Difference Between the Intercrest Distance and the Interspinous Distance in a normally formed Small Pelvis is about 3 cm.

— External Conjugate (Baudelocque Diameter) (~20 cm)

— Obsteteric Conjugate Vera (~11 cm)

5.179a,b Lumbosacral Rhomboid (Venus [Michael's] Rhomboid) in a Young Woman. **a** Pelvic Ring, Corresponding Bone Points: Dorsal View. **b** The Spinous Process of the Fourth Lumbar Vertebra Lies on the Connecting Line of the Iliac Crests. [69]

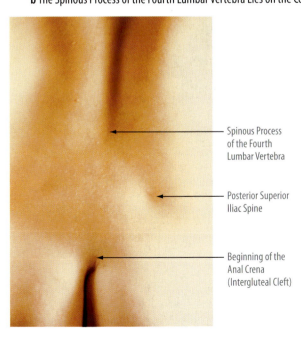

Spinous Process of the Fourth Lumbar Vertebra

Posterior Superior Iliac Spine

Beginning of the Anal Crena (Intergluteal Cleft)

a

Spinous Process Lumbar Vertebra L4

Transiliac Line

Iliac Crest

Posterior Superior Iliac Spine

Sacrum

Greater Trochanter

Ischial Spine

Coccyx

b

ℹ Deviations from the normal form (Equilateral Rectangle) of the Michael's Rhomboid define the Pathologic Changes of the Bony Birth Canal, e.g., a Generally Constricted Pelvis or a Diagonally Constricted Pelvis.

ℹ On the Connecting Line of the Iliac Crests ▬ Lies the Spinous Process of the Fourth Lumbar Vertebra, which serves as the Orientation Point for Lumbar Puncture and for Intrathecal or Epidural (Peridural) Anesthesia.

Pelvic Cavity

Interior Diameters of the Pelvis

5.180a–c Interior Diameters of the Pelvis. [15]

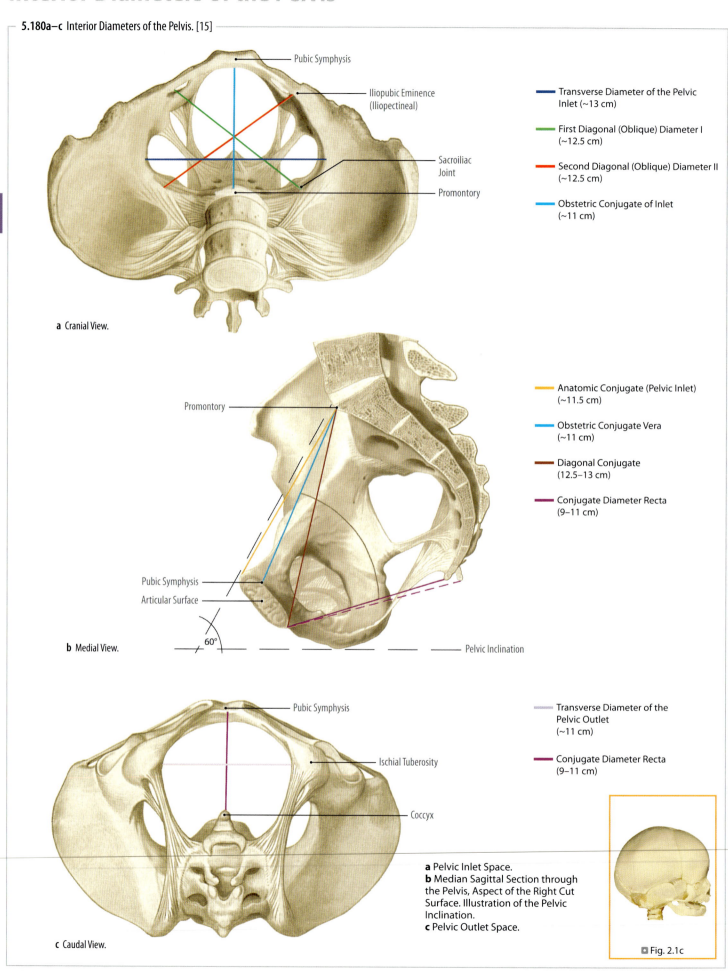

Pubic Symphysis

Iliopubic Eminence (Iliopectineal)

Sacroiliac Joint

Promontory

a Cranial View.

━━ Transverse Diameter of the Pelvic Inlet (~13 cm)

━━ First Diagonal (Oblique) Diameter I (~12.5 cm)

━━ Second Diagonal (Oblique) Diameter II (~12.5 cm)

━━ Obstetric Conjugate of Inlet (~11 cm)

Promontory

Pubic Symphysis

Articular Surface

60°

Pelvic Inclination

b Medial View.

━━ Anatomic Conjugate (Pelvic Inlet) (~11.5 cm)

━━ Obstetric Conjugate Vera (~11 cm)

━━ Diagonal Conjugate (12.5–13 cm)

━━ Conjugate Diameter Recta (9–11 cm)

Pubic Symphysis

Ischial Tuberosity

Coccyx

c Caudal View.

━━ Transverse Diameter of the Pelvic Outlet (~11 cm)

━━ Conjugate Diameter Recta (9–11 cm)

a Pelvic Inlet Space.
b Median Sagittal Section through the Pelvis, Aspect of the Right Cut Surface. Illustration of the Pelvic Inclination.
c Pelvic Outlet Space.

▫ Fig. 2.1c

Bony Birth Canal

5.181a–c Bony Birth Canal. [97]

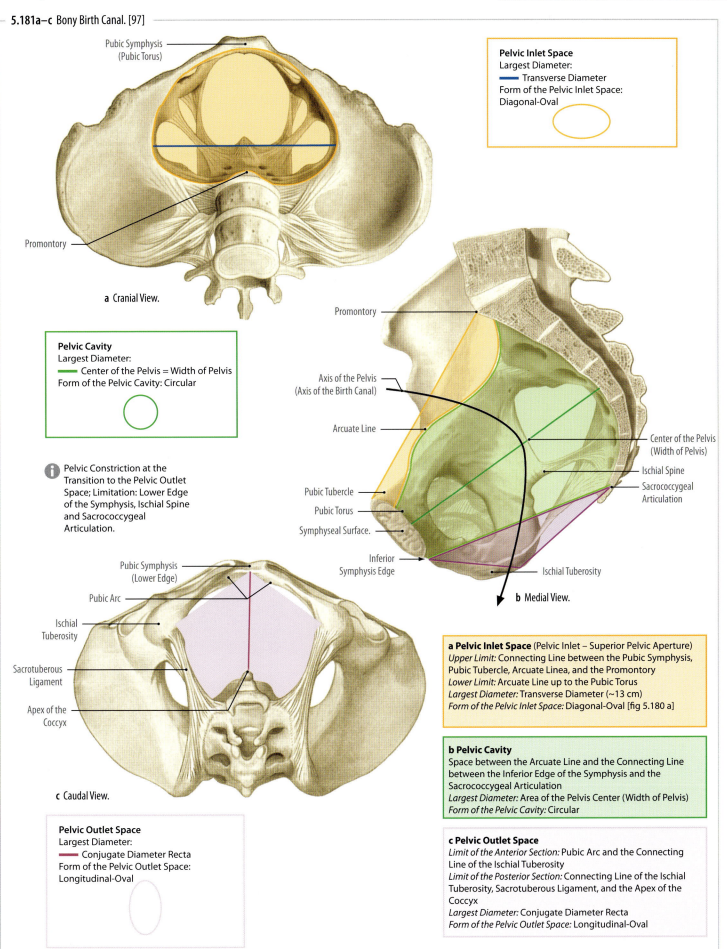

a Cranial View.

b Medial View.

c Caudal View.

Pelvic Inlet Space
Largest Diameter:
━━ Transverse Diameter
Form of the Pelvic Inlet Space:
Diagonal-Oval

Pelvic Cavity
Largest Diameter:
━━ Center of the Pelvis = Width of Pelvis
Form of the Pelvic Cavity: Circular

ⓘ Pelvic Constriction at the Transition to the Pelvic Outlet Space; Limitation: Lower Edge of the Symphysis, Ischial Spine and Sacrococcygeal Articulation.

Pelvic Outlet Space
Largest Diameter:
━━ Conjugate Diameter Recta
Form of the Pelvic Outlet Space:
Longitudinal-Oval

a Pelvic Inlet Space (Pelvic Inlet – Superior Pelvic Aperture)
Upper Limit: Connecting Line between the Pubic Symphysis, Pubic Tubercle, Arcuate Linea, and the Promontory
Lower Limit: Arcuate Line up to the Pubic Torus
Largest Diameter: Transverse Diameter (~13 cm)
Form of the Pelvic Inlet Space: Diagonal-Oval [fig 5.180 a]

b Pelvic Cavity
Space between the Arcuate Line and the Connecting Line between the Inferior Edge of the Symphysis and the Sacrococcygeal Articulation
Largest Diameter: Area of the Pelvis Center (Width of Pelvis)
Form of the Pelvic Cavity: Circular

c Pelvic Outlet Space
Limit of the Anterior Section: Pubic Arc and the Connecting Line of the Ischial Tuberosity
Limit of the Posterior Section: Connecting Line of the Ischial Tuberosity, Sacrotuberous Ligament, and the Apex of the Coccyx
Largest Diameter: Conjugate Diameter Recta
Form of the Pelvic Outlet Space: Longitudinal-Oval

Pelvic Cavity

5.182 Levator Ani M.(Pelvic Diaphragm) of a Woman: Superior View. [1]

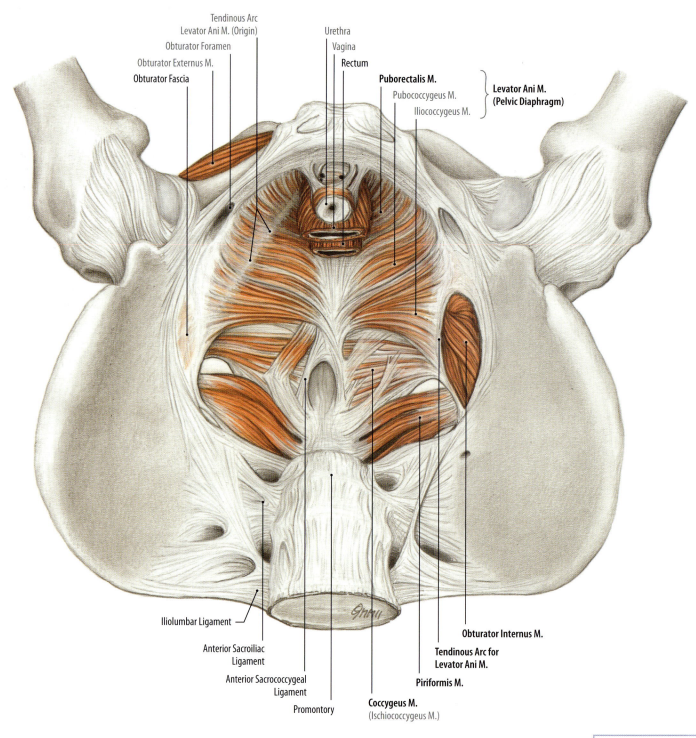

Tendinous Arc
Levator Ani M. (Origin)
Obturator Foramen
Obturator Externus M.
Obturator Fascia

Urethra
Vagina
Rectum

Puborectalis M.
Pubococcygeus M.
Iliococcygeus M.

} **Levator Ani M. (Pelvic Diaphragm)**

Iliolumbar Ligament

Anterior Sacroiliac Ligament

Anterior Sacrococcygeal Ligament

Promontory

Coccygeus M.
(Ischiococcygeus M.)

Piriformis M.

Tendinous Arc for Levator Ani M.

Obturator Internus M.

The Urethra, Vagina, and Rectum have been Resected; the Obturator Fascia on the Right Side has been Fenestrated.

An Insufficiency of the Pelvic Floor Muscles following Adiposis or Overexpansion and Injuries during the Birth Process Leads to a Lowering (Descent) of the Pelvic Organs. In a Prolapse of the Uterus, the Cervical Portion of the Vagina may Descend into the Vulva Fissure (Partial Prolapse of the Uterus), in extreme cases, the Entire Uterus Lies in Front of the Vaginal Orifice (Total Prolapse of the Uterus). Should the Vaginal Walls Descend (Vagi-

nal Prolapse), the Posterior Wall of the Urinary Bladder Arches as a Cystocele and Urethrocele in the Anterior Vaginal Wall. This Descent Interferes with the Sphincter of the Bladder, causing Urinary Incontinence. The Anterior Rectal Wall Arches into the Posterior Vaginal Wall as a Rectocele. This Interferes with the the Sphincter of the Anal Canal, resulting in Anal Incontinence (▣ Fig. 5.223).

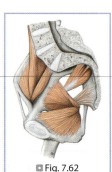

▣ Fig. 7.62

Perineal and Pelvic Floor Muscles

5.183a,b Muscles of the Pelvic Floor and the Perineum of a Man, Paramedian Sagittal Sections through the Pelvis: Medial View of the Right Side of the Body. [48]

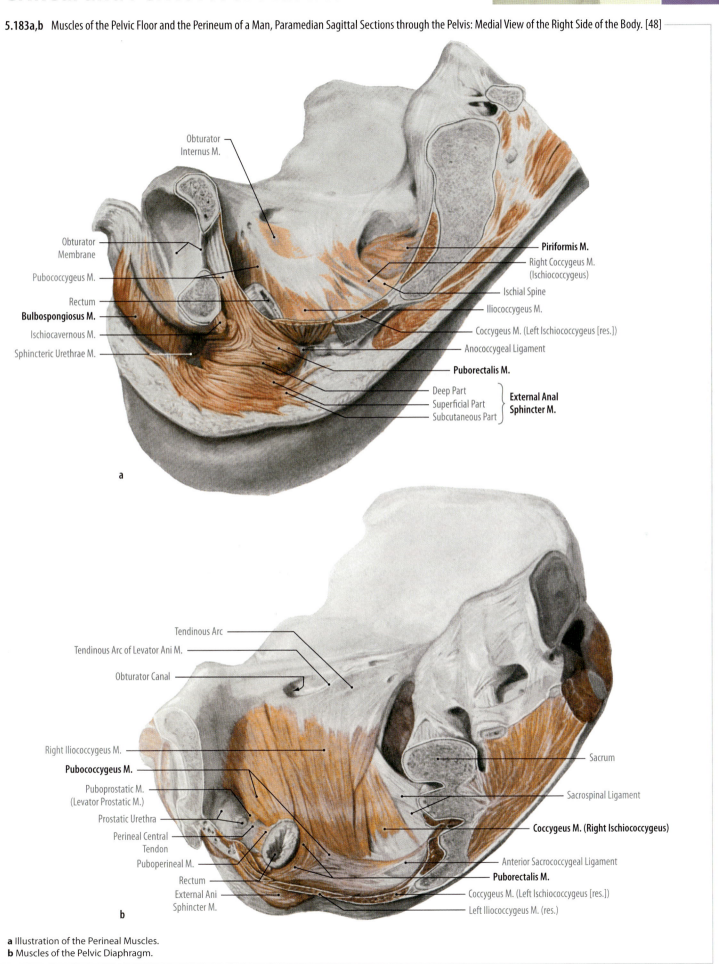

Obturator Internus M.

Obturator Membrane

Pubococcygeus M.

Rectum

Bulbospongiosus M.

Ischiocavernous M.

Sphincteric Urethrae M.

Piriformis M.

Right Coccygeus M. (Ischiococcygeus)

Ischial Spine

Iliococcygeus M.

Coccygeus M. (Left Ischiococcygeus [res.])

Anococcygeal Ligament

Puborectalis M.

Deep Part
Superficial Part   **External Anal Sphincter M.**
Subcutaneous Part

a

Tendinous Arc

Tendinous Arc of Levator Ani M.

Obturator Canal

Right Iliococcygeus M.

Pubococcygeus M.

Puboprostatic M. (Levator Prostatic M.)

Prostatic Urethra

Perineal Central Tendon

Puboperineal M.

Rectum

External Ani Sphincter M.

b

Sacrum

Sacrospinal Ligament

Coccygeus M. (Right Ischiococcygeus)

Anterior Sacrococcygeal Ligament

Puborectalis M.

Coccygeus M. (Left Ischiococcygeus [res.])

Left Iliococcygeus M. (res.)

a Illustration of the Perineal Muscles.
b Muscles of the Pelvic Diaphragm.

Pelvic Cavity

Perineal and Pelvic Floor Muscles

5.184 Perineal Region of the Man: Posteroinferior View. [48]

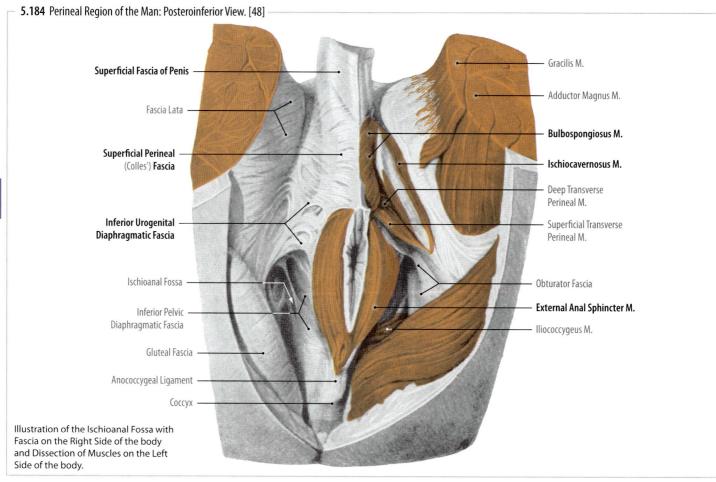

Superficial Fascia of Penis — Gracilis M.

Fascia Lata — Adductor Magnus M.

Superficial Perineal (Colles') **Fascia** — **Bulbospongiosus M.**

— **Ischiocavernosus M.**

Deep Transverse Perineal M.

Inferior Urogenital Diaphragmatic Fascia — Superficial Transverse Perineal M.

Ischioanal Fossa — Obturator Fascia

Inferior Pelvic Diaphragmatic Fascia — **External Anal Sphincter M.**

Iliococcygeus M.

Gluteal Fascia

Anococcygeal Ligament

Coccyx

Illustration of the Ischioanal Fossa with Fascia on the Right Side of the body and Dissection of Muscles on the Left Side of the body.

5.185 Perineal Region of the Woman: Posteroinferior View. [1]

As a Prophylaxis to avoid a Perineal Laceration when the Child's Head Passes Through, a Relieving Incision (Episiotomy) is often Made.

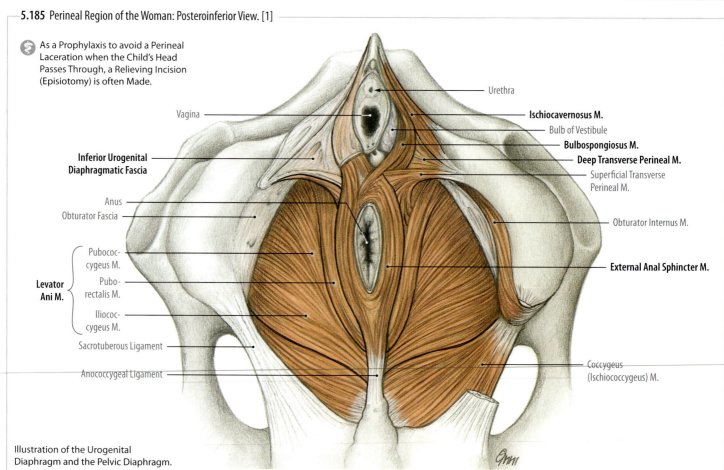

Vagina — Urethra

— **Ischiocavernosus M.**

Bulb of Vestibule

Inferior Urogenital Diaphragmatic Fascia — **Bulbospongiosus M.**

— **Deep Transverse Perineal M.**

Superficial Transverse Perineal M.

Anus — Obturator Internus M.

Obturator Fascia

Pubococ-cygeus M.

Levator Ani M. — Pubo-rectalis M. — **External Anal Sphincter M.**

Iliococ-cygeus M.

Sacrotuberous Ligament

Anococcygeal Ligament — Coccygeus (Ischiococcygeus) M.

Illustration of the Urogenital Diaphragm and the Pelvic Diaphragm.

5.186 Urogenital Diaphragm of the Man. [48]

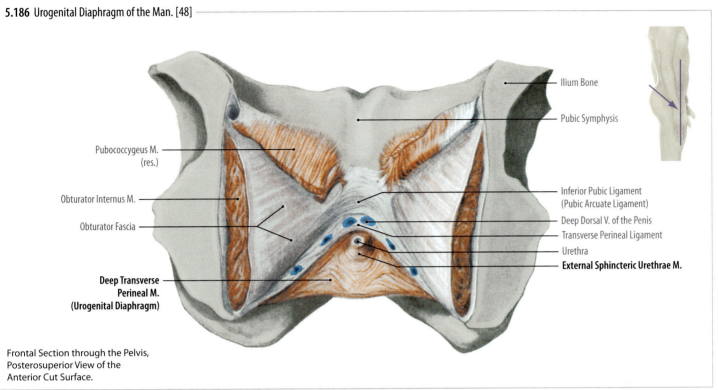

Ilium Bone

Pubic Symphysis

Pubococcygeus M. (res.)

Obturator Internus M.

Obturator Fascia

Inferior Pubic Ligament (Pubic Arcuate Ligament)

Deep Dorsal V. of the Penis

Transverse Perineal Ligament

Urethra

External Sphincteric Urethrae M.

Deep Transverse Perineal M. (Urogenital Diaphragm)

Frontal Section through the Pelvis, Posterosuperior View of the Anterior Cut Surface.

5.187 Muscles and Fascias of the Pelvic Floor and the Perineal and Hip Region of the Woman: Posteroinferior View. [1]

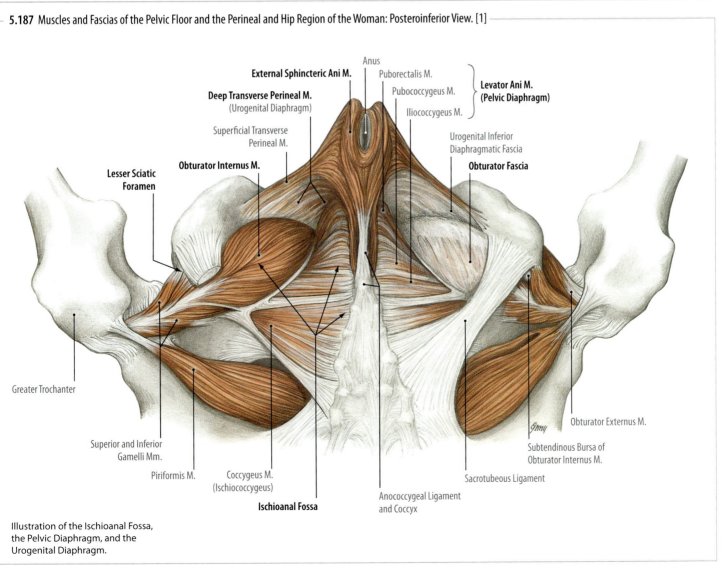

Anus

External Sphincteric Ani M.

Puborectalis M.

Pubococcygeus M.

Levator Ani M. (Pelvic Diaphragm)

Deep Transverse Perineal M. (Urogenital Diaphragm)

Iliococcygeus M.

Superficial Transverse Perineal M.

Urogenital Inferior Diaphragmatic Fascia

Obturator Internus M.

Obturator Fascia

Lesser Sciatic Foramen

Greater Trochanter

Obturator Externus M.

Superior and Inferior Gamelli Mm.

Subtendinous Bursa of Obturator Internus M.

Piriformis M.

Coccygeus M. (Ischiococcygeus)

Sacrotuberous Ligament

Ischioanal Fossa

Anococcygeal Ligament and Coccyx

Illustration of the Ischioanal Fossa, the Pelvic Diaphragm, and the Urogenital Diaphragm.

Pelvic Cavity

5.188 Pelvic Diaphragm and Ischioanal Fossa: Posteroinferior View. [48]

5

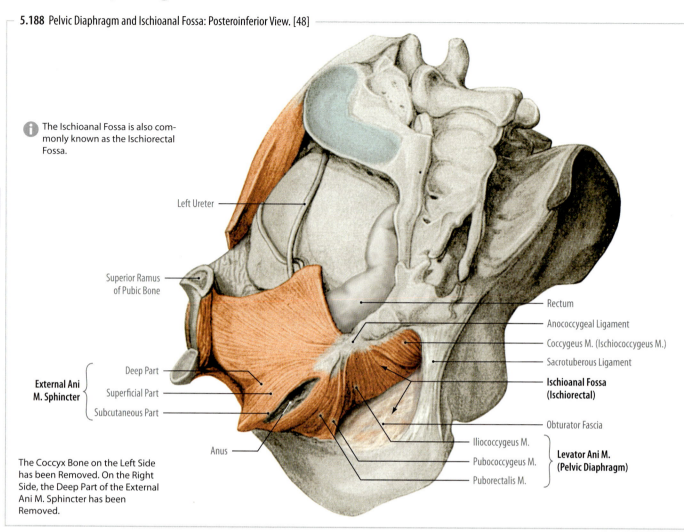

ⓘ The Ischioanal Fossa is also commonly known as the Ischiorectal Fossa.

Left Ureter

Superior Ramus of Pubic Bone

External Ani M. Sphincter
- Deep Part
- Superficial Part
- Subcutaneous Part

Anus

The Coccyx Bone on the Left Side has been Removed. On the Right Side, the Deep Part of the External Ani M. Sphincter has been Removed.

Rectum

Anococcygeal Ligament

Coccygeus M. (Ischiococcygeus M.)

Sacrotuberous Ligament

Ischioanal Fossa (Ischiorectal)

Obturator Fascia

Iliococcygeus M.

Pubococcygeus M.

Puborectalis M.

Levator Ani M. (Pelvic Diaphragm)

5.189 Frontal Section through the Pelvis in the Area of the Rectum and the Anal Canal. [23]

ⓢ **Inflammations in the Perianal Area (Anorectal Sepsis) may Present as Fistulae (Chronic) or as Abscesses (Acute). The Outcome of such Infections can take Two Paths:**
1. Transsphincteric Fistulae to the Outside
2. Through the External Anal Sphincter into the Ischioanal Fossa

Such Inflammations may Lead to:
a. An Ischioanal (Infralevatoric) Abscess
b. A Supralevator Fistulae, which Lies Outside of the Sphincter System Above the Pelvic Diaphragm. The Distal Part of the Anus (Anal Column and Crypt) is where the Causative Bacteria Enters (□ Fig. 5.216).

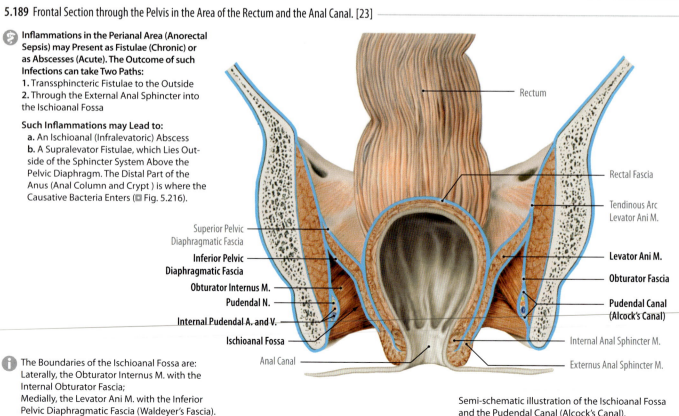

Rectum

Rectal Fascia

Tendinous Arc Levator Ani M.

Superior Pelvic Diaphragmatic Fascia

Inferior Pelvic Diaphragmatic Fascia

Obturator Internus M.

Pudendal N.

Internal Pudendal A. and V.

Ischioanal Fossa

Anal Canal

Levator Ani M.

Obturator Fascia

Pudendal Canal (Alcock's Canal)

Internal Anal Sphincter M.

Externus Anal Sphincter M.

ⓘ The Boundaries of the Ischioanal Fossa are:
Laterally, the Obturator Internus M. with the Internal Obturator Fascia;
Medially, the Levator Ani M. with the Inferior Pelvic Diaphragmatic Fascia (Waldeyer's Fascia).

Semi-schematic illustration of the Ischioanal Fossa and the Pudendal Canal (Alcock's Canal).

Urogenital Diaphragm

5.190 Male Pelvis in the Area of the Prostate and the Urinary Bladder: Frontal Section. [23, 15]

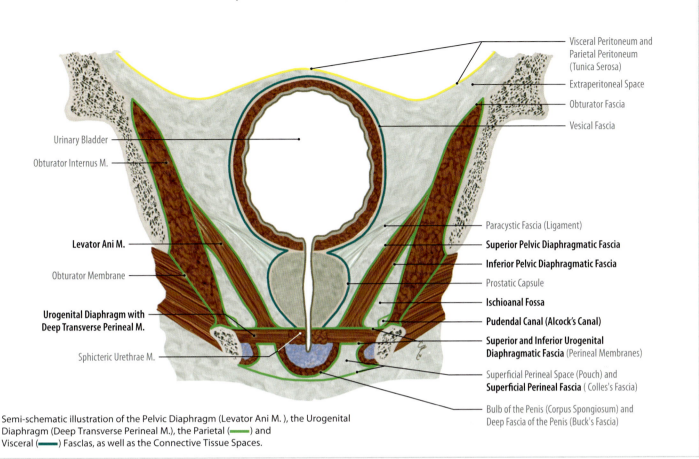

Urinary Bladder

Obturator Internus M.

Levator Ani M.

Obturator Membrane

Urogenital Diaphragm with Deep Transverse Perineal M.

Sphicteric Urethrae M.

Visceral Peritoneum and Parietal Peritoneum (Tunica Serosa)

Extraperitoneal Space

Obturator Fascia

Vesical Fascia

Paracystic Fascia (Ligament)

Superior Pelvic Diaphragmatic Fascia

Inferior Pelvic Diaphragmatic Fascia

Prostatic Capsule

Ischioanal Fossa

Pudendal Canal (Alcock's Canal)

Superior and Inferior Urogenital Diaphragmatic Fascia (Perineal Membranes)

Superficial Perineal Space (Pouch) and **Superficial Perineal Fascia** (Colles's Fascia)

Bulb of the Penis (Corpus Spongiosum) and Deep Fascia of the Penis (Buck's Fascia)

Semi-schematic illustration of the Pelvic Diaphragm (Levator Ani M.), the Urogenital Diaphragm (Deep Transverse Perineal M.), the Parietal () and Visceral ( ) Fasclas, as well as the Connective Tissue Spaces.

5.191 Female Pelvis in the Area of the Vagina and the Uterus: View of the Posterior Cut Surface, Frontal Section. [23]

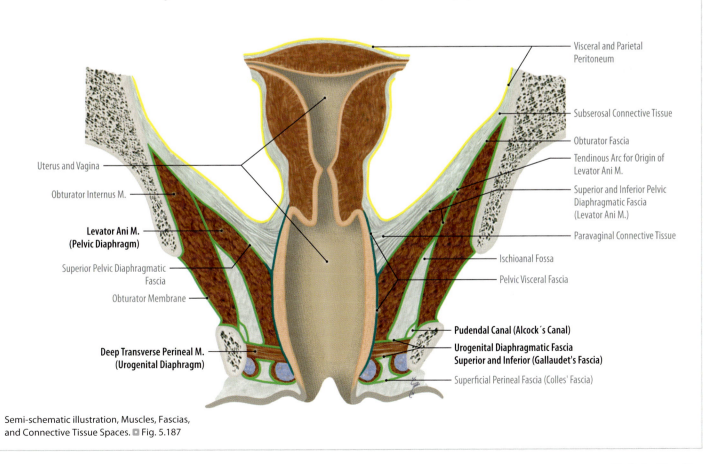

Uterus and Vagina

Obturator Internus M.

Levator Ani M. (Pelvic Diaphragm)

Superior Pelvic Diaphragmatic Fascia

Obturator Membrane

Deep Transverse Perineal M. (Urogenital Diaphragm)

Visceral and Parietal Peritoneum

Subserosal Connective Tissue

Obturator Fascia

Tendinous Arc for Origin of Levator Ani M.

Superior and Inferior Pelvic Diaphragmatic Fascia (Levator Ani M.)

Paravaginal Connective Tissue

Ischioanal Fossa

Pelvic Visceral Fascia

Pudendal Canal (Alcock´s Canal)

Urogenital Diaphragmatic Fascia Superior and Inferior (Gallaudet's Fascia)

Superficial Perineal Fascia (Colles' Fascia)

Semi-schematic illustration, Muscles, Fascias, and Connective Tissue Spaces. ⊡ Fig. 5.187

Pelvic Cavity

5.192 Arteries of the Pelvis: Medial Aspect of the Right Half of the Pelvis, Sagittal Section. [13]

Abdominal Aorta

Common Iliac A.

Iliacus A.

Iliolumbar A.

Spinal A.

Lumbar A.

Ascending Branch of the
Deep Circumflex Iliac A.

External Iliac A.

Umbilical A.

Uterine A. ♀/
Ductus Deferens A. ♂

Obturator A.

Medial Umbilical Ligament

Deep Circumflex Iliac A.

Inferior Epigastic A.

Pubic Branch of Inferior Epigastric A.

Obturator Anastomsis

Corona Mortis

Pubic Branch of the Obturator A.

Superior Vesical Aa.

Median Sacral A.

Internal Iliac A.

Iliolumbar A.

Spinal Branches of the
Lateral Sacral A.

Lateral Sacral A.

Superior Gluteal A.

Suprapiriform Foramen
Superior Gluteal Foramen)

Middle Rectal A.

Inferior Gluteal A.

Infrapiriform (Inferior Gluteal) Foramen

Internal Pudendal A.

Vaginal A. ♀

Inferior Vesical A.

Branches of the Internal Iliac A.

Internal Iliac A.
- Iliolumbar A.
  - Lumbar A.
  - Spinal A.
  - Iliacus A.
- Lateral Sacral Aa.
  - Spinal A.
- Obturator A. (◻ Fig. 5.196)
  - Pubic A.
  - Acetabular A.
  - Anterior Branch
  - Posterior Branch
- Superior Gluteal A. (◻ Fig. 7.95)
- Inferior Gluteal A. (◻ Fig. 7.95)
- Umbilical A.
  - Ductus Deferens A. ♂
    - Ureteric Aa.
  - Superior Vesical Aa.
  - (Umbilical Cordal A.)
- Inferior Vesical A.
  - Prostatic Aa. ♂
- Uterine A. ♀ (◻ Fig. 5.230)
- Vaginal A. ♀
- Middle Rectal A.
  - Vaginal Aa. ♀
  - Prostatic Aa. ♂
- Internal Pudendal A. (◻ Fig. 5.195)

◻ Fig. 7.94

◻ Fig. 7.95

Pelvic Arteries

5.193a,b Internal Iliac A., Variations: Right Half of the Pelvis, Medial View. [51]

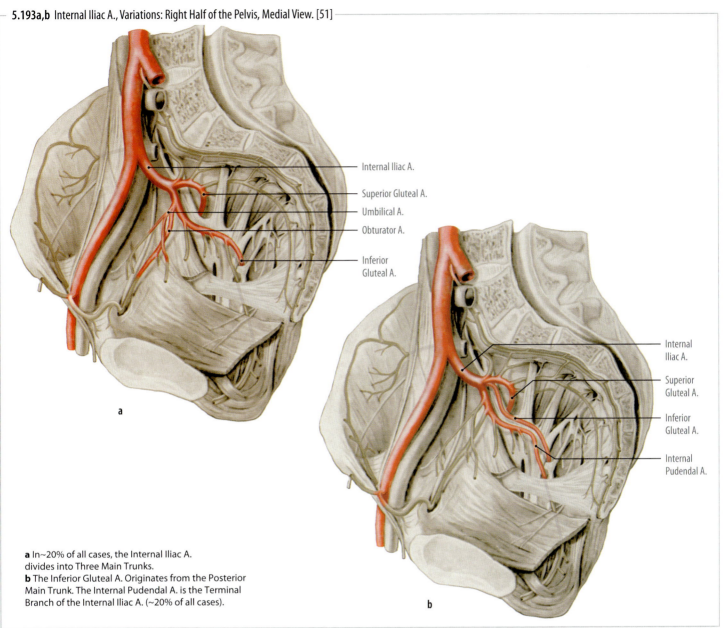

Internal Iliac A.

Superior Gluteal A.

Umbilical A.

Obturator A.

Inferior Gluteal A.

a

Internal Iliac A.

Superior Gluteal A.

Inferior Gluteal A.

Internal Pudendal A.

a In ~20% of all cases, the Internal Iliac A. divides into Three Main Trunks.
b The Inferior Gluteal A. Originates from the Posterior Main Trunk. The Internal Pudendal A. is the Terminal Branch of the Internal Iliac A. (~20% of all cases).

b

5.194 Median Sacral A., Coccygeal Glomus, and Caudal Glomera. Coccyx: Ventral View. [48, 98]

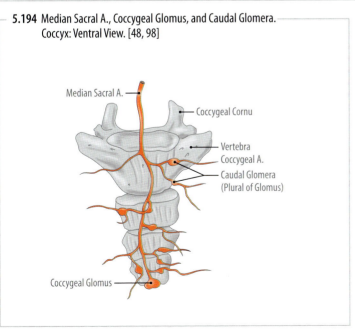

Median Sacral A.

Coccygeal Cornu

Vertebra

Coccygeal A.

Caudal Glomera (Plural of Glomus)

Coccygeal Glomus

5.195 Blood Supply of the External Female Genitalia through the Internal Pudendal A.: Anteroinferior View.

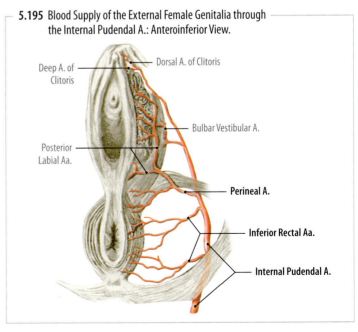

Deep A. of Clitoris

Dorsal A. of Clitoris

Bulbar Vestibular A.

Posterior Labial Aa.

Perineal A.

Inferior Rectal Aa.

Internal Pudendal A.

Pelvic Cavity

Obturator A.

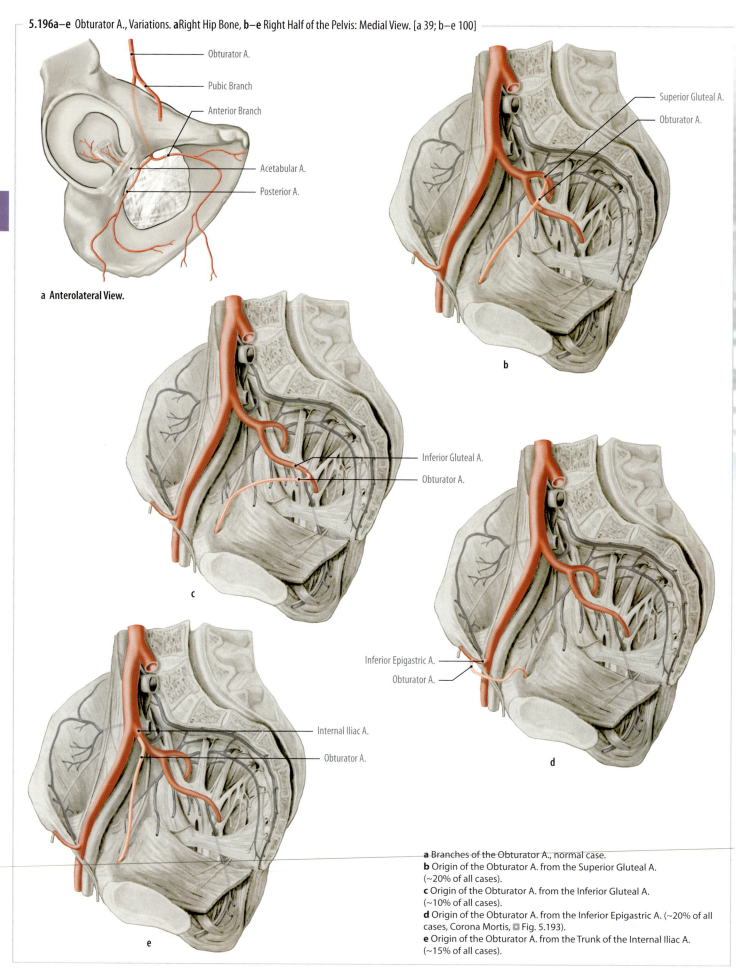

Obturator A.

Pubic Branch

Anterior Branch

Acetabular A.

Posterior A.

a Anterolateral View.

Superior Gluteal A.

Obturator A.

b

Inferior Gluteal A.

Obturator A.

c

Inferior Epigastric A.

Obturator A.

d

Internal Iliac A.

Obturator A.

e

a Branches of the Obturator A., normal case.
b Origin of the Obturator A. from the Superior Gluteal A. (~20% of all cases).
c Origin of the Obturator A. from the Inferior Gluteal A. (~10% of all cases).
d Origin of the Obturator A. from the Inferior Epigastric A. (~20% of all cases, Corona Mortis, ▢ Fig. 5.193).
e Origin of the Obturator A. from the Trunk of the Internal Iliac A. (~15% of all cases).

Pelvis: Veins · Lymph Nodes

5.197 Veins of the Female Pelvis. [48]

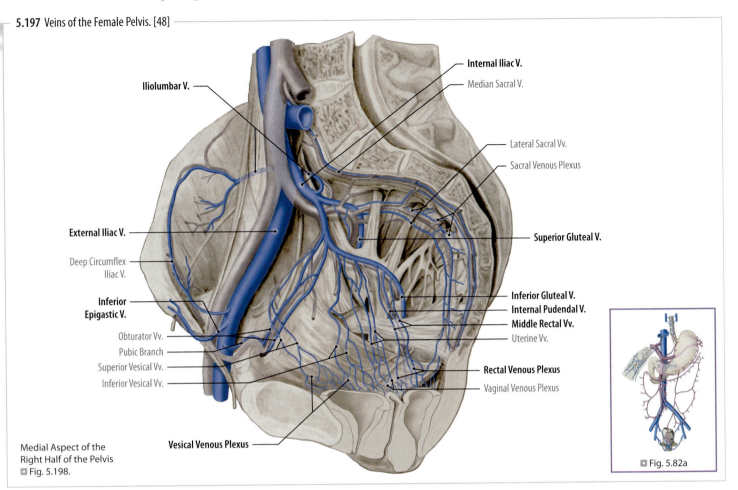

Iliolumbar V.

Internal Iliac V.

Median Sacral V.

Lateral Sacral Vv.

Sacral Venous Plexus

External Iliac V.

Superior Gluteal V.

Deep Circumflex Iliac V.

Inferior Epigastic V.

Inferior Gluteal V.

Internal Pudendal V.

Middle Rectal Vv.

Obturator Vv.

Pubic Branch

Superior Vesical Vv.

Inferior Vesical Vv.

Uterine Vv.

Rectal Venous Plexus

Vaginal Venous Plexus

Vesical Venous Plexus

Medial Aspect of the Right Half of the Pelvis
◻ Fig. 5.198.

◻ Fig. 5.82a

5.198 Lymph Nodes of the Pelvic Wall (Pelvic Parietal Lymph Nodes).

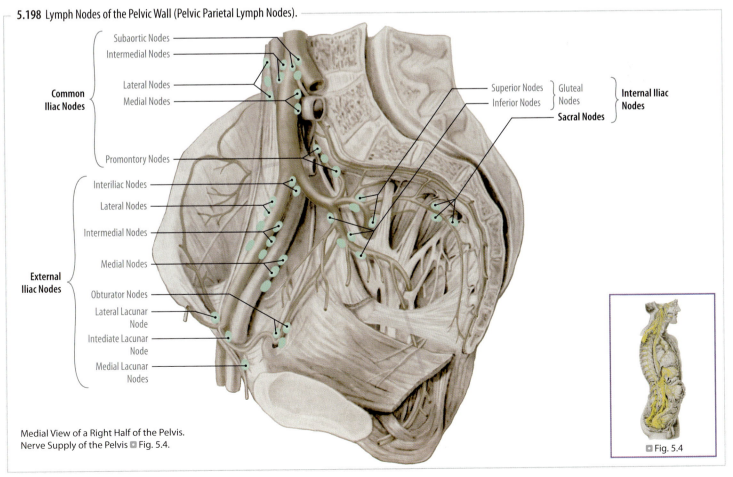

Common Iliac Nodes

Subaortic Nodes

Intermedial Nodes

Lateral Nodes

Medial Nodes

Superior Nodes

Inferior Nodes

Gluteal Nodes

Internal Iliac Nodes

Sacral Nodes

Promontory Nodes

External Iliac Nodes

Interiliac Nodes

Lateral Nodes

Intermedial Nodes

Medial Nodes

Obturator Nodes

Lateral Lacunar Node

Intediate Lacunar Node

Medial Lacunar Nodes

Medial View of a Right Half of the Pelvis.
Nerve Supply of the Pelvis ◻ Fig. 5.4.

◻ Fig. 5.4

Pelvic Cavity

5.199 Lymphatic Vessels and Lymph Nodes in the Area of the Pelvis and the Thighs, Bipedal Lymphography (Enema Phase — Early Storage Phase). [10]

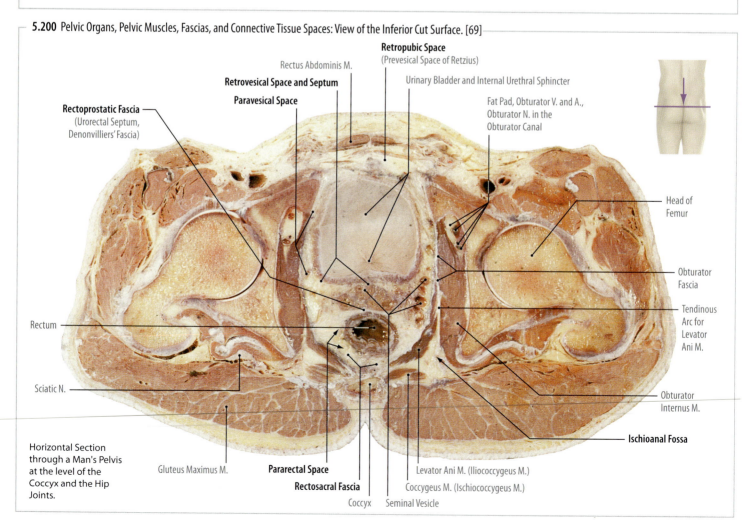

Inner Lymphatic Vessels

External Lymphatic Vessels

Common Iliac Nodes

External Iliac Nodes

Lacunar Nodes

Superficial Inguinal Nodes (Inferior Nodes)

5.200 Pelvic Organs, Pelvic Muscles, Fascias, and Connective Tissue Spaces: View of the Inferior Cut Surface. [69]

Rectus Abdominis M.

Retropubic Space (Prevesical Space of Retzius)

Retrovesical Space and Septum

Urinary Bladder and Internal Urethral Sphincter

Paravesical Space

Fat Pad, Obturator V. and A., Obturator N. in the Obturator Canal

Rectoprostatic Fascia (Urorectal Septum, Denonvilliers' Fascia)

Head of Femur

Obturator Fascia

Tendinous Arc for Levator Ani M.

Rectum

Sciatic N.

Obturator Internus M.

Ischioanal Fossa

Horizontal Section through a Man's Pelvis at the level of the Coccyx and the Hip Joints.

Gluteus Maximus M.

Pararectal Space

Rectosacral Fascia

Coccyx

Levator Ani M. (Iliococcygeus M.)

Coccygeus M. (Ischiococcygeus M.)

Seminal Vesicle

Interior Pelvic Wall: Nerves and Blood Vessels

2.201a,b Structures of the Interior Pelvic Wall: Right Side, Median Sagittal Section, Medial View. [15]

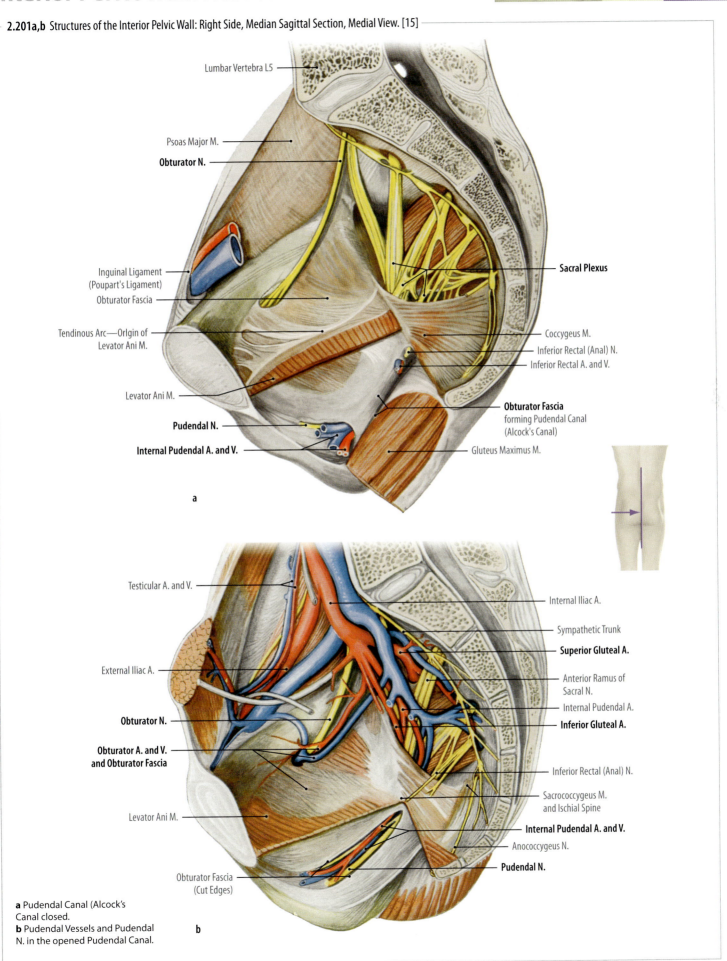

Lumbar Vertebra L5

Psoas Major M.

Obturator N.

Inguinal Ligament
(Poupart's Ligament)

Obturator Fascia

Tendinous Arc—Origin of
Levator Ani M.

Levator Ani M.

Pudendal N.

Internal Pudendal A. and V.

Sacral Plexus

Coccygeus M.

Inferior Rectal (Anal) N.

Inferior Rectal A. and V.

Obturator Fascia
forming Pudendal Canal
(Alcock's Canal)

Gluteus Maximus M.

a

Testicular A. and V.

External Iliac A.

Obturator N.

**Obturator A. and V.
and Obturator Fascia**

Levator Ani M.

Obturator Fascia
(Cut Edges)

Internal Iliac A.

Sympathetic Trunk

Superior Gluteal A.

Anterior Ramus of
Sacral N.

Internal Pudendal A.

Inferior Gluteal A.

Inferior Rectal (Anal) N.

Sacrococcygeus M.
and Ischial Spine

Internal Pudendal A. and V.

Anococcygeus N.

Pudendal N.

b

a Pudendal Canal (Alcock's
Canal closed.
b Pudendal Vessels and Pudendal
N. in the opened Pudendal Canal.

Pelvic Cavity

5.202a,b Blood and Nerve Supply of the Perineal Region and the External Genitalia: Inferior View. [23]

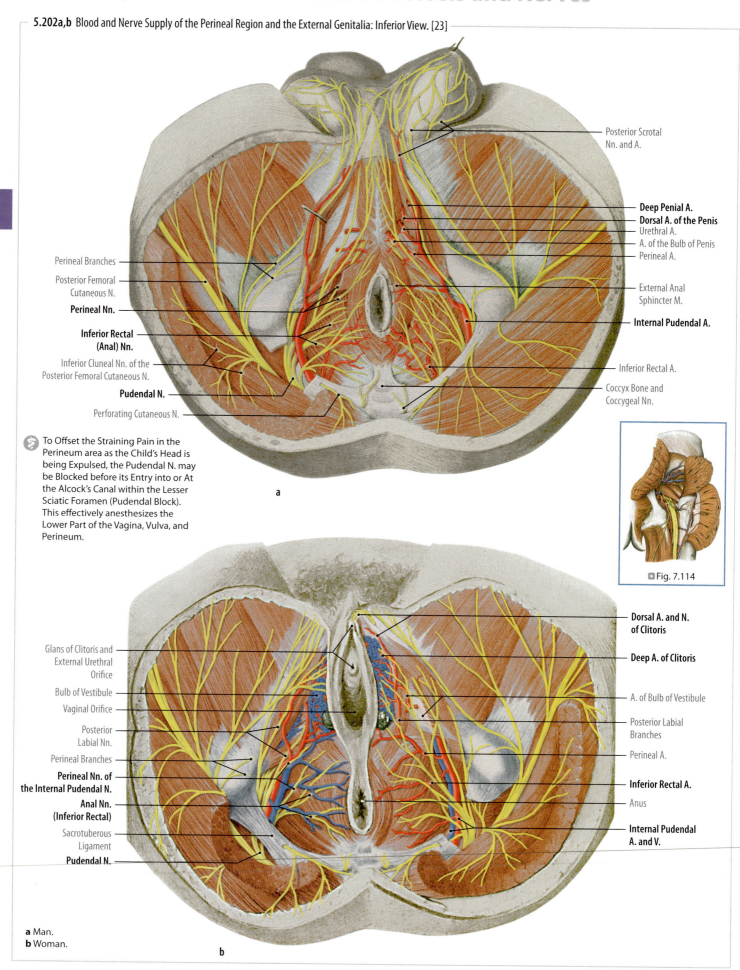

Posterior Scrotal
Nn. and A.

Deep Penial A.
Dorsal A. of the Penis
Urethral A.
A. of the Bulb of Penis
Perineal A.

External Anal
Sphincter M.

Internal Pudendal A.

Inferior Rectal A.

Coccyx Bone and
Coccygeal Nn.

Perineal Branches

Posterior Femoral
Cutaneous N.

Perineal Nn.

**Inferior Rectal
(Anal) Nn.**

Inferior Cluneal Nn. of the
Posterior Femoral Cutaneous N.

Pudendal N.

Perforating Cutaneous N.

To Offset the Straining Pain in the
Perineum area as the Child's Head is
being Expulsed, the Pudendal N. may
be Blocked before its Entry into or At
the Alcock's Canal within the Lesser
Sciatic Foramen (Pudendal Block).
This effectively anesthesizes the
Lower Part of the Vagina, Vulva, and
Perineum.

a

◨ Fig. 7.114

**Dorsal A. and N.
of Clitoris**

Deep A. of Clitoris

A. of Bulb of Vestibule

Posterior Labial
Branches

Perineal A.

Inferior Rectal A.

Anus

**Internal Pudendal
A. and V.**

Glans of Clitoris and
External Urethral
Orifice

Bulb of Vestibule

Vaginal Orifice

Posterior
Labial Nn.

Perineal Branches

**Perineal Nn. of
the Internal Pudendal N.**

**Anal Nn.
(Inferior Rectal)**

Sacrotuberous
Ligament

Pudendal N.

a Man.
b Woman.

b

Pelvic Organs, Peritoneal Relationships

5.203a,b Pelvic Organs and Peritoneal Relationships. [6]

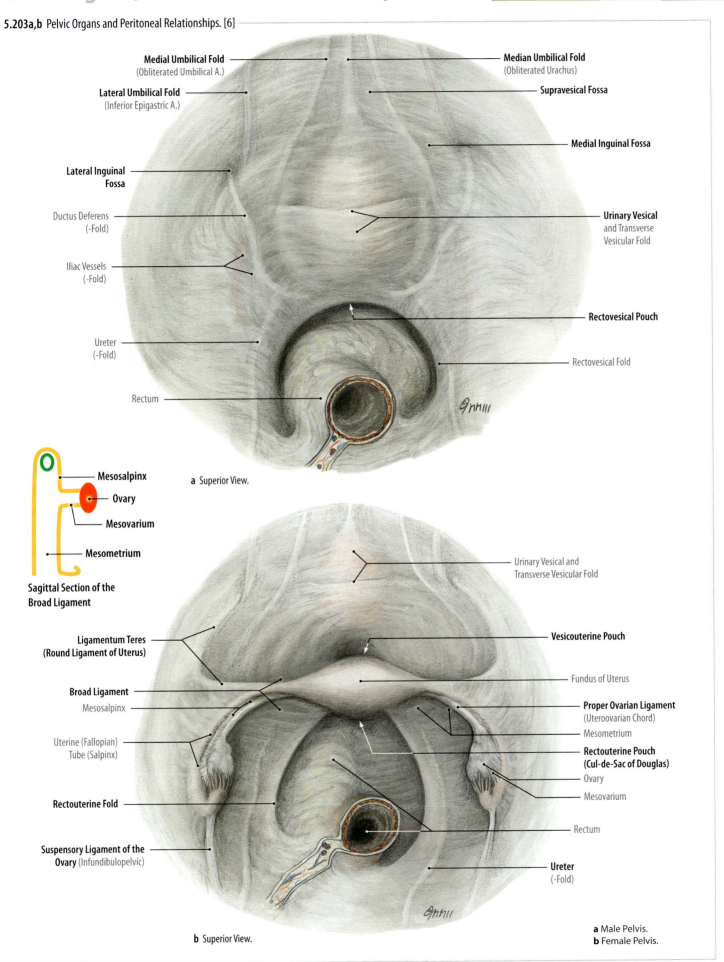

Medial Umbilical Fold
(Obliterated Umbilical A.)

Median Umbilical Fold
(Obliterated Urachus)

Lateral Umbilical Fold
(Inferior Epigastric A.)

Supravesical Fossa

Medial Inguinal Fossa

Lateral Inguinal Fossa

Ductus Deferens
(-Fold)

Urinary Vesical
and Transverse
Vesicular Fold

Iliac Vessels
(-Fold)

Rectovesical Pouch

Ureter
(-Fold)

Rectovesical Fold

Rectum

a Superior View.

Mesosalpinx

Ovary

Mesovarium

Mesometrium

Sagittal Section of the Broad Ligament

Urinary Vesical and
Transverse Vesicular Fold

Ligamentum Teres
(Round Ligament of Uterus)

Vesicouterine Pouch

Fundus of Uterus

Broad Ligament

Mesosalpinx

Proper Ovarian Ligament
(Uteroovarian Chord)

Mesometrium

Uterine (Fallopian)
Tube (Salpinx)

Rectouterine Pouch
(Cul-de-Sac of Douglas)

Ovary

Mesovarium

Rectouterine Fold

Rectum

Suspensory Ligament of the Ovary (Infundibulopelvic)

Ureter
(-Fold)

b Superior View.

a Male Pelvis.
b Female Pelvis.

Pelvic Cavity

5.204 Pelvic Organs of the Man and Peritoneal Relations of the Pelvis: Paramedian Sagittal Section, Right Lateral View. [6, 48]

5

Prostate and Seminal Vesicles are examined Rectally through Palpation and through Transrectal Sonography (Fig. 5.250). The Rectal Fascia (Waldeyer's Fascia) and the Rectoprostatic Fascia (Denonvilliers' Fascia) are important in Staging the Spread of Rectal and Prostate Cancer. A Surgical Approach to the Prostate can be done by Suprapubic Access Extraperitoneally, Retropubically through Retzius' Space, transversically (Through the Bladder), or Transperoneally.

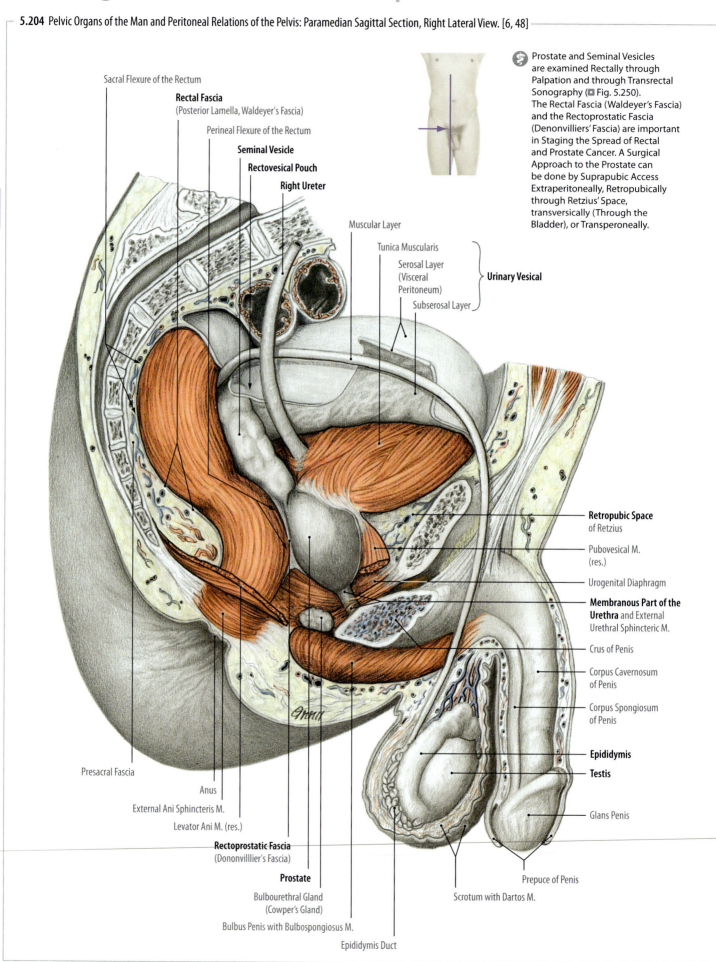

Sacral Flexure of the Rectum

Rectal Fascia
(Posterior Lamella, Waldeyer's Fascia)

Perineal Flexure of the Rectum

Seminal Vesicle

Rectovesical Pouch

Right Ureter

Muscular Layer

Tunica Muscularis

Serosal Layer
(Visceral
Peritoneum)

Subserosal Layer

Urinary Vesical

Retropubic Space
of Retzius

Pubovesical M.
(res.)

Urogenital Diaphragm

Membranous Part of the Urethra and External Urethral Sphincteric M.

Crus of Penis

Corpus Cavernosum
of Penis

Corpus Spongiosum
of Penis

Epididymis

Testis

Glans Penis

Presacral Fascia

Anus

External Ani Sphincteris M.

Levator Ani M. (res.)

Rectoprostatic Fascia
(Dononvilllier's Fascia)

Prostate

Bulbourethral Gland
(Cowper's Gland)

Bulbus Penis with Bulbospongiosus M.

Epididymis Duct

Scrotum with Dartos M.

Prepuce of Penis

Pelvic Organs, Peritoneal Relationships

5.205 Pelvic Organs of the Woman and Peritoneal Relationshps of the Pelvis: Paramedian Sagittal Section, Left Lateral View. [6]

Primary Malignant Tumors of the Vagina are relatively Rare (1–2% of all malignant tumors in women); they are mostly Squamous-Cell Carcinomas, which Spread into the Connective Tissue in the area between the Vagina and the Urinary Bladder and between the Vagina and the Rectum. First, the Tumors Metastasize into the Deep Internal Iliac Lymph Nodes or the Superficial Inguinal Nodes (□ Fig. 5.231). More common is Tumor Infiltration of the Vagina's Neighboring Organs, promoting Cervical, Bladder, or Rectal Carcinoma.

Right Ureter

Uterine Tube and Broad Ligament (res.)

Ovary

Uterine Tube and Mesosalpinx

Suspensory Ligament (Infundibulopelvic Ligament)

Ligamentum Teres (Round Ligament of Uterus)

Transverse Vesical Fold

Lateral Umbilical Fold

Medial Umbilical Fold

Mesometrium

Cut Edge of the Peritoneum

Uterine A. (Cardinal Ligament)

Muscular Layer of the Rectum

Rectouterine Fold

Transverse Fold of the Rectum

Vesicouterine Pouch

Rectouterine Pouch (Cul-de-Sac of Douglas)

Vagina

Rectovaginal Septum (Denonvilliers')

Levator Ani M. (res.)

External Ani Sphicteric M.

Anus

Adductor M. (res.)

Urinary Vesical

Urethra

Bulb of Vestibule

Deep Transverse Perineal M. (res.)

Left Ureter

Major Vestibular Gland (Bartholin's Gland)

Pelvic Cavity

5.206 Male Pelvis in the Area of the Prostate: Frontal Section, View of the Posterior Cut Surface. [6, 31]

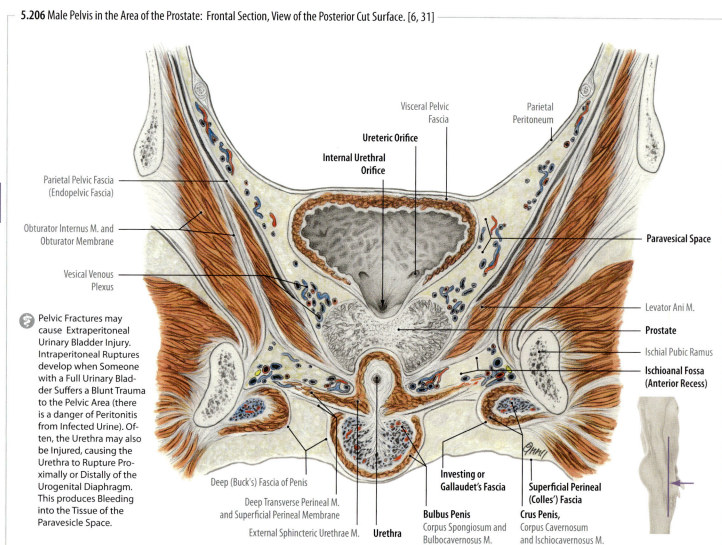

Visceral Pelvic Fascia

Parietal Peritoneum

Ureteric Orifice

Internal Urethral Orifice

Parietal Pelvic Fascia (Endopelvic Fascia)

Obturator Internus M. and Obturator Membrane

Vesical Venous Plexus

Paravesical Space

Levator Ani M.

Prostate

Ischial Pubic Ramus

Ischioanal Fossa (Anterior Recess)

Pelvic Fractures may cause Extraperitoneal Urinary Bladder Injury. Intraperitoneal Ruptures develop when Someone with a Full Urinary Bladder Suffers a Blunt Trauma to the Pelvic Area (there is a danger of Peritonitis from Infected Urine). Often, the Urethra may also be Injured, causing the Urethra to Rupture Proximally or Distally of the Urogenital Diaphragm. This produces Bleeding into the Tissue of the Paravesicle Space.

Deep (Buck's) Fascia of Penis

Deep Transverse Perineal M. and Superficial Perineal Membrane

External Sphincteric Urethrae M.

Urethra

Investing or Gallaudet's Fascia

Bulbus Penis
Corpus Spongiosum and Bulbocavernosus M.

Superficial Perineal (Colles') Fascia

Crus Penis,
Corpus Cavernosum and Ischiocavernosus M.

5.207 Anterior Pelvic Region of a Man: Median Sagittal Section, View of the Cut Surface of the Right Side. [92]

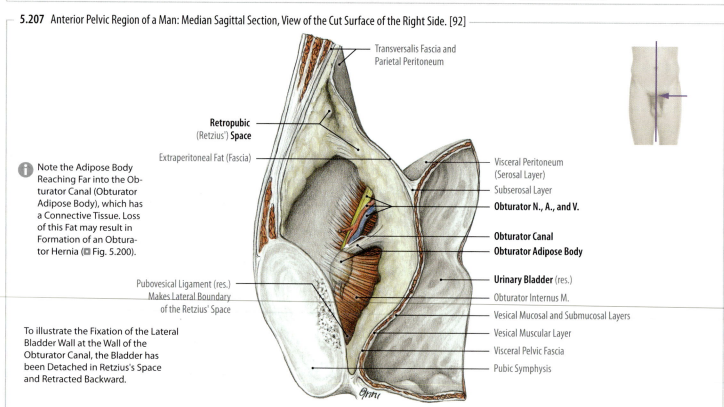

Transversalis Fascia and Parietal Peritoneum

Retropubic (Retzius') **Space**

Extraperitoneal Fat (Fascia)

Note the Adipose Body Reaching Far into the Obturator Canal (Obturator Adipose Body), which has a Connective Tissue. Loss of this Fat may result in Formation of an Obturator Hernia (�‣ Fig. 5.200).

Pubovesical Ligament (res.)
Makes Lateral Boundary of the Retzius' Space

To illustrate the Fixation of the Lateral Bladder Wall at the Wall of the Obturator Canal, the Bladder has been Detached in Retzius's Space and Retracted Backward.

Visceral Peritoneum (Serosal Layer)

Subserosal Layer

Obturator N., A., and V.

Obturator Canal

Obturator Adipose Body

Urinary Bladder (res.)

Obturator Internus M.

Vesical Mucosal and Submucosal Layers

Vesical Muscular Layer

Visceral Pelvic Fascia

Pubic Symphysis

Urinary Bladder

5.208 Urinary Bladder of a Man: Dorsal View. [6]

In Men, the Internal Urethral Sphincter of the Bladder Extends around the Proximal Prostatic Urethra. It is called the Preprostatic Portion of the Internal Urethral Sphincter, also known as the Supra-collicular Sphincter. This Sphincter does Not exist In Women.

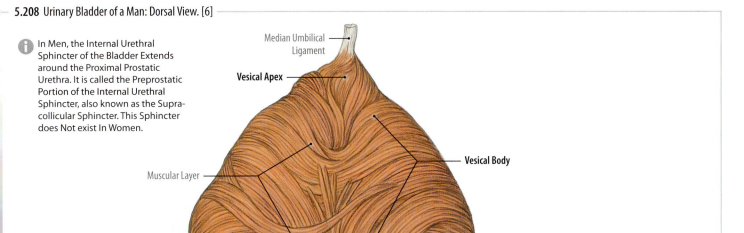

Median Umbilical Ligament

Vesical Apex

Muscular Layer

Vesical Body

Right Ureter

Fundus of Bladder

The Muscles (Muscular Layer) have been Dissected.

5.209 Floor of a Woman's Urinary Bladder with the Ureters Entering and the Urethra Exiting the Bladder: Inferior Lateral View. [99]

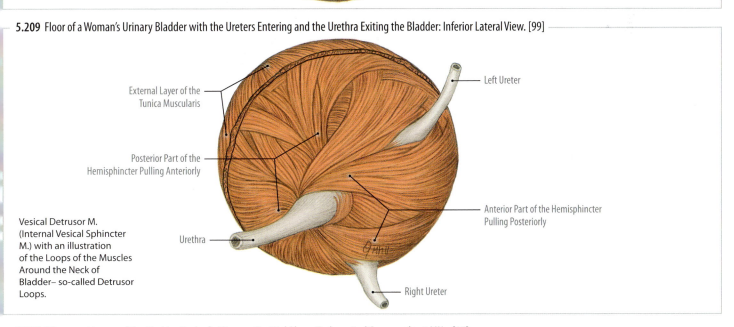

External Layer of the Tunica Muscularis

Left Ureter

Posterior Part of the Hemisphincter Pulling Anteriorly

Anterior Part of the Hemisphincter Pulling Posteriorly

Vesical Detrusor M. (Internal Vesical Sphincter M.) with an illustration of the Loops of the Muscles Around the Neck of Bladder– so-called Detrusor Loops.

Urethra

Right Ureter

5.210 Ultrasound Image of the Bladder Neck of a Woman: Sagittal Plane, Endovaginal Sonography, 4 MHz. [95]

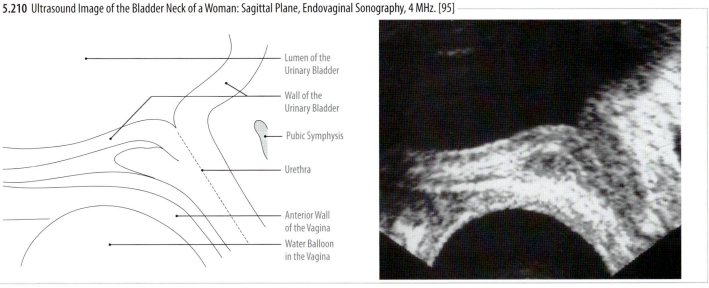

Lumen of the Urinary Bladder

Wall of the Urinary Bladder

Pubic Symphysis

Urethra

Anterior Wall of the Vagina

Water Balloon in the Vagina

Pelvic Cavity

Urinary Bladder

5.211 Muscles of the Urinary Bladder in the Area of the Vesical Trigone: Ventral View. [100]

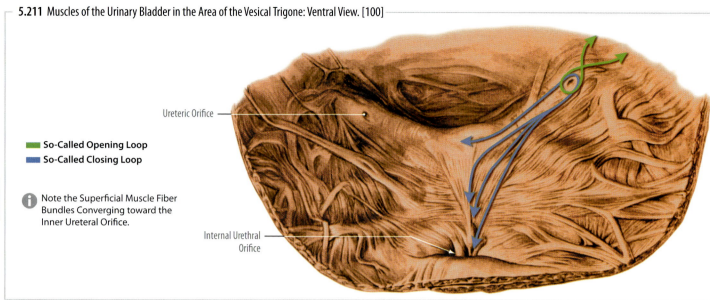

Ureteric Orifice

■ **So-Called Opening Loop**
■ **So-Called Closing Loop**

ℹ️ Note the Superficial Muscle Fiber Bundles Converging toward the Inner Ureteral Orifice.

Internal Urethral Orifice

5.212 Female Urethra with Adjacent Bladder Floor Opened from the Front: Ventral View. [2, 6]

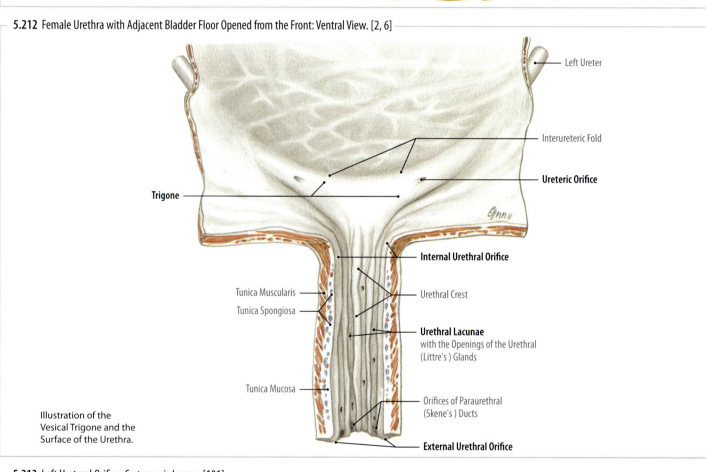

Left Ureter

Interureteric Fold

Ureteric Orifice

Trigone

Internal Urethral Orifice

Tunica Muscularis

Urethral Crest

Tunica Spongiosa

Urethral Lacunae
with the Openings of the Urethral
(Littre's) Glands

Tunica Mucosa

Orifices of Paraurethral
(Skene's) Ducts

Illustration of the
Vesical Trigone and the
Surface of the Urethra.

External Urethral Orifice

5.213 Left Ureteral Orifice: Cystoscopic Image. [101]

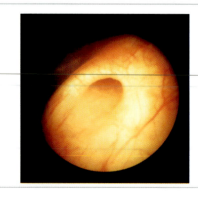

□ Fig. 5.212

Urinary Bladder, Ureter, Prostate: Vessels

5.214 Arteries and Veins of the Urinary Bladder, Ureter, and Prostate: Right Side, Lateral View. [102]

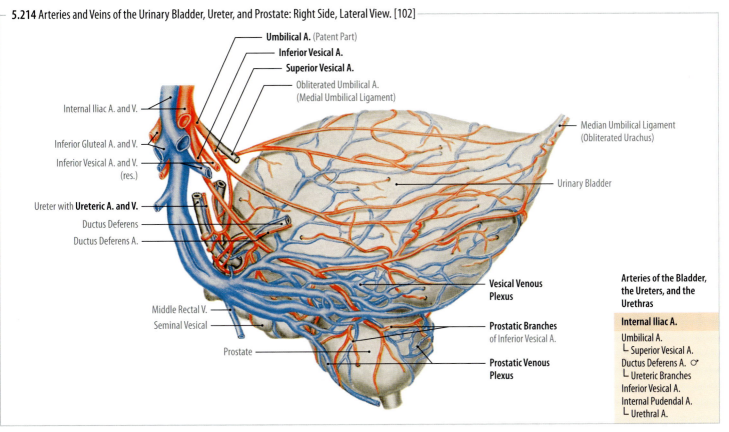

Umbilical A. (Patent Part)
Inferior Vesical A.
Superior Vesical A.
Obliterated Umbilical A.
(Medial Umbilical Ligament)

Internal Iliac A. and V.

Inferior Gluteal A. and V.

Inferior Vesical A. and V.
(res.)

Ureter with **Ureteric A. and V.**
Ductus Deferens
Ductus Deferens A.

Median Umbilical Ligament
(Obliterated Urachus)

Urinary Bladder

Vesical Venous Plexus

Middle Rectal V.
Seminal Vesical

Prostatic Branches
of Inferior Vesical A.

Prostate

Prostatic Venous Plexus

Arteries of the Bladder, the Ureters, and the Urethras

Internal Iliac A.

Umbilical A.
└ Superior Vesical A.
Ductus Deferens A. ♂
└ Ureteric Branches
Inferior Vesical A.
Internal Pudendal A.
└ Urethral A.

5.215a,b Variants of the Arterial Supply of the Bladder, Ureters, Seminal Vesicles, and Prostate: Right Lateral View. [100]

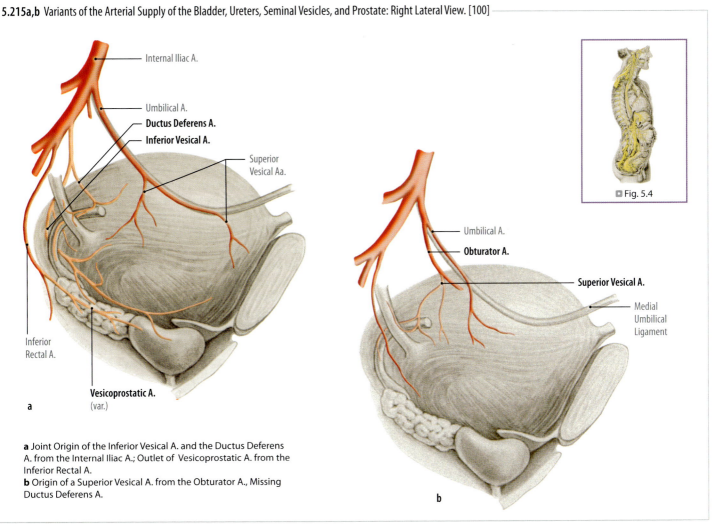

Internal Iliac A.

Umbilical A.
Ductus Deferens A.
Inferior Vesical A.
Superior Vesical Aa.

Inferior Rectal A.

Vesicoprostatic A.
(var.)

a

◻ Fig. 5.4

Umbilical A.
Obturator A.

Superior Vesical A.

Medial Umbilical Ligament

b

a Joint Origin of the Inferior Vesical A. and the Ductus Deferens A. from the Internal Iliac A.; Outlet of Vesicoprostatic A. from the Inferior Rectal A.
b Origin of a Superior Vesical A. from the Obturator A., Missing Ductus Deferens A.

Rectum and Anal Canal

5.216 Frontal Section through the Rectum and Anal Canal: Dorsal View of the Anterior Perineal Wall. [6, 92]

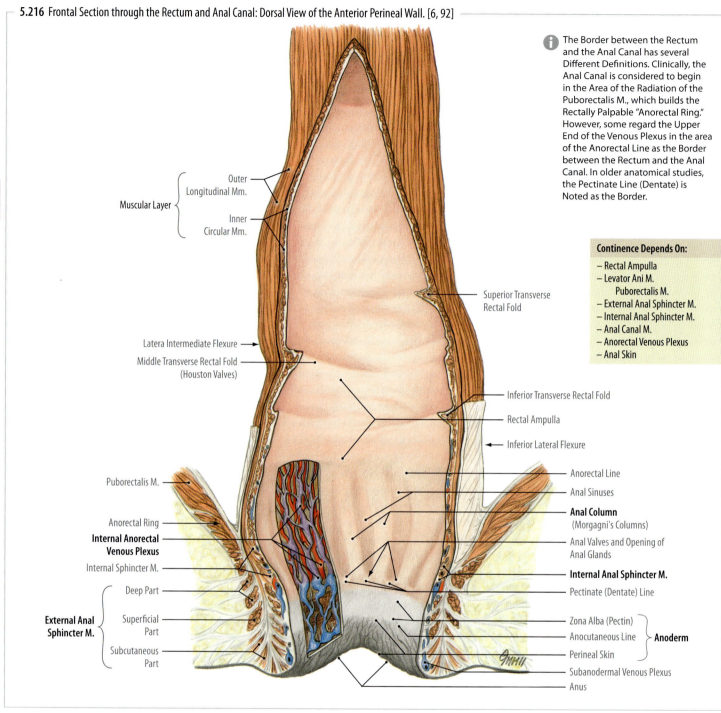

The Border between the Rectum and the Anal Canal has several Different Definitions. Clinically, the Anal Canal is considered to begin in the Area of the Radiation of the Puborectalis M., which builds the Rectally Palpable "Anorectal Ring." However, some regard the Upper End of the Venous Plexus in the area of the Anorectal Line as the Border between the Rectum and the Anal Canal. In older anatomical studies, the Pectinate Line (Dentate) is Noted as the Border.

Continence Depends On:

– Rectal Ampulla
– Levator Ani M.
    Puborectalis M.
– External Anal Sphincter M.
– Internal Anal Sphincter M.
– Anal Canal M.
– Anorectal Venous Plexus
– Anal Skin

Muscular Layer
Outer Longitudinal Mm.
Inner Circular Mm.

Superior Transverse Rectal Fold

Latera Intermediate Flexure
Middle Transverse Rectal Fold (Houston Valves)

Inferior Transverse Rectal Fold

Rectal Ampulla

Inferior Lateral Flexure

Puborectalis M.

Anorectal Line
Anal Sinuses
Anal Column (Morgagni's Columns)

Anorectal Ring
Internal Anorectal Venous Plexus
Internal Sphincter M.

Anal Valves and Opening of Anal Glands
Internal Anal Sphincter M.
Pectinate (Dentate) Line

External Anal Sphincter M.
Deep Part
Superficial Part
Subcutaneous Part

Zona Alba (Pectin)
Anocutaneous Line   **Anoderm**
Perineal Skin
Subanodermal Venous Plexus
Anus

5.217 Transrectal Ultrasound Image of the Median Area of the Rectum Showing the Layers of the Wall. [103]

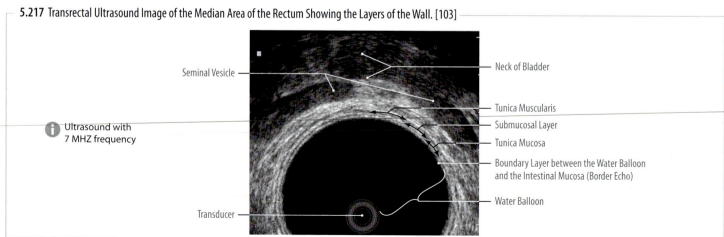

Ultrasound with 7 MHZ frequency

Seminal Vesicle

Neck of Bladder

Tunica Muscularis
Submucosal Layer
Tunica Mucosa
Boundary Layer between the Water Balloon and the Intestinal Mucosa (Border Echo)

Water Balloon

Transducer

5.218a–c Rectum and Anal Canal: Arteries, Veins, Portal Veins, and Lymphatics [2, 21]

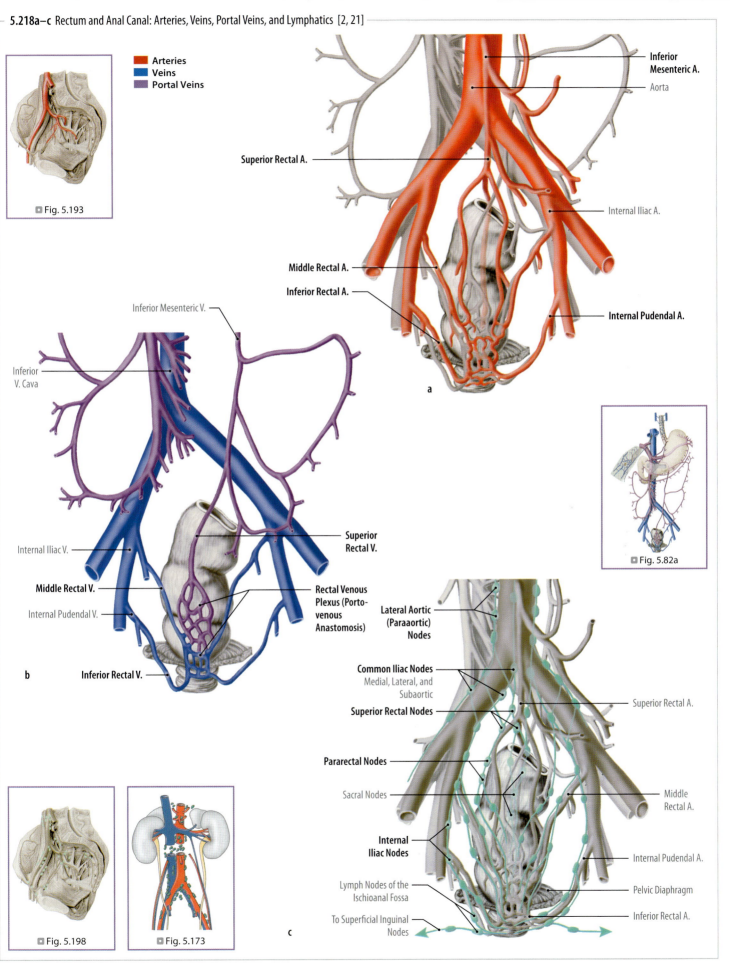

Arteries
Veins
Portal Veins

Fig. 5.193

Inferior Mesenteric A.

Aorta

Superior Rectal A.

Internal Iliac A.

Middle Rectal A.

Inferior Rectal A.

Internal Pudendal A.

a

Inferior Mesenteric V.

Inferior V. Cava

Internal Iliac V.

Superior Rectal V.

Middle Rectal V.

Internal Pudendal V.

Rectal Venous Plexus (Porto-venous Anastomosis)

Inferior Rectal V.

b

Fig. 5.82a

Lateral Aortic (Paraaortic) Nodes

Common Iliac Nodes
Medial, Lateral, and Subaortic

Superior Rectal A.

Superior Rectal Nodes

Pararectal Nodes

Sacral Nodes

Middle Rectal A.

Internal Iliac Nodes

Internal Pudendal A.

Lymph Nodes of the Ischioanal Fossa

Pelvic Diaphragm

To Superficial Inguinal Nodes

Inferior Rectal A.

Fig. 5.198

Fig. 5.173

c

Pelvic Cavity

5.219 Pelvic Organs, Pathways of the Pelvis, Diaphragm Pelvis, and Ischioanal Fossa: Dorsal View (■ Fig. 5.175). [1]

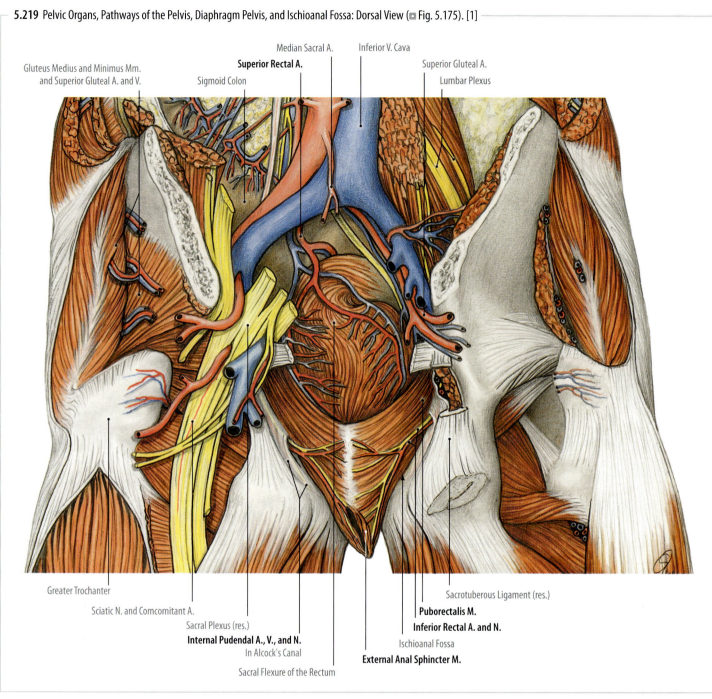

Median Sacral A.

Inferior V. Cava

Superior Rectal A.

Gluteus Medius and Minimus Mm. and Superior Gluteal A. and V.

Sigmoid Colon

Superior Gluteal A.

Lumbar Plexus

Greater Trochanter

Sciatic N. and Comcomitant A.

Sacral Plexus (res.)

Internal Pudendal A., V., and N.
In Alcock's Canal

Sacral Flexure of the Rectum

Sacrotuberous Ligament (res.)

Puborectalis M.

Inferior Rectal A. and N.

Ischioanal Fossa

External Anal Sphincter M.

5.220 Rectum and Anal Canal with Puborectal Loop of the Levator Ani M.: Median Sagittal Section, Medial View of the Right Half of the Pelvis. [48]

The Puborectalis M. (Puborectal Sling) helps to Maintain Continence following Injury of the Spincter M., e.g., after a Perineal Laceration.

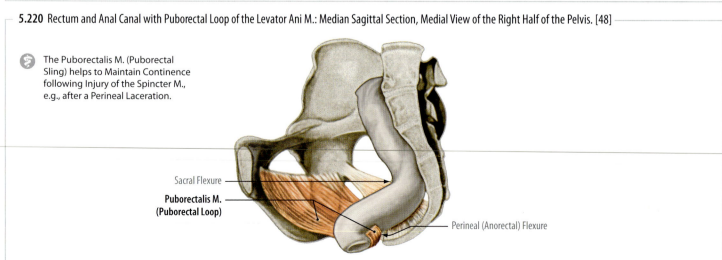

Sacral Flexure

Puborectalis M. (Puborectal Loop)

Perineal (Anorectal) Flexure

External Female Genitals

5.221 External Female Genitalia with Perineal Region: Anteroinferior View. [102]

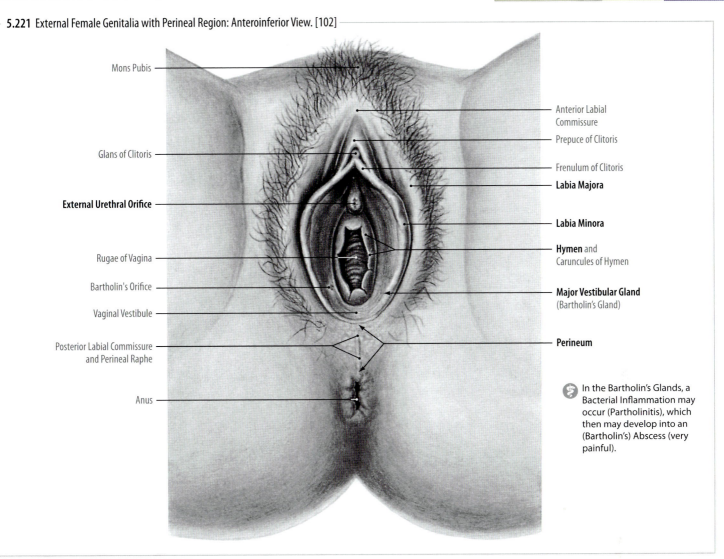

Mons Pubis

Glans of Clitoris

External Urethral Orifice

Rugae of Vagina

Bartholin's Orifice

Vaginal Vestibule

Posterior Labial Commissure
and Perineal Raphe

Anus

Anterior Labial
Commissure

Prepuce of Clitoris

Frenulum of Clitoris

Labia Majora

Labia Minora

Hymen and
Caruncles of Hymen

Major Vestibular Gland
(Bartholin's Gland)

Perineum

In the Bartholin's Glands, a
Bacterial Inflammation may
occur (Partholinitis), which
then may develop into an
(Bartholin's) Abscess (very
painful).

5.222 External Female Genitalia, Clitoris: Ventral View. [2, 23]

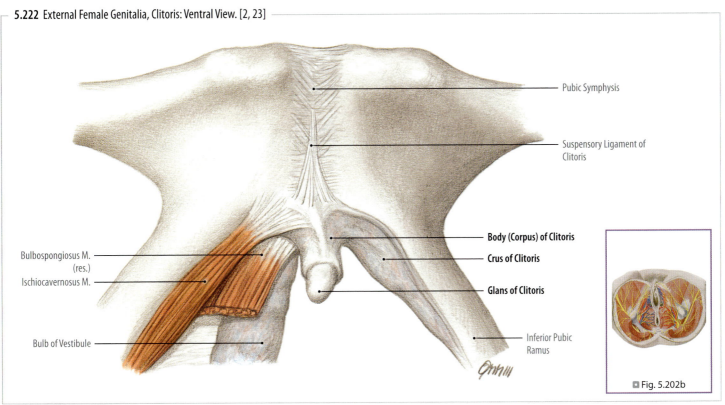

Pubic Symphysis

Suspensory Ligament of
Clitoris

Bulbospongiosus M.
(res.)

Ischiocavernosus M.

Bulb of Vestibule

Body (Corpus) of Clitoris

Crus of Clitoris

Glans of Clitoris

Inferior Pubic
Ramus

Fig. 5.202b

Pelvic Cavity

Pelvic Organs of the Woman

5.223 Pelvic Organs of the Woman: Median Sagittal Section, Medial View of the Right Cut Surface. [15]

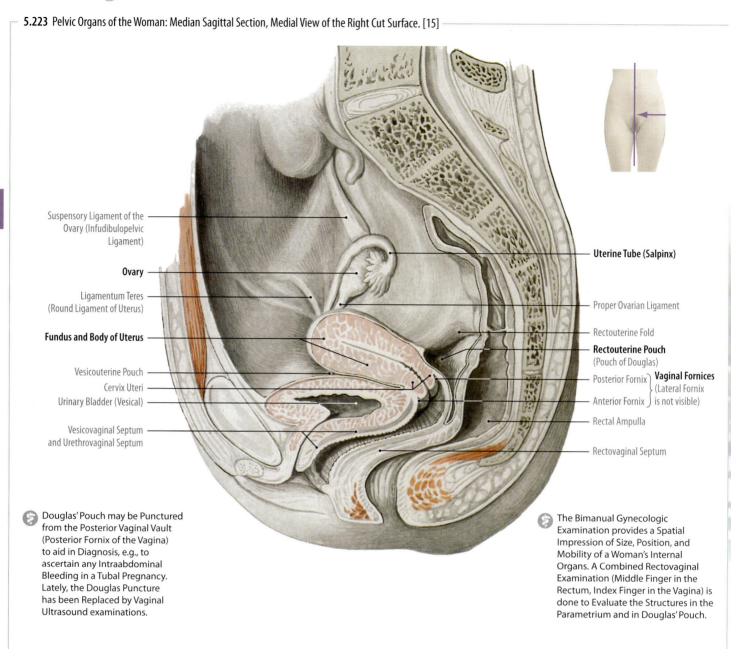

Suspensory Ligament of the Ovary (Infudibulopelvic Ligament)

Ovary

Ligamentum Teres (Round Ligament of Uterus)

Fundus and Body of Uterus

Vesicouterine Pouch

Cervix Uteri

Urinary Bladder (Vesical)

Vesicovaginal Septum and Urethrovaginal Septum

Uterine Tube (Salpinx)

Proper Ovarian Ligament

Rectouterine Fold

Rectouterine Pouch (Pouch of Douglas)

Posterior Fornix **Vaginal Fornices** (Lateral Fornix
Anterior Fornix } is not visible)

Rectal Ampulla

Rectovaginal Septum

Douglas' Pouch may be Punctured from the Posterior Vaginal Vault (Posterior Fornix of the Vagina) to aid in Diagnosis, e.g., to ascertain any Intraabdominal Bleeding in a Tubal Pregnancy. Lately, the Douglas Puncture has been Replaced by Vaginal Ultrasound examinations.

The Bimanual Gynecologic Examination provides a Spatial Impression of Size, Position, and Mobility of a Woman's Internal Organs. A Combined Rectovaginal Examination (Middle Finger in the Rectum, Index Finger in the Vagina) is done to Evaluate the Structures in the Parametrium and in Douglas' Pouch.

5.224 Schematic Illustration of Anteflexion and Anteversion: Median Sagittal Section through the Uterus and Vagina.

Normally, the Uterus, Cervix, and the Vagina have a small degree of Antiflexion (Anterior Angulation between the Axis of the Uterus and Cervix). The External Os of the Cervix faces the Posterior Wall of the Vagina. If the External Os faces the Vaginal Opening, it is called Anteversion; if it faces the Posterior Fornix, it is called Retroversion. Both conditions are Not Conducive to Semen Transport. Severe Angulation between the Body of the Uterus and the Cervix are Not Conducive for Embryo Implantation.
A Severe Anteflexion or a Reverse Flexion is called a Retroflexion.

In ~10% of all cases, the Body of the Uterus Deviates Dorsally, thus Developing a Retroflexion of the Uterus. One must Differentiate between a Mobile versus a Fixed Retroflexion of the Uterus. A Mobile Retroflexion can be corrected by Manual Repositioning. A Fixed Retroflexion requires a Surgical Intervention to Release the Adhesion of the Visceral Peritoneum between the Uterus and the Rectum.

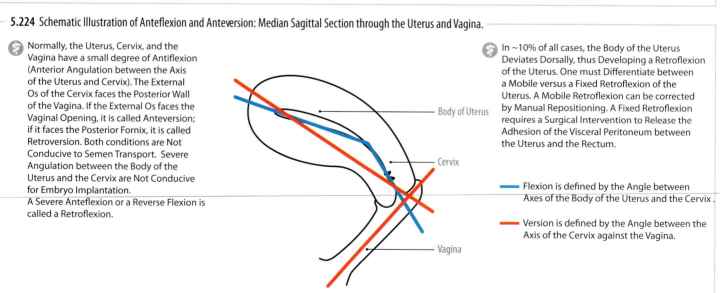

Body of Uterus

Cervix

Vagina

Flexion is defined by the Angle between Axes of the Body of the Uterus and the Cervix .

Version is defined by the Angle between the Axis of the Cervix against the Vagina.

Uterus, Tubes, Ovaries, Broad Ligament

5.225 Uterus, Tubes, Ovaries with the Broad Ligament, and the Upper Section of the Vagina: Dorsal View. [2]

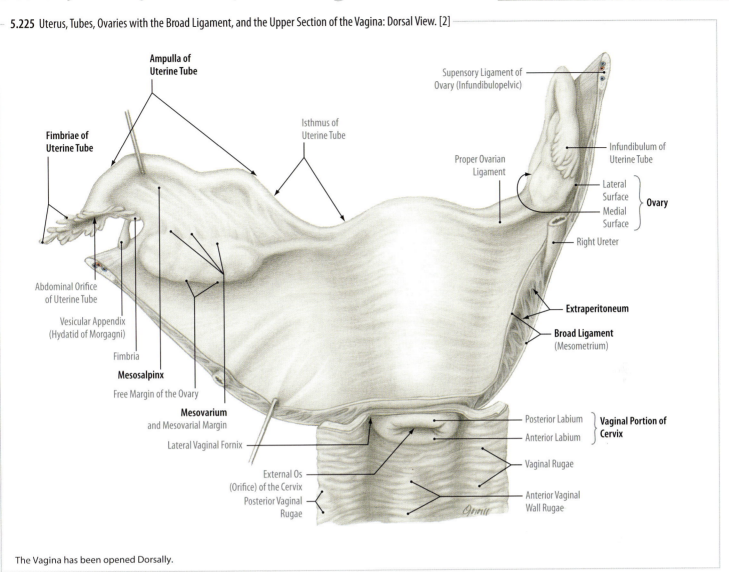

Ampulla of Uterine Tube

Fimbriae of Uterine Tube

Isthmus of Uterine Tube

Supensory Ligament of Ovary (Infundibulopelvic)

Proper Ovarian Ligament

Infundibulum of Uterine Tube

Lateral Surface

Medial Surface

Ovary

Right Ureter

Abdominal Orifice of Uterine Tube

Vesicular Appendix (Hydatid of Morgagni)

Fimbria

Extraperitoneum

Broad Ligament (Mesometrium)

Mesosalpinx

Free Margin of the Ovary

Mesovarium and Mesovarial Margin

Lateral Vaginal Fornix

Posterior Labium

Anterior Labium

Vaginal Portion of Cervix

Vaginal Rugae

External Os (Orifice) of the Cervix

Posterior Vaginal Rugae

Anterior Vaginal Wall Rugae

The Vagina has been opened Dorsally.

5.226a,b Cervix Uteri: Colposcopic Images. [104]

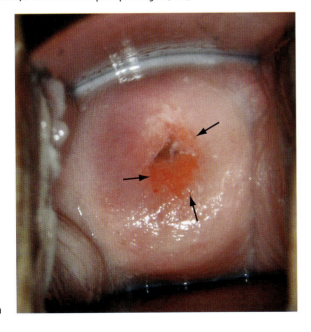 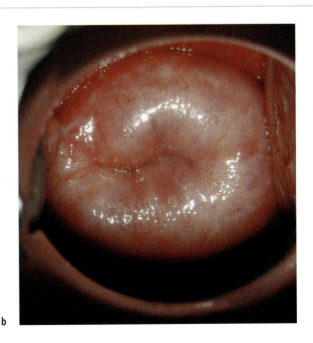

a

b

a Nullipara with Low-Grade Displasia (ectropion ➡) and Circular External Os of the Cervix Uteri in an 18-year-old girl.
b Multipara with Slit-Shaped Transversal External Os of the Uterus in a 64-year-old woman.

Pelvic Cavity

5.227 Frontal Section through the Uterus, Tube, and Ovary: Dorsal View of the Anterior Cut Surface. [31]

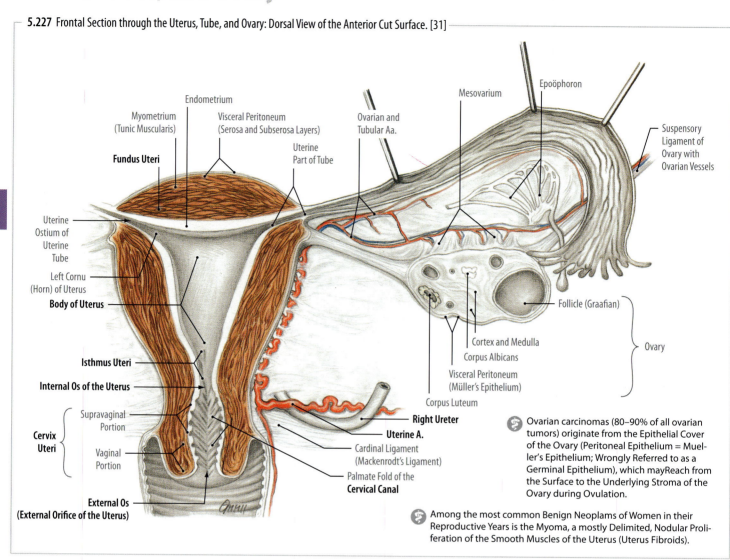

- Myometrium (Tunic Muscularis)
- Endometrium
- Visceral Peritoneum (Serosa and Subserosa Layers)
- **Fundus Uteri**
- Uterine Part of Tube
- Ovarian and Tubular Aa.
- Mesovarium
- Epoöphoron
- Suspensory Ligament of Ovary with Ovarian Vessels
- Uterine Ostium of Uterine Tube
- Left Cornu (Horn) of Uterus
- **Body of Uterus**
- Follicle (Graafian)
- Ovary
- Cortex and Medulla
- Corpus Albicans
- **Isthmus Uteri**
- **Internal Os of the Uterus**
- Visceral Peritoneum (Müller's Epithelium)
- Corpus Luteum
- **Cervix Uteri**
  - Supravaginal Portion
  - Vaginal Portion
- **Right Ureter**
- **Uterine A.**
- Cardinal Ligament (Mackenrodt's Ligament)
- Palmate Fold of the **Cervical Canal**
- **External Os (External Orifice of the Uterus)**

Ovarian carcinomas (80–90% of all ovarian tumors) originate from the Epithelial Cover of the Ovary (Peritoneal Epithelium = Mueller's Epithelium; Wrongly Referred to as a Germinal Epithelium), which mayReach from the Surface to the Underlying Stroma of the Ovary during Ovulation.

Among the most common Benign Neoplams of Women in their Reproductive Years is the Myoma, a mostly Delimited, Nodular Proliferation of the Smooth Muscles of the Uterus (Uterus Fibroids).

5.228a,b Uterus: Sagittal Section. [99]

In Pubescent Women, the Mucous Membrane often Shifts Outward physiologically from the Lower Area of the Cervical Canal and becomes visible on the Os Surface (Ectopy or Ectropion, Fig. 5.228a, Fig. 5.226a). After Menopause, the Mucous Membrane Relocates Back into the Cervical Canal so that the Portio is exclusively Covered by uncornified, multilayer Squamous Epithelium (Fig. 5.226b, Fig. 5.228b). The Border between Squamous Epithelium and Columnar Epithelium then Lies Endocervically as it does Before Puberty.
In the Area of the Ectopy, most women experience a Transformation (Metaplasia) of the Columnar Epithelium into a multilayer, uncornified Squamous Epithelium; this area of the metaplastic transformation is also known as the Transformation Zone. The Transformation Zone may be the Source of Malignant Degeneration of the Squamous Epithelium that leads to a Cervical Carcinoma via Precursors (Leukoplakia, Carcinoma in Situ). Diagnostic measures (Screening Examinations) are conducted by means of Colposcopic Inspection of the surface (Fig. 5.226, by means of Schiller's Test; Lugol's Solutions Stain Normal Glycogeneus Squamous Epithelium to Dark Brown) and by means of Cytologic Diagnostics (Smears from the area of the Cervical Canal and the External Os – called a Pap Smear).

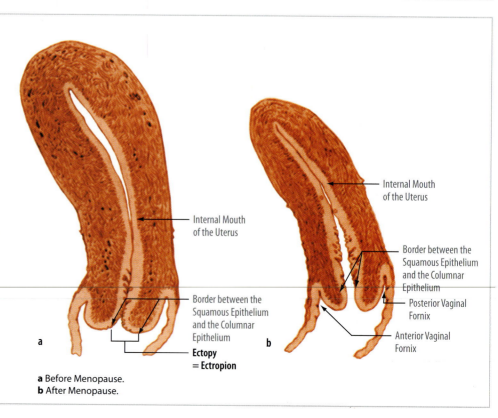

- Internal Mouth of the Uterus
- Internal Mouth of the Uterus
- Border between the Squamous Epithelium and the Columnar Epithelium
- Posterior Vaginal Fornix
- Anterior Vaginal Fornix
- Border between the Squamous Epithelium and the Columnar Epithelium
- **Ectopy = Ectropion**

a Before Menopause.
b After Menopause.

5.229 Pelvic Organs of the Woman: Anterosuperior View. [23]

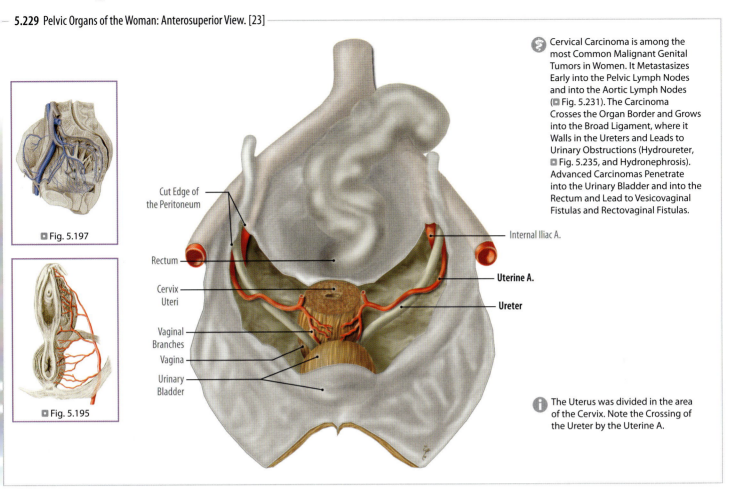

☐ Fig. 5.197

☐ Fig. 5.195

Cut Edge of
the Peritoneum

Rectum

Cervix
Uteri

Vaginal
Branches

Vagina

Urinary
Bladder

Internal Iliac A.

Uterine A.

Ureter

🔍 Cervical Carcinoma is among the
most Common Malignant Genital
Tumors in Women. It Metastasizes
Early into the Pelvic Lymph Nodes
and into the Aortic Lymph Nodes
(☐ Fig. 5.231). The Carcinoma
Crosses the Organ Border and Grows
into the Broad Ligament, where it
Walls in the Ureters and Leads to
Urinary Obstructions (Hydroureter,
☐ Fig. 5.235, and Hydronephrosis).
Advanced Carcinomas Penetrate
into the Urinary Bladder and into the
Rectum and Lead to Vesicovaginal
Fistulas and Rectovaginal Fistulas.

ℹ️ The Uterus was divided in the area
of the Cervix. Note the Crossing of
the Ureter by the Uterine A.

5.230 Arterial Supply of the Female Genitalia: Anterosuperior View. [23]

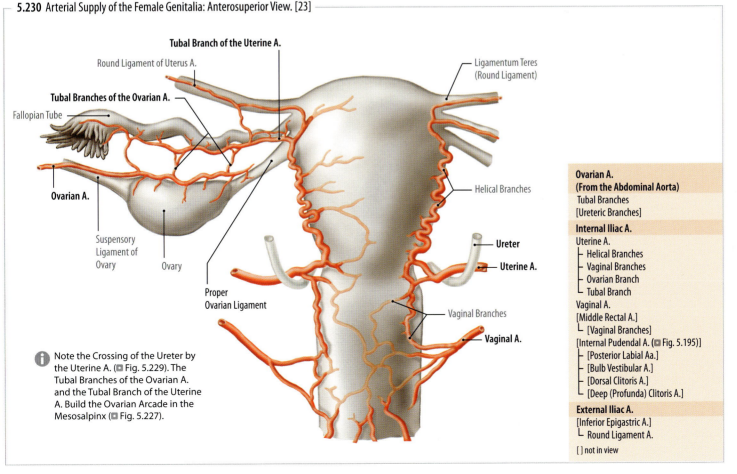

Tubal Branch of the Uterine A.

Round Ligament of Uterus A.

Tubal Branches of the Ovarian A.

Fallopian Tube

Ovarian A.

Suspensory
Ligament of
Ovary

Ovary

Proper
Ovarian Ligament

Ligamentum Teres
(Round Ligament)

Helical Branches

Ureter

Uterine A.

Vaginal Branches

Vaginal A.

ℹ️ Note the Crossing of the Ureter by
the Uterine A. (☐ Fig. 5.229). The
Tubal Branches of the Ovarian A.
and the Tubal Branch of the Uterine
A. Build the Ovarian Arcade in the
Mesosalpinx (☐ Fig. 5.227).

Ovarian A.
(From the Abdominal Aorta)
Tubal Branches
[Ureteric Branches]
Internal Iliac A.
Uterine A.
├ Helical Branches
├ Vaginal Branches
├ Ovarian Branch
└ Tubal Branch
Vaginal A.
[Middle Rectal A.]
└ [Vaginal Branches]
[Internal Pudendal A. (☐ Fig. 5.195)]
├ [Posterior Labial Aa.]
├ [Bulb Vestibular A.]
├ [Dorsal Clitoris A.]
└ [Deep (Profunda) Clitoris A.]
External Iliac A.
[Inferior Epigastric A.]
└ Round Ligament A.
[ ] not in view

Pelvic Cavity

5.231 Lymph Drains and Regional Lymph Nodes of the Internal Female Genital Organs: Ventral View. [2, 21]

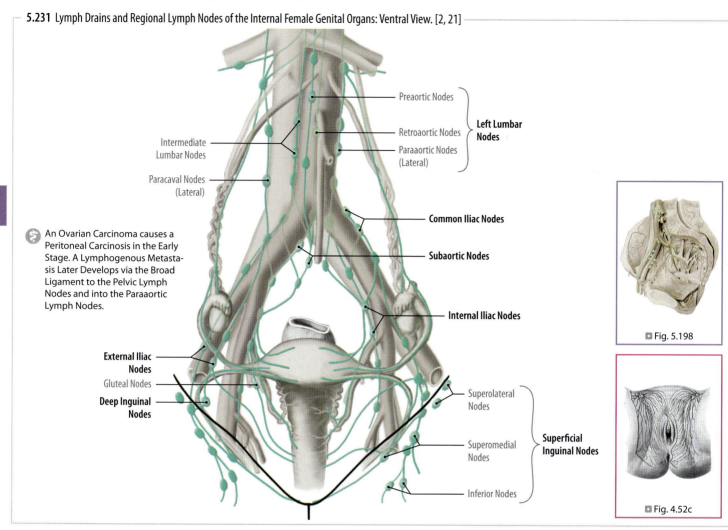

Preaortic Nodes

Retroaortic Nodes

Paraaortic Nodes (Lateral)

Left Lumbar Nodes

Intermediate Lumbar Nodes

Paracaval Nodes (Lateral)

An Ovarian Carcinoma causes a Peritoneal Carcinosis in the Early Stage. A Lymphogenous Metastasis Later Develops via the Broad Ligament to the Pelvic Lymph Nodes and into the Paraaortic Lymph Nodes.

Common Iliac Nodes

Subaortic Nodes

Internal Iliac Nodes

External Iliac Nodes

Gluteal Nodes

Deep Inguinal Nodes

Superolateral Nodes

Superomedial Nodes

Superficial Inguinal Nodes

Inferior Nodes

Fig. 5.198

Fig. 4.52c

5.232 Innervation of the Internal Female Genitalia: Anterolateral View. [23]

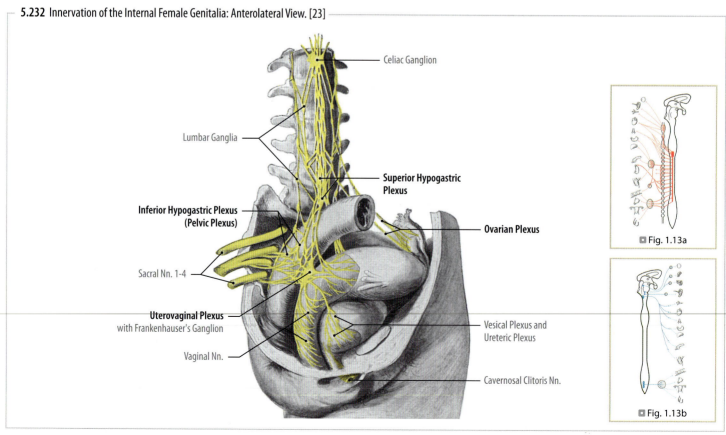

Celiac Ganglion

Lumbar Ganglia

Superior Hypogastric Plexus

Inferior Hypogastric Plexus (Pelvic Plexus)

Ovarian Plexus

Sacral Nn. 1-4

Uterovaginal Plexus
with Frankenhauser's Ganglion

Vesical Plexus and Ureteric Plexus

Vaginal Nn.

Cavernosal Clitoris Nn.

Fig. 1.13a

Fig. 1.13b

5.233 Position of the Uterus on the Diaphragma Pelvis: Superior View. [105]

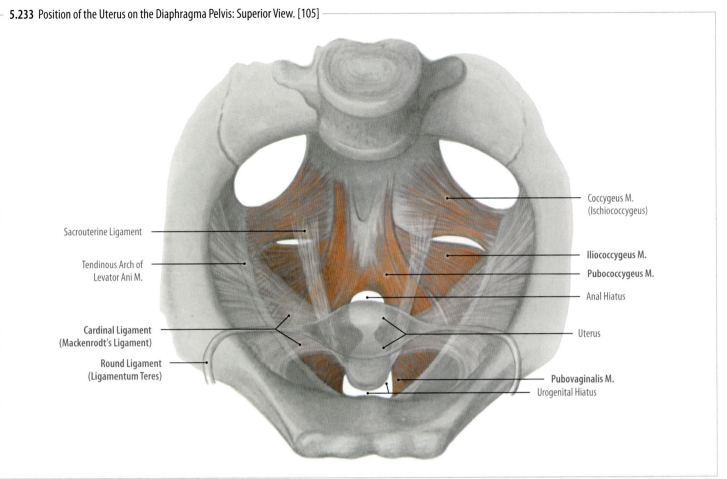

Sacrouterine Ligament

Tendinous Arch of
Levator Ani M.

**Cardinal Ligament
(Mackenrodt's Ligament)**

**Round Ligament
(Ligamentum Teres)**

Coccygeus M.
(Ischiococcygeus)

Iliococcygeus M.

Pubococcygeus M.

Anal Hiatus

Uterus

Pubovaginalis M.

Urogenital Hiatus

5.234 Ligament Structures in the Female Pelvis: Superior View. [105]

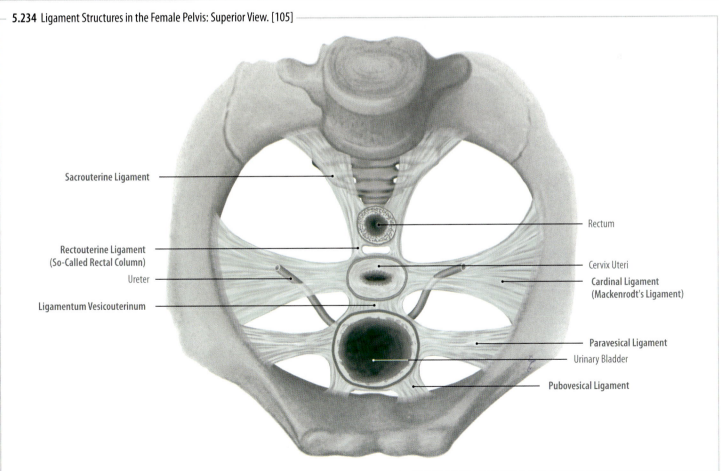

Sacrouterine Ligament

**Rectouterine Ligament
(So-Called Rectal Column)**

Ureter

Ligamentum Vesicouterinum

Rectum

Cervix Uteri

**Cardinal Ligament
(Mackenrodt's Ligament)**

Paravesical Ligament

Urinary Bladder

Pubovesical Ligament

Pelvic Cavity

5.235 Organs of the Female Pelvis: Posterosuperior View. [15]

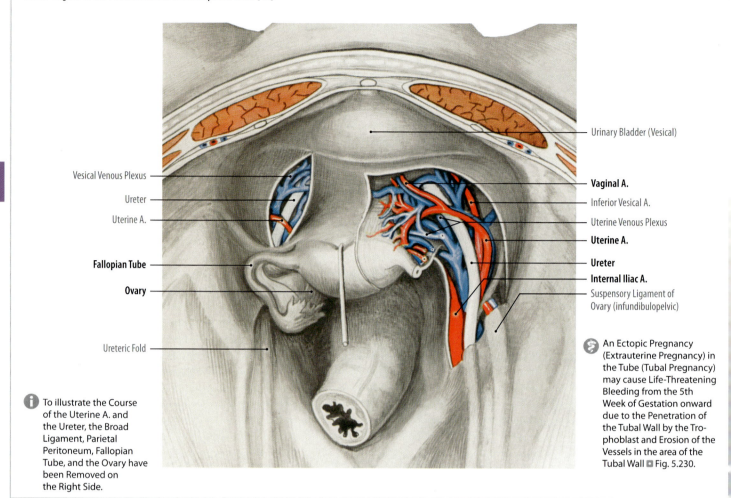

Urinary Bladder (Vesical)

Vesical Venous Plexus

Vaginal A.

Ureter

Inferior Vesical A.

Uterine A.

Uterine Venous Plexus

Uterine A.

Fallopian Tube

Ureter

Ovary

Internal Iliac A.

Suspensory Ligament of Ovary (infundibulopelvic)

Ureteric Fold

To illustrate the Course of the Uterine A. and the Ureter, the Broad Ligament, Parietal Peritoneum, Fallopian Tube, and the Ovary have been Removed on the Right Side.

An Ectopic Pregnancy (Extrauterine Pregnancy) in the Tube (Tubal Pregnancy) may cause Life-Threatening Bleeding from the 5th Week of Gestation onward due to the Penetration of the Tubal Wall by the Trophoblast and Erosion of the Vessels in the area of the Tubal Wall Fig. 5.230.

5.236 Endoscopic Image of the Uterus and Adnexa: Posterosuperior View. [106]

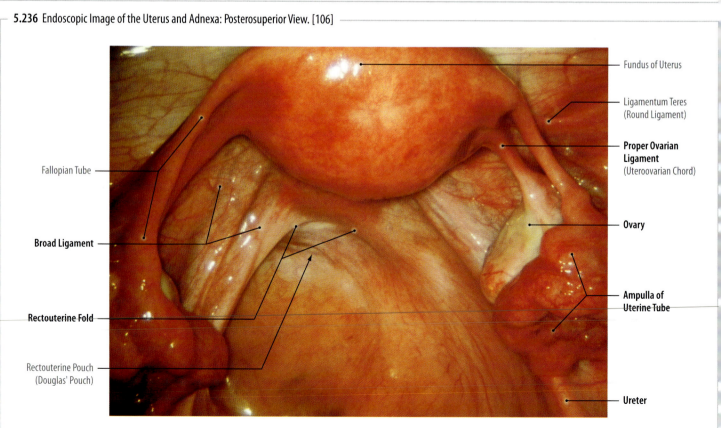

Fundus of Uterus

Ligamentum Teres (Round Ligament)

Proper Ovarian Ligament (Uteroovarian Chord)

Fallopian Tube

Ovary

Broad Ligament

Ampulla of Uterine Tube

Rectouterine Fold

Rectouterine Pouch (Douglas' Pouch)

Ureter

Male Genitals and Pelvis

5.237 External Male Genitalia.

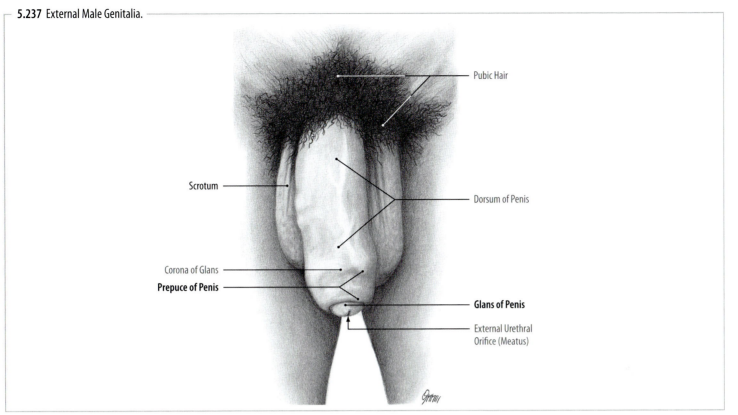

Pubic Hair

Scrotum

Dorsum of Penis

Corona of Glans

Prepuce of Penis

Glans of Penis

External Urethral
Orifice (Meatus)

5.238 Pelvic Organs of the Man: Median Sagittal Section, Medial View of the Right Cut Surface. [15]

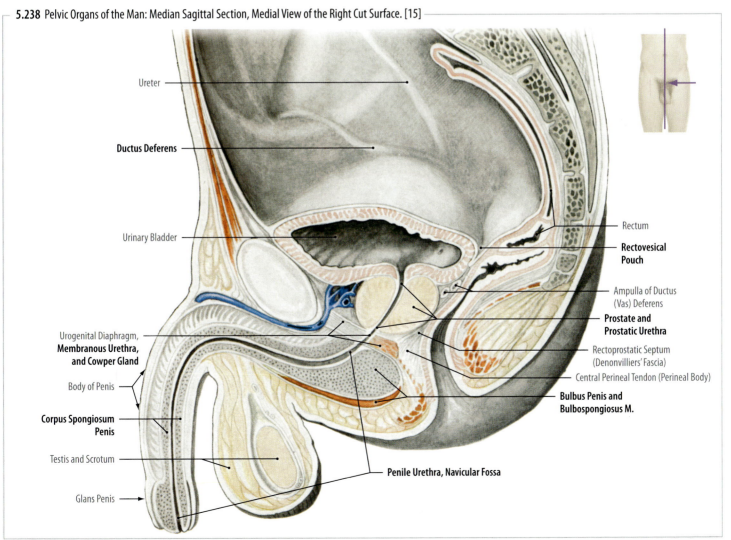

Ureter

Ductus Deferens

Urinary Bladder

Urogenital Diaphragm,
**Membranous Urethra,
and Cowper Gland**

Body of Penis

**Corpus Spongiosum
Penis**

Testis and Scrotum

Glans Penis

Rectum

**Rectovesical
Pouch**

Ampulla of Ductus
(Vas) Deferens

**Prostate and
Prostatic Urethra**

Rectoprostatic Septum
(Denonvilliers' Fascia)

Central Perineal Tendon (Perineal Body)

**Bulbus Penis and
Bulbospongiosus M.**

Penile Urethra, Navicular Fossa

Pelvic Cavity

5.239 Penis, Prostate, and Floor of the Urinary Bladder. [100]

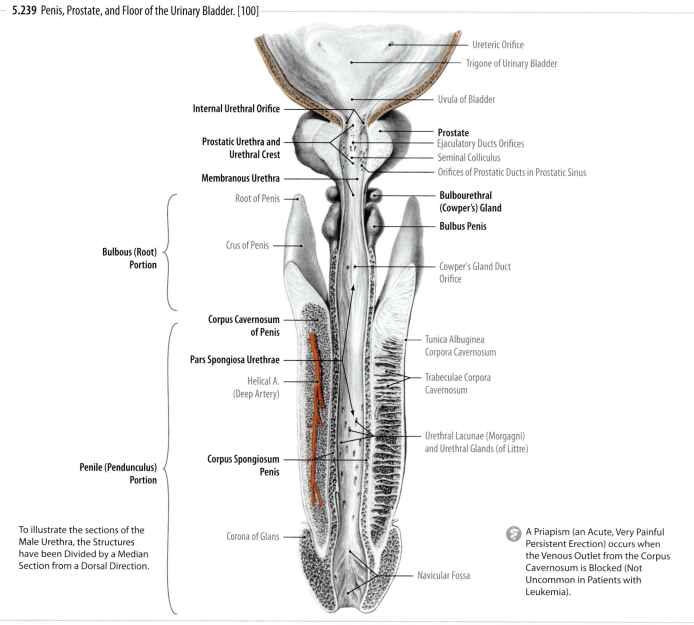

Ureteric Orifice

Trigone of Urinary Bladder

Uvula of Bladder

Internal Urethral Orifice

Prostatic Urethra and Urethral Crest

Prostate
Ejaculatory Ducts Orifices
Seminal Colliculus
Orifices of Prostatic Ducts in Prostatic Sinus

Membranous Urethra

Root of Penis

Bulbourethral (Cowper's) Gland

Bulbus Penis

Bulbous (Root) Portion

Crus of Penis

Cowper's Gland Duct Orifice

Corpus Cavernosum of Penis

Tunica Albuginea Corpora Cavernosum

Pars Spongiosa Urethrae

Trabeculae Corpora Cavernosum

Helical A. (Deep Artery)

Urethral Lacunae (Morgagni) and Urethral Glands (of Littre)

Penile (Pendunculus) Portion

Corpus Spongiosum Penis

Corona of Glans

Navicular Fossa

To illustrate the sections of the Male Urethra, the Structures have been Divided by a Median Section from a Dorsal Direction.

A Priapism (an Acute, Very Painful Persistent Erection) occurs when the Venous Outlet from the Corpus Cavernosum is Blocked (Not Uncommon in Patients with Leukemia).

5.240 Sagittal Section through the Penis in the Area of the Glans Penis. [23]

5.241 Urethra Opened from the Underside of the Penis. [100]

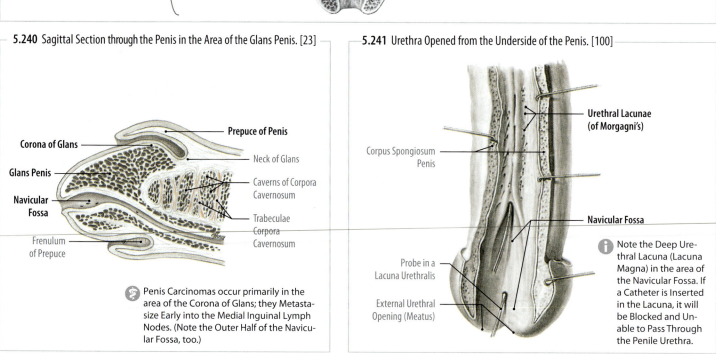

Prepuce of Penis

Corona of Glans

Neck of Glans

Glans Penis

Caverns of Corpora Cavernosum

Navicular Fossa

Trabeculae Corpora Cavernosum

Frenulum of Prepuce

Penis Carcinomas occur primarily in the area of the Corona of Glans; they Metastasize Early into the Medial Inguinal Lymph Nodes. (Note the Outer Half of the Navicular Fossa, too.)

Urethral Lacunae (of Morgagni's)

Corpus Spongiosum Penis

Navicular Fossa

Probe in a Lacuna Urethralis

External Urethral Opening (Meatus)

Note the Deep Urethral Lacuna (Lacuna Magna) in the area of the Navicular Fossa. If a Catheter is Inserted in the Lacuna, it will be Blocked and Unable to Pass Through the Penile Urethra.

5.242 Blood Supply of the Penis: Inferior View. [23, 48]

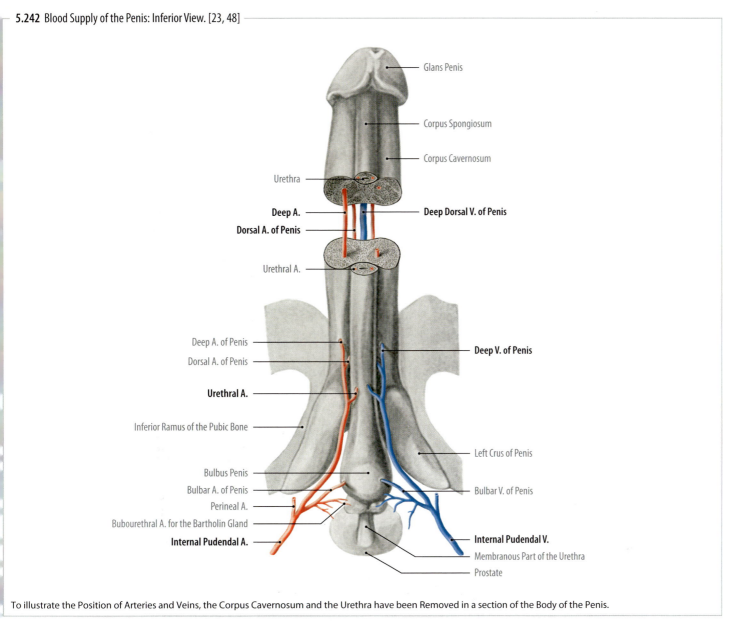

- Glans Penis
- Corpus Spongiosum
- Corpus Cavernosum
- Urethra
- **Deep A.**
- **Dorsal A. of Penis**
- **Deep Dorsal V. of Penis**
- Urethral A.
- Deep A. of Penis
- Dorsal A. of Penis
- **Deep V. of Penis**
- **Urethral A.**
- Inferior Ramus of the Pubic Bone
- Left Crus of Penis
- Bulbus Penis
- Bulbar A. of Penis
- Perineal A.
- Bubourethral A. for the Bartholin Gland
- **Internal Pudendal A.**
- Bulbar V. of Penis
- **Internal Pudendal V.**
- Membranous Part of the Urethra
- Prostate

To illustrate the Position of Arteries and Veins, the Corpus Cavernosum and the Urethra have been Removed in a section of the Body of the Penis.

5.243 Body of Penis: Cross-Section through the Median Area. [6, 78, 107]

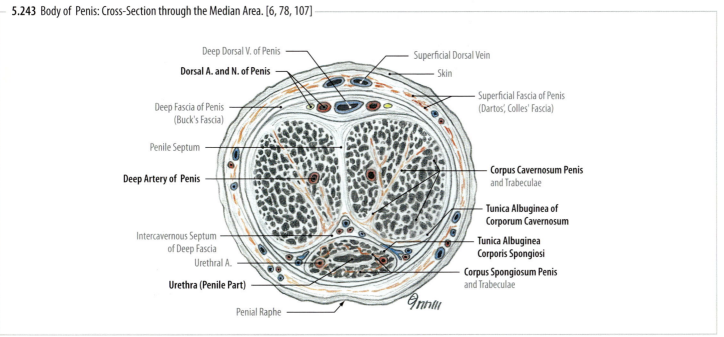

- Deep Dorsal V. of Penis
- **Dorsal A. and N. of Penis**
- Superficial Dorsal Vein
- Skin
- Deep Fascia of Penis (Buck's Fascia)
- Superficial Fascia of Penis (Dartos', Colles' Fascia)
- Penile Septum
- **Deep Artery of Penis**
- **Corpus Cavernosum Penis** and Trabeculae
- **Tunica Albuginea of Corporum Cavernosum**
- Intercavernous Septum of Deep Fascia
- Urethral A.
- **Tunica Albuginea Corporis Spongiosi**
- **Urethra (Penile Part)**
- **Corpus Spongiosum Penis** and Trabeculae
- Penial Raphe

Pelvic Cavity

5.244 Male Perineal Region: Inferior View. [100]

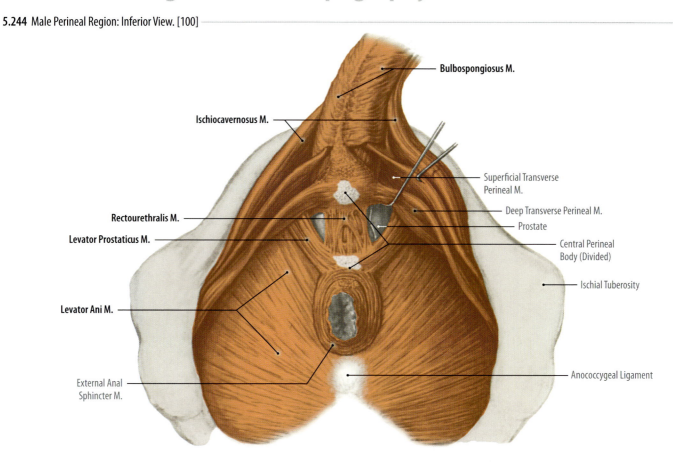

Bulbospongiosus M.

Ischiocavernosus M.

Superficial Transverse Perineal M.

Deep Transverse Perineal M.

Prostate

Rectourethralis M.

Levator Prostaticus M.

Central Perineal Body (Divided)

Levator Ani M.

Ischial Tuberosity

External Anal Sphincter M.

Anococcygeal Ligament

Following Transection of the Central Perineal Body and Resection of the Urogenital Diaphragm Forward, the Prerectal Parts of the Levator Ani M. (Levator Prostaticus M. and Rectourethral M.) can be seen.

5.245 Urinary Bladder with Ureters, Spermatic Cords and Seminal Vesicles, as well as Prostate and Bulbus Penis: Dorsal View. [48]

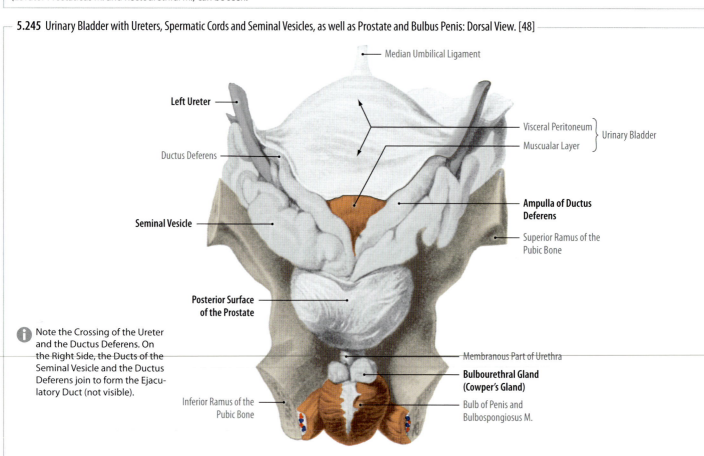

Median Umbilical Ligament

Left Ureter

Visceral Peritoneum

Muscualar Layer

Urinary Bladder

Ductus Deferens

Ampulla of Ductus Deferens

Seminal Vesicle

Superior Ramus of the Pubic Bone

Posterior Surface of the Prostate

Note the Crossing of the Ureter and the Ductus Deferens. On the Right Side, the Ducts of the Seminal Vesicle and the Ductus Deferens join to form the Ejaculatory Duct (not visible).

Membranous Part of Urethra

Bulbourethral Gland (Cowper's Gland)

Inferior Ramus of the Pubic Bone

Bulb of Penis and Bulbospongiosus M.

5.246 a Prostate, Seminal Vesicles, and Spermatic Ducts: Anterosuperior View. **b** Testis and Epididymis. [31, 2, 92]

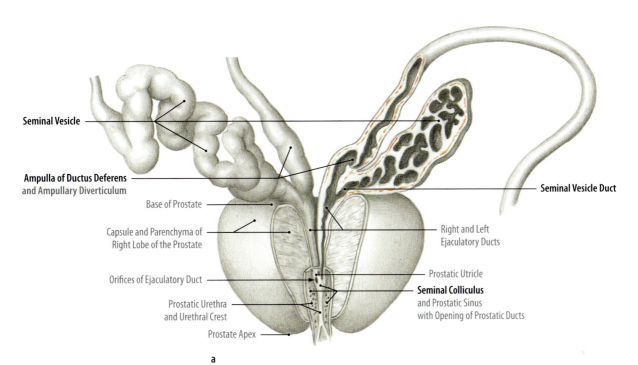

Seminal Vesicle

Ampulla of Ductus Deferens
and Ampullary Diverticulum

Base of Prostate

Capsule and Parenchyma of
Right Lobe of the Prostate

Seminal Vesicle Duct

Right and Left
Ejaculatory Ducts

Orifices of Ejaculatory Duct

Prostatic Urethra
and Urethral Crest

Prostate Apex

Prostatic Utricle

Seminal Colliculus
and Prostatic Sinus
with Opening of Prostatic Ducts

a

A Hyperplasia of the Prostate (Prostate Adenoma) is a Benign Tumor in Older Men, which Originates from the Glandular Connective Tissue of the Transitional Zone. According to the Size of the Tumor, Urinary Obstructions, Frequency (Polyuria), Residual (dribbling) Urine, and Consequential Cystitis Can Result as well. In an Advanced Stage, Decompensation of the Urinary Bladder with Backflow of the Urine into the Efferent Urinary Tracts and a Danger of an Epididymitis may result. In ~70% of all cases, Prostate Cancer develops in the Peripheral Zone of the Organ (Palpable in Rectal Examinations). It Metastasizes Early and Hematogenously via the Veins of the Pelvic Space into the Spinal Column and Pelvic Bones. The Lymphogenous Metastasis First Spreads into the Regional Iliac Lymph Nodes and then into the Paraaortic Lymph Nodes, and even into the Occipital Lymph Nodes (□ Fig. 5.198).

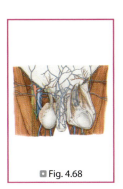

□ Fig. 4.68

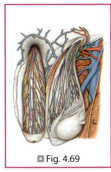

□ Fig. 4.69

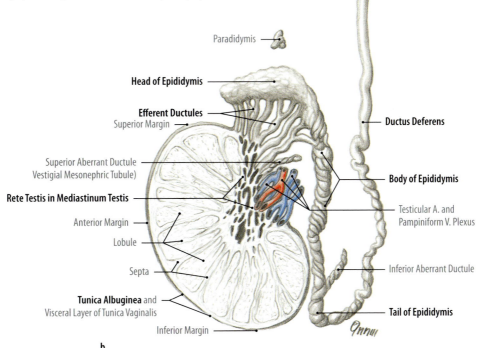

Paradidymis

Head of Epididymis

Efferent Ductules
Superior Margin

Superior Aberrant Ductule
Vestigial Mesonephric Tubule)

Rete Testis in Mediastinum Testis

Anterior Margin

Lobule

Septa

Tunica Albuginea and
Visceral Layer of Tunica Vaginalis

Inferior Margin

Ductus Deferens

Body of Epididymis

Testicular A. and
Pampiniform V. Plexus

Inferior Aberrant Ductule

Tail of Epididymis

b

a To illustrate the Path of the Ejaculatory Duct into the Prostatic Part of the Urethra, Part of the Prostate has been Removed Cuneiformly from the Front.
b Sagittal section through the Testis with Epididymis and Spermatic Duct.

Pelvic Cavity

5.247 Cross-Section through a Right Testis with Testicular Coats. [23]

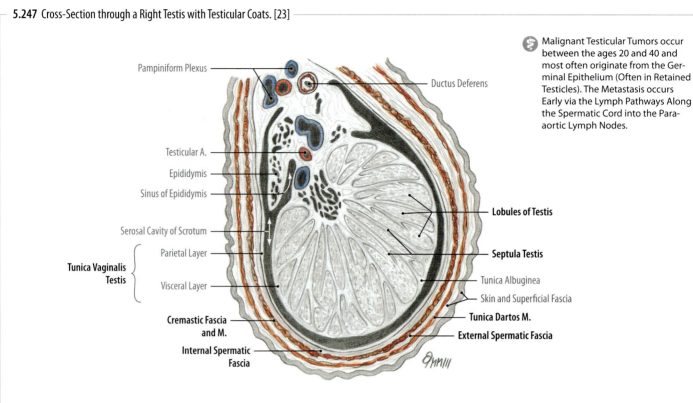

Pampiniform Plexus

Ductus Deferens

Testicular A.

Epididymis

Sinus of Epididymis

Serosal Cavity of Scrotum

Tunica Vaginalis Testis

Parietal Layer

Visceral Layer

Cremastic Fascia and M.

Internal Spermatic Fascia

Lobules of Testis

Septula Testis

Tunica Albuginea

Skin and Superficial Fascia

Tunica Dartos M.

External Spermatic Fascia

Malignant Testicular Tumors occur between the ages 20 and 40 and most often originate from the Germinal Epithelium (Often in Retained Testicles). The Metastasis occurs Early via the Lymph Pathways Along the Spermatic Cord into the Para-aortic Lymph Nodes.

5.248 Cross-Section through the Testis of a Young Man. [108]

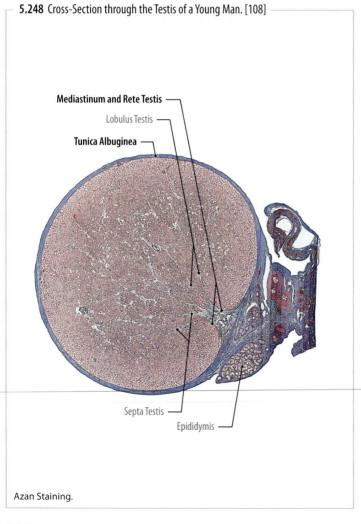

Mediastinum and Rete Testis

Lobulus Testis

Tunica Albuginea

Septa Testis

Epididymis

Azan Staining.

5.249 Arteries and Veins of the Testis, the Spermatic Cord, and the Testicular Coats. [2]

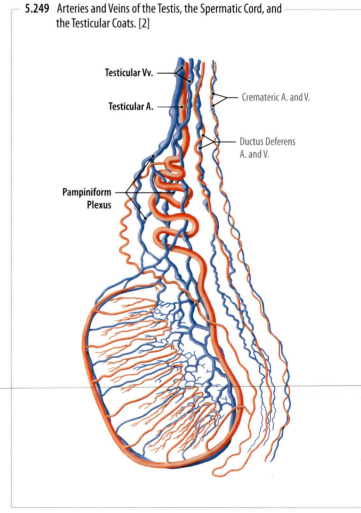

Testicular Vv.

Testicular A.

Cremateric A. and V.

Ductus Deferens A. and V.

Pampiniform Plexus

Prostate: Sonography

5.250a,b Prostate: Transrectal Sonography. [95]

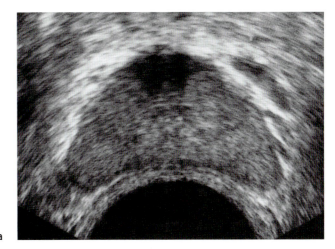

a

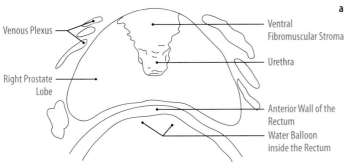

Venous Plexus

Right Prostate Lobe

Ventral Fibromuscular Stroma

Urethra

Anterior Wall of the Rectum

Water Balloon inside the Rectum

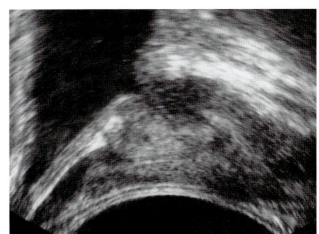

b

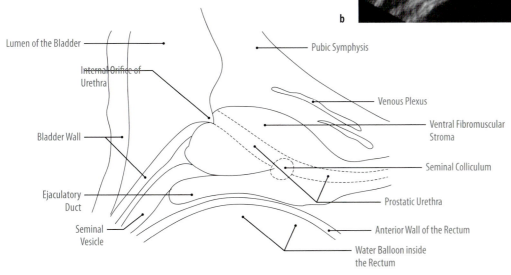

Lumen of the Bladder

Internal Orifice of Urethra

Bladder Wall

Ejaculatory Duct

Seminal Vesicle

Pubic Symphysis

Venous Plexus

Ventral Fibromuscular Stroma

Seminal Colliculum

Prostatic Urethra

Anterior Wall of the Rectum

Water Balloon inside the Rectum

a Prostate of a young man (total volume 11 ml). Sonogram in the Transversal Plane, 7.5 MHz.
b Same patient; Sonogram in the Median Sagittal Plane, 7.5 MHz.

Pelvic Cavity

5.Aa,b   Muscles of the Pelvic Floor.

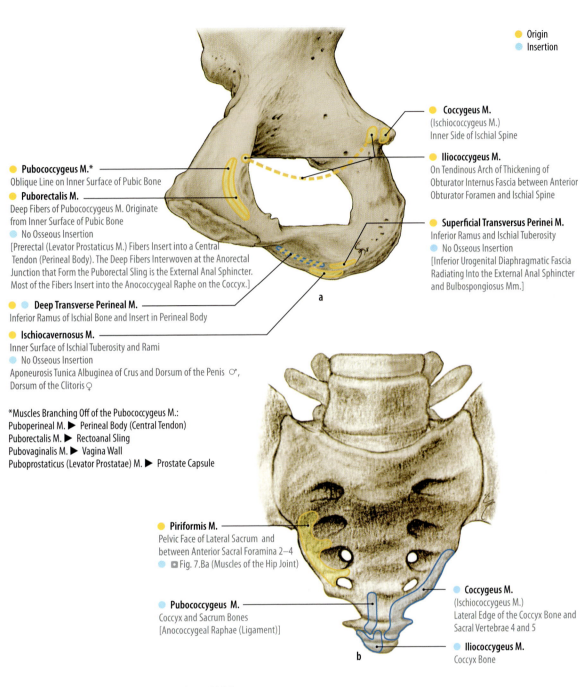

● Origin
● Insertion

● **Coccygeus M.**
(Ischiococcygeus M.)
Inner Side of Ischial Spine

● **Iliococcygeus M.**
On Tendinous Arch of Thickening of
Obturator Internus Fascia between Anterior
Obturator Foramen and Ischial Spine

● **Pubococcygeus M.***
Oblique Line on Inner Surface of Pubic Bone

● **Puborectalis M.**
Deep Fibers of Pubococcygeus M. Originate
from Inner Surface of Pubic Bone
● No Osseous Insertion
[Prerectal (Levator Prostaticus M.) Fibers Insert into a Central
Tendon (Perineal Body). The Deep Fibers Interwoven at the Anorectal
Junction that Form the Puborectal Sling is the External Anal Sphincter.
Most of the Fibers Insert into the Anococcygeal Raphe on the Coccyx.]

● **Superficial Transversus Perinei M.**
Inferior Ramus and Ischial Tuberosity
● No Osseous Insertion
[Inferior Urogenital Diaphragmatic Fascia
Radiating Into the External Anal Sphincter
and Bulbospongiosus Mm.]

● ● **Deep Transverse Perineal M.**
Inferior Ramus of Ischial Bone and Insert in Perineal Body

● **Ischiocavernosus M.**
Inner Surface of Ischial Tuberosity and Rami
● No Osseous Insertion
Aponeurosis Tunica Albuginea of Crus and Dorsum of the Penis ♂,
Dorsum of the Clitoris ♀

*Muscles Branching Off of the Pubococcygeus M.:
Puboperineal M. ▶ Perineal Body (Central Tendon)
Puborectalis M. ▶ Rectoanal Sling
Pubovaginalis M. ▶ Vagina Wall
Puboprostaticus (Levator Prostatae) M. ▶ Prostate Capsule

a

● **Piriformis M.**
Pelvic Face of Lateral Sacrum and
between Anterior Sacral Foramina 2–4
● ◻ Fig. 7.Ba (Muscles of the Hip Joint)

● **Pubococcygeus M.**
Coccyx and Sacrum Bones
[Anococcygeal Raphae (Ligament)]

● **Coccygeus M.**
(Ischiococcygeus M.)
Lateral Edge of the Coccyx Bone and
Sacral Vertebrae 4 and 5

● **Iliococcygeus M.**
Coccyx Bone

b

Muscles of the Pelvic Floor Without Osseous Insertion and Origin

Bulbospongiosus M.
(Bulbocavernosus)
♂ ● Central Perineal Tendon (Perineal Body), Median Raphe of the Bulbus Penis
● Dorsum Penis and Inferior Urogenital Diaphragmatic Fascia

♀ ● Central Perineal Tendon (Perineal Body)
● Bulb of Vestibule, Undersurface of the Clitoris and the Inferior Urogenital Diaphragmatic Fascia

External Sphincter Ani M. ● ● **Deep Part:**
Circular Muscle Cuff with Connection to the Central Perineal Tendon and Via the Anococcygeal
Ligament to the Coccyx, Crossing of the Fibers of the Right and Left Sides of the Body
● ● **Superficial Part:**
Between the Anococcygeal Ligament and the Central Perineal Tendon
● ● **Subcutaneous Part:**
Radiation into the Anal Skin

Function	Innervation	Blood Supply
Muscles of the Pelvic Diaphragm		

Levator Ani M.
 Pubococcygeus M.
 Iliococcygeus M.
    Tension of the pelvic floor
    Carries the pelvic viscera
    Lifting of the pelvic floor
 Puborectalis M.
    A Levator like the Pubococcygeus M. and the Iliococcygeus M.
    Support of rectal occlusion (part of the continence organ)
    Arbitrary constriction of the Vagina
	Sacral Nn. ((S2) S3–S4
	 (Inferior Anal [Rectal] Nn. of the Pudendal N.)
		Inferior Rectal A.
		
		 Inferior Rectal A.
		 Middle Rectal A.

Coccygeus M. (Ischiococcygeus M.) Support of the Sacrospinous Ligament in its supporting function	Sacral N. S3–S4 (S5)	Lateral Sacral A.
External Anal Sphincter M. Arbitrary occlusion of the Anal Canal (part of the continence organ)	Inferior Anal (Rectal) N. of the Pudendal N. S3–S4	Inferior Rectal A. Middle Rectal A.
Muscles of the Urogenital Diaphragm and of the Perineum		
Deep Transversus Perinei M. Tension of the pelvic floor in the area of the Pubic Bone Support of urethral occlusion (Compressor Urethrae M.)	Perineal Nn. of the Pudendal N. (S2) S3–S4	Perineal A. Bulb of Penis A. ♂/Vestibular A. ♀
Superficial Transversus Perinei M. (Tension of the perineal region)	Perineal Nn. of the Pudendal N. (S2) S3–S4	Perineal A.
Ischiocavernosus M. Support of the blood filling the Corpus Cavernosum during an erection of the Penis or of the Clitoris	Perineal Nn. of the Pudendal N. (S2) S4	Perineal A. Deep A. of Penis ♂/Clitoris ♀

Bulbospongiosus M.
 In a Man:
    Compression of the Bulbus Penis
    Support of the blood filling the Penis during an erection
    and ejaculation
 In a Woman:
    Draining of the Bulbourethral Glands
    Hypertonia of the Vaginal Orifice
	Perineal Nn. of the Pudendal N. (S2) S4	Perineal A.
		 Bulb of Penis A. ♂/Vestibular A. ♀

5

Upper Limbs

Clavicle (Collarbone) · Scapula

6.1a,b Right Clavicle. [6]

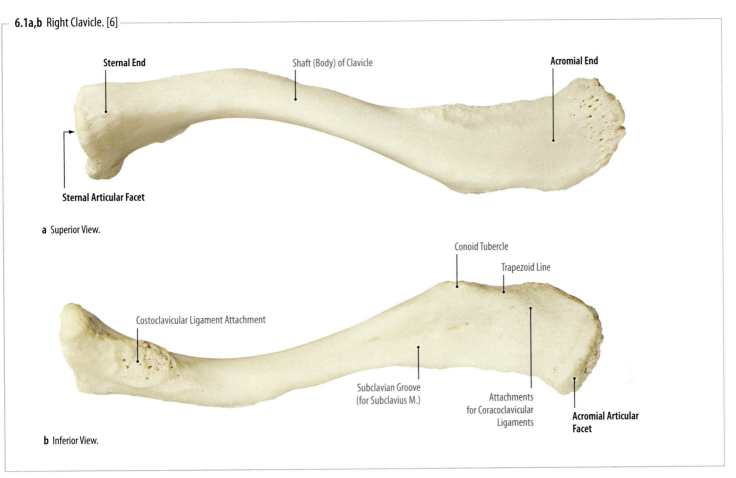

Sternal End

Shaft (Body) of Clavicle

Acromial End

Sternal Articular Facet

a Superior View.

Conoid Tubercle

Trapezoid Line

Costoclavicular Ligament Attachment

Subclavian Groove
(for Subclavius M.)

Attachments
for Coracoclavicular
Ligaments

**Acromial Articular
Facet**

b Inferior View.

6.2a,b Right Shoulder Blade (Scapula). [6]

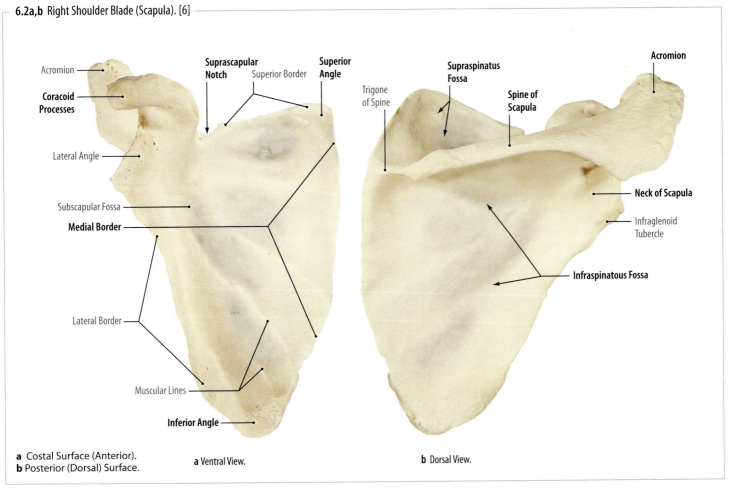

Acromion

**Coracoid
Processes**

Lateral Angle

Subscapular Fossa

Medial Border

Lateral Border

Muscular Lines

Inferior Angle

**Suprascapular
Notch** · Superior Border

**Superior
Angle**

Trigone
of Spine

**Supraspinatus
Fossa**

**Spine of
Scapula**

Acromion

Neck of Scapula

Infraglenoid
Tubercle

Infraspinatous Fossa

a Costal Surface (Anterior).
b Posterior (Dorsal) Surface.

a Ventral View.

b Dorsal View.

Skeleton

Humerus Bone

6

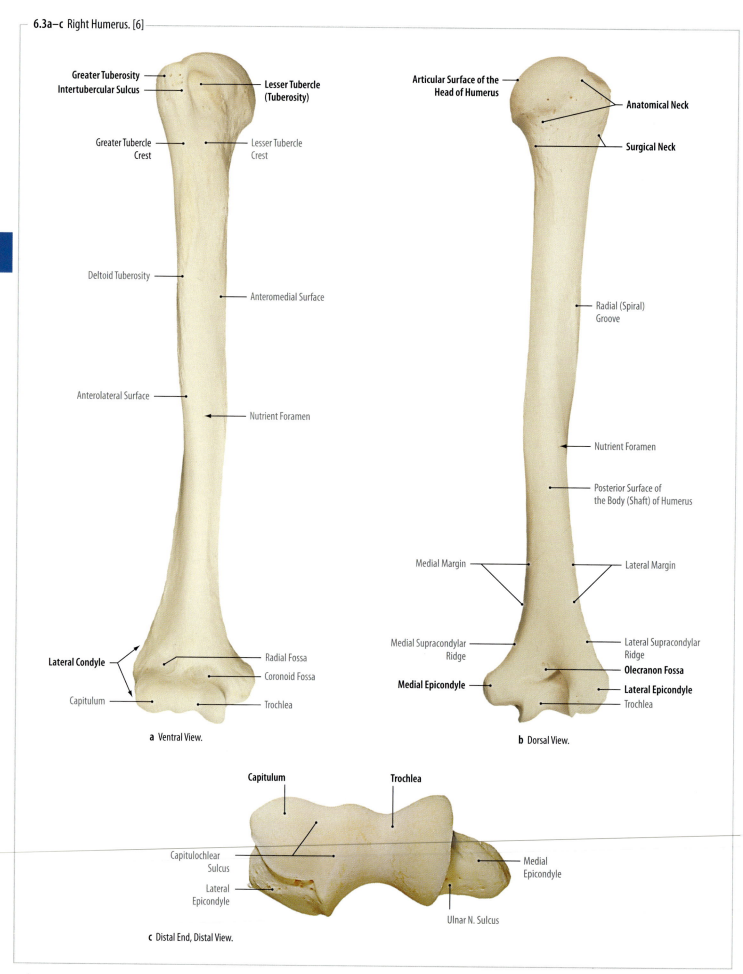

Greater Tuberosity
Intertubercular Sulcus

**Lesser Tubercle
(Tuberosity)**

Greater Tubercle
Crest

Lesser Tubercle
Crest

Deltoid Tuberosity

Anteromedial Surface

Anterolateral Surface

Nutrient Foramen

Lateral Condyle

Radial Fossa

Coronoid Fossa

Capitulum

Trochlea

a Ventral View.

**Articular Surface of the
Head of Humerus**

Anatomical Neck

Surgical Neck

Radial (Spiral)
Groove

Nutrient Foramen

Posterior Surface of
the Body (Shaft) of Humerus

Medial Margin

Lateral Margin

Medial Supracondylar
Ridge

Lateral Supracondylar
Ridge

Olecranon Fossa

Medial Epicondyle

Lateral Epicondyle

Trochlea

b Dorsal View.

Capitulum

Trochlea

Capitulochlear
Sulcus

Medial
Epicondyle

Lateral
Epicondyle

Ulnar N. Sulcus

c Distal End, Distal View.

Ulna · Radius, Forearm Bones

6.4a,b Right Ulna and Radius. [6]

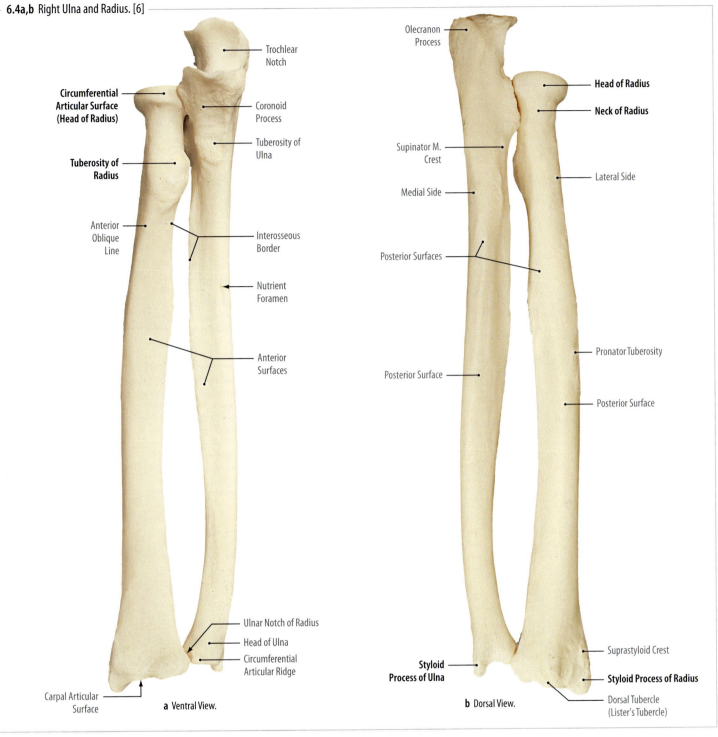

Trochlear Notch

Circumferential Articular Surface (Head of Radius)

Coronoid Process

Tuberosity of Ulna

Tuberosity of Radius

Anterior Oblique Line

Interosseous Border

Nutrient Foramen

Anterior Surfaces

Ulnar Notch of Radius

Head of Ulna

Circumferential Articular Ridge

Carpal Articular Surface

a Ventral View.

Olecranon Process

Head of Radius

Neck of Radius

Supinator M. Crest

Medial Side

Lateral Side

Posterior Surfaces

Posterior Surface

Pronator Tuberosity

Posterior Surface

Styloid Process of Ulna

Suprastyloid Crest

Styloid Process of Radius

Dorsal Tubercle (Lister's Tubercle)

b Dorsal View.

6.5 Proximal Part of a Right Ulna: Radial View. [6]

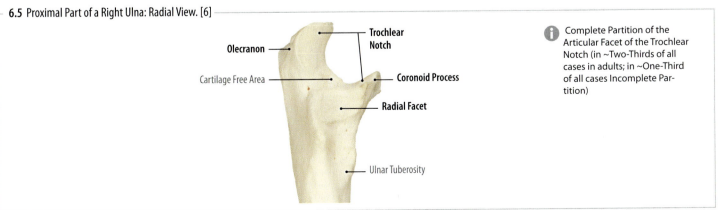

Trochlear Notch

Olecranon

Cartilage Free Area

Coronoid Process

Radial Facet

Ulnar Tuberosity

ⓘ Complete Partition of the Articular Facet of the Trochlear Notch (in ~Two-Thirds of all cases in adults; in ~One-Third of all cases Incomplete Partition)

Skeleton

Dorsal View of the Skeleton of the Hand

6.6 Skeleton of the Hand: Right Side, Dorsal View. [6]

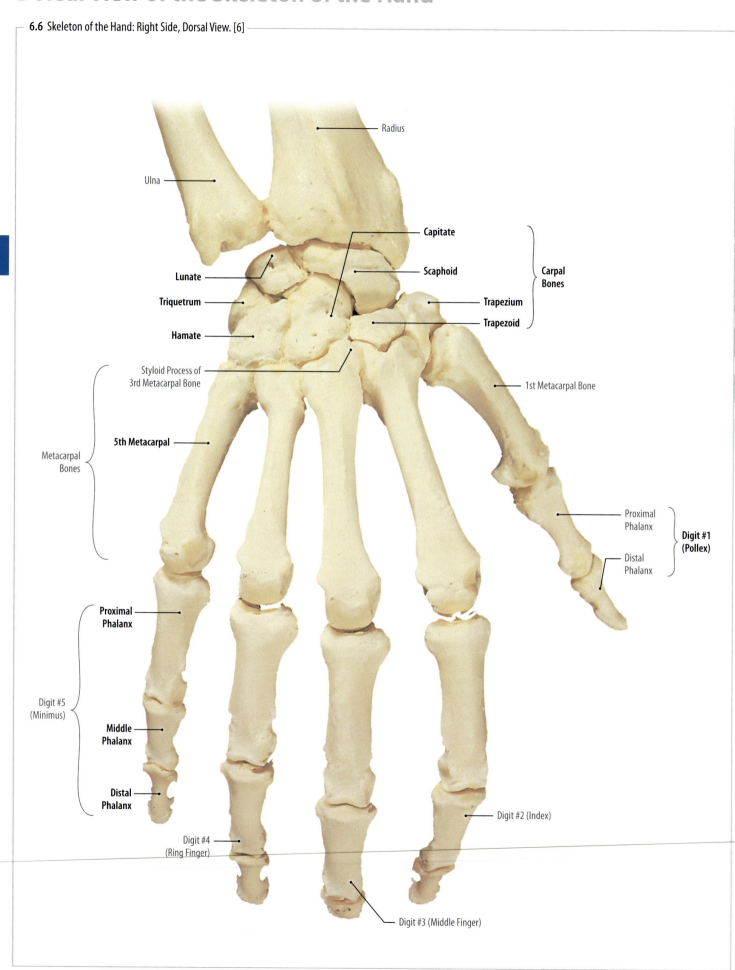

Radius

Ulna

Capitate

Scaphoid

Lunate

Trapezium

Triquetrum

Trapezoid

Carpal Bones

Hamate

Styloid Process of
3rd Metacarpal Bone

1st Metacarpal Bone

5th Metacarpal

Metacarpal
Bones

Proximal
Phalanx

Distal
Phalanx

**Digit #1
(Pollex)**

**Proximal
Phalanx**

Digit #5
(Minimus)

**Middle
Phalanx**

**Distal
Phalanx**

Digit #2 (Index)

Digit #4
(Ring Finger)

Digit #3 (Middle Finger)

6.7 Skeleton of the Hand: Right Side, Palmar View. [6]

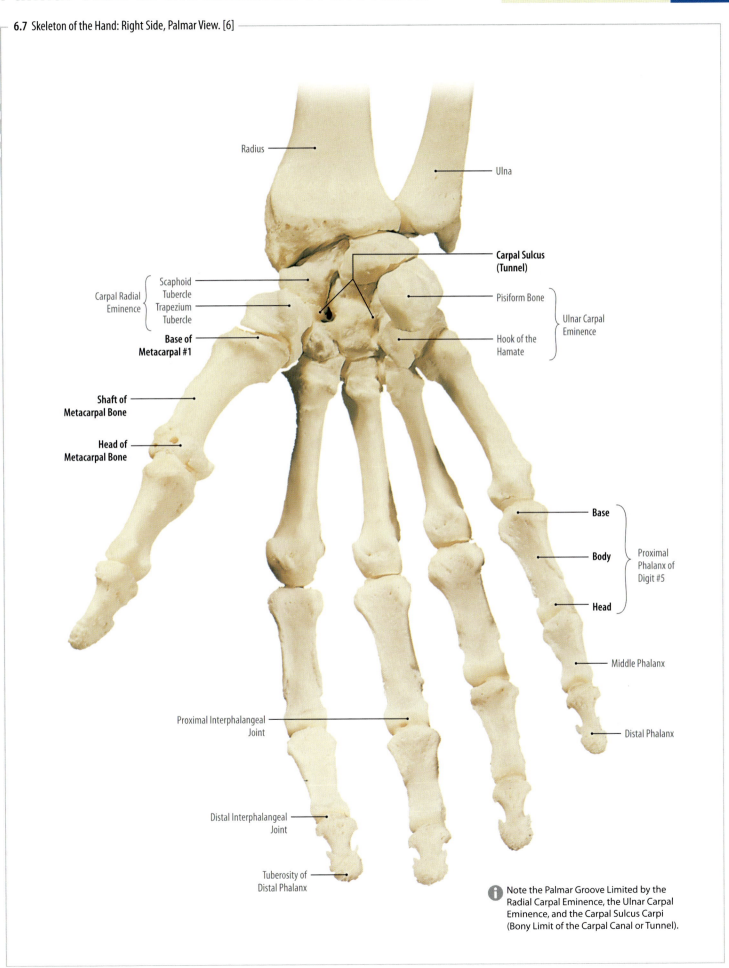

Radius

Ulna

Carpal Sulcus (Tunnel)

Carpal Radial Eminence { Scaphoid Tubercle / Trapezium Tubercle

Pisiform Bone

Ulnar Carpal Eminence

Base of Metacarpal #1

Hook of the Hamate

Shaft of Metacarpal Bone

Head of Metacarpal Bone

Base

Body

Proximal Phalanx of Digit #5

Head

Middle Phalanx

Proximal Interphalangeal Joint

Distal Phalanx

Distal Interphalangeal Joint

Tuberosity of Distal Phalanx

ⓘ Note the Palmar Groove Limited by the Radial Carpal Eminence, the Ulnar Carpal Eminence, and the Carpal Sulcus Carpi (Bony Limit of the Carpal Canal or Tunnel).

Skeleton

Joints of the Shoulder Girdle

6.8 Skeleton Parts of a Right Sternoclavicle Joint: Ventral View. [6]

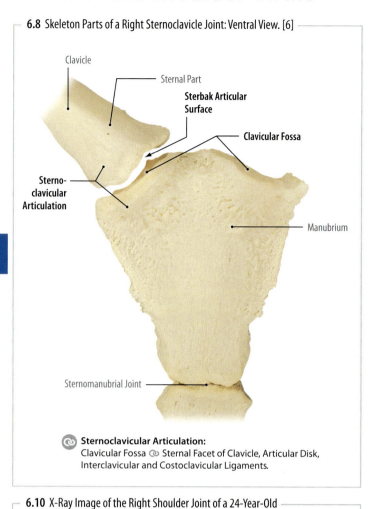

Clavicle

Sternal Part

Sterbak Articular Surface

Clavicular Fossa

Sterno-clavicular Articulation

Manubrium

Sternomanubrial Joint

Sternoclavicular Articulation:
Clavicular Fossa ⊘ Sternal Facet of Clavicle, Articular Disk, Interclavicular and Costoclavicular Ligaments.

6.9 Skeleton Parts of a Right Acromioclavicular Joint: Ventral View. [6]

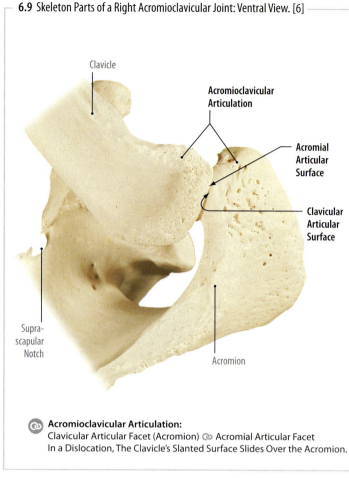

Clavicle

Acromioclavicular Articulation

Acromial Articular Surface

Clavicular Articular Surface

Supra-scapular Notch

Acromion

Acromioclavicular Articulation:
Clavicular Articular Facet (Acromion) ⊘ Acromial Articular Facet
In a Dislocation, The Clavicle's Slanted Surface Slides Over the Acromion.

6.10 X-Ray Image of the Right Shoulder Joint of a 24-Year-Old Woman in the Anteroposterior (AP) Projection. [10]

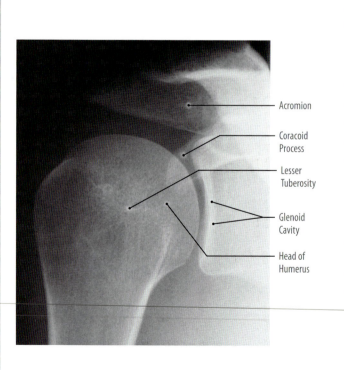

Acromion

Coracoid Process

Lesser Tuberosity

Glenoid Cavity

Head of Humerus

6.11 Skeleton Parts of a Right Shoulder Joint, View of the Articulating Surfaces. [6]

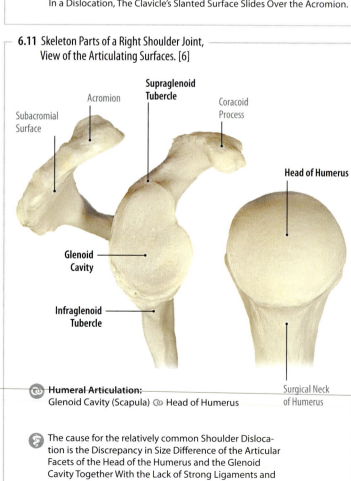

Subacromial Surface

Acromion

Supraglenoid Tubercle

Coracoid Process

Head of Humerus

Glenoid Cavity

Infraglenoid Tubercle

Surgical Neck of Humerus

Humeral Articulation:
Glenoid Cavity (Scapula) ⊘ Head of Humerus

The cause for the relatively common Shoulder Dislocation is the Discrepancy in Size Difference of the Articular Facets of the Head of the Humerus and the Glenoid Cavity Together With the Lack of Strong Ligaments and Large Bony Support.

6

Joints and Ligaments of the Shoulder Girdle

6.12 Joints and Ligaments of the Shoulder Girdle: Ventral View. [56]

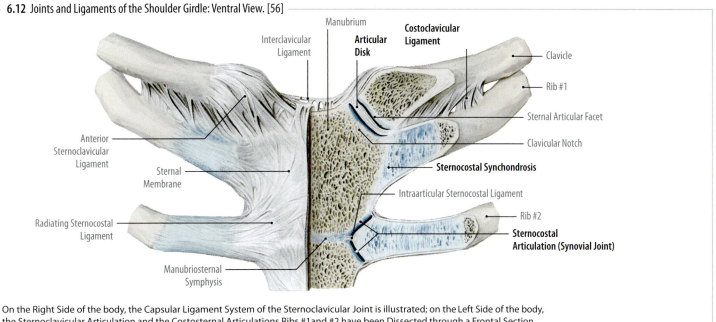

Interclavicular Ligament

Manubrium

Articular Disk

Costoclavicular Ligament

Clavicle

Rib #1

Sternal Articular Facet

Clavicular Notch

Sternocostal Synchondrosis

Intraarticular Sternocostal Ligament

Rib #2

Sternocostal Articulation (Synovial Joint)

Anterior Sternoclavicular Ligament

Sternal Membrane

Radiating Sternocostal Ligament

Manubriosternal Symphysis

On the Right Side of the body, the Capsular Ligament System of the Sternoclavicular Joint is illustrated; on the Left Side of the body, the Sternoclavicular Articulation and the Costosternal Articulations Ribs #1 and #2 have been Dissected through a Frontal Section.

6.13 Joints and Ligaments of the Right Side of the Shoulder Girdle: Anterolateral View. [56]

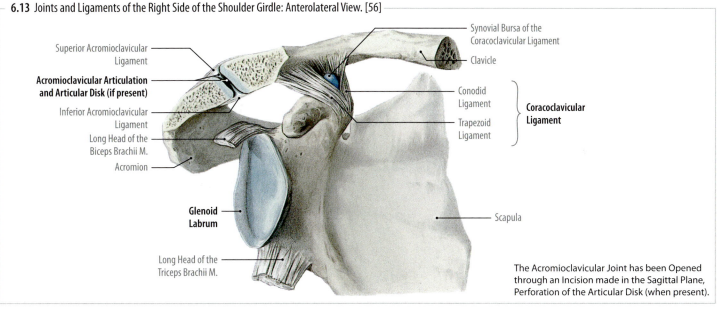

Superior Acromioclavicular Ligament

Acromioclavicular Articulation and Articular Disk (if present)

Inferior Acromioclavicular Ligament

Long Head of the Biceps Brachii M.

Acromion

Glenoid Labrum

Long Head of the Triceps Brachii M.

Synovial Bursa of the Coracoclavicular Ligament

Clavicle

Conoid Ligament

Trapezoid Ligament

Coracoclavicular Ligament

Scapula

The Acromioclavicular Joint has been Opened through an Incision made in the Sagittal Plane, Perforation of the Articular Disk (when present).

6.14 Joints and Ligaments of the Acromioclavicular Joint: Right Side, Superior View. [6]

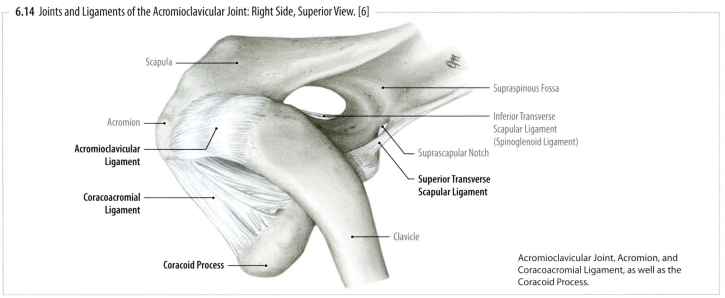

Scapula

Acromion

Acromioclavicular Ligament

Coracoacromial Ligament

Coracoid Process

Supraspinous Fossa

Inferior Transverse Scapular Ligament (Spinoglenoid Ligament)

Suprascapular Notch

Superior Transverse Scapular Ligament

Clavicle

Acromioclavicular Joint, Acromion, and Coracoacromial Ligament, as well as the Coracoid Process.

Joints and Ligaments

Shoulder Joint: Capsule-Ligament System

6.15 Capsule–Ligament System of a Right Shoulder Joint: Ventral View. [56]

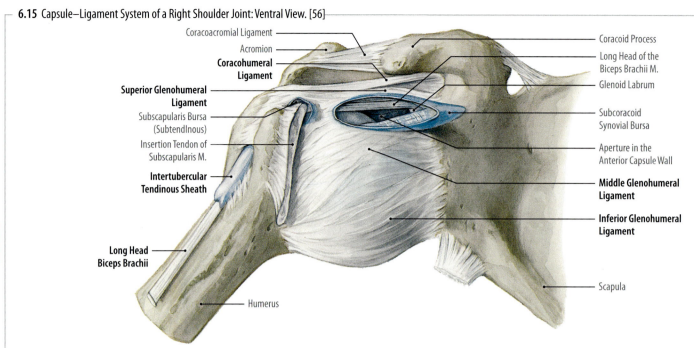

Coracoacromial Ligament

Acromion

Coracohumeral Ligament

Superior Glenohumeral Ligament

Subscapularis Bursa (Subtendinous)

Insertion Tendon of Subscapularis M.

Intertubercular Tendinous Sheath

Long Head Biceps Brachii

Humerus

Coracoid Process

Long Head of the Biceps Brachii M.

Glenoid Labrum

Subcoracoid Synovial Bursa

Aperture in the Anterior Capsule Wall

Middle Glenohumeral Ligament

Inferior Glenohumeral Ligament

Scapula

6.16 Right Acetabulum: Lateral View. [6]

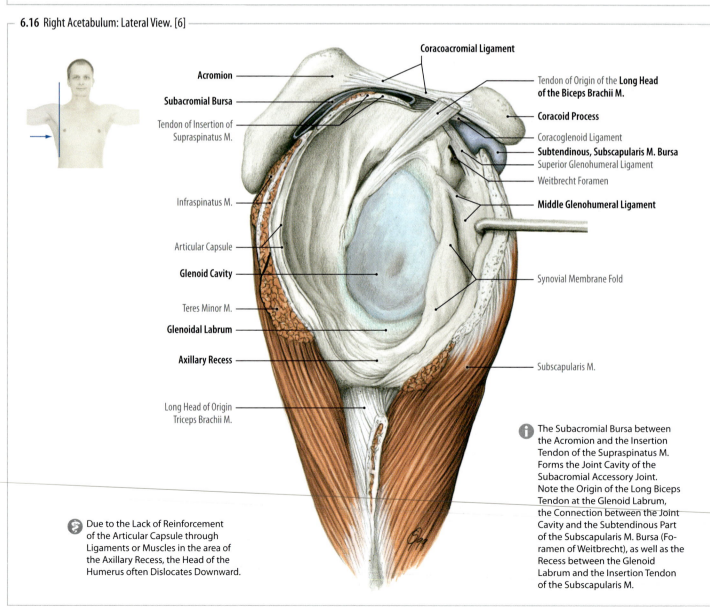

Coracoacromial Ligament

Acromion

Subacromial Bursa

Tendon of Insertion of Supraspinatus M.

Infraspinatus M.

Articular Capsule

Glenoid Cavity

Teres Minor M.

Glenoidal Labrum

Axillary Recess

Long Head of Origin Triceps Brachii M.

Tendon of Origin of the **Long Head of the Biceps Brachii M.**

Coracoid Process

Coracoglenoid Ligament

Subtendinous, Subscapularis M. Bursa

Superior Glenohumeral Ligament

Weitbrecht Foramen

Middle Glenohumeral Ligament

Synovial Membrane Fold

Subscapularis M.

ℹ The Subacromial Bursa between the Acromion and the Insertion Tendon of the Supraspinatus M. Forms the Joint Cavity of the Subacromial Accessory Joint. Note the Origin of the Long Biceps Tendon at the Glenoid Labrum, the Connection between the Joint Cavity and the Subtendinous Part of the Subscapularis M. Bursa (Foramen of Weitbrecht), as well as the Recess between the Glenoid Labrum and the Insertion Tendon of the Subscapularis M.

🔄 Due to the Lack of Reinforcement of the Articular Capsule through Ligaments or Muscles in the area of the Axillary Recess, the Head of the Humerus often Dislocates Downward.

6

6.17 Frontal Section through a Left Shoulder: Ventral View of the Posterior Cut Surface. [6]

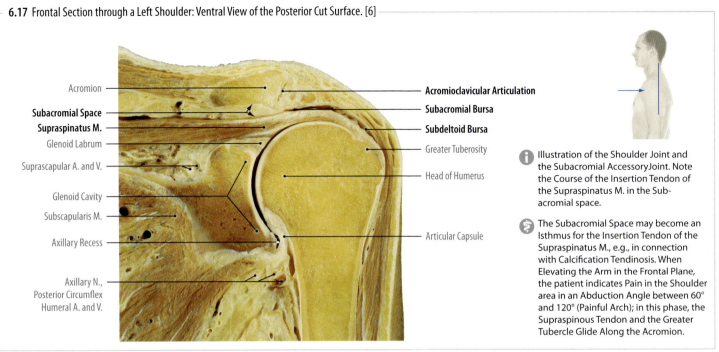

Acromion

Subacromial Space

Supraspinatus M.

Glenoid Labrum

Suprascapular A. and V.

Glenoid Cavity

Subscapularis M.

Axillary Recess

Axillary N.,
Posterior Circumflex
Humeral A. and V.

Acromioclavicular Articulation

Subacromial Bursa

Subdeltoid Bursa

Greater Tuberosity

Head of Humerus

Articular Capsule

ⓘ Illustration of the Shoulder Joint and the Subacromial Accessory Joint. Note the Course of the Insertion Tendon of the Supraspinatus M. in the Subacromial space.

⚡ The Subacromial Space may become an Isthmus for the Insertion Tendon of the Supraspinatus M., e.g., in connection with Calcification Tendinosis. When Elevating the Arm in the Frontal Plane, the patient indicates Pain in the Shoulder area in an Abduction Angle between 60° and 120° (Painful Arch); in this phase, the Supraspinous Tendon and the Greater Tubercle Glide Along the Acromion.

6.18 Sonography of the Shoulder. [73]

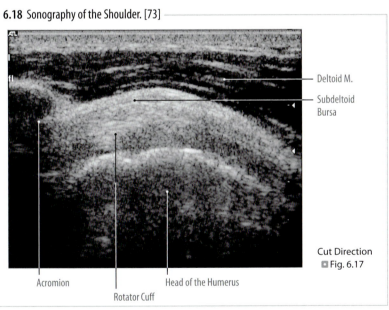

Deltoid M.

Subdeltoid
Bursa

Cut Direction
▣ Fig. 6.17

Acromion

Head of the Humerus

Rotator Cuff

6.19 Arthroscopy of the Shoulder. [109]

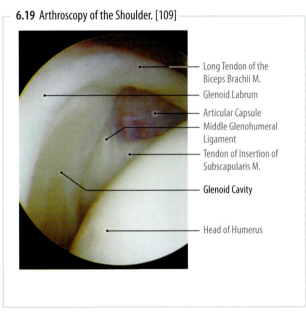

Long Tendon of the
Biceps Brachii M.

Glenoid Labrum

Articular Capsule

Middle Glenohumeral
Ligament

Tendon of Insertion of
Subscapularis M.

Glenoid Cavity

Head of Humerus

6.20 T1-Weighted MRI of the Right Shoulder of a 30-Year-Old Man: Transversal Section Plane. [10]

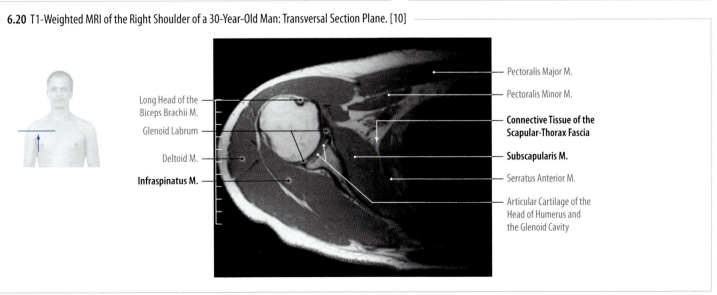

Long Head of the
Biceps Brachii M.

Glenoid Labrum

Deltoid M.

Infraspinatus M.

Pectoralis Major M.

Pectoralis Minor M.

**Connective Tissue of the
Scapular-Thorax Fascia**

Subscapularis M.

Serratus Anterior M.

Articular Cartilage of the
Head of Humerus and
the Glenoid Cavity

Joints and Ligaments

Elbow (Cubital) Joint

6.21 Skeleton Parts of a Right Elbow Joint: Ventral View. [6]

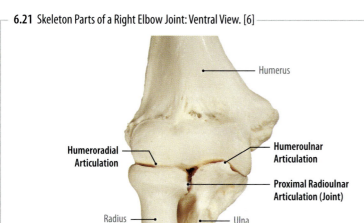

Humerus

Humeroradial Articulation

Humeroulnar Articulation

Proximal Radioulnar Articulation (Joint)

Radius

Ulna

Humeroulnar Articulation:
Trochlea of Humerus ⟳ Ulnar Trochlear Notch

Humeroradial Articulation:
Capitulum of Humerus ⟳ Articular Fossa of the Radial Head

Proximal Radioulnar Articulation:
Radial Circumferential Articular Surface ⟳ Ulnar Radial Notch

6.22a–c Capsule–Ligament System of a Right Elbow Joint. [a, b 1; c 56]

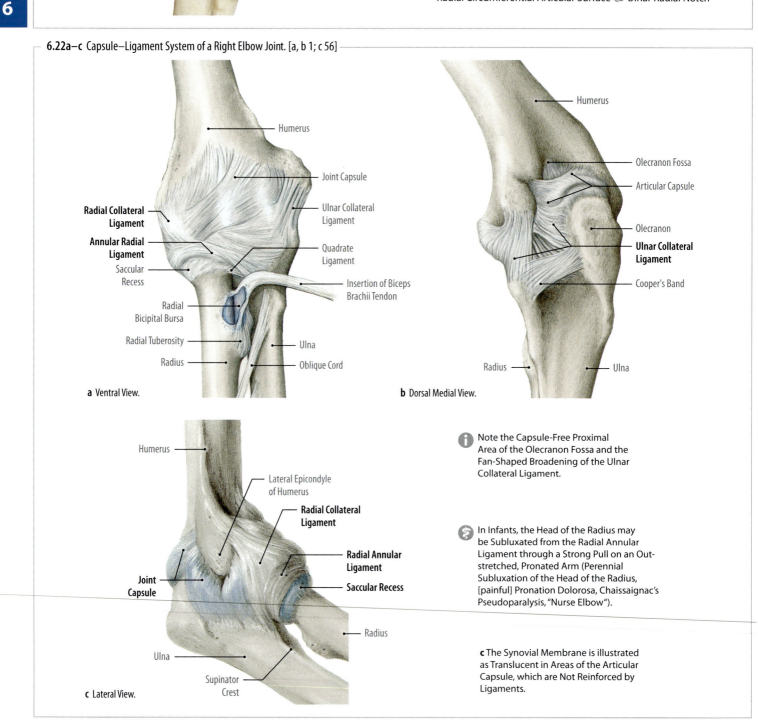

Humerus

Joint Capsule

Radial Collateral Ligament

Ulnar Collateral Ligament

Annular Radial Ligament

Quadrate Ligament

Saccular Recess

Insertion of Biceps Brachii Tendon

Radial Bicipital Bursa

Radial Tuberosity

Ulna

Radius

Oblique Cord

a Ventral View.

Humerus

Olecranon Fossa

Articular Capsule

Olecranon

Ulnar Collateral Ligament

Cooper's Band

Radius

Ulna

b Dorsal Medial View.

Humerus

Lateral Epicondyle of Humerus

Radial Collateral Ligament

Radial Annular Ligament

Joint Capsule

Saccular Recess

Radius

Ulna

Supinator Crest

c Lateral View.

ⓘ Note the Capsule-Free Proximal Area of the Olecranon Fossa and the Fan-Shaped Broadening of the Ulnar Collateral Ligament.

In Infants, the Head of the Radius may be Subluxated from the Radial Annular Ligament through a Strong Pull on an Outstretched, Pronated Arm (Perennial Subluxation of the Head of the Radius, [painful] Pronation Dolorosa, Chaissaignac's Pseudoparalysis, "Nurse Elbow").

c The Synovial Membrane is illustrated as Translucent in Areas of the Articular Capsule, which are Not Reinforced by Ligaments.

Radioulnar Joints

6.23 X-Ray Image of the Right Elbow Joint of a 30-Year-Old Woman in Flexion Position in the Lateral Projection. [10]

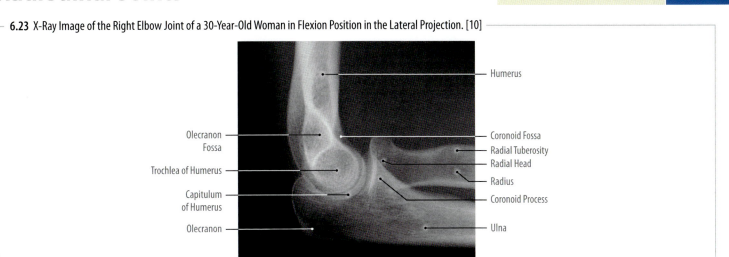

- Humerus
- Olecranon Fossa
- Trochlea of Humerus
- Capitulum of Humerus
- Olecranon
- Coronoid Fossa
- Radial Tuberosity
- Radial Head
- Radius
- Coronoid Process
- Ulna

6.24 Proximal and Distal Radioulnar Joint: Right Side, Ventral View. [56]

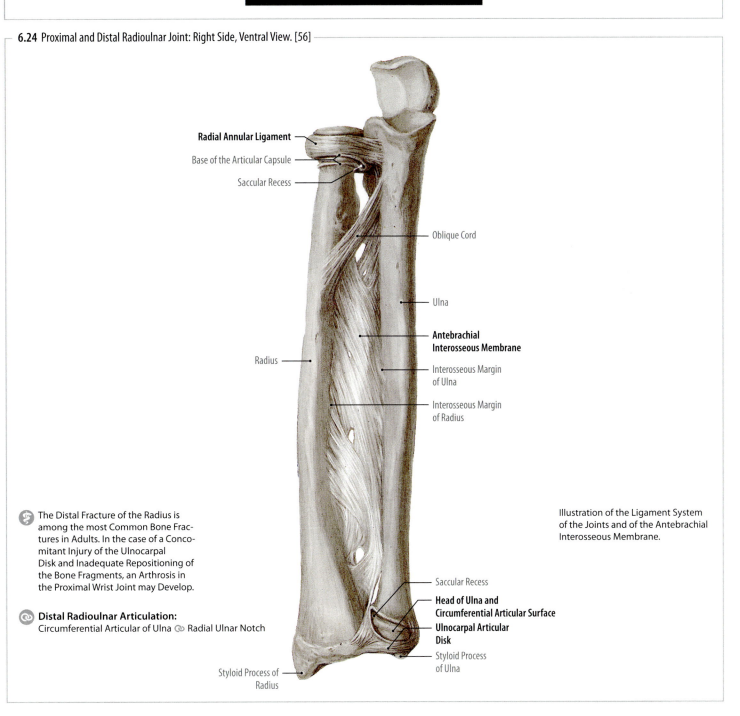

- **Radial Annular Ligament**
- Base of the Articular Capsule
- Saccular Recess
- Oblique Cord
- Ulna
- **Antebrachial Interosseous Membrane**
- Interosseous Margin of Ulna
- Interosseous Margin of Radius
- Radius
- Saccular Recess
- **Head of Ulna and Circumferential Articular Surface**
- **Ulnocarpal Articular Disk**
- Styloid Process of Ulna
- Styloid Process of Radius

The Distal Fracture of the Radius is among the most Common Bone Fractures in Adults. In the case of a Concomitant Injury of the Ulnocarpal Disk and Inadequate Repositioning of the Bone Fragments, an Arthrosis in the Proximal Wrist Joint may Develop.

Distal Radioulnar Articulation:
Circumferential Articular of Ulna ↔ Radial Ulnar Notch

Illustration of the Ligament System of the Joints and of the Antebrachial Interosseous Membrane.

Joints and Ligaments

Wrist Joints

6.25 Skeleton Parts of the Joints of the Hand of a Right Hand: Dorsal Radial View. [6]

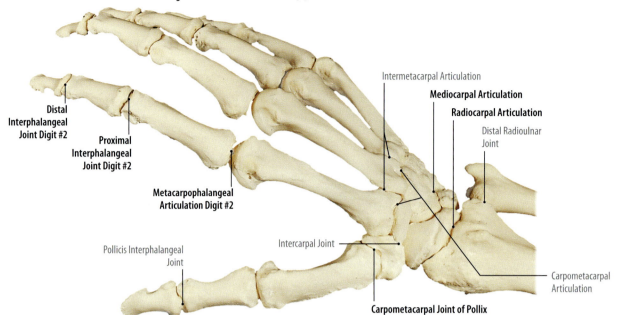

Distal Interphalangeal Joint Digit #2

Proximal Interphalangeal Joint Digit #2

Metacarpophalangeal Articulation Digit #2

Pollicis Interphalangeal Joint

Intermetacarpal Articulation

Mediocarpal Articulation

Radiocarpal Articulation

Distal Radioulnar Joint

Intercarpal Joint

Carpometacarpal Joint of Pollix

Carpometacarpal Articulation

Radiocarpal Articulation (Proximal Wrist Joint):
Radiocarpal Articulation and Articular Disk (Ulnocarpal Disk) ◷◷ Scaphoid Bone, Lunte Bone, Triquetrum Bone

Mediocarpal Articulation (Distal Wrist Joint):
Scaphoid, Lunate , Triquetrum Bones ◷◷ Trapezium, Trapezoid, Capitate, Hamat Bones

Pisiform Bone Articulation:
Pisiform Bone ◷◷ Triquetrum Bones

Carpometacarpal Articulation of the Thumb (Polex)
Carpometacarpal Joint #1 (Saddle Joint of the Thumb or CM Joint #1): Trapezium Bone ◷◷ Base of the Metacarpal Bone #1

Interphalaneal Articulation of the Pollex (Interphalangeal Joint of the Thumb = IP Joint):
Head of the Proximal Phalanx of Pollex ◷◷ Base of the Distal Phalanx of Pollex

Metacarpophalangeal Articulation (Metacarpophalangeal Joint = MP Joint):
Head of Metacarpal Bone ◷◷ Base of the Proximal Phalanx

Proximal Interphalangeal Articulation (Proximal Interphalangeal Joint = PIP Joint):
Head of the Proximal Phalanx ◷◷ Base of the Middle Phalanx

Distal Interphalangeal Articulation (Distal Interphalangeal Joint = DIP Joint):
Caput of the Middle Phalanx ◷◷ Basis of the Distal Phalanx

Amphiarthroses of the Hand:
Intercarpal Articulations, Carpometacarpal Articulations, Intermetacarpal Articulations

6.26 Joints of the Hand and Ligaments between the Fingers: Right Side, Dorsal View. [56]

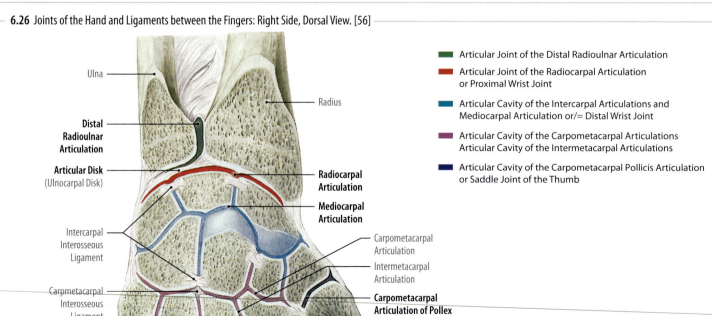

Ulna

Radius

Distal Radioulnar Articulation

Articular Disk (Ulnocarpal Disk)

Intercarpal Interosseous Ligament

Carpmetacarpal Interosseous Ligament

Metacarpal Interosseous Ligament

Radiocarpal Articulation

Mediocarpal Articulation

Carpometacarpal Articulation

Intermetacarpal Articulation

Carpometacarpal Articulation of Pollex

▬ Articular Joint of the Distal Radioulnar Articulation

▬ Articular Joint of the Radiocarpal Articulation or Proximal Wrist Joint

▬ Articular Cavity of the Intercarpal Articulations and Mediocarpal Articulation or/= Distal Wrist Joint

▬ Articular Cavity of the Carpometacarpal Articulations Articular Cavity of the Intermetacarpal Articulations

▬ Articular Cavity of the Carpometacarpal Pollicis Articulation or Saddle Joint of the Thumb

To illustrate the Articular Cavities, the Dorsal Part of the Hand has been Removed through a saw cut.

Wrist Joints: Capsule-Ligament System

6.27 Capsule–Ligament System of the Joints of the Hand: Right Side, Dorsal View. [56]

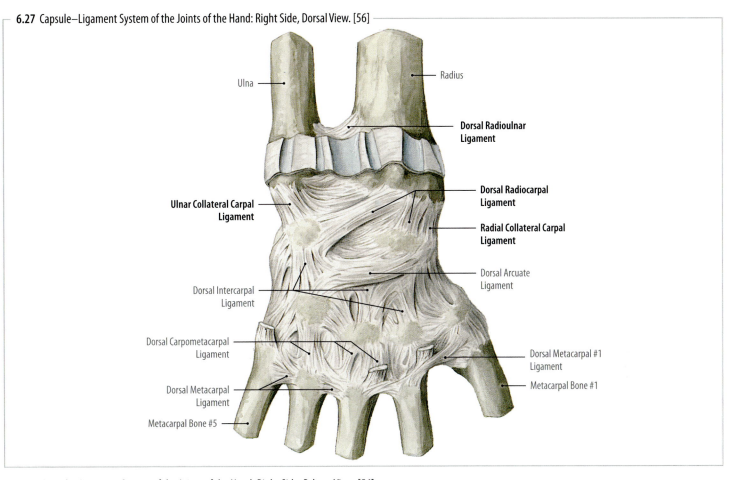

- Ulna
- Radius
- **Dorsal Radioulnar Ligament**
- **Dorsal Radiocarpal Ligament**
- **Ulnar Collateral Carpal Ligament**
- **Radial Collateral Carpal Ligament**
- Dorsal Arcuate Ligament
- Dorsal Intercarpal Ligament
- Dorsal Carpometacarpal Ligament
- Dorsal Metacarpal #1 Ligament
- Metacarpal Bone #1
- Dorsal Metacarpal Ligament
- Metacarpal Bone #5

6.28 Capsule–Ligament System of the Joints of the Hand: Right Side, Palmar View. [56]

ⓘ Guyon's Canal – Distal Ulnar Tunnel. The "Loge de Guyon" is a Triangular Osteofibrous Tunnel whose Dorsal Floor is Formed by the Flexor Retinaculum and the Pisohamate Ligament. The Palmar Roof is Limited ProxImally by the Superficial Palmar Fascia (Palmar Carpal Ligament) and Distally by the Palmaris Brevis M.
Proximally, the Insertion Tendon of the Flexor Carpi Ulnaris M. with the Pisiform Bone and Distally, the Abductor Digiti Minimi M. Join in the Composition of the Medial Wall. The Lateral Limit is the Flexor Retinaculum and Distally the Hook (Hamulus) of the Hamate Bone. The Ulnar N. and the Ulnar Vessels run through Guyon's Canal.

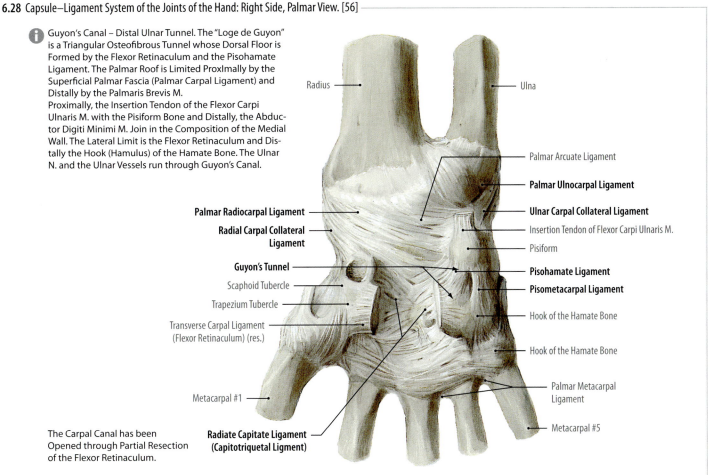

- Radius
- Ulna
- Palmar Arcuate Ligament
- **Palmar Ulnocarpal Ligament**
- **Palmar Radiocarpal Ligament**
- **Ulnar Carpal Collateral Ligament**
- **Radial Carpal Collateral Ligament**
- Insertion Tendon of Flexor Carpi Ulnaris M.
- Pisiform
- **Guyon's Tunnel**
- Scaphoid Tubercle
- Trapezium Tubercle
- **Pisohamate Ligament**
- **Pisometacarpal Ligament**
- Hook of the Hamate Bone
- Transverse Carpal Ligament (Flexor Retinaculum) (res.)
- Hook of the Hamate Bone
- Palmar Metacarpal Ligament
- Metacarpal #1
- Metacarpal #5
- The Carpal Canal has been Opened through Partial Resection of the Flexor Retinaculum.
- **Radiate Capitate Ligament (Capitotriquetal Ligment)**

Joints and Ligaments

Finger Joints

6.29 Capsule-Ligament System of a Right Index Finger: Radial View. [1]

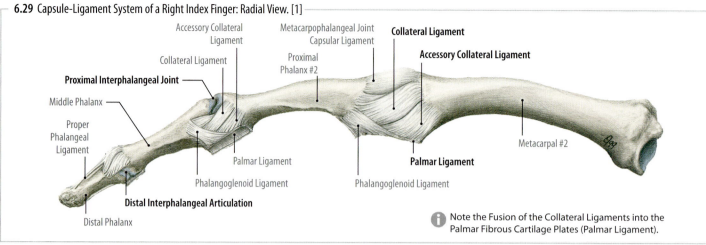

Accessory Collateral Ligament
Collateral Ligament
Proximal Interphalangeal Joint
Middle Phalanx
Proper Phalangeal Ligament
Metacarpophalangeal Joint Capsular Ligament
Proximal Phalanx #2
Collateral Ligament
Accessory Collateral Ligament
Palmar Ligament
Phalangoglenoid Ligament
Distal Interphalangeal Articulation
Palmar Ligament
Phalangoglenoid Ligament
Metacarpal #2
Distal Phalanx

ⓘ Note the Fusion of the Collateral Ligaments into the Palmar Fibrous Cartilage Plates (Palmar Ligament).

6.30 Cross-Section through the Right Middle Finger in the Area of the Metacarpophalangeal Joint: View of the Distal Cut Surface. [6]

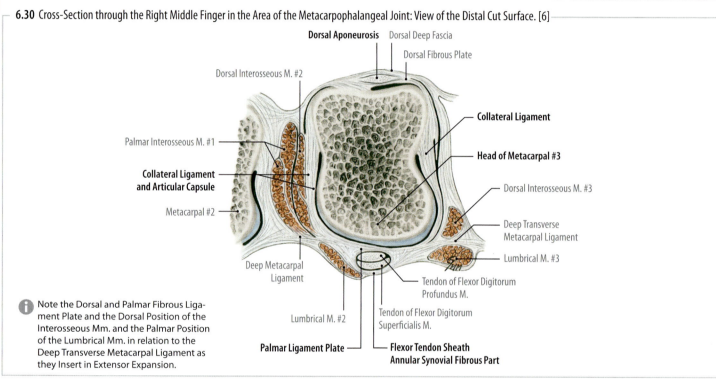

Dorsal Aponeurosis Dorsal Deep Fascia
Dorsal Fibrous Plate
Dorsal Interosseous M. #2
Palmar Interosseous M. #1
Collateral Ligament and Articular Capsule
Metacarpal #2
Collateral Ligament
Head of Metacarpal #3
Dorsal Interosseous M. #3
Deep Transverse Metacarpal Ligament
Lumbrical M. #3
Deep Metacarpal Ligament
Tendon of Flexor Digitorum Profundus M.
Lumbrical M. #2
Tendon of Flexor Digitorum Superficialis M.
Palmar Ligament Plate
Flexor Tendon Sheath Annular Synovial Fibrous Part

ⓘ Note the Dorsal and Palmar Fibrous Ligament Plate and the Dorsal Position of the Interosseous Mm. and the Palmar Position of the Lumbrical Mm. in relation to the Deep Transverse Metacarpal Ligament as they Insert in Extensor Expansion.

6.31 X-Ray Image of the Right Hand of a 22-Year-Old Woman in the Diagonal-Dorsopalmar Projection. [10]

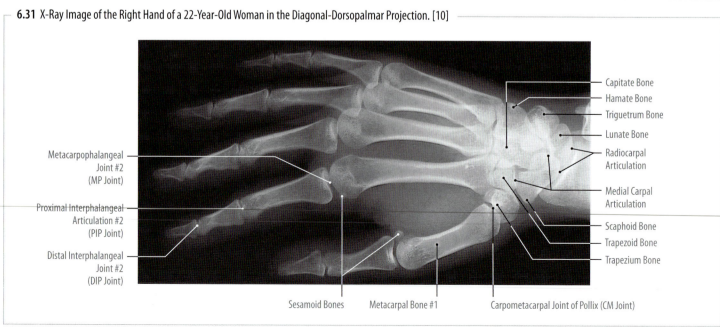

Metacarpophalangeal Joint #2 (MP Joint)
Proximal Interphalangeal Articulation #2 (PIP Joint)
Distal Interphalangeal Joint #2 (DIP Joint)
Capitate Bone
Hamate Bone
Triquetrum Bone
Lunate Bone
Radiocarpal Articulation
Medial Carpal Articulation
Scaphoid Bone
Trapezoid Bone
Trapezium Bone
Sesamoid Bones
Metacarpal Bone #1
Carpometacarpal Joint of Pollix (CM Joint)

6

404

Muscles of the Back and Shoulders

6.32 Muscles of the Back, Muscles of the Shoulder Girdle and the Shoulder Joint: Dorsal View. [6]

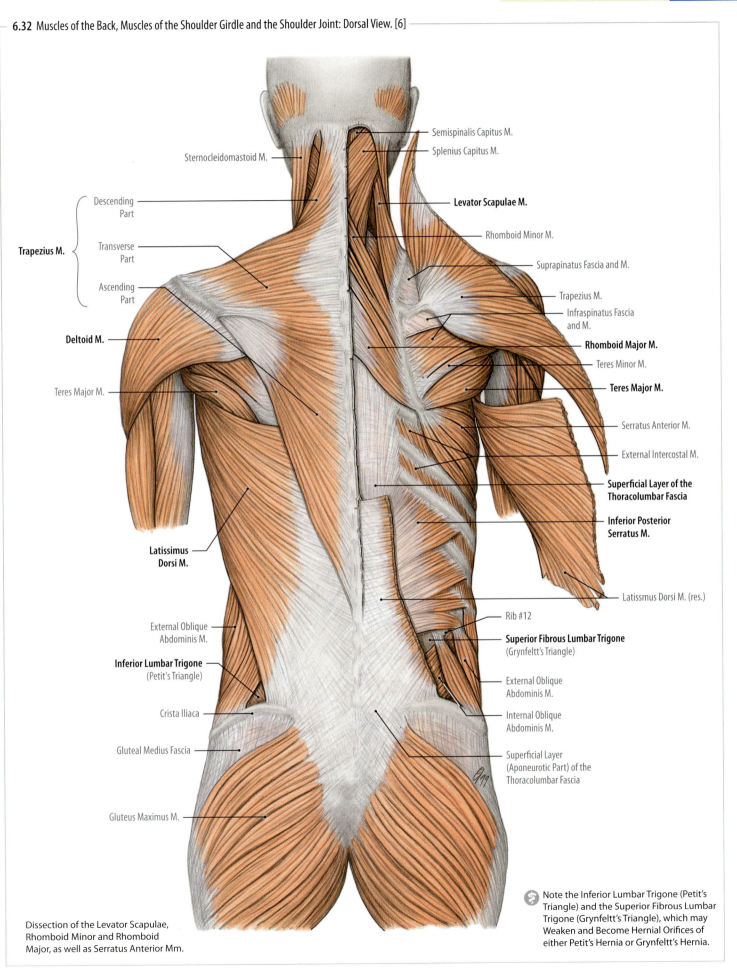

Semispinalis Capitus M.

Splenius Capitus M.

Sternocleidomastoid M.

Levator Scapulae M.

Trapezius M.
Descending Part

Transverse Part

Ascending Part

Rhomboid Minor M.

Suprapinatus Fascia and M.

Trapezius M.

Infraspinatus Fascia and M.

Rhomboid Major M.

Teres Minor M.

Deltoid M.

Teres Major M.

Teres Major M.

Serratus Anterior M.

External Intercostal M.

Superficial Layer of the Thoracolumbar Fascia

Inferior Posterior Serratus M.

Latissimus Dorsi M.

Latissmus Dorsi M. (res.)

Rib #12

Superior Fibrous Lumbar Trigone
(Grynfeltt's Triangle)

External Oblique Abdominis M.

External Oblique Abdominis M.

Inferior Lumbar Trigone
(Petit's Triangle)

Internal Oblique Abdominis M.

Crista Iliaca

Gluteal Medius Fascia

Superficial Layer (Aponeurotic Part) of the Thoracolumbar Fascia

Gluteus Maximus M.

Note the Inferior Lumbar Trigone (Petit's Triangle) and the Superior Fibrous Lumbar Trigone (Grynfeltt's Triangle), which may Weaken and Become Hernial Orifices of either Petit's Hernia or Grynfeltt's Hernia.

Dissection of the Levator Scapulae, Rhomboid Minor and Rhomboid Major, as well as Serratus Anterior Mm.

Muscles

6.33 Muscles of the Torso, the Shoulder, and the Thigh: Right Lateral View. [110]

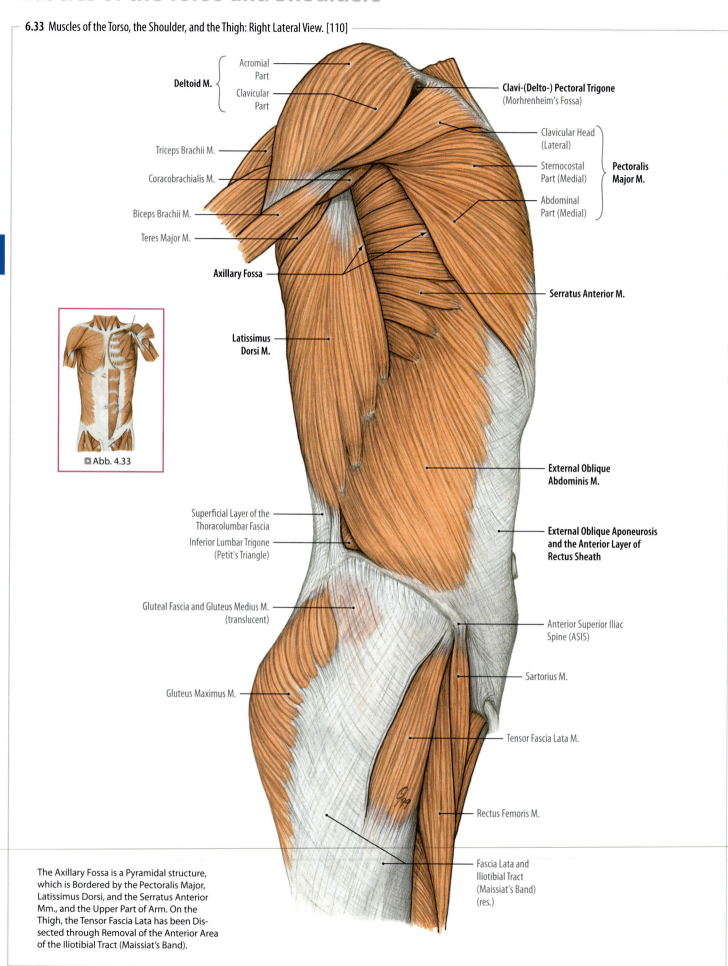

Deltoid M.
- Acromial Part
- Clavicular Part

Triceps Brachii M.

Coracobrachialis M.

Biceps Brachii M.

Teres Major M.

Axillary Fossa

Latissimus Dorsi M.

☐ Abb. 4.33

Superficial Layer of the Thoracolumbar Fascia

Inferior Lumbar Trigone (Petit's Triangle)

Gluteal Fascia and Gluteus Medius M. (translucent)

Gluteus Maximus M.

Clavi-(Delto-) Pectoral Trigone (Morhrenheim's Fossa)

Pectoralis Major M.
- Clavicular Head (Lateral)
- Sternocostal Part (Medial)
- Abdominal Part (Medial)

Serratus Anterior M.

External Oblique Abdominis M.

External Oblique Aponeurosis and the Anterior Layer of Rectus Sheath

Anterior Superior Iliac Spine (ASIS)

Sartorius M.

Tensor Fascia Lata M.

Rectus Femoris M.

Fascia Lata and Iliotibial Tract (Maissiat's Band) (res.)

The Axillary Fossa is a Pyramidal structure, which is Bordered by the Pectoralis Major, Latissimus Dorsi, and the Serratus Anterior Mm., and the Upper Part of Arm. On the Thigh, the Tensor Fascia Lata has been Dissected through Removal of the Anterior Area of the Iliotibial Tract (Maissiat's Band).

Muscles of the Torso and Shoulders

6.34 Muscles of the Torso and Shoulder of the Left Side: Anterolateral View. [1]

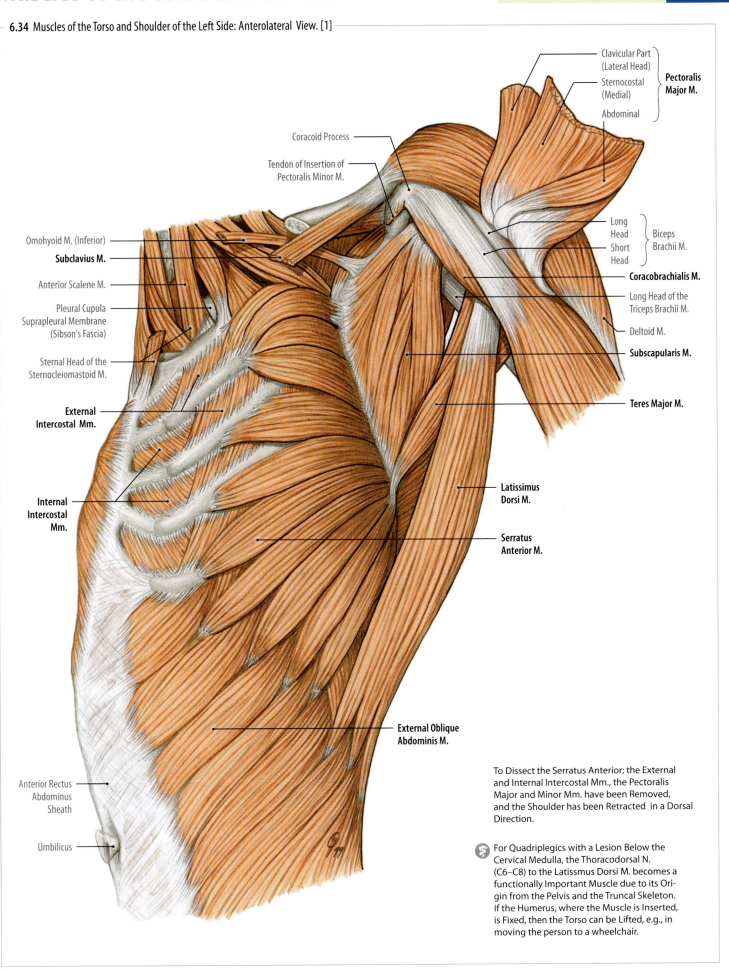

Coracoid Process

Tendon of Insertion of
Pectoralis Minor M.

Clavicular Part
(Lateral Head)

Sternocostal
(Medial)

Abdominal

**Pectoralis
Major M.**

Long
Head

Short
Head

Biceps
Brachii M.

Coracobrachialis M.

Long Head of the
Triceps Brachii M.

Deltoid M.

Subscapularis M.

Teres Major M.

Omohyoid M. (Inferior)

Subclavius M.

Anterior Scalene M.

Pleural Cupula
Suprapleural Membrane
(Sibson's Fascia)

Sternal Head of the
Sternocleiomastoid M.

**External
Intercostal Mm.**

**Internal
Intercostal
Mm.**

**Latissimus
Dorsi M.**

**Serratus
Anterior M.**

**External Oblique
Abdominis M.**

Anterior Rectus
Abdominus
Sheath

Umbilicus

To Dissect the Serratus Anterior; the External
and Internal Intercostal Mm., the Pectoralis
Major and Minor Mm. have been Removed,
and the Shoulder has been Retracted in a Dorsal
Direction.

For Quadriplegics with a Lesion Below the
Cervical Medulla, the Thoracodorsal N.
(C6–C8) to the Latissimus Dorsi M. becomes a
functionally Important Muscle due to its Origin from the Pelvis and the Truncal Skeleton.
If the Humerus, where the Muscle is Inserted,
is Fixed, then the Torso can be Lifted, e.g., in
moving the person to a wheelchair.

Muscles

Shoulder Girdle Muscles: Function

6.35a,b Functions of the Muscles of the Shoulder Girdle. [12]

a Movements of the Shoulder Girdle, Participating Muscle Groups.
Muscles of the Shoulder Girdle, Dorsal View (*Right* Side). The Trapezius M. is Not Pictured for reasons of clarity (Trapezius M., ◻ Fig. 6.32).
On the *Left* Side, the Force Directions of the Shoulder Girdle Muscles are Illustrated Schematically. The Course Directions marked with *Gray Arrows* correspond with the parts of the Trapezius M. that are Not Pictured (Descending Part 9, Transverse Part 10, Ascending Part 11).

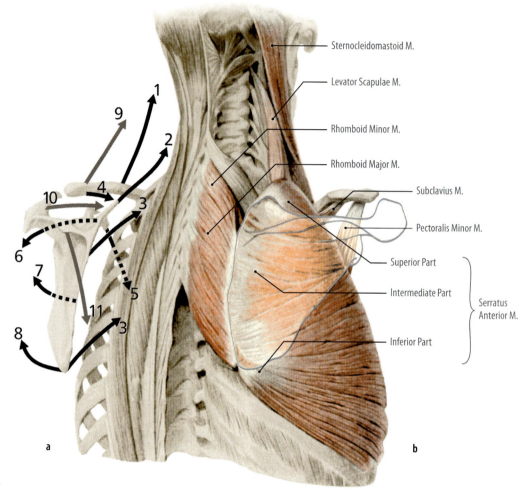

Movement of the Shoulder Girdle
Superiorly (Elevation)
Ascending Part of the Trapezius M. (9), Levator Scapulae M. (2), Rhomboid Mm. (3), Superior Part of the Serratus Anterior M. (6), Sternocleidomastoid M. (1).
Inferiorly (Depression)
Ascending Part of the Trapezius M. (11), Inferior Part of the Inferior Serratus M. (8), Pectoralis Minor M. (5), Subclavius M. (4).
Posteriorly, Dorsally (Retraction)
Transverse Part of the Trapezius M. (10), Rhomboid M. (3).
Anteriorly, Ventrally (Protraction)
Superior Part (6) and Intermediate Part of the Serratus Anterior M. (7), Pectoralis Minor M. (5).

Sternocleidomastoid M.
Levator Scapulae M.
Rhomboid Minor M.
Rhomboid Major M.
Subclavius M.
Pectoralis Minor M.
Superior Part
Intermediate Part
Serratus Anterior M.
Inferior Part

b Muscle Slings of the Shoulder Girdle.
Serratus–Rhomboid Sling:
  Course Direction Diagonal from Cranial-Dorsal to Ventral-Caudal,
  Rhomboid Major and Minor Mm. ⚍ Inferior Part of the Serratus Anterior M.
Levator Scapulae–Trapezius Sling:
  Course Direction Vertical from Cranial to Caudal, Levator Scapulae M. ⚍ Ascending Part of the Trapezius M.
Trapezius–Serratus Sling:
  Course Direction Horizontal from Ventral to Dorsal, Intermediate Part of the Serratus Anterior M. ⚍ Transverse Part of the Trapezius M.
Trapezius–Pectoralis Sling:
  Course Direction Diagonal from Cranial-Dorsal to Caudal-Ventral, Descending Part of the Trapezius M. ⚍ Pectoralis Minor M.

6.36 Rotation of the Scapula in the Shoulder Blade–Thorax Joint and in the Joints of the Shoulder Girdle, Executing Muscles.

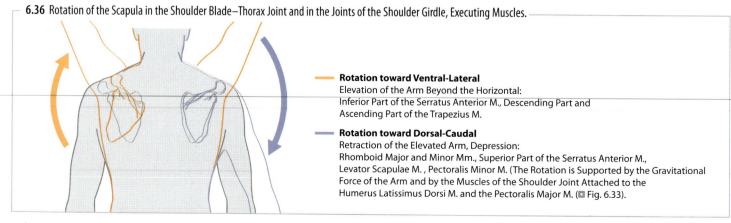

— **Rotation toward Ventral-Lateral**
Elevation of the Arm Beyond the Horizontal:
Inferior Part of the Serratus Anterior M., Descending Part and Ascending Part of the Trapezius M.

— **Rotation toward Dorsal-Caudal**
Retraction of the Elevated Arm, Depression:
Rhomboid Major and Minor Mm., Superior Part of the Serratus Anterior M., Levator Scapulae M. , Pectoralis Minor M. (The Rotation is Supported by the Gravitational Force of the Arm and by the Muscles of the Shoulder Joint Attached to the Humerus Latissimus Dorsi M. and the Pectoralis Major M. (◻ Fig. 6.33).

Muscles of the Arms

6.37a,b Muscles of the Arm of the Right Side. [56]

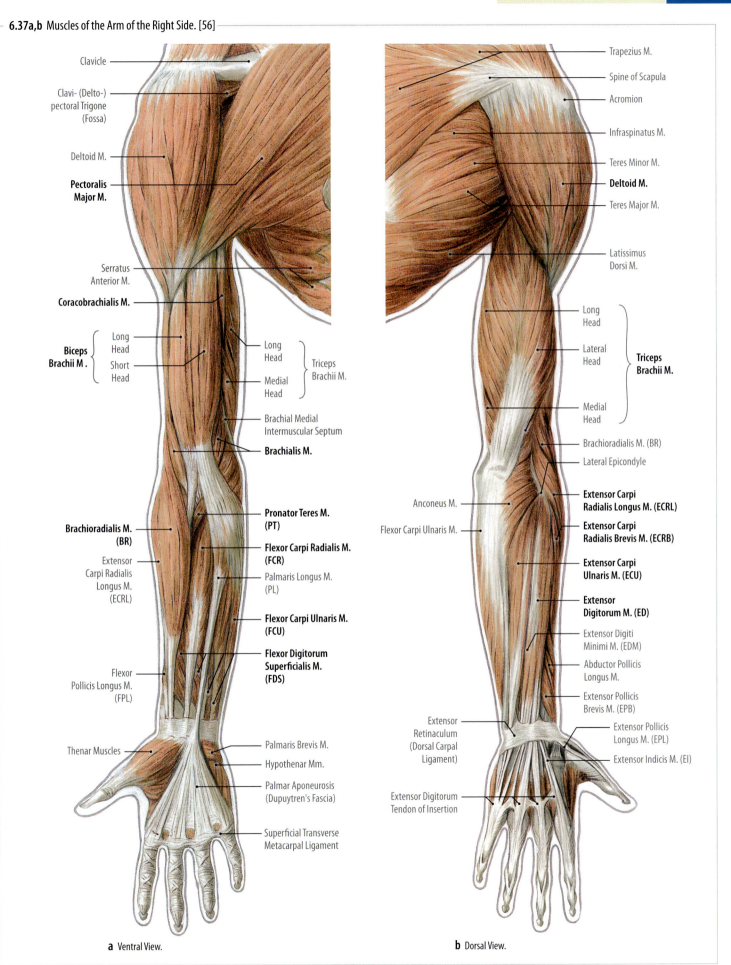

Clavicle

Clavi- (Delto-) pectoral Trigone (Fossa)

Deltoid M.

Pectoralis Major M.

Serratus Anterior M.

Coracobrachialis M.

Biceps Brachii M. — Long Head / Short Head

Brachioradialis M. (BR)

Extensor Carpi Radialis Longus M. (ECRL)

Flexor Pollicis Longus M. (FPL)

Thenar Muscles

Long Head

Medial Head

Brachial Medial Intermuscular Septum

Brachialis M.

Pronator Teres M. (PT)

Flexor Carpi Radialis M. (FCR)

Palmaris Longus M. (PL)

Flexor Carpi Ulnaris M. (FCU)

Flexor Digitorum Superficialis M. (FDS)

Palmaris Brevis M.

Hypothenar Mm.

Palmar Aponeurosis (Dupuytren's Fascia)

Superficial Transverse Metacarpal Ligament

Long Head / Medial Head — Triceps Brachii M.

Trapezius M.

Spine of Scapula

Acromion

Infraspinatus M.

Teres Minor M.

Deltoid M.

Teres Major M.

Latissimus Dorsi M.

Long Head

Lateral Head

Medial Head — **Triceps Brachii M.**

Brachioradialis M. (BR)

Lateral Epicondyle

Extensor Carpi Radialis Longus M. (ECRL)

Extensor Carpi Radialis Brevis M. (ECRB)

Extensor Carpi Ulnaris M. (ECU)

Extensor Digitorum M. (ED)

Extensor Digiti Minimi M. (EDM)

Abductor Pollicis Longus M.

Extensor Pollicis Brevis M. (EPB)

Extensor Pollicis Longus M. (EPL)

Extensor Indicis M. (EI)

Anconeus M.

Flexor Carpi Ulnaris M.

Extensor Retinaculum (Dorsal Carpal Ligament)

Extensor Digitorum Tendon of Insertion

a Ventral View.

b Dorsal View.

Muscles

Muscles of the Upper Arms

6

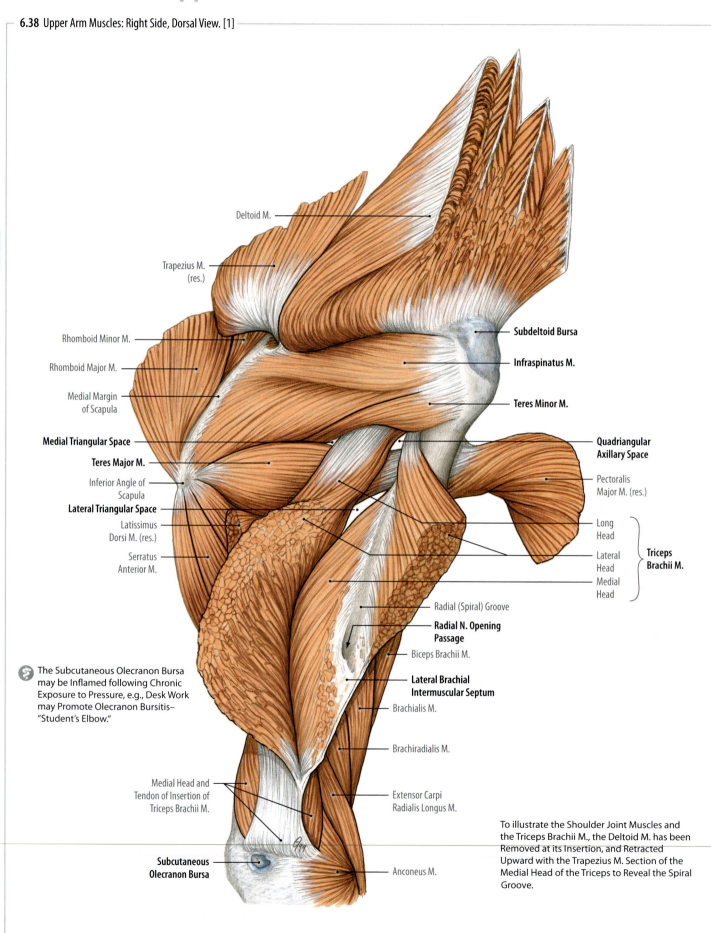

Deltoid M.

Trapezius M. (res.)

Rhomboid Minor M.

Rhomboid Major M.

Medial Margin of Scapula

Medial Triangular Space

Teres Major M.

Inferior Angle of Scapula

Lateral Triangular Space

Latissimus Dorsi M. (res.)

Serratus Anterior M.

Subdeltoid Bursa

Infraspinatus M.

Teres Minor M.

Quadriangular Axillary Space

Pectoralis Major M. (res.)

Long Head

Lateral Head

Medial Head

Triceps Brachii M.

Radial (Spiral) Groove

Radial N. Opening Passage

Biceps Brachii M.

Lateral Brachial Intermuscular Septum

Brachialis M.

Brachiradialis M.

Extensor Carpi Radialis Longus M.

Medial Head and Tendon of Insertion of Triceps Brachii M.

Subcutaneous Olecranon Bursa

Anconeus M.

The Subcutaneous Olecranon Bursa may be Inflamed following Chronic Exposure to Pressure, e.g., Desk Work may Promote Olecranon Bursitis– "Student's Elbow."

To illustrate the Shoulder Joint Muscles and the Triceps Brachii M., the Deltoid M. has been Removed at its Insertion, and Retracted Upward with the Trapezius M. Section of the Medial Head of the Triceps to Reveal the Spiral Groove.

6.39 Muscles of the Right Shoulder: Ventral View. [1]

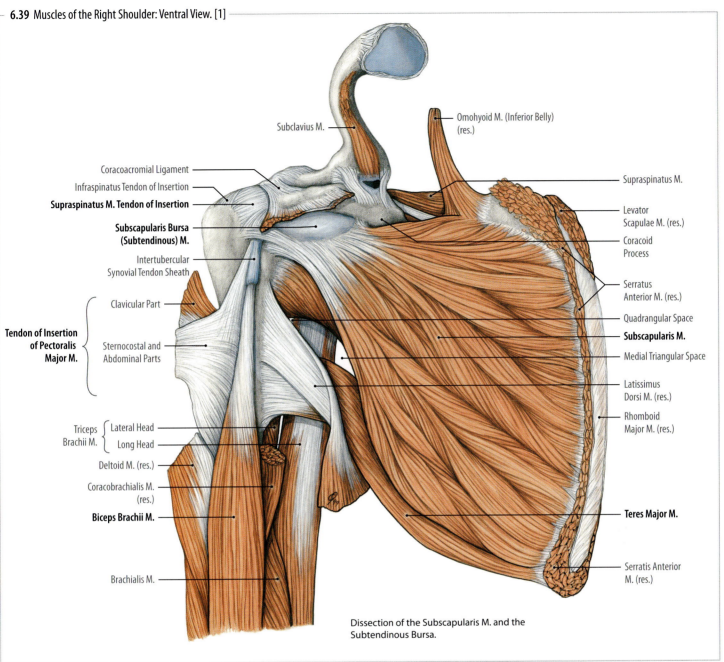

Subclavius M.

Omohyoid M. (Inferior Belly) (res.)

Coracoacromial Ligament

Infraspinatus Tendon of Insertion

Supraspinatus M. Tendon of Insertion

Subscapularis Bursa (Subtendinous) M.

Intertubercular Synovial Tendon Sheath

Supraspinatus M.

Levator Scapulae M. (res.)

Coracoid Process

Serratus Anterior M. (res.)

Quadrangular Space

Subscapularis M.

Medial Triangular Space

Latissimus Dorsi M. (res.)

Rhomboid Major M. (res.)

Tendon of Insertion of Pectoralis Major M.
- Clavicular Part
- Sternocostal and Abdominal Parts

Triceps Brachii M.
- Lateral Head
- Long Head

Deltoid M. (res.)

Coracobrachialis M. (res.)

Biceps Brachii M.

Teres Major M.

Brachialis M.

Serratis Anterior M. (res.)

Dissection of the Subscapularis M. and the Subtendinous Bursa.

6.40 Muscle Compartments of the Upper Arm: Right Superior View.

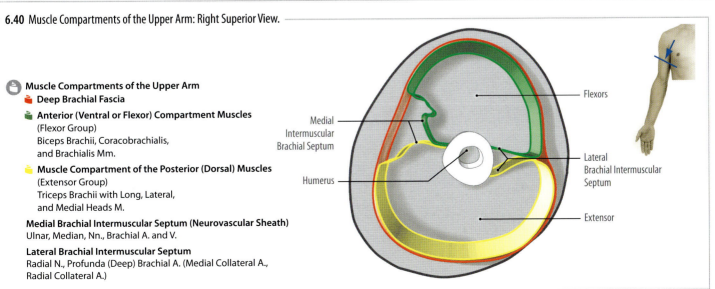

Muscle Compartments of the Upper Arm
🔴 **Deep Brachial Fascia**
🟢 **Anterior (Ventral or Flexor) Compartment Muscles**
(Flexor Group)
Biceps Brachii, Coracobrachialis, and Brachialis Mm.
🟡 **Muscle Compartment of the Posterior (Dorsal) Muscles**
(Extensor Group)
Triceps Brachii with Long, Lateral, and Medial Heads M.
Medial Brachial Intermuscular Septum (Neurovascular Sheath)
Ulnar, Median, Nn., Brachial A. and V.
Lateral Brachial Intermuscular Septum
Radial N., Profunda (Deep) Brachial A. (Medial Collateral A., Radial Collateral A.)

Medial Intermuscular Brachial Septum

Humerus

Flexors

Lateral Brachial Intermuscular Septum

Extensor

Muscles

6.41 Right Shoulder, Muscles of the Rotator Cuff: Lateral View. [8]

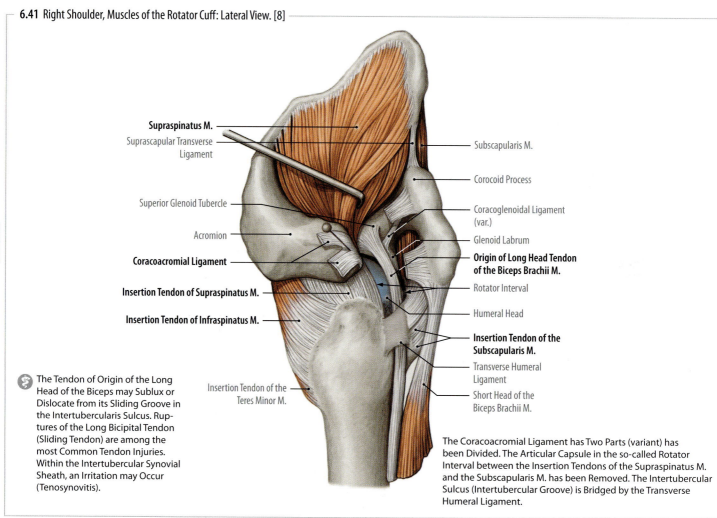

Supraspinatus M.

Suprascapular Transverse Ligament

Superior Glenoid Tubercle

Acromion

Coracoacromial Ligament

Insertion Tendon of Supraspinatus M.

Insertion Tendon of Infraspinatus M.

Subscapularis M.

Corocoid Process

Coracoglenoidal Ligament (var.)

Glenoid Labrum

Origin of Long Head Tendon of the Biceps Brachii M.

Rotator Interval

Humeral Head

Insertion Tendon of the Subscapularis M.

Transverse Humeral Ligament

Short Head of the Biceps Brachii M.

Insertion Tendon of the Teres Minor M.

The Tendon of Origin of the Long Head of the Biceps may Sublux or Dislocate from its Sliding Groove in the Intertubercularis Sulcus. Ruptures of the Long Bicipital Tendon (Sliding Tendon) are among the most Common Tendon Injuries. Within the Intertubercular Synovial Sheath, an Irritation may Occur (Tenosynovitis).

The Coracoacromial Ligament has Two Parts (variant) has been Divided. The Articular Capsule in the so-called Rotator Interval between the Insertion Tendons of the Supraspinatus M. and the Subscapularis M. has been Removed. The Intertubercular Sulcus (Intertubercular Groove) is Bridged by the Transverse Humeral Ligament.

6.42 Fornix Humeri, Rotator Cuff and Synovial Bursa: Right Side, Anterolateral View. [1]

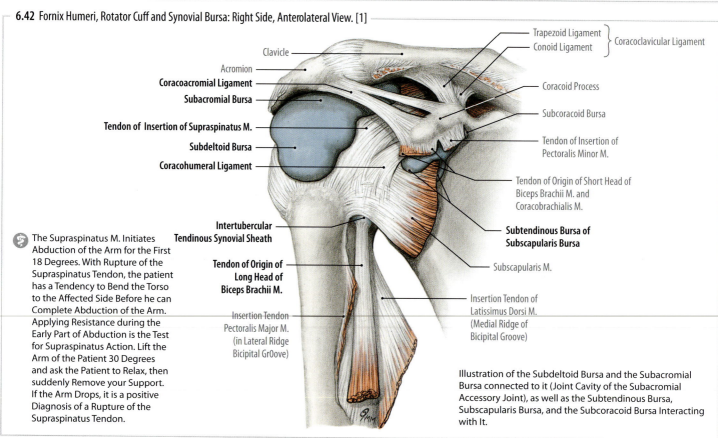

Clavicle

Acromion

Coracoacromial Ligament

Subacromial Bursa

Tendon of Insertion of Supraspinatus M.

Subdeltoid Bursa

Coracohumeral Ligament

Intertubercular Tendinous Synovial Sheath

Tendon of Origin of Long Head of Biceps Brachii M.

Insertion Tendon Pectoralis Major M. (in Lateral Ridge Bicipital GrOove)

Trapezoid Ligament

Conoid Ligament

} Coracoclavicular Ligament

Coracoid Process

Subcoracoid Bursa

Tendon of Insertion of Pectoralis Minor M.

Tendon of Origin of Short Head of Biceps Brachii M. and Coracobrachialis M.

Subtendinous Bursa of Subscapularis Bursa

Subscapularis M.

Insertion Tendon of Latissimus Dorsi M. (Medial Ridge of Bicipital Groove)

The Supraspinatus M. Initiates Abduction of the Arm for the First 18 Degrees. With Rupture of the Supraspinatus Tendon, the patient has a Tendency to Bend the Torso to the Affected Side Before he can Complete Abduction of the Arm. Applying Resistance during the Early Part of Abduction is the Test for Supraspinatus Action. Lift the Arm of the Patient 30 Degrees and ask the Patient to Relax, then suddenly Remove your Support. If the Arm Drops, it is a positive Diagnosis of a Rupture of the Supraspinatus Tendon.

Illustration of the Subdeltoid Bursa and the Subacromial Bursa connected to it (Joint Cavity of the Subacromial Accessory Joint), as well as the Subtendinous Bursa, Subscapularis Bursa, and the Subcoracoid Bursa Interacting with It.

Shoulder: Synovial Bursa, Function

6.43 Synovial Bursa in the Area of the Right Shoulder: Ventral View. [56]

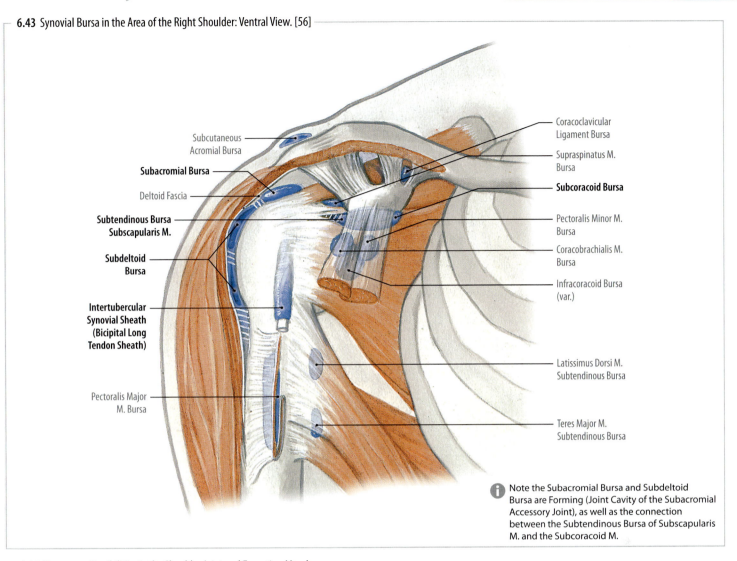

Subcutaneous Acromial Bursa

Subacromial Bursa

Deltoid Fascia

Subtendinous Bursa Subscapularis M.

Subdeltoid Bursa

Intertubercular Synovial Sheath (Bicipital Long Tendon Sheath)

Pectoralis Major M. Bursa

Coracoclavicular Ligament Bursa

Supraspinatus M. Bursa

Subcoracoid Bursa

Pectoralis Minor M. Bursa

Coracobrachialis M. Bursa

Infracoracoid Bursa (var.)

Latissimus Dorsi M. Subtendinous Bursa

Teres Major M. Subtendinous Bursa

i Note the Subacromial Bursa and Subdeltoid Bursa are Forming (Joint Cavity of the Subacromial Accessory Joint), as well as the connection between the Subtendinous Bursa of Subscapularis M. and the Subcoracoid M.

6.44 Movement Possibilities in the Shoulder Joint and Executing Muscles.

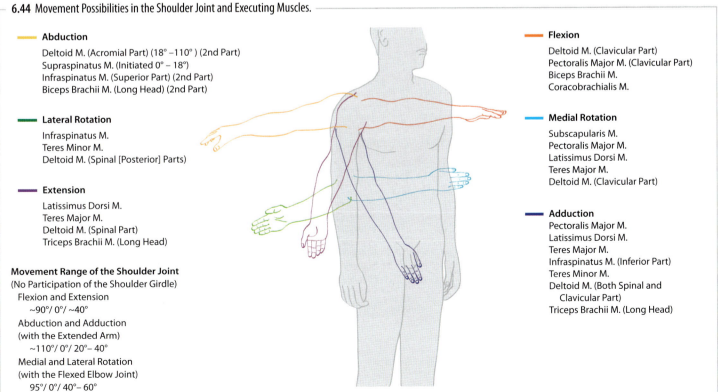

— Abduction

Deltoid M. (Acromial Part) (18° –110°) (2nd Part)
Supraspinatus M. (Initiated 0° – 18°)
Infraspinatus M. (Superior Part) (2nd Part)
Biceps Brachii M. (Long Head) (2nd Part)

— Lateral Rotation

Infraspinatus M.
Teres Minor M.
Deltoid M. (Spinal [Posterior] Parts)

— Extension

Latissimus Dorsi M.
Teres Major M.
Deltoid M. (Spinal Part)
Triceps Brachii M. (Long Head)

Movement Range of the Shoulder Joint
(No Participation of the Shoulder Girdle)
Flexion and Extension
~90°/ 0°/ ~40°
Abduction and Adduction
(with the Extended Arm)
~110°/ 0°/ 20°– 40°
Medial and Lateral Rotation
(with the Flexed Elbow Joint)
95°/ 0°/ 40°– 60°

— Flexion

Deltoid M. (Clavicular Part)
Pectoralis Major M. (Clavicular Part)
Biceps Brachii M.
Coracobrachialis M.

— Medial Rotation

Subscapularis M.
Pectoralis Major M.
Latissimus Dorsi M.
Teres Major M.
Deltoid M. (Clavicular Part)

— Adduction

Pectoralis Major M.
Latissimus Dorsi M.
Teres Major M.
Infraspinatus M. (Inferior Part)
Teres Minor M.
Deltoid M. (Both Spinal and
    Clavicular Part)
Triceps Brachii M. (Long Head)

Muscles

Muscles of the Arms

6

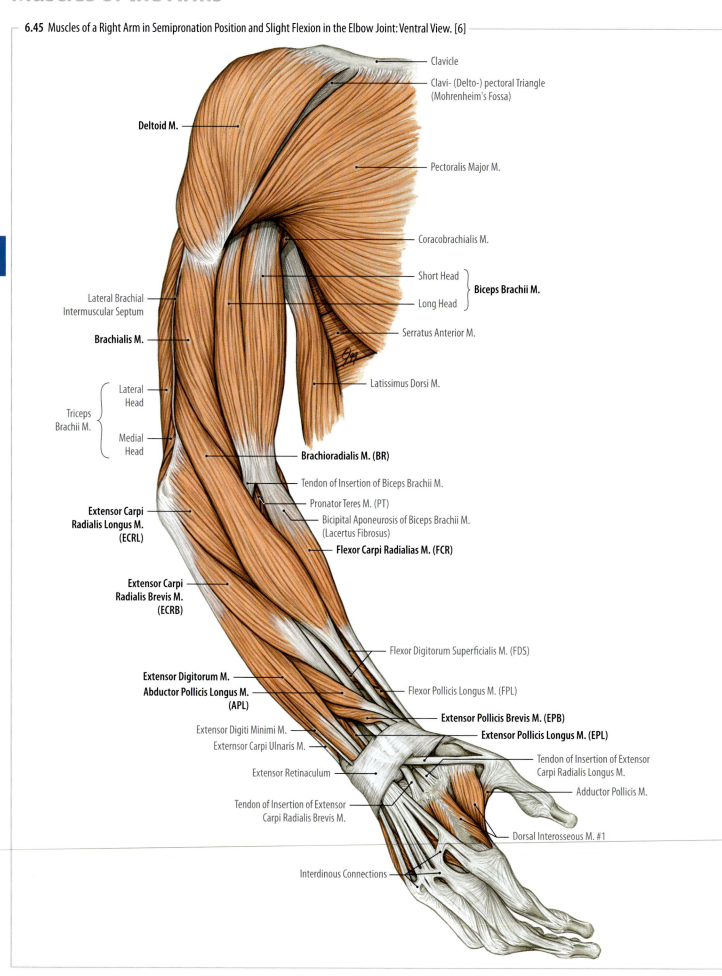

Clavicle

Clavi- (Delto-) pectoral Triangle
(Mohrenheim's Fossa)

Deltoid M.

Pectoralis Major M.

Coracobrachialis M.

Short Head
Biceps Brachii M.
Long Head

Lateral Brachial
Intermuscular Septum

Brachialis M.

Serratus Anterior M.

Lateral
Head

Latissimus Dorsi M.

Triceps
Brachii M.

Medial
Head

Brachioradialis M. (BR)

Tendon of Insertion of Biceps Brachii M.

**Extensor Carpi
Radialis Longus M.
(ECRL)**

Pronator Teres M. (PT)

Bicipital Aponeurosis of Biceps Brachii M.
(Lacertus Fibrosus)

Flexor Carpi Radialias M. (FCR)

**Extensor Carpi
Radialis Brevis M.
(ECRB)**

Flexor Digitorum Superficialis M. (FDS)

Extensor Digitorum M.
**Abductor Pollicis Longus M.
(APL)**

Flexor Pollicis Longus M. (FPL)

Extensor Pollicis Brevis M. (EPB)

Extensor Digiti Minimi M.

Extensor Pollicis Longus M. (EPL)

Externsor Carpi Ulnaris M.

Tendon of Insertion of Extensor
Carpi Radialis Longus M.

Extensor Retinaculum

Adductor Pollicis M.

Tendon of Insertion of Extensor
Carpi Radialis Brevis M.

Dorsal Interosseous M. #1

Interdinous Connections

Muscles of the Upper Arms

6.46 Muscles of the Upper Arm: Right Side, Ventral View. [6]

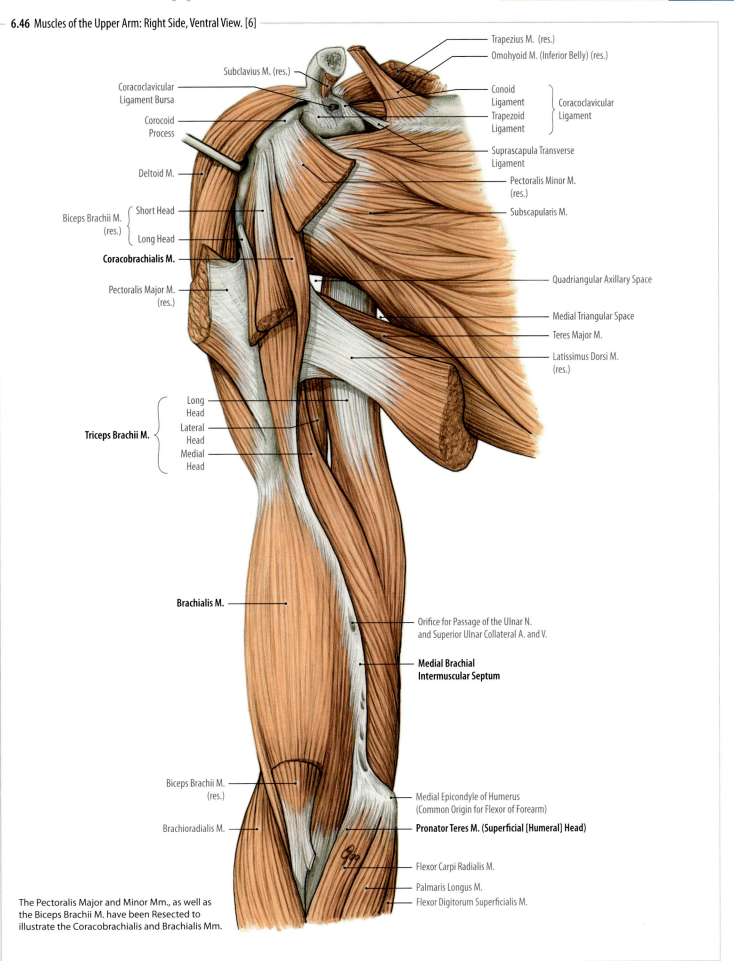

Trapezius M. (res.)
Omohyoid M. (Inferior Belly) (res.)
Subclavius M. (res.)
Coracoclavicular Ligament Bursa
Corocoid Process
Conoid Ligament
Trapezoid Ligament
Coracoclavicular Ligament
Suprascapula Transverse Ligament
Deltoid M.
Pectoralis Minor M. (res.)
Biceps Brachii M. (res.)
Short Head
Long Head
Subscapularis M.
Coracobrachialis M.
Pectoralis Major M. (res.)
Quadriangular Axillary Space
Medial Triangular Space
Teres Major M.
Latissimus Dorsi M. (res.)
Triceps Brachii M.
Long Head
Lateral Head
Medial Head
Brachialis M.
Orifice for Passage of the Ulnar N. and Superior Ulnar Collateral A. and V.
Medial Brachial Intermuscular Septum
Biceps Brachii M. (res.)
Medial Epicondyle of Humerus (Common Origin for Flexor of Forearm)
Brachioradialis M.
Pronator Teres M. (Superficial [Humeral] Head)
Flexor Carpi Radialis M.
Palmaris Longus M.
Flexor Digitorum Superficialis M.

The Pectoralis Major and Minor Mm., as well as the Biceps Brachii M. have been Resected to illustrate the Coracobrachialis and Brachialis Mm.

Muscles

Muscles of the Forearms

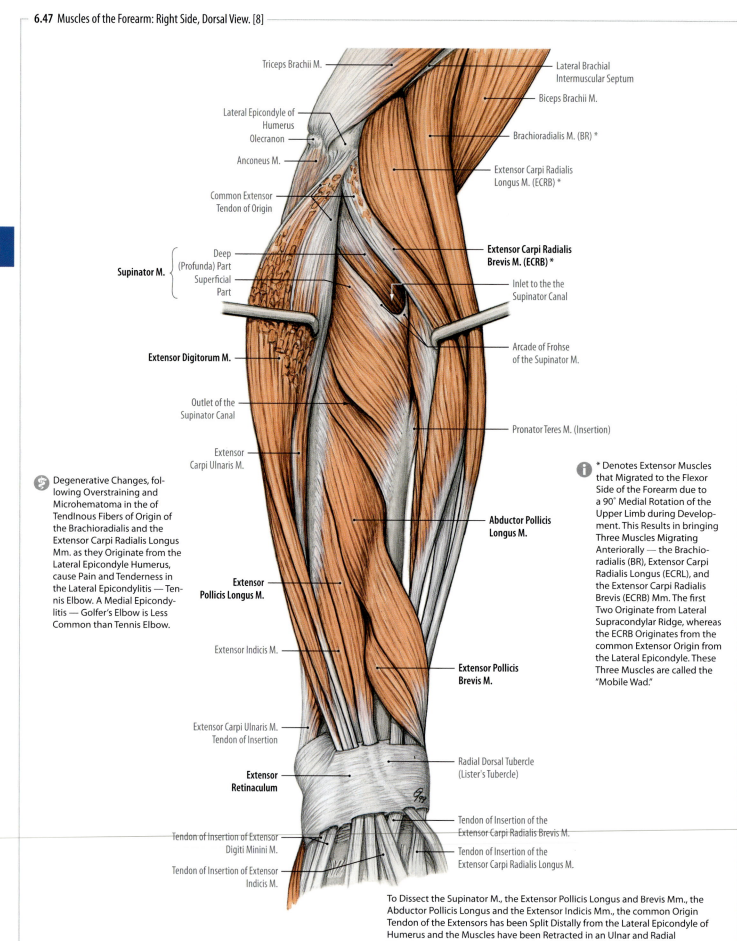

Triceps Brachii M.

Lateral Epicondyle of Humerus

Olecranon

Anconeus M.

Common Extensor Tendon of Origin

Supinator M. Deep (Profunda) Part
Superficial Part

Extensor Digitorum M.

Outlet of the Supinator Canal

Extensor Carpi Ulnaris M.

Extensor Pollicis Longus M.

Extensor Indicis M.

Extensor Carpi Ulnaris M. Tendon of Insertion

Extensor Retinaculum

Tendon of Insertion of Extensor Digiti Minini M.

Tendon of Insertion of Extensor Indicis M.

Lateral Brachial Intermuscular Septum

Biceps Brachii M.

Brachioradialis M. (BR) *

Extensor Carpi Radialis Longus M. (ECRB) *

Extensor Carpi Radialis Brevis M. (ECRB) *

Inlet to the the Supinator Canal

Arcade of Frohse of the Supinator M.

Pronator Teres M. (Insertion)

Abductor Pollicis Longus M.

Extensor Pollicis Brevis M.

Radial Dorsal Tubercle (Lister's Tubercle)

Tendon of Insertion of the Extensor Carpi Radialis Brevis M.

Tendon of Insertion of the Extensor Carpi Radialis Longus M.

Degenerative Changes, following Overstraining and Microhematoma in the of TendInous Fibers of Origin of the Brachioradialis and the Extensor Carpi Radialis Longus Mm. as they Originate from the Lateral Epicondyle Humerus, cause Pain and Tenderness in the Lateral Epicondylitis — Tennis Elbow. A Medial Epicondylitis — Golfer's Elbow is Less Common than Tennis Elbow.

* Denotes Extensor Muscles that Migrated to the Flexor Side of the Forearm due to a 90˚ Medial Rotation of the Upper Limb during Development. This Results in bringing Three Muscles Migrating Anteriorally — the Brachioradialis (BR), Extensor Carpi Radialis Longus (ECRL), and the Extensor Carpi Radialis Brevis (ECRB) Mm. The first Two Originate from Lateral Supracondylar Ridge, whereas the ECRB Originates from the common Extensor Origin from the Lateral Epicondyle. These Three Muscles are called the "Mobile Wad."

To Dissect the Supinator M., the Extensor Pollicis Longus and Brevis Mm., the Abductor Pollicis Longus and the Extensor Indicis Mm., the common Origin Tendon of the Extensors has been Split Distally from the Lateral Epicondyle of Humerus and the Muscles have been Retracted in an Ulnar and Radial Direction.

6

Elbow Joint: Function · Muscles

6.48 Movement Possibilities in the Elbow Joint and Executing Muscles.

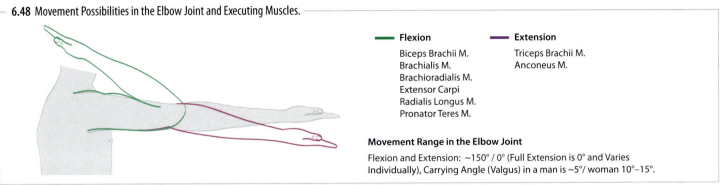

— Flexion	**— Extension**
Biceps Brachii M.	Triceps Brachii M.
Brachialis M.	Anconeus M.
Brachioradialis M.	
Extensor Carpi	
Radialis Longus M.	
Pronator Teres M.	

Movement Range in the Elbow Joint

Flexion and Extension: ~150° / 0° (Full Extension is 0° and Varies Individually), Carrying Angle (Valgus) in a man is ~5°/ woman 10°–15°.

6.49 Deep Muscles of the Elbow Region of the Right Side in Pronation Position: Posterolateral View. [8]

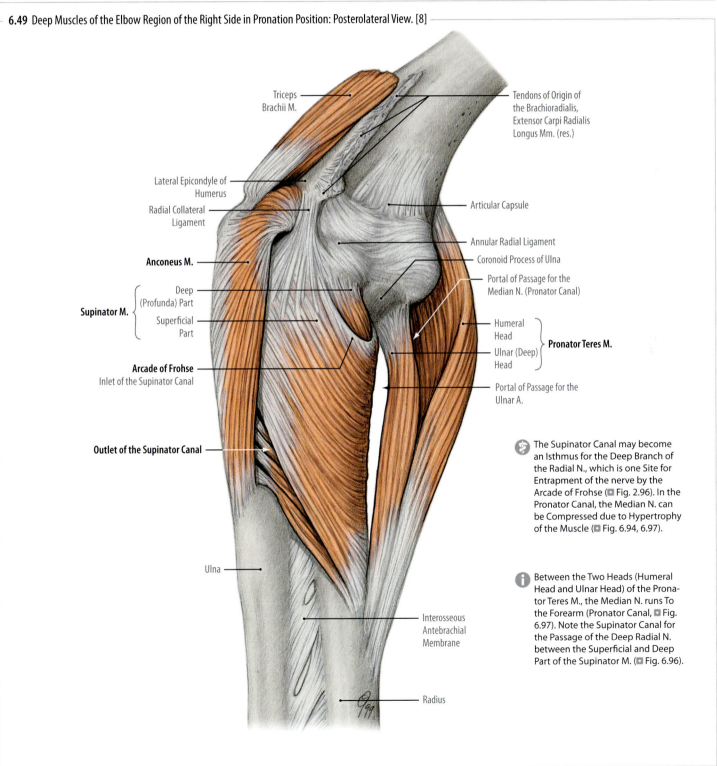

Triceps Brachii M.

Tendons of Origin of the Brachioradialis, Extensor Carpi Radialis Longus Mm. (res.)

Lateral Epicondyle of Humerus

Radial Collateral Ligament

Articular Capsule

Anconeus M.

Annular Radial Ligament

Coronoid Process of Ulna

Supinator M. { Deep (Profunda) Part — Superficial Part

Portal of Passage for the Median N. (Pronator Canal)

Humeral Head

Pronator Teres M.

Ulnar (Deep) Head

Arcade of Frohse
Inlet of the Supinator Canal

Portal of Passage for the Ulnar A.

Outlet of the Supinator Canal

The Supinator Canal may become an Isthmus for the Deep Branch of the Radial N., which is one Site for Entrapment of the nerve by the Arcade of Frohse (⬛ Fig. 2.96). In the Pronator Canal, the Median N. can be Compressed due to Hypertrophy of the Muscle (⬛ Fig. 6.94, 6.97).

Ulna

Between the Two Heads (Humeral Head and Ulnar Head) of the Pronator Teres M., the Median N. runs To the Forearm (Pronator Canal, ⬛ Fig. 6.97). Note the Supinator Canal for the Passage of the Deep Radial N. between the Superficial and Deep Part of the Supinator M. (⬛ Fig. 6.96).

Interosseous Antebrachial Membrane

Radius

Muscles

Pronator Quadratus M.

6.50a,b Pronator Quadratus Muscle: Right Side, Palmar View. [8]

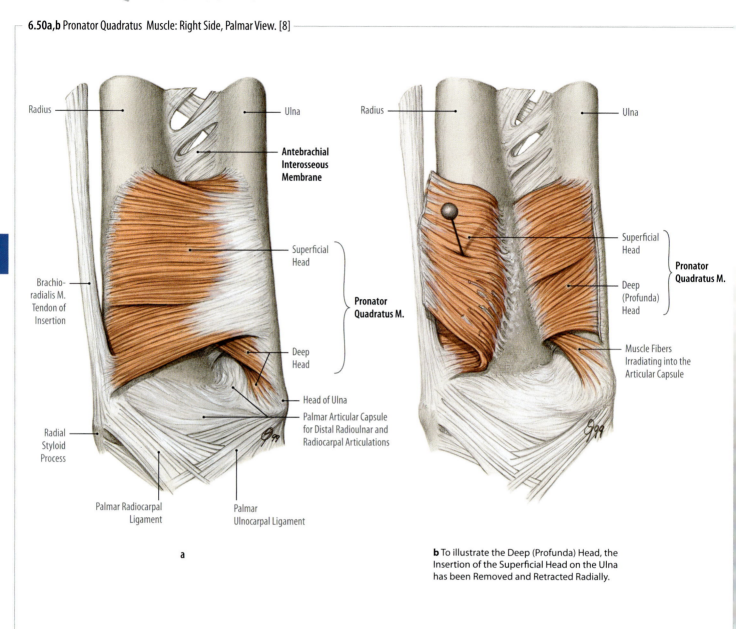

Radius

Ulna

Antebrachial Interosseous Membrane

Superficial Head

Pronator Quadratus M.

Brachio-radialis M. Tendon of Insertion

Deep Head

Radial Styloid Process

Head of Ulna

Palmar Articular Capsule for Distal Radioulnar and Radiocarpal Articulations

Palmar Radiocarpal Ligament

Palmar Ulnocarpal Ligament

a

Radius

Ulna

Superficial Head

Pronator Quadratus M.

Deep (Profunda) Head

Muscle Fibers Irradiating into the Articular Capsule

b To illustrate the Deep (Profunda) Head, the Insertion of the Superficial Head on the Ulna has been Removed and Retracted Radially.

6.51 Movement Possibilities in the Proximal and Distal Radioulnar Joint and Executing Muscles.

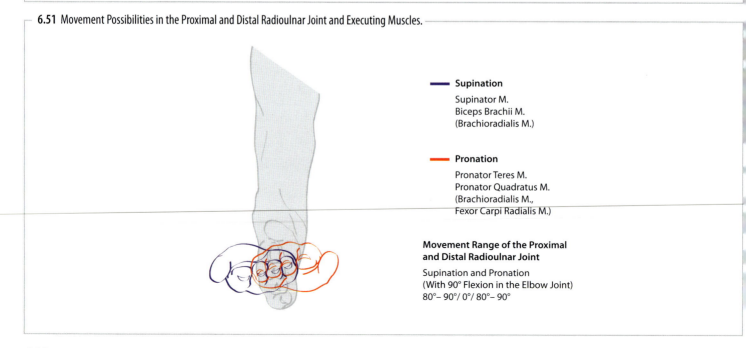

—— Supination

Supinator M.
Biceps Brachii M.
(Brachioradialis M.)

—— Pronation

Pronator Teres M.
Pronator Quadratus M.
(Brachioradialis M.,
Fexor Carpi Radialis M.)

Movement Range of the Proximal and Distal Radioulnar Joint

Supination and Pronation
(With 90° Flexion in the Elbow Joint)
80°– 90°/ 0°/ 80°– 90°

418

6.52 Muscles of the Forearm: Right Side, Palmar View. [8]

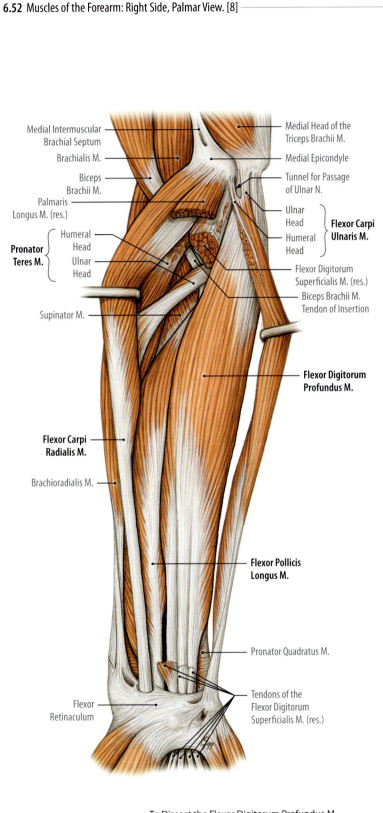

Medial Intermuscular Brachial Septum

Brachialis M.

Biceps Brachii M.

Palmaris Longus M. (res.)

Pronator Teres M. {
Humeral Head
Ulnar Head
}

Supinator M.

Flexor Carpi Radialis M.

Brachioradialis M.

Flexor Pollicis Longus M.

Flexor Retinaculum

Medial Head of the Triceps Brachii M.

Medial Epicondyle

Tunnel for Passage of Ulnar N.

Ulnar Head

Humeral Head

Flexor Carpi Ulnaris M.

Flexor Digitorum Superficialis M. (res.)

Biceps Brachii M. Tendon of Insertion

Flexor Digitorum Profundus M.

Pronator Quadratus M.

Tendons of the Flexor Digitorum Superficialis M. (res.)

To Dissect the Flexor Digitorum Profundus M., the Flexor Digitorum Superficialis M. and the Palmaris Longus M. have been largely Removed.

The Cubital Tunnel between the Ulnar Head and the Humeral Head of the Flexor Carpi Ulnaris M. may become an Isthmus for the Ulnar N. (Fig. 6.87).

6.53 Muscle Compartments of the Muscles of the Forearm: Right Side, Superior View.

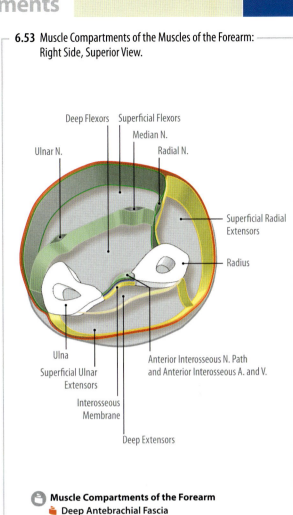

Deep Flexors   Superficial Flexors

Median N.

Ulnar N.

Radial N.

Superficial Radial Extensors

Radius

Ulna

Superficial Ulnar Extensors

Anterior Interosseous N. Path and Anterior Interosseous A. and V.

Interosseous Membrane

Deep Extensors

Muscle Compartments of the Forearm

Deep Antebrachial Fascia

Anterior (Ventral) Muscle Compartment of the Flexor Muscles Group

Superficial Anterior (Ventral) Muscles
Flexor Digitorum Superficialis, Pronator Teres, Flexor Carpi Radialis Mm.
Flexor Carpi Ulnaris, Palmaris Longus Mm.

Deep Anterior (Ventral) Muscles
Flexor Digitorum Profundus M.,
Flexor Pollicis Longus, Pronator Quadratus Mm.

Muscle Compartment of the Posterior (Dorsal) Muscles (Extensor Group)

Deep Posterior (Dorsal) Muscles
Supinator, Abductor Pollicis Longus,
Extensor Pollicis Brevis, Extensor Indicis Mm.

Superficial Posterior (Dorsal) Muscles
Ulnar Group:
Extensor Digitorum, Extensor Carpi Ulnaris Mm.
Radial Group:
Brachioradialis, Extensor Carpi Radialis Longus, Extensor Carpi Radialis Brevis Mm.

Muscles

6.54 Muscles of the Forearm: Right Side, Palmar View. [12]

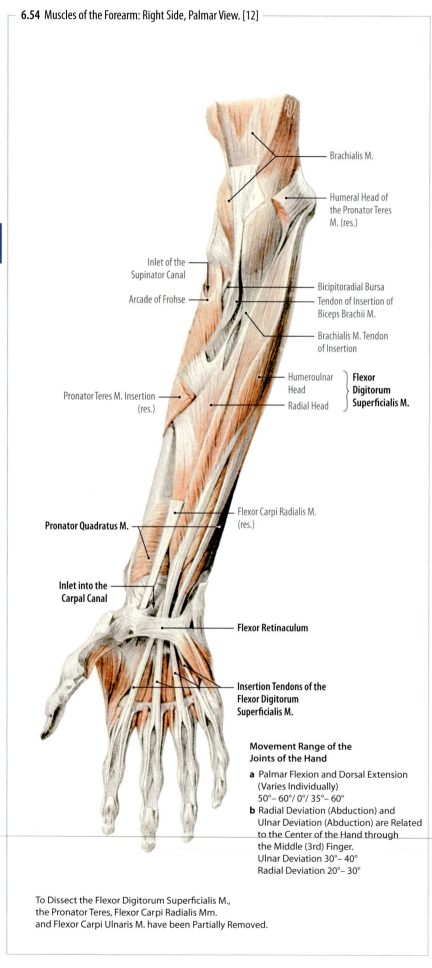

Brachialis M.

Humeral Head of the Pronator Teres M. (res.)

Inlet of the Supinator Canal

Bicipitoradial Bursa

Arcade of Frohse

Tendon of Insertion of Biceps Brachii M.

Brachialis M. Tendon of Insertion

Humeroulnar Head

Flexor Digitorum Superficialis M.

Pronator Teres M. Insertion (res.)

Radial Head

Pronator Quadratus M.

Flexor Carpi Radialis M. (res.)

Inlet into the Carpal Canal

Flexor Retinaculum

Insertion Tendons of the Flexor Digitorum Superficialis M.

Movement Range of the Joints of the Hand

a Palmar Flexion and Dorsal Extension (Varies Individually)
50°– 60°/ 0°/ 35°– 60°

b Radial Deviation (Abduction) and Ulnar Deviation (Abduction) are Related to the Center of the Hand through the Middle (3rd) Finger.
Ulnar Deviation 30°– 40°
Radial Deviation 20°– 30°

To Dissect the Flexor Digitorum Superficialis M., the Pronator Teres, Flexor Carpi Radialis Mm. and Flexor Carpi Ulnaris M. have been Partially Removed.

6.55a,b Movement Possibilities in the Joints of the Hand and Executing Muscles.

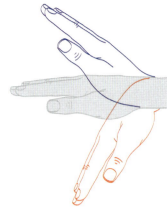

a

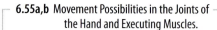

—— **Dorsal Extension**

Extensor Digitorum M.
Extensor Carpi Radialis Longus M.
Extensor Carpi Radialis Brevis M.
Extensor Carpi Ulnaris M.
Extensor Pollicis Longus M.
Extensor Digiti Minimi M.
Extensor Indicis M.

—— **Palmar Flexion**

Flexor Digitorum Profundus M.
Flexor Digitorum Superficialis M.
Flexor Carpi Radialis M.
Flexor Carpi Ulnaris M.
Flexor Pollicis Longus M.
Abductor Pollicis Longus M.

b

—— **Ulnar Deviation (Abduction)**

Flexor Carpi Ulnaris M.
Extensor Carpi Ulnaris M.
Extensor Digitorum M.
Flexor Digitorum Profundus M.
Extensor Digiti Minimi M.

—— **Radial Deviation (Abduction)**

Flexor Carpi Radialis M.
Extensor Carpi Radialis Longus M.
Extensor Carpi Radialis Brevis M.
Flexor Pollicis Longus M.
Extensor Pollicis Brevis M.
Extensor Pollicis Longus M.

6

6.56 Tendons, Tendon Sheaths, and Synovial Bursa of the Extensor (Back) of the Hand. [56]

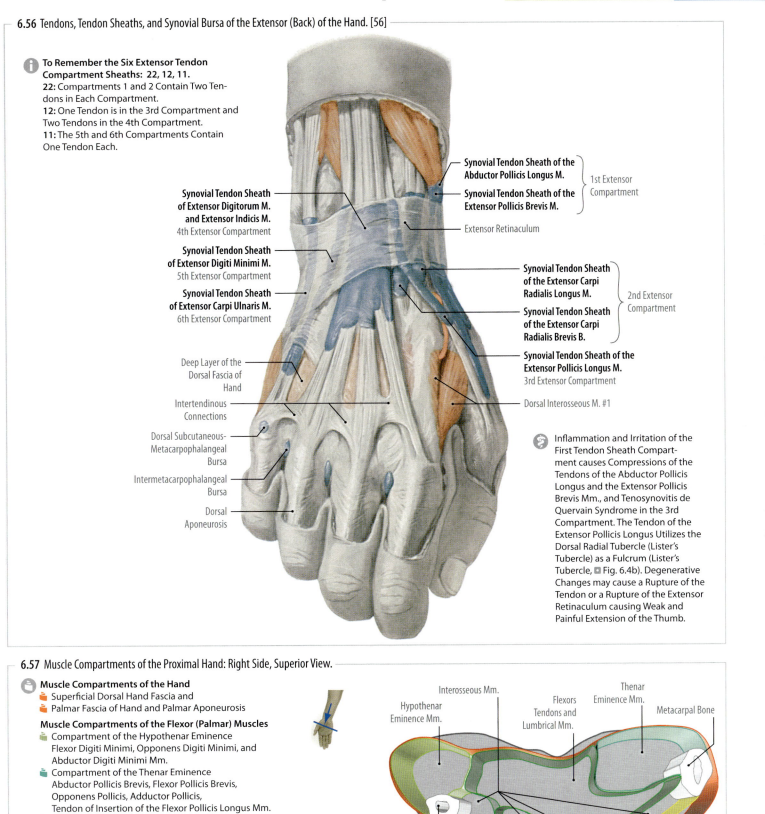

To Remember the Six Extensor Tendon Compartment Sheaths: 22, 12, 11.
22: Compartments 1 and 2 Contain Two Tendons in Each Compartment.
12: One Tendon is in the 3rd Compartment and Two Tendons in the 4th Compartment.
11: The 5th and 6th Compartments Contain One Tendon Each.

Synovial Tendon Sheath of the Abductor Pollicis Longus M.

Synovial Tendon Sheath of the Extensor Pollicis Brevis M.

1st Extensor Compartment

Synovial Tendon Sheath of Extensor Digitorum M. and Extensor Indicis M.
4th Extensor Compartment

Extensor Retinaculum

Synovial Tendon Sheath of Extensor Digiti Minimi M.
5th Extensor Compartment

Synovial Tendon Sheath of the Extensor Carpi Radialis Longus M.

2nd Extensor Compartment

Synovial Tendon Sheath of Extensor Carpi Ulnaris M.
6th Extensor Compartment

Synovial Tendon Sheath of the Extensor Carpi Radialis Brevis B.

Synovial Tendon Sheath of the Extensor Pollicis Longus M.
3rd Extensor Compartment

Deep Layer of the Dorsal Fascia of Hand

Intertendinous Connections

Dorsal Interosseous M. #1

Dorsal Subcutaneous-Metacarpophalangeal Bursa

Intermetacarpophalangeal Bursa

Dorsal Aponeurosis

Inflammation and Irritation of the First Tendon Sheath Compartment causes Compressions of the Tendons of the Abductor Pollicis Longus and the Extensor Pollicis Brevis Mm., and Tenosynovitis de Quervain Syndrome in the 3rd Compartment. The Tendon of the Extensor Pollicis Longus Utilizes the Dorsal Radial Tubercle (Lister's Tubercle) as a Fulcrum (Lister's Tubercle, ◘ Fig. 6.4b). Degenerative Changes may cause a Rupture of the Tendon or a Rupture of the Extensor Retinaculum causing Weak and Painful Extension of the Thumb.

6.57 Muscle Compartments of the Proximal Hand: Right Side, Superior View.

Muscle Compartments of the Hand
- Superficial Dorsal Hand Fascia and
- Palmar Fascia of Hand and Palmar Aponeurosis

Muscle Compartments of the Flexor (Palmar) Muscles
- Compartment of the Hypothenar Eminence
  Flexor Digiti Minimi, Opponens Digiti Minimi, and Abductor Digiti Minimi Mm.
- Compartment of the Thenar Eminence
  Abductor Pollicis Brevis, Flexor Pollicis Brevis, Opponens Pollicis, Adductor Pollicis, Tendon of Insertion of the Flexor Pollicis Longus Mm.
- Median Compartment
  Tendon of Insertion of the Flexor Digitorum Superficialis and the Flexor Digitorum Profundus Mm. with Lumbrical Mm.

Muscle Compartments in the Area of the Metacarpal Bones (Interosseous Spaces)
Between the ▪ Deep Layer of the Dorsal Fascia of Hand and the ▪ Deep Layer of the Palmar Fascia of Palmar of Hand: Dorsal Interossei Mm., Palmar Interossei Mm.

Muscle Compartments of the Posterior (Dorsal) Muscles
Between the ▪ Superficial and the ▪ Deep Layer of the Dorsal Hand Fascia: Insertion Tendons of the Extensor Digitorum, Extensor Indicis, Extensor Digiti Minimi, Extensor Pollicis Longus, Extensor Pollicis Brevis and Abductor Pollicis Longus Mm.

Interosseous Mm.

Hypothenar Eminence Mm.

Flexors Tendons and Lumbrical Mm.

Thenar Eminence Mm.

Metacarpal Bone

5th Metcarpal Bone

Extensor (Tendons)

Muscles of the Hand

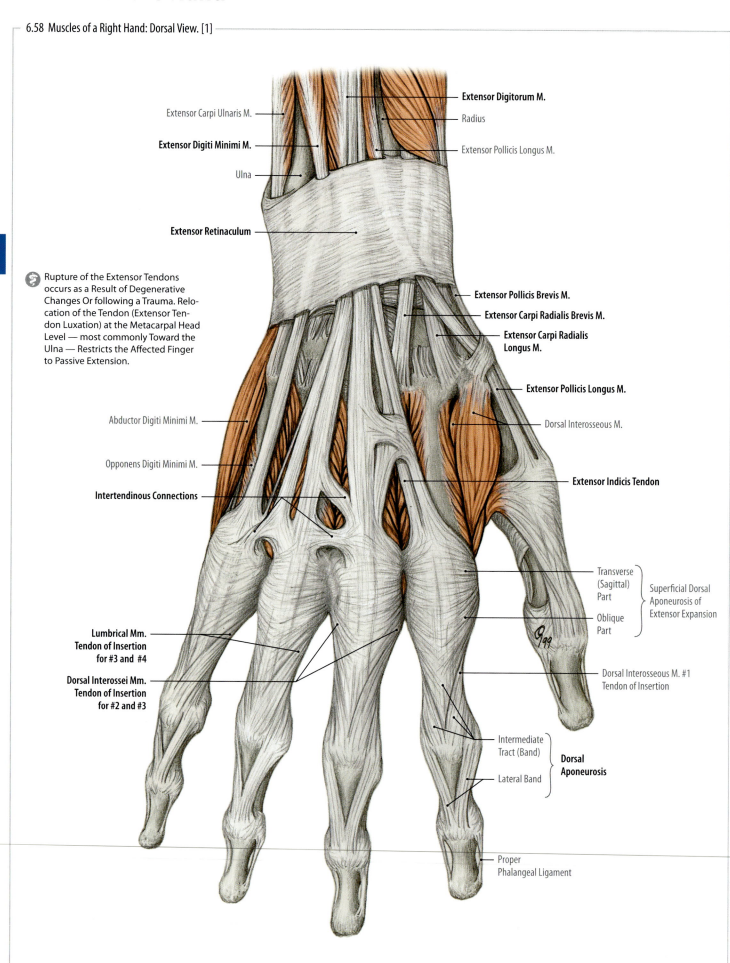

Extensor Carpi Ulnaris M.

Extensor Digiti Minimi M.

Ulna

Extensor Retinaculum

Rupture of the Extensor Tendons occurs as a Result of Degenerative Changes Or following a Trauma. Relocation of the Tendon (Extensor Tendon Luxation) at the Metacarpal Head Level — most commonly Toward the Ulna — Restricts the Affected Finger to Passive Extension.

Abductor Digiti Minimi M.

Opponens Digiti Minimi M.

Intertendinous Connections

**Lumbrical Mm.
Tendon of Insertion
for #3 and #4**

**Dorsal Interossei Mm.
Tendon of Insertion
for #2 and #3**

Extensor Digitorum M.

Radius

Extensor Pollicis Longus M.

Extensor Pollicis Brevis M.

Extensor Carpi Radialis Brevis M.

**Extensor Carpi Radialis
Longus M.**

Extensor Pollicis Longus M.

Dorsal Interosseous M.

Extensor Indicis Tendon

Transverse
(Sagittal)
Part

Oblique
Part

Superficial Dorsal
Aponeurosis of
Extensor Expansion

Dorsal Interosseous M. #1
Tendon of Insertion

Intermediate
Tract (Band)

Lateral Band

**Dorsal
Aponeurosis**

Proper
Phalangeal Ligament

422

6.59 Muscles of the Right Hand: Dorsal View. [8]

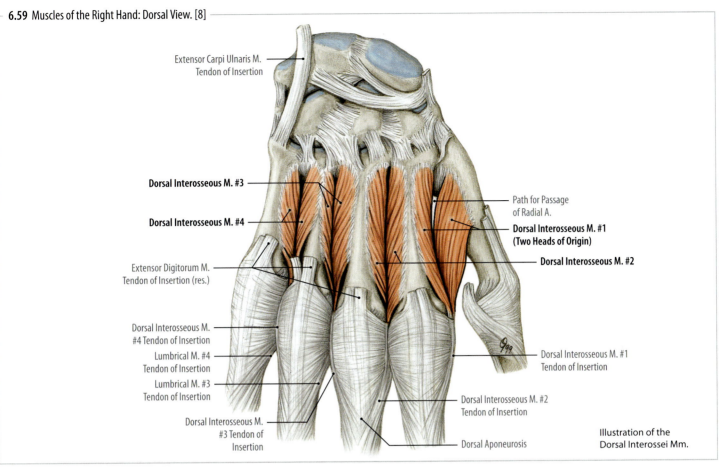

Extensor Carpi Ulnaris M.
Tendon of Insertion

Dorsal Interosseous M. #3

Dorsal Interosseous M. #4

Extensor Digitorum M.
Tendon of Insertion (res.)

Dorsal Interosseous M.
#4 Tendon of Insertion

Lumbrical M. #4
Tendon of Insertion

Lumbrical M. #3
Tendon of Insertion

Dorsal Interosseous M.
#3 Tendon of
Insertion

Path for Passage
of Radial A.

**Dorsal Interosseous M. #1
(Two Heads of Origin)**

Dorsal Interosseous M. #2

Dorsal Interosseous M. #1
Tendon of Insertion

Dorsal Interosseous M. #2
Tendon of Insertion

Dorsal Aponeurosis

Illustration of the
Dorsal Interossei Mm.

6.60 Muscles of the Right Hand with Palmar Aponeurosis and Palmaris Brevis M.: Palmar View. [1]

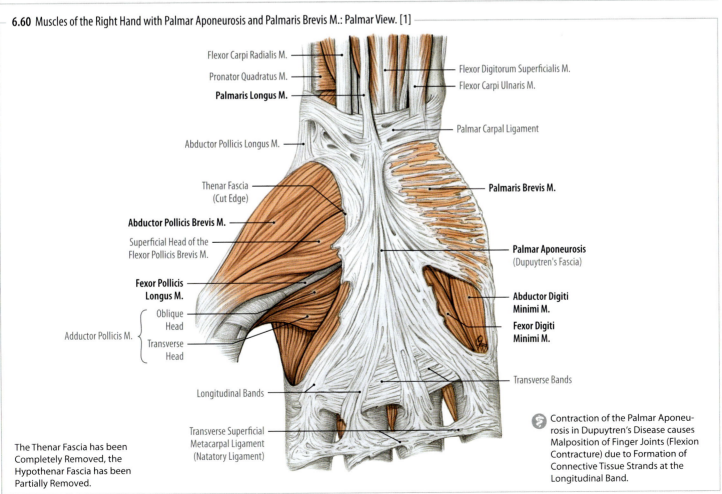

Flexor Carpi Radialis M.

Pronator Quadratus M.

Palmaris Longus M.

Abductor Pollicis Longus M.

Thenar Fascia
(Cut Edge)

Abductor Pollicis Brevis M.

Superficial Head of the
Flexor Pollicis Brevis M.

**Fexor Pollicis
Longus M.**

Oblique
Head

Adductor Pollicis M.

Transverse
Head

Longitudinal Bands

Transverse Superficial
Metacarpal Ligament
(Natatory Ligament)

The Thenar Fascia has been
Completely Removed, the
Hypothenar Fascia has been
Partially Removed.

Flexor Digitorum Superficialis M.

Flexor Carpi Ulnaris M.

Palmar Carpal Ligament

Palmaris Brevis M.

Palmar Aponeurosis
(Dupuytren's Fascia)

**Abductor Digiti
Minimi M.**

**Fexor Digiti
Minimi M.**

Transverse Bands

Contraction of the Palmar Aponeu-
rosis in Dupuytren's Disease causes
Malposition of Finger Joints (Flexion
Contracture) due to Formation of
Connective Tissue Strands at the
Longitudinal Band.

Muscles

Muscles of the Hand and Tendon Sheaths

6.61 Muscles and Tendon Sheaths of the Fingers of the Right Hand: Palmar View. [1]

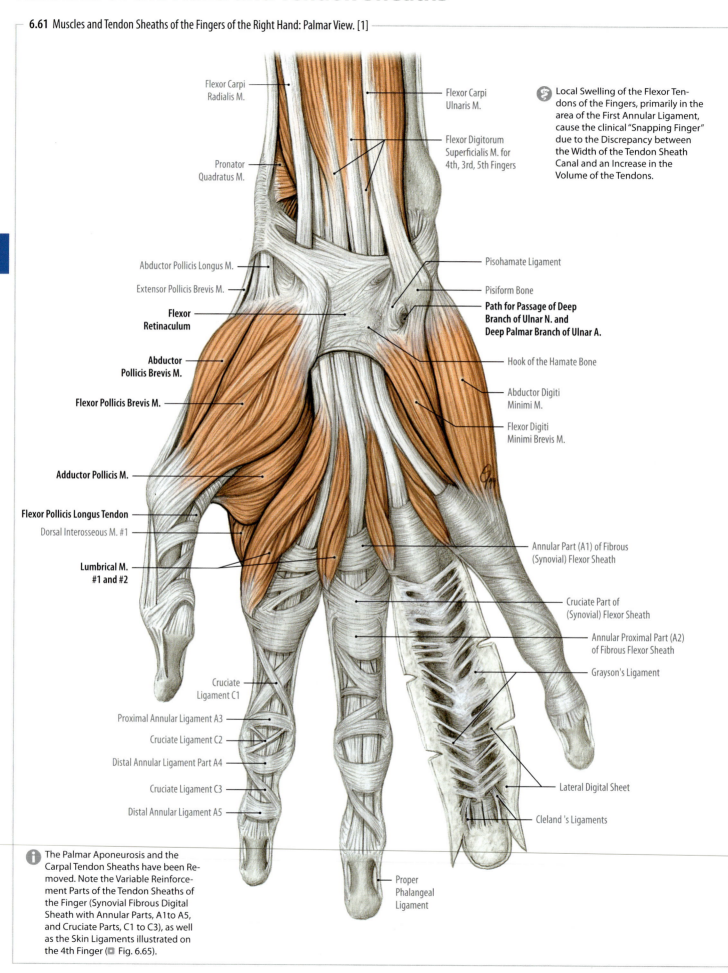

Flexor Carpi Radialis M.

Flexor Carpi Ulnaris M.

Pronator Quadratus M.

Flexor Digitorum Superficialis M. for 4th, 3rd, 5th Fingers

Abductor Pollicis Longus M.

Extensor Pollicis Brevis M.

Flexor Retinaculum

Abductor Pollicis Brevis M.

Flexor Pollicis Brevis M.

Adductor Pollicis M.

Flexor Pollicis Longus Tendon

Dorsal Interosseous M. #1

Lumbrical M. #1 and #2

Pisohamate Ligament

Pisiform Bone

Path for Passage of Deep Branch of Ulnar N. and Deep Palmar Branch of Ulnar A.

Hook of the Hamate Bone

Abductor Digiti Minimi M.

Flexor Digiti Minimi Brevis M.

Annular Part (A1) of Fibrous (Synovial) Flexor Sheath

Cruciate Part of (Synovial) Flexor Sheath

Annular Proximal Part (A2) of Fibrous Flexor Sheath

Grayson's Ligament

Lateral Digital Sheet

Cleland's Ligaments

Cruciate Ligament C1

Proximal Annular Ligament A3

Cruciate Ligament C2

Distal Annular Ligament Part A4

Cruciate Ligament C3

Distal Annular Ligament A5

Proper Phalangeal Ligament

> Local Swelling of the Flexor Tendons of the Fingers, primarily in the area of the First Annular Ligament, cause the clinical "Snapping Finger" due to the Discrepancy between the Width of the Tendon Sheath Canal and an Increase in the Volume of the Tendons.

> The Palmar Aponeurosis and the Carpal Tendon Sheaths have been Removed. Note the Variable Reinforcement Parts of the Tendon Sheaths of the Finger (Synovial Fibrous Digital Sheath with Annular Parts, A1 to A5, and Cruciate Parts, C1 to C3), as well as the Skin Ligaments illustrated on the 4th Finger (Fig. 6.65).

Palmar Tendon Sheaths

6.62 Tendon Sheaths in the Area of the Palm and the Fingers of a Right Hand: Palmar View. [56]

ⓘ The Tendons of the Fingers are Covered by Synovial Sheath and Reinforced by Fibrous Digital Sheath. The Five Annular Band Ligaments are very Strong. The Annular Ligaments are Identified from Proximal toward Distal as (A1– A5). Between the Annular Ligaments lie Three Variably Formed Cruciate or Y-Shaped Ligaments, which are Designated from Proximal toward Distal Fingers as C1, C2, and C3 Ligaments and are Opposite the Metacarpophalangeal (MP), Proximal Interphalangeal (PIP), and Distal Interphalangeal (DIP) Joints.

ⓘ Inflammations of the Palmar Tendon Sheaths may Spread from the Carpal Canal to the Fingers (and Vice Versa) depending on the Connection between the Carpal Tendon Sheaths and the Tendon Sheaths of the Fingers. The Palmar Ulnar Bursa and the Flexor Pollicis Longus Sheath are Connected and Form a Horse-Shoe Shaped Synovial Sheath. An Infection at the Tip of the 5th Finger may Spread to the Thumb. The Other Three Fingers are Not Connected (🔲 Fig. 6.63a).

Flexor Carpi Ulnaris M.

Synovial Tendinous Sheath of Flexor Carpi Radialis M.

Median N.

Flexor Retinaculum

Common Synovial Tendinous Sheath (Ulnar Bursa)

Synovial Tendinous Sheath of Flexor Pollicis Longus M.

Synovial Tendinous Sheath of 5th Finger Flexor Digiti Minimi M.

Annular Part A1 (Accessory Synovial Ligament)

Annular Part A2 (Proximal Proper Synovial Ligament)

Cruciate Part C1 (Cruciate Ligament)

Cruciate Part C2

Cruciate Part C3 (Cruciate Ligament)

Annular Part A5 (Distal Articular Ligament)

Annular Part A3 (Proximal Articular Ligament)

Annular Part A4 (Distal Proper Synovial Ligament)

6.63a–d Palmar Tendon Sheaths of the Hand; Variable Development of the Carpal Palmar Synovial Tendon Sheath and the Fingers (Digital Synovial Sheath). [56]

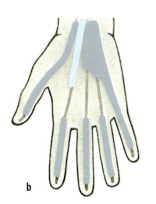

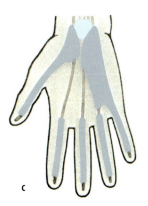

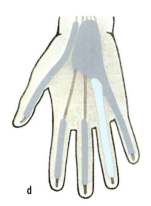

a Most common form.
b The Joint Tendon Sheath of the Carpal Canal (Common Flexor Tendon Sheath) is Divided (Independent Index Finger Tendon Sheath).
c In the area of the Carpal Canal, the Tendon Sheath of the Flexor Pollicis Longus M. Encroaches on the Tendon Sheath of the Index Finger.
d On the Ring Finger, the Tendon Sheaths of the Palm (Ulnar Bursa) and the Finger are Connected to Each Other.

Muscles of the Interior of the Hand

6.64a,b Muscles of the Right Hand: Palmar View. [8]

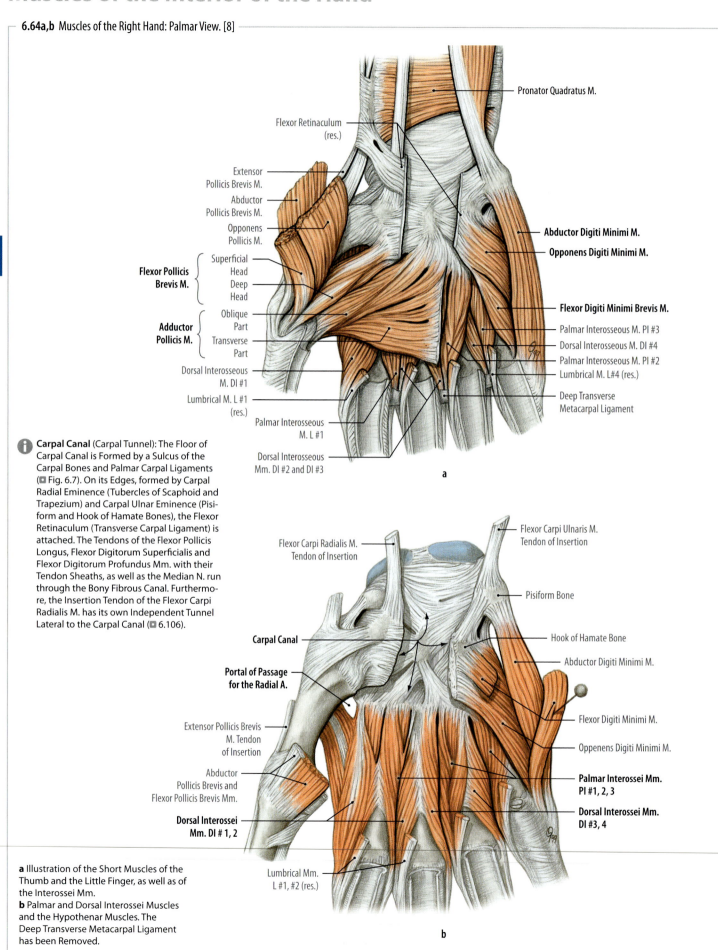

Pronator Quadratus M.

Flexor Retinaculum (res.)

Extensor Pollicis Brevis M.

Abductor Pollicis Brevis M.

Opponens Pollicis M.

Abductor Digiti Minimi M.

Opponens Digiti Minimi M.

Flexor Pollicis Brevis M.
- Superficial Head
- Deep Head

Flexor Digiti Minimi Brevis M.

Adductor Pollicis M.
- Oblique Part
- Transverse Part

Palmar Interosseous M. PI #3

Dorsal Interosseous M. DI #4

Palmar Interosseous M. PI #2

Lumbrical M. L#4 (res.)

Dorsal Interosseous M. DI #1

Lumbrical M. L #1 (res.)

Deep Transverse Metacarpal Ligament

Palmar Interosseous M. L #1

Dorsal Interosseous Mm. DI #2 and DI #3

a

ⓘ Carpal Canal (Carpal Tunnel): The Floor of Carpal Canal is Formed by a Sulcus of the Carpal Bones and Palmar Carpal Ligaments (◻ Fig. 6.7). On its Edges, formed by Carpal Radial Eminence (Tubercles of Scaphoid and Trapezium) and Carpal Ulnar Eminence (Pisiform and Hook of Hamate Bones), the Flexor Retinaculum (Transverse Carpal Ligament) is attached. The Tendons of the Flexor Pollicis Longus, Flexor Digitorum Superficialis and Flexor Digitorum Profundus Mm. with their Tendon Sheaths, as well as the Median N. run through the Bony Fibrous Canal. Furthermore, the Insertion Tendon of the Flexor Carpi Radialis M. has its own Independent Tunnel Lateral to the Carpal Canal (◻ 6.106).

Flexor Carpi Ulnaris M. Tendon of Insertion

Flexor Carpi Radialis M. Tendon of Insertion

Pisiform Bone

Carpal Canal

Hook of Hamate Bone

Abductor Digiti Minimi M.

Portal of Passage for the Radial A.

Flexor Digiti Minimi M.

Oppenens Digiti Minimi M.

Extensor Pollicis Brevis M. Tendon of Insertion

Palmar Interossei Mm. PI #1, 2, 3

Abductor Pollicis Brevis and Flexor Pollicis Brevis Mm.

Dorsal Interossei Mm. DI #1, 2

Dorsal Interossei Mm. DI #3, 4

Lumbrical Mm. L #1, #2 (res.)

a Illustration of the Short Muscles of the Thumb and the Little Finger, as well as of the Interossei Mm.
b Palmar and Dorsal Interossei Muscles and the Hypothenar Muscles. The Deep Transverse Metacarpal Ligament has been Removed.

b

Finger: Muscles, Tendons, Ligaments

6.65 Dorsal Aponeurosis, Muscles, and Tendons of the Right Index Finger: Radial View. [1]

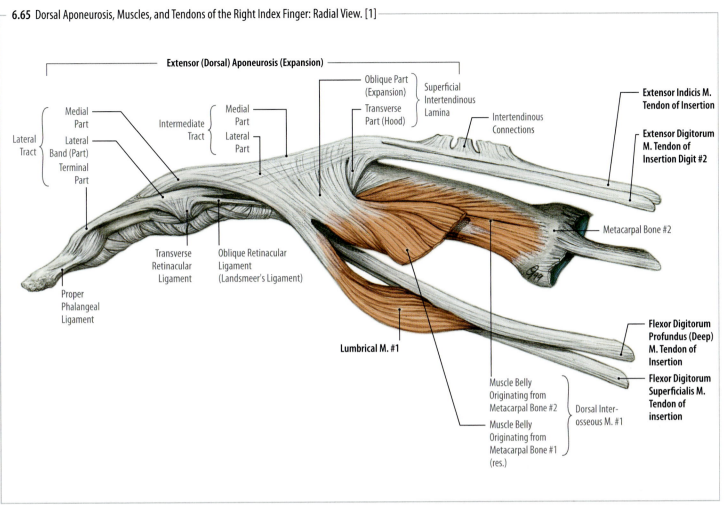

Extensor (Dorsal) Aponeurosis (Expansion)

Oblique Part (Expansion)

Transverse Part (Hood)

Superficial Intertendinous Lamina

Intertendinous Connections

Medial Part

Lateral Band (Part)

Terminal Part

Lateral Tract

Intermediate Tract

Medial Part

Lateral Part

Extensor Indicis M. Tendon of Insertion

Extensor Digitorum M. Tendon of Insertion Digit #2

Metacarpal Bone #2

Transverse Retinacular Ligament

Oblique Retinacular Ligament (Landsmeer's Ligament)

Proper Phalangeal Ligament

Lumbrical M. #1

Flexor Digitorum Profundus (Deep) M. Tendon of Insertion

Flexor Digitorum Superficialis M. Tendon of insertion

Muscle Belly Originating from Metacarpal Bone #2

Muscle Belly Originating from Metacarpal Bone #1 (res.)

Dorsal Interosseous M. #1

6.66 Tendons and Joints of the Right Index Finger: Radial View. [56]

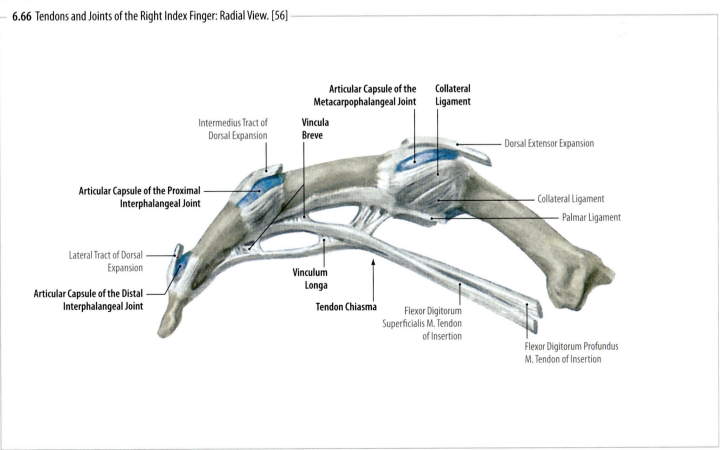

Intermedius Tract of Dorsal Expansion

Vincula Breve

Articular Capsule of the Metacarpophalangeal Joint

Collateral Ligament

Dorsal Extensor Expansion

Articular Capsule of the Proximal Interphalangeal Joint

Collateral Ligament

Palmar Ligament

Lateral Tract of Dorsal Expansion

Articular Capsule of the Distal Interphalangeal Joint

Vinculum Longa

Tendon Chiasma

Flexor Digitorum Superficialis M. Tendon of Insertion

Flexor Digitorum Profundus M. Tendon of Insertion

Muscles

Finger Joints: Function

6.67 Movement Possibilities in the Finger Joints and Executing Muscles.

Metacarpophalangeal Joints (MP) (Digits 2–5)

— **Flexion (0°–90°)**
Lumbrical Mm. (Primary Muscle of Flexion)
Interossei Mm.
Flexor Digitorum Superficialis M.
Flexor Digitorum Profundus M.

— **Extension (0°–30°/45°)**
Extensor Digitorum M. (Digits 2-5)
(Extensor Indicis M. Digit 2,
Extensor Digiti Minimi M. Digit 5)

Abduction (Spreading) of the Fingers 2, 4, and 5
and the Thumb from the Middle Finger (20°)
Dorsal Interossei Mm.
Abductor Digiti Minimi M.
Abductor Pollicis Longus M.
Abductor Pollicis Brevis M.
Extensor Pollicis Brevis M.

Adduction of the Fingers 2, 4, and 5
Towards the Middle Finger and the Thumb (20°)
Palmar Interossei Mm.
Flexor Digitorum Superficialis M.
Flexor Digitorum Profundus M.
Adductor Pollicis M.
Extensor Pollicis Longus M.

Proximal Interphalangeal Joints PIP (Digits 2–5)

— **Flexion (0°–100°)**
Flexor Digitorum Superficialis M.
Flexor Digitorum Profundus M.

— **Extension**
Interossei Mm.
Lumbrical Mm.
Extensor Digitorum M.

Movement Range of the Finger Joints
Metacarpophalangeal (MP) Joints
Flexion and Extension
90°/ 0°/ 10°– 45°
Ulnar and Radial Abduction Away From the Middle Finger
as the Center of the Hand and Towards as Adduction

Proximal Interphalangeal (PIP) Joints
Flexion and Extension
100° – 110°/ 0°/ (Individually Possible
via the Neutral-0-Position)

Distal Interphalangeal (DIP) Joints
Flexion and Extension

Distal Interphalangeal Joints DIP (Digits 2–5)

— **Flexion (0°–90°)**
Flexor Digitorum Profundus M.

— **Extension (0°–10°)**
Interossei Mm.
Lumbrical Mm.
Extensor Digitorum M.

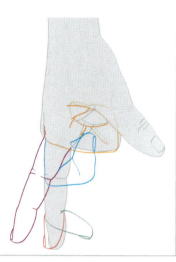

6.68a,b Movement Range in the Thumb Joints and Executing Muscles.

Thumb Saddle Joint

— **Flexion**
Flexor Pollicis Brevis M.
Opponens Pollicis M.

— **Extension**
Extensor Pollicis Longus M.
Extensor Pollicis Brevis M.

— **Adduction**
Adductor Pollicis Brevis M.
Opponens Pollicis M.
Flexor Pollicis Brevis M.
Extensor Pollicis Longus M.

Metacarpophalangeal Joint of the Thumb

— **Flexion**
Flexor Pollicis Brevis M.
Flexor Pollicis Longus M.

— **Extension**
Extensor Pollicis Brevis M.
Extensor Pollicis Longus M.

Distal Interphalangeal Joint of the Thumb

— **Flexion**
Flexor Pollicis Longus M.

— **Extension**
Extensor Pollicis Longus M.

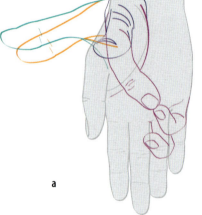

a

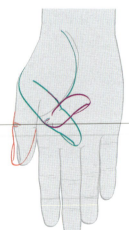

b

— **Abduction**
Abductor Pollicis Longus M.
Extensor Pollicis Brevis M.
Abductor Pollicis Brevis M.
Opponens Pollicis M.

— **Inward Rotation (Pronation)**
Opponens Pollicis M.
Adductor Pollicis M.

— **Outward Rotation (Supination)**
Abductor Pollicis Longus M.
Extensor Pollicis Brevis M.
Extensor Pollicis Longus M.

Movement Range of the Thumb Joints

Thumb Saddle Joint
Inward Rotation, Outward Rotation
~30°

Abduction, Adduction to the
Neutral-0-Position 70°

Flexion

Metacarpophalangeal Joint
Flexion, Extension to the
Neutral-0-Position 50°

Distal Interphalangeal Joint
Flexion, Extension
70°– 80°/ 0°/ 5°– 10°

Opposition Movement
Reposition Movement

Arm: Arteries

6.69 Overview of the Arteries of the Upper Limbs.

The Right Subclavian A. Originates from the Brachiocephalic Trunk. The Left Subclavian A. Originates from the Aortic Arch. When it reaches the Free Upper Limbs at the Outer Edge of the First Rib between the Clavicle and the First Rib, it becomes the Axillary A. The Subclavian A. Supplies the Thoracic Wall and Cavity, the Lower Part of the Anterior Neck including the Thyroid Glands, Shoulder Girdle Posteriorly, Spinal Cord, and Brain.

The Axillary A. runs through the Armpit (Axilla). The Arteries Branching from it Supply the Shoulder Region and the Thoracic Wall. On the Distal Edge of the Latissmis Dorsi M., the Axillary A. Emerges into the Brachial A. In an emergency, the Axillaris A. may only be Ligated via the Shoulder Blade Proximal Arcade of the Outlet of the Subscapular A. to Maintain the Collateral Circulation between the Subclavian A. and Axillary A. (Compare Figs. 6.71, 6.85, 6.86).

The Brachial A. runs in the Upper Arm in the Medial Bicipital Groove down to the Elbow, where it usually Divides into the Radial and Ulnar Aa. at the Cubital Fossa, at the Level of the Radial Neck. The Brachial A. Supplies the Muscles of the Upper Arm and Builds a Collateral Circulatory System with the Arteries of the Forearm in the Area of the Elbow.

The Brachial A. may be Compressed Against the Humerus in Injuries of the Upper Arm. To Maintain Collateral Circulation in the Cubital Area, the Brachial A. may be Ligated Distally to the Outlet of the Deep (Profunda) Brachial A. or Distally to the Outlet of the Inferior Ulnar Collateral A. (Fig. 6.70).

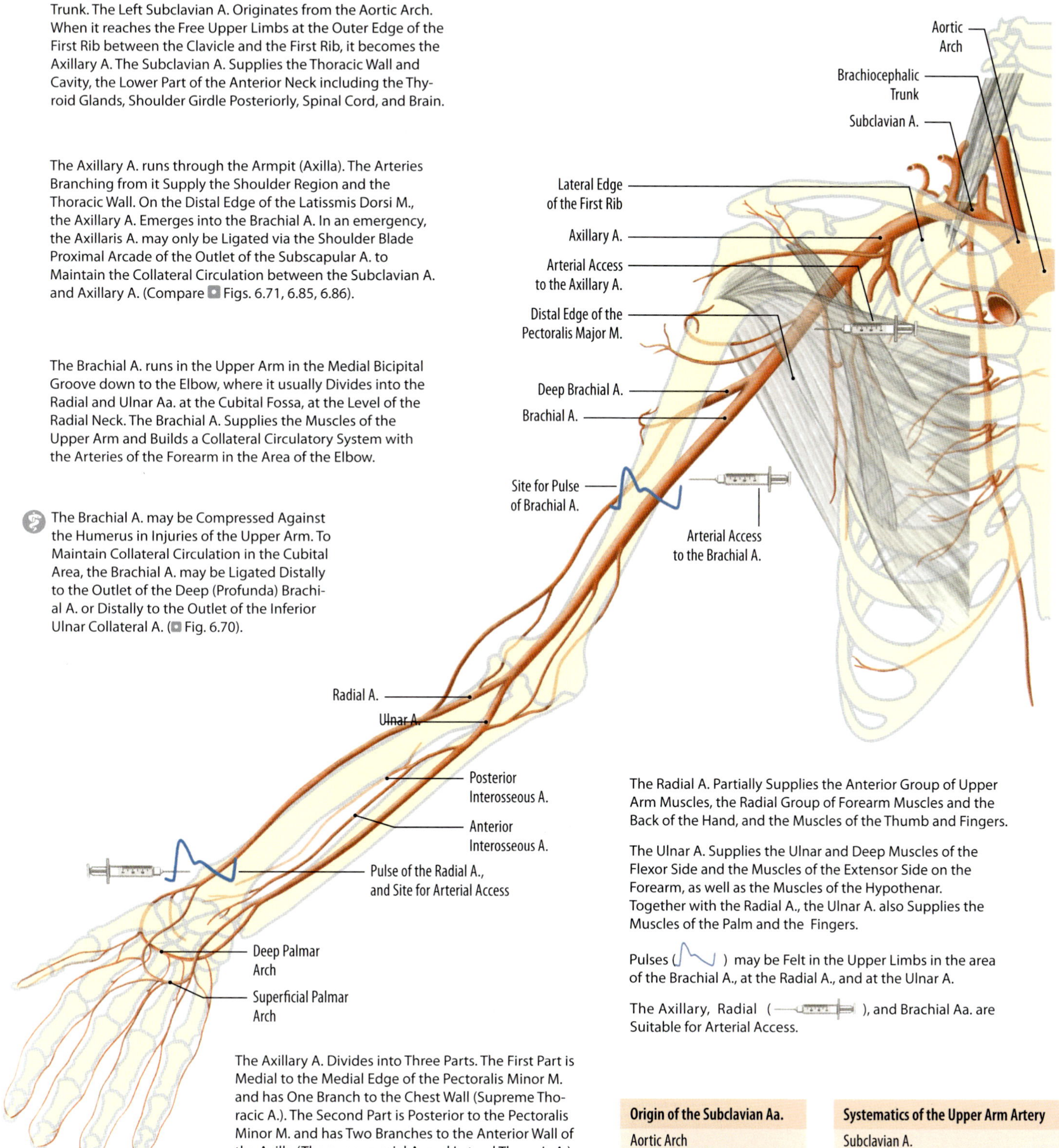

The Axillary A. Divides into Three Parts. The First Part is Medial to the Medial Edge of the Pectoralis Minor M. and has One Branch to the Chest Wall (Supreme Thoracic A.). The Second Part is Posterior to the Pectoralis Minor M. and has Two Branches to the Anterior Wall of the Axilla (Thoracoacromial A. and Lateral Thoracic A.). The Third Part from the Lateral Edge of the Pectoralis Minor M. to the Outer Edge of Latissimus Dorsi M. and has Three Branches to supply the Posterior Wall of the Axilla (Subscapular A.) and the Lateral Wall of the Axilla by Two Arteries (Anterior and Posterior Circumflex Humeral Aa.) Encircling the Surgical Neck of the Humerus.

Labels on figure:
- Aortic Arch
- Brachiocephalic Trunk
- Subclavian A.
- Lateral Edge of the First Rib
- Axillary A.
- Arterial Access to the Axillary A.
- Distal Edge of the Pectoralis Major M.
- Deep Brachial A.
- Brachial A.
- Site for Pulse of Brachial A.
- Arterial Access to the Brachial A.
- Radial A.
- Ulnar A.
- Posterior Interosseous A.
- Anterior Interosseous A.
- Pulse of the Radial A., and Site for Arterial Access
- Deep Palmar Arch
- Superficial Palmar Arch

The Radial A. Partially Supplies the Anterior Group of Upper Arm Muscles, the Radial Group of Forearm Muscles and the Back of the Hand, and the Muscles of the Thumb and Fingers.

The Ulnar A. Supplies the Ulnar and Deep Muscles of the Flexor Side and the Muscles of the Extensor Side on the Forearm, as well as the Muscles of the Hypothenar. Together with the Radial A., the Ulnar A. also Supplies the Muscles of the Palm and the Fingers.

Pulses ( ) may be Felt in the Upper Limbs in the area of the Brachial A., at the Radial A., and at the Ulnar A.

The Axillary, Radial ( ), and Brachial Aa. are Suitable for Arterial Access.

Origin of the Subclavian Aa.

Aortic Arch
├ Left Subclavian A.
└ Brachiocephalic Trunk
　└ Right Subclavian A.

Systematics of the Upper Arm Artery

Subclavian A.
▶ To the Lateral Edge of the First Rib, from There Onward
Axillary A.
▶ To the Distal Edge of the Latissimus Dorsi M., from There Onward
Brachial A.
▶ Division at the Level of the Radial Neck
├ Radial A.
└ Ulnar A.

Pathways and Topography

6.70 Arteries of the Shoulder Region and the Upper Arm: Ventral View. [13]

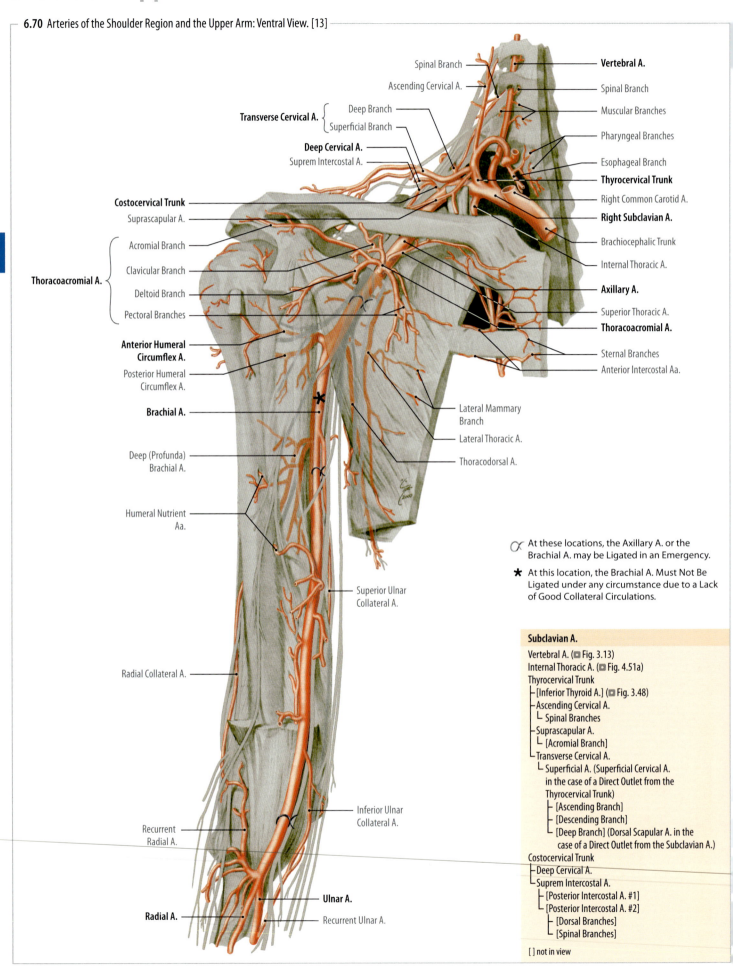

Spinal Branch

Ascending Cervical A.

Transverse Cervical A. {
Deep Branch
Superficial Branch
}

Deep Cervical A.

Suprem Intercostal A.

Costocervical Trunk

Suprascapular A.

Acromial Branch

Clavicular Branch

Thoracoacromial A. {

Deltoid Branch

Pectoral Branches

Anterior Humeral Circumflex A.

Posterior Humeral Circumflex A.

Brachial A.

Deep (Profunda) Brachial A.

Humeral Nutrient Aa.

Radial Collateral A.

Recurrent Radial A.

Radial A.

Vertebral A.

Spinal Branch

Muscular Branches

Pharyngeal Branches

Esophageal Branch

Thyrocervical Trunk

Right Common Carotid A.

Right Subclavian A.

Brachiocephalic Trunk

Internal Thoracic A.

Axillary A.

Superior Thoracic A.

Thoracoacromial A.

Sternal Branches

Anterior Intercostal Aa.

Lateral Mammary Branch

Lateral Thoracic A.

Thoracodorsal A.

Superior Ulnar Collateral A.

Inferior Ulnar Collateral A.

Ulnar A.

Recurrent Ulnar A.

ᗢ At these locations, the Axillary A. or the Brachial A. may be Ligated in an Emergency.

★ At this location, the Brachial A. Must Not Be Ligated under any circumstance due to a Lack of Good Collateral Circulations.

Subclavian A.

Vertebral A. (▣ Fig. 3.13)
Internal Thoracic A. (▣ Fig. 4.51a)
Thyrocervical Trunk
 ├[Inferior Thyroid A.] (▣ Fig. 3.48)
 ├Ascending Cervical A.
 │ └ Spinal Branches
 ├Suprascapular A.
 │ └ [Acromial Branch]
 └Transverse Cervical A.
    └ Superficial A. (Superficial Cervical A. in the case of a Direct Outlet from the Thyrocervical Trunk)
       ├ [Ascending Branch]
       ├ [Descending Branch]
       └ [Deep Branch] (Dorsal Scapular A. in the case of a Direct Outlet from the Subclavian A.)
Costocervical Trunk
 ├Deep Cervical A.
 └Suprem Intercostal A.
    ├ [Posterior Intercostal A. #1]
    └ [Posterior Intercostal A. #2]
       ├ [Dorsal Branches]
       └ [Spinal Branches]

[ ] not in view

6

6.71 Arteries of the Shoulder Region and the Upper Arm: Dorsal View. [13]

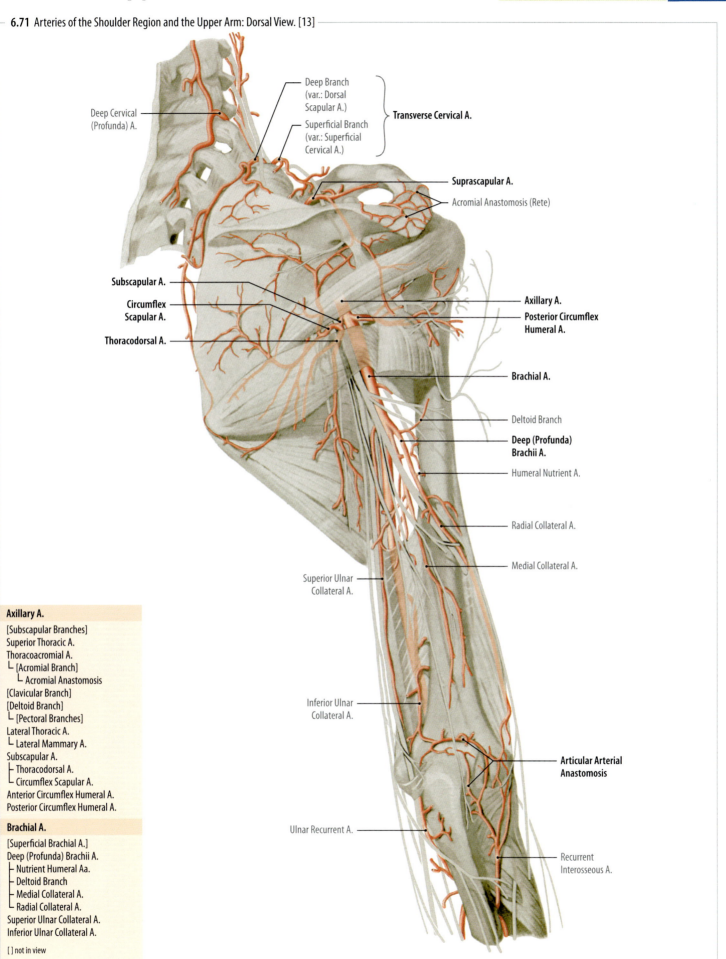

Deep Cervical (Profunda) A.

Deep Branch (var.: Dorsal Scapular A.)

Superficial Branch (var.: Superficial Cervical A.)

Transverse Cervical A.

Suprascapular A.

Acromial Anastomosis (Rete)

Subscapular A.

Circumflex Scapular A.

Thoracodorsal A.

Axillary A.

Posterior Circumflex Humeral A.

Brachial A.

Deltoid Branch

Deep (Profunda) Brachii A.

Humeral Nutrient A.

Radial Collateral A.

Medial Collateral A.

Superior Ulnar Collateral A.

Inferior Ulnar Collateral A.

Articular Arterial Anastomosis

Ulnar Recurrent A.

Recurrent Interosseous A.

Axillary A.

[Subscapular Branches]
Superior Thoracic A.
Thoracoacromial A.
 └ [Acromial Branch]
   └ Acromial Anastomosis
[Clavicular Branch]
[Deltoid Branch]
 └ [Pectoral Branches]
Lateral Thoracic A.
 └ Lateral Mammary A.
Subscapular A.
 ├ Thoracodorsal A.
 └ Circumflex Scapular A.
Anterior Circumflex Humeral A.
Posterior Circumflex Humeral A.

Brachial A.

[Superficial Brachial A.]
Deep (Profunda) Brachii A.
 ├ Nutrient Humeral Aa.
 ├ Deltoid Branch
 ├ Medial Collateral A.
 └ Radial Collateral A.
Superior Ulnar Collateral A.
Inferior Ulnar Collateral A.

[ ] not in view

Pathways and Topography

Brachial Plexus

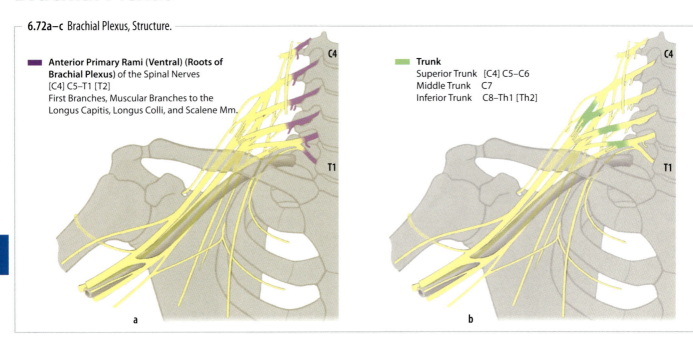

Anterior Primary Rami (Ventral) (Roots of Brachial Plexus) of the Spinal Nerves
[C4] C5–T1 [T2]
First Branches, Muscular Branches to the Longus Capitis, Longus Colli, and Scalene Mm.

Trunk
Superior Trunk   [C4] C5–C6
Middle Trunk   C7
Inferior Trunk   C8–Th1 [Th2]

a

b

6.73a,b Nerves of the Brachial Plexus.

ⓘ The Brachial Plexus is formed by the Anterior Primary Rami C5–T1 ± C4 or T2. It is Divided into Four distinct Areas:

A: Roots of Brachial Plexus Anterior Primary Rami of [C4] C5–T1 [T2] give Motor Innervations to Muscles attached to the Axial Skeleton Prevertebral Cervical Mm., Direct Nerves, and Scalene Mm., Levator Scapulae, Rhomboids Mm. via Dorsal Scapular N. (C5), Subclavius M. (C5,6), and Serratus Anterior M. (C5,6,7) Rootlets.

B: Three Trunks organized in Superior to Inferior Direction. The Only Superior Trunk formed by the Union of C5 and C6 Roots, gives a Suprascapular N. (C5,6) to the Muscles on the Back Surface of the Scapula.

C: Divisions—the Trunks are Divided into Anterior and Posterior Divisions. No Branches emerge From the Divisions. A Line (Clavicle) Across the Divisions can Divide the Brachial Plexus into a Supraclavicular Part and Inferior to this Line as an Infraclavicular Part. All Anterior Divisions supply Muscles Anterior to the Bones of the Upper Limb (Flexors), and all the Posterior Divisions supply the Dorsal Muscle of the Limb (Extensors).

D: Three Cords are formed; All Posterior Divisions of the Trunks Form:
1. The Posterior Cord of the Brachial Plexus —Supplies the Posterior (Extensor) Muscles in the Axilla, Arm, and Forearm.
2. The Lateral Cord— Formed by the Anterior Divisions of Both Superior and Middle Trunks. It gives Innervations to the Flexor Muscle in the Arm, the Forearm, and the Thenar Eminence.
3. Medial Cord— Formed by the Anterior Division of the Inferior Trunk and gives Innervations to the Anterior Axillary Wall and Medial Muscle in Forearm and Deep Small Muscles of the Hand.

Supraclavicular Part (Motor Parts, Nerves Originating from the Roots and Superior Trunk):		
Nerve	**Spinal Cord Segment**	**Innervated Muscle**
Long Thoracic N.	C5, C6, C7 (Roots)	Serratus Anterior M.
Dorsal Scapular N.	C4, C5 (Roots)	Levator Scapulae and Rhomboid Major and Minor Mm.
Subclavius N.	C4, C5, C6 (Roots)	Subclavius M.
Suprascapular N.	C4, C5, C6 (Superior Trunk)	Supraspinatus and Infraspinatus Mm.
Medial and Lateral Pectoral Nn.	C5–T1 (Cords)	Pectoralis Major and Minor Mm.
Thoracodorsal N.	C6–C8 (Posterior Cord))	Latissimus Dorsi M.
Subscapular N.	C5–C7 (C8) (Posterior Cord)	Subscapularis and Teres Major Mm.

Ⓢ The Regional Anesthesia of the Brachial Plexus can be Administered via Four Approaches:
1. Interscalene Block: Injection at Scalene Cleft aiming at the Chassaignac Tubercle
2. Supraclavicular Block: Approach the Plexus through the Posterior Cervical Triangle
3. Infraclavicular Block: Enter from the Costoclavicular Space into the Infraclavicular Fossa
4. Axillary Block: Injection into the Medial Arm to the Axillary Sheath

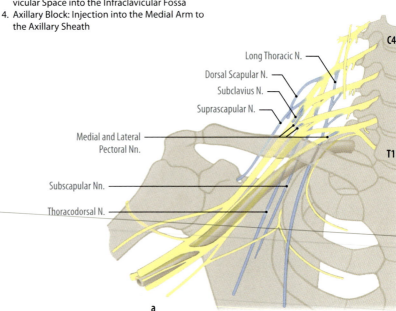

Long Thoracic N.
Dorsal Scapular N.
Subclavius N.
Suprascapular N.
Medial and Lateral Pectoral Nn.
Subscapular Nn.
Thoracodorsal N.

a

Brachial Plexus

ⓘ Each of the Three Cords has Two Types of Branches:
Collateral Branches of the Path of the Cord through the Axilla; and Terminal Branches, which are the Ends of the Cords. Each Cord has Two Terminal Branches.
Collateral Branches of:
Lateral Cord
   Lateral Pectoral N.
Medial Cord
   Medial Pectoral N.,
   Medial Brachial Cutaneous N.
   Medial Antebrachial Cutaneous N.
Posterior Cord
   Upper (Superior) Subscapular N.
   Middle Subscapular N.
     (Thoracodorsal)
   Lower (Inferior) Subscapular N.

   ■ **Dorsal Divisions**
   ■ **Posterior Cord**   C5–T1
     Radial N.
     Axillary N.
   ■ **Ventral Divisions**
   ■ **Medial Cord**   C8–T1 [T2]
     Ulnar N.
     Medial Root of the Median N.
   ■ **Lateral Cord**   C5–C7
     Musculocutaneous N.
     (Lateral Antebrachial Cutaneous N.)
     Lateral Root of the Median N.

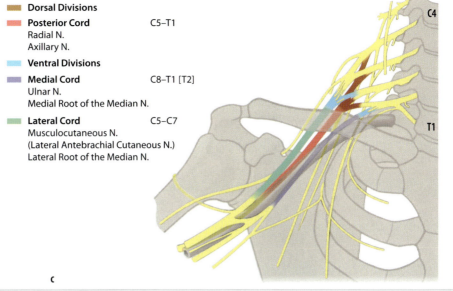

c

Infraclavicular Part (Motor Parts)

Nerve	Spinal Cord Segment	Innervated Muscle
Axillary N.	(C4) C5– C6 ▶	Deltoid Teres Minor Mm.
Radial N.	C5– C8 (T1) ▶	Triceps Brachii Anconeus Brachioradialis Brachialis (Lateral 1/5th) Extensor Carpi Radialis Longus Extensor Carpi Radialis Brevis Supinator Extensor Carpi Ulnaris Extensor Digitorum Extensor Digiti Minimi Abductor Pollicis Longus Extensor Pollicis Longus Extensor Pollicis Brevis Extensor Indicis
Musculocutaneous N.	C6– T1 ▶	Biceps Brachii Coracobrachialis Brachialis

Nerve	Spinal Cord Segment	Innervated Muscle
Ulnar N.	C8– T1 ▶	Flexor Carpi Ulnar Flexor Digitorum Profundus (4th and 5th) Abductor Digiti Minimi Opponens Digiti Minimi Flexor Digiti Minimi Brevis Lumbrical (3rd and 4th) Palmar Interossei Dorsal Interossei Adductor Pollicis Flexor Pollicis Brevis (Deep Head) Mm.
Median N.	C6– T1 ▶	Pronator Teres Flexor Carpi Radialis Flexor Digitorum Superficialis Flexor Digitorum Profundus (2nd and 3rd) Flexor Pollicis Longus Lumbrical (1st and 2nd) Opponens Pollicis Flexor Pollicis Brevis (Superficial Head) Abductor Pollicis Brevis

ⓢ With Damage to the Plexus Brachialis through Overstraining (Birth Palsy) or through Nerve Root Avulsion (Motorcycle Accidents), one Differentiates between an Upper Plexus Paresis (Duchenne-Erb Paralysis) with Involvement of the Segments C5–C6 and a Lower Plexus Paresis (Déjerine-Klumpke Paralysis) with Failure of the Segments C8–T1. An Upper Plexus Paresis results in Paralysis of the Deltoid, Biceps, Brachialis, and Brachioradialis Mm.; the Upper Limb in the Adducted Shoulder; the Medially Rotated Arm; and the Extended Elbow. In a Lower Plexus Paresis, the Small (Intrinsic) Muscles are Affected; a Clawhand Results.

Musculocutaneous N.
Axillary N.
Median N.
Medial Antebrachial Cutaneous N.
Radial N.
Ulnar N.
C4
T1
Intercostobrachial N.
Intercostal N. #2
Medial Brachial Cutaneous N.

b

Pathways and Topography

6.74 Nerves of the Shoulder Region and the Upper Arm: Ventral View. [15]

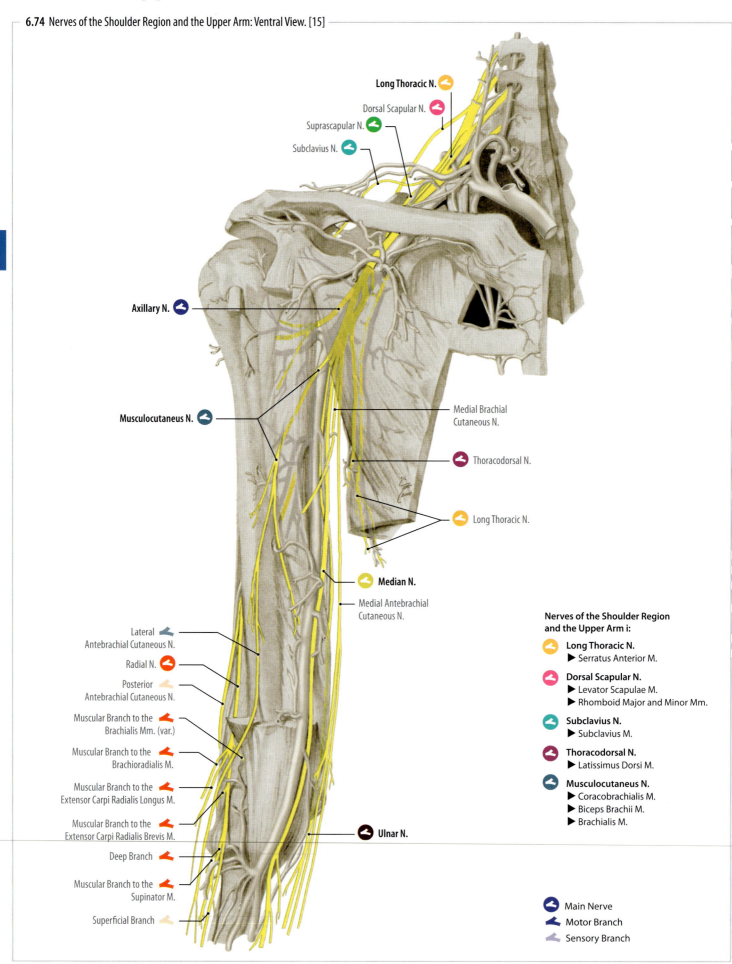

Long Thoracic N.

Dorsal Scapular N.

Suprascapular N.

Subclavius N.

Axillary N.

Musculocutaneus N.

Medial Brachial
Cutaneous N.

Thoracodorsal N.

Long Thoracic N.

Median N.

Medial Antebrachial
Cutaneous N.

Lateral
Antebrachial Cutaneous N.

Radial N.

Posterior
Antebrachial Cutaneous N.

Muscular Branch to the
Brachialis Mm. (var.)

Muscular Branch to the
Brachioradialis M.

Muscular Branch to the
Extensor Carpi Radialis Longus M.

Muscular Branch to the
Extensor Carpi Radialis Brevis M.

Deep Branch

Muscular Branch to the
Supinator M.

Superficial Branch

Ulnar N.

Nerves of the Shoulder Region and the Upper Arm i:

Long Thoracic N.
▶ Serratus Anterior M.

Dorsal Scapular N.
▶ Levator Scapulae M.
▶ Rhomboid Major and Minor Mm.

Subclavius N.
▶ Subclavius M.

Thoracodorsal N.
▶ Latissimus Dorsi M.

Musculocutaneus N.
▶ Coracobrachialis M.
▶ Biceps Brachii M.
▶ Brachialis M.

⬤ Main Nerve
◀ Motor Branch
◀ Sensory Branch

6.75 Nerves of the Shoulder Region and the Upper Arm: Dorsal View. [13]

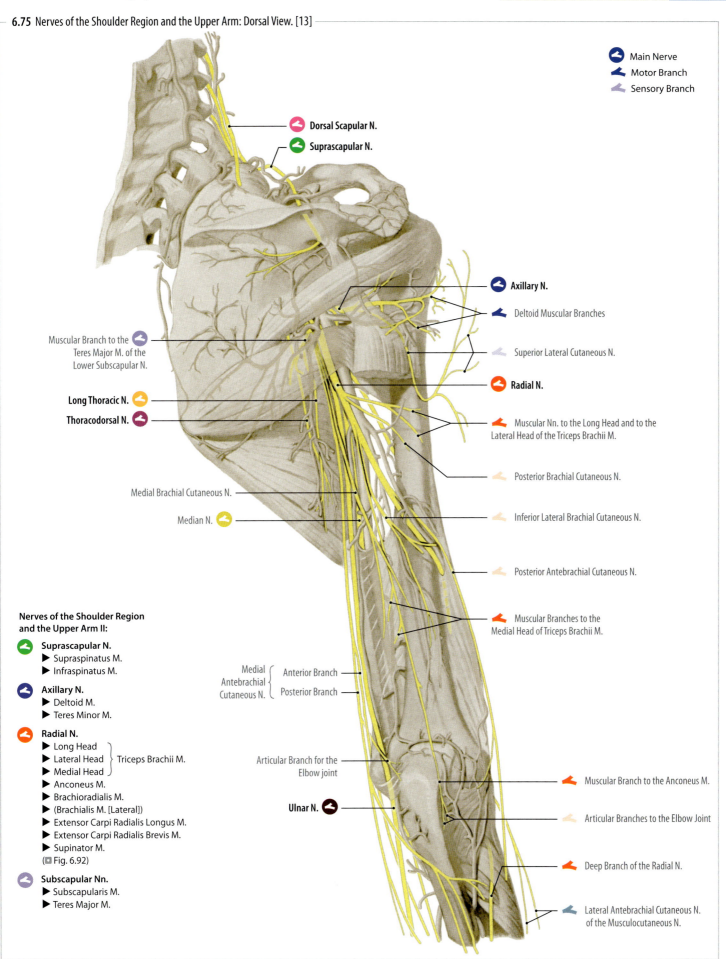

Main Nerve
Motor Branch
Sensory Branch

Dorsal Scapular N.

Suprascapular N.

Axillary N.

Deltoid Muscular Branches

Superior Lateral Cutaneous N.

Muscular Branch to the
Teres Major M. of the
Lower Subscapular N.

Radial N.

Muscular Nn. to the Long Head and to the
Lateral Head of the Triceps Brachii M.

Long Thoracic N.

Thoracodorsal N.

Posterior Brachial Cutaneous N.

Medial Brachial Cutaneous N.

Inferior Lateral Brachial Cutaneous N.

Median N.

Posterior Antebrachial Cutaneous N.

Muscular Branches to the
Medial Head of Triceps Brachii M.

**Nerves of the Shoulder Region
and the Upper Arm II:**

Suprascapular N.
▶ Supraspinatus M.
▶ Infraspinatus M.

Axillary N.
▶ Deltoid M.
▶ Teres Minor M.

Radial N.
▶ Long Head
▶ Lateral Head ⎱ Triceps Brachii M.
▶ Medial Head ⎰
▶ Anconeus M.
▶ Brachioradialis M.
▶ (Brachialis M. [Lateral])
▶ Extensor Carpi Radialis Longus M.
▶ Extensor Carpi Radialis Brevis M.
▶ Supinator M.
(⬚ Fig. 6.92)

Subscapular Nn.
▶ Subscapularis M.
▶ Teres Major M.

Medial
Antebrachial ⎰ Anterior Branch
Cutaneous N. ⎱ Posterior Branch

Articular Branch for the
Elbow joint

Ulnar N.

Muscular Branch to the Anconeus M.

Articular Branches to the Elbow Joint

Deep Branch of the Radial N.

Lateral Antebrachial Cutaneous N.
of the Musculocutaneous N.

Pathways and Topography

6.76 Superficial Nerves and Veins of the Right Arm: Ventral View. [56]

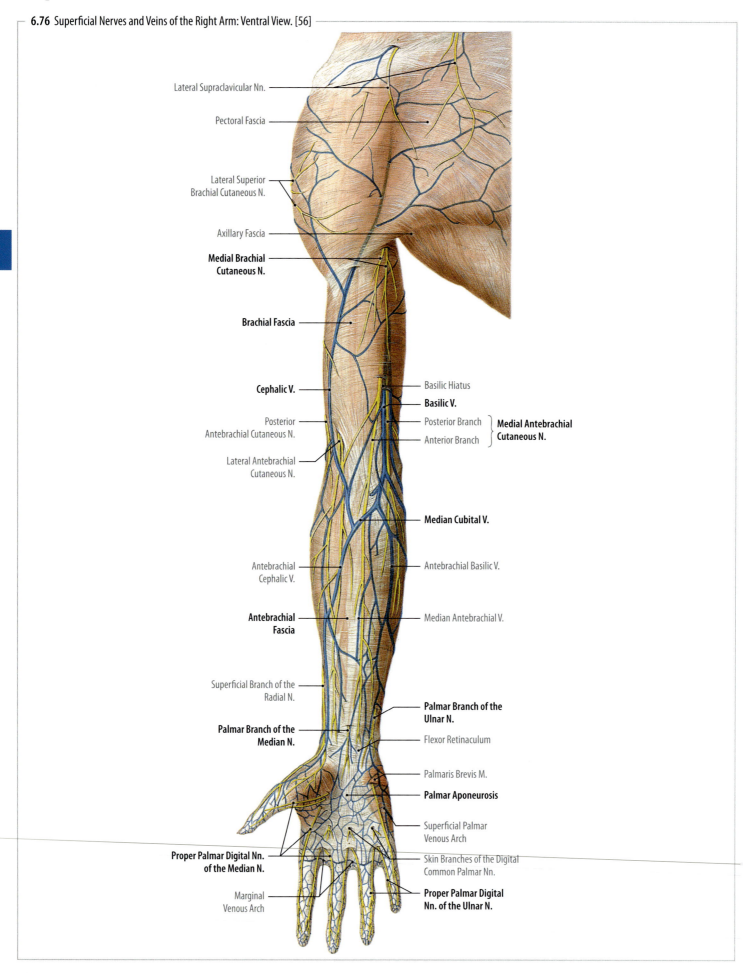

Lateral Supraclavicular Nn.

Pectoral Fascia

Lateral Superior
Brachial Cutaneous N.

Axillary Fascia

**Medial Brachial
Cutaneous N.**

Brachial Fascia

Cephalic V.

Posterior
Antebrachial Cutaneous N.

Lateral Antebrachial
Cutaneous N.

Antebrachial
Cephalic V.

**Antebrachial
Fascia**

Superficial Branch of the
Radial N.

**Palmar Branch of the
Median N.**

Proper Palmar Digital Nn.
of the Median N.

Marginal
Venous Arch

Basilic Hiatus

Basilic V.

Posterior Branch } **Medial Antebrachial
Anterior Branch } Cutaneous N.**

Median Cubital V.

Antebrachial Basilic V.

Median Antebrachial V.

**Palmar Branch of the
Ulnar N.**

Flexor Retinaculum

Palmaris Brevis M.

Palmar Aponeurosis

Superficial Palmar
Venous Arch

Skin Branches of the Digital
Common Palmar Nn.

**Proper Palmar Digital
Nn. of the Ulnar N.**

Superficial Nerves and Veins

6.77 Superficial Nerves and Veins of the Right Arm: Dorsal View. [56]

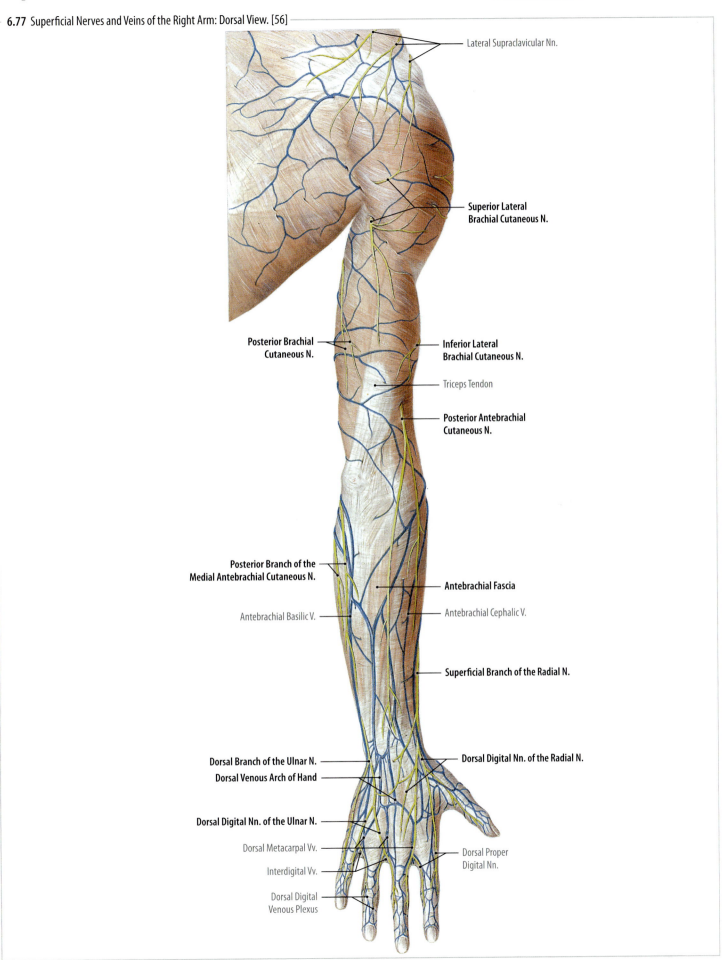

Lateral Supraclavicular Nn.

Superior Lateral
Brachial Cutaneous N.

Posterior Brachial
Cutaneous N.

Inferior Lateral
Brachial Cutaneous N.

Triceps Tendon

Posterior Antebrachial
Cutaneous N.

Posterior Branch of the
Medial Antebrachial Cutaneous N.

Antebrachial Fascia

Antebrachial Basilic V.

Antebrachial Cephalic V.

Superficial Branch of the Radial N.

Dorsal Branch of the Ulnar N.

Dorsal Digital Nn. of the Radial N.

Dorsal Venous Arch of Hand

Dorsal Digital Nn. of the Ulnar N.

Dorsal Metacarpal Vv.

Dorsal Proper
Digital Nn.

Interdigital Vv.

Dorsal Digital
Venous Plexus

Pathways and Topography

Sensory Supply, Dermatomes

6.78a,b Sensory Supply of the Skin and Segmental Classification. [65]

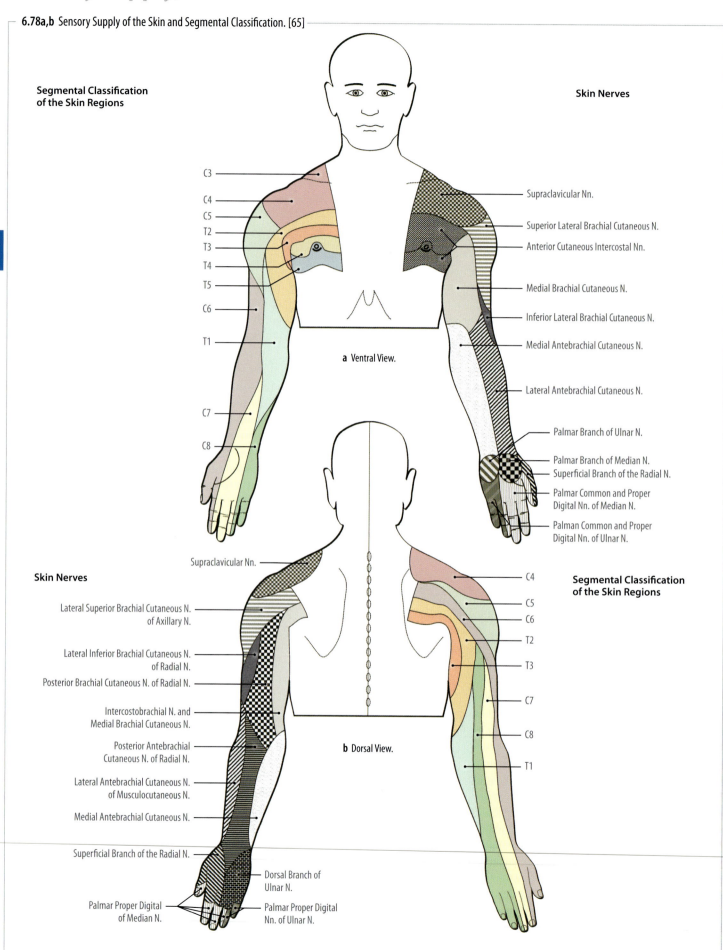

Segmental Classification of the Skin Regions

C3
C4
C5
T2
T3
T4
T5
C6
T1
C7
C8

Skin Nerves

Supraclavicular Nn.
Superior Lateral Brachial Cutaneous N.
Anterior Cutaneous Intercostal Nn.
Medial Brachial Cutaneous N.
Inferior Lateral Brachial Cutaneous N.
Medial Antebrachial Cutaneous N.
Lateral Antebrachial Cutaneous N.
Palmar Branch of Ulnar N.
Palmar Branch of Median N.
Superficial Branch of the Radial N.
Palmar Common and Proper Digital Nn. of Median N.
Palman Common and Proper Digital Nn. of Ulnar N.

a Ventral View.

Skin Nerves

Supraclavicular Nn.

Lateral Superior Brachial Cutaneous N. of Axillary N.

Lateral Inferior Brachial Cutaneous N. of Radial N.

Posterior Brachial Cutaneous N. of Radial N.

Intercostobrachial N. and Medial Brachial Cutaneous N.

Posterior Antebrachial Cutaneous N. of Radial N.

Lateral Antebrachial Cutaneous N. of Musculocutaneous N.

Medial Antebrachial Cutaneous N.

Superficial Branch of the Radial N.

Palmar Proper Digital of Median N.

Dorsal Branch of Ulnar N.

Palmar Proper Digital Nn. of Ulnar N.

b Dorsal View.

Segmental Classification of the Skin Regions

C4
C5
C6
T2
T3
C7
C8
T1

6

Axilla: Pathways

6.79 Epifascial Pathways and Lymph Nodes of the Right Armpit: Lateral View. [56]

The Axilla is a Square-Based Pyramid with a Truncated Apex. It has Four Walls:
1: The Anterior (Pectoral) Wall
2: Medially is the Lateral Thoracic Wall for the Superior 5 Intercostal Space
3: The Posterior Wall of the Ventral Surface of the Scapula with Muscle Attached Laterally
4: The Lateral Wall is a Narrow Short Wall of Humerus.
The Base is formed by the Skin of the Armpit Attached by Fascia extending Through the Anterior Wall to the Clavicle.

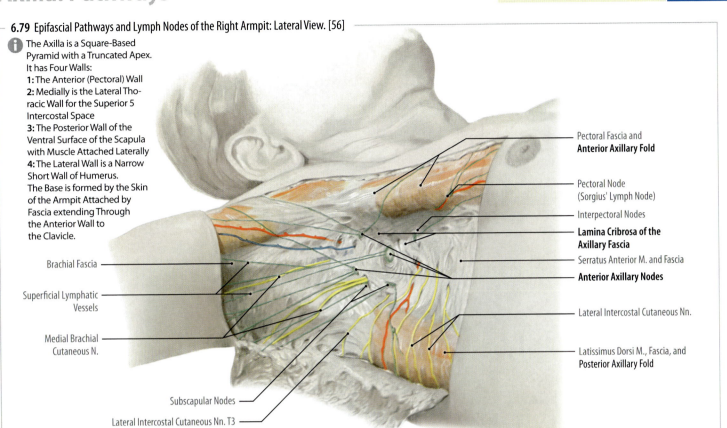

Pectoral Fascia and **Anterior Axillary Fold**

Pectoral Node (Sorgius' Lymph Node)

Interpectoral Nodes

Lamina Cribrosa of the Axillary Fascia

Serratus Anterior M. and Fascia

Anterior Axillary Nodes

Lateral Intercostal Cutaneous Nn.

Latissimus Dorsi M., Fascia, and **Posterior Axillary Fold**

Brachial Fascia

Superficial Lymphatic Vessels

Medial Brachial Cutaneous N.

Subscapular Nodes

Lateral Intercostal Cutaneous Nn. T3

6.80 Fascias and Pathways of the Right Armpit: Ventral View. [15]

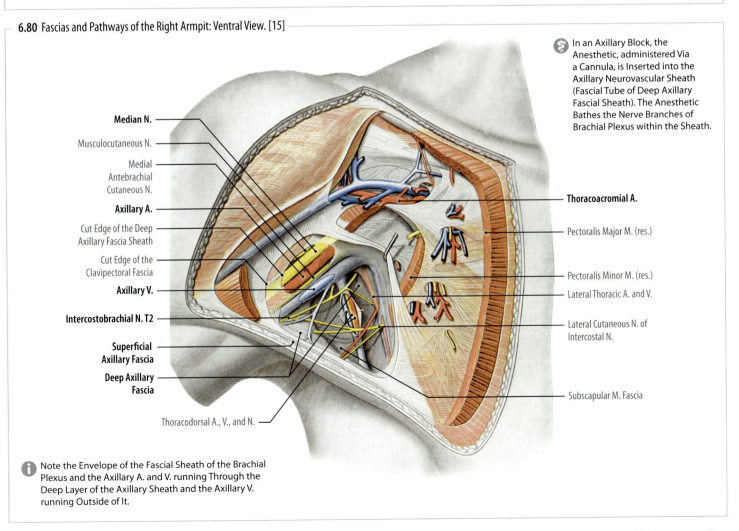

In an Axillary Block, the Anesthetic, administered Via a Cannula, is Inserted into the Axillary Neurovascular Sheath (Fascial Tube of Deep Axillary Fascial Sheath). The Anesthetic Bathes the Nerve Branches of Brachial Plexus within the Sheath.

Median N.

Musculocutaneous N.

Medial Antebrachial Cutaneous N.

Axillary A.

Cut Edge of the Deep Axillary Fascia Sheath

Cut Edge of the Clavipectoral Fascia

Axillary V.

Intercostobrachial N. T2

Superficial Axillary Fascia

Deep Axillary Fascia

Thoracodorsal A., V., and N.

Thoracoacromial A.

Pectoralis Major M. (res.)

Pectoralis Minor M. (res.)

Lateral Thoracic A. and V.

Lateral Cutaneous N. of Intercostal N.

Subscapular M. Fascia

Note the Envelope of the Fascial Sheath of the Brachial Plexus and the Axillary A. and V. running Through the Deep Layer of the Axillary Sheath and the Axillary V. running Outside of It.

Pathways and Topography

6.81 Pathways and Lymph Nodes of a Right Axilla: Anterolateral View. [56]

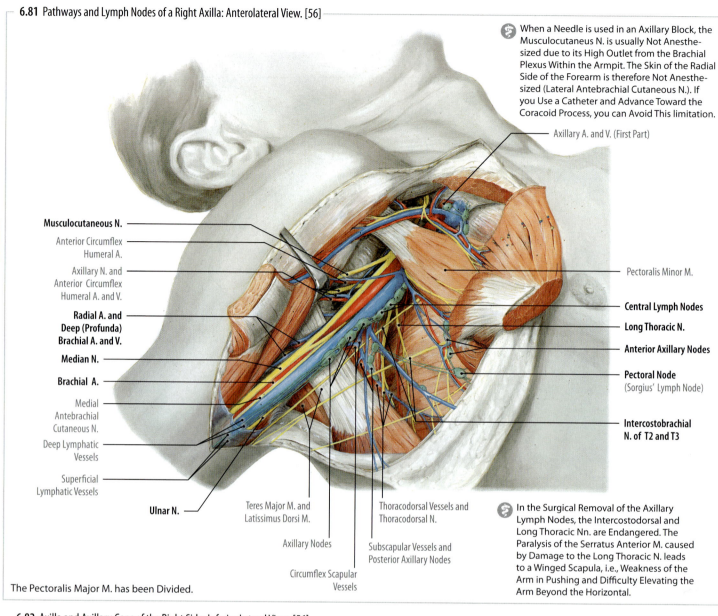

When a Needle is used in an Axillary Block, the Musculocutaneus N. is usually Not Anesthesized due to its High Outlet from the Brachial Plexus Within the Armpit. The Skin of the Radial Side of the Forearm is therefore Not Anesthesized (Lateral Antebrachial Cutaneous N.). If you Use a Catheter and Advance Toward the Coracoid Process, you can Avoid This limitation.

Axillary A. and V. (First Part)

Musculocutaneous N.

Anterior Circumflex Humeral A.

Axillary N. and Anterior Circumflex Humeral A. and V.

Radial A. and Deep (Profunda) Brachial A. and V.

Median N.

Brachial A.

Medial Antebrachial Cutaneous N.

Deep Lymphatic Vessels

Superficial Lymphatic Vessels

Ulnar N.

Teres Major M. and Latissimus Dorsi M.

Axillary Nodes

Subscapular Vessels and Posterior Axillary Nodes

Circumflex Scapular Vessels

Thoracodorsal Vessels and Thoracodorsal N.

Pectoralis Minor M.

Central Lymph Nodes

Long Thoracic N.

Anterior Axillary Nodes

Pectoral Node (Sorgius' Lymph Node)

Intercostobrachial N. of T2 and T3

In the Surgical Removal of the Axillary Lymph Nodes, the Intercostodorsal and Long Thoracic Nn. are Endangered. The Paralysis of the Serratus Anterior M. caused by Damage to the Long Thoracic N. leads to a Winged Scapula, i.e., Weakness of the Arm in Pushing and Difficulty Elevating the Arm Beyond the Horizontal.

The Pectoralis Major M. has been Divided.

6.82 Axilla and Axillary Gaps of the Right Side: Inferior Lateral View. [56]

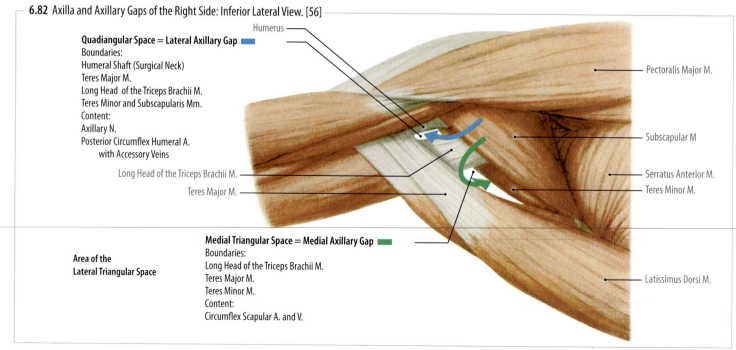

Humerus

Quadiangular Space = Lateral Axillary Gap
Boundaries:
Humeral Shaft (Surgical Neck)
Teres Major M.
Long Head of the Triceps Brachii M.
Teres Minor and Subscapularis Mm.
Content:
Axillary N.
Posterior Circumflex Humeral A.
   with Accessory Veins

Long Head of the Triceps Brachii M.

Teres Major M.

Pectoralis Major M.

Subscapular M

Serratus Anterior M.

Teres Minor M.

Latissimus Dorsi M.

Area of the Lateral Triangular Space

Medial Triangular Space = Medial Axillary Gap
Boundaries:
Long Head of the Triceps Brachii M.
Teres Major M.
Teres Minor M.
Content:
Circumflex Scapular A. and V.

6.83 Axillary N. and Posterior Circumflex Humeral Vessels of the Right Shoulder: Lateral View. [56]

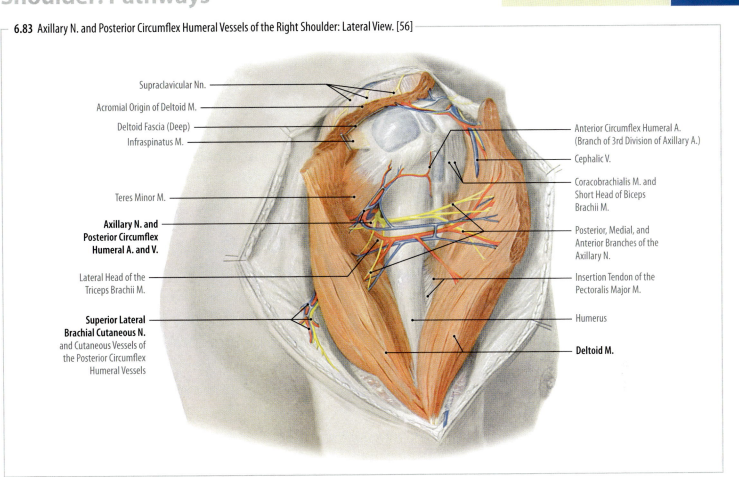

Supraclavicular Nn.

Acromial Origin of Deltoid M.

Deltoid Fascia (Deep)

Infraspinatus M.

Teres Minor M.

Axillary N. and Posterior Circumflex Humeral A. and V.

Lateral Head of the Triceps Brachii M.

Superior Lateral Brachial Cutaneous N. and Cutaneous Vessels of the Posterior Circumflex Humeral Vessels

Anterior Circumflex Humeral A. (Branch of 3rd Division of Axillary A.)

Cephalic V.

Coracobrachialis M. and Short Head of Biceps Brachii M.

Posterior, Medial, and Anterior Branches of the Axillary N.

Insertion Tendon of the Pectoralis Major M.

Humerus

Deltoid M.

6.84 Pathways of the Deep Shoulder Region, the Axilla and the Clavi- (Delto-) Pectoral Trigone (Mohrenheim's Fossa) of the Right Shoulder: Lateral View. [56]

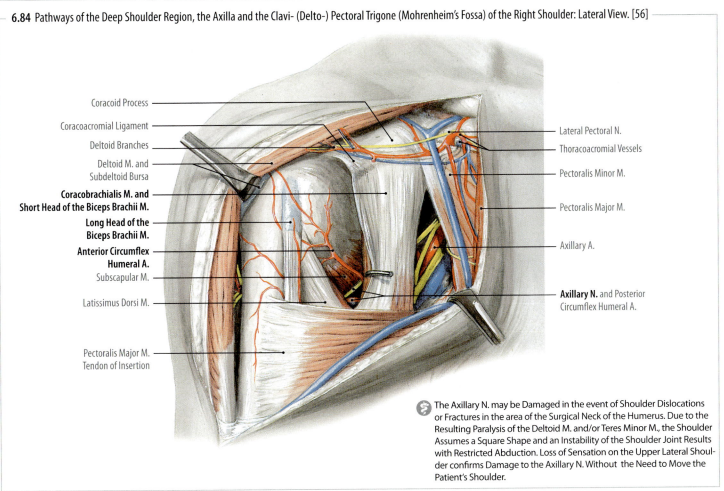

Coracoid Process

Coracoacromial Ligament

Deltoid Branches

Deltoid M. and Subdeltoid Bursa

Coracobrachialis M. and Short Head of the Biceps Brachii M.

Long Head of the Biceps Brachii M.

Anterior Circumflex Humeral A.

Subscapular M.

Latissimus Dorsi M.

Pectoralis Major M. Tendon of Insertion

Lateral Pectoral N.

Thoracoacromial Vessels

Pectoralis Minor M.

Pectoralis Major M.

Axillary A.

Axillary N. and Posterior Circumflex Humeral A.

The Axillary N. may be Damaged in the event of Shoulder Dislocations or Fractures in the area of the Surgical Neck of the Humerus. Due to the Resulting Paralysis of the Deltoid M. and/or Teres Minor M., the Shoulder Assumes a Square Shape and an Instability of the Shoulder Joint Results with Restricted Abduction. Loss of Sensation on the Upper Lateral Shoulder confirms Damage to the Axillary N. Without the Need to Move the Patient's Shoulder.

Pathways and Topography

6.85 Muscles and Pathways of the Right Shoulder: Dorsal View. [1]

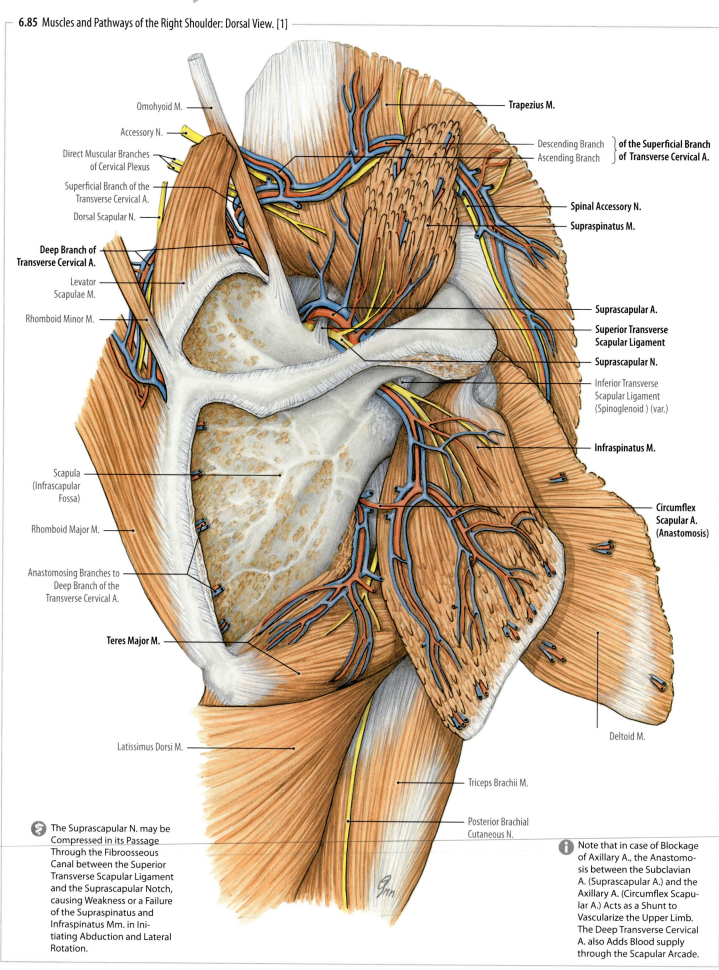

Omohyoid M.

Accessory N.

Direct Muscular Branches of Cervical Plexus

Superficial Branch of the Transverse Cervical A.

Dorsal Scapular N.

Deep Branch of Transverse Cervical A.

Levator Scapulae M.

Rhomboid Minor M.

Scapula (Infrascapular Fossa)

Rhomboid Major M.

Anastomosing Branches to Deep Branch of the Transverse Cervical A.

Teres Major M.

Latissimus Dorsi M.

Trapezius M.

Descending Branch } **of the Superficial Branch**
Ascending Branch } **of Transverse Cervical A.**

Spinal Accessory N.

Supraspinatus M.

Suprascapular A.

Superior Transverse Scapular Ligament

Suprascapular N.

Inferior Transverse Scapular Ligament (Spinoglenoid) (var.)

Infraspinatus M.

Circumflex Scapular A. (Anastomosis)

Deltoid M.

Triceps Brachii M.

Posterior Brachial Cutaneous N.

The Suprascapular N. may be Compressed in its Passage Through the Fibroosseous Canal between the Superior Transverse Scapular Ligament and the Suprascapular Notch, causing Weakness or a Failure of the Supraspinatus and Infraspinatus Mm. in Initiating Abduction and Lateral Rotation.

Note that in case of Blockage of Axillary A., the Anastomosis between the Subclavian A. (Suprascapular A.) and the Axillary A. (Circumflex Scapular A.) Acts as a Shunt to Vascularize the Upper Limb. The Deep Transverse Cervical A. also Adds Blood supply through the Scapular Arcade.

6.86 Shoulder Region and Upper Arm: Right Side, Dorsal View. [8]

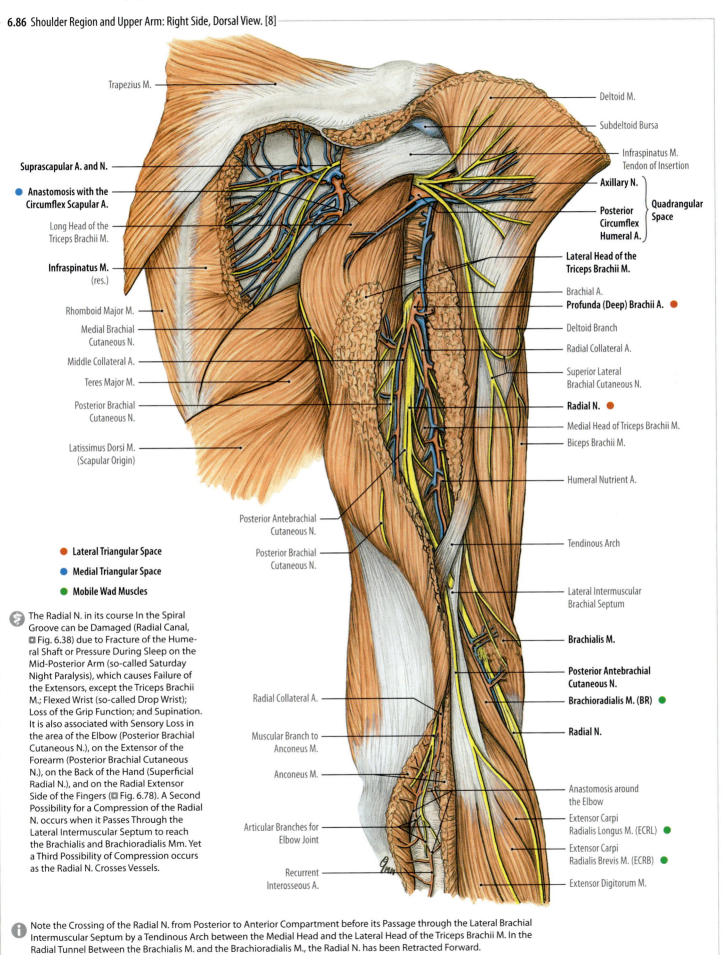

Trapezius M.

Deltoid M.

Subdeltoid Bursa

Infraspinatus M.
Tendon of Insertion

Suprascapular A. and N.

● **Anastomosis with the
Circumflex Scapular A.**

Axillary N.

**Posterior
Circumflex
Humeral A.**

} Quadrangular
Space

Long Head of the
Triceps Brachii M.

**Lateral Head of the
Triceps Brachii M.**

Infraspinatus M.
(res.)

Brachial A.

Profunda (Deep) Brachii A. ●

Rhomboid Major M.

Deltoid Branch

Medial Brachial
Cutaneous N.

Radial Collateral A.

Middle Collateral A.

Superior Lateral
Brachial Cutaneous N.

Teres Major M.

Radial N. ●

Posterior Brachial
Cutaneous N.

Medial Head of Triceps Brachii M.

Biceps Brachii M.

Latissimus Dorsi M.
(Scapular Origin)

Humeral Nutrient A.

Posterior Antebrachial
Cutaneous N.

Tendinous Arch

Posterior Brachial
Cutaneous N.

● **Lateral Triangular Space**

● **Medial Triangular Space**

● **Mobile Wad Muscles**

Lateral Intermuscular
Brachial Septum

Brachialis M.

The Radial N. in its course In the Spiral
Groove can be Damaged (Radial Canal,
☐ Fig. 6.38) due to Fracture of the Hume-
ral Shaft or Pressure During Sleep on the
Mid-Posterior Arm (so-called Saturday
Night Paralysis), which causes Failure of
the Extensors, except the Triceps Brachii
M.; Flexed Wrist (so-called Drop Wrist);
Loss of the Grip Function; and Supination.
It is also associated with Sensory Loss in
the area of the Elbow (Posterior Brachial
Cutaneous N.), on the Extensor of the
Forearm (Posterior Brachial Cutaneous
N.), on the Back of the Hand (Superficial
Radial N.), and on the Radial Extensor
Side of the Fingers (☐ Fig. 6.78). A Second
Possibility for a Compression of the Radial
N. occurs when it Passes Through the
Lateral Intermuscular Septum to reach
the Brachialis and Brachioradialis Mm. Yet
a Third Possibility of Compression occurs
as the Radial N. Crosses Vessels.

**Posterior Antebrachial
Cutaneous N.**

Brachioradialis M. (BR) ●

Radial Collateral A.

Radial N.

Muscular Branch to
Anconeus M.

Anconeus M.

Anastomosis around
the Elbow

Extensor Carpi
Radialis Longus M. (ECRL) ●

Articular Branches for
Elbow Joint

Extensor Carpi
Radialis Brevis M. (ECRB) ●

Recurrent
Interosseous A.

Extensor Digitorum M.

ℹ Note the Crossing of the Radial N. from Posterior to Anterior Compartment before its Passage through the Lateral Brachial
Intermuscular Septum by a Tendinous Arch between the Medial Head and the Lateral Head of the Triceps Brachii M. In the
Radial Tunnel Between the Brachialis M. and the Brachioradialis M., the Radial N. has been Retracted Forward.

Pathways and Topography

6.87 Muscles and Pathways on a Right Arm: Ventral View. [8]

6

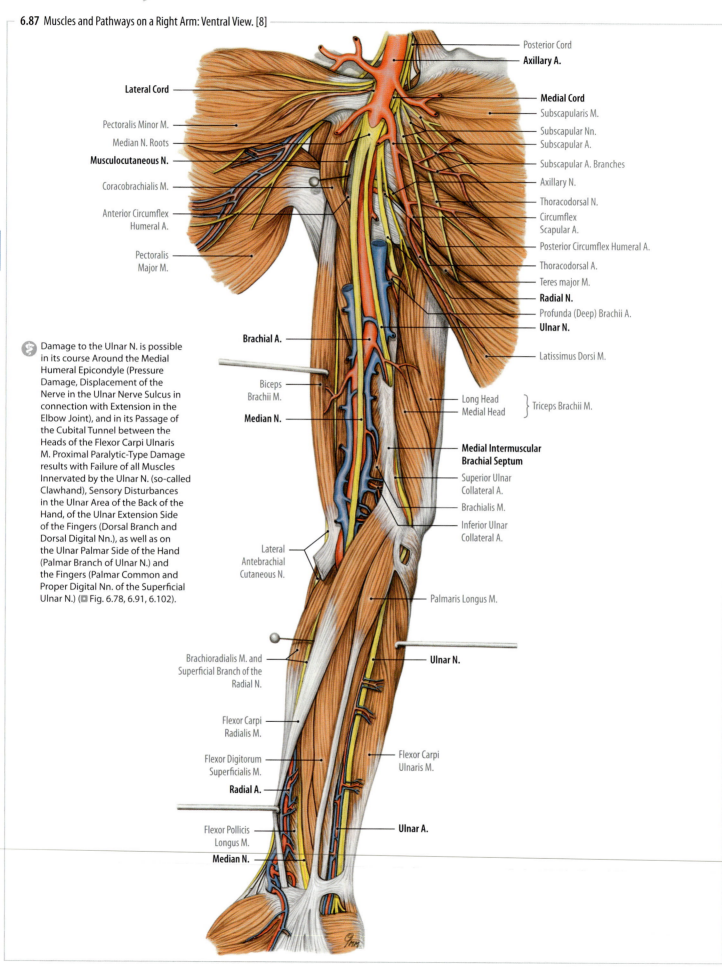

Posterior Cord

Axillary A.

Lateral Cord

Medial Cord

Pectoralis Minor M.

Subscapularis M.

Median N. Roots

Subscapular Nn.

Musculocutaneous N.

Subscapular A.

Coracobrachialis M.

Subscapular A. Branches

Anterior Circumflex Humeral A.

Axillary N.

Thoracodorsal N.

Circumflex Scapular A.

Pectoralis Major M.

Posterior Circumflex Humeral A.

Thoracodorsal A.

Teres major M.

Radial N.

Profunda (Deep) Brachii A.

Ulnar N.

Brachial A.

Latissimus Dorsi M.

Biceps Brachii M.

Long Head
Medial Head } Triceps Brachii M.

Median N.

Medial Intermuscular Brachial Septum

Superior Ulnar Collateral A.

Brachialis M.

Inferior Ulnar Collateral A.

Lateral Antebrachial Cutaneous N.

Palmaris Longus M.

Brachioradialis M. and Superficial Branch of the Radial N.

Ulnar N.

Flexor Carpi Radialis M.

Flexor Digitorum Superficialis M.

Flexor Carpi Ulnaris M.

Radial A.

Flexor Pollicis Longus M.

Ulnar A.

Median N.

Damage to the Ulnar N. is possible in its course Around the Medial Humeral Epicondyle (Pressure Damage, Displacement of the Nerve in the Ulnar Nerve Sulcus in connection with Extension in the Elbow Joint), and in its Passage of the Cubital Tunnel between the Heads of the Flexor Carpi Ulnaris M. Proximal Paralytic-Type Damage results with Failure of all Muscles Innervated by the Ulnar N. (so-called Clawhand), Sensory Disturbances in the Ulnar Area of the Back of the Hand, of the Ulnar Extension Side of the Fingers (Dorsal Branch and Dorsal Digital Nn.), as well as on the Ulnar Palmar Side of the Hand (Palmar Branch of Ulnar N.) and the Fingers (Palmar Common and Proper Digital Nn. of the Superficial Ulnar N.) (◨ Fig. 6.78, 6.91, 6.102).

6.88a,b Muscles and Pathways of the Right Upper Arm. [a 56, b 1]

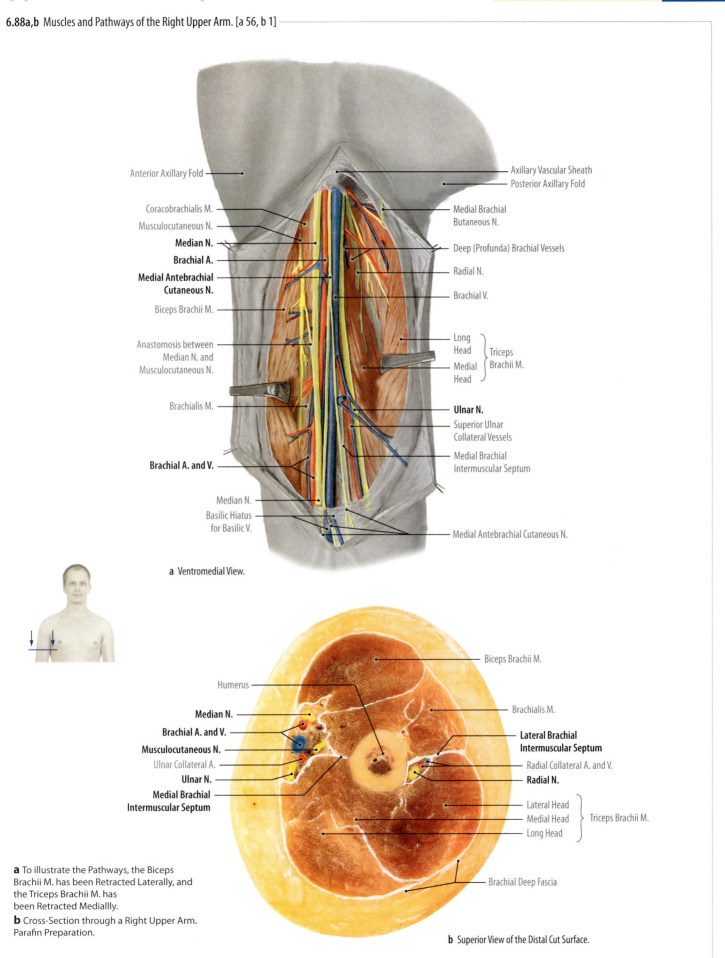

Anterior Axillary Fold

Coracobrachialis M.

Musculocutaneous N.

Median N.

Brachial A.

Medial Antebrachial Cutaneous N.

Biceps Brachii M.

Anastomosis between Median N. and Musculocutaneous N.

Brachialis M.

Brachial A. and V.

Median N.

Basilic Hiatus for Basilic V.

Axillary Vascular Sheath

Posterior Axillary Fold

Medial Brachial Butaneous N.

Deep (Profunda) Brachial Vessels

Radial N.

Brachial V.

Long Head } Triceps Brachii M.

Medial Head

Ulnar N.

Superior Ulnar Collateral Vessels

Medial Brachial Intermuscular Septum

Medial Antebrachial Cutaneous N.

a Ventromedial View.

Biceps Brachii M.

Humerus

Median N.

Brachial A. and V.

Musculocutaneous N.

Ulnar Collateral A.

Ulnar N.

Medial Brachial Intermuscular Septum

Brachialis M.

Lateral Brachial Intermuscular Septum

Radial Collateral A. and V.

Radial N.

Lateral Head

Medial Head } Triceps Brachii M.

Long Head

Brachial Deep Fascia

a To illustrate the Pathways, the Biceps Brachii M. has been Retracted Laterally, and the Triceps Brachii M. has been Retracted Mediallly.
b Cross-Section through a Right Upper Arm. Parafin Preparation.

b Superior View of the Distal Cut Surface.

Pathways and Topography

6.89 Arteries of the Forearm and the Hand: Ventral View. [13]

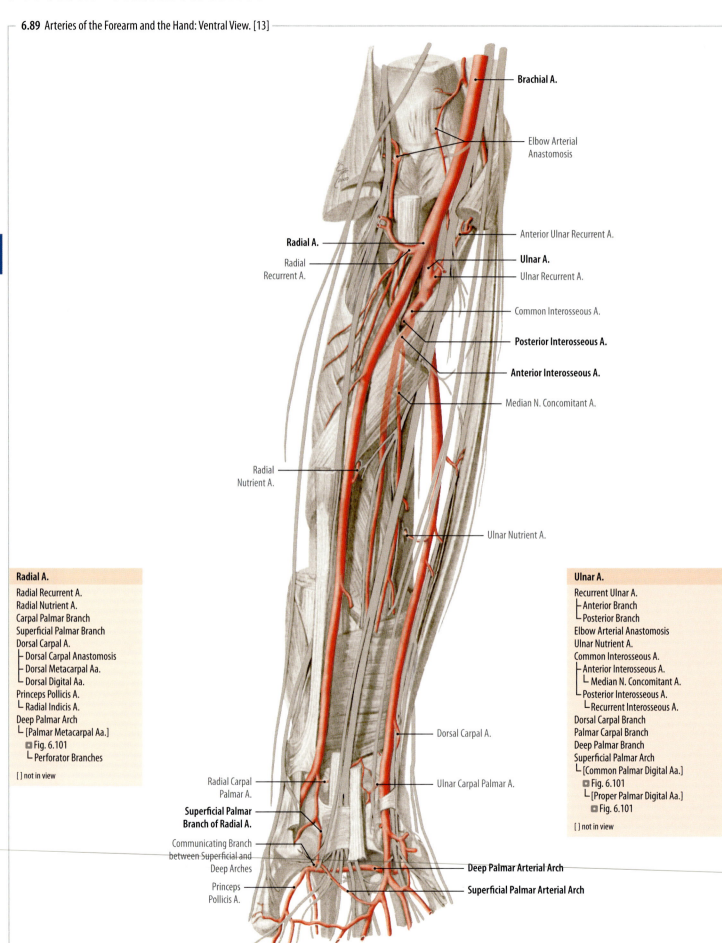

Brachial A.

Elbow Arterial Anastomosis

Radial A.

Anterior Ulnar Recurrent A.

Radial Recurrent A.

Ulnar A.

Ulnar Recurrent A.

Common Interosseous A.

Posterior Interosseous A.

Anterior Interosseous A.

Median N. Concomitant A.

Radial Nutrient A.

Ulnar Nutrient A.

Radial A.

Radial Recurrent A.
Radial Nutrient A.
Carpal Palmar Branch
Superficial Palmar Branch
Dorsal Carpal A.
├ Dorsal Carpal Anastomosis
├ Dorsal Metacarpal Aa.
└ Dorsal Digital Aa.
Princeps Pollicis A.
└ Radial Indicis A.
Deep Palmar Arch
└ [Palmar Metacarpal Aa.]
　▣ Fig. 6.101
　└ Perforator Branches

[ ] not in view

Ulnar A.

Recurrent Ulnar A.
├ Anterior Branch
└ Posterior Branch
Elbow Arterial Anastomosis
Ulnar Nutrient A.
Common Interosseous A.
├ Anterior Interosseous A.
│ └ Median N. Concomitant A.
└ Posterior Interosseous A.
　└ Recurrent Interosseous A.
Dorsal Carpal Branch
Palmar Carpal Branch
Deep Palmar Branch
Superficial Palmar Arch
└ [Common Palmar Digital Aa.]
　▣ Fig. 6.101
　└ [Proper Palmar Digital Aa.]
　　▣ Fig. 6.101

[ ] not in view

Dorsal Carpal A.

Radial Carpal Palmar A.

Ulnar Carpal Palmar A.

Superficial Palmar Branch of Radial A.

Communicating Branch between Superficial and Deep Arches

Deep Palmar Arterial Arch

Princeps Pollicis A.

Superficial Palmar Arterial Arch

6.90 Arteries of the Forearm and the Hand: Dorsal View. [13]

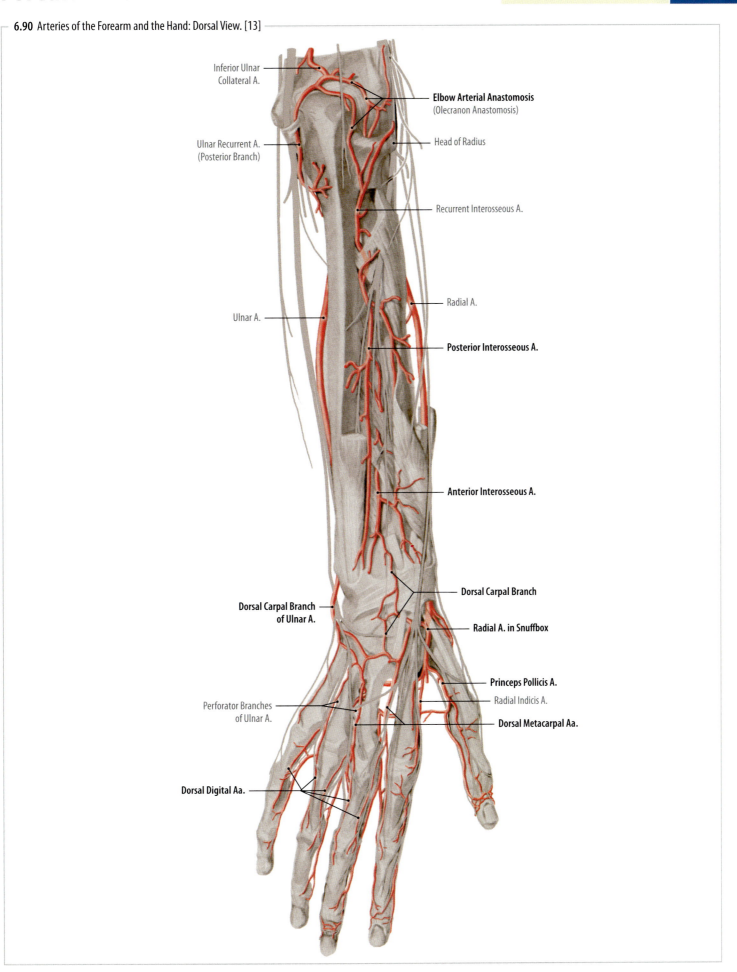

Inferior Ulnar Collateral A.

Elbow Arterial Anastomosis (Olecranon Anastomosis)

Head of Radius

Ulnar Recurrent A. (Posterior Branch)

Recurrent Interosseous A.

Radial A.

Ulnar A.

Posterior Interosseous A.

Anterior Interosseous A.

Dorsal Carpal Branch

Dorsal Carpal Branch of Ulnar A.

Radial A. in Snuffbox

Princeps Pollicis A.

Radial Indicis A.

Perforator Branches of Ulnar A.

Dorsal Metacarpal Aa.

Dorsal Digital Aa.

6.91 Nerves of the Forearm and the Hand: Ventral View. [13]

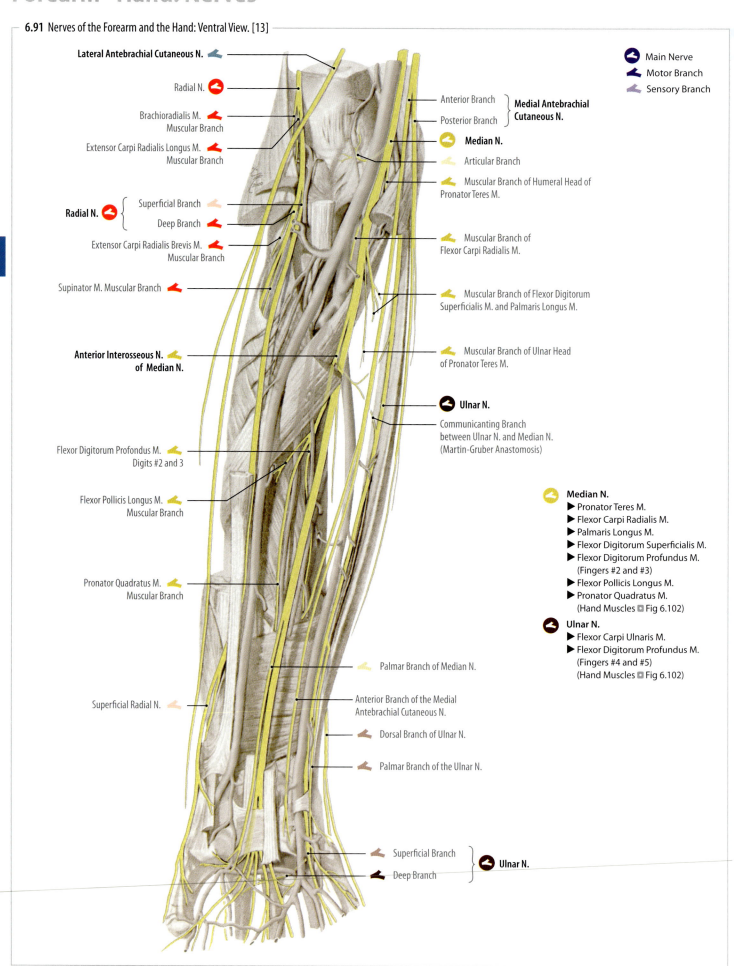

Lateral Antebrachial Cutaneous N.

Radial N.

Brachioradialis M.
Muscular Branch

Extensor Carpi Radialis Longus M.
Muscular Branch

Radial N.
— Superficial Branch
— Deep Branch

Extensor Carpi Radialis Brevis M.
Muscular Branch

Supinator M. Muscular Branch

Anterior Interosseous N.
of Median N.

Flexor Digitorum Profondus M.
Digits #2 and 3

Flexor Pollicis Longus M.
Muscular Branch

Pronator Quadratus M.
Muscular Branch

Superficial Radial N.

Main Nerve
Motor Branch
Sensory Branch

Anterior Branch
Posterior Branch
} Medial Antebrachial
Cutaneous N.

Median N.

Articular Branch

Muscular Branch of Humeral Head of
Pronator Teres M.

Muscular Branch of
Flexor Carpi Radialis M.

Muscular Branch of Flexor Digitorum
Superficialis M. and Palmaris Longus M.

Muscular Branch of Ulnar Head
of Pronator Teres M.

Ulnar N.

Communicating Branch
between Ulnar N. and Median N.
(Martin-Gruber Anastomosis)

Median N.
► Pronator Teres M.
► Flexor Carpi Radialis M.
► Palmaris Longus M.
► Flexor Digitorum Superficialis M.
► Flexor Digitorum Profundus M.
   (Fingers #2 and #3)
► Flexor Pollicis Longus M.
► Pronator Quadratus M.
   (Hand Muscles ▣ Fig 6.102)

Ulnar N.
► Flexor Carpi Ulnaris M.
► Flexor Digitorum Profundus M.
   (Fingers #4 and #5)
   (Hand Muscles ▣ Fig 6.102)

Palmar Branch of Median N.

Anterior Branch of the Medial
Antebrachial Cutaneous N.

Dorsal Branch of Ulnar N.

Palmar Branch of the Ulnar N.

Superficial Branch
Deep Branch
} Ulnar N.

6

6.92 Nerves of the Forearm and the Hand: Dorsal View. [13]

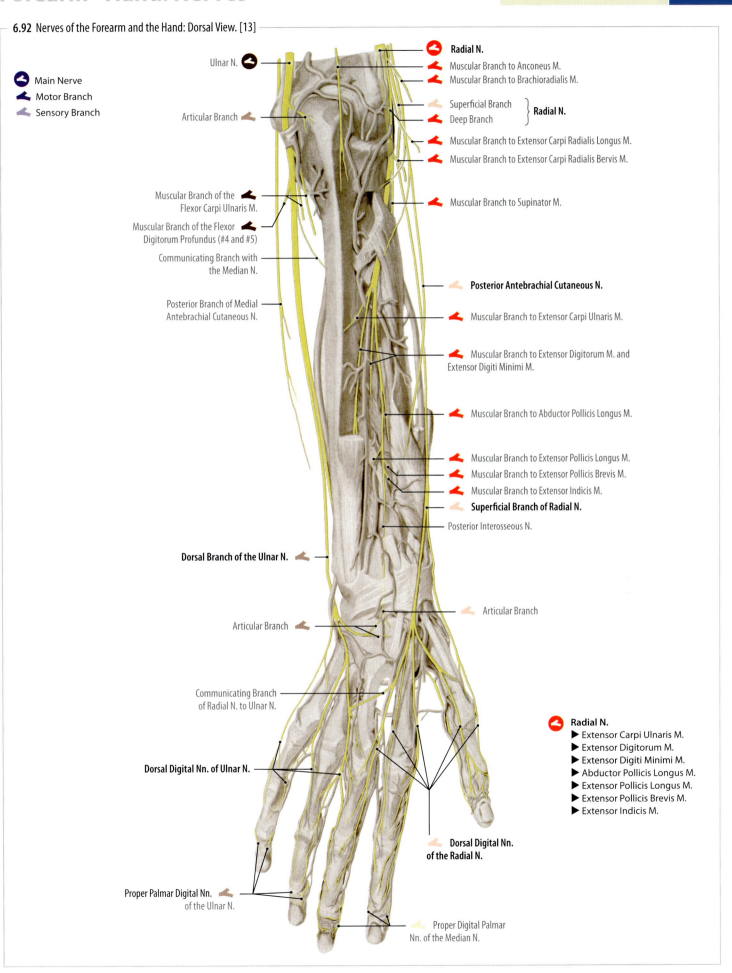

Main Nerve
Motor Branch
Sensory Branch

Ulnar N.

Articular Branch

Muscular Branch of the
Flexor Carpi Ulnaris M.

Muscular Branch of the Flexor
Digitorum Profundus (#4 and #5)

Communicating Branch with
the Median N.

Posterior Branch of Medial
Antebrachial Cutaneous N.

Radial N.
Muscular Branch to Anconeus M.
Muscular Branch to Brachioradialis M.

Superficial Branch
Deep Branch } **Radial N.**

Muscular Branch to Extensor Carpi Radialis Longus M.
Muscular Branch to Extensor Carpi Radialis Bervis M.

Muscular Branch to Supinator M.

Posterior Antebrachial Cutaneous N.

Muscular Branch to Extensor Carpi Ulnaris M.

Muscular Branch to Extensor Digitorum M. and
Extensor Digiti Minimi M.

Muscular Branch to Abductor Pollicis Longus M.

Muscular Branch to Extensor Pollicis Longus M.
Muscular Branch to Extensor Pollicis Brevis M.
Muscular Branch to Extensor Indicis M.

Superficial Branch of Radial N.

Posterior Interosseous N.

Dorsal Branch of the Ulnar N.

Articular Branch

Articular Branch

Communicating Branch
of Radial N. to Ulnar N.

Radial N.
▶ Extensor Carpi Ulnaris M.
▶ Extensor Digitorum M.
▶ Extensor Digiti Minimi M.
▶ Abductor Pollicis Longus M.
▶ Extensor Pollicis Longus M.
▶ Extensor Pollicis Brevis M.
▶ Extensor Indicis M.

Dorsal Digital Nn. of Ulnar N.

**Dorsal Digital Nn.
of the Radial N.**

Proper Palmar Digital Nn.
of the Ulnar N.

Proper Digital Palmar
Nn. of the Median N.

Pathways and Topography

6.93a,b Pathways of the Elbow Region (Cubital Fossa): Right Side, Ventral View. [56]

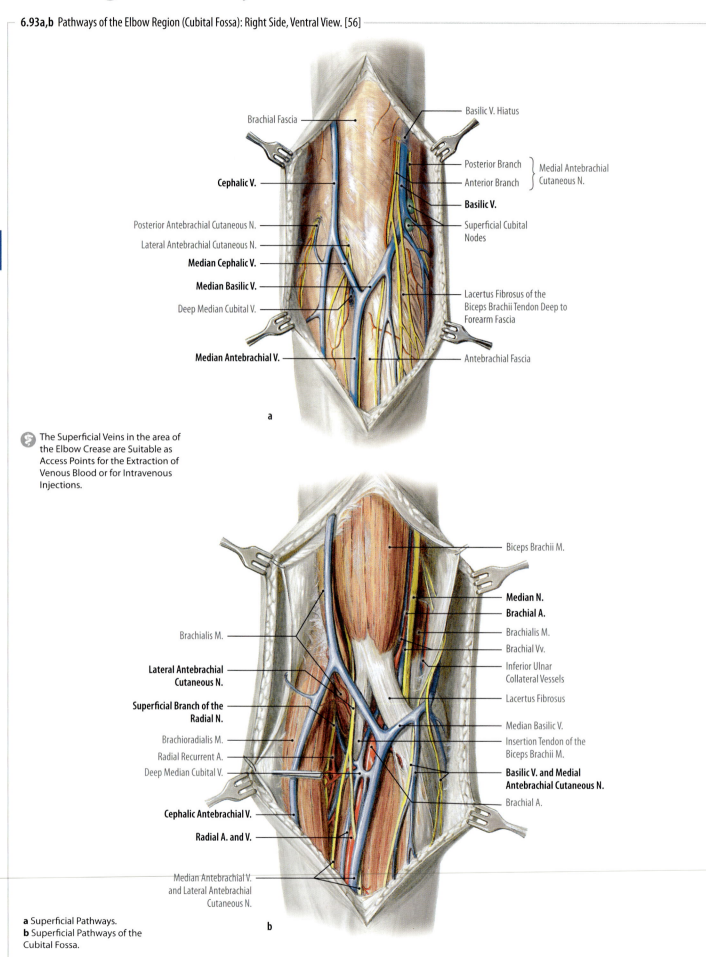

Brachial Fascia

Basilic V. Hiatus

Cephalic V.

Posterior Branch ⎫ Medial Antebrachial
Anterior Branch ⎭ Cutaneous N.

Basilic V.

Posterior Antebrachial Cutaneous N.

Superficial Cubital Nodes

Lateral Antebrachial Cutaneous N.

Median Cephalic V.

Median Basilic V.

Deep Median Cubital V.

Lacertus Fibrosus of the Biceps Brachii Tendon Deep to Forearm Fascia

Median Antebrachial V.

Antebrachial Fascia

a

The Superficial Veins in the area of the Elbow Crease are Suitable as Access Points for the Extraction of Venous Blood or for Intravenous Injections.

Biceps Brachii M.

Median N.

Brachial A.

Brachialis M.

Brachialis M.

Lateral Antebrachial Cutaneous N.

Brachial Vv.

Inferior Ulnar Collateral Vessels

Superficial Branch of the Radial N.

Lacertus Fibrosus

Brachioradialis M.

Median Basilic V.

Radial Recurrent A.

Insertion Tendon of the Biceps Brachii M.

Deep Median Cubital V.

Basilic V. and Medial Antebrachial Cutaneous N.

Cephalic Antebrachial V.

Brachial A.

Radial A. and V.

Median Antebrachial V. and Lateral Antebrachial Cutaneous N.

b

a Superficial Pathways.
b Superficial Pathways of the Cubital Fossa.

Elbow Crease: Deep Pathways

6.94 Deep Pathways of the Right Cubital Fossa: Ventral View. [56]

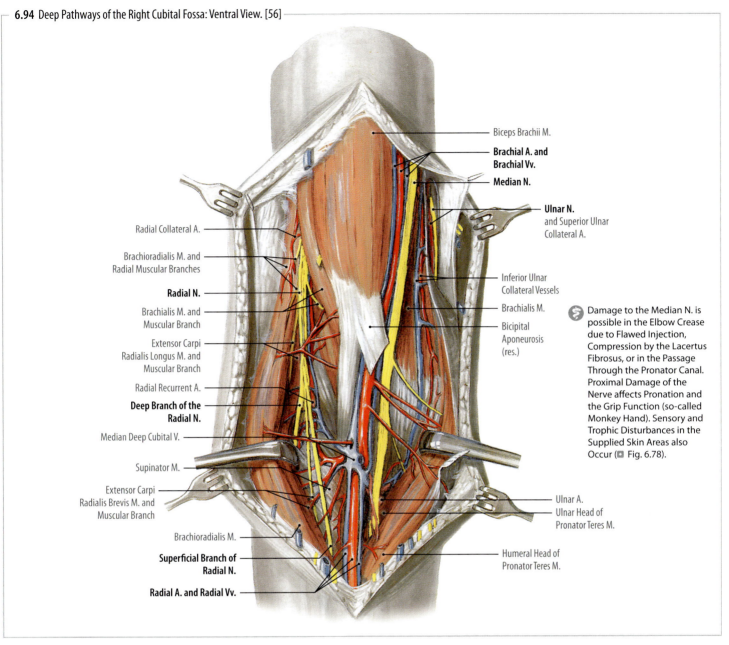

Radial Collateral A.

Brachioradialis M. and
Radial Muscular Branches

Radial N.

Brachialis M. and
Muscular Branch

Extensor Carpi
Radialis Longus M. and
Muscular Branch

Radial Recurrent A.

**Deep Branch of the
Radial N.**

Median Deep Cubital V.

Supinator M.

Extensor Carpi
Radialis Brevis M. and
Muscular Branch

Brachioradialis M.

**Superficial Branch of
Radial N.**

Radial A. and Radial Vv.

Biceps Brachii M.

**Brachial A. and
Brachial Vv.**

Median N.

Ulnar N.
and Superior Ulnar
Collateral A.

Inferior Ulnar
Collateral Vessels

Brachialis M.

Bicipital
Aponeurosis
(res.)

Ulnar A.

Ulnar Head of
Pronator Teres M.

Humeral Head of
Pronator Teres M.

Damage to the Median N. is
possible in the Elbow Crease
due to Flawed Injection,
Compression by the Lacertus
Fibrosus, or in the Passage
Through the Pronator Canal.
Proximal Damage of the
Nerve affects Pronation and
the Grip Function (so-called
Monkey Hand). Sensory and
Trophic Disturbances in the
Supplied Skin Areas also
Occur (Fig. 6.78).

6.95 Arteries of the Elbow Region: Ventral View. [15]

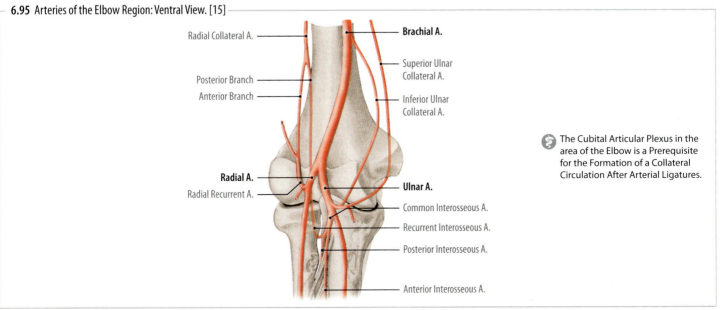

Radial Collateral A.

Posterior Branch

Anterior Branch

Radial A.
Radial Recurrent A.

Brachial A.

Superior Ulnar
Collateral A.

Inferior Ulnar
Collateral A.

Ulnar A.

Common Interosseous A.

Recurrent Interosseous A.

Posterior Interosseous A.

Anterior Interosseous A.

The Cubital Articular Plexus in the
area of the Elbow is a Prerequisite
for the Formation of a Collateral
Circulation After Arterial Ligatures.

Pathways and Topography

6.96 Muscles and Pathways of the Back of the Right Forearm (Posterior Antebrachial Region). [8]

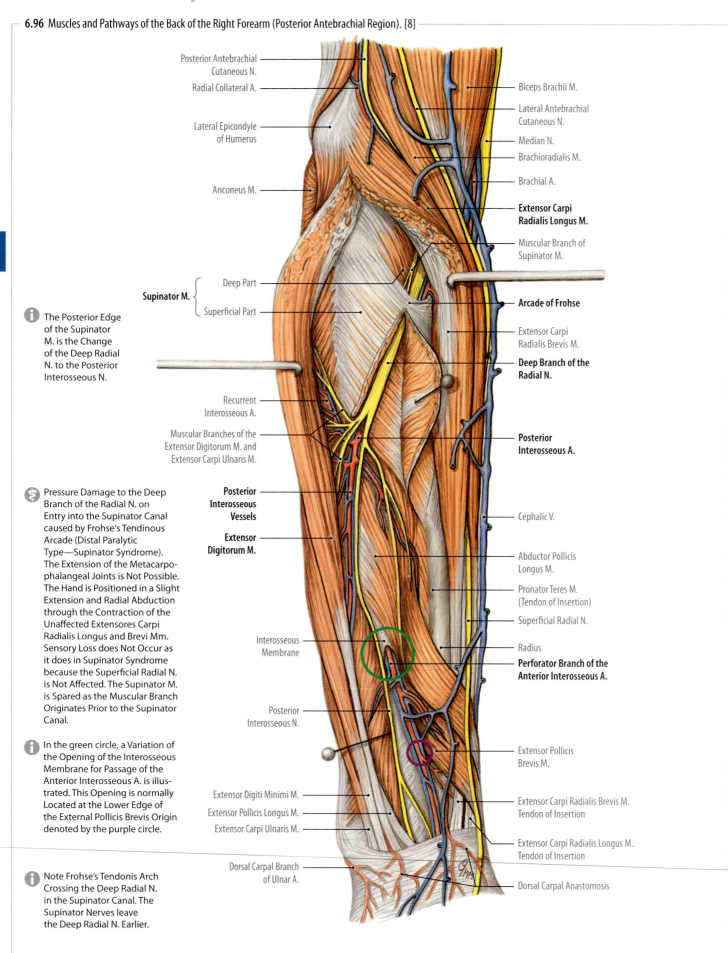

Posterior Antebrachial Cutaneous N.

Radial Collateral A.

Lateral Epicondyle of Humerus

Anconeus M.

Supinator M. {
Deep Part
Superficial Part
}

Recurrent Interosseous A.

Muscular Branches of the Extensor Digitorum M. and Extensor Carpi Ulnaris M.

Posterior Interosseous Vessels

Extensor Digitorum M.

Interosseous Membrane

Posterior Interosseous N.

Extensor Digiti Minimi M.

Extensor Pollicis Longus M.

Extensor Carpi Ulnaris M.

Dorsal Carpal Branch of Ulnar A.

Biceps Brachii M.

Lateral Antebrachial Cutaneous N.

Median N.

Brachioradialis M.

Brachial A.

Extensor Carpi Radialis Longus M.

Muscular Branch of Supinator M.

Arcade of Frohse

Extensor Carpi Radialis Brevis M.

Deep Branch of the Radial N.

Posterior Interosseous A.

Cephalic V.

Abductor Pollicis Longus M.

Pronator Teres M. (Tendon of Insertion)

Superficial Radial N.

Radius

Perforator Branch of the Anterior Interosseous A.

Extensor Pollicis Brevis M.

Extensor Carpi Radialis Brevis M. Tendon of Insertion

Extensor Carpi Radialis Longus M. Tendon of Insertion

Dorsal Carpal Anastomosis

ⓘ The Posterior Edge of the Supinator M. is the Change of the Deep Radial N. to the Posterior Interosseous N.

🔄 Pressure Damage to the Deep Branch of the Radial N. on Entry into the Supinator Canal caused by Frohse's Tendinous Arcade (Distal Paralytic Type—Supinator Syndrome). The Extension of the Metacarpophalangeal Joints is Not Possible. The Hand is Positioned in a Slight Extension and Radial Abduction through the Contraction of the Unaffected Extensores Carpi Radialis Longus and Brevi Mm. Sensory Loss does Not Occur as it does in Supinator Syndrome because the Superficial Radial N. is Not Affected. The Supinator M. is Spared as the Muscular Branch Originates Prior to the Supinator Canal.

ⓘ In the green circle, a Variation of the Opening of the Interosseous Membrane for Passage of the Anterior Interosseous A. is illustrated. This Opening is normally Located at the Lower Edge of the External Pollicis Brevis Origin denoted by the purple circle.

ⓘ Note Frohse's Tendonis Arch Crossing the Deep Radial N. in the Supinator Canal. The Supinator Nerves leave the Deep Radial N. Earlier.

6

Forearm: Pathways

6.97 Muscles and Pathways of the Flexor (Palmar) Side of a Right Forearm.

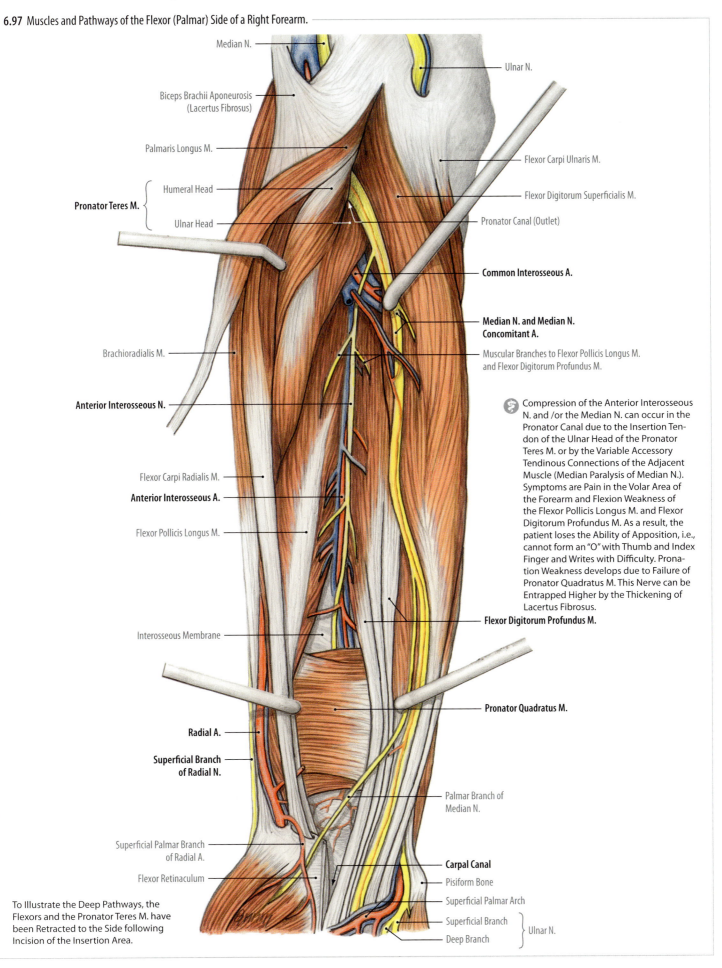

Median N.

Ulnar N.

Biceps Brachii Aponeurosis
(Lacertus Fibrosus)

Palmaris Longus M.

Flexor Carpi Ulnaris M.

Humeral Head

Flexor Digitorum Superficialis M.

Pronator Teres M.

Ulnar Head

Pronator Canal (Outlet)

Common Interosseous A.

**Median N. and Median N.
Concomitant A.**

Brachioradialis M.

Muscular Branches to Flexor Pollicis Longus M.
and Flexor Digitorum Profundus M.

Anterior Interosseous N.

Flexor Carpi Radialis M.

Anterior Interosseous A.

Flexor Pollicis Longus M.

Interosseous Membrane

Flexor Digitorum Profundus M.

Pronator Quadratus M.

Radial A.

**Superficial Branch
of Radial N.**

Palmar Branch of
Median N.

Superficial Palmar Branch
of Radial A.

Carpal Canal

Flexor Retinaculum

Pisiform Bone

Superficial Palmar Arch

Superficial Branch

Deep Branch

} Ulnar N.

Compression of the Anterior Interosseous N. and /or the Median N. can occur in the Pronator Canal due to the Insertion Tendon of the Ulnar Head of the Pronator Teres M. or by the Variable Accessory Tendinous Connections of the Adjacent Muscle (Median Paralysis of Median N.). Symptoms are Pain in the Volar Area of the Forearm and Flexion Weakness of the Flexor Pollicis Longus M. and Flexor Digitorum Profundus M. As a result, the patient loses the Ability of Apposition, i.e., cannot form an "O" with Thumb and Index Finger and Writes with Difficulty. Pronation Weakness develops due to Failure of Pronator Quadratus M. This Nerve can be Entrapped Higher by the Thickening of Lacertus Fibrosus.

To Illustrate the Deep Pathways, the Flexors and the Pronator Teres M. have been Retracted to the Side following Incision of the Insertion Area.

Pathways and Topography

6.98 Median N. and High Division of the Median N. on a Right Forearm: Ventral View. [6]

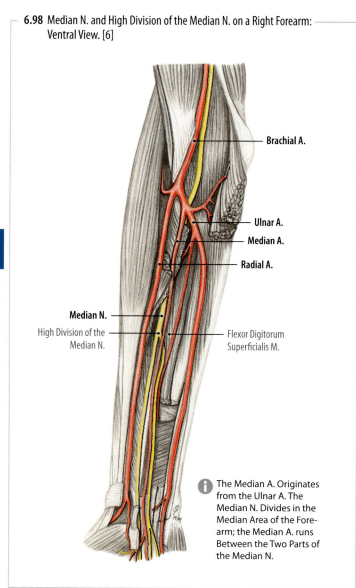

Brachial A.

Ulnar A.

Median A.

Radial A.

Median N.

High Division of the Median N.

Flexor Digitorum Superficialis M.

ℹ️ The Median A. Originates from the Ulnar A. The Median N. Divides in the Median Area of the Forearm; the Median A. runs Between the Two Parts of the Median N.

6.99 Anastomoses between the Median N. and the Ulnar N. on a Right Forearm: Ventral View. [111]

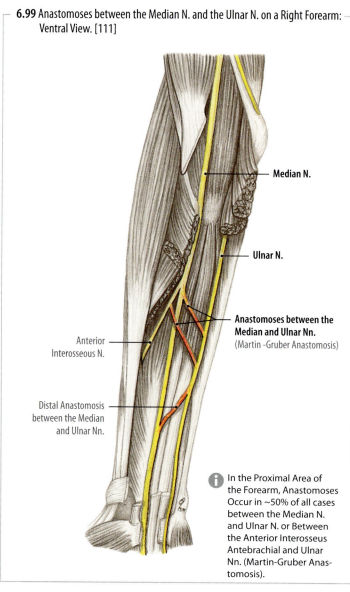

Median N.

Ulnar N.

Anastomoses between the Median and Ulnar Nn. (Martin -Gruber Anastomosis)

Anterior Interosseous N.

Distal Anastomosis between the Median and Ulnar Nn.

ℹ️ In the Proximal Area of the Forearm, Anastomoses Occur in ~50% of all cases between the Median N. and Ulnar N. or Between the Anterior Interosseus Antebrachial and Ulnar Nn. (Martin-Gruber Anastomosis).

6.100 Cross-Section through a Right Forearm in the Median Third: Ventral View of the Distal Cut Surface. [56]

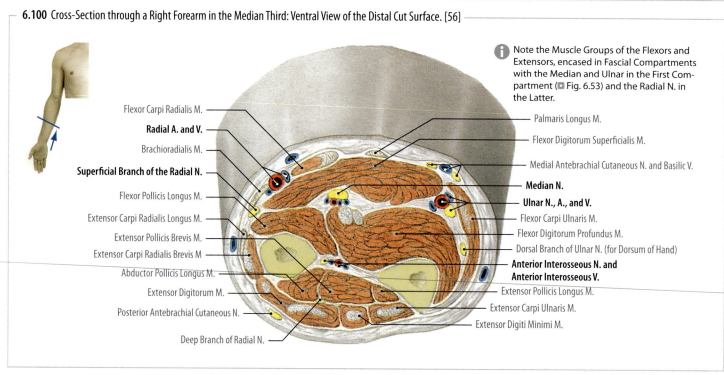

ℹ️ Note the Muscle Groups of the Flexors and Extensors, encased in Fascial Compartments with the Median and Ulnar in the First Compartment (🔲 Fig. 6.53) and the Radial N. in the Latter.

Flexor Carpi Radialis M.

Radial A. and V.

Brachioradialis M.

Superficial Branch of the Radial N.

Flexor Pollicis Longus M.

Extensor Carpi Radialis Longus M.

Extensor Pollicis Brevis M.

Extensor Carpi Radialis Brevis M

Abductor Pollicis Longus M.

Extensor Digitorum M.

Posterior Antebrachial Cutaneous N.

Deep Branch of Radial N.

Palmaris Longus M.

Flexor Digitorum Superficialis M.

Medial Antebrachial Cutaneous N. and Basilic V.

Median N.

Ulnar N., A., and V.

Flexor Carpi Ulnaris M.

Flexor Digitorum Profundus M.

Dorsal Branch of Ulnar N. (for Dorsum of Hand)

Anterior Interosseous N. and Anterior Interosseous V.

Extensor Pollicis Longus M.

Extensor Carpi Ulnaris M.

Extensor Digiti Minimi M.

6

Hand: Arteries

6.101 Arteries of the Hand: Ventral View. [13]

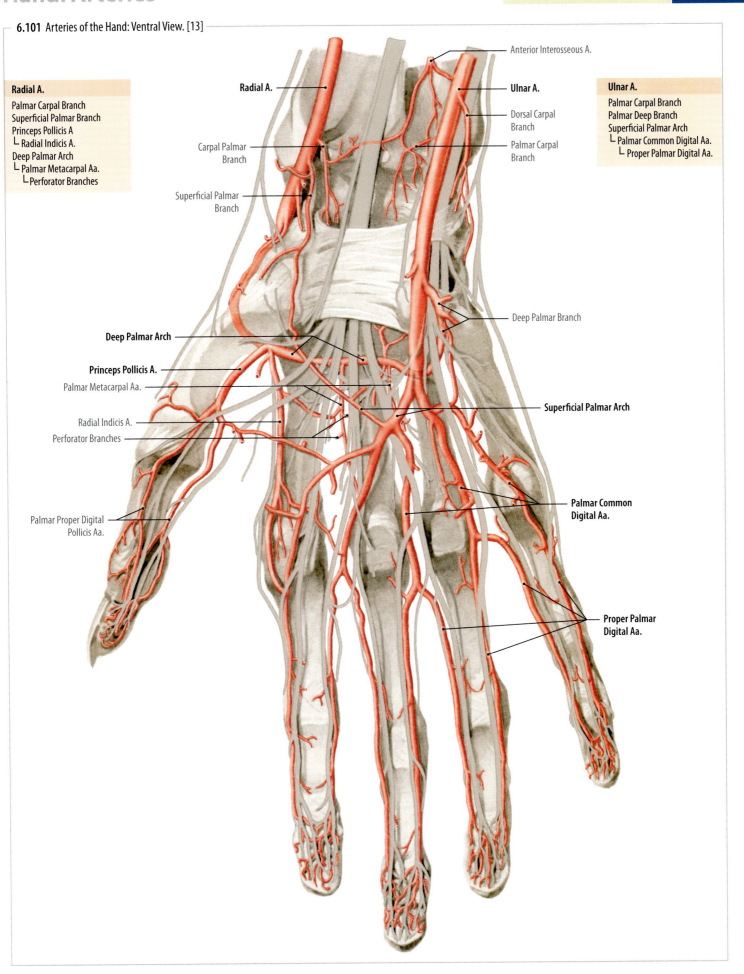

Radial A.
Palmar Carpal Branch
Superficial Palmar Branch
Princeps Pollicis A
  └ Radial Indicis A.
Deep Palmar Arch
  └ Palmar Metacarpal Aa.
    └ Perforator Branches

Radial A.

Carpal Palmar Branch

Superficial Palmar Branch

Deep Palmar Arch

Princeps Pollicis A.

Palmar Metacarpal Aa.

Radial Indicis A.

Perforator Branches

Palmar Proper Digital Pollicis Aa.

Anterior Interosseous A.

Ulnar A.

Dorsal Carpal Branch

Palmar Carpal Branch

Deep Palmar Branch

Superficial Palmar Arch

Palmar Common Digital Aa.

Proper Palmar Digital Aa.

Ulnar A.
Palmar Carpal Branch
Palmar Deep Branch
Superficial Palmar Arch
  └ Palmar Common Digital Aa.
    └ Proper Palmar Digital Aa.

Pathways and Topography

Hand: Nerves

6.102 Nerves of the Hand: Ventral View. [13]

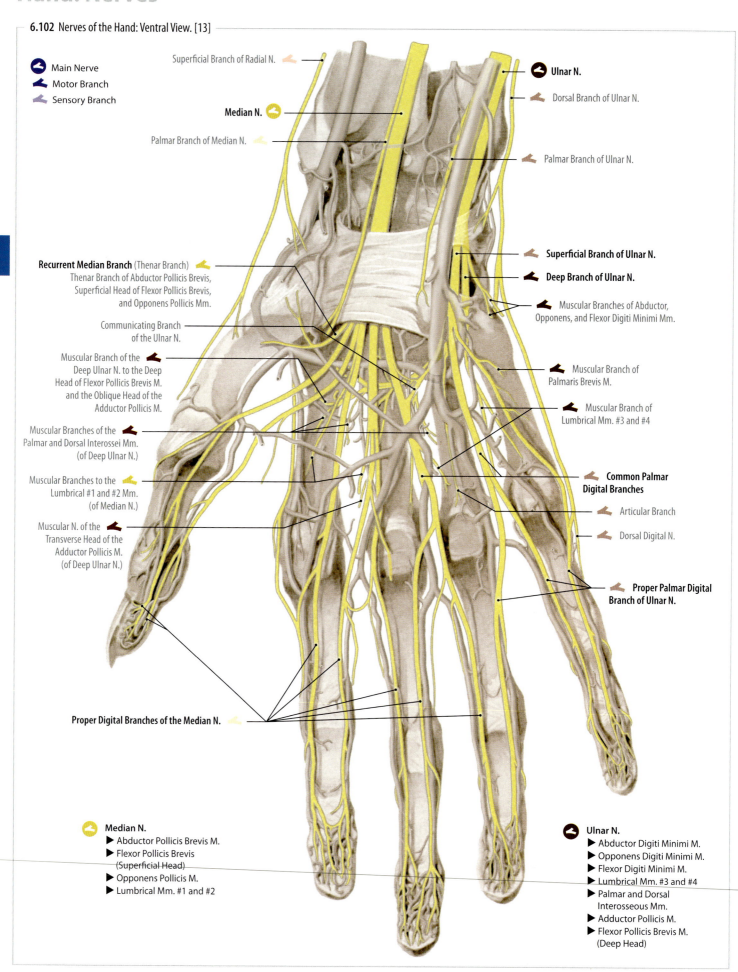

Main Nerve
Motor Branch
Sensory Branch

Superficial Branch of Radial N.

Median N.

Palmar Branch of Median N.

Ulnar N.

Dorsal Branch of Ulnar N.

Palmar Branch of Ulnar N.

Recurrent Median Branch (Thenar Branch)
Thenar Branch of Abductor Pollicis Brevis,
Superficial Head of Flexor Pollicis Brevis,
and Opponens Pollicis Mm.

Superficial Branch of Ulnar N.

Deep Branch of Ulnar N.

Communicating Branch
of the Ulnar N.

Muscular Branches of Abductor,
Opponens, and Flexor Digiti Minimi Mm.

Muscular Branch of the
Deep Ulnar N. to the Deep
Head of Flexor Pollicis Brevis M.
and the Oblique Head of the
Adductor Pollicis M.

Muscular Branch of
Palmaris Brevis M.

Muscular Branches of the
Palmar and Dorsal Interossei Mm.
(of Deep Ulnar N.)

Muscular Branch of
Lumbrical Mm. #3 and #4

Muscular Branches to the
Lumbrical #1 and #2 Mm.
(of Median N.)

**Common Palmar
Digital Branches**

Articular Branch

Muscular N. of the
Transverse Head of the
Adductor Pollicis M.
(of Deep Ulnar N.)

Dorsal Digital N.

**Proper Palmar Digital
Branch of Ulnar N.**

Proper Digital Branches of the Median N.

Median N.
▶ Abductor Pollicis Brevis M.
▶ Flexor Pollicis Brevis
(Superficial Head)
▶ Opponens Pollicis M.
▶ Lumbrical Mm. #1 and #2

Ulnar N.
▶ Abductor Digiti Minimi M.
▶ Opponens Digiti Minimi M.
▶ Flexor Digiti Minimi M.
▶ Lumbrical Mm. #3 and #4
▶ Palmar and Dorsal
Interosseous Mm.
▶ Adductor Pollicis M.
▶ Flexor Pollicis Brevis M.
(Deep Head)

6.103a,b Pathways of the Back (Dorsum) of the Hand: Right Side. [56]

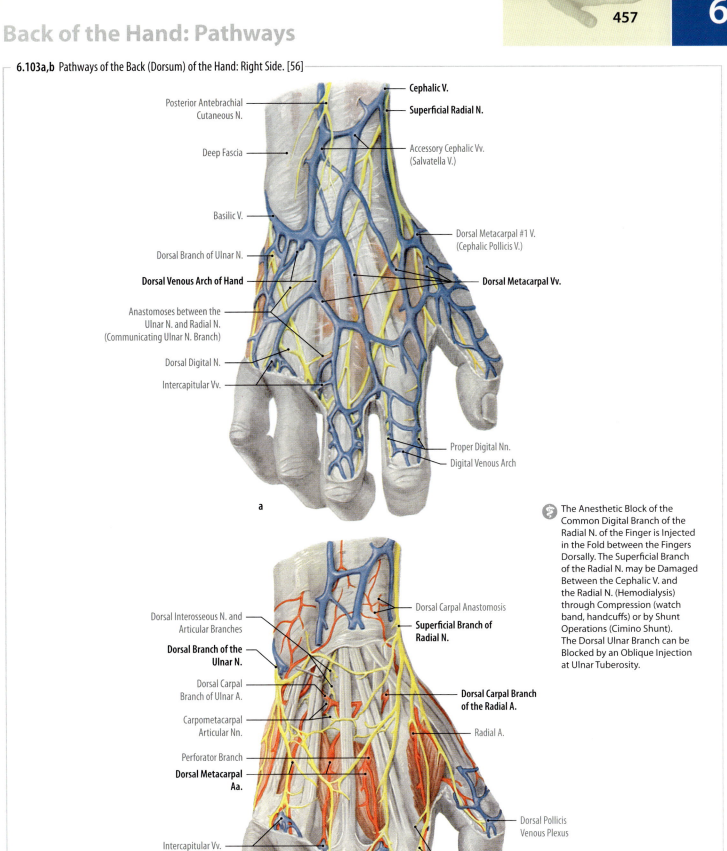

Posterior Antebrachial Cutaneous N.

Deep Fascia

Basilic V.

Dorsal Branch of Ulnar N.

Dorsal Venous Arch of Hand

Anastomoses between the Ulnar N. and Radial N. (Communicating Ulnar N. Branch)

Dorsal Digital N.

Intercapitular Vv.

Cephalic V.

Superficial Radial N.

Accessory Cephalic Vv. (Salvatella V.)

Dorsal Metacarpal #1 V. (Cephalic Pollicis V.)

Dorsal Metacarpal Vv.

Proper Digital Nn.

Digital Venous Arch

a

The Anesthetic Block of the Common Digital Branch of the Radial N. of the Finger is Injected in the Fold between the Fingers Dorsally. The Superficial Branch of the Radial N. may be Damaged Between the Cephalic V. and the Radial N. (Hemodialysis) through Compression (watch band, handcuffs) or by Shunt Operations (Cimino Shunt). The Dorsal Ulnar Branch can be Blocked by an Oblique Injection at Ulnar Tuberosity.

Dorsal Interosseous N. and Articular Branches

Dorsal Branch of the Ulnar N.

Dorsal Carpal Branch of Ulnar A.

Carpometacarpal Articular Nn.

Perforator Branch

Dorsal Metacarpal Aa.

Intercapitular Vv.

Dorsal Digital A. and N.

Dorsal Carpal Anastomosis

Superficial Branch of Radial N.

Dorsal Carpal Branch of the Radial A.

Radial A.

Dorsal Pollicis Venous Plexus

Dorsal Metacarpophalangeal Articular Branches

Dorsal Proximal Interphalangeal Articular Branches

b

a Illustration of the Superficial Pathways.
b Illustration of the Pathways following Removal of the Dorsal Fascia of the Hand.

Pathways and Topography

6.104 Pathways of the Right Palm: Superficial Layer. [56]

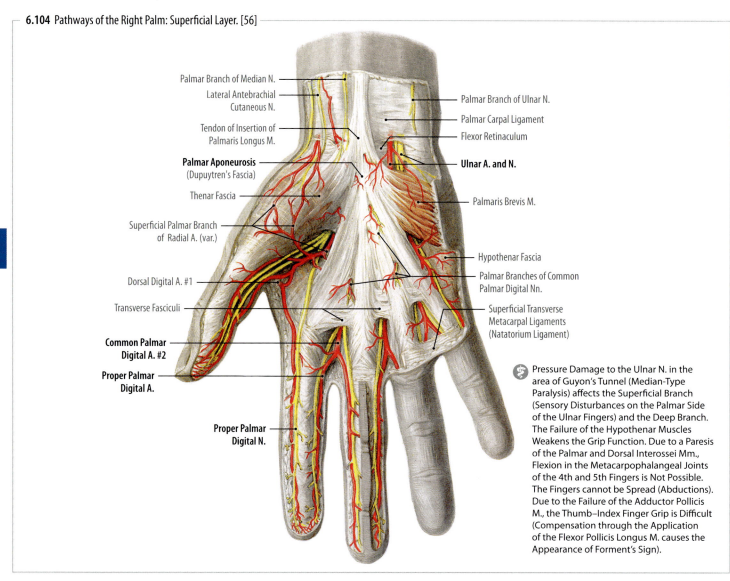

Palmar Branch of Median N.
Lateral Antebrachial Cutaneous N.
Tendon of Insertion of Palmaris Longus M.
Palmar Aponeurosis (Dupuytren's Fascia)
Thenar Fascia
Superficial Palmar Branch of Radial A. (var.)
Dorsal Digital A. #1
Transverse Fasciculi
Common Palmar Digital A. #2
Proper Palmar Digital A.
Proper Palmar Digital N.

Palmar Branch of Ulnar N.
Palmar Carpal Ligament
Flexor Retinaculum
Ulnar A. and N.
Palmaris Brevis M.
Hypothenar Fascia
Palmar Branches of Common Palmar Digital Nn.
Superficial Transverse Metacarpal Ligaments (Natatorium Ligament)

Pressure Damage to the Ulnar N. in the area of Guyon's Tunnel (Median-Type Paralysis) affects the Superficial Branch (Sensory Disturbances on the Palmar Side of the Ulnar Fingers) and the Deep Branch. The Failure of the Hypothenar Muscles Weakens the Grip Function. Due to a Paresis of the Palmar and Dorsal Interossei Mm., Flexion in the Metacarpophalangeal Joints of the 4th and 5th Fingers is Not Possible. The Fingers cannot be Spread (Abductions). Due to the Failure of the Adductor Pollicis M., the Thumb–Index Finger Grip is Difficult (Compensation through the Application of the Flexor Pollicis Longus M. causes the Appearance of Forment's Sign).

6.105 Cross-Sections through the Right Hand. **a** In the Area of the Bases of the Metacarpal Bones, **b** At the Level of the Thumb Basal Joint: View of the Distal Cut Surfaces. [56]

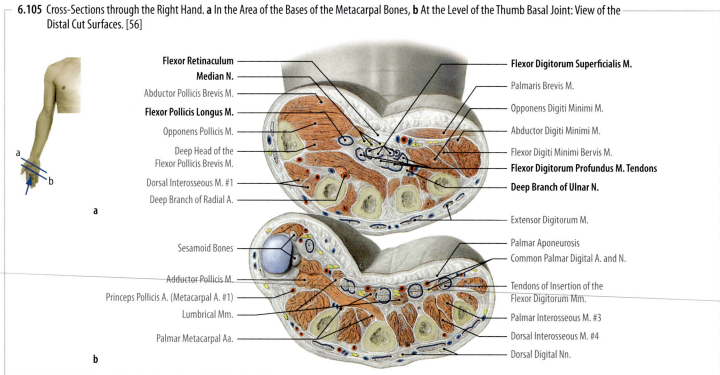

Flexor Retinaculum
Median N.
Abductor Pollicis Brevis M.
Flexor Pollicis Longus M.
Opponens Pollicis M.
Deep Head of the Flexor Pollicis Brevis M.
Dorsal Interosseous M. #1
Deep Branch of Radial A.

Flexor Digitorum Superficialis M.
Palmaris Brevis M.
Opponens Digiti Minimi M.
Abductor Digiti Minimi M.
Flexor Digiti Minimi Bervis M.
Flexor Digitorum Profundus M. Tendons
Deep Branch of Ulnar N.

Sesamoid Bones
Adductor Pollicis M.
Princeps Pollicis A. (Metacarpal A. #1)
Lumbrical Mm.
Palmar Metacarpal Aa.

Extensor Digitorum M.
Palmar Aponeurosis
Common Palmar Digital A. and N.
Tendons of Insertion of the Flexor Digitorum Mm.
Palmar Interosseous M. #3
Dorsal Interosseous M. #4
Dorsal Digital Nn.

Palm: Pathways

6.106 Muscles and Pathways of the Right Palm. [1]

The most common Damage to a Peripheral Nerve is Compression of the Median N. in the Carpal Tunnel (Carpal Tunnel Syndrome), Constriction of the Canal in Rheumatics, Tenosynovitis, and through Muscle Variants). This Leads to Sensory Disturbances (Paresthesias and Dysesthesias—primarily At Night) in the Thumb, Index and Middle Fingers, as well as Motor Weakness in the Thenar Muscles supplied by the Recurrent Thenar Branch (Abductor Pollicis Brevis, Opponens Pollicis, Flexor Pollicis Brevis [Superficial Head]) with Weakness of Differentiated Gripping Movements.

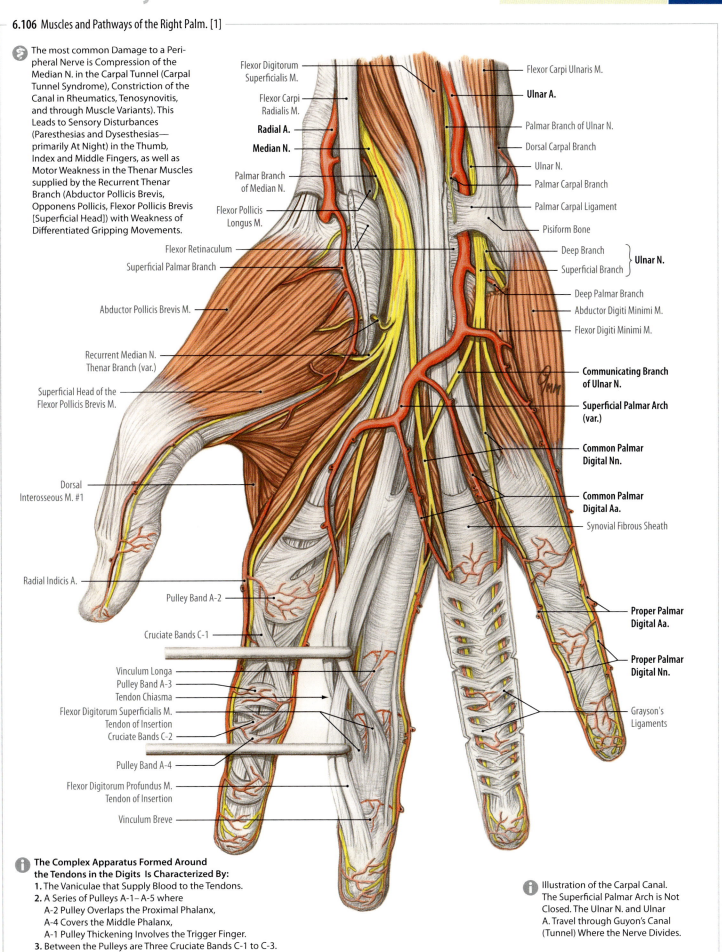

Flexor Digitorum Superficialis M.

Flexor Carpi Radialis M.

Radial A.

Median N.

Palmar Branch of Median N.

Flexor Pollicis Longus M.

Flexor Retinaculum

Superficial Palmar Branch

Abductor Pollicis Brevis M.

Recurrent Median N. Thenar Branch (var.)

Superficial Head of the Flexor Pollicis Brevis M.

Dorsal Interosseous M. #1

Radial Indicis A.

Pulley Band A-2

Cruciate Bands C-1

Vinculum Longa

Pulley Band A-3

Tendon Chiasma

Flexor Digitorum Superficialis M. Tendon of Insertion

Cruciate Bands C-2

Pulley Band A-4

Flexor Digitorum Profundus M. Tendon of Insertion

Vinculum Breve

Flexor Carpi Ulnaris M.

Ulnar A.

Palmar Branch of Ulnar N.

Dorsal Carpal Branch

Ulnar N.

Palmar Carpal Branch

Palmar Carpal Ligament

Pisiform Bone

Deep Branch
Superficial Branch } **Ulnar N.**

Deep Palmar Branch

Abductor Digiti Minimi M.

Flexor Digiti Minimi M.

Communicating Branch of Ulnar N.

Superficial Palmar Arch (var.)

Common Palmar Digital Nn.

Common Palmar Digital Aa.

Synovial Fibrous Sheath

Proper Palmar Digital Aa.

Proper Palmar Digital Nn.

Grayson's Ligaments

The Complex Apparatus Formed Around the Tendons in the Digits Is Characterized By:
1. The Vaniculae that Supply Blood to the Tendons.
2. A Series of Pulleys A-1– A-5 where
   A-2 Pulley Overlaps the Proximal Phalanx,
   A-4 Covers the Middle Phalanx,
   A-1 Pulley Thickening Involves the Trigger Finger.
3. Between the Pulleys are Three Cruciate Bands C-1 to C-3.

Illustration of the Carpal Canal. The Superficial Palmar Arch is Not Closed. The Ulnar N. and Ulnar A. Travel through Guyon's Canal (Tunnel) Where the Nerve Divides.

Pathways and Topography

6.107 Muscles and Pathways of the Palmar Side of a Right Forearm. [8]

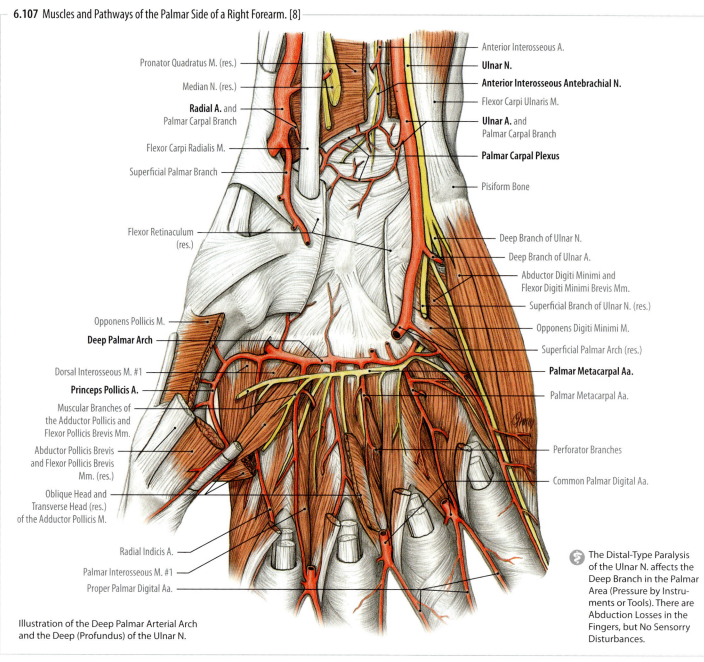

Pronator Quadratus M. (res.)

Median N. (res.)

Radial A. and Palmar Carpal Branch

Flexor Carpi Radialis M.

Superficial Palmar Branch

Flexor Retinaculum (res.)

Opponens Pollicis M.

Deep Palmar Arch

Dorsal Interosseous M. #1

Princeps Pollicis A.

Muscular Branches of the Adductor Pollicis and Flexor Pollicis Brevis Mm.

Abductor Pollicis Brevis and Flexor Pollicis Brevis Mm. (res.)

Oblique Head and Transverse Head (res.) of the Adductor Pollicis M.

Radial Indicis A.

Palmar Interosseous M. #1

Proper Palmar Digital Aa.

Anterior Interosseous A.

Ulnar N.

Anterior Interosseous Antebrachial N.

Flexor Carpi Ulnaris M.

Ulnar A. and Palmar Carpal Branch

Palmar Carpal Plexus

Pisiform Bone

Deep Branch of Ulnar N.

Deep Branch of Ulnar A.

Abductor Digiti Minimi and Flexor Digiti Minimi Brevis Mm.

Superficial Branch of Ulnar N. (res.)

Opponens Digiti Minimi M.

Superficial Palmar Arch (res.)

Palmar Metacarpal Aa.

Palmar Metacarpal Aa.

Perforator Branches

Common Palmar Digital Aa.

The Distal-Type Paralysis of the Ulnar N. affects the Deep Branch in the Palmar Area (Pressure by Instruments or Tools). There are Abduction Losses in the Fingers, but No Sensorry Disturbances.

Illustration of the Deep Palmar Arterial Arch and the Deep (Profundus) of the Ulnar N.

6.108a–c Variants of the Median N. and the Origin of Thenar (Recurrent) Branch in the Carpal Canal on the Right Hand: Palmar View. [112]

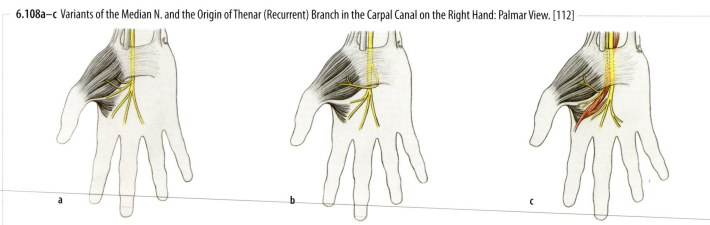

a   b   c

a Outside of the Carpal Canal, Two Thenar Branches Originate.
b The Thenar Branch Originates in the Carpal Canal on the Medial Side of the Median N., Turns in an Ulnar Direction, and then Runs in a Lateral Direction into the Thenar Muscles. In such cases, the Thenar Branch may also Run on the Flexor Retinaculum.

c High Division of the Median N. From the Weak Radial Part, the Thenar Branch Originates at an Atypical Location (High Division of the Median N. with Concurrent Existence of the Median A. ▫ Fig. 6.98). An Accessory Lumbrical M. runs through the Carpal Canal.

Finger: Pathways

6.109 Pathways of the Index Finger of a Right Hand: Radial View. [56]

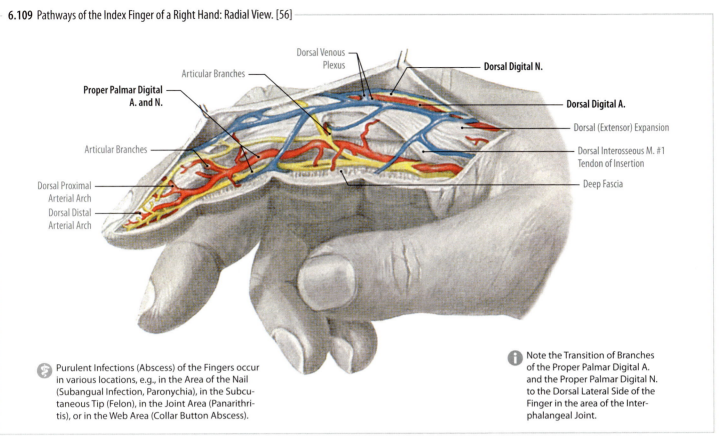

Dorsal Venous Plexus

Articular Branches

Proper Palmar Digital A. and N.

Articular Branches

Dorsal Proximal Arterial Arch

Dorsal Distal Arterial Arch

Dorsal Digital N.

Dorsal Digital A.

Dorsal (Extensor) Expansion

Dorsal Interosseous M. #1 Tendon of Insertion

Deep Fascia

Purulent Infections (Abscess) of the Fingers occur in various locations, e.g., in the Area of the Nail (Subangual Infection, Paronychia), in the Subcutaneous Tip (Felon), in the Joint Area (Panarithritis), or in the Web Area (Collar Button Abscess).

Note the Transition of Branches of the Proper Palmar Digital A. and the Proper Palmar Digital N. to the Dorsal Lateral Side of the Finger in the area of the Interphalangeal Joint.

6.110 Cross-Section through a Right Index Finger in the Area of the Proximal Interphalangeal Joint: View of the Distal Cut Surface. [56]

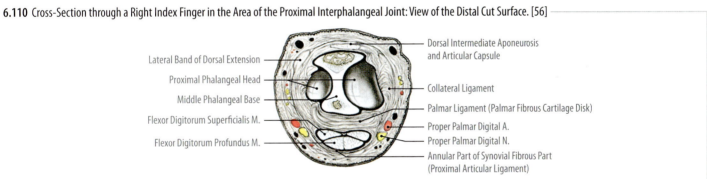

Lateral Band of Dorsal Extension

Proximal Phalangeal Head

Middle Phalangeal Base

Flexor Digitorum Superficialis M.

Flexor Digitorum Profundus M.

Dorsal Intermediate Aponeurosis and Articular Capsule

Collateral Ligament

Palmar Ligament (Palmar Fibrous Cartilage Disk)

Proper Palmar Digital A.

Proper Palmar Digital N.

Annular Part of Synovial Fibrous Part (Proximal Articular Ligament)

6.111 Fingernail of a Right Index Finger: Dorsal View. [56]

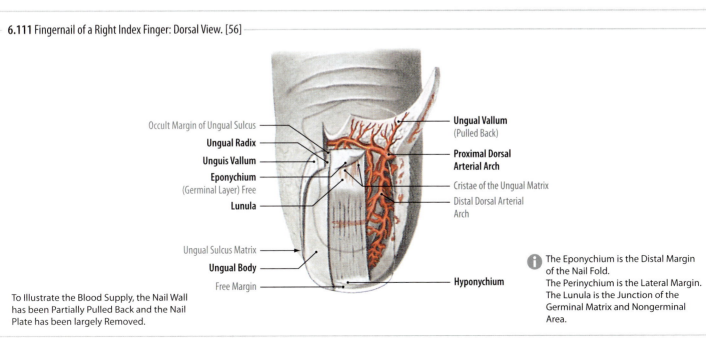

Occult Margin of Ungual Sulcus

Ungual Radix

Unguis Vallum

Eponychium (Germinal Layer) Free

Lunula

Ungual Sulcus Matrix

Ungual Body

Free Margin

Ungual Vallum (Pulled Back)

Proximal Dorsal Arterial Arch

Cristae of the Ungual Matrix

Distal Dorsal Arterial Arch

Hyponychium

To Illustrate the Blood Supply, the Nail Wall has been Partially Pulled Back and the Nail Plate has been largely Removed.

The Eponychium is the Distal Margin of the Nail Fold.
The Perinychium is the Lateral Margin.
The Lunula is the Junction of the Germinal Matrix and Nongerminal Area.

Pathways and Topography

6.Aa,b Muscles of the Shoulder (Muscles of the Shoulder Girdle): Origins and Insertions on the Skeleton of the Trunk and on the Skull.

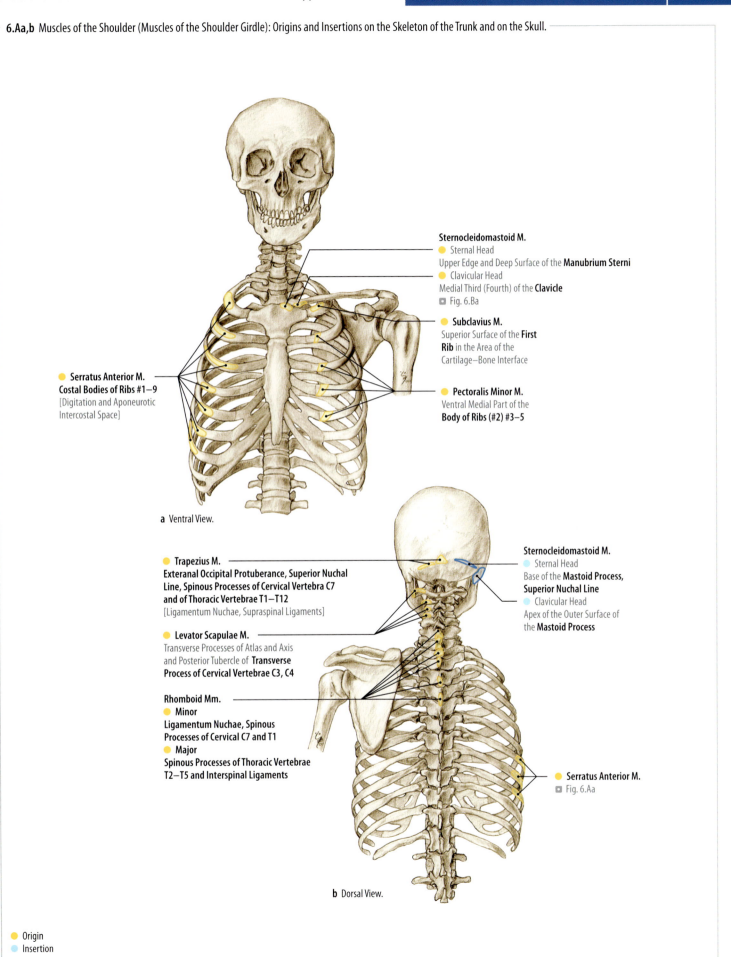

Sternocleidomastoid M.
● Sternal Head
Upper Edge and Deep Surface of the **Manubrium Sterni**
● Clavicular Head
Medial Third (Fourth) of the **Clavicle**
▣ Fig. 6.Ba

● **Subclavius M.**
Superior Surface of the **First Rib** in the Area of the Cartilage–Bone Interface

● **Serratus Anterior M.**
Costal Bodies of Ribs #1–9
[Digitation and Aponeurotic Intercostal Space]

● **Pectoralis Minor M.**
Ventral Medial Part of the **Body of Ribs (#2) #3–5**

a Ventral View.

● **Trapezius M.**
Exteranal Occipital Protuberance, Superior Nuchal Line, Spinous Processes of Cervical Vertebra C7 and of Thoracic Vertebrae T1–T12
[Ligamentum Nuchae, Supraspinal Ligaments]

● **Levator Scapulae M.**
Transverse Processes of Atlas and Axis and Posterior Tubercle of **Transverse Process of Cervical Vertebrae C3, C4**

Rhomboid Mm.
● **Minor**
Ligamentum Nuchae, Spinous Processes of Cervical C7 and T1
● **Major**
Spinous Processes of Thoracic Vertebrae T2–T5 and Interspinal Ligaments

Sternocleidomastoid M.
● Sternal Head
Base of the **Mastoid Process, Superior Nuchal Line**
● Clavicular Head
Apex of the Outer Surface of the **Mastoid Process**

● **Serratus Anterior M.**
▣ Fig. 6.Aa

b Dorsal View.

● Origin
● Insertion

6.Ba,b Muscles of the Shoulder (Muscles of the Shoulder Girdle): Origins and Insertions on the Clavicle.

6

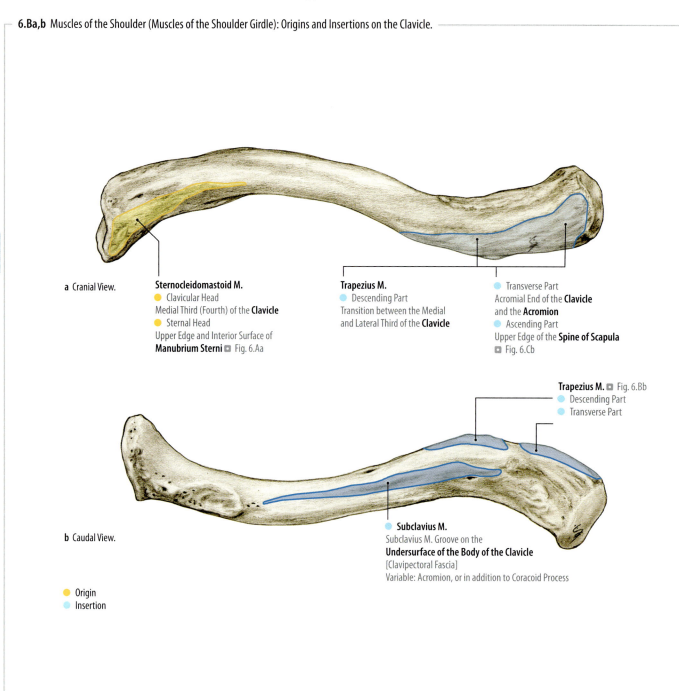

a Cranial View.

Sternocleidomastoid M.
🟡 Clavicular Head
Medial Third (Fourth) of the **Clavicle**
🟡 Sternal Head
Upper Edge and Interior Surface of
Manubrium Sterni ◼ Fig. 6.Aa

Trapezius M.
🔵 Descending Part
Transition between the Medial
and Lateral Third of the **Clavicle**

🔵 Transverse Part
Acromial End of the **Clavicle**
and the **Acromion**
🔵 Ascending Part
Upper Edge of the **Spine of Scapula**
◼ Fig. 6.Cb

Trapezius M. ◼ Fig. 6.Bb
🔵 Descending Part
🔵 Transverse Part

b Caudal View.

🔵 **Subclavius M.**
Subclavius M. Groove on the
Undersurface of the Body of the Clavicle
[Clavipectoral Fascia]
Variable: Acromion, or in addition to Coracoid Process

🟡 Origin
🔵 Insertion

6.Ca,b Muscles of the Shoulder Girdle: Origins and Insertions on the Scapula.

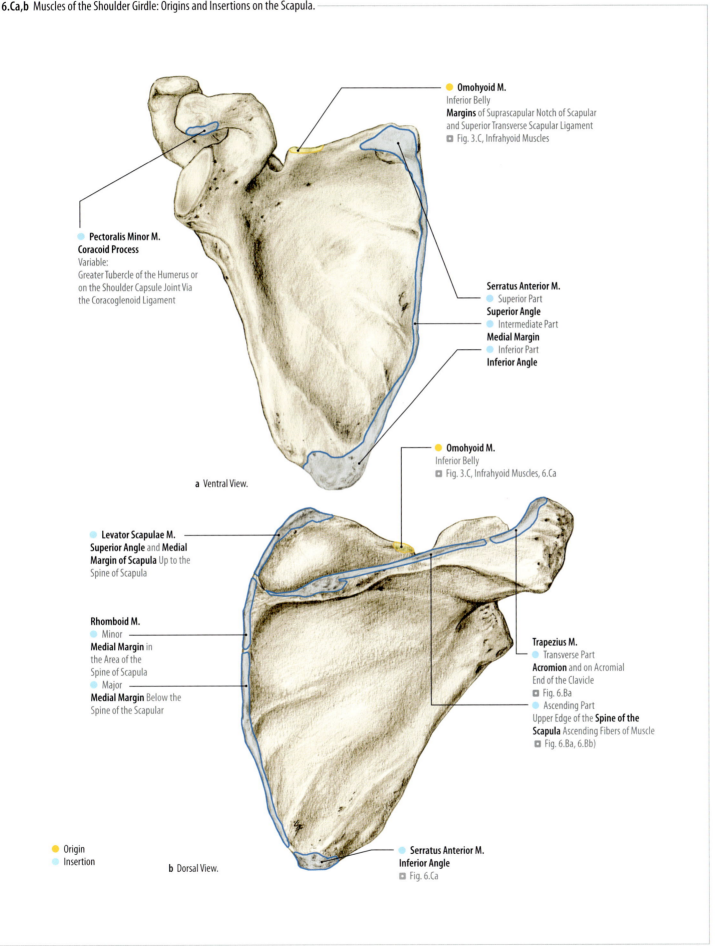

● **Omohyoid M.**
Inferior Belly
Margins of Suprascapular Notch of Scapular
and Superior Transverse Scapular Ligament
▶ Fig. 3.C, Infrahyoid Muscles

● **Pectoralis Minor M.**
Coracoid Process
Variable:
Greater Tubercle of the Humerus or
on the Shoulder Capsule Joint Via
the Coracoglenoid Ligament

Serratus Anterior M.
● Superior Part
Superior Angle
● Intermediate Part
Medial Margin
● Inferior Part
Inferior Angle

a Ventral View.

● **Omohyoid M.**
Inferior Belly
▶ Fig. 3.C, Infrahyoid Muscles, 6.Ca

● **Levator Scapulae M.**
Superior Angle and **Medial
Margin of Scapula** Up to the
Spine of Scapula

Rhomboid M.
● Minor
Medial Margin in
the Area of the
Spine of Scapula
● Major
Medial Margin Below the
Spine of the Scapular

Trapezius M.
● Transverse Part
Acromion and on Acromial
End of the Clavicle
▶ Fig. 6.Ba
● Ascending Part
Upper Edge of the **Spine of the
Scapula** Ascending Fibers of Muscle
▶ Fig. 6.Ba, 6.Bb)

● Origin
● Insertion

b Dorsal View.

Serratus Anterior M.
Inferior Angle
▶ Fig. 6.Ca

Muscles of the Arm

6

Function	Innervation	Blood Supply
Muscles of the Shoulder Girdle (Migrated Muscles of the Trunk – Thoracic Mm.)		
Dorsal Group		
Rhomboid M. (Rhomboid Major and Minor Mm.) Return of the elevated Arm to the neutral-0-position, Relocation of the Scapula to a cranial medial position, Rotation of the Scapula's inferior angle in a medial direction	Dorsal Scapular N. C4–C5	Descending Branch of the Superficial and Deep Branch of the Transverse Cervical Aa. Posterior Intercostal Aa.
Levator Scapulae M. Return of the elevated Arm to the neutral-0-position, Relocation of the Scapula to a cranial position, With a Fixated Shoulder Girdle: Extension of the Cervical Spine	Dorsal Scapular N. (C2) C3–C5	Ascending Cervical A. Vertebral A. Transverse Cervical A.
Serratus Anterior M. **Inferior and Intermediate Parts:** Rotation of the Scapula in a lateral cranial direction for the elevation of the Arm above the horizontal **Superior Part:** Support of the return of the elevated Arm, Relocation of the Scapula to a cranial position **Entire Muscle:** Relocation of the Scapula to a lateral ventral position Fixation of the Medial Scapula edge on the Thorax together with the Rhomboid Mm. With a Fixated Shoulder Girdle: Lifting of the Ribs (support of inspiration)	Long Thoracic N. C5–C7 (C8)	Lateral Thoracic A. Thoracodorsal A. Deep Branch of the Transverse Cervical A. Suprem Intercostal A. Posterior Intercostal Aa.
Ventral Group		
Subclavius M. Lowering of the Clavicle Fixation of the Clavicle in the Sternoclavicular Joint Tension of the Clavipectoral Fascia (keeping the Subclavian V. open)	Subclavius N. (C4) C5–C6	Suprascapular A.
Omohyoid M. ▣ Muscles of the Neck Fig. 3.C		
Muscles of the Shoulder Girdle (Mixed Head-Trunk-Muscles – Craniothoracic Mm.)		
Trapezius M. **Descending and Ascending Parts:** Rotation of the Scapula in a lateral cranial direction for the elevation of the Arm above the horizontal **Transverse Part:** Relocation of the Scapula to a medial position **Descending Part:** Relocation of the Scapula to a cranial position **Entire Muscle:** Bilateral Activity: Extension of the Cervical Spine Unilateral Activity: Rotation of the Head and Cervical Spine to the opposite side • *Subtendinous Trapezial M. Bursa*	Spina Accessory N. External part of CN XI , Branches of the Cervical Plexus (C2) C3–C4	Transverse Cervical A. Suprascapular A. Posterior Intercostal Aa. Occipital A.
Sternocleidomastoid M. With a Fixated Shoulder Girdle: Unilateral Activity: Inclination of the Head and Cervical Spine to the ipsilateral side Rotation of the Head and the Cervical Spine to the contralateral side Bilateral Activity: Tilting of the Head in the Head Joints in a dorsal direction and ventral movement of the extended Cervical Spine Lifting of the Superior Thorax Aperture (support of inspiration)	Spinal Accessory N. External part of CN XI, Muscular Branches of the Cervical Nerves C1–C2 (C3)	Sternocleidomastoid Branch of the Occipital A (or of the External Carotid A. directly) Superior Thyroid A. Posterior Auricular A. Transverse Cervical A.

• Bursa = Synovial Bursa assigned to a muscle.

6.Da,b Muscles of the Shoulder Joint: Origins on the Skeleton of the Trunk.

ⓘ Pectoralis Major M. Variations:
The Sternocostal Head may Cross the Sternum. Deficiency or Absence of the Sternocostal Head is more Common than the Clavical Head. The Clavicular Part Fuses with the Deltoid M. The Costocoracoid M. Separates the Muscular Band and Individually Inserts Deeply in the Humerus.

Pectoralis Major M. —
- Clavicular Part
- ☐ Fig. 6.Fa
- Sternocostal Part

Anterior Surface of the Sternum Cartilage of Ribs #2—7
and Anterior Costal Membrane
- Abdominal Part

No Bony Origin:
Anterior Layer of Rectus Sheath

[**Pectoralis Minor M.**
- ☐ Fig. 6.Aa,
- ☐ Fig. 6.Ca,
Muscles of the Shoulder Girdle

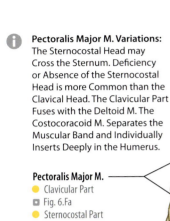

a Ventral View.

ⓘ Latissimus Dorsi M. Variations:
The number of Thoracic Vertebrae varies from Four to Eight, so Costal Attachments Vary, and Muscle Fiber may Not Reach the Iliac Crest.

Latissimus Dorsi M.
- Scapular Part (inconstant) —
Inferior Angle

- Costal Part —
Dorsal Part of Ribs #9—12
(variable)

- Vertebral Part —
(Via the Aponeurosis of Thoracolumbar Fascia)
Spinous Processes of Thoracic Vertebrae T6—12, of Lumbar Vertebrae L1—5, Median Sacral Crest

- Iliac Part —
Posterior Third of the **External Lip of the Iliac Crest**

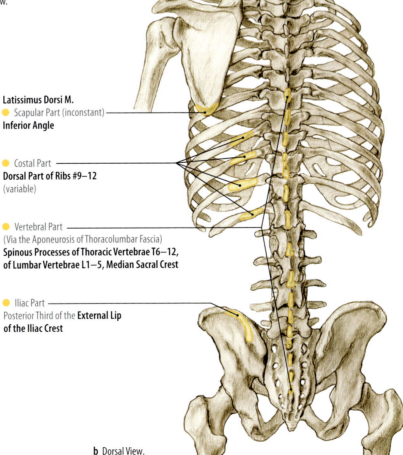

- Origin
- Insertion

b Dorsal View.

6.Ea,b Muscles of the Shoulder Joint: Origins on the Scapula.

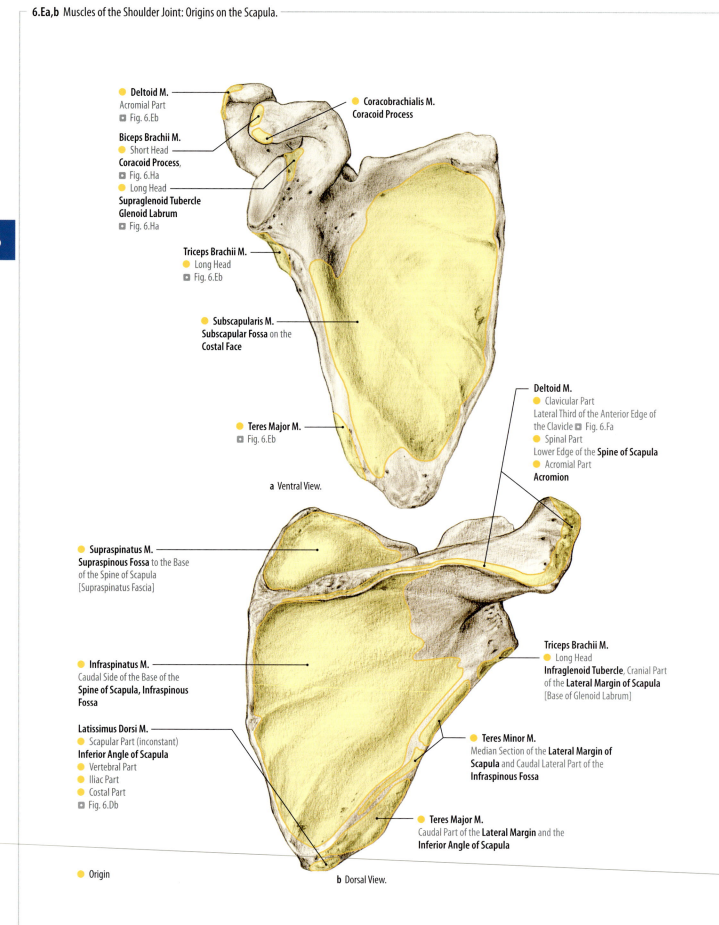

Deltoid M.
Acromial Part
☐ Fig. 6.Eb

Biceps Brachii M.
Short Head
Coracoid Process,
☐ Fig. 6.Ha
Long Head
Supraglenoid Tubercle
Glenoid Labrum
☐ Fig. 6.Ha

Coracobrachialis M.
Coracoid Process

Triceps Brachii M.
Long Head
☐ Fig. 6.Eb

Subscapularis M.
Subscapular Fossa on the
Costal Face

Teres Major M.
☐ Fig. 6.Eb

Deltoid M.
Clavicular Part
Lateral Third of the Anterior Edge of
the Clavicle ☐ Fig. 6.Fa
Spinal Part
Lower Edge of the **Spine of Scapula**
Acromial Part
Acromion

a Ventral View.

Supraspinatus M.
Supraspinous Fossa to the Base
of the Spine of Scapula
[Supraspinatus Fascia]

Infraspinatus M.
Caudal Side of the Base of the
Spine of Scapula, Infraspinous
Fossa

Latissimus Dorsi M.
Scapular Part (inconstant)
Inferior Angle of Scapula
Vertebral Part
Iliac Part
Costal Part
☐ Fig. 6.Db

Triceps Brachii M.
Long Head
Infraglenoid Tubercle, Cranial Part
of the **Lateral Margin of Scapula**
[Base of Glenoid Labrum]

Teres Minor M.
Median Section of the **Lateral Margin of**
Scapula and Caudal Lateral Part of the
Infraspinous Fossa

Teres Major M.
Caudal Part of the **Lateral Margin** and the
Inferior Angle of Scapula

Origin

b Dorsal View.

6.Fa,b Muscles of the Shoulder Joint: Origins on the Clavicle.

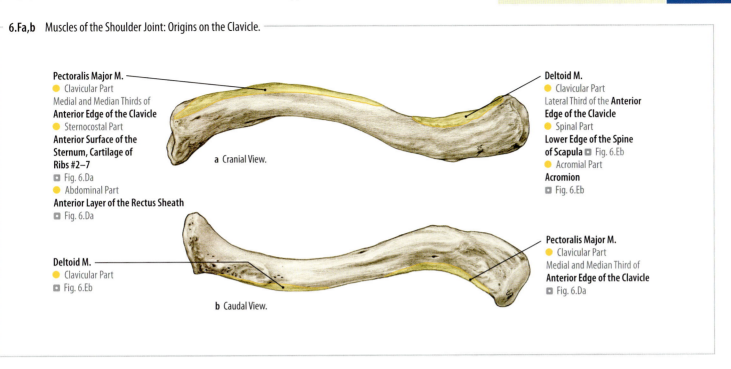

Pectoralis Major M.
- Clavicular Part
Medial and Median Thirds of
Anterior Edge of the Clavicle
- Sternocostal Part
**Anterior Surface of the
Sternum, Cartilage of
Ribs #2–7**
▢ Fig. 6.Da
- Abdominal Part
Anterior Layer of the Rectus Sheath
▢ Fig. 6.Da

Deltoid M.
- Clavicular Part
▢ Fig. 6.Eb

a Cranial View.

b Caudal View.

Deltoid M.
- Clavicular Part
Lateral Third of the **Anterior
Edge of the Clavicle**
- Spinal Part
**Lower Edge of the Spine
of Scapula** ▢ Fig. 6.Eb
- Acromial Part
Acromion
▢ Fig. 6.Eb

Pectoralis Major M.
- Clavicular Part
Medial and Median Third of
Anterior Edge of the Clavicle
▢ Fig. 6.Da

6.Ga,b Muscles of the Shoulder Joint: Insertions on the Humerus.

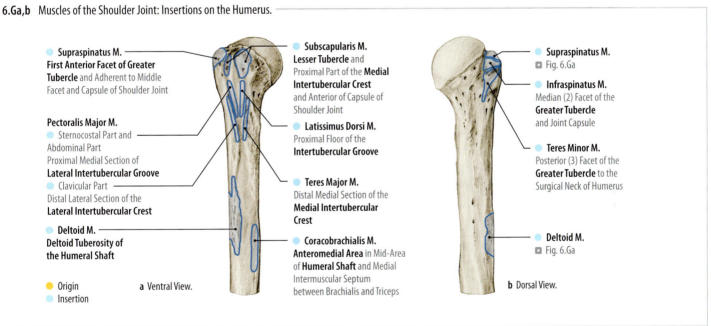

Supraspinatus M.
**First Anterior Facet of Greater
Tubercle** and Adherent to Middle
Facet and Capsule of Shoulder Joint

Pectoralis Major M.
- Sternocostal Part and
Abdominal Part
Proximal Medial Section of
Lateral Intertubercular Groove
- Clavicular Part
Distal Lateral Section of the
Lateral Intertubercular Crest

Deltoid M.
**Deltoid Tuberosity of
the Humeral Shaft**

- Origin
- Insertion

a Ventral View.

Subscapularis M.
Lesser Tubercle and
Proximal Part of the **Medial
Intertubercular Crest**
and Anterior of Capsule of
Shoulder Joint

Latissimus Dorsi M.
Proximal Floor of the
Intertubercular Groove

Teres Major M.
Distal Medial Section of the
**Medial Intertubercular
Crest**

Coracobrachialis M.
Anteromedial Area in Mid-Area
of **Humeral Shaft** and Medial
Intermuscular Septum
between Brachialis and Triceps

Supraspinatus M.
▢ Fig. 6.Ga

Infraspinatus M.
Median (2) Facet of the
Greater Tubercle
and Joint Capsule

Teres Minor M.
Posterior (3) Facet of the
Greater Tubercle to the
Surgical Neck of Humerus

Deltoid M.
▢ Fig. 6.Ga

b Dorsal View.

Function	Innervation	Blood Supply
Dorsal Group (Dorsal Brachial Mm.)		
Deltoid M.	Axillary N. (C4) C5–C6	Posterior Circumflex Humeral A.
Acromial Part:		Thoracoacromial A.
Abduction in the Shoulder Joint		Deltoid Branch
Clavicular Part:		of the Deep Brachial A.
Flexion, medial rotation, adduction in the Shoulder Joint from the neutral-0 degree, support of abduction in the approximately 80-degree abducted Arm		
Spinal Part:		
Extension, lateral rotation, adduction in the shoulder joint from the neutral-0 degree, support of abduction in the abducted Arm		
Entire Muscle:		
Carries the weight of the Arm, muscular direction of the Shoulder Joint		
• *Subdeltoid Bursa*		

• Bursa = Synovial Bursa assigned to a muscle.
Ⓢ Axillary Nerve: Segment indicating Deltoid M. for the Spinal Cord Segment C5

Muscles of the Arm

Function	Innervation	Blood Supply
Muscles of the Rotator Cuff		
Supraspinatus M. Abduction in the Shoulder Joint (18°), support of lateral rotation, with an extended Arm support of medial rotation, centering of the Humeral Head in the Glenoid Fossa, tension of the Joint Capsule ◙ Fig. 6.Eb • *Subacromial Bursa*	Suprascapular N. C4–C6	Suprascapular A. Circumflex Scapular A. Thoracoacromial A. Transverse Cervical A.
Infraspinatus M. Lateral rotation in the Shoulder Joint, support of abduction (cranial part) and of adduction (caudal part), Tension of the Joint Capsule • *Infraspinatus Subtendinous Bursa*	Suprascapular N. C4–C6	Suprascapular A. Circumflex Scapular A.
Teres Minor M. Lateral rotation and adduction in the Shoulder Joint	Axillary N. C5–C6	Circumflex Scapular A.
Subscapularis M. Medial rotation in the Shoulder Joint, support of abduction (cranial part) and of adduction with an elevated Arm • *Subscapular Subtendinous Bursa (Subtendinous Recess)* • *Subcoracoid Bursa*	Subscapular N. C5–C7 (C8)	Subscapular Branch of the Axillary A. Subscapular A. Muscular Branches of the Thoracodorsal A.
Teres Major M. Medial rotation, adduction, and extension in the Shoulder Joint • *Teres Major Subtendinous Bursa*	Subscapular N. and/or Thoracodorsal N. C5–C7	Thoracodorsal A.
Latissimus Dorsi M. Medial rotation, adduction, and extension in the Shoulder Joint, lowering of the elevated Arm With Humerus in Fixed Position: Lifting of the Trunk and support of forced expiration, support of the extension of the Lumbar Spine • *Latissimus Dorsi Subtendinous Bursa*	Thoracodorsal N. C6–C8	Thoracodorsal A. Posterior Intercostal Aa.
Ventral Group (Ventral Brachial Mm.)		
Coracobrachialis M. Flexion and adduction in the Shoulder Joint Supporting muscle for the Arm • *Coracobrachialis Bursa*	Musculocutaneus N. C6–C7 (C8)	Anterior and Posterior Circumflex Humeral Aa.

Pectoralis Major M.
Entire Muscle:
Adduction and medial rotation in the Shoulder Joint, lowering of the elevated Arm, leading the Arm in front of the body to the opposite side,
With the Humerus in Fixed Position:
    Moving forward and lowering of the shoulder and movement of the Trunk toward the Arm (climbing and pull-up)
Clavicular Part:
Flexion in the Shoulder Joint with an abducted Arm
Sternocostal Part:
With the Humerus in Fixed Position:
    Lifting the Ribs (support of inspiration)
• *Pectoralis Major Bursa*
	Medial Pectoral N. (C8–T1)
	Lateral Pectoral N. (C5–C7)
		Pectoral Branches of the Thoracoacromial A.
		Lateral Thoracic A.
		Branches of the Posterior Intercostal Aa.
		Medial Mammary Branches of the Perforator Branches from the Internal Thoracic A.

Pectoralis Minor M. (The muscles belong functionally to the muscles of the Shoulder Girdle, and embryologically to the group of the ventral muscles of the Shoulder Joint; they may insert via the Coracoglenoid Ligament on the Humerus.) Lowering and tilting of the Scapula, rotation of the inferior angle in a dorso-medial direction With a Fixated Shoulder Girdle: Lifting of the Ribs (support of inspiration)	Medial Pectoral N. (C8–T1) and Lateral Pectoral N. (variation) (C5–C7)	Thoracoacromial A. Intercostal Aa.

• Bursa = Synovial Bursa assigned to a muscle.

🔵 Suprascapular N.: Segment indicating Infraspinatus M. for the Spinal Cord Segment C4, Scapulohumeral Reflex.

6.Ha,b Muscles of the Upper Arm and Forearm (Muscles of the Elbow and Shoulder Joints): Origins on the Humerus.

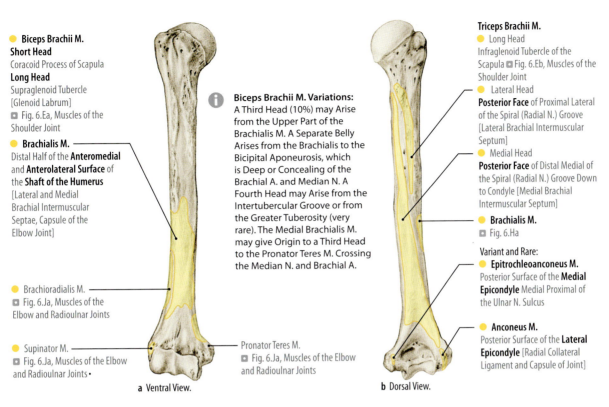

● **Biceps Brachii M.**
Short Head
Coracoid Process of Scapula
Long Head
Supraglenoid Tubercle
[Glenoid Labrum]
□ Fig. 6.Ea, Muscles of the
Shoulder Joint

● **Brachialis M.**
Distal Half of the **Anteromedial**
and **Anterolateral Surface** of
the **Shaft of the Humerus**
[Lateral and Medial
Brachial Intermuscular
Septae, Capsule of the
Elbow Joint]

● Brachioradialis M.
□ Fig. 6.Ja, Muscles of the
Elbow and Radioulnar Joints

● Supinator M.
□ Fig. 6.Ja, Muscles of the
Elbow and Radioulnar Joints ·

ⓘ **Biceps Brachii M. Variations:**
A Third Head (10%) may Arise
from the Upper Part of the
Brachialis M. A Separate Belly
Arises from the Brachialis to the
Bicipital Aponeurosis, which
is Deep or Concealing of the
Brachial A. and Median N. A
Fourth Head may Arise from the
Intertubercular Groove or from
the Greater Tuberosity (very
rare). The Medial Brachialis M.
may give Origin to a Third Head
to the Pronator Teres M. Crossing
the Median N. and Brachial A.

Pronator Teres M.
□ Fig. 6.Ja, Muscles of the Elbow
and Radioulnar Joints

Triceps Brachii M.
● Long Head
Infraglenoid Tubercle of the
Scapula □ Fig. 6.Eb, Muscles of the
Shoulder Joint

● Lateral Head
Posterior Face of Proximal Lateral
of the Spiral (Radial N.) Groove
[Lateral Brachial Intermuscular
Septum]

● Medial Head
Posterior Face of Distal Medial of
the Spiral (Radial N.) Groove Down
to Condyle [Medial Brachial
Intermuscular Septum]

● **Brachialis M.**
□ Fig. 6.Ha

Variant and Rare:
● **Epitrochleoanconeus M.**
Posterior Surface of the **Medial
Epicondyle** Medial Proximal of
the Ulnar N. Sulcus

● **Anconeus M.**
Posterior Surface of the **Lateral
Epicondyle** [Radial Collateral
Ligament and Capsule of Joint]

a Ventral View.

b Dorsal View.

6.Ia,b Muscles of the Upper Arm and Forearm (Muscles of the Elbow and Shoulder Joints): Insertions on Radius and Ulna.

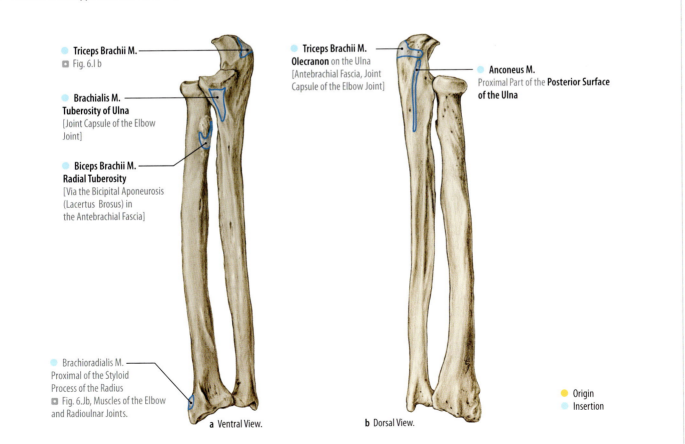

● Triceps Brachii M.
□ Fig. 6.I b

● **Brachialis M.**
Tuberosity of Ulna
[Joint Capsule of the Elbow
Joint]

● **Biceps Brachii M.**
Radial Tuberosity
[Via the Bicipital Aponeurosis
(Lacertus Brosus) in
the Antebrachial Fascia]

● Triceps Brachii M.
Olecranon on the Ulna
[Antebrachial Fascia, Joint
Capsule of the Elbow Joint]

● **Anconeus M.**
Proximal Part of the **Posterior Surface
of the Ulna**

● Brachioradialis M.
Proximal of the Styloid
Process of the Radius
□ Fig. 6.Jb, Muscles of the Elbow
and Radioulnar Joints.

● Origin
● Insertion

a Ventral View.

b Dorsal View.

Muscles of the Arm

Function	Innervation	Blood Supply
Anterior (Ventral) Muscles		
Biceps Brachii M. **Long Head** **Short Head** Flexion in the Elbow Joint (in supination position) Supination (with a flexed Elbow Joint) Medial rotation and abduction in the Shoulder Joint (long head) Adduction in the Shoulder Joint (short head) • *Intertubercular (bicipital long head) Tendinis* • *Bicipitoradial Bursa*	Musculocutaneus N. C5–C6	Muscular Branches of the Axillary A. (Anterior Circumflex Humeral A.) and of the Brachial A.
Brachialis M. Flexion in the Elbow Joint (in supination and pronation position)	Musculocutaneus N. and Radial N. C5–C6 (C7)	Muscles of the Brachial A. Superior Ulnar Collateral A. Inferior Ulnar Collateral A. Recurrent Radial A.
Posterior (Dorsal) Muscles		
Triceps Brachii M. **Long Head** **Lateral Head** **Medial Head** Extension in the Elbow Joint Adduction in the Shoulder Joint (long head) Carrying the weight of the Arm (long head)	Radial N. C6–C8 (T1)	Posterior Circumflex Humeral A. Deep Brachial A. Superior Ulnar Collateral A.
Anconeus M. Extension in the Elbow Joint Tension of the Joint Capsule • *Olecranon Subcutaneous Bursa* • *Olecranon Intratendinous Bursa* • *Subtendinous Triceps Brachii M. Bursa*	Radial N. C7–C8	Recurrent Interosseous A. from the Posterior Interosseous A.

• Bursa = Synovial Bursa assigned to a muscle.

🔁 Musculocutaneus N. C5–C6: Biceps Brachii Reflex.
   Radial N. C6–C8 (T1): Segment indicating Triceps Brachii M. for the Spinal Cord Segment C7, Triceps Brachii Reflex.

6.J Muscles of the Forearm (Muscles of the Proximal and Distal Radioulnar Joints and of the Elbow Joint): Origins and Insertions on: **a** the Humerus, and **b** on the Radius and Ulna. Ventral View.

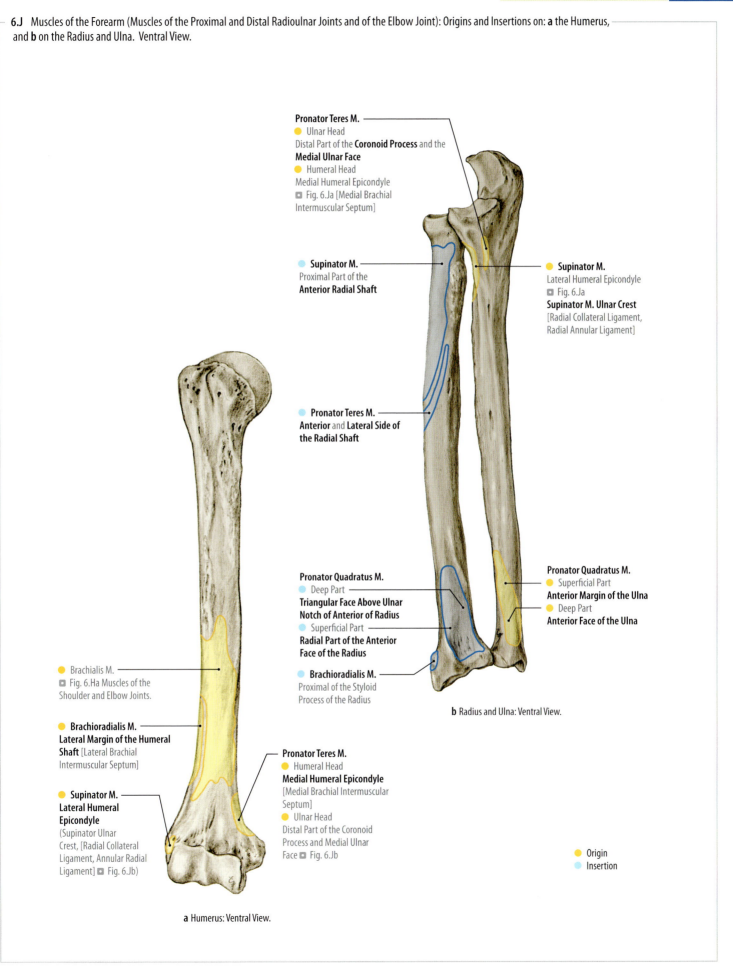

Pronator Teres M.
● Ulnar Head
Distal Part of the **Coronoid Process** and the **Medial Ulnar Face**
● Humeral Head
Medial Humeral Epicondyle
□ Fig. 6.Ja [Medial Brachial Intermuscular Septum]

● **Supinator M.**
Proximal Part of the **Anterior Radial Shaft**

● **Supinator M.**
Lateral Humeral Epicondyle
□ Fig. 6.Ja
Supinator M. Ulnar Crest
[Radial Collateral Ligament, Radial Annular Ligament]

● **Pronator Teres M.**
Anterior and **Lateral Side of the Radial Shaft**

Pronator Quadratus M.
● Deep Part
Triangular Face Above Ulnar Notch of Anterior of Radius
● Superficial Part
Radial Part of the Anterior Face of the Radius

Pronator Quadratus M.
● Superficial Part
Anterior Margin of the Ulna
● Deep Part
Anterior Face of the Ulna

● **Brachioradialis M.**
Proximal of the Styloid Process of the Radius

● Brachialis M.
□ Fig. 6.Ha Muscles of the Shoulder and Elbow Joints.

● **Brachioradialis M.**
Lateral Margin of the Humeral Shaft [Lateral Brachial Intermuscular Septum]

● **Supinator M.**
Lateral Humeral Epicondyle
(Supinator Ulnar Crest, [Radial Collateral Ligament, Annular Radial Ligament] □ Fig. 6.Jb)

b Radius and Ulna: Ventral View.

Pronator Teres M.
● Humeral Head
Medial Humeral Epicondyle
[Medial Brachial Intermuscular Septum]
● Ulnar Head
Distal Part of the Coronoid Process and Medial Ulnar Face □ Fig. 6.Jb

● Origin
● Insertion

a Humerus: Ventral View.

Muscles of the Arm

Function	Innervation	Blood Supply
Group of the Posterior (Dorsal), Superficial, Radial Muscles		
Brachioradialis M. Flexion in the Elbow Joint (in neutral-0-position of the Arm) Support of the pronation with a supinated Forearm and of the supination with a pronated Forearm, up to the neutral-0-position, respectively Tension banding effect for the radius	Radial N. C5–C6	Radial Collateral A. Radial Recurrent A. Muscular Branches of the Radial A.
Group of the Anterior (Ventral), Superficial Muscles		

Pronator Teres M.
 Humeral Head
 Ulnar Head
  Pronation (both heads),
  Support of the flexion in the Elbow Joint (Humeral Head)
	Median N. C6–C7	Muscular Branches of the Brachial,
		Ulnar and Radial Aa.

Group of the Anterior (Ventral), Deep Muscles		
Pronator Quadratus M. Pronation	Anterior Interosseous N. of the Median N. (C7) C8–T1	Anterior Interosseous A. form the Common Interosseous A. of Ulnar A.
Group of the Posterior (Dorsal), Deep Muscles		
Supinator M. Supination (in flexion and extension position of the Elbow Joint)	Deep Branch of the Radial N.	Recurrent Interosseous A. from the Ulnar A. Radial Recurrent A. from the Radial A.

Radial N. C5–C6: Segment indicating Brachioradialis M. for the Spinal Cord Segment C6, Brachioradialis Reflex.

6

6.Ka,b Muscles of the Forearm (Muscles of the Hand and Finger Joints): Origins on the Humerus.

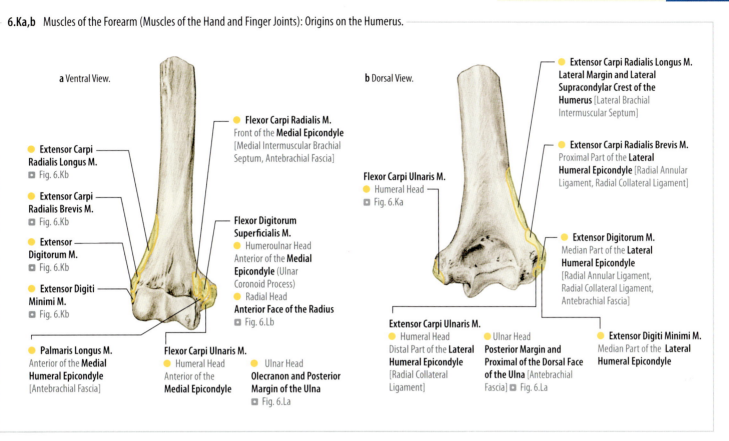

a Ventral View.

● Extensor Carpi Radialis Longus M.
▢ Fig. 6.Kb

● Extensor Carpi Radialis Brevis M.
▢ Fig. 6.Kb

● Extensor Digitorum M.
▢ Fig. 6.Kb

● Extensor Digiti Minimi M.
▢ Fig. 6.Kb

● Palmaris Longus M.
Anterior of the **Medial Humeral Epicondyle** [Antebrachial Fascia]

● Flexor Carpi Radialis M.
Front of the **Medial Epicondyle** [Medial Intermuscular Brachial Septum, Antebrachial Fascia]

● Flexor Digitorum Superficialis M.
● Humeroulnar Head
Anterior of the **Medial Epicondyle** (Ulnar Coronoid Process)
● Radial Head
Anterior Face of the Radius
▢ Fig. 6.Lb

Flexor Carpi Ulnaris M.
● Humeral Head
Anterior of the **Medial Epicondyle**
● Ulnar Head
Olecranon and Posterior Margin of the Ulna
▢ Fig. 6.La

b Dorsal View.

Flexor Carpi Ulnaris M.
● Humeral Head
▢ Fig. 6.Ka

● Extensor Carpi Radialis Longus M.
Lateral Margin and Lateral Supracondylar Crest of the **Humerus** [Lateral Brachial Intermuscular Septum]

● Extensor Carpi Radialis Brevis M.
Proximal Part of the **Lateral Humeral Epicondyle** [Radial Annular Ligament, Radial Collateral Ligament]

● Extensor Digitorum M.
Median Part of the **Lateral Humeral Epicondyle** [Radial Annular Ligament, Radial Collateral Ligament, Antebrachial Fascia]

● Extensor Digiti Minimi M.
Median Part of the **Lateral Humeral Epicondyle**

Extensor Carpi Ulnaris M.
● Humeral Head
Distal Part of the **Lateral Humeral Epicondyle** [Radial Collateral Ligament]
● Ulnar Head
Posterior Margin and Proximal of the Dorsal Face of the Ulna [Antebrachial Fascia] ▢ Fig. 6.La

6.La,b Muscles of the Forearm (Muscles of the Hand and Finger Joints): Origins on the Radius and the Ulna.

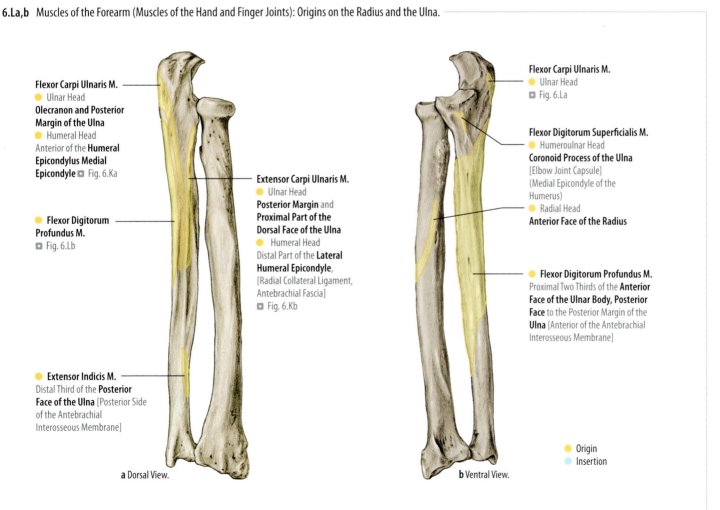

Flexor Carpi Ulnaris M.
● Ulnar Head
Olecranon and Posterior Margin of the Ulna
● Humeral Head
Anterior of the **Humeral Epicondylus Medial Epicondyle** ▢ Fig. 6.Ka

● Flexor Digitorum Profundus M.
▢ Fig. 6.Lb

● Extensor Indicis M.
Distal Third of the **Posterior Face of the Ulna** [Posterior Side of the Antebrachial Interosseous Membrane]

Extensor Carpi Ulnaris M.
● Ulnar Head
Posterior Margin and **Proximal Part of the Dorsal Face of the Ulna**
● Humeral Head
Distal Part of the **Lateral Humeral Epicondyle**, [Radial Collateral Ligament, Antebrachial Fascia]
▢ Fig. 6.Kb

Flexor Carpi Ulnaris M.
● Ulnar Head
▢ Fig. 6.La

Flexor Digitorum Superficialis M.
● Humeroulnar Head
Coronoid Process of the Ulna [Elbow Joint Capsule] (Medial Epicondyle of the Humerus)
● Radial Head
Anterior Face of the Radius

● Flexor Digitorum Profundus M.
Proximal Two Thirds of the **Anterior Face of the Ulnar Body, Posterior Face** to the Posterior Margin of the **Ulna** [Anterior of the Antebrachial Interosseous Membrane]

● Origin
● Insertion

a Dorsal View.

b Ventral View.

Muscles of the Arm

6.Ma Muscles of the Forearm and Long Muscles of the Fingers (Muscles of the Hand and Finger Joints): Insertions on the Skeleton of the Hand, Palmar View.

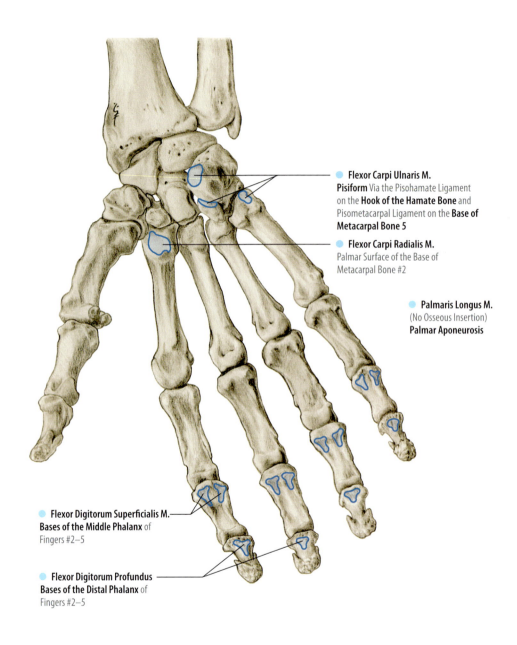

6

● **Flexor Carpi Ulnaris M.**
Pisiform Via the Pisohamate Ligament
on the **Hook of the Hamate Bone** and
Pisometacarpal Ligament on the **Base of
Metacarpal Bone 5**

● **Flexor Carpi Radialis M.**
Palmar Surface of the Base of
Metacarpal Bone #2

● **Palmaris Longus M.**
(No Osseous Insertion)
Palmar Aponeurosis

● **Flexor Digitorum Superficialis M.**
Bases of the Middle Phalanx of
Fingers #2–5

● **Flexor Digitorum Profundus**
Bases of the Distal Phalanx of
Fingers #2–5

● Origin
● Insertion

6.Mb Muscles of the Forearm and Long Muscles of the Hand (Muscles of the Hand and Finger Joints): Insertions on the Skeleton of the Hand, Dorsal View.

● **Extensor Carpi Radialis Brevis M.**
Base and Styloid Process of the 3rd Metacarpal Bone, Variable on the Base of Metacarpal Bone #2

● **Extensor Carpi Ulnaris M.**
Base of the Metacarpal Bone #5

● **Extensor Carpi Radialis Longus M.**
Radial Part of the **Base of Metacarpal Bone #2**

● **Extensor Digiti Minimi M.**
Via Extensor (Dorsal) Expansion in Ulnar Area of the **Bases of the Middle and Distal Phalanges of the Small Finger**

● **Extensor Digitorum M.**
Via Extensor (Dorsal) Expansion of the **Bases of Middle and Distal Phalanges of the Fingers #2–5**
[In the Metacarpophalangeal Joints on the Dorsal Fibrous Cartilaginous Plates and on the Capsules of the Metacarpophalangeal and Proximal Interphalangeal Joints]

● **Extensor Indicis M.**
Via the Dorsal (Extensor) Expansion in the Ulnar Area of the **Bases of the Middle and Distal Phalanges of the Index Finger**

● Origin
● Insertion

Muscles of the Arm

Function	Innervation	Blood Supply
Group of the Anterior (Ventral), Superficial Muscles		
Flexor Carpi Radialis M. Palmar flexion and radial abduction in the Hand Joints Support of flexion in the Elbow Joint and of pronation	Median N. (C5), C6–C7 (C8)	Muscular Branches of the Radial A.
Flexor Carpi Ulnaris M. Palmar flexion and ulnar abduction in the Hand Joints	Ulnar N. C7–T1	Superior Ulnar Collateral A. from the Brachial A. Recurrent Ulnar A. Muscular Branches of the Ulnar A.
Palmaris Longus M. [The muscle is missing in ~20% of all cases] Support of palmar flexion and of radial abduction in the Hand Joints	Median N. C8–T1	Muscular Branches of the Ulnar A.
Flexor Digitorum Superficialis M. Palmar flexion in the hand joints Flexion in the Proximal Interphalangeal Joints of the Fingers #2–5, Support of flexion in the Metacarpophalangeal Joints and of the adduction of the spread-apart Fingers	Median N. (Variable also from the Ulnar N. (C6) C7–T1	Muscular Branches of the Radial A. and of the Ulnar A.
Group of the Anterior (Ventral), Deep Muscles		
Flexor Digitorum Profundus M. Palmar flexion and ulnar abduction in the Hand Joints, flexion in the Distal Interphalangeal Joints of the Fingers #2–5 Support of flexion in the Metacarpophalangeal and Proximal Interphalangeal Joints, as well as support of adduction of the spread-apart Fingers	Anterior Antebrachial Interosseous of the Median N. (Finger #2) Median N. and Ulnar N. (Fingers #3 and 4) Ulnar N. (Finger #5) C6–T1	Anterior Interosseous A. and Muscular Branches of the Ulnar A.
Group of the Posterior (Dorsal), Superficial, Ulnar Muscles		
Extensor Digitorum M. Dorsal extension and Ulnar abduction in the Hand Joints Extension in the Metacarpophalangeal Joints of the Fingers #2–5 Support of extension in the Proximal Interphalangeal and Distal Interphalangeal Joints with flexed Hand Joints Adduction of the spread-apart Fingers and the abduction of the adducted Fingers	Deep Branch of the Radial N. C6–C8	Posterior Interosseous A. of the Ulnar A.
Extensor Digiti Minimi M. Extension and abduction of the Little Finger in the Metacarpophalangeal Joint, dorsal extension and ulnar abduction in the Hand Joints	Deep Branch of the Radial N. C7–C8	Posterior Interosseous A. of the Ulnar A.
Extensor Carpi Ulnaris M. Ulnar abduction and support of dorsal extension in the Hand Joints	Radial N. C7–C8	Posterior Interosseous A. of the Ulnar A.
Group of the Posterior (Dorsal), Superficial, Radial Muscles		
Extensor Carpi Radialis Brevis M. Dorsal extension in the Hand Joints Support of the return of the Ulnar Abducted Hand to the neutral-0-position (function with fist closure, see below)	Deep Branch of the Radial N. C6–C7	Radial Collateral A. from the Deep Brachial A. Recurrent Radial A. and Muscular Branches of the Radial A.
Extensor Carpi Radialis Longus M. Dorsal extension and radial abduction in the Hand Joints Support of flexion of the Fingers (fist closure) through stabilization of the Hand Joints and through forward extension of the Flexors Support of flexion in the Elbow Joint (Brachioradialis M., ◼ Fig. 6.6Jb)	Deep Branch of the Radial N. C6–C7	Radial Collateral A. from the Deep Brachial A. Radial Recurrent A. and Muscular Branches of the Radial A.
Group of the Posterior (Dorsal), Deep Muscles		
Extensor Indicis M. Extension of the Index Finger in the Metacarpophalangeal Joint Support of extension in the Proximal Interphalangeal and Distal Interphalangeal Joints as well as in the Hand Joints	Deep Branch of the Radial N. C7–C8	Posterior Interosseous A. of the Ulnar A.

6

6.Na,b Muscles of the Forearm (Muscles of the Thumb Joint): Origins on the Radius and the Ulna.

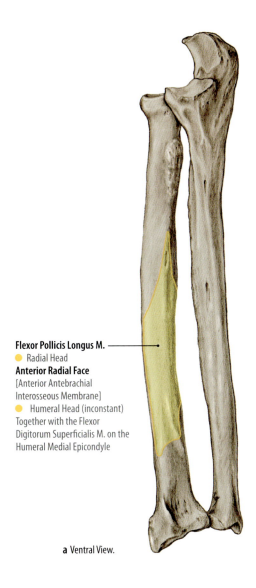

Flexor Pollicis Longus M.
● Radial Head
Anterior Radial Face
[Anterior Antebrachial
Interosseous Membrane]
● Humeral Head (inconstant)
Together with the Flexor
Digitorum Superficialis M. on the
Humeral Medial Epicondyle

a Ventral View.

ℹ **Flexor Pollicis Longus M. Variations:**
Muscular slips of Flexor Digitorum Superficialis M.,
Flexor Digitorum Profundus M., or Pronator Teres.

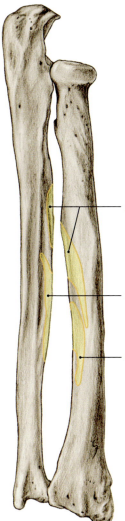

● **Abductor Pollicis Longus M.**
Medial Third of the **Posterior Radial
and Posterior Ulnar Faces**
[Posterior Side of the Antebrachial
Interosseous Membrane]

● **Extensor Pollicis Longus M.**
Medial Third of the **Posterior and
Margin Face Interosseus Ulnar
Membrane**

● **Extensor Pollicis Brevis M.**
Transition between the Medial and
Distal Third of the **Posterior Face
and the Radial Margin Interosseous
Membrane**, Inconstant on the Margin
Ulna Interosseous Membrane [Posterior
of Antebrachial Interosseous Membrane]

b Dorsal View.

● Origin
● Insertion

6.0a Muscles of the Forearm and the Hand (Muscles of the Thumb Joint), Origins and Insertions on the Skeleton of the Hand, Palmar View.

6

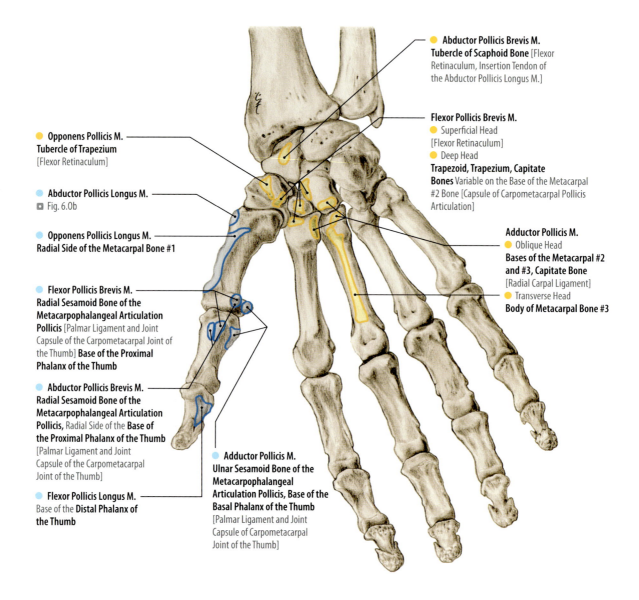

● **Opponens Pollicis M.**
Tubercle of Trapezium
[Flexor Retinaculum]

● **Abductor Pollicis Longus M.**
☐ Fig. 6.0b

● **Opponens Pollicis Longus M.**
Radial Side of the Metacarpal Bone #1

● **Flexor Pollicis Brevis M.**
Radial Sesamoid Bone of the
Metacarpophalangeal Articulation
Pollicis [Palmar Ligament and Joint
Capsule of the Carpometacarpal Joint of
the Thumb] **Base of the Proximal**
Phalanx of the Thumb

● **Abductor Pollicis Brevis M.**
Radial Sesamoid Bone of the
Metacarpophalangeal Articulation
Pollicis, Radial Side of the **Base of**
the Proximal Phalanx of the Thumb
[Palmar Ligament and Joint
Capsule of the Carpometacarpal
Joint of the Thumb]

● **Flexor Pollicis Longus M.**
Base of the **Distal Phalanx of**
the Thumb

● **Adductor Pollicis M.**
Ulnar Sesamoid Bone of the
Metacarpophalangeal
Articulation Pollicis, Base of the
Basal Phalanx of the Thumb
[Palmar Ligament and Joint
Capsule of Carpometacarpal
Joint of the Thumb]

● **Abductor Pollicis Brevis M.**
Tubercle of Scaphoid Bone [Flexor
Retinaculum, Insertion Tendon of
the Abductor Pollicis Longus M.]

● **Flexor Pollicis Brevis M.**
● Superficial Head
[Flexor Retinaculum]
● Deep Head
Trapezoid, Trapezium, Capitate
Bones Variable on the Base of the Metacarpal
#2 Bone [Capsule of Carpometacarpal Pollicis
Articulation]

Adductor Pollicis M.
● Oblique Head
Bases of the Metacarpal #2
and #3, Capitate Bone
[Radial Carpal Ligament]
● Transverse Head
Body of Metacarpal Bone #3

● Origin
● Insertion

6.0b Muscles of the Forearm and Hand (Muscles of the Thumb Joint): Insertions on the Skeleton of the Hand, Dorsal View.

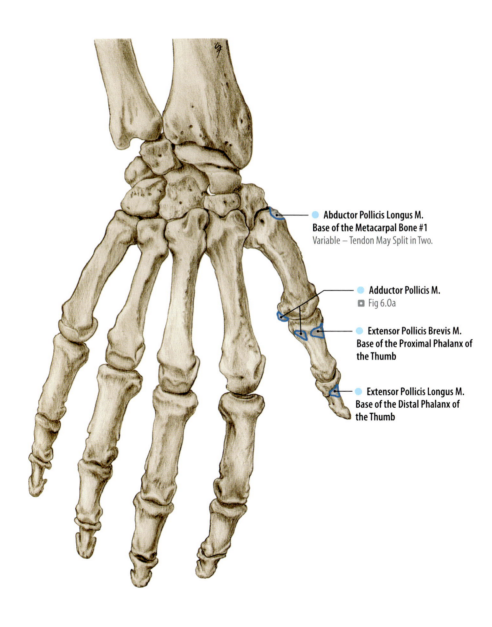

● **Abductor Pollicis Longus M.**
Base of the Metacarpal Bone #1
Variable – Tendon May Split in Two.

● **Adductor Pollicis M.**
▣ Fig 6.0a

● **Extensor Pollicis Brevis M.**
Base of the Proximal Phalanx of the Thumb

● **Extensor Pollicis Longus M.**
Base of the Distal Phalanx of the Thumb

● Origin
● Insertion

Function	Innervation	Blood Supply
Group of the Anterior (Ventral), Deep Muscles		
Flexor Pollicis Longus M. Flexion in the Metacarpophalangeal and Distal Interphalangeal Joints of the Thumb Support of opposition movement in the Carpometacarpal Joint Support of flexion and radial abduction in the Hand Joints	Anterior Interosseous N. of the Median N. (C6) C7–C8 (T1)	Muscular Branches of the Radial A. Anterior Interosseous A. Muscular Branches of the Ulnar A.
Group of the Posterior (Dorsal), Deep Muscles		
Abductor Pollicis Longus M. Abduction and extension of the Carpometacarpal Joint (repositioning of the Thumb) Radial abduction and flexion in the Hand Joints	Deep Branch of the Radial N. (C6) C7–C8	Posterior Interosseous A. of the Ulnar A. Muscular Branches of the Radial A.
Extensor Pollicis Brevis M. Extension in the Metacarpophalangeal Joint of the Thumb Support of extension and abduction in the Carpometacarpal Joint (repositioning of the Thumb) as well as of radial abduction in the Hand Joints	Deep Branch of the Radial N. C6–C7	Posterior Interosseous A. of the Ulnar A. Muscular Branches of the Radial A.
Extensor Pollicis Longus M. Extension in the Interphalangeal Joint of the Thumb and in the Metacarpophalangeal Joint of the Thumb Adduction and extension of the Thumb in the Carpometacarpal Joint (repositioning of the Thumb) Dorsal extension and radial abduction in the Hand Joints	Deep Branch of the Radial N. C6–C7	Posterior Interosseous A. of the Ulnar A.
Muscles of the Thenar (Thenar Muscles)		
Abductor Pollicis Brevis M. Abduction in the Carpometacarpal Joint Slight flexion in the metacarpophalangeal Joint of the Thumb (opening of the hand for the grasping movement)	Median N. C6–C7	Muscular Branches of the Superficial Palmar Arch and of the Radial A.
Opponens Pollicis M. Inward rotation, adduction, and flexion in the Carpometacarpal Joint (in connection with opposition movement)	Median N. C6–C7	Muscular Branches of the Superficial Palmar Arch Princeps Pollicis A. from the Radial A.
Flexor Pollicis Brevis M. **Superficial Head and Deep Head:** Flexion in the Metacarpophalangeal Joint of the Thumb **Deep Head:** Flexion, adduction, and inward rotation in the Carpometacarpal Joint (in connection with opposite movement)	Median N. (Superficial Head) Deep Branch of the Ulnar N. (Deep Head) C7–T1	Muscular Branches of the Superficial Palmar Arch Princeps Pollicis A. from the Radial A.
Adductor Pollicis M. Adduction and inward rotation in the Carpometacarpal Joint (in connection with opposition movement) Flexion in the Metacarpophalangeal Joint Support of extension in the Distal Interphalangeal Joint of the Thumb	Deep Branch of the Ulnar N. C8–T1	Muscular Branches of the Deep Palmar Arch

⊘ Anterior Interosseous N. of the Median N. (C6) C7–C8 (T1): Segment indicating Flexor Pollicis Longus M. Spinal Cord Segment C8, Flexor Pollicis Longus Tendon Reflex [Thumb reflex].

6.Pa Short Muscles of the Hand (Muscles of the Finger Joints): Origins and Insertions on the Skeleton of the Hand, Palmar View.

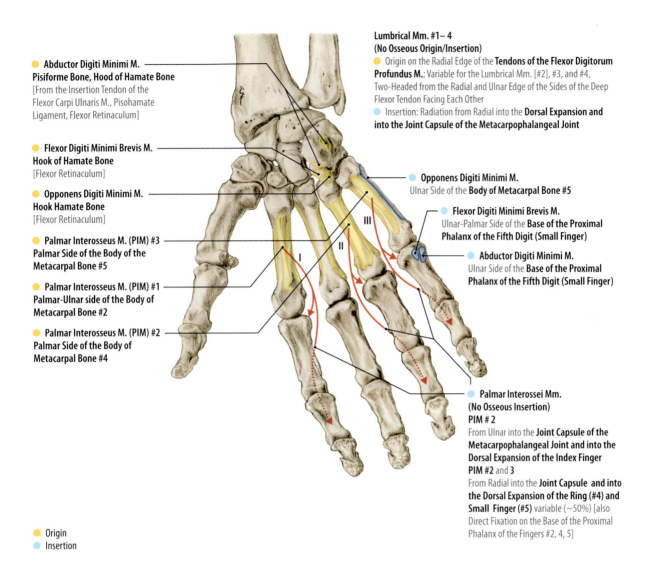

● **Abductor Digiti Minimi M.**
Pisiforme Bone, Hood of Hamate Bone
[From the Insertion Tendon of the
Flexor Carpi Ulnaris M., Pisohamate
Ligament, Flexor Retinaculum]

● **Flexor Digiti Minimi Brevis M.**
Hook of Hamate Bone
[Flexor Retinaculum]

● **Opponens Digiti Minimi M.**
Hook Hamate Bone
[Flexor Retinaculum]

● **Palmar Interosseus M. (PIM) #3**
**Palmar Side of the Body of the
Metacarpal Bone #5**

● **Palmar Interosseus M. (PIM) #1**
**Palmar-Ulnar side of the Body of
Metacarpal Bone #2**

● **Palmar Interosseus M. (PIM) #2**
**Palmar Side of the Body of
Metacarpal Bone #4**

Lumbrical Mm. #1– 4
(No Osseous Origin/Insertion)
● Origin on the Radial Edge of the **Tendons of the Flexor Digitorum
Profundus M.**; Variable for the Lumbrical Mm. [#2], #3, and #4,
Two-Headed from the Radial and Ulnar Edge of the Sides of the Deep
Flexor Tendon Facing Each Other
● Insertion: Radiation from Radial into the **Dorsal Expansion and
into the Joint Capsule of the Metacarpophalangeal Joint**

● **Opponens Digiti Minimi M.**
Ulnar Side of the **Body of Metacarpal Bone #5**

● **Flexor Digiti Minimi Brevis M.**
Ulnar-Palmar Side of the **Base of the Proximal
Phalanx of the Fifth Digit (Small Finger)**

● **Abductor Digiti Minimi M.**
Ulnar Side of the **Base of the Proximal
Phalanx of the Fifth Digit (Small Finger)**

● **Palmar Interossei Mm.**
(No Osseous Insertion)
PIM # 2
From Ulnar into the **Joint Capsule of the
Metacarpophalangeal Joint and into the
Dorsal Expansion of the Index Finger**
PIM #2 and 3
From Radial into the **Joint Capsule and into
the Dorsal Expansion of the Ring (#4) and
Small Finger (#5)** variable (~50%) [also
Direct Fixation on the Base of the Proximal
Phalanx of the Fingers #2, 4, 5]

● Origin
● Insertion

Function	Innervation	Blood Supply
Muscles of the Palm		
Lumbrical Mm. #1–4 Flexion in the Metacarpophalangeal Joints of the Fingers #2–5 ("starting muscles" during flexion) support of extension in the Proximal Interphalangeal and Distal Interphalangeal Joints of the Fingers #1–3	Median N. (Lumbrical Mm. #1, 2) Ulnar N. (Lumbrical Mm. #3, 4)	Muscular Branches of the Superficial Palmar Arch
Palmar Interossei Mm. #1–3 Flexion in the Metacarpophalangeal Joints of the Fingers #2, 4, 5 Extension in the Proximal Interphalangeal and Distal Interphalangeal Joints of the Fingers #2, 4, 5 Adduction of the index, ring, and little fingers to the middle Finger	Deep Branch of the Ulnar N. C8–T1	Muscular Branches of the Deep Palmar Arch
Dorsal Interossei Mm. #1–4 Flexion in the Metacarpophalangeal Joints of the Fingers #2–4, Extension in the Proximal Interphalangeal and Distal Interphalangeal Joints of the Fingers #2–4 Abduction of the index and ring fingers from the middle Finger (spreading of the Fingers)	Deep Branch of the Ulnar N. C8–T1	Muscular Branches of the Deep Palmar Arch

Muscles of the Arm

6.Pb Short Muscles of the Hand (Muscles of the Finger Joints): Origins and Insertions on the Skeleton of the Hand, Dorsal View.

6

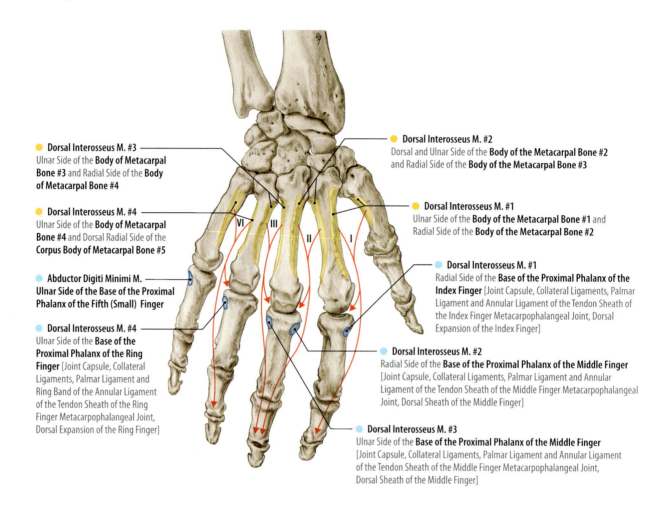

● Dorsal Interosseus M. #3
Ulnar Side of the **Body of Metacarpal Bone #3** and Radial Side of the **Body of Metacarpal Bone #4**

● Dorsal Interosseus M. #4
Ulnar Side of the **Body of Metacarpal Bone #4** and Dorsal Radial Side of the **Corpus Body of Metacarpal Bone #5**

● Abductor Digiti Minimi M.
Ulnar Side of the Base of the Proximal Phalanx of the Fifth (Small) Finger

● Dorsal Interosseus M. #4
Ulnar Side of the **Base of the Proximal Phalanx of the Ring Finger** [Joint Capsule, Collateral Ligaments, Palmar Ligament and Ring Band of the Annular Ligament of the Tendon Sheath of the Ring Finger Metacarpophalangeal Joint, Dorsal Expansion of the Ring Finger]

● Dorsal Interosseus M. #2
Dorsal and Ulnar Side of the **Body of the Metacarpal Bone #2** and Radial Side of the **Body of the Metacarpal Bone #3**

● Dorsal Interosseus M. #1
Ulnar Side of the **Body of the Metacarpal Bone #1** and Radial Side of the **Body of the Metacarpal Bone #2**

● Dorsal Interosseus M. #1
Radial Side of the **Base of the Proximal Phalanx of the Index Finger** [Joint Capsule, Collateral Ligaments, Palmar Ligament and Annular Ligament of the Tendon Sheath of the Index Finger Metacarpophalangeal Joint, Dorsal Expansion of the Index Finger]

● Dorsal Interosseus M. #2
Radial Side of the **Base of the Proximal Phalanx of the Middle Finger** [Joint Capsule, Collateral Ligaments, Palmar Ligament and Annular Ligament of the Tendon Sheath of the Middle Finger Metacarpophalangeal Joint, Dorsal Sheath of the Middle Finger]

● Dorsal Interosseus M. #3
Ulnar Side of the **Base of the Proximal Phalanx of the Middle Finger** [Joint Capsule, Collateral Ligaments, Palmar Ligament and Annular Ligament of the Tendon Sheath of the Middle Finger Metacarpophalangeal Joint, Dorsal Sheath of the Middle Finger]

● Origin
● Insertion

Function	Innervation	Blood Supply
Muscles of the Hypothenar (Hypothenar Muscles)		
Abductor Digiti Minimi M. Abduction of the extended little Finger Flexion in the Metacarpophalangeal Joint Extension in the Proximal Interphalangeal and Distal Interphalangeal Joints of the Little Finger	Deep Branch of the Ulnar N. C8–T1	Muscular Branches of the Superficial Palmar Arch Common Palmar Digital A. #5
Flexor Digiti Minimi Brevis M. Flexion in the Metacarpophalangeal Joint of the little Finger, Slight rotation of the Metacarpal Bone #5 in the Carpometacarpal Joint (in connection with opposition movement)	Deep Branch of the Ulnar N. C8–T1	Muscular Branches of the Superficial Palmar Arch Common Palmar Digital A. #5
Opponens Digiti Minimi M. Slight rotation of the Metacarpal Bone #5 in the Carpometacarpal Joint	Deep Branch of the Ulnar N. C8–T1	Muscular Branches of the Superficial Palmar Arch Common Palmar Digital A. #5

⊘ Deep Branch of the Ulnar N. C8–T1: Segment indicating Abductor Digiti Minimi M. for the Spinal Cord Segment T1.

Lower Limbs

Hip Bone

7.1a,b Right Hip Bone. [6]

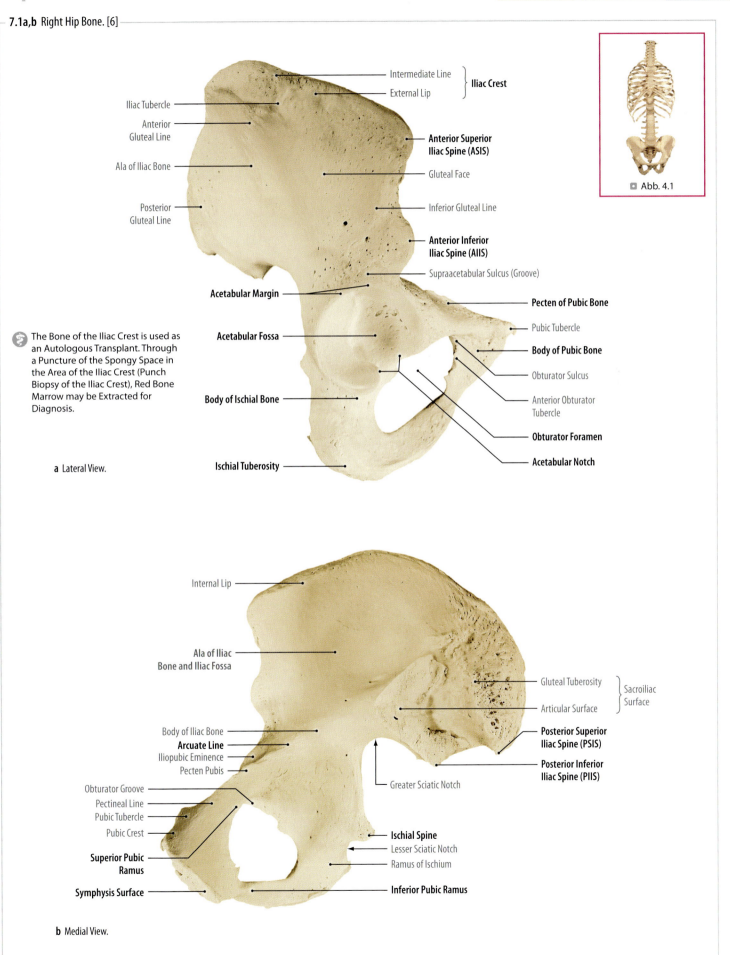

□ Abb. 4.1

Intermediate Line
External Lip
} **Iliac Crest**

Iliac Tubercle

Anterior
Gluteal Line

Ala of Iliac Bone

Posterior
Gluteal Line

**Anterior Superior
Iliac Spine (ASIS)**

Gluteal Face

Inferior Gluteal Line

**Anterior Inferior
Iliac Spine (AIIS)**

Supraacetabular Sulcus (Groove)

Acetabular Margin

Pecten of Pubic Bone

Pubic Tubercle

The Bone of the Iliac Crest is used as an Autologous Transplant. Through a Puncture of the Spongy Space in the Area of the Iliac Crest (Punch Biopsy of the Iliac Crest), Red Bone Marrow may be Extracted for Diagnosis.

Acetabular Fossa

Body of Pubic Bone

Obturator Sulcus

Anterior Obturator
Tubercle

Body of Ischial Bone

Obturator Foramen

Ischial Tuberosity

Acetabular Notch

a Lateral View.

Internal Lip

**Ala of Iliac
Bone and Iliac Fossa**

Gluteal Tuberosity
} Sacroiliac
Surface

Articular Surface

Body of Iliac Bone

Arcuate Line

Iliopubic Eminence

Pecten Pubis

**Posterior Superior
Iliac Spine (PSIS)**

**Posterior Inferior
Iliac Spine (PIIS)**

Greater Sciatic Notch

Obturator Groove

Pectineal Line

Pubic Tubercle

Pubic Crest

**Superior Pubic
Ramus**

Ischial Spine

Lesser Sciatic Notch

Ramus of Ischium

Symphysis Surface

Inferior Pubic Ramus

b Medial View.

Hip Bone – Development

7.2a–c Hip Bone, Development. [a, c 6; b 35]

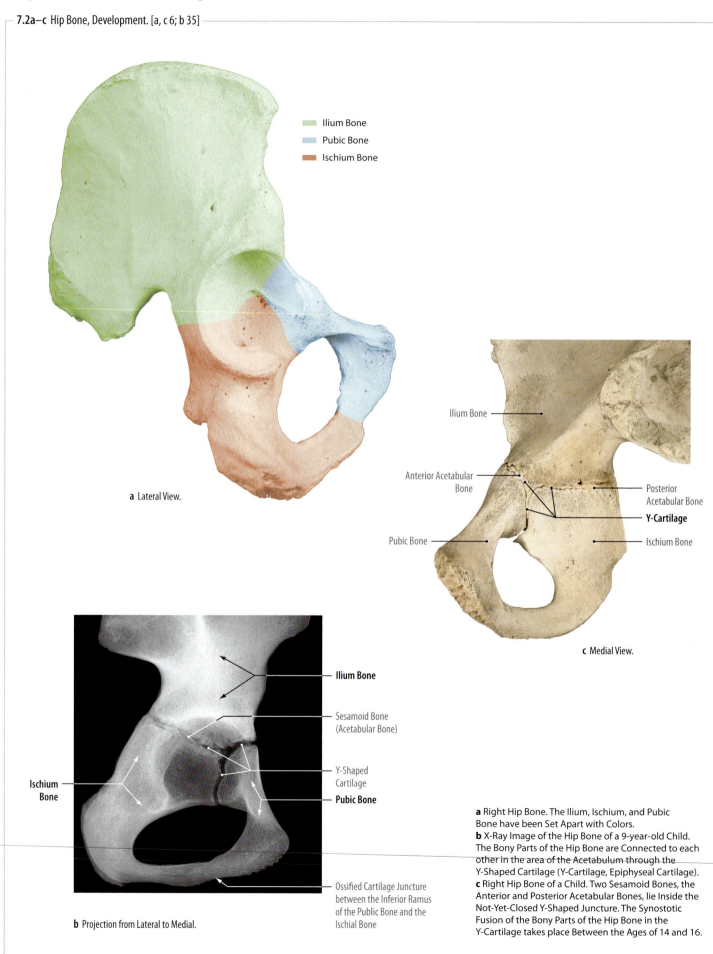

Ilium Bone
Pubic Bone
Ischium Bone

a Lateral View.

Ilium Bone

Anterior Acetabular
Bone

Pubic Bone

Posterior
Acetabular Bone

Y-Cartilage

Ischium Bone

c Medial View.

Ilium Bone

Sesamoid Bone
(Acetabular Bone)

Y-Shaped
Cartilage

Pubic Bone

Ischium
Bone

Ossified Cartilage Juncture
between the Inferior Ramus
of the Public Bone and the
Ischial Bone

b Projection from Lateral to Medial.

a Right Hip Bone. The Ilium, Ischium, and Pubic
Bone have been Set Apart with Colors.
b X-Ray Image of the Hip Bone of a 9-year-old Child.
The Bony Parts of the Hip Bone are Connected to each
other in the area of the Acetabulum through the
Y-Shaped Cartilage (Y-Cartilage, Epiphyseal Cartilage).
c Right Hip Bone of a Child. Two Sesamoid Bones, the
Anterior and Posterior Acetabular Bones, lie Inside the
Not-Yet-Closed Y-Shaped Juncture. The Synostotic
Fusion of the Bony Parts of the Hip Bone in the
Y-Cartilage takes place Between the Ages of 14 and 16.

7

Femur

7.3a,b Right Femur. [6]

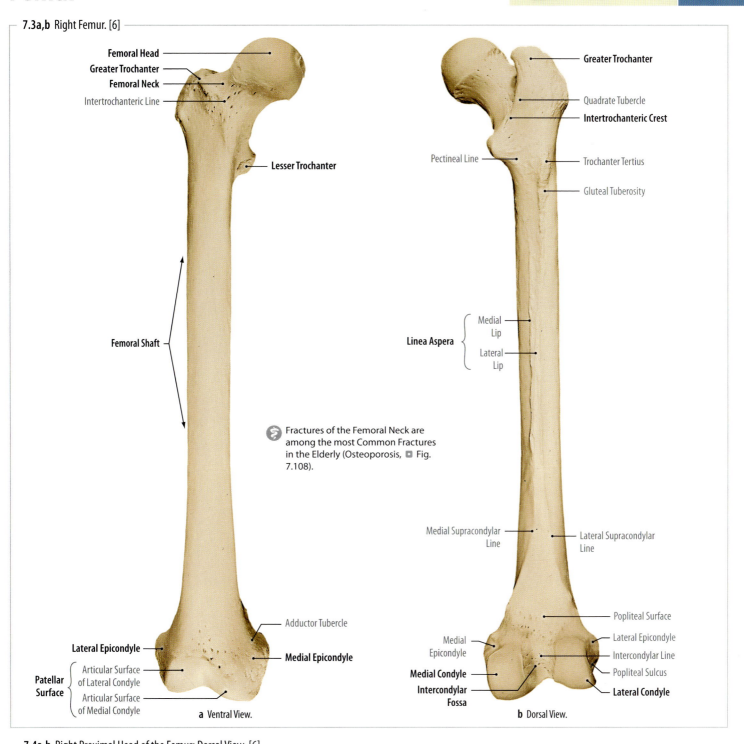

Femoral Head
Greater Trochanter
Femoral Neck
Intertrochanteric Line

Lesser Trochanter

Femoral Shaft

ⓢ Fractures of the Femoral Neck are among the most Common Fractures in the Elderly (Osteoporosis, ▣ Fig. 7.108).

Lateral Epicondyle

Patellar Surface
Articular Surface of Lateral Condyle
Articular Surface of Medial Condyle

Adductor Tubercle

Medial Epicondyle

a Ventral View.

Greater Trochanter
Quadrate Tubercle
Intertrochanteric Crest
Pectineal Line
Trochanter Tertius
Gluteal Tuberosity

Linea Aspera
Medial Lip
Lateral Lip

Medial Supracondylar Line
Lateral Supracondylar Line

Popliteal Surface
Medial Epicondyle
Lateral Epicondyle
Intercondylar Line
Medial Condyle
Popliteal Sulcus
Intercondylar Fossa
Lateral Condyle

b Dorsal View.

7.4a,b Right Proximal Head of the Femur: Dorsal View. [6]

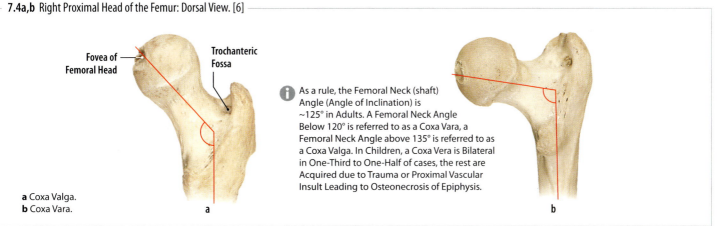

Fovea of Femoral Head
Trochanteric Fossa

ⓘ As a rule, the Femoral Neck (shaft) Angle (Angle of Inclination) is ~125° in Adults. A Femoral Neck Angle Below 120° is referred to as a Coxa Vara, a Femoral Neck Angle above 135° is referred to as a Coxa Valga. In Children, a Coxa Vera is Bilateral in One-Third to One-Half of cases, the rest are Acquired due to Trauma or Proximal Vascular Insult Leading to Osteonecrosis of Epiphysis.

a Coxa Valga.
b Coxa Vara.

a

b

Skeleton

Patella · Fibula and Tibia

7.5a,b Right Kneecap (Patella). [6]

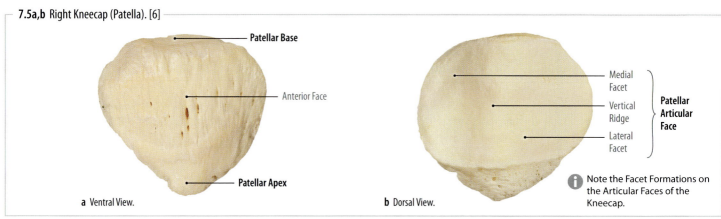

Patellar Base

Anterior Face

Patellar Apex

a Ventral View.

Medial Facet

Vertical Ridge

Lateral Facet

Patellar Articular Face

b Dorsal View.

Note the Facet Formations on the Articular Faces of the Kneecap.

7.6a,b Right Fibula and Tibia. [6]

7

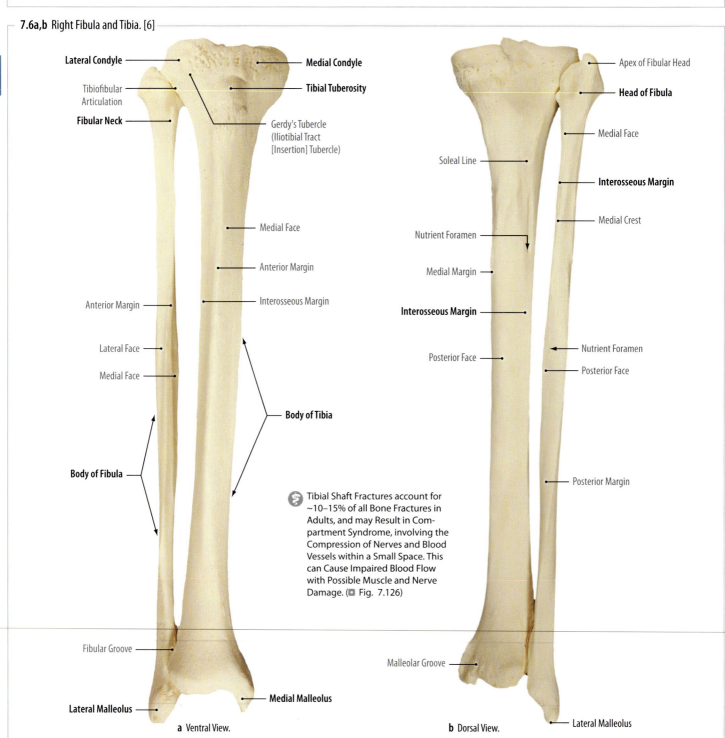

Lateral Condyle

Tibiofibular Articulation

Fibular Neck

Medial Condyle

Tibial Tuberosity

Gerdy's Tubercle (Iliotibial Tract [Insertion] Tubercle)

Medial Face

Anterior Margin

Interosseous Margin

Anterior Margin

Lateral Face

Medial Face

Body of Fibula

Body of Tibia

Fibular Groove

Lateral Malleolus

Medial Malleolus

a Ventral View.

Tibial Shaft Fractures account for ~10–15% of all Bone Fractures in Adults, and may Result in Compartment Syndrome, involving the Compression of Nerves and Blood Vessels within a Small Space. This can Cause Impaired Blood Flow with Possible Muscle and Nerve Damage. (□ Fig. 7.126)

Apex of Fibular Head

Head of Fibula

Medial Face

Soleal Line

Interosseous Margin

Medial Crest

Nutrient Foramen

Medial Margin

Interosseous Margin

Nutrient Foramen

Posterior Face

Posterior Face

Posterior Margin

Malleolar Groove

b Dorsal View.

Lateral Malleolus

7.7 Right Proximal Head of the Tibia (Tibial Plateau): Superior View. [6]

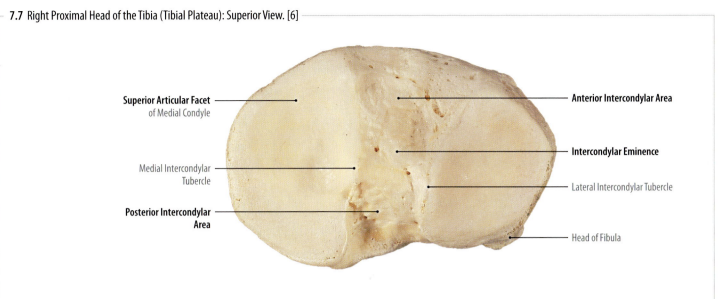

Superior Articular Facet
of Medial Condyle

Anterior Intercondylar Area

Medial Intercondylar Tubercle

Intercondylar Eminence

Lateral Intercondylar Tubercle

Posterior Intercondylar Area

Head of Fibula

7.8a Right Tibia, **b** Right Fibula. [6]

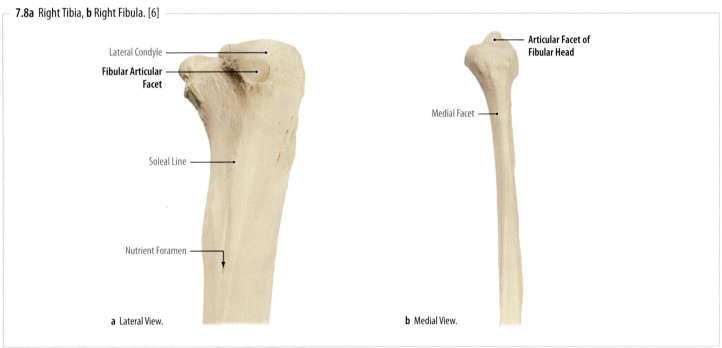

Lateral Condyle

Articular Facet of Fibular Head

Fibular Articular Facet

Medial Facet

Soleal Line

Nutrient Foramen

a Lateral View.

b Medial View.

7.9 Right Distal Heads of the Tibia and Fibula, Ankle Joint (Malleolar) Fork: Plantar View. [6]

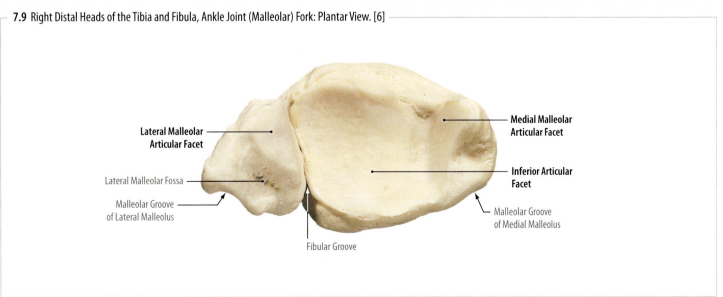

Lateral Malleolar Articular Facet

Medial Malleolar Articular Facet

Lateral Malleolar Fossa

Malleolar Groove of Lateral Malleolus

Inferior Articular Facet

Malleolar Groove of Medial Malleolus

Fibular Groove

Skeleton

Skeleton of the Foot

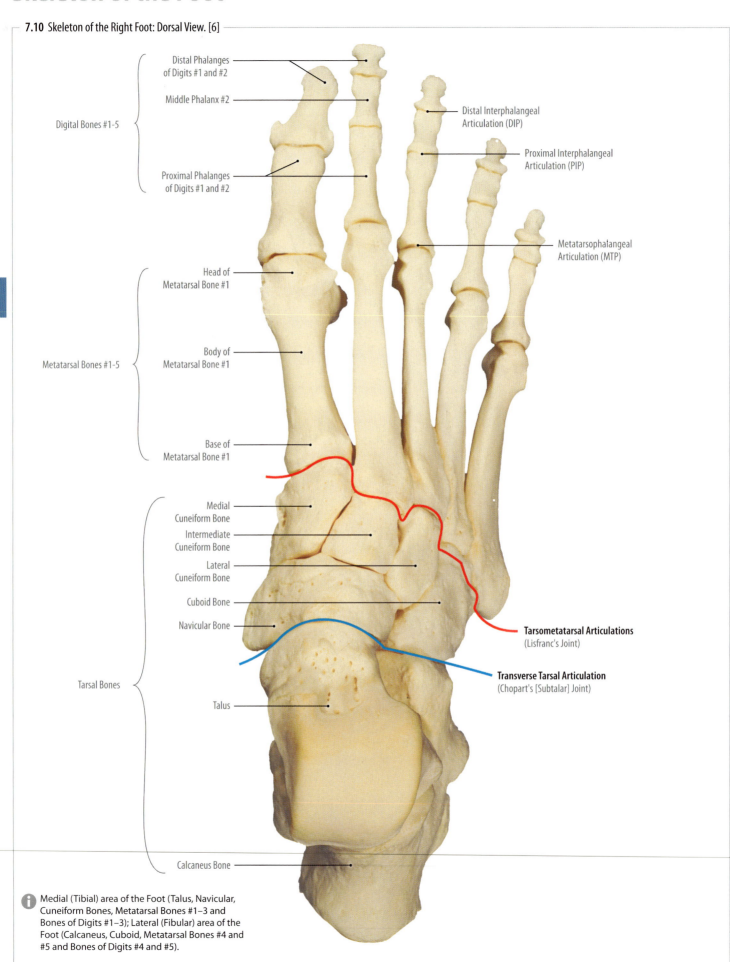

Distal Phalanges
of Digits #1 and #2

Middle Phalanx #2

Digital Bones #1-5

Proximal Phalanges
of Digits #1 and #2

Distal Interphalangeal
Articulation (DIP)

Proximal Interphalangeal
Articulation (PIP)

Metatarsophalangeal
Articulation (MTP)

Head of
Metatarsal Bone #1

Metatarsal Bones #1-5

Body of
Metatarsal Bone #1

Base of
Metatarsal Bone #1

Medial
Cuneiform Bone

Intermediate
Cuneiform Bone

Lateral
Cuneiform Bone

Cuboid Bone

Navicular Bone

Tarsometatarsal Articulations
(Lisfranc's Joint)

Transverse Tarsal Articulation
(Chopart's [Subtalar] Joint)

Tarsal Bones

Talus

Calcaneus Bone

🛈 Medial (Tibial) area of the Foot (Talus, Navicular,
Cuneiform Bones, Metatarsal Bones #1–3 and
Bones of Digits #1–3); Lateral (Fibular) area of the
Foot (Calcaneus, Cuboid, Metatarsal Bones #4 and
#5 and Bones of Digits #4 and #5).

7

Skeleton of the Foot

7.11 Skeleton of the Right Foot: Plantar View. [6]

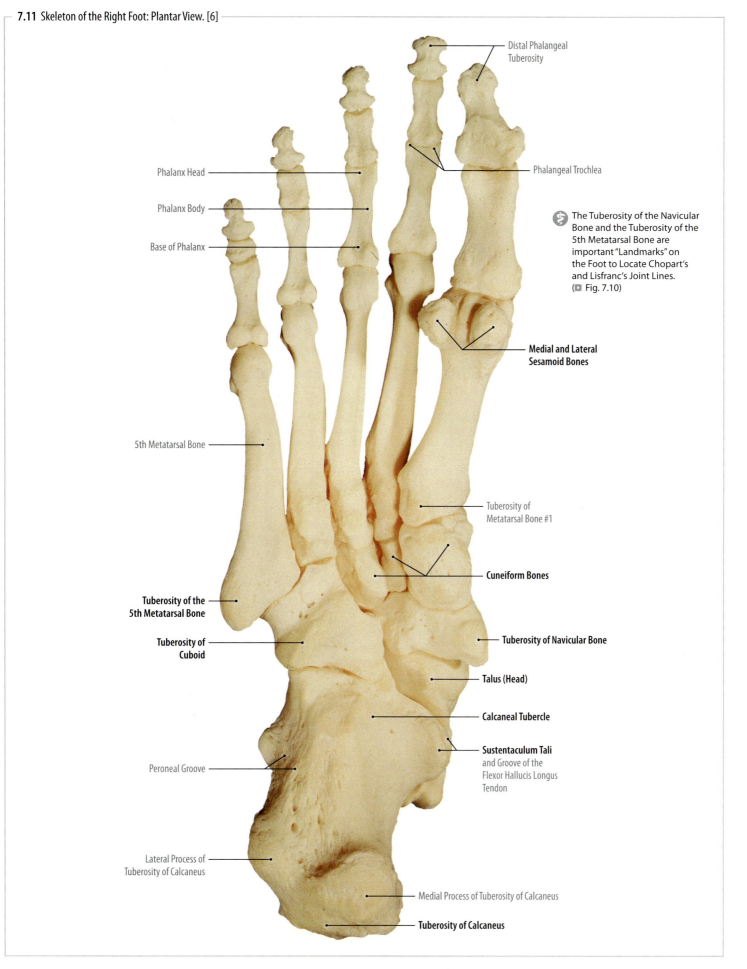

Distal Phalangeal Tuberosity

Phalanx Head

Phalanx Body

Base of Phalanx

Phalangeal Trochlea

The Tuberosity of the Navicular Bone and the Tuberosity of the 5th Metatarsal Bone are important "Landmarks" on the Foot to Locate Chopart's and Lisfranc's Joint Lines. (◨ Fig. 7.10)

Medial and Lateral Sesamoid Bones

5th Metatarsal Bone

Tuberosity of Metatarsal Bone #1

Cuneiform Bones

Tuberosity of the 5th Metatarsal Bone

Tuberosity of Cuboid

Tuberosity of Navicular Bone

Talus (Head)

Calcaneal Tubercle

Sustentaculum Tali and Groove of the Flexor Hallucis Longus Tendon

Peroneal Groove

Lateral Process of Tuberosity of Calcaneus

Medial Process of Tuberosity of Calcaneus

Tuberosity of Calcaneus

Skeleton

Talus, Calcaneus and Navicular Bone

7.12a,b Right Ankle Bone (Talus). [6]

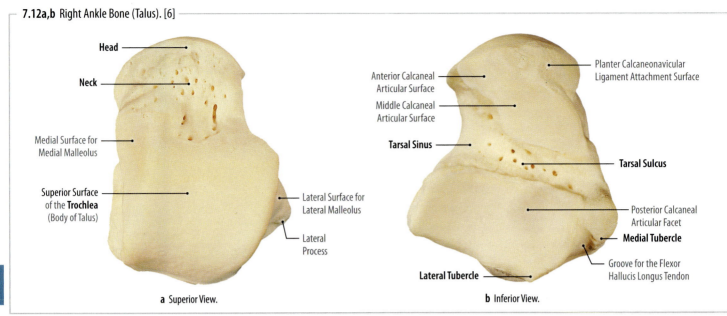

Head

Neck

Medial Surface for
Medial Malleolus

Superior Surface
of the **Trochlea**
(Body of Talus)

Lateral Surface for
Lateral Malleolus

Lateral
Process

a Superior View.

Anterior Calcaneal
Articular Surface

Middle Calcaneal
Articular Surface

Tarsal Sinus

Planter Calcaneonavicular
Ligament Attachment Surface

Tarsal Sulcus

Posterior Calcaneal
Articular Facet

Medial Tubercle

Groove for the Flexor
Hallucis Longus Tendon

Lateral Tubercle

b Inferior View.

7.13a,b Right Heel Bone (Calcaneus). [6]

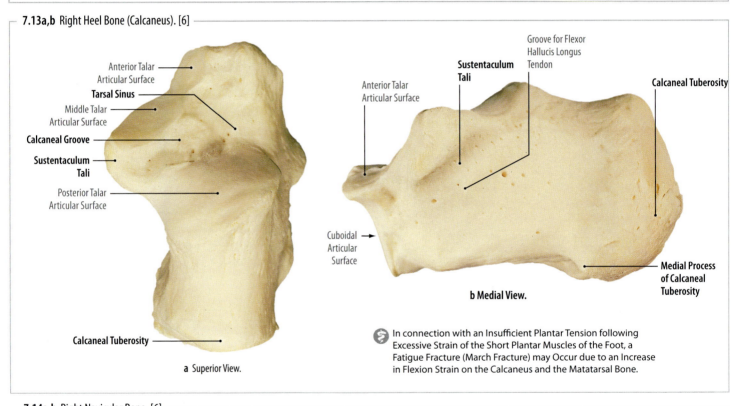

Anterior Talar
Articular Surface

Tarsal Sinus

Middle Talar
Articular Surface

Calcaneal Groove

**Sustentaculum
Tali**

Posterior Talar
Articular Surface

Calcaneal Tuberosity

a Superior View.

Groove for Flexor
Hallucis Longus
Tendon

**Sustentaculum
Tali**

Anterior Talar
Articular Surface

Calcaneal Tuberosity

Cuboidal
Articular
Surface

**Medial Process
of Calcaneal
Tuberosity**

b Medial View.

In connection with an Insufficient Plantar Tension following
Excessive Strain of the Short Plantar Muscles of the Foot, a
Fatigue Fracture (March Fracture) may Occur due to an Increase
in Flexion Strain on the Calcaneus and the Matatarsal Bone.

7.14a,b Right Navicular Bone. [6]

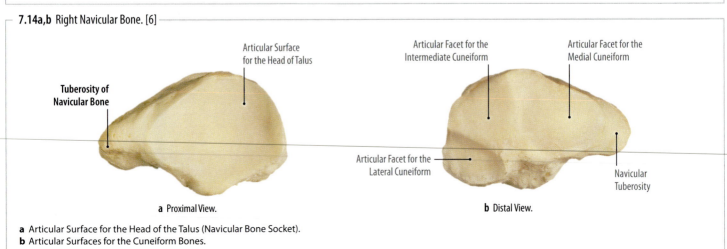

Articular Surface
for the Head of Talus

**Tuberosity of
Navicular Bone**

a Proximal View.

Articular Facet for the
Intermediate Cuneiform

Articular Facet for the
Medial Cuneiform

Articular Facet for the
Lateral Cuneiform

Navicular
Tuberosity

b Distal View.

a Articular Surface for the Head of the Talus (Navicular Bone Socket).
b Articular Surfaces for the Cuneiform Bones.

Cuboid, Cuneiform Bones; Metatarsal Bones

7.15a,b Right Cuboid Bone. [6]

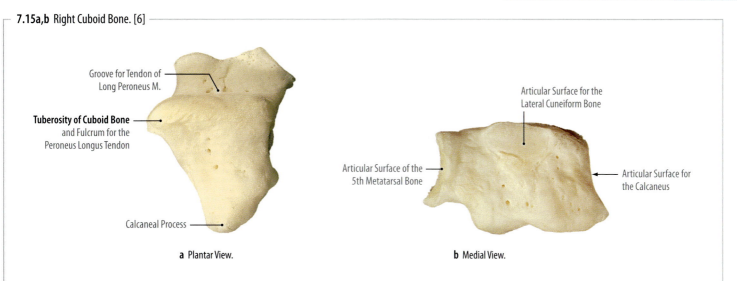

Groove for Tendon of
Long Peroneus M.

Tuberosity of Cuboid Bone
and Fulcrum for the
Peroneus Longus Tendon

Calcaneal Process

a Plantar View.

Articular Surface for the
Lateral Cuneiform Bone

Articular Surface of the
5th Metatarsal Bone

Articular Surface for
the Calcaneus

b Medial View.

7.16 Cuneiform Bones and Cuboid Bone of the Right Foot. [6]

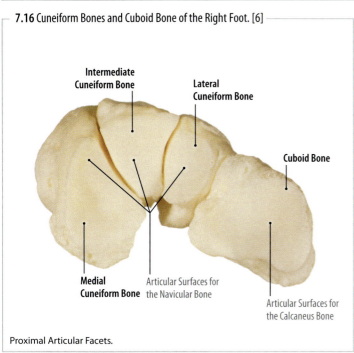

**Intermediate
Cuneiform Bone**

**Lateral
Cuneiform Bone**

Cuboid Bone

**Medial
Cuneiform Bone**

Articular Surfaces for
the Navicular Bone

Articular Surfaces for
the Calcaneus Bone

Proximal Articular Facets.

7.17 Right Second Metatarsal Bone: Medial View. [6]

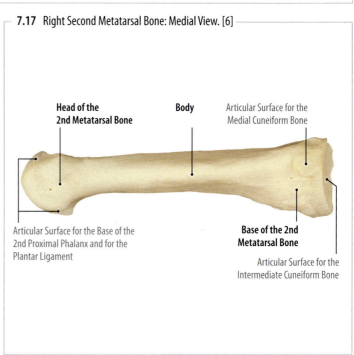

**Head of the
2nd Metatarsal Bone**

Body

Articular Surface for the
Medial Cuneiform Bone

Articular Surface for the Base of the
2nd Proximal Phalanx and for the
Plantar Ligament

**Base of the 2nd
Metatarsal Bone**

Articular Surface for the
Intermediate Cuneiform Bone

7.18 Articular Surfaces of the Bases of the Metatarsal Bones 1–5 (Distal Articular Facets) of the Tarsometatarsal Articulations (Lisfranc's Joint): Right Side. [6]

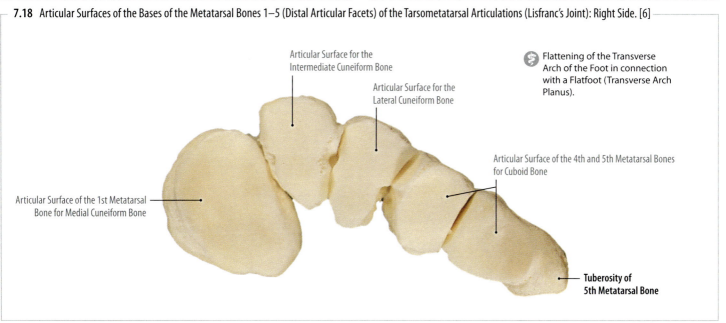

Articular Surface for the
Intermediate Cuneiform Bone

Articular Surface for the
Lateral Cuneiform Bone

Flattening of the Transverse
Arch of the Foot in connection
with a Flatfoot (Transverse Arch
Planus).

Articular Surface of the 1st Metatarsal
Bone for Medial Cuneiform Bone

Articular Surface of the 4th and 5th Metatarsal Bones
for Cuboid Bone

**Tuberosity of
5th Metatarsal Bone**

Skeleton

7.19 Articular Surfaces of a Right Sacroiliac Joint. [6]

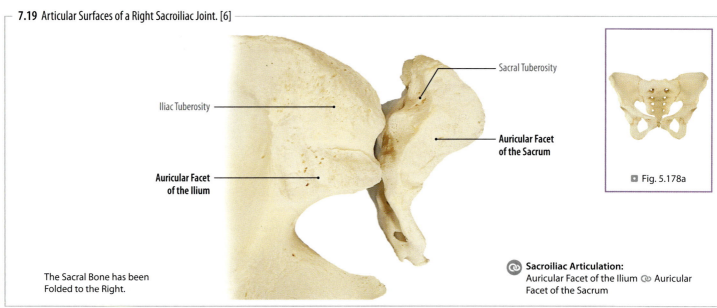

Iliac Tuberosity

Sacral Tuberosity

**Auricular Facet
of the Sacrum**

**Auricular Facet
of the Ilium**

☑ Fig. 5.178a

The Sacral Bone has been
Folded to the Right.

Sacroiliac Articulation:
Auricular Facet of the Ilium ⚭ Auricular
Facet of the Sacrum

7.20 Hip Joint: Ventral View. [6]

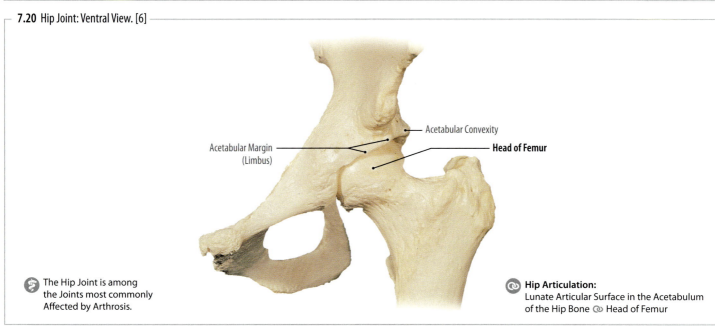

Acetabular Convexity

Acetabular Margin
(Limbus)

Head of Femur

The Hip Joint is among
the Joints most commonly
Affected by Arthrosis.

Hip Articulation:
Lunate Articular Surface in the Acetabulum
of the Hip Bone ⚭ Head of Femur

7.21 Right Socket of the Hip Joint: Lateral View. [6]

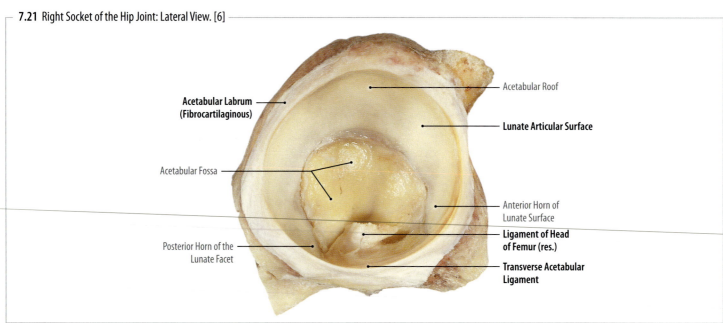

**Acetabular Labrum
(Fibrocartilaginous)**

Acetabular Roof

Lunate Articular Surface

Acetabular Fossa

Anterior Horn of
Lunate Surface

**Ligament of Head
of Femur (res.)**

Posterior Horn of the
Lunate Facet

**Transverse Acetabular
Ligament**

Symphysis · Pelvic Ring and Hip Joint

7.22 Frontal Section through the Pubic Symphysis of a Man. [12]

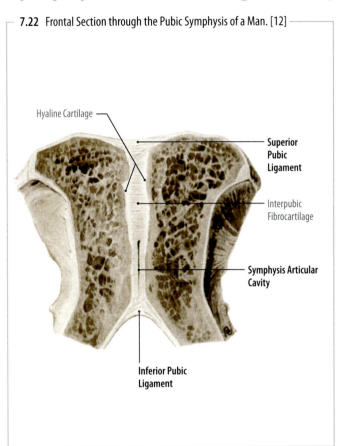

Hyaline Cartilage

Superior Pubic Ligament

Interpubic Fibrocartilage

Symphysis Articular Cavity

Inferior Pubic Ligament

7.23 Ligament System of the Articular Connections between the Sacral Bone and the Coccyx, as well as between the Hip Bone and the Sacral Bone: Right Side, Dorsal View. [12]

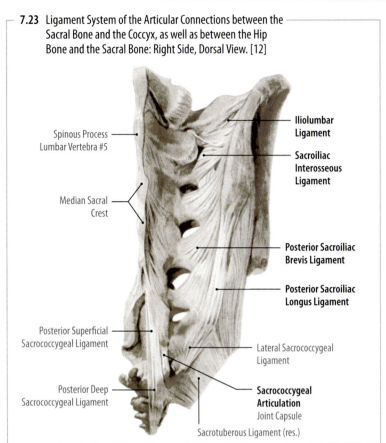

Spinous Process Lumbar Vertebra #5

Median Sacral Crest

Iliolumbar Ligament

Sacroiliac Interosseous Ligament

Posterior Sacroiliac Brevis Ligament

Posterior Sacroiliac Longus Ligament

Posterior Superficial Sacrococcygeal Ligament

Posterior Deep Sacrococcygeal Ligament

Lateral Sacrococcygeal Ligament

Sacrococcygeal Articulation Joint Capsule

Sacrotuberous Ligament (res.)

7.24 Ligament System of the Pelvic Ring and the Hip Joint: Right Side, Dorsal View. [46]

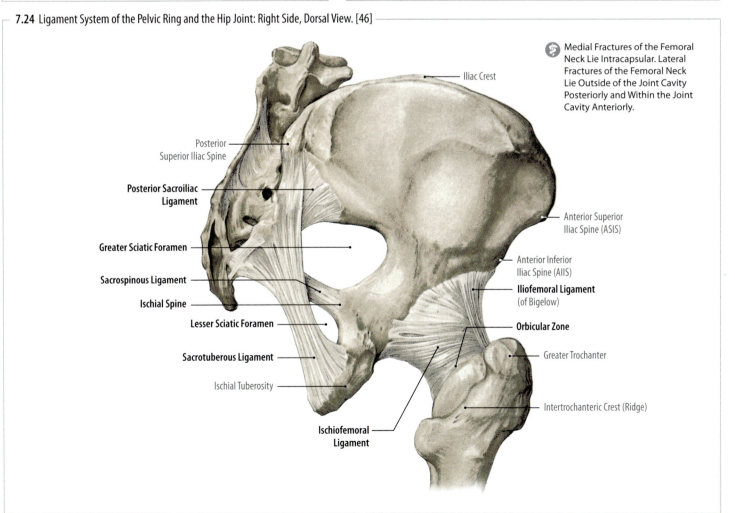

Iliac Crest

Ⓢ Medial Fractures of the Femoral Neck Lie Intracapsular. Lateral Fractures of the Femoral Neck Lie Outside of the Joint Cavity Posteriorly and Within the Joint Cavity Anteriorly.

Posterior Superior Iliac Spine

Posterior Sacroiliac Ligament

Greater Sciatic Foramen

Sacrospinous Ligament

Ischial Spine

Lesser Sciatic Foramen

Sacrotuberous Ligament

Ischial Tuberosity

Ischiofemoral Ligament

Anterior Superior Iliac Spine (ASIS)

Anterior Inferior Iliac Spine (AIIS)

Iliofemoral Ligament (of Bigelow)

Orbicular Zone

Greater Trochanter

Intertrochanteric Crest (Ridge)

Joints and Ligaments

7.25 Capsule–Ligament System of a Right Hip Joint: Ventral View. [46]

The Iliofemoral Ligament of Bigelow with the Pubofemoral Ligament form an "N"-Shaped Strong Ligament to the Anterior Capsule, strong enough to Extend the Head of Femur against it, if you are Standing for a Long Time Without Using your Muscles. The Ischiofemoral Ligament forms a Triangle with its Apex attached on the Anterior of the Trochanteric area to allow for Freedom of Motion.

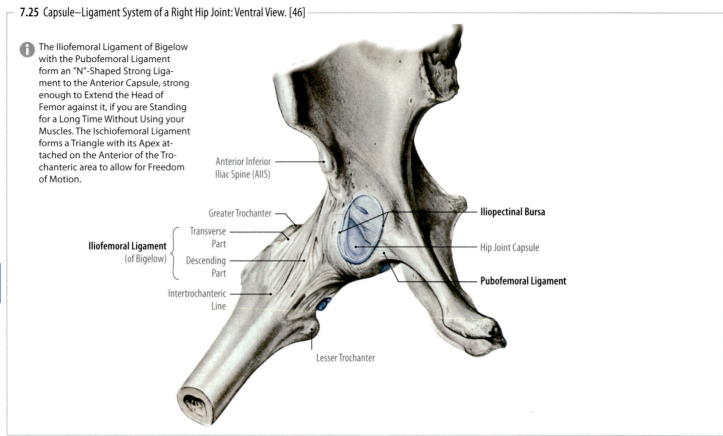

Anterior Inferior Iliac Spine (AIIS)

Greater Trochanter

Iliopectinal Bursa

Iliofemoral Ligament (of Bigelow)

Transverse Part

Descending Part

Hip Joint Capsule

Intertrochanteric Line

Pubofemoral Ligament

Lesser Trochanter

7.26 X-Ray Image of a Right Hip Joint of a 33-Year-Old Man in the AnteroPosterior (AP) Projection. [10]

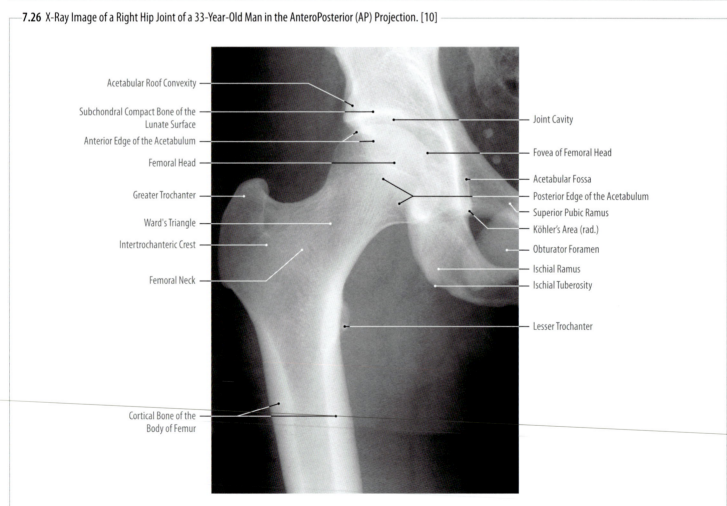

Acetabular Roof Convexity

Subchondral Compact Bone of the Lunate Surface

Anterior Edge of the Acetabulum

Femoral Head

Greater Trochanter

Ward's Triangle

Intertrochanteric Crest

Femoral Neck

Joint Cavity

Fovea of Femoral Head

Acetabular Fossa

Posterior Edge of the Acetabulum

Superior Pubic Ramus

Köhler's Area (rad.)

Obturator Foramen

Ischial Ramus

Ischial Tuberosity

Lesser Trochanter

Cortical Bone of the Body of Femur

7.27 Joints and Ligaments of the Pelvic Ring and the Hip Joint: Right Side, Ventral View. [6]

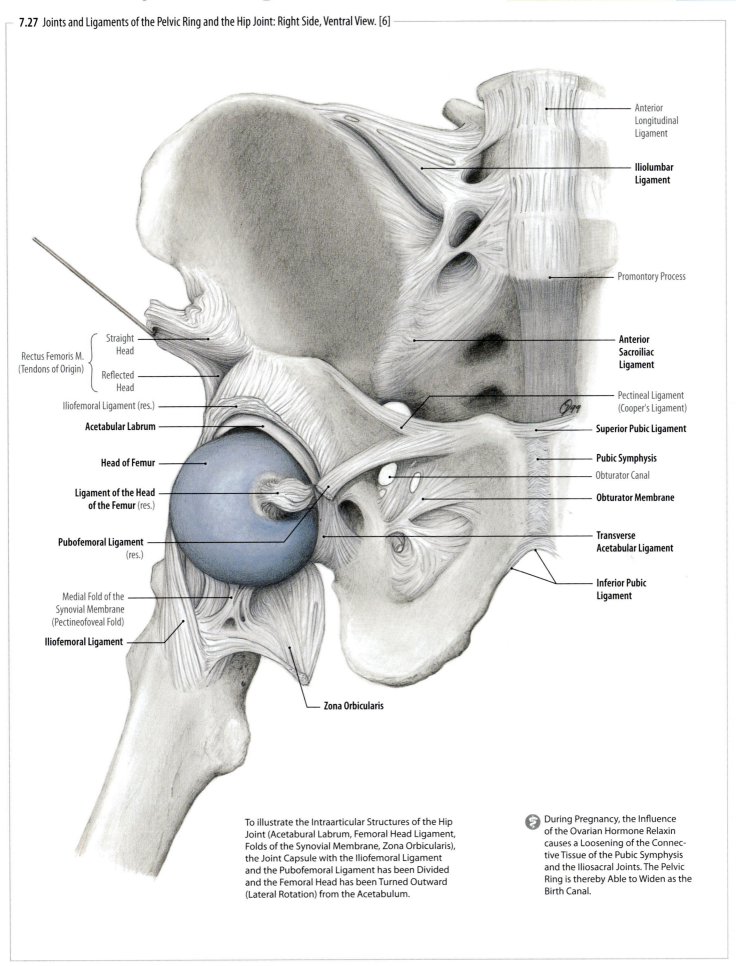

Anterior Longitudinal Ligament

Iliolumbar Ligament

Promontory Process

Anterior Sacroiliac Ligament

Pectineal Ligament (Cooper's Ligament)

Superior Pubic Ligament

Pubic Symphysis

Obturator Canal

Obturator Membrane

Transverse Acetabular Ligament

Inferior Pubic Ligament

Rectus Femoris M. (Tendons of Origin)
Straight Head
Reflected Head

Iliofemoral Ligament (res.)

Acetabular Labrum

Head of Femur

Ligament of the Head of the Femur (res.)

Pubofemoral Ligament (res.)

Medial Fold of the Synovial Membrane (Pectineofoveal Fold)

Iliofemoral Ligament

Zona Orbicularis

To illustrate the Intraarticular Structures of the Hip Joint (Acetabural Labrum, Femoral Head Ligament, Folds of the Synovial Membrane, Zona Orbicularis), the Joint Capsule with the Iliofemoral Ligament and the Pubofemoral Ligament has been Divided and the Femoral Head has been Turned Outward (Lateral Rotation) from the Acetabulum.

During Pregnancy, the Influence of the Ovarian Hormone Relaxin causes a Loosening of the Connective Tissue of the Pubic Symphysis and the Iliosacral Joints. The Pelvic Ring is thereby Able to Widen as the Birth Canal.

Joints and Ligaments

7.28 Three-Dimensional Reconstruction of the Skeletal Parts of the Knee Joint of the Right Side on CT Images: Anterolateral View. [84]

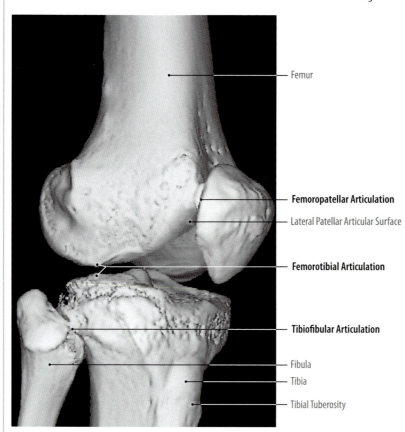

Femur

Femoropatellar Articulation

Lateral Patellar Articular Surface

Femorotibial Articulation

Tibiofibular Articulation

Fibula

Tibia

Tibial Tuberosity

Femoropatellar Articulation:
Patellar Surface (Femoral) ⟳ Articular Surface (Patellar)

Femorotibial Articulation:
Medial Condyle and Lateral Condyle (Femoral) ⟳ Superior Articular Surface (Tibial)

Tibiofibular Articulation:
Fibular Articular Surface (Tibial) ⟳ Articular Surface of Head of Fibula

7.29 Skeletal Parts of a Left Knee Joint and a Left Tibiofibular Joint: Dorsal View. [6]

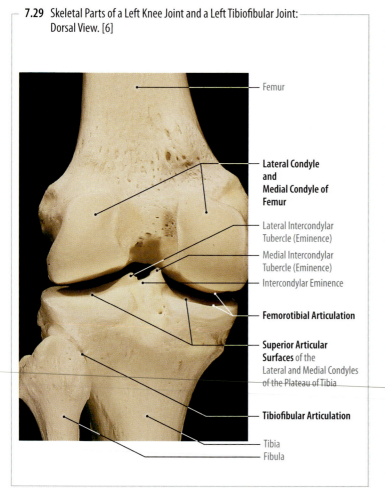

Femur

Lateral Condyle and Medial Condyle of Femur

Lateral Intercondylar Tubercle (Eminence)

Medial Intercondylar Tubercle (Eminence)

Intercondylar Eminence

Femorotibial Articulation

Superior Articular Surfaces of the Lateral and Medial Condyles of the Plateau of Tibia

Tibiofibular Articulation

Tibia

Fibula

7.30 X-Ray Image of a Left Knee Joint of a 47-Year-Old Woman in the Lateral Projection. [10]

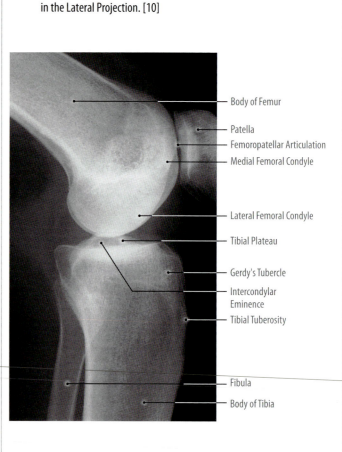

Body of Femur

Patella

Femoropatellar Articulation

Medial Femoral Condyle

Lateral Femoral Condyle

Tibial Plateau

Gerdy's Tubercle

Intercondylar Eminence

Tibial Tuberosity

Fibula

Body of Tibia

7

7.31a,b Right Knee Joints: Ventral View. [6]

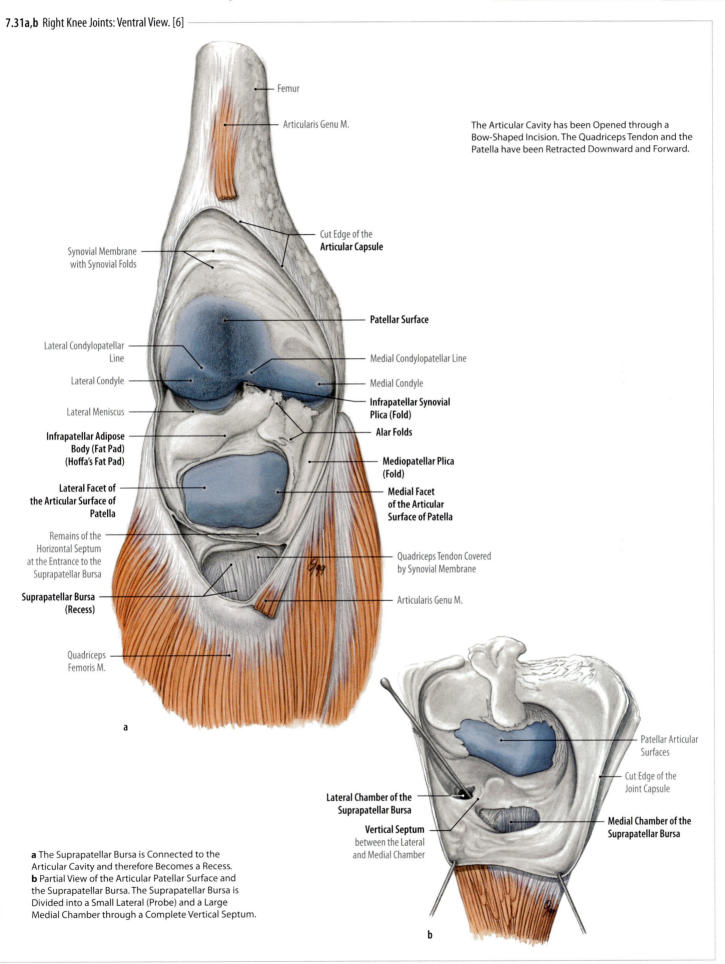

Femur

Articularis Genu M.

The Articular Cavity has been Opened through a Bow-Shaped Incision. The Quadriceps Tendon and the Patella have been Retracted Downward and Forward.

Cut Edge of the
Articular Capsule

Synovial Membrane
with Synovial Folds

Patellar Surface

Lateral Condylopatellar
Line

Medial Condylopatellar Line

Lateral Condyle

Medial Condyle

Lateral Meniscus

**Infrapatellar Synovial
Plica (Fold)**

**Infrapatellar Adipose
Body (Fat Pad)
(Hoffa's Fat Pad)**

Alar Folds

**Mediopatellar Plica
(Fold)**

**Lateral Facet of
the Articular Surface of
Patella**

**Medial Facet
of the Articular
Surface of Patella**

Remains of the
Horizontal Septum
at the Entrance to the
Suprapatellar Bursa

Quadriceps Tendon Covered
by Synovial Membrane

**Suprapatellar Bursa
(Recess)**

Articularis Genu M.

Quadriceps
Femoris M.

a

Patellar Articular
Surfaces

Cut Edge of the
Joint Capsule

**Lateral Chamber of the
Suprapatellar Bursa**

Vertical Septum
between the Lateral
and Medial Chamber

**Medial Chamber of the
Suprapatellar Bursa**

b

a The Suprapatellar Bursa is Connected to the Articular Cavity and therefore Becomes a Recess.
b Partial View of the Articular Patellar Surface and the Suprapatellar Bursa. The Suprapatellar Bursa is Divided into a Small Lateral (Probe) and a Large Medial Chamber through a Complete Vertical Septum.

Joints and Ligaments

Knee Joint: Capsule–Ligament System

7.32a,b Capsule–Ligament System of a Right Knee Joint. [46]

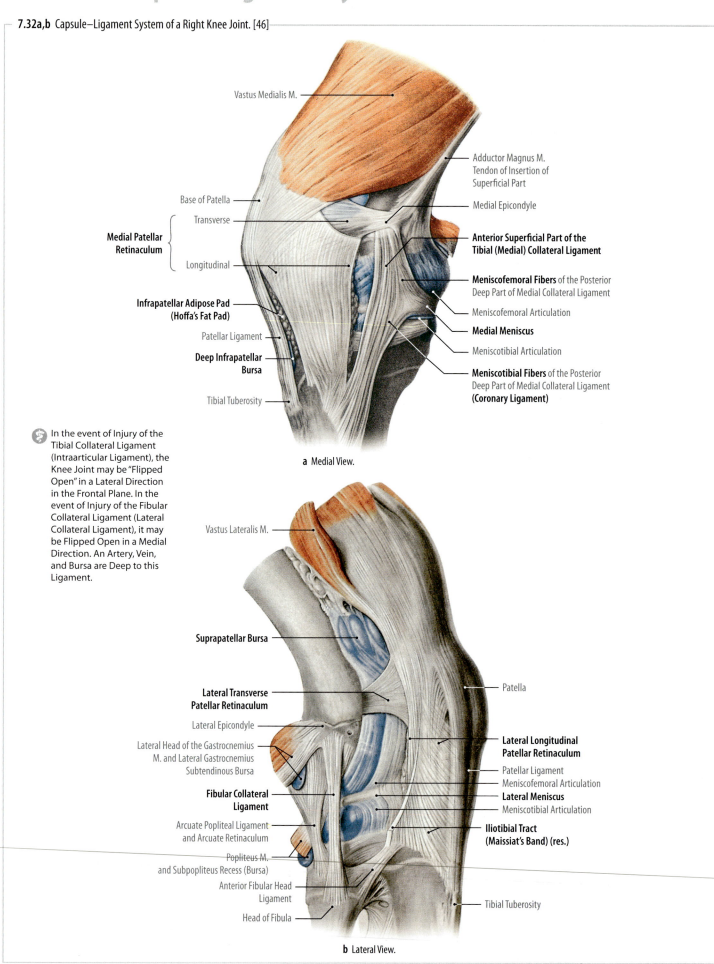

Vastus Medialis M.

Adductor Magnus M. Tendon of Insertion of Superficial Part

Base of Patella

Medial Epicondyle

Transverse

Anterior Superficial Part of the Tibial (Medial) Collateral Ligament

Medial Patellar Retinaculum

Longitudinal

Meniscofemoral Fibers of the Posterior Deep Part of Medial Collateral Ligament

Meniscofemoral Articulation

Infrapatellar Adipose Pad (Hoffa's Fat Pad)

Medial Meniscus

Patellar Ligament

Meniscotibial Articulation

Deep Infrapatellar Bursa

Meniscotibial Fibers of the Posterior Deep Part of Medial Collateral Ligament **(Coronary Ligament)**

Tibial Tuberosity

a Medial View.

🔷 In the event of Injury of the Tibial Collateral Ligament (Intraarticular Ligament), the Knee Joint may be "Flipped Open" in a Lateral Direction in the Frontal Plane. In the event of Injury of the Fibular Collateral Ligament (Lateral Collateral Ligament), it may be Flipped Open in a Medial Direction. An Artery, Vein, and Bursa are Deep to this Ligament.

Vastus Lateralis M.

Suprapatellar Bursa

Lateral Transverse Patellar Retinaculum

Patella

Lateral Epicondyle

Lateral Head of the Gastrocnemius M. and Lateral Gastrocnemius Subtendinous Bursa

Lateral Longitudinal Patellar Retinaculum

Patellar Ligament

Meniscofemoral Articulation

Fibular Collateral Ligament

Lateral Meniscus

Meniscotibial Articulation

Arcuate Popliteal Ligament and Arcuate Retinaculum

Iliotibial Tract (Maissiat's Band) (res.)

Popliteus M. and Subpopliteus Recess (Bursa)

Anterior Fibular Head Ligament

Tibial Tuberosity

Head of Fibula

b Lateral View.

Knee Joint: Ligaments, Internal Structure

7.33a,b Collateral Ligaments and Internal Structure of a Right Knee Joint. [46]

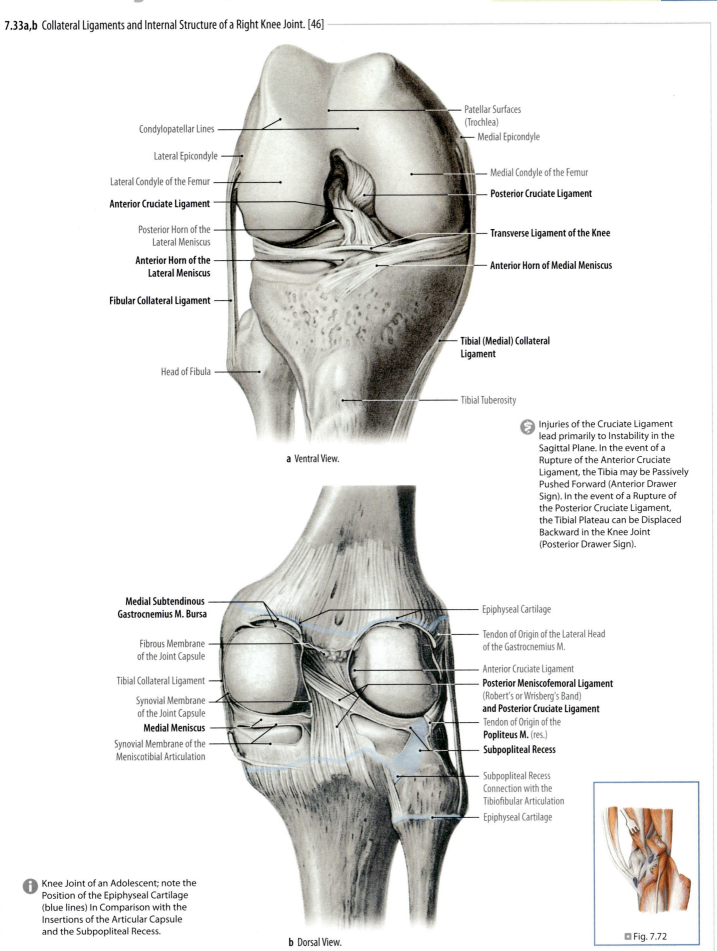

Condylopatellar Lines

Lateral Epicondyle

Lateral Condyle of the Femur

Anterior Cruciate Ligament

Posterior Horn of the Lateral Meniscus

Anterior Horn of the Lateral Meniscus

Fibular Collateral Ligament

Head of Fibula

Patellar Surfaces (Trochlea)

Medial Epicondyle

Medial Condyle of the Femur

Posterior Cruciate Ligament

Transverse Ligament of the Knee

Anterior Horn of Medial Meniscus

Tibial (Medial) Collateral Ligament

Tibial Tuberosity

a Ventral View.

Injuries of the Cruciate Ligament lead primarily to Instability in the Sagittal Plane. In the event of a Rupture of the Anterior Cruciate Ligament, the Tibia may be Passively Pushed Forward (Anterior Drawer Sign). In the event of a Rupture of the Posterior Cruciate Ligament, the Tibial Plateau can be Displaced Backward in the Knee Joint (Posterior Drawer Sign).

Medial Subtendinous Gastrocnemius M. Bursa

Fibrous Membrane of the Joint Capsule

Tibial Collateral Ligament

Synovial Membrane of the Joint Capsule

Medial Meniscus

Synovial Membrane of the Meniscotibial Articulation

Epiphyseal Cartilage

Tendon of Origin of the Lateral Head of the Gastrocnemius M.

Anterior Cruciate Ligament

Posterior Meniscofemoral Ligament (Robert's or Wrisberg's Band) **and Posterior Cruciate Ligament**

Tendon of Origin of the **Popliteus M.** (res.)

Subpopliteal Recess

Subpopliteal Recess Connection with the Tibiofibular Articulation

Epiphyseal Cartilage

☐ Fig. 7.72

ⓘ Knee Joint of an Adolescent; note the Position of the Epiphyseal Cartilage (blue lines) In Comparison with the Insertions of the Articular Capsule and the Subpopliteal Recess.

b Dorsal View.

Joints and Ligaments

7.34 Tibial Plateau with Menisci, Cruciate Ligaments, and Collateral Ligaments: Posterosuperior View. [1]

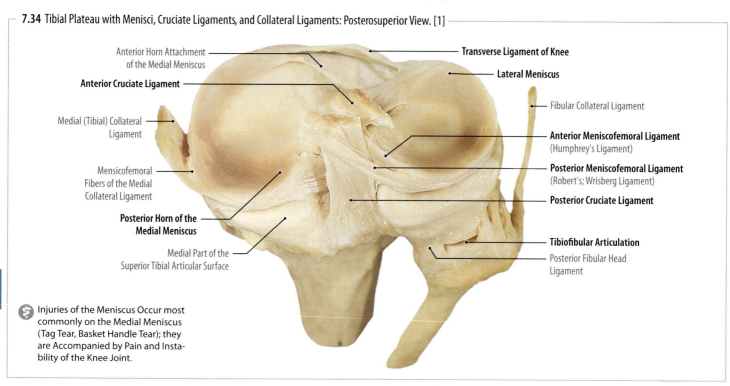

Anterior Horn Attachment of the Medial Meniscus

Anterior Cruciate Ligament

Medial (Tibial) Collateral Ligament

Mensicofemoral Fibers of the Medial Collateral Ligament

Posterior Horn of the Medial Meniscus

Medial Part of the Superior Tibial Articular Surface

Transverse Ligament of Knee

Lateral Meniscus

Fibular Collateral Ligament

Anterior Meniscofemoral Ligament (Humphrey's Ligament)

Posterior Meniscofemoral Ligament (Robert's; Wrisberg Ligament)

Posterior Cruciate Ligament

Tibiofibular Articulation

Posterior Fibular Head Ligament

Injuries of the Meniscus Occur most commonly on the Medial Meniscus (Tag Tear, Basket Handle Tear); they are Accompanied by Pain and Instability of the Knee Joint.

7.35a,b Insertion Areas of the Anterior (Green) and the Posterior (Yellow) Cruciate Ligament, as well as of the Medial (Red) and the Lateral (Blue) Meniscus.

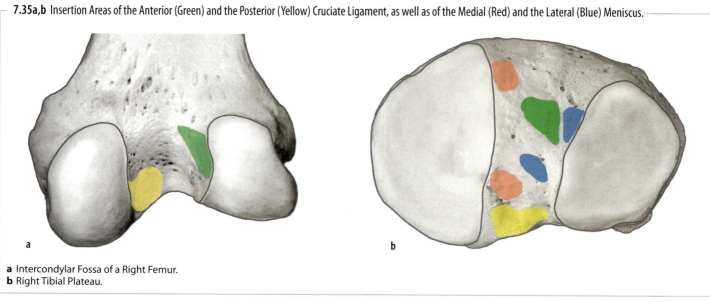

a

b

a Intercondylar Fossa of a Right Femur.
b Right Tibial Plateau.

7.36 Arthroscopy of the Left Knee Joint of a 22-Year-Old Woman: Anteromedial View; Illustration of the Medial Meniscus in the Transition Area between the Anterior Horn and the Intermediate Part. [109]

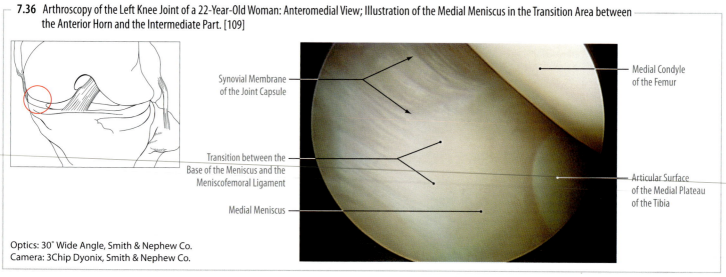

Synovial Membrane of the Joint Capsule

Transition between the Base of the Meniscus and the Meniscofemoral Ligament

Medial Meniscus

Medial Condyle of the Femur

Articular Surface of the Medial Plateau of the Tibia

Optics: 30° Wide Angle, Smith & Nephew Co.
Camera: 3Chip Dyonix, Smith & Nephew Co.

482

7.37 Sagittal Section through the Median Area of a Right Knee Joint: View of the Medial Cut Surface. [6]

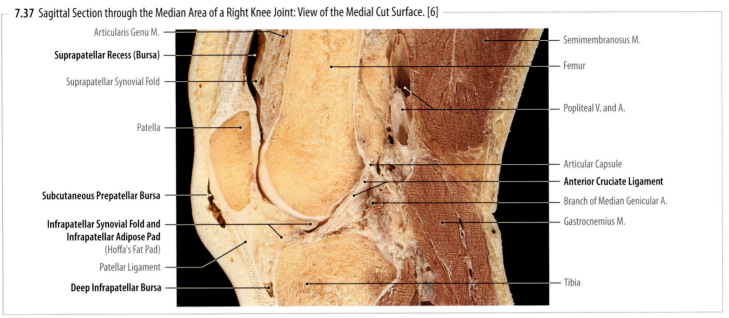

Articularis Genu M.

Suprapatellar Recess (Bursa)

Suprapatellar Synovial Fold

Patella

Subcutaneous Prepatellar Bursa

**Infrapatellar Synovial Fold and
Infrapatellar Adipose Pad**
(Hoffa's Fat Pad)

Patellar Ligament

Deep Infrapatellar Bursa

Semimembranosus M.

Femur

Popliteal V. and A.

Articular Capsule

Anterior Cruciate Ligament

Branch of Median Genicular A.

Gastrocnemius M.

Tibia

7.38 T1-Weighted MRI of the Right Knee Joint of a 36-Year-Old Man: Sagittal Section Plane. [10]

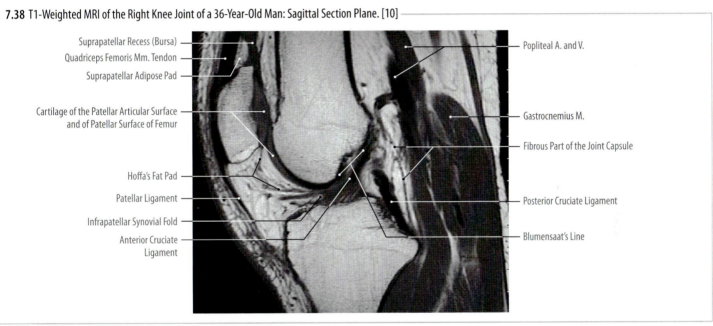

Suprapatellar Recess (Bursa)

Quadriceps Femoris Mm. Tendon

Suprapatellar Adipose Pad

Cartilage of the Patellar Articular Surface
and of Patellar Surface of Femur

Hoffa's Fat Pad

Patellar Ligament

Infrapatellar Synovial Fold

Anterior Cruciate
Ligament

Popliteal A. and V.

Gastrocnemius M.

Fibrous Part of the Joint Capsule

Posterior Cruciate Ligament

Blumensaat's Line

7.39 Cross-Section through the Right Knee Joint of a Woman in Slightly Flexed Position: View of the Distal Cut Surface. [6]

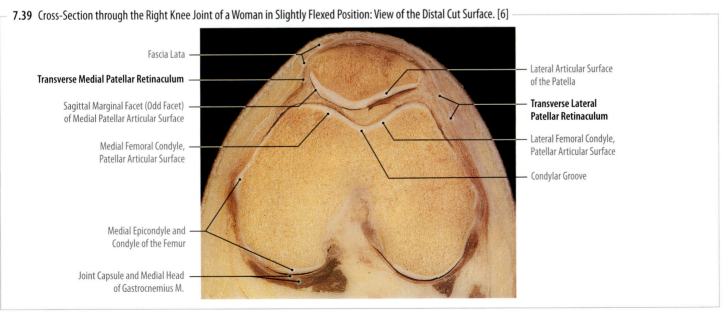

Fascia Lata

Transverse Medial Patellar Retinaculum

Sagittal Marginal Facet (Odd Facet)
of Medial Patellar Articular Surface

Medial Femoral Condyle,
Patellar Articular Surface

Medial Epicondyle and
Condyle of the Femur

Joint Capsule and Medial Head
of Gastrocnemius M.

Lateral Articular Surface
of the Patella

**Transverse Lateral
Patellar Retinaculum**

Lateral Femoral Condyle,
Patellar Articular Surface

Condylar Groove

Joints and Ligaments

Knee Joint: Synovial Bursa

7.40a,b Synovial Bursae in the Proximity of the Knee Joint: Right Side. [46]

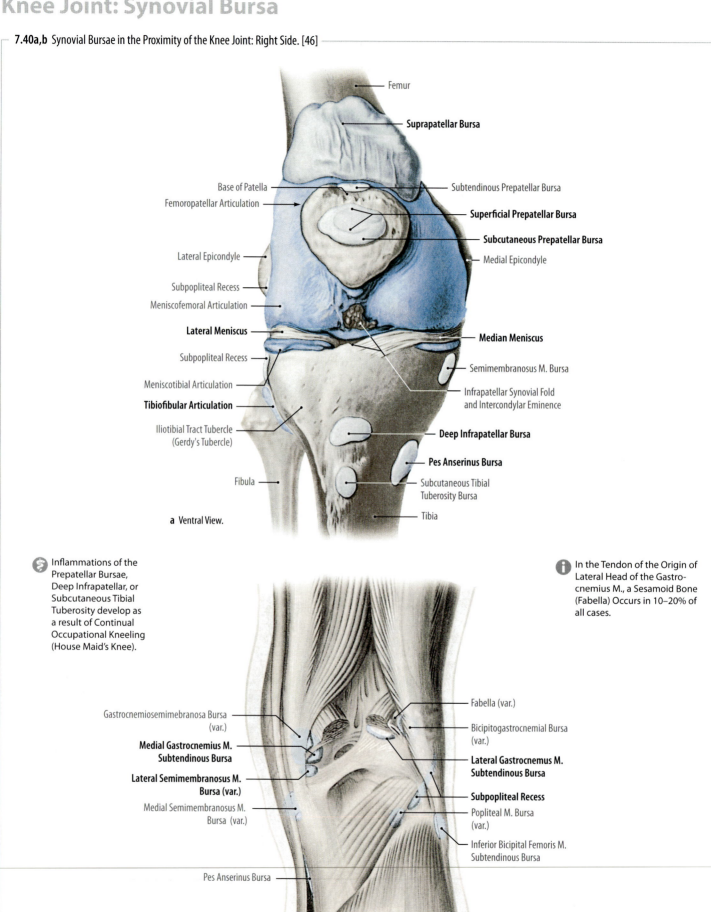

Femur

Suprapatellar Bursa

Base of Patella

Femoropatellar Articulation

Subtendinous Prepatellar Bursa

Superficial Prepatellar Bursa

Subcutaneous Prepatellar Bursa

Lateral Epicondyle

Medial Epicondyle

Subpopliteal Recess

Meniscofemoral Articulation

Lateral Meniscus

Median Meniscus

Subpopliteal Recess

Semimembranosus M. Bursa

Meniscotibial Articulation

Infrapatellar Synovial Fold
and Intercondylar Eminence

Tibiofibular Articulation

Iliotibial Tract Tubercle
(Gerdy's Tubercle)

Deep Infrapatellar Bursa

Pes Anserinus Bursa

Fibula

Subcutaneous Tibial
Tuberosity Bursa

Tibia

a Ventral View.

Inflammations of the
Prepatellar Bursae,
Deep Infrapatellar, or
Subcutaneous Tibial
Tuberosity develop as
a result of Continual
Occupational Kneeling
(House Maid's Knee).

In the Tendon of the Origin of
Lateral Head of the Gastrocnemius M., a Sesamoid Bone
(Fabella) Occurs in 10–20% of
all cases.

Gastrocnemiosemimebranosa Bursa
(var.)

Fabella (var.)

Bicipitogastrocnemial Bursa
(var.)

**Medial Gastrocnemius M.
Subtendinous Bursa**

**Lateral Gastrocnemus M.
Subtendinous Bursa**

**Lateral Semimembranosus M.
Bursa (var.)**

Subpopliteal Recess

Medial Semimembranosus M.
Bursa (var.)

Popliteal M. Bursa
(var.)

Inferior Bicipital Femoris M.
Subtendinous Bursa

Pes Anserinus Bursa

b Dorsal View.

Syndesmosis · Upper Ankle Joint

7.41 Joint and Ligament Connections between the Fibula and Tibia: Fibulotibial Joints, Ventral View. [46]

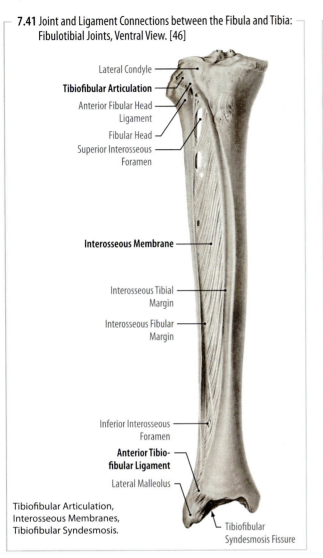

Lateral Condyle

Tibiofibular Articulation

Anterior Fibular Head Ligament

Fibular Head

Superior Interosseous Foramen

Interosseous Membrane

Interosseous Tibial Margin

Interosseous Fibular Margin

Inferior Interosseous Foramen

Anterior Tibio-fibular Ligament

Lateral Malleolus

Tibiofibular Articulation, Interosseous Membranes, Tibiofibular Syndesmosis.

Tibiofibular Syndesmosis Fissure

7.42 Skeletal Parts of a Right Superior Ankle Joint (Talocrural Articulation) and a Right Inferior Ankle Joint (Talocalcaneonavicular and Subtalar Articulations): Ventral View. [6]

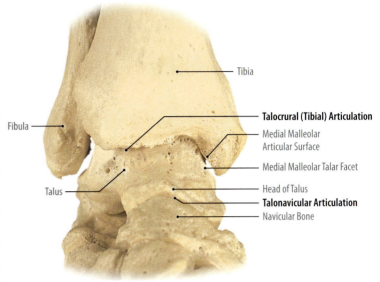

Tibia

Fibula

Talocrural (Tibial) Articulation

Medial Malleolar Articular Surface

Medial Malleolar Talar Facet

Talus

Head of Talus

Talonavicular Articulation

Navicular Bone

Talocrural Articulation:
Inferior Articular Facet (Tibia) ⟳ Superior Articular Surface of Trochlea Tali
Subtalar Articulation (Posterior Chamber of the Inferior Ankle Joint):
Posterior Calcaneal Articular Facet (Tali) ⟳ Posterior Talar Articular Facet (Calcanei)
Talocalcaneonavicular Articulations (Anterior Chamber of the Inferior Ankle Joint):
Anterior Calcaneal Articular Facet (Tali) ⟳ Anterior Talar Articular Facet (Calcaneum)
Middle Calcaneal Articular Facet (Tali) ⟳ Middle Articular Facet (Canlcanei)
Navicular Articular Facet (Tali) ⟳ Socket of the Navicular Bone

7.43 Mortice: Right Side, Ventral Inferior View. [6]

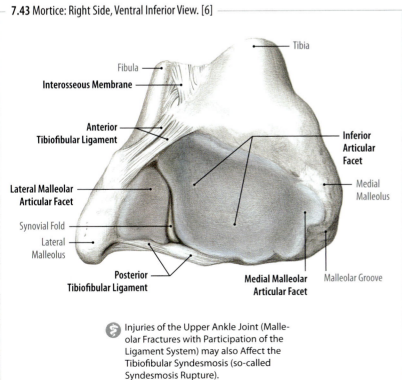

Tibia

Fibula

Interosseous Membrane

Anterior Tibiofibular Ligament

Inferior Articular Facet

Medial Malleolus

Lateral Malleolar Articular Facet

Synovial Fold

Lateral Malleolus

Posterior Tibiofibular Ligament

Medial Malleolar Articular Facet

Malleolar Groove

Injuries of the Upper Ankle Joint (Malleolar Fractures with Participation of the Ligament System) may also Affect the Tibiofibular Syndesmosis (so-called Syndesmosis Rupture).

7.44 X-Ray Image of a Right Superior Ankle Joint of a 21-Year-Old Woman in the AP Projection. [10]

Lateral Malleolus

Trochlea of Talus

Talocrural Articulation

Medial Malleolus

Joints and Ligaments

Upper and Lower Ankle Joint

7.45 Capsule–Ligament System of the Ankle Joints and the Joints of the Foot: Right Side, Ventral View. [6]

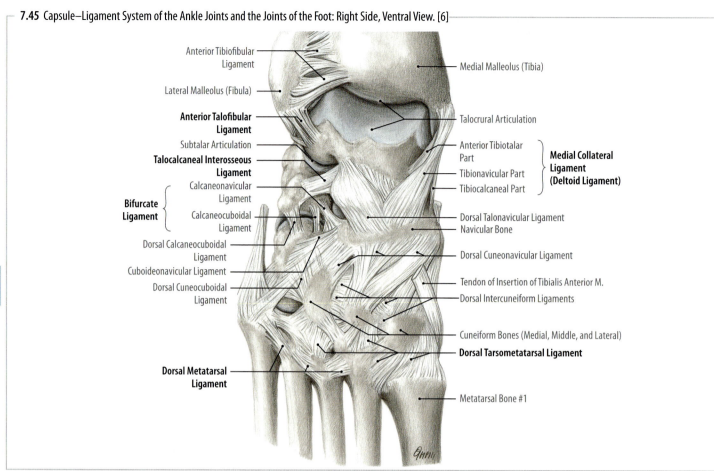

Anterior Tibiofibular Ligament

Lateral Malleolus (Fibula)

Anterior Talofibular Ligament

Subtalar Articulation

Talocalcaneal Interosseous Ligament

Calcaneonavicular Ligament

Bifurcate Ligament

Calcaneocuboidal Ligament

Dorsal Calcaneocuboidal Ligament

Cuboideonavicular Ligament

Dorsal Cuneocuboidal Ligament

Dorsal Metatarsal Ligament

Medial Malleolus (Tibia)

Talocrural Articulation

Anterior Tibiotalar Part

Tibionavicular Part

Tibiocalcaneal Part

Medial Collateral Ligament (Deltoid Ligament)

Dorsal Talonavicular Ligament

Navicular Bone

Dorsal Cuneonavicular Ligament

Tendon of Insertion of Tibialis Anterior M.

Dorsal Intercuneiform Ligaments

Cuneiform Bones (Medial, Middle, and Lateral)

Dorsal Tarsometatarsal Ligament

Metatarsal Bone #1

7.46 Capsule–Ligament System of the Ankle Joints: Right Side, Medial View. [6]

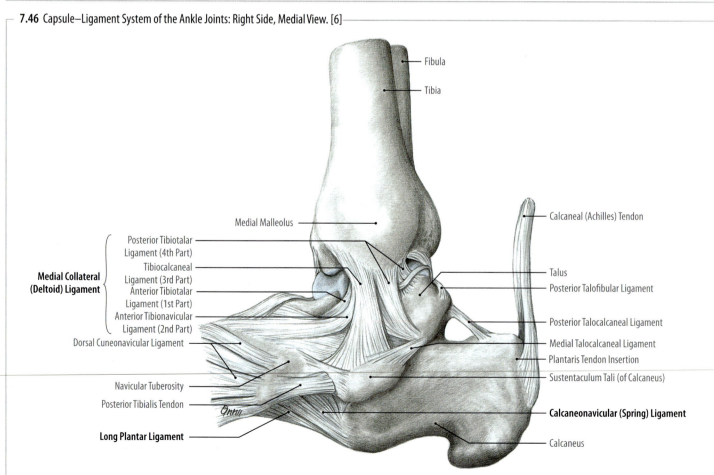

Fibula

Tibia

Medial Malleolus

Medial Collateral (Deltoid) Ligament

Posterior Tibiotalar Ligament (4th Part)

Tibiocalcaneal Ligament (3rd Part)

Anterior Tibiotalar Ligament (1st Part)

Anterior Tibionavicular Ligament (2nd Part)

Dorsal Cuneonavicular Ligament

Navicular Tuberosity

Posterior Tibialis Tendon

Long Plantar Ligament

Calcaneal (Achilles) Tendon

Talus

Posterior Talofibular Ligament

Posterior Talocalcaneal Ligament

Medial Talocalcaneal Ligament

Plantaris Tendon Insertion

Sustentaculum Tali (of Calcaneus)

Calcaneonavicular (Spring) Ligament

Calcaneus

Upper and Lower Ankle Joint

7.47 Capsule–Ligament System of the Ankle Joints: Right Side, Dorsal View. [6]

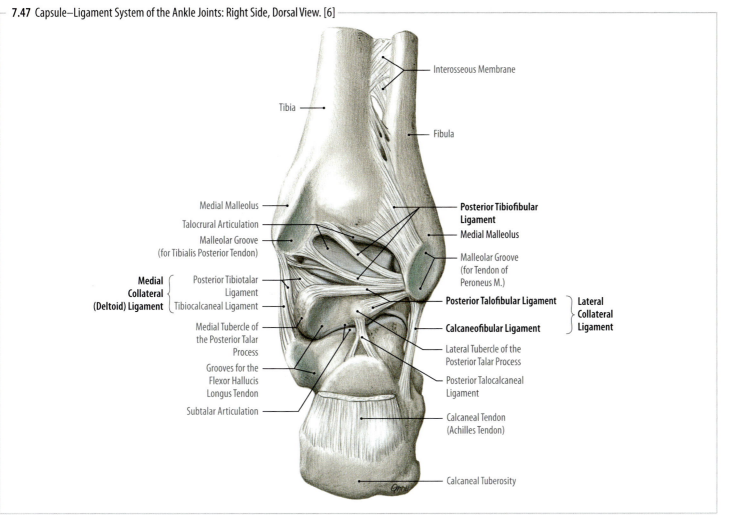

- Interosseous Membrane
- Tibia
- Fibula
- Medial Malleolus
- Talocrural Articulation
- Malleolar Groove (for Tibialis Posterior Tendon)
- **Posterior Tibiofibular Ligament**
- **Medial Malleolus**
- **Medial Collateral (Deltoid) Ligament**
  - Posterior Tibiotalar Ligament
  - Tibiocalcaneal Ligament
- Malleolar Groove (for Tendon of Peroneus M.)
- **Posterior Talofibular Ligament**
- **Calcaneofibular Ligament**
- **Lateral Collateral Ligament**
- Medial Tubercle of the Posterior Talar Process
- Grooves for the Flexor Hallucis Longus Tendon
- Subtalar Articulation
- Lateral Tubercle of the Posterior Talar Process
- Posterior Talocalcaneal Ligament
- Calcaneal Tendon (Achilles Tendon)
- Calcaneal Tuberosity

7.48 Capsule–Ligament System of the Ankle Joints: Right Side, Lateral View. [6]

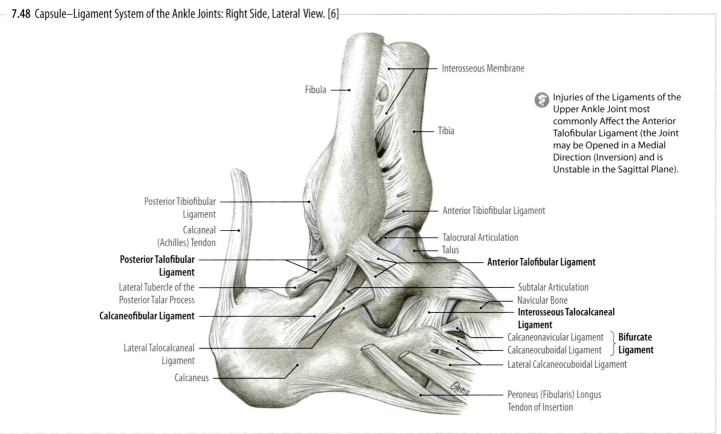

- Interosseous Membrane
- Fibula
- Tibia
- Posterior Tibiofibular Ligament
- Calcaneal (Achilles) Tendon
- **Posterior Talofibular Ligament**
- Lateral Tubercle of the Posterior Talar Process
- **Calcaneofibular Ligament**
- Lateral Talocalcaneal Ligament
- Calcaneus
- Anterior Tibiofibular Ligament
- Talocrural Articulation
- Talus
- **Anterior Talofibular Ligament**
- Subtalar Articulation
- Navicular Bone
- **Interosseous Talocalcaneal Ligament**
- Calcaneonavicular Ligament
- Calcaneocuboidal Ligament
- **Bifurcate Ligament**
- Lateral Calcaneocuboidal Ligament
- Peroneus (Fibularis) Longus Tendon of Insertion

Injuries of the Ligaments of the Upper Ankle Joint most commonly Affect the Anterior Talofibular Ligament (the Joint may be Opened in a Medial Direction (Inversion) and is Unstable in the Sagittal Plane).

Joints and Ligaments

7.49 Right Inferior Ankle Joint (Talocalcaneonavicular Articulation and Subtalar Articulation): Superior View. [6]

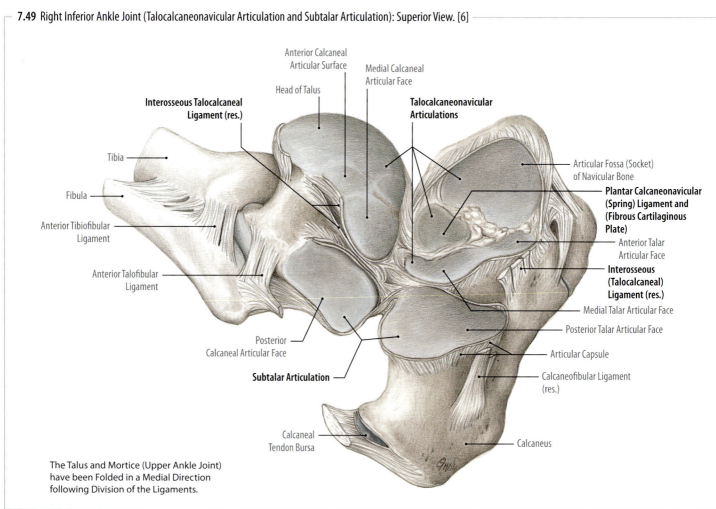

Anterior Calcaneal
Articular Surface

Medial Calcaneal
Articular Face

Head of Talus

**Interosseous Talocalcaneal
Ligament (res.)**

**Talocalcaneonavicular
Articulations**

Tibia

Fibula

Anterior Tibiofibular
Ligament

Anterior Talofibular
Ligament

Posterior
Calcaneal Articular Face

Subtalar Articulation

Calcaneal
Tendon Bursa

Articular Fossa (Socket)
of Navicular Bone

**Plantar Calcaneonavicular
(Spring) Ligament and
(Fibrous Cartilaginous
Plate)**

Anterior Talar
Articular Face

**Interosseous
(Talocalcaneal)
Ligament (res.)**

Medial Talar Articular Face

Posterior Talar Articular Face

Articular Capsule

Calcaneofibular Ligament
(res.)

Calcaneus

The Talus and Mortice (Upper Ankle Joint)
have been Folded in a Medial Direction
following Division of the Ligaments.

7.50 Right Foot, Illustration of the Synovial Membranes of the Superior and the Inferior Ankle Joints: Lateral View. [46]

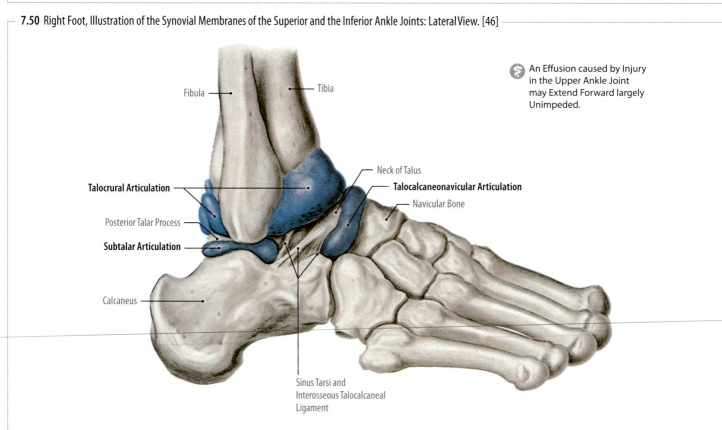

An Effusion caused by Injury
in the Upper Ankle Joint
may Extend Forward largely
Unimpeded.

Fibula

Tibia

Neck of Talus

Talocrural Articulation

Talocalcaneonavicular Articulation

Posterior Talar Process

Navicular Bone

Subtalar Articulation

Calcaneus

Sinus Tarsi and
Interosseous Talocalcaneal
Ligament

7.51a,b Right Foot, Capsule–Ligament System of the Joints of the Foot: Plantar View. [46]

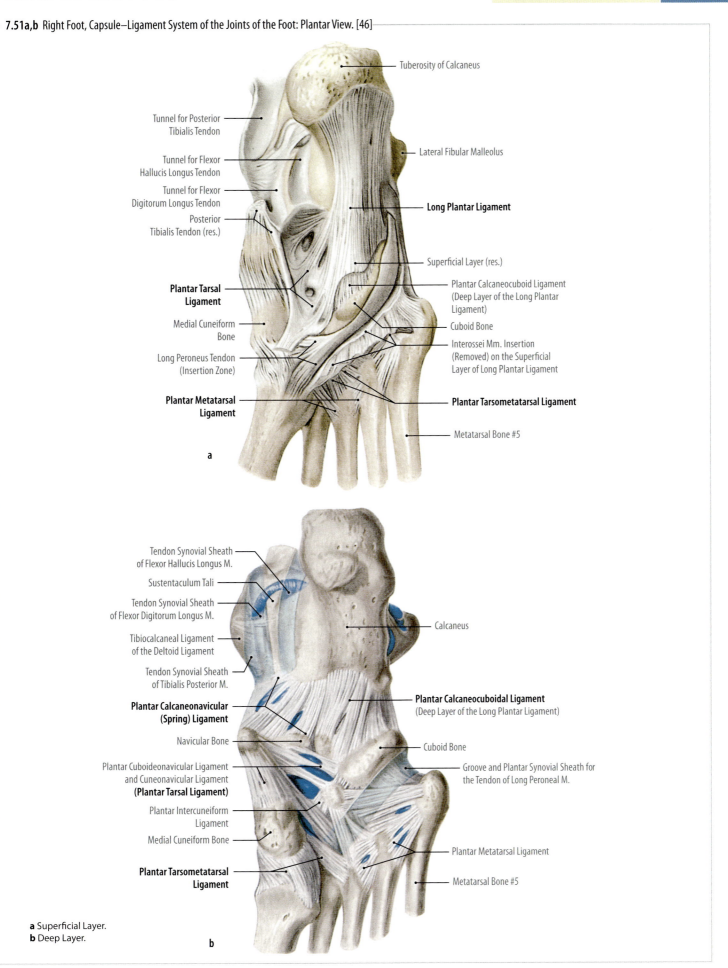

Tuberosity of Calcaneus

Tunnel for Posterior Tibialis Tendon

Lateral Fibular Malleolus

Tunnel for Flexor Hallucis Longus Tendon

Tunnel for Flexor Digitorum Longus Tendon

Posterior Tibialis Tendon (res.)

Long Plantar Ligament

Superficial Layer (res.)

Plantar Tarsal Ligament

Plantar Calcaneocuboid Ligament (Deep Layer of the Long Plantar Ligament)

Medial Cuneiform Bone

Cuboid Bone

Interossei Mm. Insertion (Removed) on the Superficial Layer of Long Plantar Ligament

Long Peroneus Tendon (Insertion Zone)

Plantar Metatarsal Ligament

Plantar Tarsometatarsal Ligament

Metatarsal Bone #5

a

Tendon Synovial Sheath of Flexor Hallucis Longus M.

Sustentaculum Tali

Tendon Synovial Sheath of Flexor Digitorum Longus M.

Tibiocalcaneal Ligament of the Deltoid Ligament

Calcaneus

Tendon Synovial Sheath of Tibialis Posterior M.

Plantar Calcaneonavicular (Spring) Ligament

Plantar Calcaneocuboidal Ligament (Deep Layer of the Long Plantar Ligament)

Navicular Bone

Cuboid Bone

Plantar Cuboideonavicular Ligament and Cuneonavicular Ligament **(Plantar Tarsal Ligament)**

Groove and Plantar Synovial Sheath for the Tendon of Long Peroneal M.

Plantar Intercuneiform Ligament

Medial Cuneiform Bone

Plantar Metatarsal Ligament

Plantar Tarsometatarsal Ligament

Metatarsal Bone #5

a Superficial Layer.
b Deep Layer.

b

Joints and Ligaments

Joints of the Foot

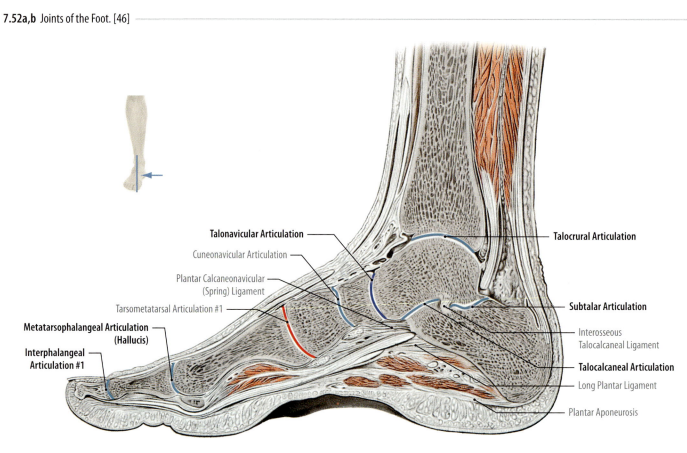

Talonavicular Articulation

Cuneonavicular Articulation

Plantar Calcaneonavicular
(Spring) Ligament

Tarsometatarsal Articulation #1

Metatarsophalangeal Articulation
(Hallucis)

Interphalangeal
Articulation #1

Talocrural Articulation

Subtalar Articulation

Interosseous
Talocalcaneal Ligament

Talocalcaneal Articulation

Long Plantar Ligament

Plantar Aponeurosis

a View of the Lateral Cut Surface.

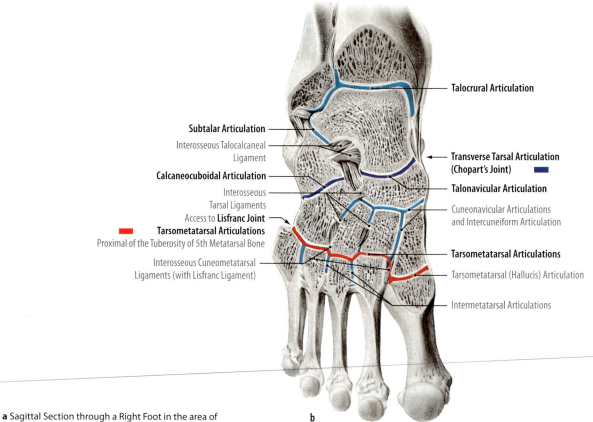

Subtalar Articulation

Interosseous Talocalcaneal
Ligament

Calcaneocuboidal Articulation

Interosseous
Tarsal Ligaments

Access to Lisfranc Joint

Tarsometatarsal Articulations
Proximal of the Tuberosity of 5th Metatarsal Bone

Interosseous Cuneometatarsal
Ligaments (with Lisfranc Ligament)

Talocrural Articulation

Transverse Tarsal Articulation
(Chopart's Joint)

Talonavicular Articulation

Cuneonavicular Articulations
and Intercuneiform Articulation

Tarsometatarsal Articulations

Tarsometatarsal (Hallucis) Articulation

Intermetatarsal Articulations

a Sagittal Section through a Right Foot in the area of
the Hallux.
b Dissection of the Joints of the Foot through Removal
of the Bone in the area of the Dorsum of the Foot.

b

7

Leg: Superficial Fascias, Muscles

7.56a,b Superficial Fasciae (a) and Muscles (b) on a Right Leg: Dorsal View. [46]

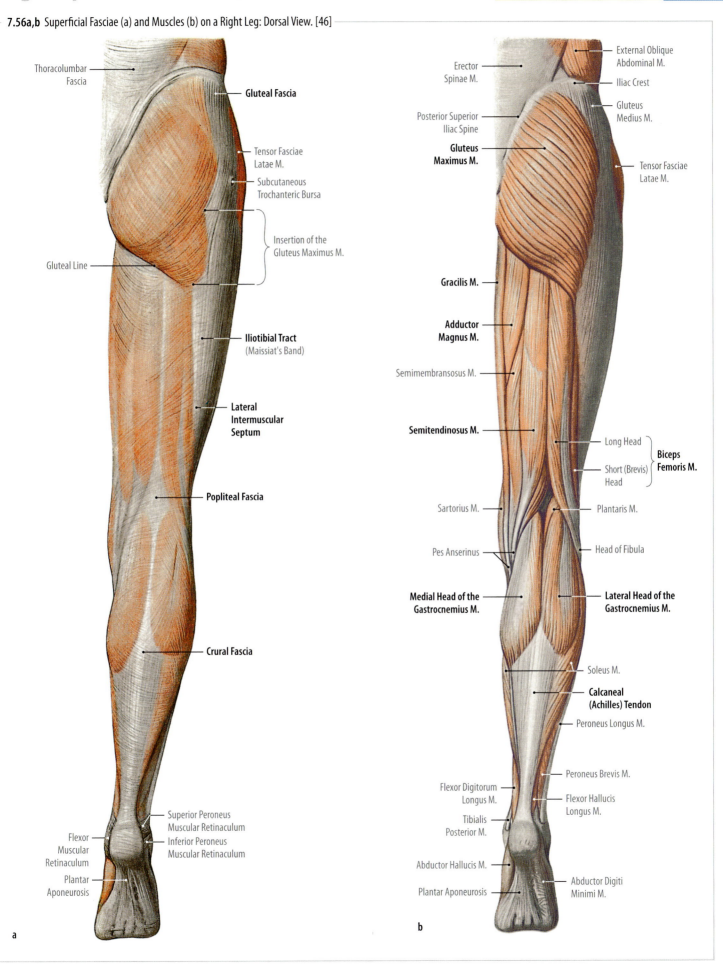

a — Left illustration labels:

Thoracolumbar Fascia

Gluteal Fascia

Tensor Fasciae Latae M.

Subcutaneous Trochanteric Bursa

Insertion of the Gluteus Maximus M.

Gluteal Line

Iliotibial Tract (Maissiat's Band)

Lateral Intermuscular Septum

Popliteal Fascia

Crural Fascia

Superior Peroneus Muscular Retinaculum

Inferior Peroneus Muscular Retinaculum

Flexor Muscular Retinaculum

Plantar Aponeurosis

b — Right illustration labels:

Erector Spinae M.

External Oblique Abdominal M.

Iliac Crest

Gluteus Medius M.

Posterior Superior Iliac Spine

Gluteus Maximus M.

Tensor Fasciae Latae M.

Gracilis M.

Adductor Magnus M.

Semimembransosus M.

Semitendinosus M.

Long Head

Short (Brevis) Head

Biceps Femoris M.

Sartorius M.

Plantaris M.

Pes Anserinus

Head of Fibula

Medial Head of the Gastrocnemius M.

Lateral Head of the Gastrocnemius M.

Soleus M.

Calcaneal (Achilles) Tendon

Peroneus Longus M.

Peroneus Brevis M.

Flexor Digitorum Longus M.

Flexor Hallucis Longus M.

Tibialis Posterior M.

Abductor Hallucis M.

Plantar Aponeurosis

Abductor Digiti Minimi M.

Muscles

Muscles of the Leg

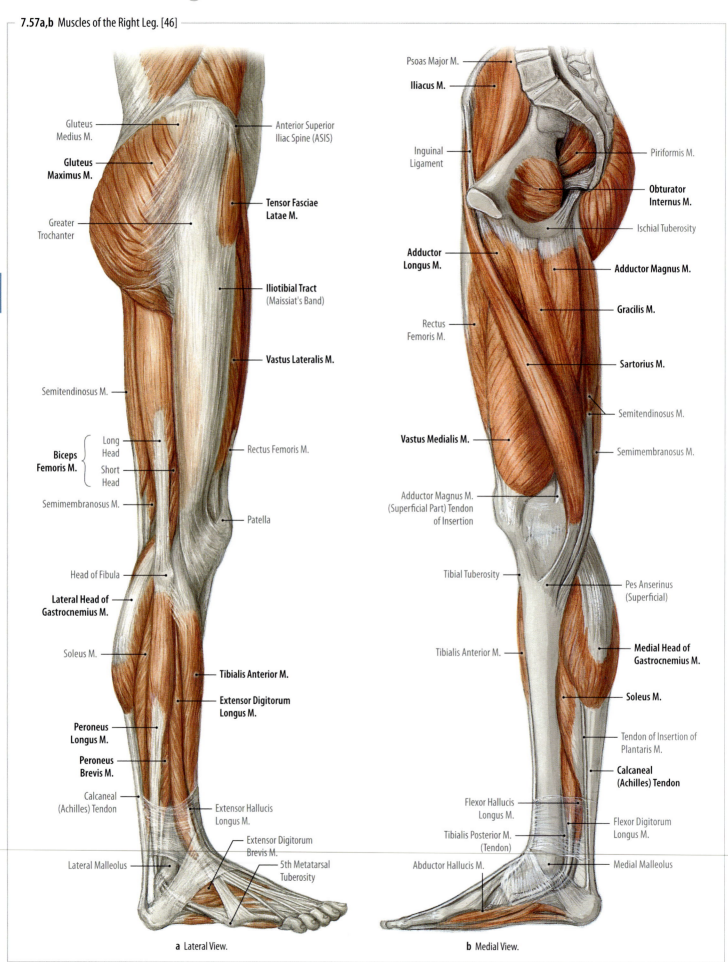

Gluteus Medius M.

Gluteus Maximus M.

Greater Trochanter

Semitendinosus M.

Biceps Femoris M. { Long Head / Short Head }

Semimembranosus M.

Head of Fibula

Lateral Head of Gastrocnemius M.

Soleus M.

Peroneus Longus M.

Peroneus Brevis M.

Calcaneal (Achilles) Tendon

Lateral Malleolus

Anterior Superior Iliac Spine (ASIS)

Tensor Fasciae Latae M.

Iliotibial Tract (Maissiat's Band)

Vastus Lateralis M.

Rectus Femoris M.

Patella

Tibialis Anterior M.

Extensor Digitorum Longus M.

Extensor Hallucis Longus M.

Extensor Digitorum Brevis M.

5th Metatarsal Tuberosity

a Lateral View.

Psoas Major M.

Iliacus M.

Inguinal Ligament

Adductor Longus M.

Rectus Femoris M.

Vastus Medialis M.

Adductor Magnus M. (Superficial Part) Tendon of Insertion

Tibial Tuberosity

Tibialis Anterior M.

Flexor Hallucis Longus M.

Tibialis Posterior M. (Tendon)

Abductor Hallucis M.

Piriformis M.

Obturator Internus M.

Ischial Tuberosity

Adductor Magnus M.

Gracilis M.

Sartorius M.

Semitendinosus M.

Semimembranosus M.

Pes Anserinus (Superficial)

Medial Head of Gastrocnemius M.

Soleus M.

Tendon of Insertion of Plantaris M.

Calcaneal (Achilles) Tendon

Flexor Digitorum Longus M.

Medial Malleolus

b Medial View.

7.58 Muscles and Fasciae of the Lumbar and Hip Region: Ventral View. [1]

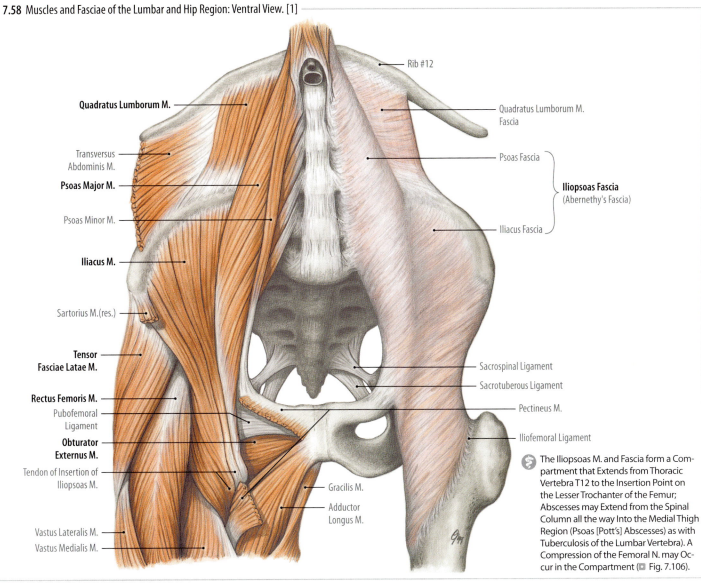

- Rib #12
- Quadratus Lumborum M.
- Quadratus Lumborum M. Fascia
- Transversus Abdominis M.
- Psoas Fascia
- Psoas Major M.
- **Iliopsoas Fascia** (Abernethy's Fascia)
- Psoas Minor M.
- Iliacus Fascia
- **Iliacus M.**
- Sartorius M.(res.)
- **Tensor Fasciae Latae M.**
- Sacrospinal Ligament
- Sacrotuberous Ligament
- **Rectus Femoris M.**
- Pectineus M.
- Pubofemoral Ligament
- **Obturator Externus M.**
- Iliofemoral Ligament
- Tendon of Insertion of Iliopsoas M.
- Gracilis M.
- Adductor Longus M.
- Vastus Lateralis M.
- Vastus Medialis M.

The Iliopsoas M. and Fascia form a Compartment that Extends from Thoracic Vertebra T12 to the Insertion Point on the Lesser Trochanter of the Femur; Abscesses may Extend from the Spinal Column all the way Into the Medial Thigh Region (Psoas [Pott's] Abscesses) as with Tuberculosis of the Lumbar Vertebra). A Compression of the Femoral N. may Occur in the Compartment (☐ Fig. 7.106).

7.59a,b Right Hip Region: Ventral View. [1]

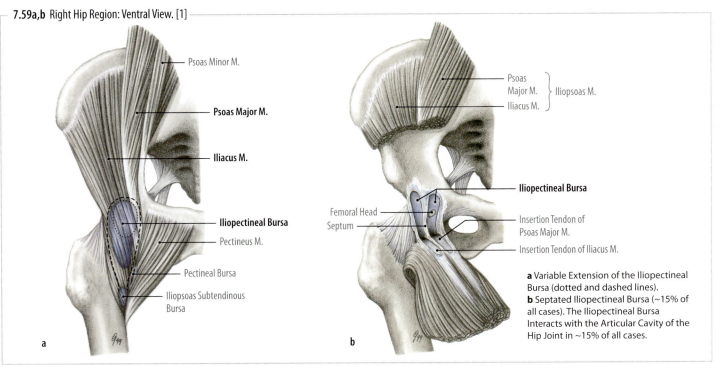

- Psoas Minor M.
- Psoas Major M.
- Psoas Major M. / Iliacus M. } Iliopsoas M.
- **Psoas Major M.**
- **Iliacus M.**
- **Iliopectineal Bursa**
- **Iliopectineal Bursa**
- Pectineus M.
- Femoral Head Septum
- Insertion Tendon of Psoas Major M.
- Pectineal Bursa
- Insertion Tendon of Iliacus M.
- Iliopsoas Subtendinous Bursa

a Variable Extension of the Iliopectineal Bursa (dotted and dashed lines).
b Septated Iliopectineal Bursa (~15% of all cases). The Iliopectineal Bursa Interacts with the Articular Cavity of the Hip Joint in ~15% of all cases.

a   b

Muscles

7.60 Synovial Bursa of the Gluteal Region: Dorsal View. [46]

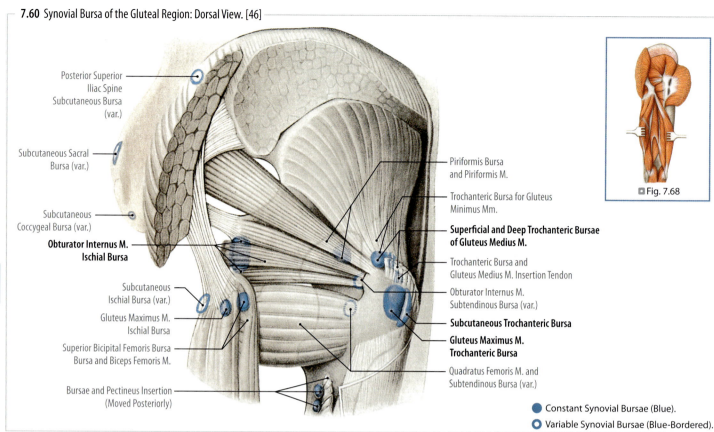

Posterior Superior
Iliac Spine
Subcutaneous Bursa
(var.)

Subcutaneous Sacral
Bursa (var.)

Subcutaneous
Coccygeal Bursa (var.)

**Obturator Internus M.
Ischial Bursa**

Subcutaneous
Ischial Bursa (var.)

Gluteus Maximus M.
Ischial Bursa

Superior Bicipital Femoris Bursa
Bursa and Biceps Femoris M.

Bursae and Pectineus Insertion
(Moved Posteriorly)

Piriformis Bursa
and Piriformis M.

Trochanteric Bursa for Gluteus
Minimus Mm.

**Superficial and Deep Trochanteric Bursae
of Gluteus Medius M.**

Trochanteric Bursa and
Gluteus Medius M. Insertion Tendon

Obturator Internus M.
Subtendinous Bursa (var.)

Subcutaneous Trochanteric Bursa

**Gluteus Maximus M.
Trochanteric Bursa**

Quadratus Femoris M. and
Subtendinous Bursa (var.)

◾ Fig. 7.68

● Constant Synovial Bursae (Blue).
◯ Variable Synovial Bursae (Blue-Bordered).

7.61 Right Hip Region: Dorsal View. [1]

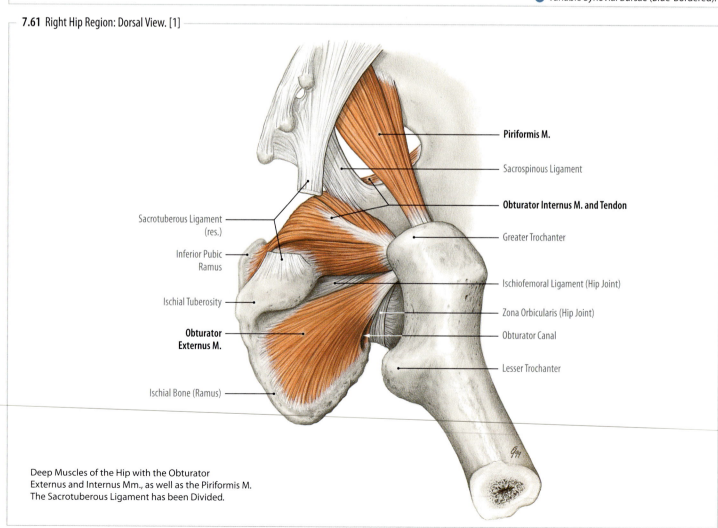

Sacrotuberous Ligament
(res.)

Inferior Pubic
Ramus

Ischial Tuberosity

**Obturator
Externus M.**

Ischial Bone (Ramus)

Piriformis M.

Sacrospinous Ligament

Obturator Internus M. and Tendon

Greater Trochanter

Ischiofemoral Ligament (Hip Joint)

Zona Orbicularis (Hip Joint)

Obturator Canal

Lesser Trochanter

Deep Muscles of the Hip with the Obturator
Externus and Internus Mm., as well as the Piriformis M.
The Sacrotuberous Ligament has been Divided.

496

7.62 Muscles of the Pelvic Wall, Right Half of the Pelvis: Medial View. [1]

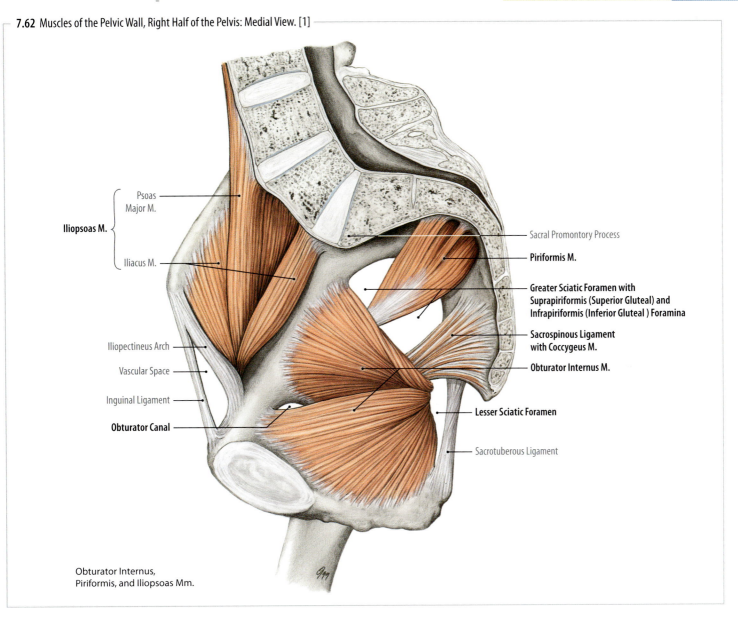

- Psoas Major M.
- Iliopsoas M.
- Iliacus M.
- Iliopectineus Arch
- Vascular Space
- Inguinal Ligament
- **Obturator Canal**
- Sacral Promontory Process
- **Piriformis M.**
- **Greater Sciatic Foramen with Suprapiriformis (Superior Gluteal) and Infrapiriformis (Inferior Gluteal) Foramina**
- **Sacrospinous Ligament with Coccygeus M.**
- **Obturator Internus M.**
- **Lesser Sciatic Foramen**
- Sacrotuberous Ligament

Obturator Internus, Piriformis, and Iliopsoas Mm.

7.63 Scope of Movement in the Hip Joint and Executing Muscles.

Abduction
Gluteus Medius M.
Gluteus Minimus M.
Piriformis M.
Tensor Fasciae Latae M.
Gluteus Maximus (Superior Fibers)
[Support of the Abduction:
Rectus Femoris M.
Sartorius M.]

Adduction
Adductor Longus M.
Adductor Brevis M.
Adductor Magnus M.
Pectineus M.
Gluteus Maximus M. (Inferior Part)
Quadratus Femoris M.
Obturator and Gemelli Mm.

Medial Rotation
Tensor Fasciae Latae M.
Gluteus Medius M. (Anterior Part)
Gluteus Minimus M.
Adductor Magnus M.
Adductor Longus M.
Gracilis M.

Range of Movement of the Hip Joint
Flexion (Knee Joint Flexed) and Extension
130°–140° / 0° / 10°–15°
Abduction and Adduction
30°–50° / 0° / 20°–30°
Medial Rotation and Lateral Rotation
30°–40° / 0° / 40°–50°

Flexion
Iliopsoas M.
Rectus Femoris M.
Tensor Fasciae Latae M.
Gluteus Medius M. (Anterior Part)
Sartorius M.
[Support of the Flexion:
Gracilis M.
Pectineus M.
Adductor Longus M.
Adductor Brevis M.
Adductor Magnus M. (Deep Part)]

Extension
Gluteus Maximus M.
Semimembranosus M.
Semitendinosus M.
Long Head of the Biceps Femoris M.
Gluteus Medius M. (Posterior Part)
Adductor Magnus M. (Superficial Part)
[Support of the Extension:
Quadratus Femoris M.
Obturators and Gemelli Mm.]

Lateral Rotation
Gluteus Maximus M.
Gluteus Medius (Posterior Part)
Piriformis M.
Quadratus Femoris M.
Obturators and Gemelli Mm.
Pectineus M.
Sartorius M.
[Support of the Lateral Rotation:
Long Head of the Biceps Femoris M.
Rectus Femoris M.]

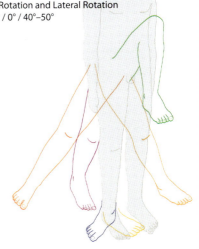

Muscles

7.64 Muscles of the Thigh: Right Side, Anteromedial View. [6]

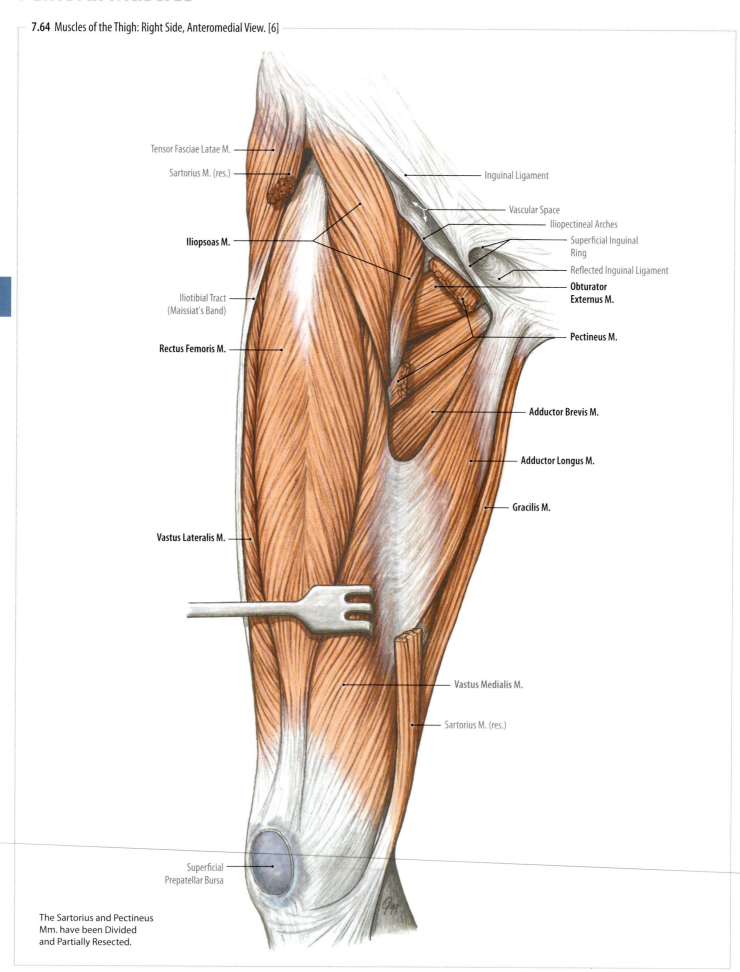

Tensor Fasciae Latae M.

Sartorius M. (res.)

Iliopsoas M.

Iliotibial Tract
(Maissiat's Band)

Rectus Femoris M.

Vastus Lateralis M.

Inguinal Ligament

Vascular Space

Iliopectineal Arches

Superficial Inguinal
Ring

Reflected Inguinal Ligament

**Obturator
Externus M.**

Pectineus M.

Adductor Brevis M.

Adductor Longus M.

Gracilis M.

Vastus Medialis M.

Sartorius M. (res.)

Superficial
Prepatellar Bursa

The Sartorius and Pectineus
Mm. have been Divided
and Partially Resected.

7

7.65 Muscles of the Thigh: Right Side, Anteromedial View. [6]

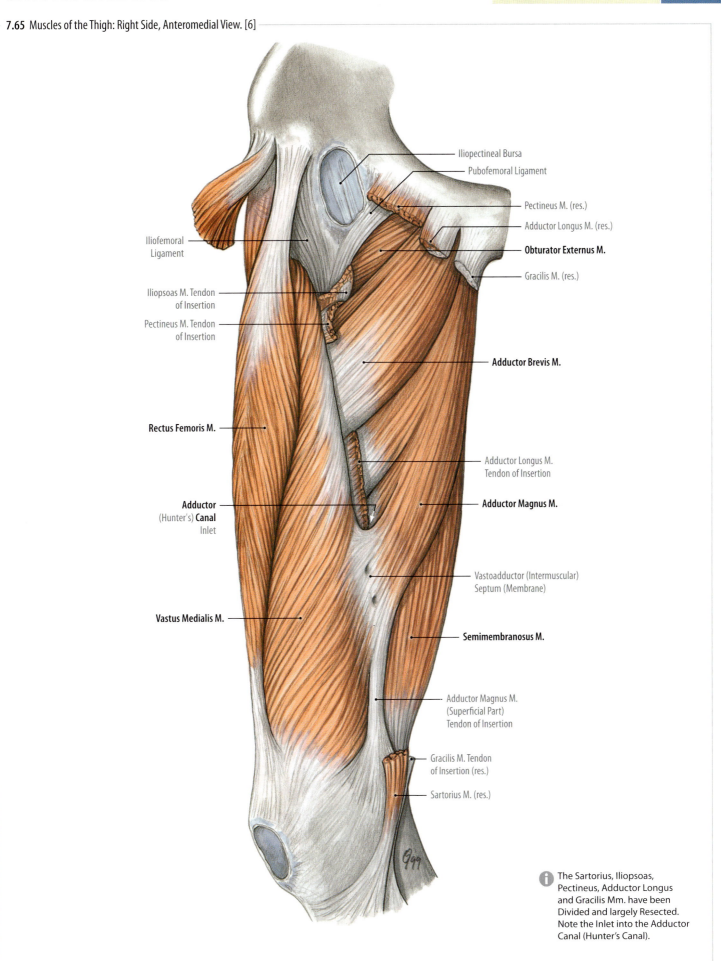

Iliopectineal Bursa

Pubofemoral Ligament

Pectineus M. (res.)

Adductor Longus M. (res.)

Obturator Externus M.

Gracilis M. (res.)

Iliofemoral
Ligament

Iliopsoas M. Tendon
of Insertion

Pectineus M. Tendon
of Insertion

Adductor Brevis M.

Rectus Femoris M.

Adductor Longus M.
Tendon of Insertion

Adductor Magnus M.

**Adductor
(Hunter's) Canal**
Inlet

Vastoadductor (Intermuscular)
Septum (Membrane)

Vastus Medialis M.

Semimembranosus M.

Adductor Magnus M.
(Superficial Part)
Tendon of Insertion

Gracilis M. Tendon
of Insertion (res.)

Sartorius M. (res.)

ⓘ The Sartorius, Iliopsoas,
Pectineus, Adductor Longus
and Gracilis Mm. have been
Divided and largely Resected.
Note the Inlet into the Adductor
Canal (Hunter's Canal).

Muscles

7.66 Muscles of the Thigh: Right Side, Medial Ventral View. [6]

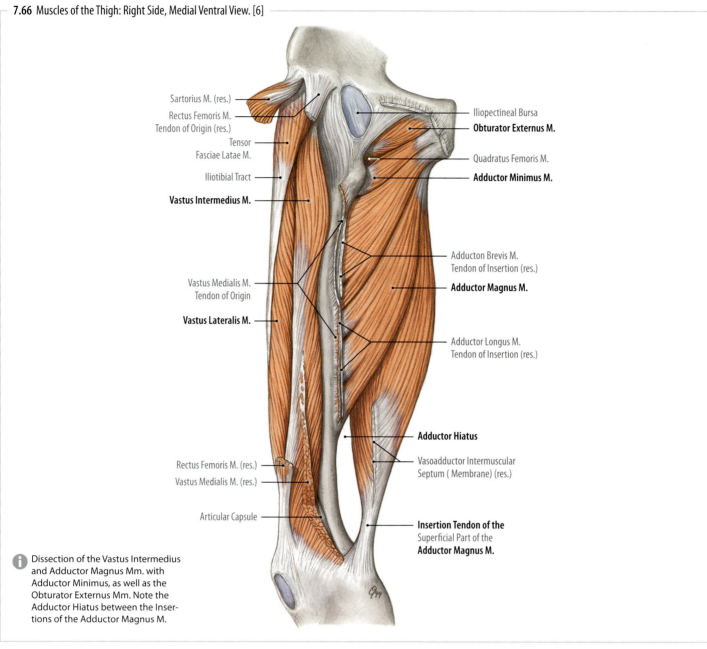

Sartorius M. (res.)

Rectus Femoris M.
Tendon of Origin (res.)

Tensor
Fasciae Latae M.

Iliotibial Tract

Vastus Intermedius M.

**Vastus Medialis M.
Tendon of Origin**

Vastus Lateralis M.

Rectus Femoris M. (res.)

Vastus Medialis M. (res.)

Articular Capsule

Iliopectineal Bursa

Obturator Externus M.

Quadratus Femoris M.

Adductor Minimus M.

Adducton Brevis M.
Tendon of Insertion (res.)

Adductor Magnus M.

Adductor Longus M.
Tendon of Insertion (res.)

Adductor Hiatus

Vasoadductor Intermuscular
Septum (Membrane) (res.)

Insertion Tendon of the
Superficial Part of the
Adductor Magnus M.

ℹ️ Dissection of the Vastus Intermedius
and Adductor Magnus Mm. with
Adductor Minimus, as well as the
Obturator Externus Mm. Note the
Adductor Hiatus between the Inser-
tions of the Adductor Magnus M.

7.67 Muscles and Muscle Compartments of the Thigh of the Right Side: Superior View Following a Transversal Section.

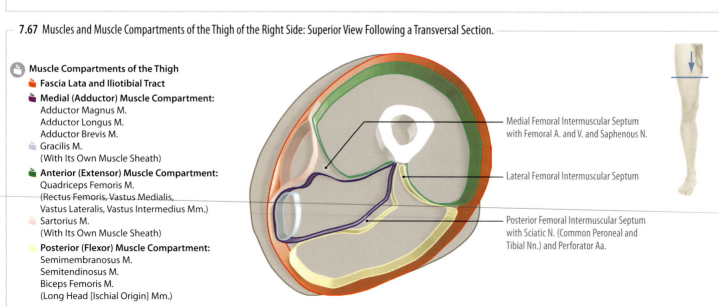

Muscle Compartments of the Thigh

🟥 **Fascia Lata and Iliotibial Tract**

🟪 **Medial (Adductor) Muscle Compartment:**
Adductor Magnus M.
Adductor Longus M.
Adductor Brevis M.
🔵 Gracilis M.
(With Its Own Muscle Sheath)

🟩 **Anterior (Extensor) Muscle Compartment:**
Quadriceps Femoris M.
(Rectus Femoris, Vastus Medialis,
Vastus Lateralis, Vastus Intermedius Mm.)
🔴 Sartorius M.
(With Its Own Muscle Sheath)

🟨 **Posterior (Flexor) Muscle Compartment:**
Semimembranosus M.
Semitendinosus M.
Biceps Femoris M.
(Long Head [Ischial Origin] Mm.)

Medial Femoral Intermuscular Septum
with Femoral A. and V. and Saphenous N.

Lateral Femoral Intermuscular Septum

Posterior Femoral Intermuscular Septum
with Sciatic N. (Common Peroneal and
Tibial Nn.) and Perforator Aa.

7.68 Gluteal and Posterior Thigh Muscles: Right Side, Dorsal View. [6]

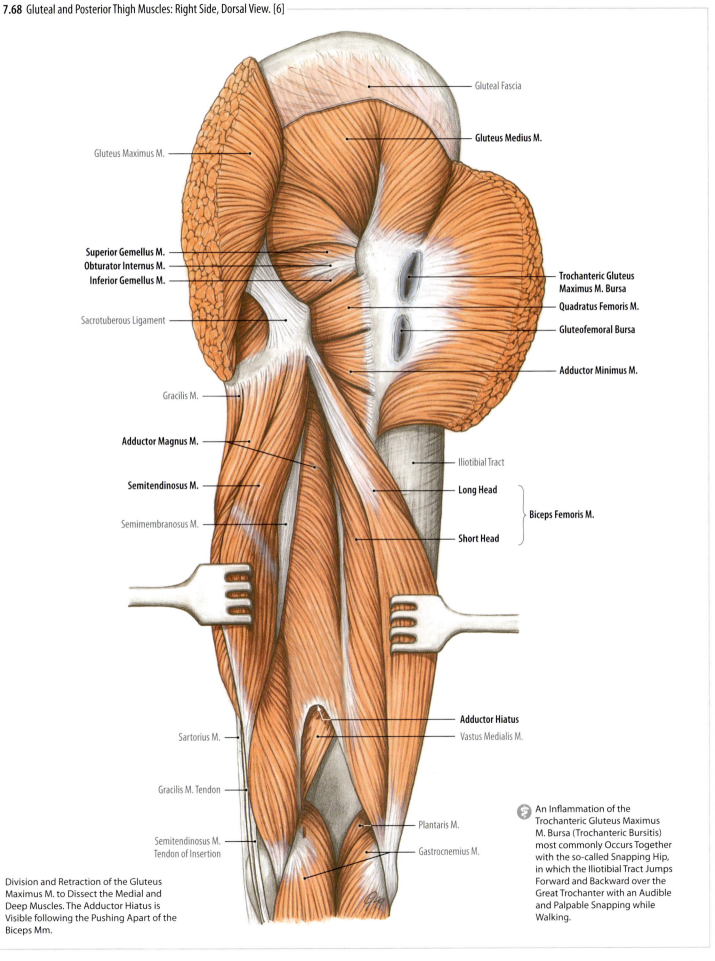

Gluteal Fascia

Gluteus Medius M.

Gluteus Maximus M.

Superior Gemellus M.
Obturator Internus M.
Inferior Gemellus M.

Trochanteric Gluteus
Maximus M. Bursa

Quadratus Femoris M.

Gluteofemoral Bursa

Sacrotuberous Ligament

Adductor Minimus M.

Gracilis M.

Adductor Magnus M.

Iliotibial Tract

Semitendinosus M.

Long Head

Semimembranosus M.

Biceps Femoris M.

Short Head

Adductor Hiatus

Sartorius M.

Vastus Medialis M.

Gracilis M. Tendon

Plantaris M.

Semitendinosus M.
Tendon of Insertion

Gastrocnemius M.

Division and Retraction of the Gluteus
Maximus M. to Dissect the Medial and
Deep Muscles. The Adductor Hiatus is
Visible following the Pushing Apart of the
Biceps Mm.

An Inflammation of the
Trochanteric Gluteus Maximus
M. Bursa (Trochanteric Bursitis)
most commonly Occurs Together
with the so-called Snapping Hip,
in which the Iliotibial Tract Jumps
Forward and Backward over the
Great Trochanter with an Audible
and Palpable Snapping while
Walking.

Muscles

Femoral Muscles

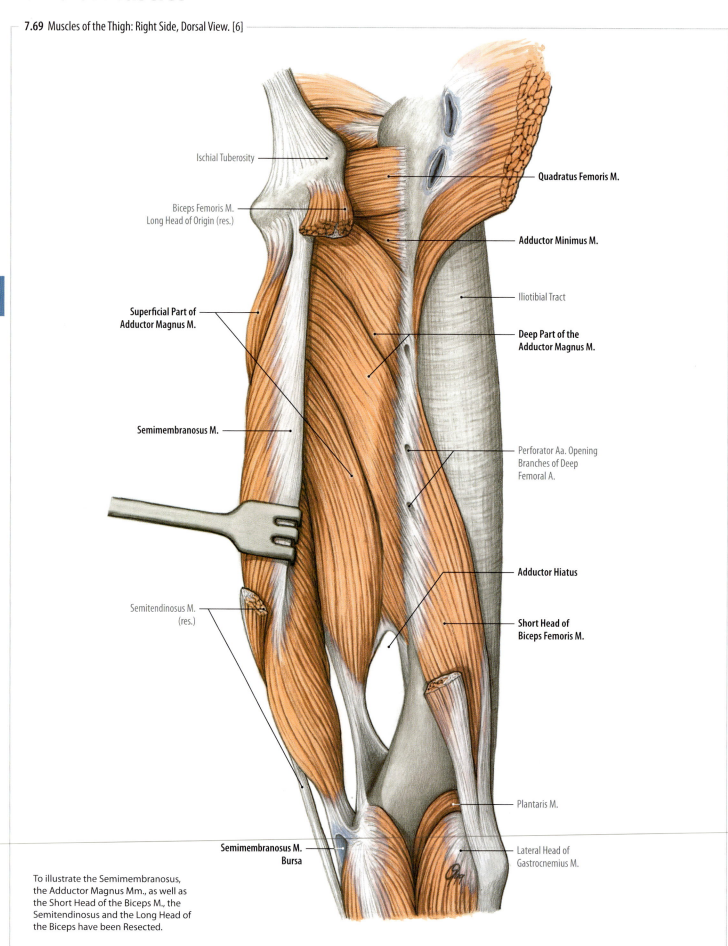

Ischial Tuberosity

Biceps Femoris M.
Long Head of Origin (res.)

**Superficial Part of
Adductor Magnus M.**

Semimembranosus M.

Quadratus Femoris M.

Adductor Minimus M.

Iliotibial Tract

**Deep Part of the
Adductor Magnus M.**

Perforator Aa. Opening
Branches of Deep
Femoral A.

Semitendinosus M.
(res.)

Adductor Hiatus

**Short Head of
Biceps Femoris M.**

Plantaris M.

**Semimembranosus M.
Bursa**

Lateral Head of
Gastrocnemius M.

To illustrate the Semimembranosus,
the Adductor Magnus Mm., as well as
the Short Head of the Biceps M., the
Semitendinosus and the Long Head of
the Biceps have been Resected.

7.70 Right Femur: Anterolateral View. [1]

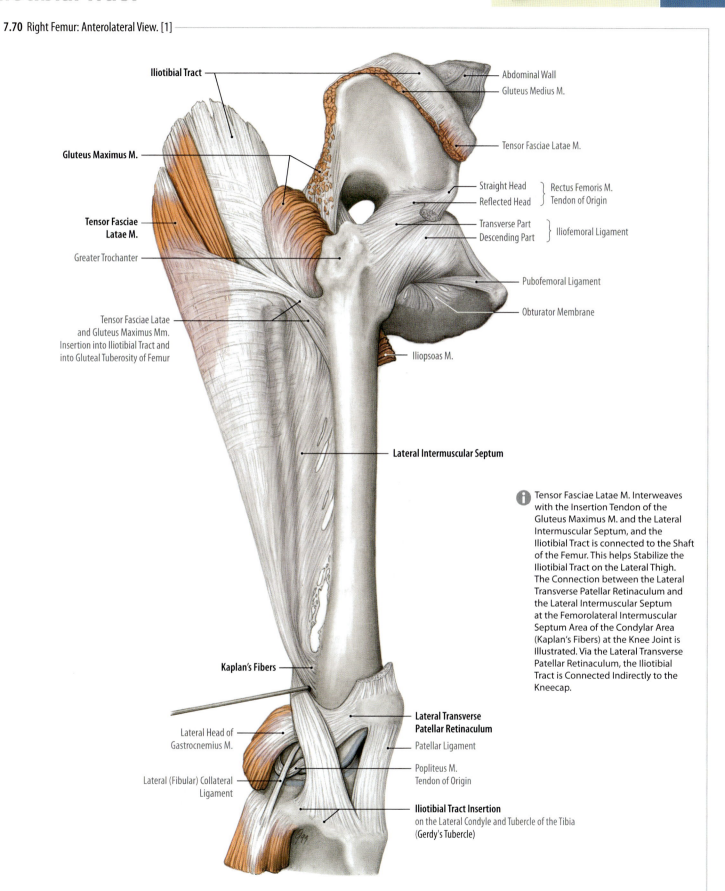

Iliotibial Tract

Abdominal Wall

Gluteus Medius M.

Gluteus Maximus M.

Tensor Fasciae Latae M.

Straight Head ⎤ Rectus Femoris M.
Reflected Head ⎦ Tendon of Origin

Tensor Fasciae
Latae M.

Transverse Part ⎤ Iliofemoral Ligament
Descending Part ⎦

Greater Trochanter

Pubofemoral Ligament

Obturator Membrane

Tensor Fasciae Latae
and Gluteus Maximus Mm.
Insertion into Iliotibial Tract and
into Gluteal Tuberosity of Femur

Iliopsoas M.

Lateral Intermuscular Septum

Kaplan's Fibers

Lateral Transverse
Patellar Retinaculum

Lateral Head of
Gastrocnemius M.

Patellar Ligament

Popliteus M.
Tendon of Origin

Lateral (Fibular) Collateral
Ligament

Iliotibial Tract Insertion
on the Lateral Condyle and Tubercle of the Tibia
(Gerdy's Tubercle)

ⓘ Tensor Fasciae Latae M. Interweaves
with the Insertion Tendon of the
Gluteus Maximus M. and the Lateral
Intermuscular Septum, and the
Iliotibial Tract is connected to the Shaft
of the Femur. This helps Stabilize the
Iliotibial Tract on the Lateral Thigh.
The Connection between the Lateral
Transverse Patellar Retinaculum and
the Lateral Intermuscular Septum
at the Femorolateral Intermuscular
Septum Area of the Condylar Area
(Kaplan's Fibers) at the Knee Joint is
Illustrated. Via the Lateral Transverse
Patellar Retinaculum, the Iliotibial
Tract is Connected Indirectly to the
Kneecap.

To illustrate the Iliotibial Tract (Maissiat's Band), the Muscles of the
Thigh have been Removed. The Iliotibial Tract has been Removed from
the Iliac Crest, along With the Tensor Fasciae Latae M.

7.71 Frontal Section through the Pelvis and Femur: View of the Anterior Cut Surface. [46]

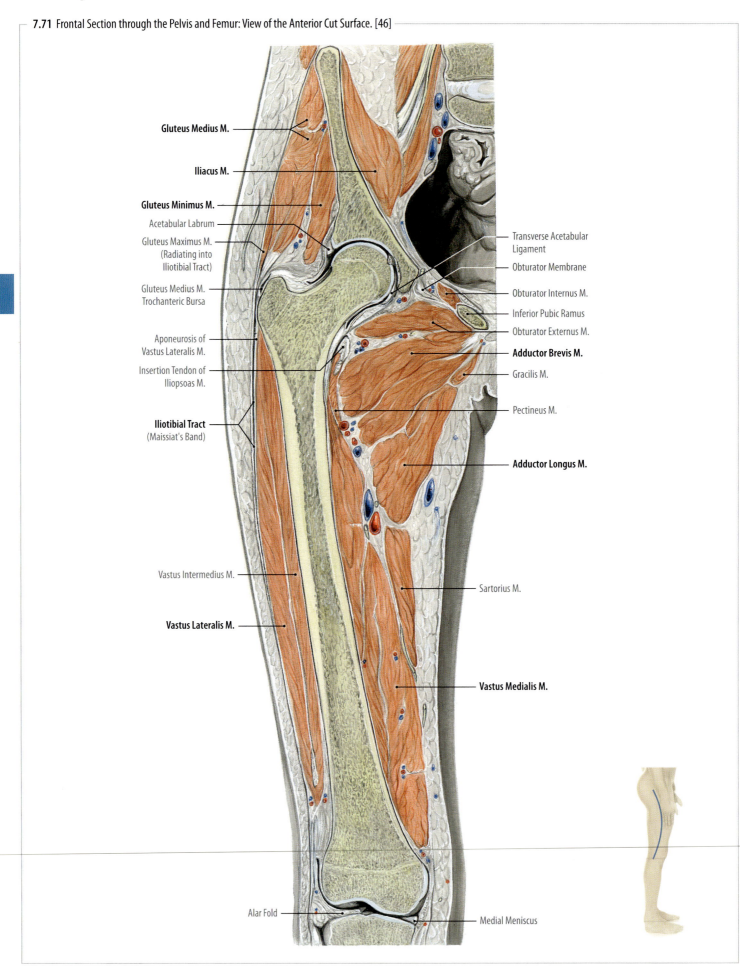

Gluteus Medius M.

Iliacus M.

Gluteus Minimus M.

Acetabular Labrum

Gluteus Maximus M.
(Radiating into
Iliotibial Tract)

Gluteus Medius M.
Trochanteric Bursa

Aponeurosis of
Vastus Lateralis M.

Insertion Tendon of
Iliopsoas M.

Iliotibial Tract
(Maissiat's Band)

Vastus Intermedius M.

Vastus Lateralis M.

Transverse Acetabular
Ligament

Obturator Membrane

Obturator Internus M.

Inferior Pubic Ramus

Obturator Externus M.

Adductor Brevis M.

Gracilis M.

Pectineus M.

Adductor Longus M.

Sartorius M.

Vastus Medialis M.

Alar Fold

Medial Meniscus

7

7.72 Knee Area of the Right Side: Dorsal View; Insertions of the Femoral Muscles and Origins of the Muscles of the Leg. [8]

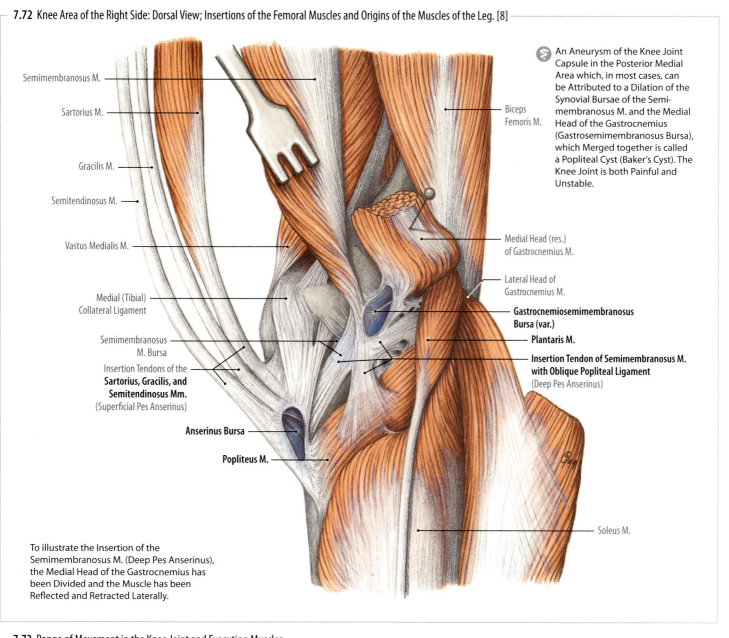

Semimembranosus M.

Sartorius M.

Gracilis M.

Semitendinosus M.

Vastus Medialis M.

Medial (Tibial) Collateral Ligament

Semimembranosus M. Bursa

Insertion Tendons of the **Sartorius, Gracilis, and Semitendinosus Mm.** (Superficial Pes Anserinus)

Anserinus Bursa

Popliteus M.

Biceps Femoris M.

Medial Head (res.) of Gastrocnemius M.

Lateral Head of Gastrocnemius M.

Gastrocnemiosemimembranosus Bursa (var.)

Plantaris M.

Insertion Tendon of Semimembranosus M. with Oblique Popliteal Ligament (Deep Pes Anserinus)

Soleus M.

An Aneurysm of the Knee Joint Capsule in the Posterior Medial Area which, in most cases, can be Attributed to a Dilation of the Synovial Bursae of the Semimembranosus M. and the Medial Head of the Gastrocnemius (Gastrosemimembranosus Bursa), which Merged together is called a Popliteal Cyst (Baker's Cyst). The Knee Joint is both Painful and Unstable.

To illustrate the Insertion of the Semimembranosus M. (Deep Pes Anserinus), the Medial Head of the Gastrocnemius has been Divided and the Muscle has been Reflected and Retracted Laterally.

7.73 Range of Movement in the Knee Joint and Executing Muscles.

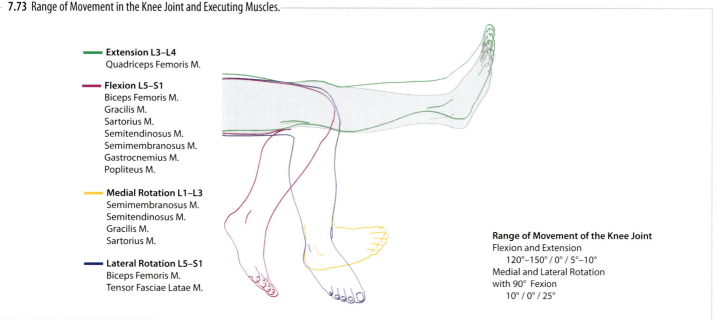

Extension L3–L4
Quadriceps Femoris M.

Flexion L5–S1
Biceps Femoris M.
Gracilis M.
Sartorius M.
Semitendinosus M.
Semimembranosus M.
Gastrocnemius M.
Popliteus M.

Medial Rotation L1–L3
Semimembranosus M.
Semitendinosus M.
Gracilis M.
Sartorius M.

Lateral Rotation L5–S1
Biceps Femoris M.
Tensor Fasciae Latae M.

Range of Movement of the Knee Joint
Flexion and Extension
120°–150° / 0° / 5°–10°
Medial and Lateral Rotation
with 90° Fexion
10° / 0° / 25°

Muscles

Muscles of the Lower Leg

7.74a,b Muscles of the Lower Leg: Right Side, Dorsal View. [6]

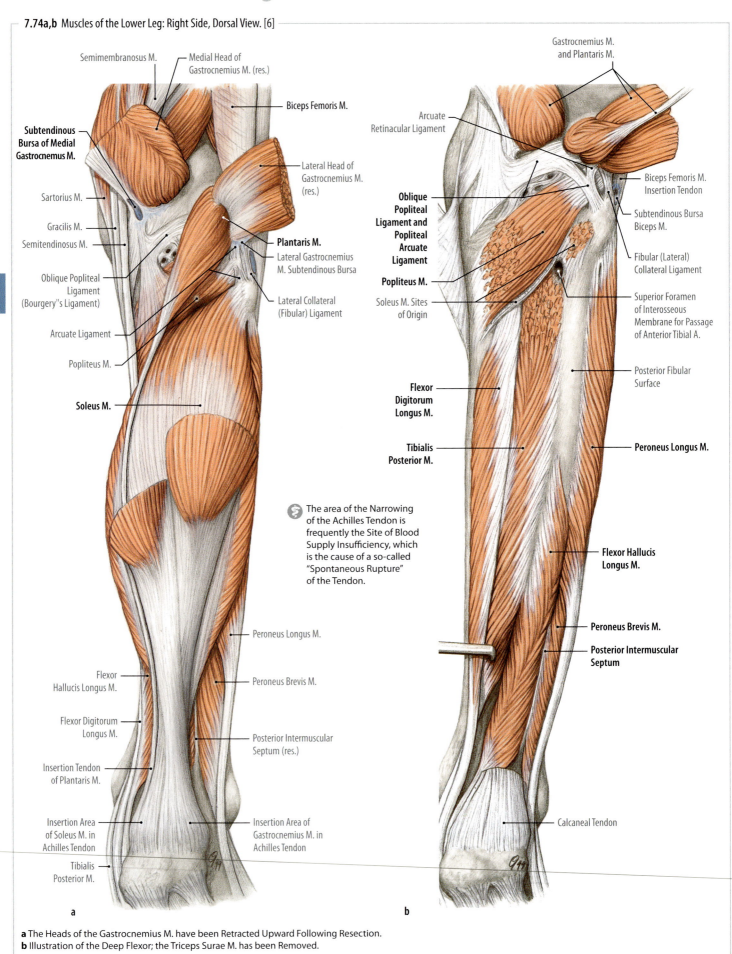

Semimembranosus M.

Medial Head of Gastrocnemius M. (res.)

Biceps Femoris M.

Subtendinous Bursa of Medial Gastrocnemius M.

Sartorius M.

Gracilis M.

Semitendinosus M.

Oblique Popliteal Ligament (Bourgery"s Ligament)

Arcuate Ligament

Popliteus M.

Soleus M.

Lateral Head of Gastrocnemius M. (res.)

Plantaris M.

Lateral Gastrocnemius M. Subtendinous Bursa

Lateral Collateral (Fibular) Ligament

Flexor Hallucis Longus M.

Flexor Digitorum Longus M.

Insertion Tendon of Plantaris M.

Insertion Area of Soleus M. in Achilles Tendon

Tibialis Posterior M.

Peroneus Longus M.

Peroneus Brevis M.

Posterior Intermuscular Septum (res.)

Insertion Area of Gastrocnemius M. in Achilles Tendon

Gastrocnemius M. and Plantaris M.

Arcuate Retinacular Ligament

Oblique Popliteal Ligament and Popliteal Arcuate Ligament

Popliteus M.

Soleus M. Sites of Origin

Flexor Digitorum Longus M.

Tibialis Posterior M.

Biceps Femoris M. Insertion Tendon

Subtendinous Bursa Biceps M.

Fibular (Lateral) Collateral Ligament

Superior Foramen of Interosseous Membrane for Passage of Anterior Tibial A.

Posterior Fibular Surface

Peroneus Longus M.

Flexor Hallucis Longus M.

Peroneus Brevis M.

Posterior Intermuscular Septum

Calcaneal Tendon

The area of the Narrowing of the Achilles Tendon is frequently the Site of Blood Supply Insufficiency, which is the cause of a so-called "Spontaneous Rupture" of the Tendon.

a

b

a The Heads of the Gastrocnemius M. have been Retracted Upward Following Resection.
b Illustration of the Deep Flexor; the Triceps Surae M. has been Removed.

7

Mucles of the Lower Leg

7.75a,b Muscles of the Lower Leg: Right Side, Anterolateral View. [6]

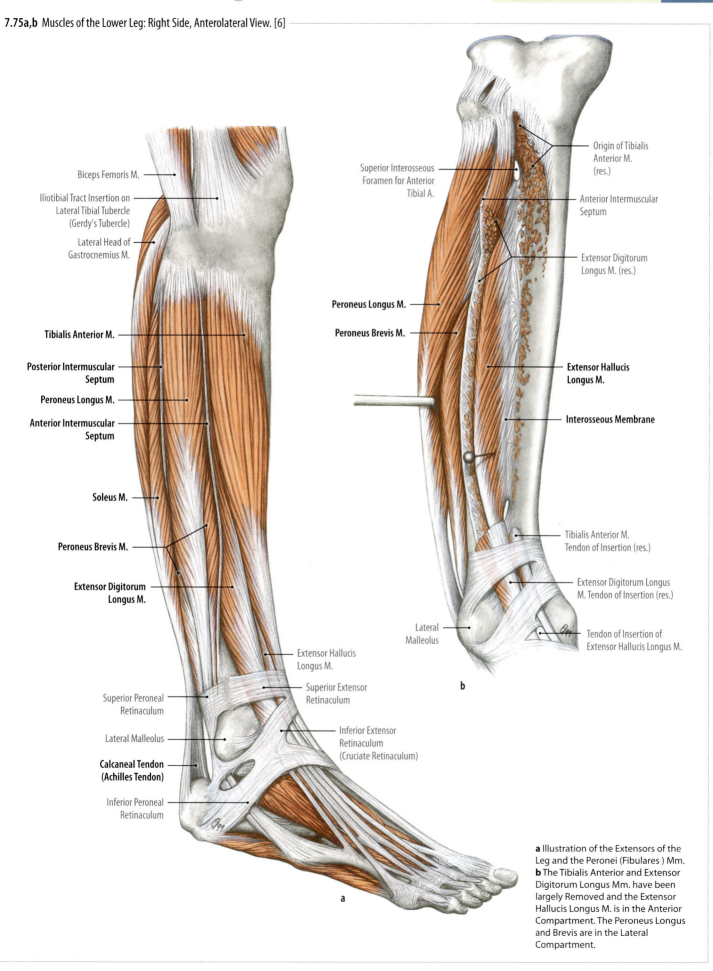

Biceps Femoris M.

Iliotibial Tract Insertion on Lateral Tibial Tubercle (Gerdy's Tubercle)

Lateral Head of Gastrocnemius M.

Tibialis Anterior M.

Posterior Intermuscular Septum

Peroneus Longus M.

Anterior Intermuscular Septum

Soleus M.

Peroneus Brevis M.

Extensor Digitorum Longus M.

Superior Peroneal Retinaculum

Lateral Malleolus

Calcaneal Tendon (Achilles Tendon)

Inferior Peroneal Retinaculum

Extensor Hallucis Longus M.

Superior Extensor Retinaculum

Inferior Extensor Retinaculum (Cruciate Retinaculum)

a

Superior Interosseous Foramen for Anterior Tibial A.

Peroneus Longus M.

Peroneus Brevis M.

Origin of Tibialis Anterior M. (res.)

Anterior Intermuscular Septum

Extensor Digitorum Longus M. (res.)

Extensor Hallucis Longus M.

Interosseous Membrane

Tibialis Anterior M. Tendon of Insertion (res.)

Extensor Digitorum Longus M. Tendon of Insertion (res.)

Lateral Malleolus

Tendon of Insertion of Extensor Hallucis Longus M.

b

a Illustration of the Extensors of the Leg and the Peronei (Fibulares) Mm.
b The Tibialis Anterior and Extensor Digitorum Longus Mm. have been largely Removed and the Extensor Hallucis Longus M. is in the Anterior Compartment. The Peroneus Longus and Brevis are in the Lateral Compartment.

Muscles

7.76 Compartment of the Muscles of the Leg: Right Side, Superior View following a Transverse Section.

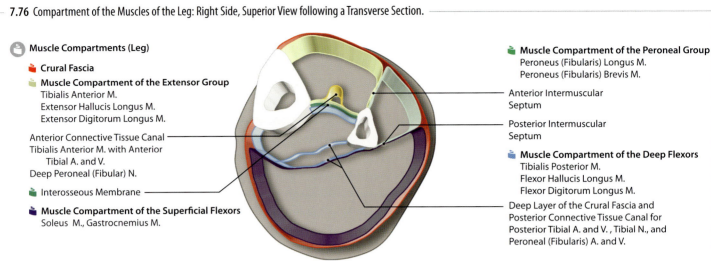

Muscle Compartments (Leg)

Crural Fascia

Muscle Compartment of the Extensor Group
Tibialis Anterior M.
Extensor Hallucis Longus M.
Extensor Digitorum Longus M.

Anterior Connective Tissue Canal
Tibialis Anterior M. with Anterior
   Tibial A. and V.
Deep Peroneal (Fibular) N.

Interosseous Membrane

Muscle Compartment of the Superficial Flexors
Soleus M., Gastrocnemius M.

Muscle Compartment of the Peroneal Group
Peroneus (Fibularis) Longus M.
Peroneus (Fibularis) Brevis M.

Anterior Intermuscular
Septum

Posterior Intermuscular
Septum

Muscle Compartment of the Deep Flexors
Tibialis Posterior M.
Flexor Hallucis Longus M.
Flexor Digitorum Longus M.

Deep Layer of the Crural Fascia and
Posterior Connective Tissue Canal for
Posterior Tibial A. and V. , Tibial N., and
Peroneal (Fibularis) A. and V.

7.77 Muscles of the Dorsum of the Foot, Superficial Layer: Lateral Superior View. [8]

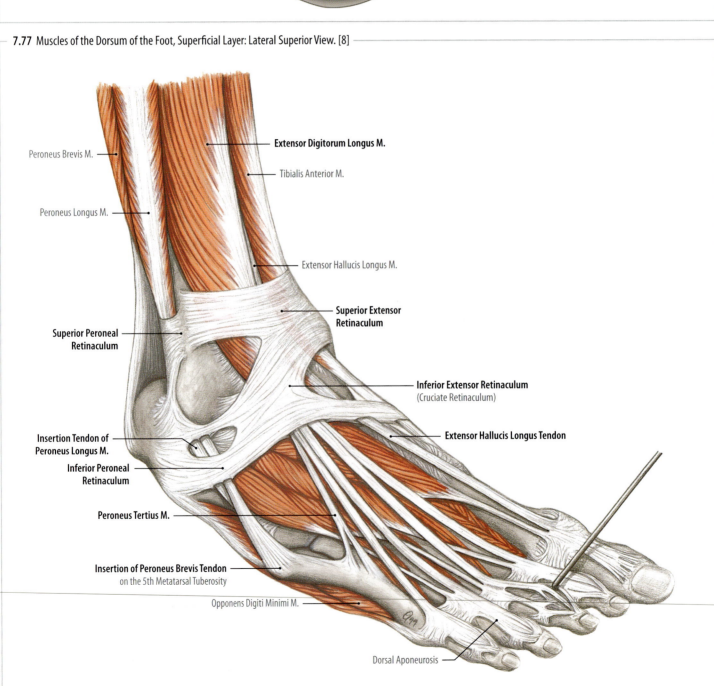

Peroneus Brevis M.

Peroneus Longus M.

Superior Peroneal
Retinaculum

Insertion Tendon of
Peroneus Longus M.

Inferior Peroneal
Retinaculum

Peroneus Tertius M.

Insertion of Peroneus Brevis Tendon
on the 5th Metatarsal Tuberosity

Opponens Digiti Minimi M.

Dorsal Aponeurosis

Extensor Digitorum Longus M.

Tibialis Anterior M.

Extensor Hallucis Longus M.

**Superior Extensor
Retinaculum**

Inferior Extensor Retinaculum
(Cruciate Retinaculum)

Extensor Hallucis Longus Tendon

Muscles of the Foot · Ankle Joints: Function

7.78 Muscles of the Dorsum of the Foot, Deep Layer: Lateral Superior View. [8]

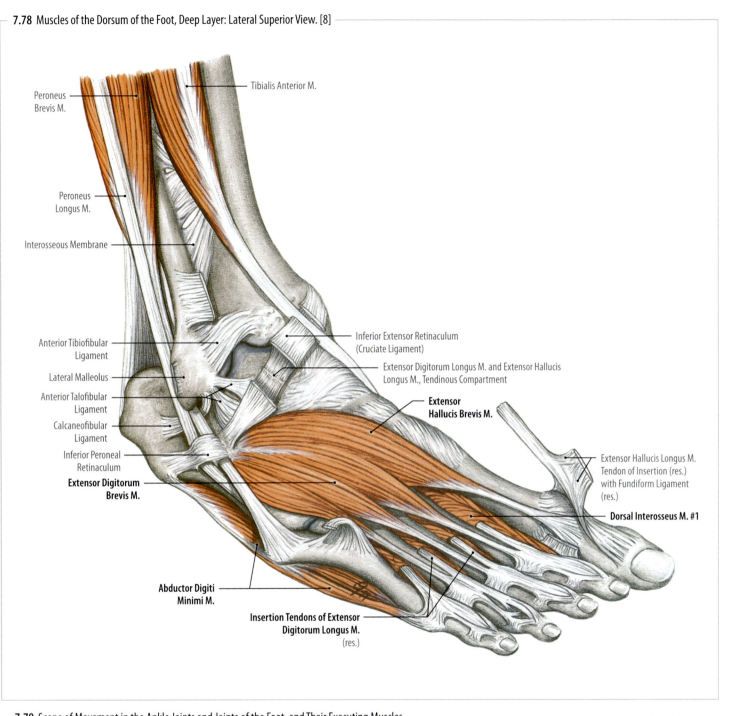

Peroneus Brevis M.

Tibialis Anterior M.

Peroneus Longus M.

Interosseous Membrane

Anterior Tibiofibular Ligament

Lateral Malleolus

Anterior Talofibular Ligament

Calcaneofibular Ligament

Inferior Peroneal Retinaculum

Extensor Digitorum Brevis M.

Inferior Extensor Retinaculum (Cruciate Ligament)

Extensor Digitorum Longus M. and Extensor Hallucis Longus M., Tendinous Compartment

Extensor Hallucis Brevis M.

Extensor Hallucis Longus M. Tendon of Insertion (res.) with Fundiform Ligament (res.)

Dorsal Interosseus M. #1

Abductor Digiti Minimi M.

Insertion Tendons of Extensor Digitorum Longus M. (res.)

7.79 Scope of Movement in the Ankle Joints and Joints of the Foot, and Their Executing Muscles.

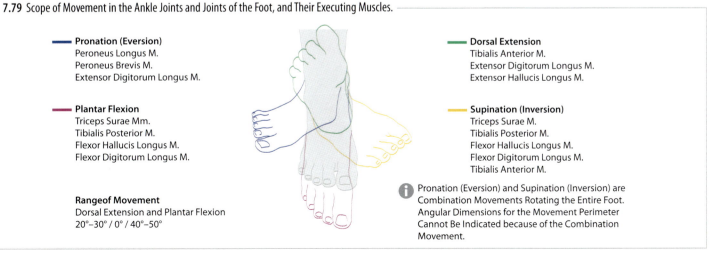

Pronation (Eversion)
Peroneus Longus M.
Peroneus Brevis M.
Extensor Digitorum Longus M.

Plantar Flexion
Triceps Surae Mm.
Tibialis Posterior M.
Flexor Hallucis Longus M.
Flexor Digitorum Longus M.

Rangeof Movement
Dorsal Extension and Plantar Flexion
20°–30° / 0° / 40°–50°

Dorsal Extension
Tibialis Anterior M.
Extensor Digitorum Longus M.
Extensor Hallucis Longus M.

Supination (Inversion)
Triceps Surae M.
Tibialis Posterior M.
Flexor Hallucis Longus M.
Flexor Digitorum Longus M.
Tibialis Anterior M.

ⓘ Pronation (Eversion) and Supination (Inversion) are Combination Movements Rotating the Entire Foot. Angular Dimensions for the Movement Perimeter Cannot Be Indicated because of the Combination Movement.

Muscles

7.80 Tension of the Plantar Arch on the Right Foot: Plantar Medial View. [1]

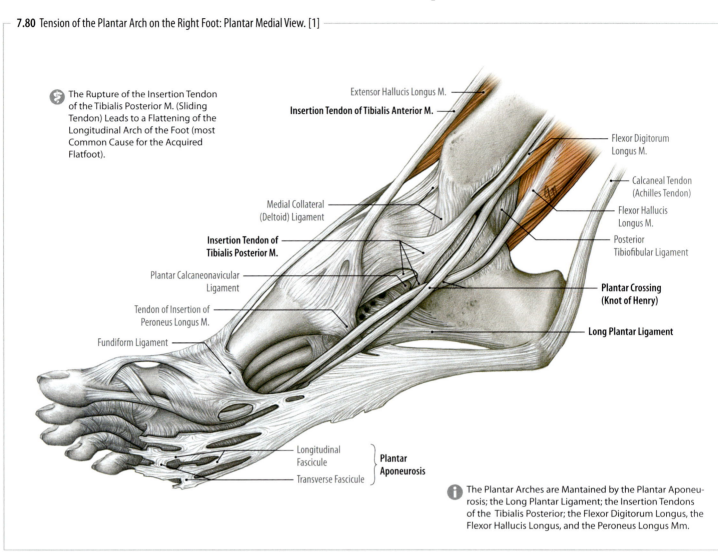

The Rupture of the Insertion Tendon of the Tibialis Posterior M. (Sliding Tendon) Leads to a Flattening of the Longitudinal Arch of the Foot (most Common Cause for the Acquired Flatfoot).

Extensor Hallucis Longus M.

Insertion Tendon of Tibialis Anterior M.

Flexor Digitorum Longus M.

Medial Collateral (Deltoid) Ligament

Calcaneal Tendon (Achilles Tendon)

Flexor Hallucis Longus M.

Insertion Tendon of Tibialis Posterior M.

Posterior Tibiofibular Ligament

Plantar Calcaneonavicular Ligament

Plantar Crossing (Knot of Henry)

Tendon of Insertion of Peroneus Longus M.

Long Plantar Ligament

Fundiform Ligament

Longitudinal Fascicule

Transverse Fascicule

Plantar Aponeurosis

The Plantar Arches are Mantained by the Plantar Aponeurosis; the Long Plantar Ligament; the Insertion Tendons of the Tibialis Posterior; the Flexor Digitorum Longus, the Flexor Hallucis Longus, and the Peroneus Longus Mm.

7.81 Cross-Section through a Right Foot in the Area of the Medial and Intermediate Cuneiform and Metatarsal Bones #3–5: View of the Distal Cut Surface.

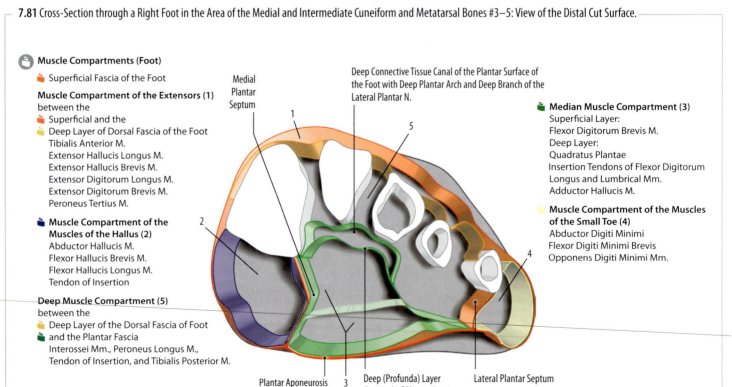

Muscle Compartments (Foot)

Superficial Fascia of the Foot

Muscle Compartment of the Extensors (1)
between the
Superficial and the
Deep Layer of Dorsal Fascia of the Foot
Tibialis Anterior M.
Extensor Hallucis Longus M.
Extensor Hallucis Brevis M.
Extensor Digitorum Longus M.
Extensor Digitorum Brevis M.
Peroneus Tertius M.

Muscle Compartment of the Muscles of the Hallus (2)
Abductor Hallucis M.
Flexor Hallucis Brevis M.
Flexor Hallucis Longus M.
Tendon of Insertion

Deep Muscle Compartment (5)
between the
Deep Layer of the Dorsal Fascia of Foot
and the Plantar Fascia
Interossei Mm., Peroneus Longus M.,
Tendon of Insertion, and Tibialis Posterior M.

Medial Plantar Septum

Deep Connective Tissue Canal of the Plantar Surface of the Foot with Deep Plantar Arch and Deep Branch of the Lateral Plantar N.

Median Muscle Compartment (3)
Superficial Layer:
Flexor Digitorum Brevis M.
Deep Layer:
Quadratus Plantae
Insertion Tendons of Flexor Digitorum Longus and Lumbrical Mm.
Adductor Hallucis M.

Muscle Compartment of the Muscles of the Small Toe (4)
Abductor Digiti Minimi
Flexor Digiti Minimi Brevis
Opponens Digiti Minimi Mm.

Plantar Aponeurosis

Deep (Profunda) Layer (Lamina) of Plantar Fascia

Lateral Plantar Septum

Muscles of the Foot: Superficial, Median Layer

7.82a,b Muscles of the Sole of the Foot: Right Side, Plantar View. [8]

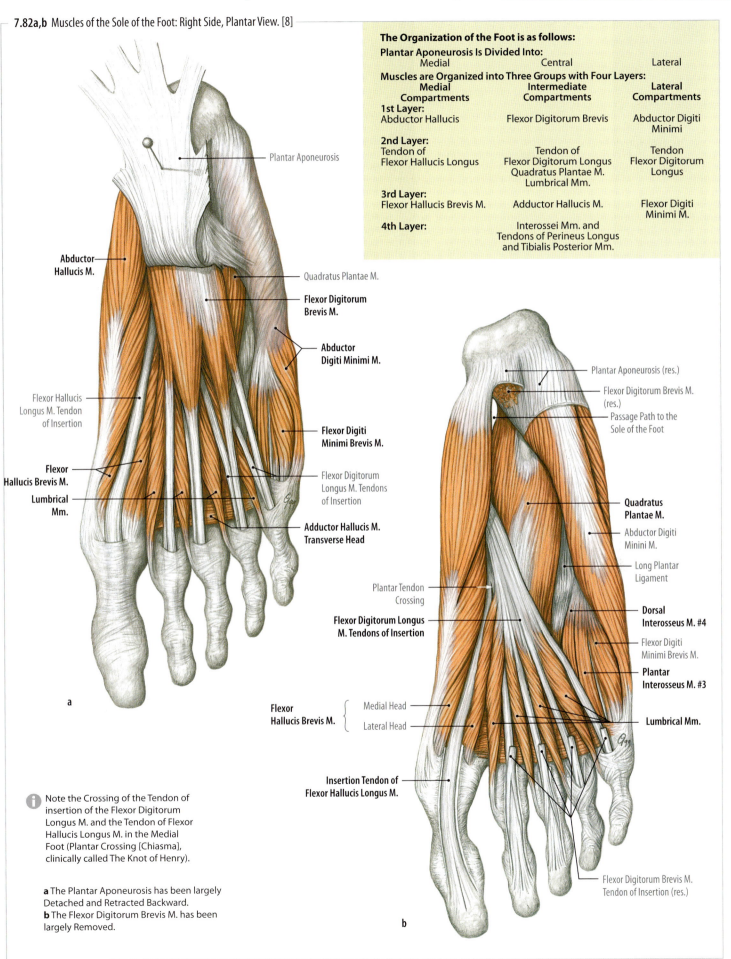

The Organization of the Foot is as follows:

Plantar Aponeurosis Is Divided Into:

Medial	Central	Lateral

Muscles are Organized into Three Groups with Four Layers:

Medial Compartments	Intermediate Compartments	Lateral Compartments
1st Layer:		
Abductor Hallucis	Flexor Digitorum Brevis	Abductor Digiti Minimi
2nd Layer:		
Tendon of Flexor Hallucis Longus	Tendon of Flexor Digitorum Longus Quadratus Plantae M. Lumbrical Mm.	Tendon Flexor Digitorum Longus
3rd Layer:		
Flexor Hallucis Brevis M.	Adductor Hallucis M.	Flexor Digiti Minimi M.
4th Layer:	Interossei Mm. and Tendons of Perineus Longus and Tibialis Posterior Mm.	

Plantar Aponeurosis

Abductor Hallucis M.

Quadratus Plantae M.

Flexor Digitorum Brevis M.

Abductor Digiti Minimi M.

Flexor Hallucis Longus M. Tendon of Insertion

Flexor Digiti Minimi Brevis M.

Flexor Hallucis Brevis M.

Flexor Digitorum Longus M. Tendons of Insertion

Lumbrical Mm.

Adductor Hallucis M. Transverse Head

a

Plantar Aponeurosis (res.)

Flexor Digitorum Brevis M. (res.)

Passage Path to the Sole of the Foot

Quadratus Plantae M.

Abductor Digiti Minini M.

Long Plantar Ligament

Plantar Tendon Crossing

Dorsal Interosseus M. #4

Flexor Digitorum Longus M. Tendons of Insertion

Flexor Digiti Minimi Brevis M.

Plantar Interosseus M. #3

Flexor Hallucis Brevis M. { Medial Head / Lateral Head }

Lumbrical Mm.

Insertion Tendon of Flexor Hallucis Longus M.

Flexor Digitorum Brevis M. Tendon of Insertion (res.)

b

ⓘ Note the Crossing of the Tendon of insertion of the Flexor Digitorum Longus M. and the Tendon of Flexor Hallucis Longus M. in the Medial Foot (Plantar Crossing [Chiasma], clinically called The Knot of Henry).

a The Plantar Aponeurosis has been largely Detached and Retracted Backward.
b The Flexor Digitorum Brevis M. has been largely Removed.

Muscles

7.83a,b Muscles of the Sole of the Foot: Right Side, Plantar View. [8]

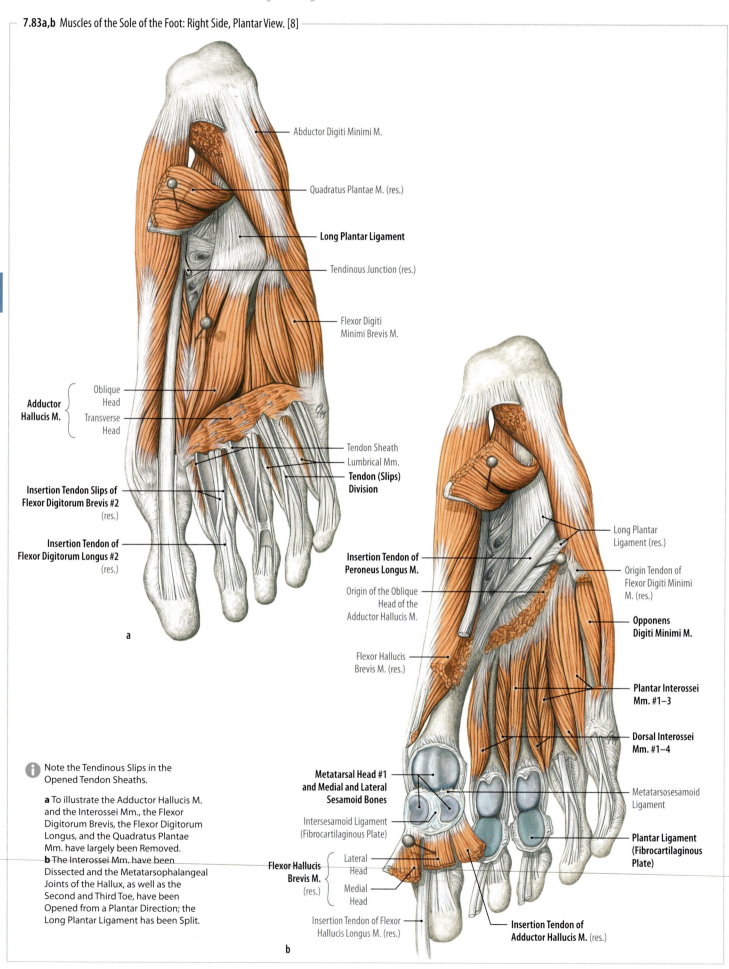

Abductor Digiti Minimi M.

Quadratus Plantae M. (res.)

Long Plantar Ligament

Tendinous Junction (res.)

Flexor Digiti
Minimi Brevis M.

**Adductor
Hallucis M.** { Oblique
Head
Transverse
Head

Tendon Sheath
Lumbrical Mm.
**Tendon (Slips)
Division**

**Insertion Tendon Slips of
Flexor Digitorum Brevis #2**
(res.)

**Insertion Tendon of
Flexor Digitorum Longus #2**
(res.)

**Insertion Tendon of
Peroneus Longus M.**

Origin of the Oblique
Head of the
Adductor Hallucis M.

Flexor Hallucis
Brevis M. (res.)

Long Plantar
Ligament (res.)

Origin Tendon of
Flexor Digiti Minimi
M. (res.)

**Opponens
Digiti Minimi M.**

**Plantar Interossei
Mm. #1–3**

**Dorsal Interossei
Mm. #1–4**

Metatarsosesamoid
Ligament

**Plantar Ligament
(Fibrocartilaginous
Plate)**

**Metatarsal Head #1
and Medial and Lateral
Sesamoid Bones**

Intersesamoid Ligament
(Fibrocartilaginous Plate)

**Flexor Hallucis
Brevis M.**
(res.) { Lateral
Head
Medial
Head

Insertion Tendon of Flexor
Hallucis Longus M. (res.)

**Insertion Tendon of
Adductor Hallucis M.** (res.)

a

b

ⓘ Note the Tendinous Slips in the
Opened Tendon Sheaths.

a To illustrate the Adductor Hallucis M.
and the Interossei Mm., the Flexor
Digitorum Brevis, the Flexor Digitorum
Longus, and the Quadratus Plantae
Mm. have largely been Removed.
b The Interossei Mm. have been
Dissected and the Metatarsophalangeal
Joints of the Hallux, as well as the
Second and Third Toe, have been
Opened from a Plantar Direction; the
Long Plantar Ligament has been Split.

Muscles of the Foot: Deep Layer

7.84 Muscles of the Foot: Right Side, Dorsal View. [1]

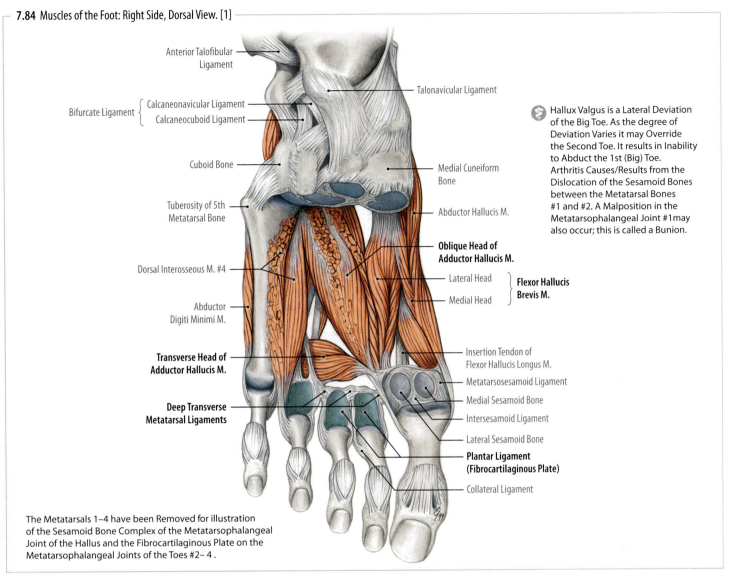

Anterior Talofibular Ligament

Talonavicular Ligament

Bifurcate Ligament { Calcaneonavicular Ligament / Calcaneocuboid Ligament

Cuboid Bone

Medial Cuneiform Bone

Tuberosity of 5th Metatarsal Bone

Abductor Hallucis M.

Dorsal Interosseous M. #4

Oblique Head of Adductor Hallucis M.

Lateral Head } **Flexor Hallucis**
Medial Head } **Brevis M.**

Abductor Digiti Minimi M.

Insertion Tendon of Flexor Hallucis Longus M.

Transverse Head of Adductor Hallucis M.

Metatarsosesamoid Ligament

Medial Sesamoid Bone

Deep Transverse Metatarsal Ligaments

Intersesamoid Ligament

Lateral Sesamoid Bone

Plantar Ligament (Fibrocartilaginous Plate)

Collateral Ligament

Hallux Valgus is a Lateral Deviation of the Big Toe. As the degree of Deviation Varies it may Override the Second Toe. It results in Inability to Abduct the 1st (Big) Toe. Arthritis Causes/Results from the Dislocation of the Sesamoid Bones between the Metatarsal Bones #1 and #2. A Malposition in the Metatarsophalangeal Joint #1may also occur; this is called a Bunion.

The Metatarsals 1–4 have been Removed for illustration of the Sesamoid Bone Complex of the Metatarsophalangeal Joint of the Hallus and the Fibrocartilaginous Plate on the Metatarsophalangeal Joints of the Toes #2– 4 .

7.85 Muscles of the Second Toe of a Right Foot: Medial View. [1]

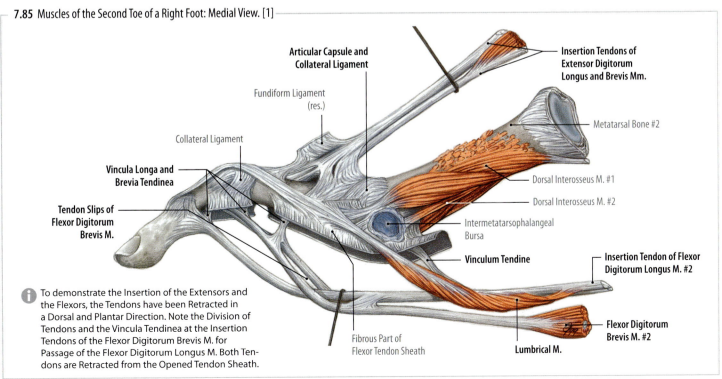

Articular Capsule and Collateral Ligament

Insertion Tendons of Extensor Digitorum Longus and Brevis Mm.

Fundiform Ligament (res.)

Collateral Ligament

Metatarsal Bone #2

Vincula Longa and Brevia Tendinea

Dorsal Interosseus M. #1

Dorsal Interosseus M. #2

Tendon Slips of Flexor Digitorum Brevis M.

Intermetatarsophalangeal Bursa

Vinculum Tendine

Insertion Tendon of Flexor Digitorum Longus M. #2

Fibrous Part of Flexor Tendon Sheath

Lumbrical M.

Flexor Digitorum Brevis M. #2

To demonstrate the Insertion of the Extensors and the Flexors, the Tendons have been Retracted in a Dorsal and Plantar Direction. Note the Division of Tendons and the Vincula Tendinea at the Insertion Tendons of the Flexor Digitorum Brevis M. for Passage of the Flexor Digitorum Longus M. Both Tendons are Retracted from the Opened Tendon Sheath.

Muscles

Foot: Tendon Sheaths, Synovial Bursa

7.86a,b Tendon Sheaths and Synovial Bursa of a Right Foot. [46]

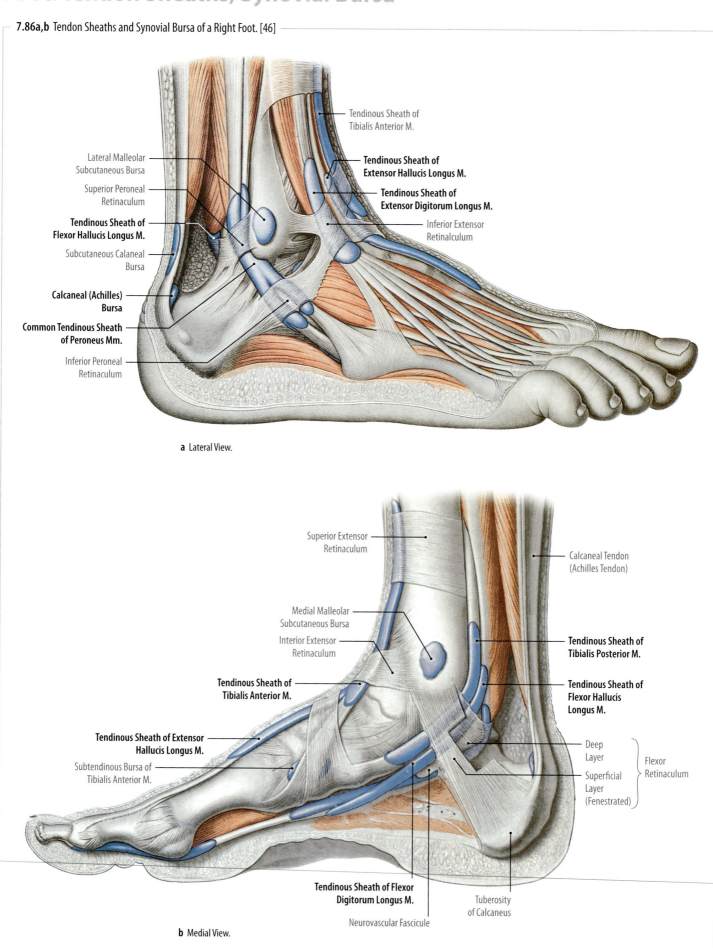

Tendinous Sheath of
Tibialis Anterior M.

Lateral Malleolar
Subcutaneous Bursa

Superior Peroneal
Retinaculum

**Tendinous Sheath of
Flexor Hallucis Longus M.**

Subcutaneous Calaneal
Bursa

**Calcaneal (Achilles)
Bursa**

**Common Tendinous Sheath
of Peroneus Mm.**

Inferior Peroneal
Retinaculum

**Tendinous Sheath of
Extensor Hallucis Longus M.**

**Tendinous Sheath of
Extensor Digitorum Longus M.**

Inferior Extensor
Retinalculum

a Lateral View.

Superior Extensor
Retinaculum

Calcaneal Tendon
(Achilles Tendon)

Medial Malleolar
Subcutaneous Bursa

Interior Extensor
Retinaculum

**Tendinous Sheath of
Tibialis Anterior M.**

**Tendinous Sheath of Extensor
Hallucis Longus M.**

Subtendinous Bursa of
Tibialis Anterior M.

**Tendinous Sheath of
Tibialis Posterior M.**

**Tendinous Sheath of
Flexor Hallucis
Longus M.**

Deep
Layer

Superficial
Layer
(Fenestrated)

Flexor
Retinaculum

**Tendinous Sheath of Flexor
Digitorum Longus M.**

Neurovascular Fascicule

Tuberosity
of Calcaneus

b Medial View.

Foot: Tendon Sheaths, Synovial Bursa

7.87a,b Tendon Sheaths and Synovial Bursa of a Right Foot. 46]

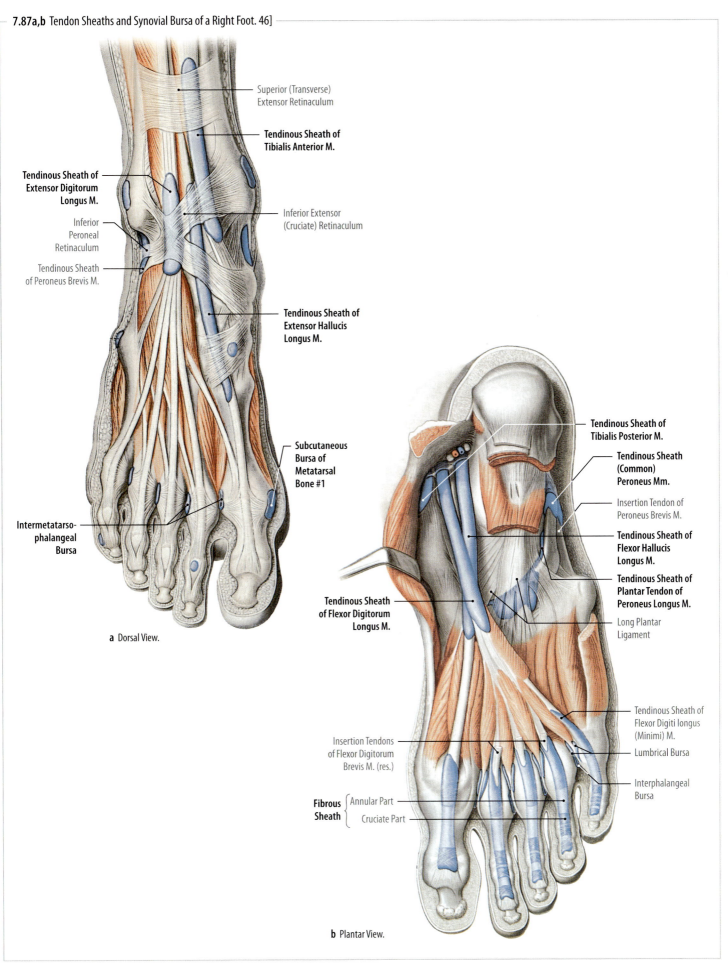

Superior (Transverse) Extensor Retinaculum

Tendinous Sheath of Tibialis Anterior M.

Tendinous Sheath of Extensor Digitorum Longus M.

Inferior Peroneal Retinaculum

Inferior Extensor (Cruciate) Retinaculum

Tendinous Sheath of Peroneus Brevis M.

Tendinous Sheath of Extensor Hallucis Longus M.

Subcutaneous Bursa of Metatarsal Bone #1

Intermetatarso-phalangeal Bursa

a Dorsal View.

Tendinous Sheath of Tibialis Posterior M.

Tendinous Sheath (Common) Peroneus Mm.

Insertion Tendon of Peroneus Brevis M.

Tendinous Sheath of Flexor Hallucis Longus M.

Tendinous Sheath of Plantar Tendon of Peroneus Longus M.

Long Plantar Ligament

Tendinous Sheath of Flexor Digitorum Longus M.

Insertion Tendons of Flexor Digitorum Brevis M. (res.)

Fibrous Sheath { Annular Part / Cruciate Part

Tendinous Sheath of Flexor Digiti longus (Minimi) M.

Lumbrical Bursa

Interphalangeal Bursa

b Plantar View.

Muscles

Arteries: Overview Leg and Pelvis

7.88 Overview of the Arteries of the Free Lower Limbs and the Pelvis.

The Common Iliac A. Divides at the Sacroiliac Joint into the **External Iliac A. and the Internal Iliac A.**; The Internal Iliac A. Supplies the Pelvic Organs and Muscles Below the Pelvic Ring.

The **External Iliac A.** Crosses the Mid-Inguinal Ligament into the Common Femoral A.

In the clinic, the **Femoral A.** is also referred to as the Common Femoral A. 2 cm Before its Division into the Deep (Profunda) Femoral A. and Superficial Femoral A. , which is a Continuation of the Femoral A.

The **Superficial Femoral A.** primarily Supplies the Lower Leg and the Foot. The Femoral Artery Reaches the Popliteal Space via the Adductor Canal (Hunter's Canal). At the Adductor Hiatus, the Superficial Femoral A. Continues at the Posterior Thigh and the Posterior Leg as the Popliteal A.

The **Deep (Profunda) Femoral A.** Originates from the Common Femoral A. and Supplies the Femoral (Thigh) Muscles Anteriorly and Posteriorly.

The **Popliteal A.** has Branches to the Knee region. In the area of the Popliteus M., the Popliteal A. usually Bifurcates into the Arteries of the Lower Leg.

The **Posterior Tibial A.** forms the Continuation of the Popliteal A. and Supplies the Muscles of the Flexor Compartments Together With the Peroneal (Fibular) A.

The **Peroneal (Fibular) A.** Originates from the Posterior Tibial A. and has Branches to the Peroneus Longus and Brevis Mm.

The **Anterior Tibial A.** passes Through the Superior Gap in the Interosseous Membrane into the Extensor (Anterior) Compartment. It Supplies the Muscle Group of the Extensors and, in part, the Peroneus Longus and Brevis Mm. to a Lesser Extent.

The **Dorsalis Pedis A.** is a Continuation of the Anterior Tibial A. on the Dorsum of the Foot Distal to the Inferior Extensor Retinaculum and Supplies the Dorsum of the Foot.

The **Medial and Lateral Plantar Aa.** Originate from the Posterior Tibial A. in the area of the Abductor Hallucis M. and Supply the structures of the Sole of the Foot.

Pulses (⌇) are Palpable on the Lower Limbs in the area of the Femoral, Popliteal, Dorsalis Pedis, and Posterior Tibial A.

The Femoral A. below the Mid-inguinal Ligament is suitable as a Point of Access (▭) for Arterial Catheterization.

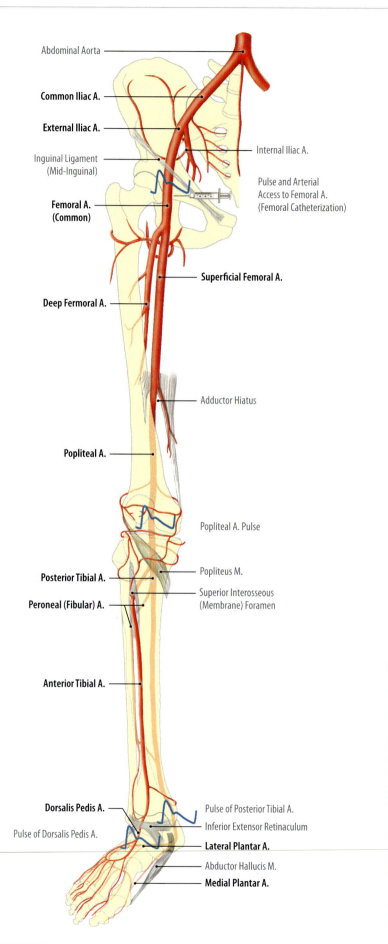

Abdominal Aorta

Common Iliac A.

External Iliac A.

Inguinal Ligament (Mid-Inguinal)

Internal Iliac A.

Pulse and Arterial Access to Femoral A. (Femoral Catheterization)

Femoral A. (Common)

Superficial Femoral A.

Deep Fermoral A.

Adductor Hiatus

Popliteal A.

Popliteal A. Pulse

Posterior Tibial A.

Popliteus M.

Peroneal (Fibular) A.

Superior Interosseous (Membrane) Foramen

Anterior Tibial A.

Dorsalis Pedis A.

Pulse of Dorsalis Pedis A.

Pulse of Posterior Tibial A.

Inferior Extensor Retinaculum

Lateral Plantar A.

Abductor Hallucis M.

Medial Plantar A.

7

Superficial and Deep Veins

7.89a–c   a,b Superficial (Cutaneous) Veins on a Right Leg; c Superficial and Deep Veins of the Leg of the Right Side. [46]

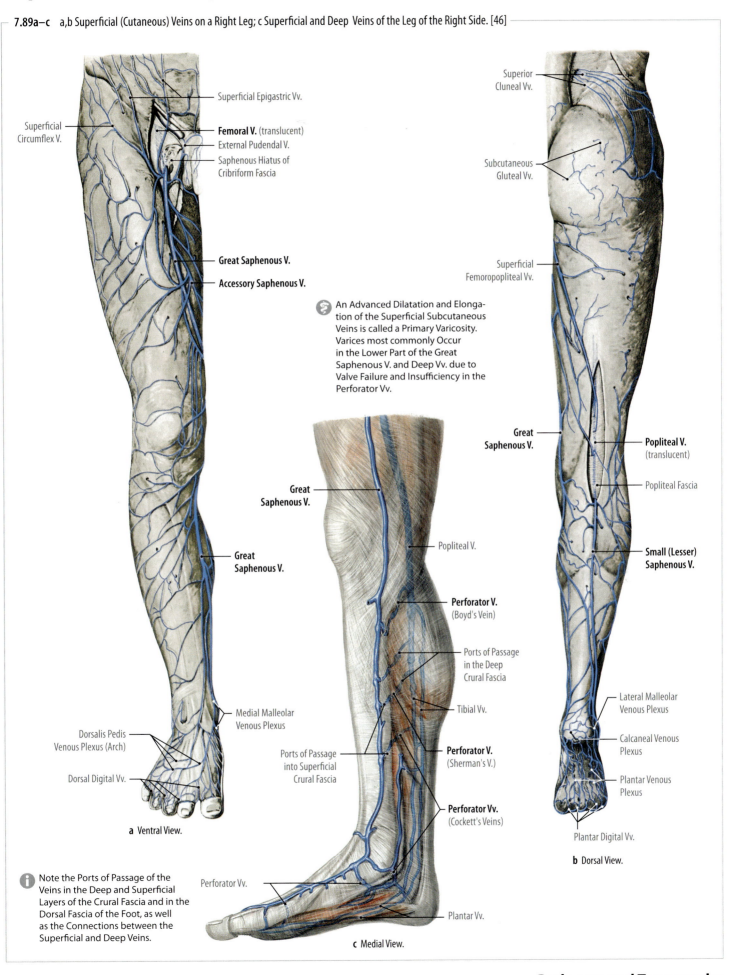

Superficial Epigastric Vv.

Superficial Circumflex V.

Femoral V. (translucent)

External Pudendal V.

Saphenous Hiatus of Cribriform Fascia

Great Saphenous V.

Accessory Saphenous V.

Superior Cluneal Vv.

Subcutaneous Gluteal Vv.

Superficial Femoropopliteal Vv.

An Advanced Dilatation and Elonga-
tion of the Superficial Subcutaneous
Veins is called a Primary Varicosity.
Varices most commonly Occur
in the Lower Part of the Great
Saphenous V. and Deep Vv. due to
Valve Failure and Insufficiency in the
Perforator Vv.

Great Saphenous V.

Great Saphenous V.

Popliteal V. (translucent)

Popliteal Fascia

Great Saphenous V.

Popliteal V.

Perforator V. (Boyd's Vein)

Ports of Passage in the Deep Crural Fascia

Tibial Vv.

Small (Lesser) Saphenous V.

Lateral Malleolar Venous Plexus

Medial Malleolar Venous Plexus

Dorsalis Pedis Venous Plexus (Arch)

Dorsal Digital Vv.

Ports of Passage into Superficial Crural Fascia

Perforator V. (Sherman's V.)

Perforator Vv. (Cockett's Veins)

Calcaneal Venous Plexus

Plantar Venous Plexus

Plantar Digital Vv.

a Ventral View.

b Dorsal View.

Note the Ports of Passage of the
Veins in the Deep and Superficial
Layers of the Crural Fascia and in the
Dorsal Fascia of the Foot, as well
as the Connections between the
Superficial and Deep Veins.

Perforator Vv.

Plantar Vv.

c Medial View.

Pathways and Topography

7.90 Pelvis – Leg Arteriography. [10]

There are Five Lumbar Arteries with the Five Lumbar Vertebrae. Four of the Lumbar Arteries Originate from Descending Aorta, The Fifth Lumbar Artery Originates from Median Sacral A.

Lumbar Aa. #3 and #4

Common Iliac A.

Iliolumbar A.

Medial Femoral Circumflex A.

Deep Femoral A.

Femoral A. (**Superficial Femoral A.**)

Abdominal Aorta

Inferior Mesenteric A.

Median Sacral A.

External Iliac A.

Internal Iliac A.

Superior Gluteal A.

Obturator A.

Femoral A. (**Rad.: Common Femoral A.**)

Internal Pudendal A.

Deep Femoral A.

Lateral Femoral Circumflex A.

Descending Branch of Lateral Femoral Circumflex A.

Rad.: Descending Branch of Profunda (Deep) Femoral A.

Muscular Branches of Femoral A.

Descending Genicular A.

Popliteal A.

Sural Aa.

Anterior Tibial A.

Rad.: Tibiofibular Trunk

Posterior Tibial A.

Peroneal A.

Digital Subtraction Angiography (DSA) of a 60-Year-Old Woman

Rad. = Radiological Term

7.91 Phlebogram (Venogram) of the Left Leg of a 37-Year-Old Woman. [10]

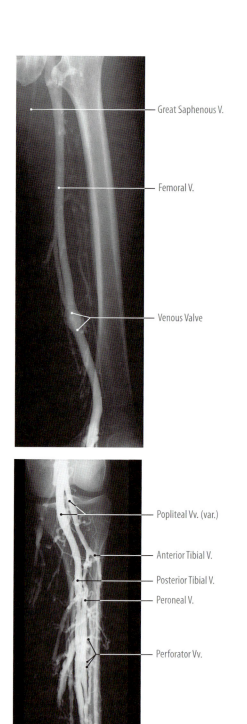

Great Saphenous V.

Femoral V.

Venous Valve

Popliteal Vv. (var.)

Anterior Tibial V.

Posterior Tibial V.

Peroneal V.

Perforator Vv.

Note the Doubled Popliteal Vv. and Perforator Vv. on the Leg.

7.92a,b Lymph Vessels and Lymph Nodes on a Right Leg. [46]

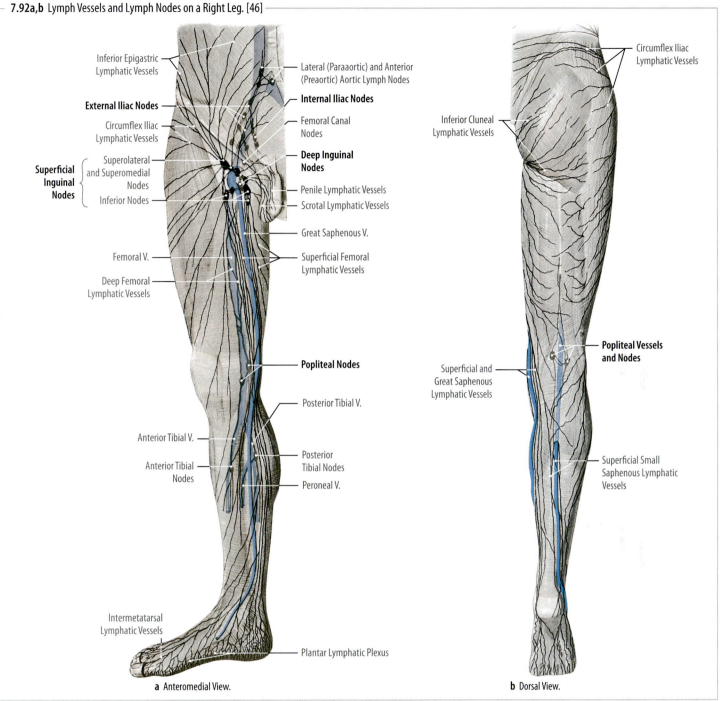

Inferior Epigastric Lymphatic Vessels

Lateral (Paraaortic) and Anterior (Preaortic) Aortic Lymph Nodes

External Iliac Nodes

Internal Iliac Nodes

Circumflex Iliac Lymphatic Vessels

Femoral Canal Nodes

Superficial Inguinal Nodes

Superolateral and Superomedial Nodes

Deep Inguinal Nodes

Inferior Nodes

Penile Lymphatic Vessels

Scrotal Lymphatic Vessels

Great Saphenous V.

Femoral V.

Superficial Femoral Lymphatic Vessels

Deep Femoral Lymphatic Vessels

Popliteal Nodes

Posterior Tibial V.

Anterior Tibial V.

Posterior Tibial Nodes

Anterior Tibial Nodes

Peroneal V.

Intermetatarsal Lymphatic Vessels

Plantar Lymphatic Plexus

a Anteromedial View.

Circumflex Iliac Lymphatic Vessels

Inferior Cluneal Lymphatic Vessels

Popliteal Vessels and Nodes

Superficial and Great Saphenous Lymphatic Vessels

Superficial Small Saphenous Lymphatic Vessels

b Dorsal View.

7.93 Portals of Passage in the Inguinal Region, Anterior Femoral and Gluteal. [46]

Muscular Space
Borders:
Pelvic Edge between the Anterior Superior Iliac Spine and the Arch of Iliopectineus; Inguinal Ligament.
Content:
Iliopsoas M., Lateral Femoral Cutaneous N., and Femoral N.

Vascular Space
Borders:
Superior Pubic Ramus , Arch of Iliopectineus, Inguinal Ligament, and Lacunar Ligament
Content:
Femoral A. and V., Femoral V., Femoral Branch of the Genitofemoral N., Lymphatic Vessels

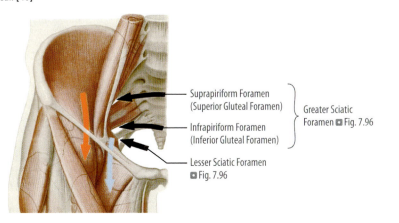

Suprapiriform Foramen (Superior Gluteal Foramen)

Infrapiriform Foramen (Inferior Gluteal Foramen)

Greater Sciatic Foramen ◘ Fig. 7.96

Lesser Sciatic Foramen
◘ Fig. 7.96

Pathways and Topography

7.94 Arteries of the Pelvis and the Proximal Area of the Thigh: Ventral View. [13]

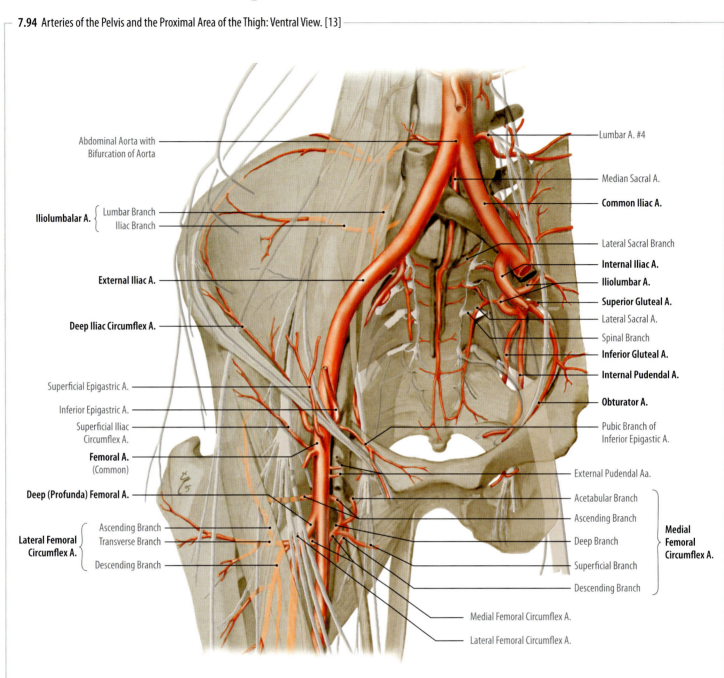

Abdominal Aorta with Bifurcation of Aorta

Iliolumbalar A. { Lumbar Branch / Iliac Branch

External Iliac A.

Deep Iliac Circumflex A.

Superficial Epigastric A.

Inferior Epigastric A.

Superficial Iliac Circumflex A.

Femoral A. (Common)

Deep (Profunda) Femoral A.

Lateral Femoral Circumflex A. { Ascending Branch / Transverse Branch / Descending Branch

Lumbar A. #4

Median Sacral A.

Common Iliac A.

Lateral Sacral Branch

Internal Iliac A.

Iliolumbar A.

Superior Gluteal A.

Lateral Sacral A.

Spinal Branch

Inferior Gluteal A.

Internal Pudendal A.

Obturator A.

Pubic Branch of Inferior Epigastic A.

External Pudendal Aa.

Acetabular Branch

Ascending Branch

Deep Branch

Superficial Branch

Descending Branch

Medial Femoral Circumflex A.

Medial Femoral Circumflex A.

Lateral Femoral Circumflex A.

Common Iliac A.

└ Internal Iliac A.
└ External Iliac A.

Internal Iliac A.

Iliolumbar A.
└ Lumbar Branch
└ Iliac Branch
Lateral Sacral A.
└ Spinal Branch
Obturator A. (◘ 5.197)
Superior Gluteal A. (◘ 7.95)
Inferior Gluteal A. (◘ 7.95)
Additional Branches ◘ Fig. 5.195

External Iliac A.

Inferior Epigastric A.
└ Pubic Branch
Deep Iliac Circumflex A.

Common Femoral A.

Superficial Epigastric A.
Superficial Iliac Circumflex A.
External Pudendal Aa.
Deep (Profunda) Femoral A.
└ Medial Femoral Circumflex A.
  └ Acetabular Branch
  └ Ascending Branch
  └ Deep (Profunda) Branch
  └ Superficial Branch
  └ Descending Branch
└ Lateral Femoral Circumflex A.
  └ Ascending Branch
  └ Transverse Branch
  └ Descending Branch

7

Gluteal and Perineal Region: Arteries

7.95 Arteries of the Gluteal Region and the Perineal Region. [13]

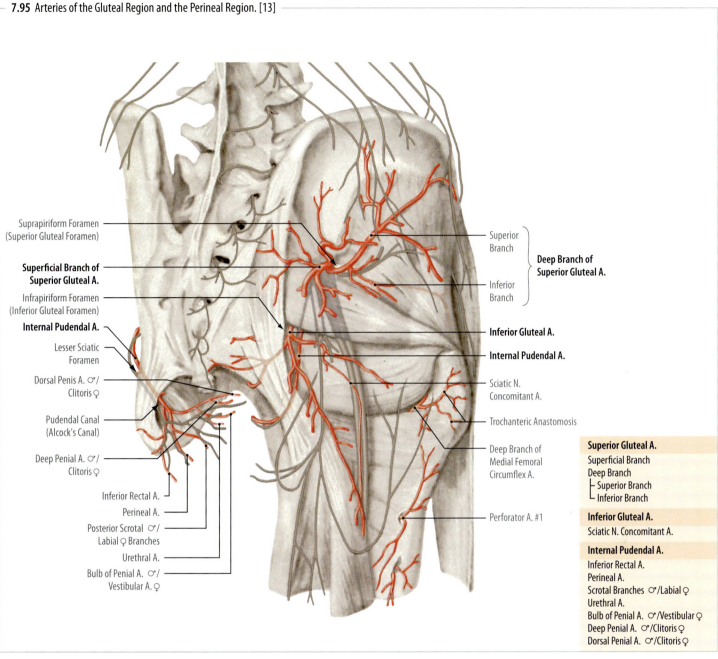

Suprapiriform Foramen (Superior Gluteal Foramen)

Superficial Branch of Superior Gluteal A.

Infrapiriform Foramen (Inferior Gluteal Foramen)

Internal Pudendal A.

Lesser Sciatic Foramen

Dorsal Penis A. ♂/ Clitoris ♀

Pudendal Canal (Alcock's Canal)

Deep Penial A. ♂/ Clitoris ♀

Inferior Rectal A.

Perineal A.

Posterior Scrotal ♂/ Labial ♀ Branches

Urethral A.

Bulb of Penial A. ♂/ Vestibular A. ♀

Superior Branch

Inferior Branch

Deep Branch of Superior Gluteal A.

Inferior Gluteal A.

Internal Pudendal A.

Sciatic N. Concomitant A.

Trochanteric Anastomosis

Deep Branch of Medial Femoral Circumflex A.

Perforator A. #1

Superior Gluteal A.
Superficial Branch
Deep Branch
├ Superior Branch
└ Inferior Branch

Inferior Gluteal A.
Sciatic N. Concomitant A.

Internal Pudendal A.
Inferior Rectal A.
Perineal A.
Scrotal Branches ♂/Labial ♀
Urethral A.
Bulb of Penial A. ♂/Vestibular ♀
Deep Penial A. ♂/Clitoris ♀
Dorsal Penial A. ♂/Clitoris ♀

7.96 Portals of Passage of the Gluteal Region. [46]

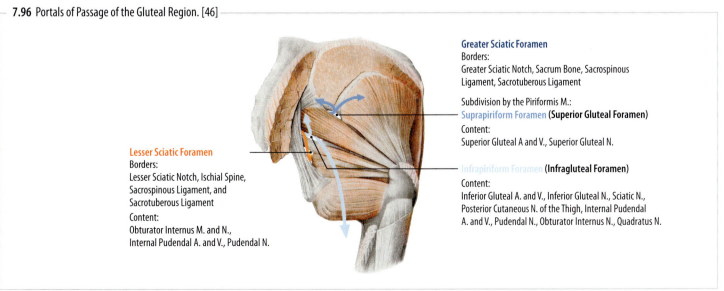

Greater Sciatic Foramen
Borders:
Greater Sciatic Notch, Sacrum Bone, Sacrospinous Ligament, Sacrotuberous Ligament

Subdivision by the Piriformis M.:
Suprapiriform Foramen (Superior Gluteal Foramen)
Content:
Superior Gluteal A and V., Superior Gluteal N.

Infrapiriform Foramen (Infragluteal Foramen)
Content:
Inferior Gluteal A. and V., Inferior Gluteal N., Sciatic N., Posterior Cutaneous N. of the Thigh, Internal Pudendal A. and V., Pudendal N., Obturator Internus N., Quadratus N.

Lesser Sciatic Foramen
Borders:
Lesser Sciatic Notch, Ischial Spine, Sacrospinous Ligament, and Sacrotuberous Ligament
Content:
Obturator Internus M. and N., Internal Pudendal A. and V., Pudendal N.

Pathways and Topography

Lumbar, Sacral Plexuses: Schematic Order

7.97 Schematic Illustration of the Lumbar Plexus, the Sacral Plexus, and the Pudendal N. [46]

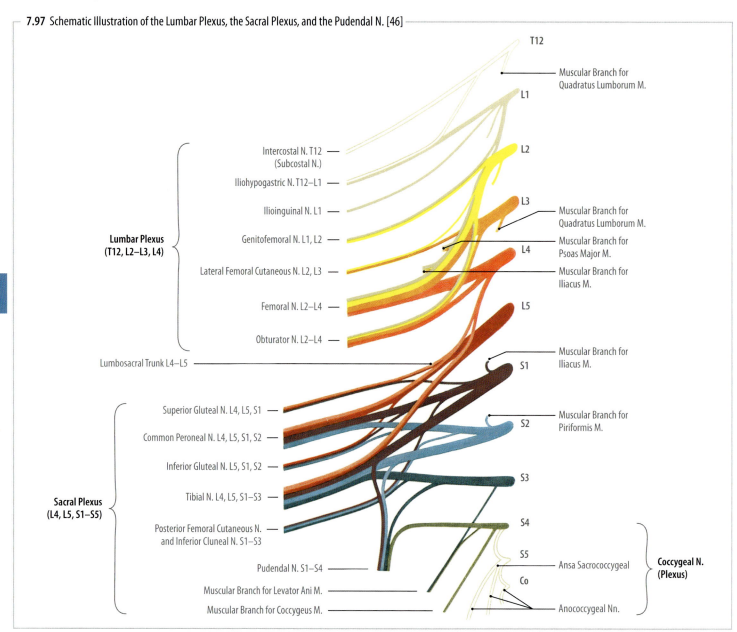

T12

Muscular Branch for
Quadratus Lumborum M.

L1

Intercostal N. T12
(Subcostal N.)

Iliohypogastric N. T12–L1

Ilioinguinal N. L1

Genitofemoral N. L1, L2

Lateral Femoral Cutaneous N. L2, L3

Femoral N. L2–L4

Obturator N. L2–L4

**Lumbar Plexus
(T12, L2–L3, L4)**

L2

L3

Muscular Branch for
Quadratus Lumborum M.

Muscular Branch for
Psoas Major M.

L4

Muscular Branch for
Iliacus M.

L5

Lumbosacral Trunk L4–L5

Muscular Branch for
Iliacus M.

S1

Superior Gluteal N. L4, L5, S1

Common Peroneal N. L4, L5, S1, S2

Inferior Gluteal N. L5, S1, S2

Tibial N. L4, L5, S1–S3

Posterior Femoral Cutaneous N.
and Inferior Cluneal N. S1–S3

Pudendal N. S1–S4

Muscular Branch for Levator Ani M.

Muscular Branch for Coccygeus M.

**Sacral Plexus
(L4, L5, S1–S5)**

S2

Muscular Branch for
Piriformis M.

S3

S4

S5

Ansa Sacrococcygeal

Co

Anococcygeal Nn.

**Coccygeal N.
(Plexus)**

7.98a–c Composition of the Lumbosacral Plexus. [46]

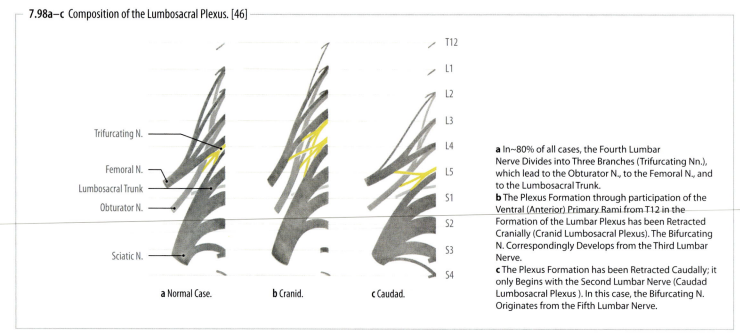

Trifurcating N.

Femoral N.

Lumbosacral Trunk

Obturator N.

Sciatic N.

a Normal Case.   **b** Cranid.   **c** Caudad.

T12
L1
L2
L3
L4
L5
S1
S2
S3
S4

a In ~80% of all cases, the Fourth Lumbar
Nerve Divides into Three Branches (Trifurcating Nn.),
which lead to the Obturator N., to the Femoral N., and
to the Lumbosacral Trunk.
b The Plexus Formation through participation of the
Ventral (Anterior) Primary Rami from T12 in the
Formation of the Lumbar Plexus has been Retracted
Cranially (Cranid Lumbosacral Plexus). The Bifurcating
N. Correspondingly Develops from the Third Lumbar
Nerve.
c The Plexus Formation has been Retracted
Caudally; it only Begins with the Second Lumbar Nerve (Caudad
Lumbosacral Plexus). In this case, the Bifurcating N.
Originates from the Fifth Lumbar Nerve.

7.99 Lumbar Plexus, Sacral Plexus, and Nerves for the Lower Limbs: Dorsal View. [13]

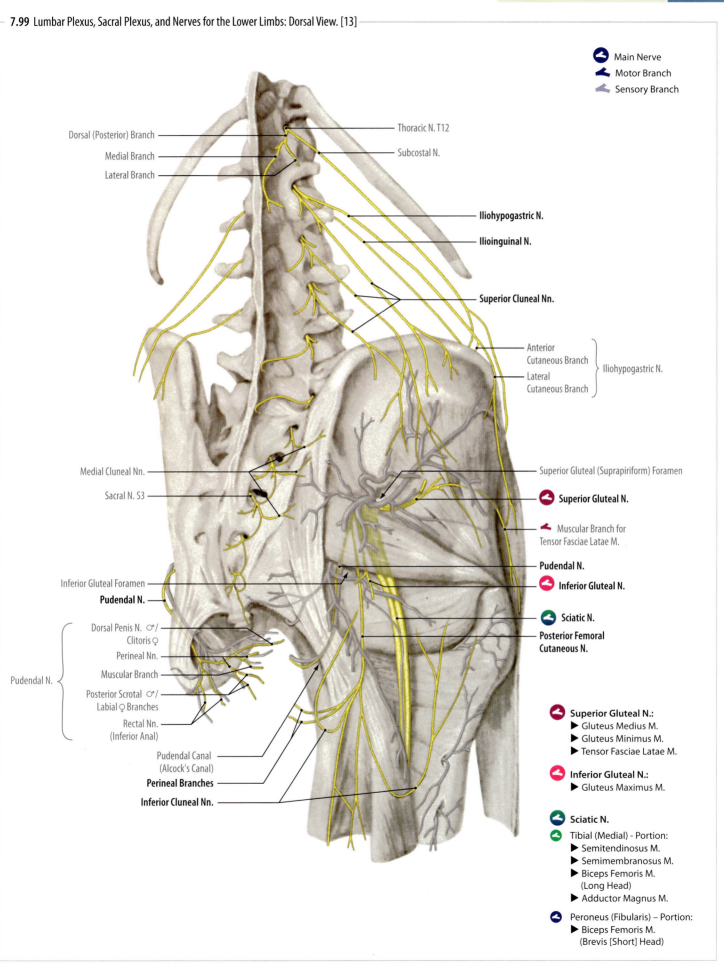

Main Nerve
Motor Branch
Sensory Branch

Dorsal (Posterior) Branch
Medial Branch
Lateral Branch

Thoracic N. T12
Subcostal N.

Iliohypogastric N.

Ilioinguinal N.

Superior Cluneal Nn.

Anterior Cutaneous Branch
Lateral Cutaneous Branch
} Iliohypogastric N.

Medial Cluneal Nn.
Sacral N. S3

Superior Gluteal (Suprapiriform) Foramen
Superior Gluteal N.

Muscular Branch for Tensor Fasciae Latae M.

Pudendal N.
Inferior Gluteal N.

Inferior Gluteal Foramen
Pudendal N.

Sciatic N.
Posterior Femoral Cutaneous N.

Dorsal Penis N. ♂/
Clitoris ♀
Perineal Nn.
Muscular Branch
Posterior Scrotal ♂/
Labial ♀ Branches
Rectal Nn.
(Inferior Anal)

Pudendal N. {

Pudendal Canal
(Alcock's Canal)
Perineal Branches
Inferior Cluneal Nn.

Superior Gluteal N.:
▶ Gluteus Medius M.
▶ Gluteus Minimus M.
▶ Tensor Fasciae Latae M.

Inferior Gluteal N.:
▶ Gluteus Maximus M.

Sciatic N.

Tibial (Medial) - Portion:
▶ Semitendinosus M.
▶ Semimembranosus M.
▶ Biceps Femoris M. (Long Head)
▶ Adductor Magnus M.

Peroneus (Fibularis) – Portion:
▶ Biceps Femoris M. (Brevis [Short] Head)

Pathways and Topography

Lumbar, Sacral Plexuses

7.100 Lumbar Plexus, Sacral Plexus, and Nerves for the Lower Limbs: Ventral View. [13]

Subcostal N.:
▶ External Oblique Abdominis M.
▶ Rectus Abdominis M.

Subcostal, Iliohypogastric, Ilioinguinal, Genitofemoral Nn.:
▶ Internal Oblique Abdominis M.
▶ Transversus Abdominis M.

Obturator N.
Anterior Branch:
▶ Adductor Brevis M.
▶ Adductor Longus M.
▶ Gracilis M.
▶ Pectineus M. (Rare)

Posterior Branch:
▶ Adductor Magnus
  (and Minimus) M.
▶ Obturator Externus M.

Femoral N. :
▶ Quadriceps Femoris M.
▶ Sartorius M.
▶ Pectineus M.
▶ Iliacus M.

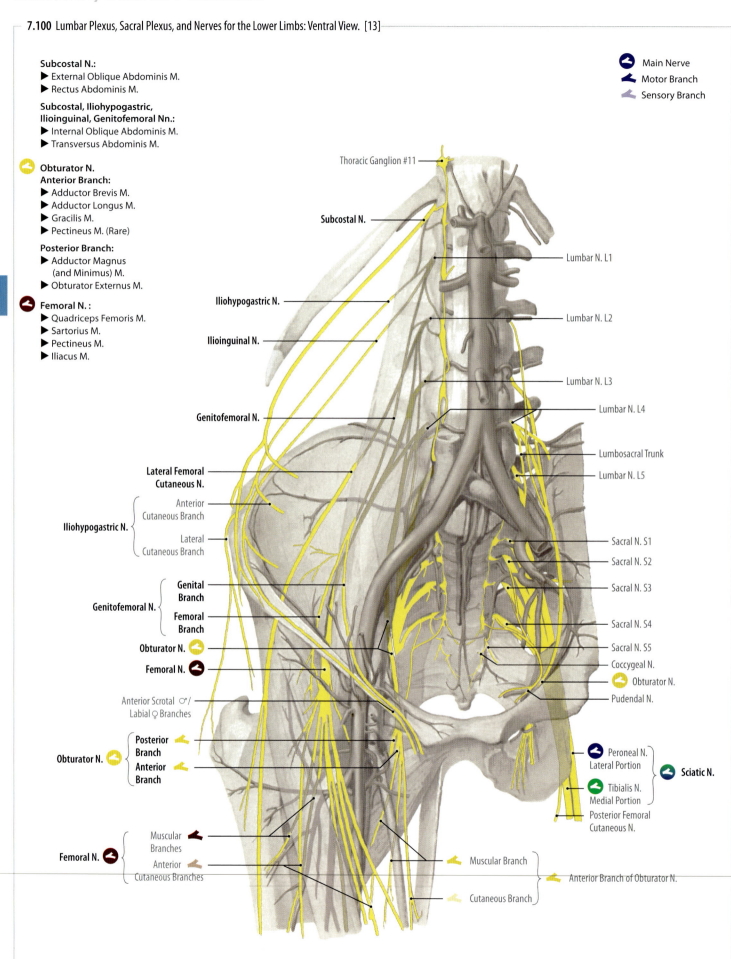

Main Nerve
Motor Branch
Sensory Branch

Thoracic Ganglion #11
Subcostal N.
Lumbar N. L1
Iliohypogastric N.
Lumbar N. L2
Ilioinguinal N.
Lumbar N. L3
Lumbar N. L4
Genitofemoral N.
Lumbosacral Trunk
Lumbar N. L5
Lateral Femoral Cutaneous N.
Anterior Cutaneous Branch
Iliohypogastric N.
Lateral Cutaneous Branch
Sacral N. S1
Sacral N. S2
Genital Branch
Sacral N. S3
Genitofemoral N.
Femoral Branch
Sacral N. S4
Obturator N.
Sacral N. S5
Femoral N.
Coccygeal N.
Obturator N.
Anterior Scrotal ♂ / Labial ♀ Branches
Pudendal N.
Posterior Branch
Anterior Branch
Obturator N.
Peroneal N. Lateral Portion
Sciatic N.
Tibialis N. Medial Portion
Posterior Femoral Cutaneous N.
Muscular Branches
Femoral N.
Anterior Cutaneous Branches
Muscular Branch
Anterior Branch of Obturator N.
Cutaneous Branch

7

Sensory Supply, Dermatomes

7.101a,b Sensory (Cutaneous Nerves) Supply of the Skin on the Left Side and Segmental Innervation of the Skin Areas on the Right Side of the Lower Limbs. [65]

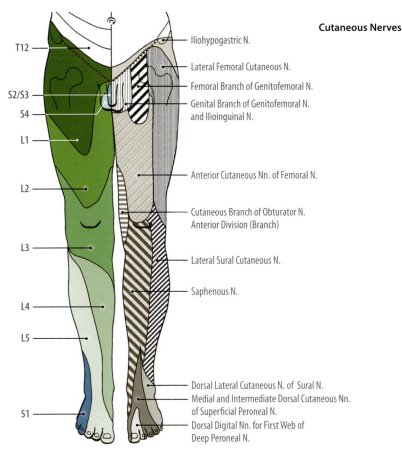

Segmental (Dermatomal) Classification of the Skin Areas

T12
S2/S3
S4
L1
L2
L3
L4
L5
S1

a Ventral View.

Cutaneous Nerves

Iliohypogastric N.
Lateral Femoral Cutaneous N.
Femoral Branch of Genitofemoral N.
Genital Branch of Genitofemoral N. and Ilioinguinal N.
Anterior Cutaneous Nn. of Femoral N.
Cutaneous Branch of Obturator N. Anterior Division (Branch)
Lateral Sural Cutaneous N.
Saphenous N.
Dorsal Lateral Cutaneous N. of Sural N.
Medial and Intermediate Dorsal Cutaneous Nn. of Superficial Peroneal N.
Dorsal Digital Nn. for First Web of Deep Peroneal N.

Cutaneous Nerves

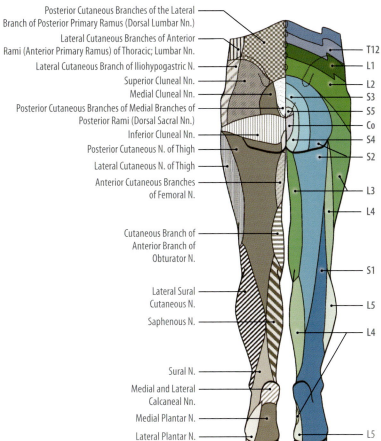

Posterior Cutaneous Branches of the Lateral Branch of Posterior Primary Ramus (Dorsal Lumbar Nn.)
Lateral Cutaneous Branches of Anterior Rami (Anterior Primary Ramus) of Thoracic; Lumbar Nn.
Lateral Cutaneous Branch of Iliohypogastric N.
Superior Cluneal Nn.
Medial Cluneal Nn.
Posterior Cutaneous Branches of Medial Branches of Posterior Rami (Dorsal Sacral Nn.)
Inferior Cluneal Nn.
Posterior Cutaneous N. of Thigh
Lateral Cutaneous N. of Thigh
Anterior Cutaneous Branches of Femoral N.
Cutaneous Branch of Anterior Branch of Obturator N.
Lateral Sural Cutaneous N.
Saphenous N.
Sural N.
Medial and Lateral Calcaneal Nn.
Medial Plantar N.
Lateral Plantar N.

T12
L1
L2
S3
S5
Co
S4
S2
L3
L4
S1
L5
L4
L5

Segmental (Dermatomal) Classification of the Skin Areas

b Dorsal View.

Pathways and Topography

Thigh: Superficial Pathways

7.102 Superficial Pathways of the Thigh and of the Inguinal Region: Right Side, Ventral View. [6]

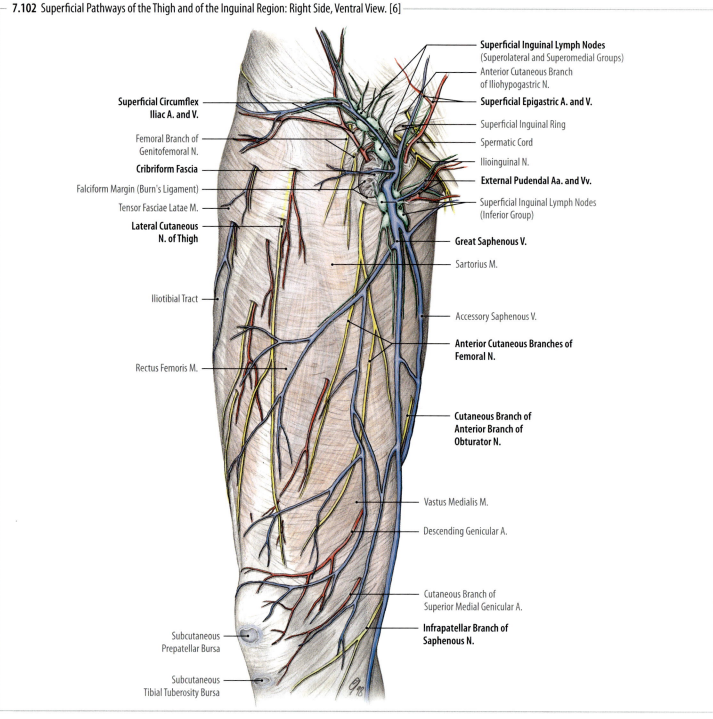

Superficial Circumflex Iliac A. and V.

Femoral Branch of Genitofemoral N.

Cribriform Fascia

Falciform Margin (Burn's Ligament)

Tensor Fasciae Latae M.

Lateral Cutaneous N. of Thigh

Iliotibial Tract

Rectus Femoris M.

Subcutaneous Prepatellar Bursa

Subcutaneous Tibial Tuberosity Bursa

Superficial Inguinal Lymph Nodes (Superolateral and Superomedial Groups)

Anterior Cutaneous Branch of Iliohypogastric N.

Superficial Epigastric A. and V.

Superficial Inguinal Ring

Spermatic Cord

Ilioinguinal N.

External Pudendal Aa. and Vv.

Superficial Inguinal Lymph Nodes (Inferior Group)

Great Saphenous V.

Sartorius M.

Accessory Saphenous V.

Anterior Cutaneous Branches of Femoral N.

Cutaneous Branch of Anterior Branch of Obturator N.

Vastus Medialis M.

Descending Genicular A.

Cutaneous Branch of Superior Medial Genicular A.

Infrapatellar Branch of Saphenous N.

7.103a–c Examples of Variants of the Superfical Veins in the Area of the Saphenous Hiatus. [46]

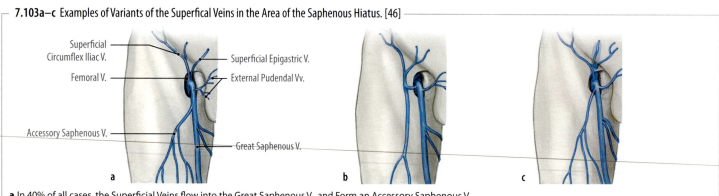

Superficial Circumflex Iliac V.

Femoral V.

Accessory Saphenous V.

Superficial Epigastric V.

External Pudendal Vv.

Great Saphenous V.

a In 40% of all cases, the Superficial Veins flow into the Great Saphenous V., and Form an Accessory Saphenous V.
b Course of the Veins in ~9% of all cases. The Accessory Saphenous Vv., Superficial Iliac, and Superficial Epigastric Vv. flow via a Common Trunk.
c The Superficial Iliac and Superficial Epigastric Vv. flow Directly into the Femoral V.

Thigh: Superficial Pathways

7.104 Superficial Pathways of the Hip and Thigh Region: Right Side, Dorsal View. [6]

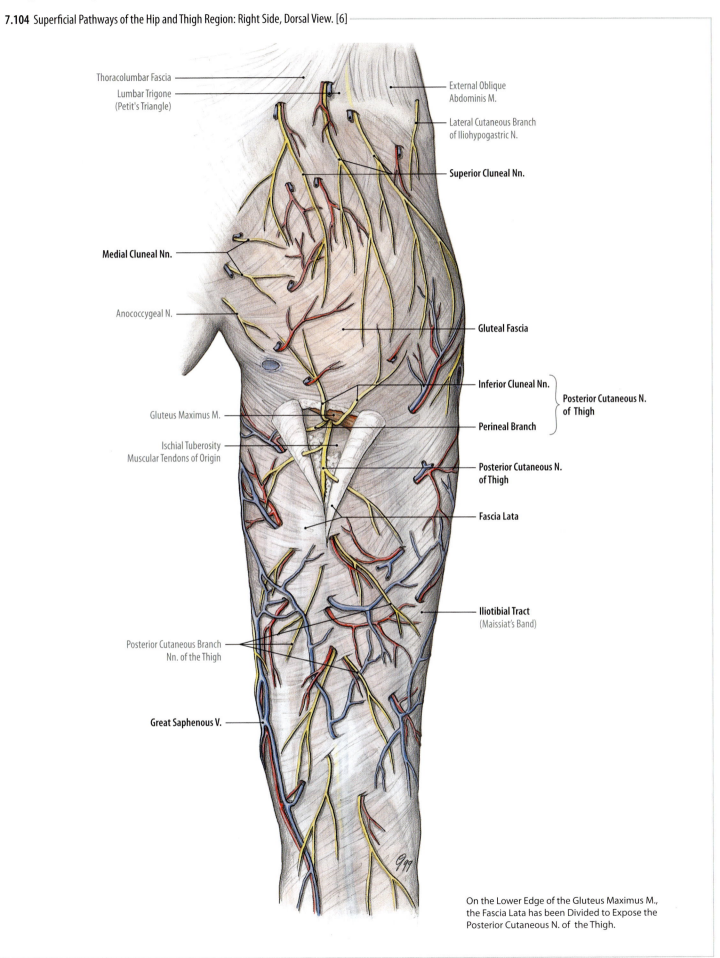

Thoracolumbar Fascia

Lumbar Trigone
(Petit's Triangle)

External Oblique
Abdominis M.

Lateral Cutaneous Branch
of Iliohypogastric N.

Superior Cluneal Nn.

Medial Cluneal Nn.

Anococcygeal N.

Gluteal Fascia

Inferior Cluneal Nn.

**Posterior Cutaneous N.
of Thigh**

Gluteus Maximus M.

Perineal Branch

Ischial Tuberosity
Muscular Tendons of Origin

**Posterior Cutaneous N.
of Thigh**

Fascia Lata

Iliotibial Tract
(Maissiat's Band)

Posterior Cutaneous Branch
Nn. of the Thigh

Great Saphenous V.

On the Lower Edge of the Gluteus Maximus M.,
the Fascia Lata has been Divided to Expose the
Posterior Cutaneous N. of the Thigh.

Pathways and Topography

7.105 Muscles and Pathways of the Thigh: Right Side, Ventral View. [6]

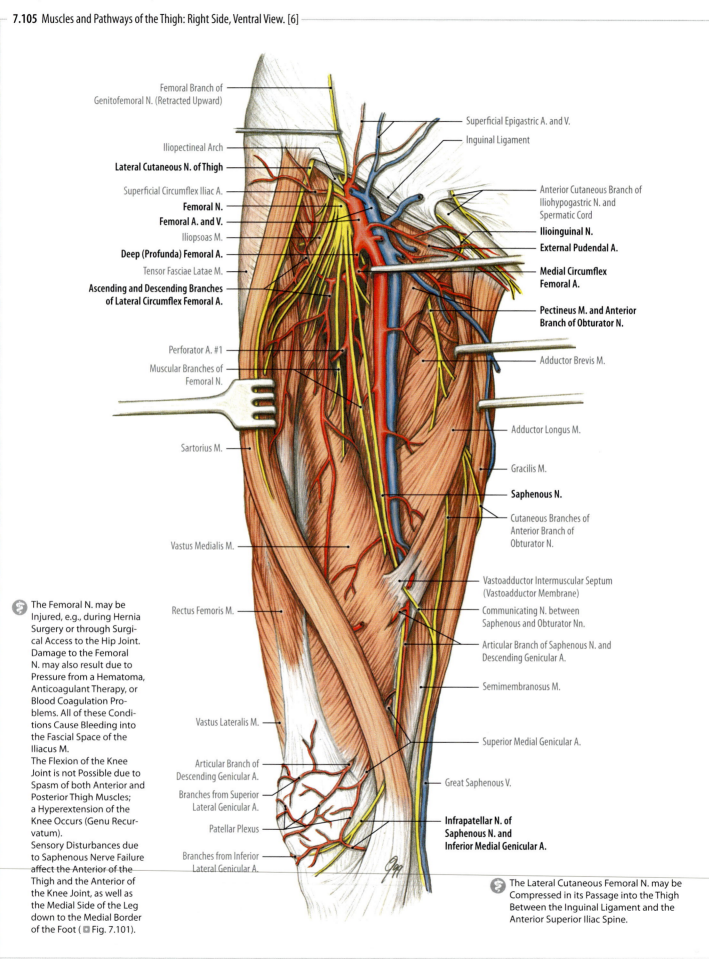

Femoral Branch of Genitofemoral N. (Retracted Upward)

Iliopectineal Arch

Lateral Cutaneous N. of Thigh

Superficial Circumflex Iliac A.

Femoral N.

Femoral A. and V.

Iliopsoas M.

Deep (Profunda) Femoral A.

Tensor Fasciae Latae M.

Ascending and Descending Branches of Lateral Circumflex Femoral A.

Perforator A. #1

Muscular Branches of Femoral N.

Sartorius M.

Vastus Medialis M.

Rectus Femoris M.

Vastus Lateralis M.

Articular Branch of Descending Genicular A.

Branches from Superior Lateral Genicular A.

Patellar Plexus

Branches from Inferior Lateral Genicular A.

Superficial Epigastric A. and V.

Inguinal Ligament

Anterior Cutaneous Branch of Iliohypogastric N. and Spermatic Cord

Ilioinguinal N.

External Pudendal A.

Medial Circumflex Femoral A.

Pectineus M. and Anterior Branch of Obturator N.

Adductor Brevis M.

Adductor Longus M.

Gracilis M.

Saphenous N.

Cutaneous Branches of Anterior Branch of Obturator N.

Vastoadductor Intermuscular Septum (Vastoadductor Membrane)

Communicating N. between Saphenous and Obturator Nn.

Articular Branch of Saphenous N. and Descending Genicular A.

Semimembranosus M.

Superior Medial Genicular A.

Great Saphenous V.

Infrapatellar N. of Saphenous N. and Inferior Medial Genicular A.

The Femoral N. may be Injured, e.g., during Hernia Surgery or through Surgical Access to the Hip Joint. Damage to the Femoral N. may also result due to Pressure from a Hematoma, Anticoagulant Therapy, or Blood Coagulation Problems. All of these Conditions Cause Bleeding into the Fascial Space of the Iliacus M.
The Flexion of the Knee Joint is not Possible due to Spasm of both Anterior and Posterior Thigh Muscles; a Hyperextension of the Knee Occurs (Genu Recurvatum).
Sensory Disturbances due to Saphenous Nerve Failure affect the Anterior of the Thigh and the Anterior of the Knee Joint, as well as the Medial Side of the Leg down to the Medial Border of the Foot (Fig. 7.101).

The Lateral Cutaneous Femoral N. may be Compressed in its Passage into the Thigh Between the Inguinal Ligament and the Anterior Superior Iliac Spine.

Femoral Triangle: Pathways

7.106 Muscles and Pathways of the Pelvis, the Inguinal Region, and the Femoral Triangle: Right Side, Ventral View. [46]

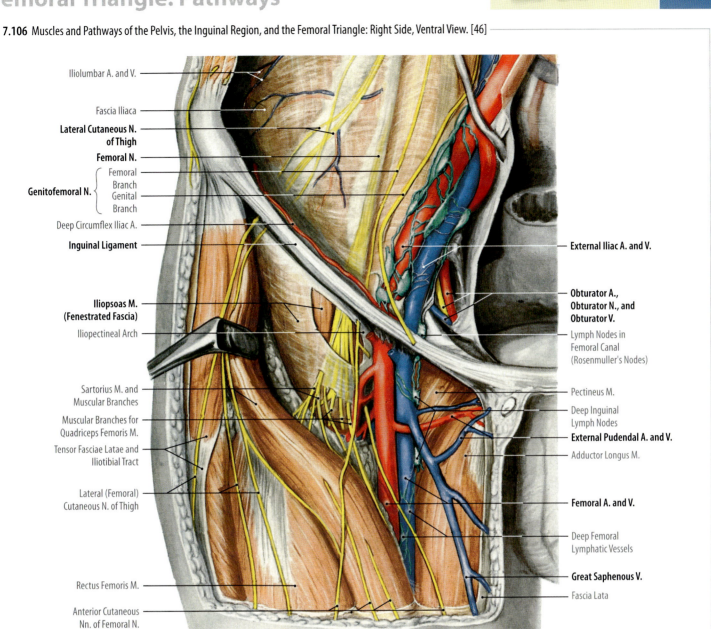

Iliolumbar A. and V.

Fascia Iliaca

Lateral Cutaneous N. of Thigh

Femoral N.

Genitofemoral N. { Femoral Branch / Genital Branch

Deep Circumflex Iliac A.

Inguinal Ligament

Iliopsoas M. (Fenestrated Fascia)

Iliopectineal Arch

Sartorius M. and Muscular Branches

Muscular Branches for Quadriceps Femoris M.

Tensor Fasciae Latae and Iliotibial Tract

Lateral (Femoral) Cutaneous N. of Thigh

Rectus Femoris M.

Anterior Cutaneous Nn. of Femoral N.

External Iliac A. and V.

Obturator A., Obturator N., and Obturator V.

Lymph Nodes in Femoral Canal (Rosenmuller's Nodes)

Pectineus M.

Deep Inguinal Lymph Nodes

External Pudendal A. and V.

Adductor Longus M.

Femoral A. and V.

Deep Femoral Lymphatic Vessels

Great Saphenous V.

Fascia Lata

ℹ️ Note the Iliopsoas Muscle Compartments, the Passage of the Femoral N. through the Iliopsoas Muscular Sheath, as well as the Course of the Femoral A., V., and the Lymphatics through the Vascular Sheath (Femoral Sheath) (◨ 7.110).

7.107a–d Schematic Illustration of the Arteries of the Femoral Triangle and Examples of the Variants. [46]

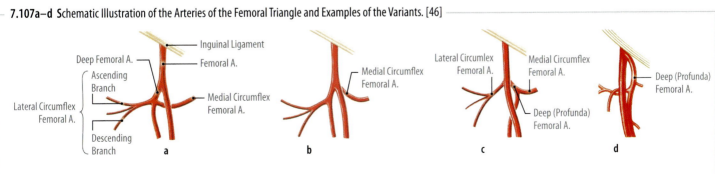

Inguinal Ligament

Deep Femoral A.

Femoral A.

Lateral Circumflex Femoral A. { Ascending Branch / Descending Branch

Medial Circumflex Femoral A.

a

Medial Circumflex Femoral A.

b

Lateral Circumflex Femoral A.

Medial Circumflex Femoral A.

Deep (Profunda) Femoral A.

c

Deep (Profunda) Femoral A.

d

a In ~60% of all cases, the Medial and Lateral Circumflex Femoral Aa. Originate from the Deep (Profunda) Femoral A. In about Half of all cases, the Deep (Profunda) Femoral A. Lies Lateral to the Femoral A.
b In ~20% of all cases, the Medial Circumflex Femoral A. Originates from the Femoral A.

c In ~15% of all cases, the Medial Circumflex Femoral A. Originates from the Deep (Profunda) Femoral and the Lateral Circumflex Femoral A. of the Femoral A.
d In ~40% of all cases, the Deep (Profunda) Femoral A. Originates from the Femoral A. in the area of the Inguinal Ligament (so-called High Origin of the Deep [Profunda] Femoral A.).

Pathways and Topography

7.108 Muscles and Pathways of the Obturator Region of a Right Thigh: Ventral View. [46]

Fractures of the Pelvis occasionally lead to Injury of the Obturator N. Compression of the Nerves may result from Obturator Hernia, Metastases in the Pelvis, or Pressure of the Child's Head During Birth. Adduction is strongly Restricted from Double Innervation of the Adductor Magnus M. from the Obturator N. and the Sciatic N., as well as the Adductor Longus M. from the Obturator N. and the Femoral N. The Sensory Failure may be Tested in the Cutaneous Area on the Medial Thigh, slightly Above the Knee Joint.

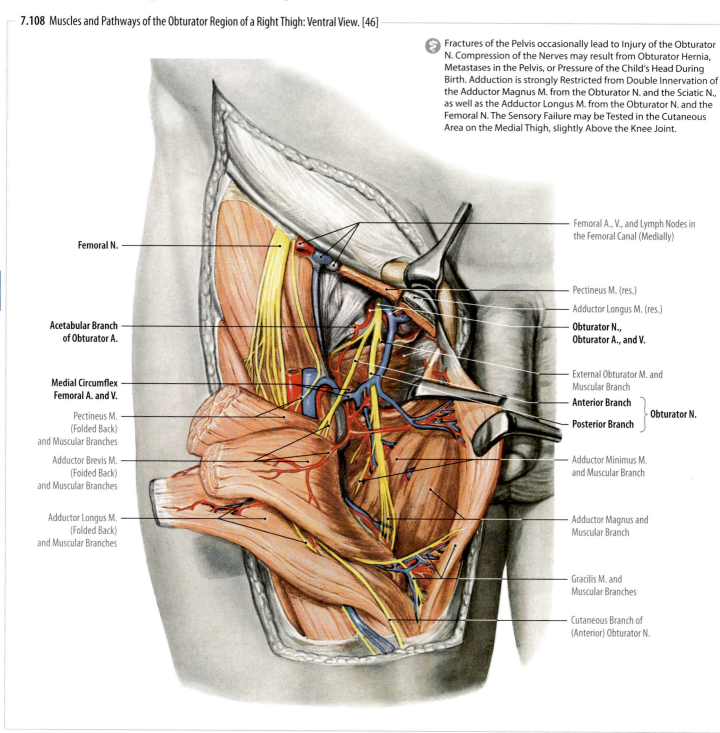

Femoral N.

Acetabular Branch of Obturator A.

Medial Circumflex Femoral A. and V.

Pectineus M. (Folded Back) and Muscular Branches

Adductor Brevis M. (Foided Back) and Muscular Branches

Adductor Longus M. (Folded Back) and Muscular Branches

Femoral A., V., and Lymph Nodes in the Femoral Canal (Medially)

Pectineus M. (res.)

Adductor Longus M. (res.)

Obturator N., Obturator A., and V.

External Obturator M. and Muscular Branch

Anterior Branch } **Obturator N.**
Posterior Branch

Adductor Minimus M. and Muscular Branch

Adductor Magnus and Muscular Branch

Gracilis M. and Muscular Branches

Cutaneous Branch of (Anterior) Obturator N.

7.109a–c Relationship of the Femoral N. to the Ascending and Descending Branches of the Lateral Circumflex Femoral A. [46]

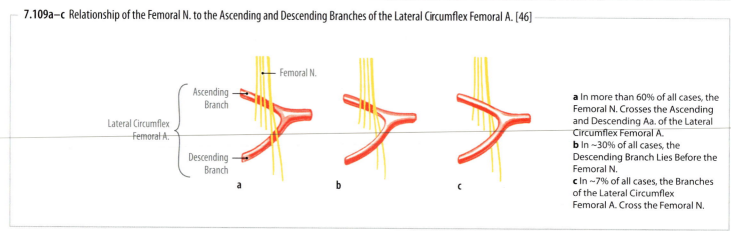

Femoral N.

Ascending Branch

Lateral Circumflex Femoral A.

Descending Branch

a   b   c

a In more than 60% of all cases, the Femoral N. Crosses the Ascending and Descending Aa. of the Lateral Circumflex Femoral A.
b In ~30% of all cases, the Descending Branch Lies Before the Femoral N.
c In ~7% of all cases, the Branches of the Lateral Circumflex Femoral A. Cross the Femoral N.

Muscular and Vascular Lacunae (Space)

7.110 Muscular Space and Vascular Space of a Right Half of the Pelvis: Lateral View. [46]

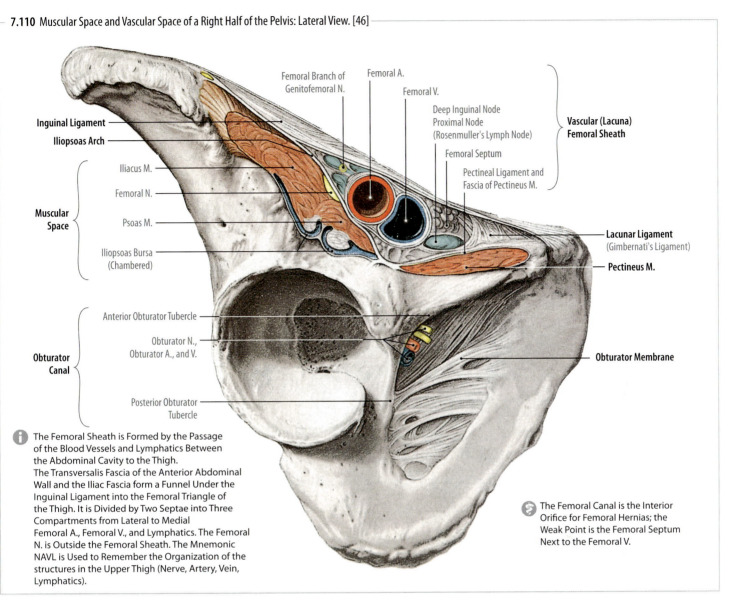

Femoral Branch of Genitofemoral N.

Femoral A.

Femoral V.

Deep Inguinal Node
Proximal Node
(Rosenmuller's Lymph Node)

Femoral Septum

Pectineal Ligament and
Fascia of Pectineus M.

Vascular (Lacuna)
Femoral Sheath

Inguinal Ligament

Iliopsoas Arch

Iliacus M.

Femoral N.

Muscular
Space

Psoas M.

Iliopsoas Bursa
(Chambered)

Lacunar Ligament
(Gimbernati's Ligament)

Pectineus M.

Anterior Obturator Tubercle

Obturator N.,
Obturator A., and V.

Obturator
Canal

Obturator Membrane

Posterior Obturator
Tubercle

ℹ️ The Femoral Sheath is Formed by the Passage
of the Blood Vessels and Lymphatics Between
the Abdominal Cavity to the Thigh.
The Transversalis Fascia of the Anterior Abdominal
Wall and the Iliac Fascia form a Funnel Under the
Inguinal Ligament into the Femoral Triangle of
the Thigh. It is Divided by Two Septae into Three
Compartments from Lateral to Medial
Femoral A., Femoral V., and Lymphatics. The Femoral
N. is Outside the Femoral Sheath. The Mnemonic
NAVL is Used to Remember the Organization of the
structures in the Upper Thigh (Nerve, Artery, Vein,
Lymphatics).

🔄 The Femoral Canal is the Interior
Orifice for Femoral Hernias; the
Weak Point is the Femoral Septum
Next to the Femoral V.

7.111a,b Arterial Supply of the Femoral Head and the Femoral Neck: Proximal Part of a Right Femur. [46]

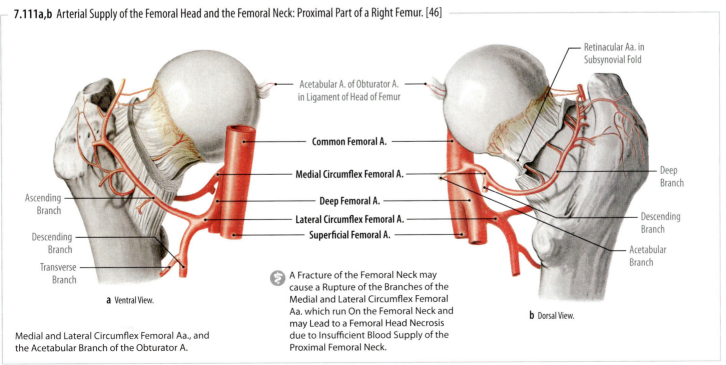

Acetabular A. of Obturator A.
in Ligament of Head of Femur

Retinacular Aa. in
Subsynovial Fold

Common Femoral A.

Medial Circumflex Femoral A.

Deep Femoral A.

Lateral Circumflex Femoral A.

Superficial Femoral A.

Deep
Branch

Descending
Branch

Acetabular
Branch

Ascending
Branch

Descending
Branch

Transverse
Branch

🔄 A Fracture of the Femoral Neck May
cause a Rupture of the Branches of the
Medial and Lateral Circumflex Femoral
Aa. which run On the Femoral Neck and
may Lead to a Femoral Head Necrosis
due to Insufficient Blood Supply of the
Proximal Femoral Neck.

a Ventral View.

b Dorsal View.

Medial and Lateral Circumflex Femoral Aa., and
the Acetabular Branch of the Obturator A.

Pathways and Topography

7.112 Muscles and Pathways of a Right Thigh: Dorsal View. [46]

Perineal Branches

Inferior Cluneal Nn.

Sciatic N.

Gluteus Maximus M.

Perforator Aa. and Vv. #1

Muscular Branches

Gluteal Tuberosity for Insertion of Gluteus Maximus M.

Posterior Cutaneous N. of Thigh

Adductor Magnus M.

Lateral Femoral Intermuscular Septum

Short Head

Long Head

Biceps Femoris M.

Femoropopliteal V.

Sartorius M.

Great Saphenous V.

Fascia Lata (Cut Edge)

Tendon of Insertion of Gracilis M.

Tendon of Insertion of Semitendinosus M.

Semimembranosus M.

Tibial N.

Deep Fascia of Muscular Layer and Popliteal Vessels

Common Peroneal N.

Gastrocnemius M.

Posterior Cutaneous N. of Thigh

Sural N.

Small Saphenous V.

Through the Division and Retraction of the Fascia Lata in a Medial and Lateral direction, the Group Fasciae of the Flexors and Adductors of the Thigh become Visible. The Common Flexor Fascia has also been Divided in the Distal Section so that the entry of the Pathways into the Popliteal Space becomes Visible.

7

Posterior Thigh, Gluteal Region: Pathways

7.113 Muscles and Pathways of the Gluteal Region, the Back of the Thigh, and the Popliteal Space: Dorsal View. [6]

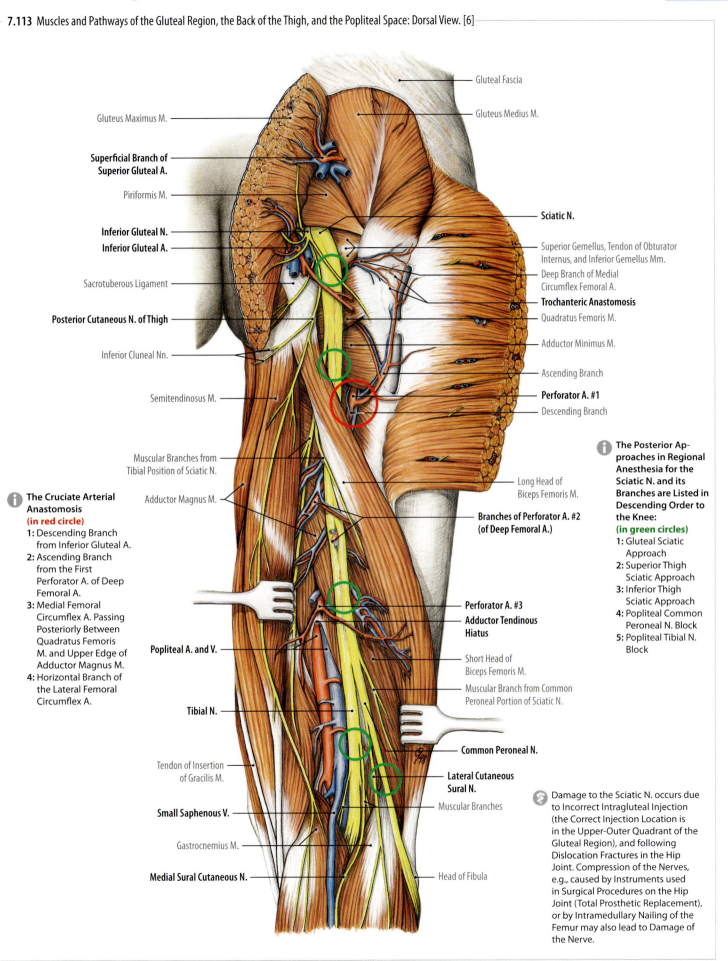

Gluteal Fascia

Gluteus Maximus M.

Gluteus Medius M.

Superficial Branch of Superior Gluteal A.

Piriformis M.

Sciatic N.

Inferior Gluteal N.
Inferior Gluteal A.

Superior Gemellus, Tendon of Obturator Internus, and Inferior Gemellus Mm.

Deep Branch of Medial Circumflex Femoral A.

Sacrotuberous Ligament

Trochanteric Anastomosis

Quadratus Femoris M.

Posterior Cutaneous N. of Thigh

Adductor Minimus M.

Inferior Cluneal Nn.

Ascending Branch

Perforator A. #1

Semitendinosus M.

Descending Branch

Muscular Branches from Tibial Position of Sciatic N.

Long Head of Biceps Femoris M.

The Cruciate Arterial Anastomosis (in red circle)
1: Descending Branch from Inferior Gluteal A.
2: Ascending Branch from the First Perforator A. of Deep Femoral A.
3: Medial Femoral Circumflex A. Passing Posteriorly Between Quadratus Femoris M. and Upper Edge of Adductor Magnus M.
4: Horizontal Branch of the Lateral Femoral Circumflex A.

Adductor Magnus M.

Branches of Perforator A. #2 (of Deep Femoral A.)

The Posterior Approaches in Regional Anesthesia for the Sciatic N. and its Branches are Listed in Descending Order to the Knee:
(in green circles)
1: Gluteal Sciatic Approach
2: Superior Thigh Sciatic Approach
3: Inferior Thigh Sciatic Approach
4: Popliteal Common Peroneal N. Block
5: Popliteal Tibial N. Block

Perforator A. #3
Adductor Tendinous Hiatus

Short Head of Biceps Femoris M.

Popliteal A. and V.

Muscular Branch from Common Peroneal Portion of Sciatic N.

Tibial N.

Common Peroneal N.

Tendon of Insertion of Gracilis M.

Lateral Cutaneous Sural N.

Muscular Branches

Small Saphenous V.

Damage to the Sciatic N. occurs due to Incorrect Intragluteal Injection (the Correct Injection Location is in the Upper-Outer Quadrant of the Gluteal Region), and following Dislocation Fractures in the Hip Joint. Compression of the Nerves, e.g., caused by Instruments used in Surgical Procedures on the Hip Joint (Total Prosthetic Replacement), or by Intramedullary Nailing of the Femur may also lead to Damage of the Nerve.

Gastrocnemius M.

Medial Sural Cutaneous N.

Head of Fibula

Pathways and Topography

7.114 Muscles and Pathways of the Deep Gluteal Region and the Ischioanal Fossa: Right Side, Dorsal View. [6]

Damage to the Superior Gluteal N. occurs due to Incorrect Intragluteal Injections (Also to the Inferior Gluteal N., but less frequently ◨ Fig. 7.113) or in connection with Hip Surgery. An Abduction Weakness in the Hip Joint results, and through Insufficiency of the Gluteus Minimus and Medius Mm. on the Supporting Leg, the Pelvis Sinks onto the Free Leg (Trendelenburg's Sign), which leads to Limping at the Hip and Gluteus Medius Lurch-Walk.

With Damage to the Inferior Gluteal N., Hip Joint Extension, Getting Up from a Sitting Position or Walking Up Stairs is strongly Restricted due to a Paresis of the Gluteus Maximus M.

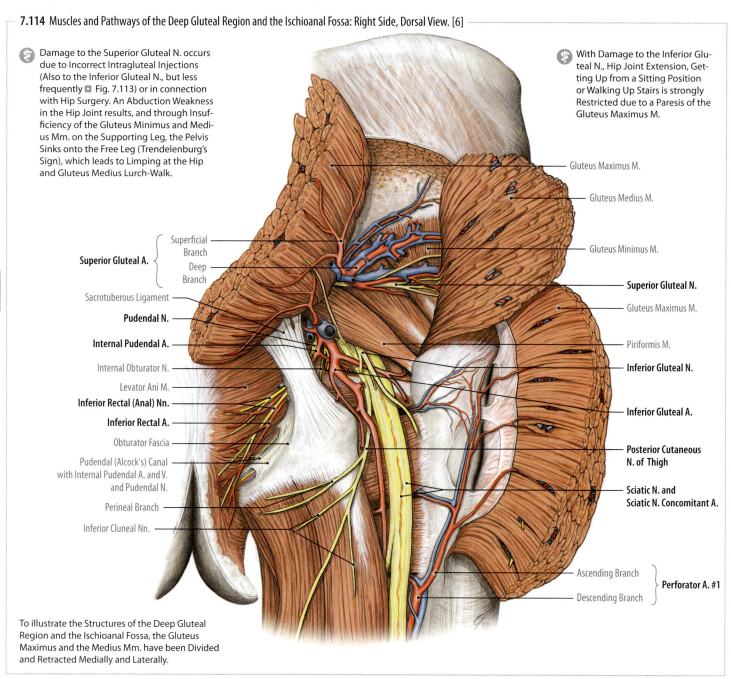

Gluteus Maximus M.

Gluteus Medius M.

Gluteus Minimus M.

Superior Gluteal A. { Superficial Branch / Deep Branch }

Superior Gluteal N.

Gluteus Maximus M.

Sacrotuberous Ligament

Piriformis M.

Pudendal N.

Inferior Gluteal N.

Internal Pudendal A.

Internal Obturator N.

Levator Ani M.

Inferior Rectal (Anal) Nn.

Inferior Gluteal A.

Inferior Rectal A.

Posterior Cutaneous N. of Thigh

Obturator Fascia

Pudendal (Alcock's) Canal with Internal Pudendal A. and V. and Pudendal N.

Sciatic N. and Sciatic N. Concomitant A.

Perineal Branch

Inferior Cluneal Nn.

Ascending Branch

Descending Branch } **Perforator A. #1**

To illustrate the Structures of the Deep Gluteal Region and the Ischioanal Fossa, the Gluteus Maximus and the Medius Mm. have been Divided and Retracted Medially and Laterally.

7.115 High Partition of the Sciatic N. (~15% of All Cases), Gluteal Region: Right Side, Dorsal View. [6]

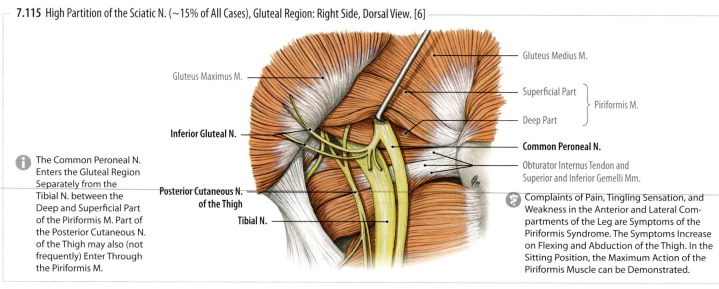

Gluteus Medius M.

Gluteus Maximus M.

Superficial Part

Deep Part } Piriformis M.

Inferior Gluteal N.

Common Peroneal N.

Obturator Internus Tendon and Superior and Inferior Gemelli Mm.

Posterior Cutaneous N. of the Thigh

Tibial N.

The Common Peroneal N. Enters the Gluteal Region Separately from the Tibial N. between the Deep and Superficial Part of the Piriformis M. Part of the Posterior Cutaneous N. of the Thigh may also (not frequently) Enter Through the Piriformis M.

Complaints of Pain, Tingling Sensation, and Weakness in the Anterior and Lateral Compartments of the Leg are Symptoms of the Piriformis Syndrome. The Symptoms Increase on Flexing and Abduction of the Thigh. In the Sitting Position, the Maximum Action of the Piriformis Muscle can be Demonstrated.

534

Thigh: Cross-Sections

7.116 Cross-Sections through the Proximal, Median, and Distal Area of a Right Thigh: View of the Distal Cut Surfaces. [46]

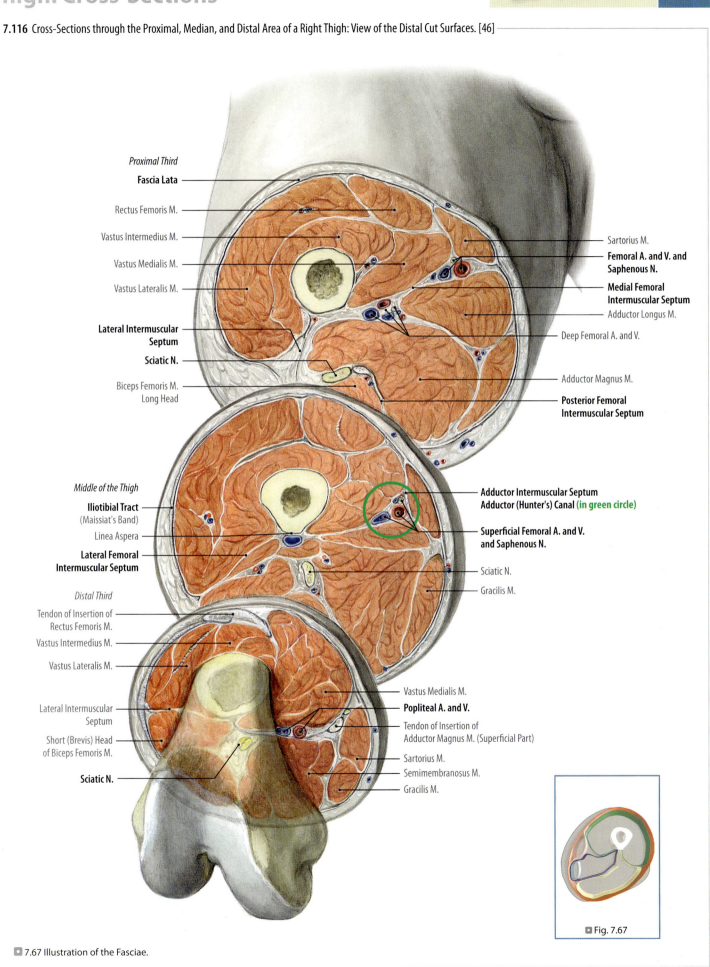

Proximal Third
Fascia Lata

Rectus Femoris M.

Vastus Intermedius M.

Vastus Medialis M.

Vastus Lateralis M.

Lateral Intermuscular Septum

Sciatic N.

Biceps Femoris M. Long Head

Sartorius M.

Femoral A. and V. and Saphenous N.

Medial Femoral Intermuscular Septum

Adductor Longus M.

Deep Femoral A. and V.

Adductor Magnus M.

Posterior Femoral Intermuscular Septum

Middle of the Thigh

Iliotibial Tract (Maissiat's Band)

Linea Aspera

Lateral Femoral Intermuscular Septum

Adductor Intermuscular Septum
Adductor (Hunter's) Canal (in green circle)

Superficial Femoral A. and V. and Saphenous N.

Sciatic N.

Gracilis M.

Distal Third

Tendon of Insertion of Rectus Femoris M.

Vastus Intermedius M.

Vastus Lateralis M.

Lateral Intermuscular Septum

Short (Brevis) Head of Biceps Femoris M.

Sciatic N.

Vastus Medialis M.

Popliteal A. and V.

Tendon of Insertion of Adductor Magnus M. (Superficial Part)

Sartorius M.

Semimembranosus M.

Gracilis M.

▶ Fig. 7.67

▶ 7.67 Illustration of the Fasciae.

Pathways and Topography

7.117 Arteries on the Front of the Knee and Leg, and on the Dorsum of the Foot of the Right Side. [13]

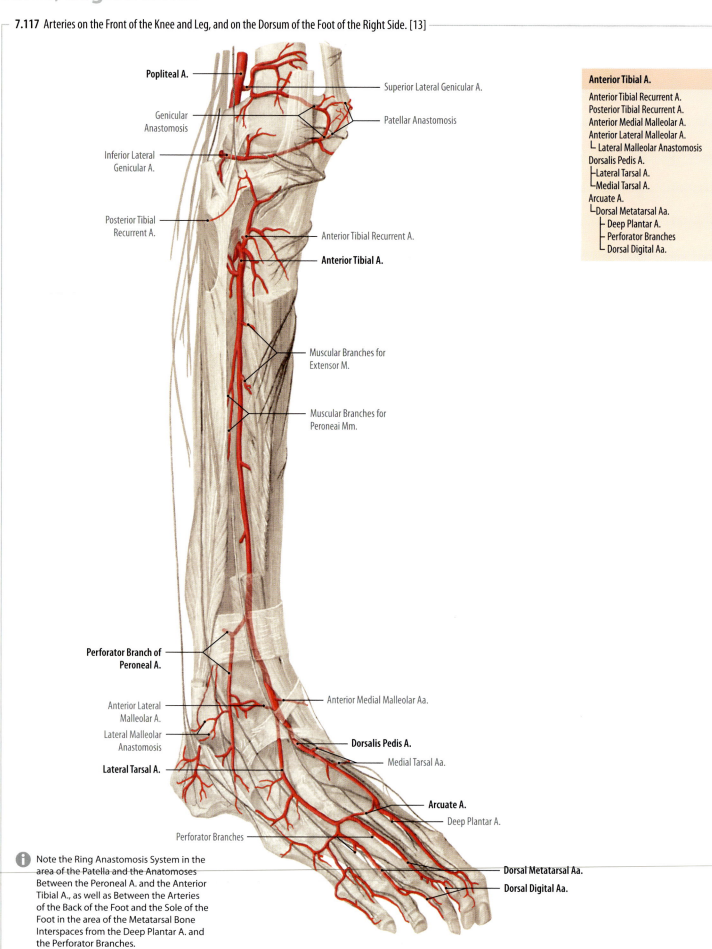

Popliteal A.

Superior Lateral Genicular A.

Genicular
Anastomosis

Patellar Anastomosis

Inferior Lateral
Genicular A.

Posterior Tibial
Recurrent A.

Anterior Tibial Recurrent A.

Anterior Tibial A.

Muscular Branches for
Extensor M.

Muscular Branches for
Peroneai Mm.

Perforator Branch of
Peroneal A.

Anterior Medial Malleolar Aa.

Anterior Lateral
Malleolar A.

Lateral Malleolar
Anastomosis

Dorsalis Pedis A.

Medial Tarsal Aa.

Lateral Tarsal A.

Arcuate A.

Deep Plantar A.

Perforator Branches

Dorsal Metatarsal Aa.

Dorsal Digital Aa.

Anterior Tibial A.

Anterior Tibial Recurrent A.
Posterior Tibial Recurrent A.
Anterior Medial Malleolar A.
Anterior Lateral Malleolar A.
└ Lateral Malleolar Anastomosis
Dorsalis Pedis A.
├Lateral Tarsal A.
└Medial Tarsal A.
Arcuate A.
└Dorsal Metatarsal Aa.
├ Deep Plantar A.
├ Perforator Branches
└ Dorsal Digital Aa.

ⓘ Note the Ring Anastomosis System in the
area of the Patella and the Anatomoses
Between the Peroneal A. and the Anterior
Tibial A., as well as Between the Arteries
of the Back of the Foot and the Sole of the
Foot in the area of the Metatarsal Bone
Interspaces from the Deep Plantar A. and
the Perforator Branches.

7

Knee, Leg: Arteries

7.118a–d Arteries on the Back of the Knee and Leg: Right Side. [13]

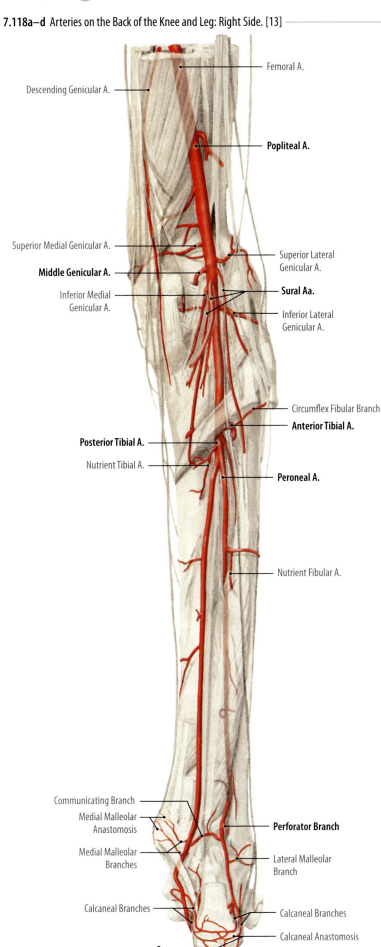

Femoral A.

Descending Genicular A.

Popliteal A.

Superior Medial Genicular A.

Middle Genicular A.

Inferior Medial Genicular A.

Superior Lateral Genicular A.

Sural Aa.

Inferior Lateral Genicular A.

Circumflex Fibular Branch

Anterior Tibial A.

Posterior Tibial A.

Nutrient Tibial A.

Peroneal A.

Nutrient Fibular A.

Communicating Branch

Medial Malleolar Anastomosis

Medial Malleolar Branches

Perforator Branch

Lateral Malleolar Branch

Calcaneal Branches

Calcaneal Branches

Calcaneal Anastomosis

a

Popliteal A.

Superior Lateral Genicular A.
Superior Medial Genicular A.
Inferior Lateral Genicular A.
Inferior Medial Genicular A.
└ Genicular Anastomosis
 └ Patellar Anastomosis
Medial Genicular A.
Sural Aa.

Posterior Tibial A.

Circumflex Peroneal Branch
Peroneal A.
Nutrient Tibial A.
Medial Malleolar Branches
├ Medial Malleolar Anastomosis
└ Calcaneal Aa.
 └ Calcaneal Anastomosis

Peroneal (Fibular) A.

├Nutrient Fibular A.
├Perforator Branch
├Communicating Branch
├Lateral Malleolar Aa.
└ Calcaneal Aa.
 └ Calcaneal Anastomosis

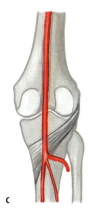

Popliteal A.

Popliteus M.

Anterior Tibial A.

Posterior Tibial A.

Peroneal (Fibular) A.

b

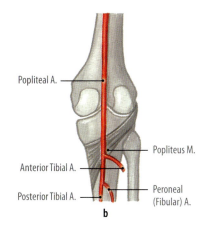

c

d

b In ~90% of all cases, the Anterior Tibialis A. Originates from the Popliteal A. on the Lower Edge of the Popliteus M.
c In ~4% of all cases, the Popliteal A. Trifurcates into the Posterior Tibial A., Anterior Tibial A., and Peroneal (Fibularis) A. on the Distal Edge of the Popliteus M.
d In ~3% of all cases, the Anterior Tibial A. Originates from the Popliteal A. Above the Popliteus M.— "High Division."

Pathways and Topography

7.119 Nerves of the Anterior and Lateral Sides of the Right Leg. [13]

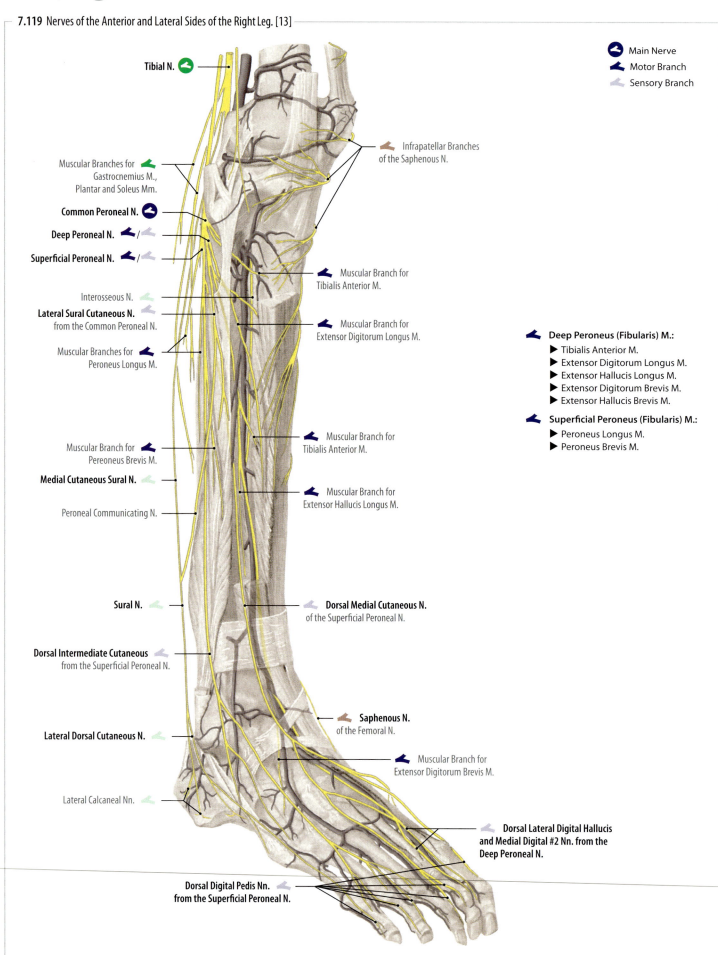

Main Nerve
Motor Branch
Sensory Branch

Tibial N.

Muscular Branches for
Gastrocnemius M.,
Plantar and Soleus Mm.

Common Peroneal N.

Deep Peroneal N.

Superficial Peroneal N.

Interosseous N.

Lateral Sural Cutaneous N.
from the Common Peroneal N.

Muscular Branches for
Peroneus Longus M.

Muscular Branch for
Pereoneus Brevis M.

Medial Cutaneous Sural N.

Peroneal Communicating N.

Sural N.

Dorsal Intermediate Cutaneous
from the Superficial Peroneal N.

Lateral Dorsal Cutaneous N.

Lateral Calcaneal Nn.

Dorsal Digital Pedis Nn.
from the Superficial Peroneal N.

Infrapatellar Branches
of the Saphenous N.

Muscular Branch for
Tibialis Anterior M.

Muscular Branch for
Extensor Digitorum Longus M.

Muscular Branch for
Tibialis Anterior M.

Muscular Branch for
Extensor Hallucis Longus M.

Dorsal Medial Cutaneous N.
of the Superficial Peroneal N.

Saphenous N.
of the Femoral N.

Muscular Branch for
Extensor Digitorum Brevis M.

Dorsal Lateral Digital Hallucis
and Medial Digital #2 Nn. from the
Deep Peroneal N.

Deep Peroneus (Fibularis) M.:
▶ Tibialis Anterior M.
▶ Extensor Digitorum Longus M.
▶ Extensor Hallucis Longus M.
▶ Extensor Digitorum Brevis M.
▶ Extensor Hallucis Brevis M.

Superficial Peroneus (Fibularis) M.:
▶ Peroneus Longus M.
▶ Peroneus Brevis M.

7

7.120 Nerves of the Back of the Leg. [13]

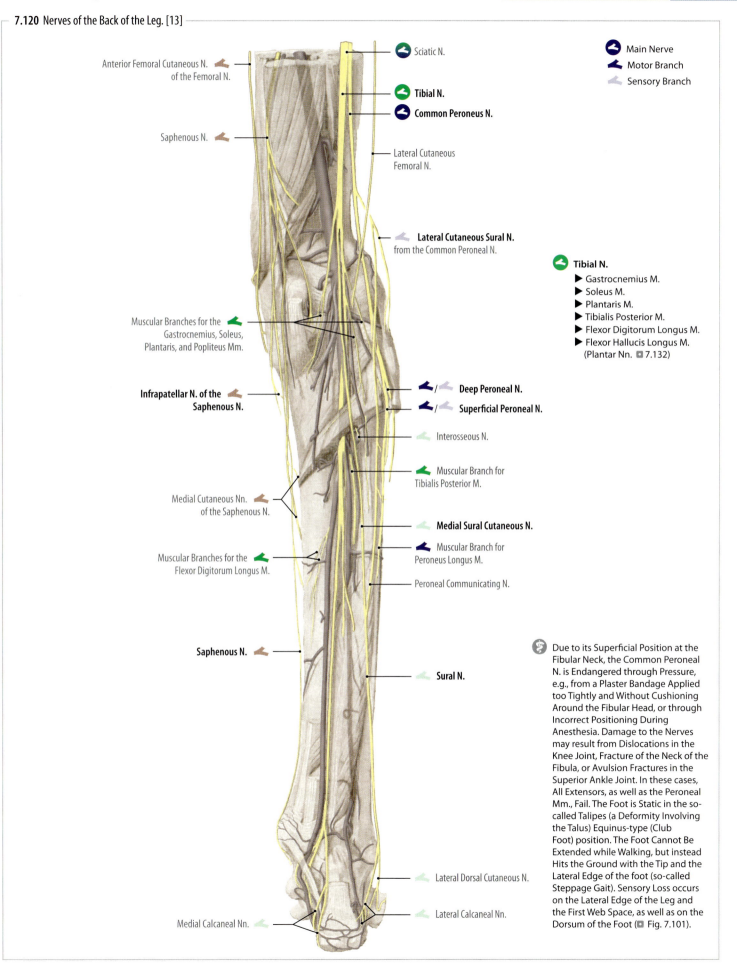

Anterior Femoral Cutaneous N. of the Femoral N.

Saphenous N.

Muscular Branches for the Gastrocnemius, Soleus, Plantaris, and Popliteus Mm.

Infrapatellar N. of the Saphenous N.

Medial Cutaneous Nn. of the Saphenous N.

Muscular Branches for the Flexor Digitorum Longus M.

Saphenous N.

Medial Calcaneal Nn.

Sciatic N.

Tibial N.

Common Peroneus N.

Lateral Cutaneous Femoral N.

Lateral Cutaneous Sural N. from the Common Peroneal N.

Deep Peroneal N.

Superficial Peroneal N.

Interosseous N.

Muscular Branch for Tibialis Posterior M.

Medial Sural Cutaneous N.

Muscular Branch for Peroneus Longus M.

Peroneal Communicating N.

Sural N.

Lateral Dorsal Cutaneous N.

Lateral Calcaneal Nn.

Main Nerve
Motor Branch
Sensory Branch

Tibial N.
► Gastrocnemius M.
► Soleus M.
► Plantaris M.
► Tibialis Posterior M.
► Flexor Digitorum Longus M.
► Flexor Hallucis Longus M.
  (Plantar Nn. 7.132)

Due to its Superficial Position at the Fibular Neck, the Common Peroneal N. is Endangered through Pressure, e.g., from a Plaster Bandage Applied too Tightly and Without Cushioning Around the Fibular Head, or through Incorrect Positioning During Anesthesia. Damage to the Nerves may result from Dislocations in the Knee Joint, Fracture of the Neck of the Fibula, or Avulsion Fractures in the Superior Ankle Joint. In these cases, All Extensors, as well as the Peroneal Mm., Fail. The Foot is Static in the so-called Talipes (a Deformity Involving the Talus) Equinus-type (Club Foot) position. The Foot Cannot Be Extended while Walking, but instead Hits the Ground with the Tip and the Lateral Edge of the foot (so-called Steppage Gait). Sensory Loss occurs on the Lateral Edge of the Leg and the First Web Space, as well as on the Dorsum of the Foot (Fig. 7.101).

Pathways and Topography

7.121 Muscles and Pathways of the Right Popliteal Space: Dorsal View. [6]

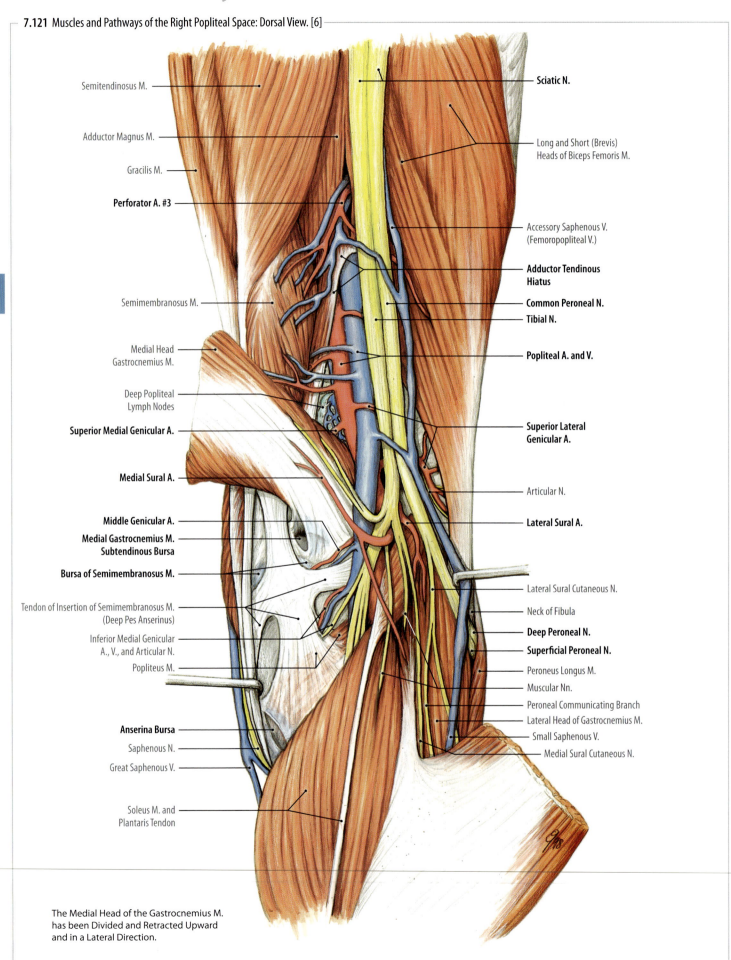

Semitendinosus M.

Adductor Magnus M.

Gracilis M.

Perforator A. #3

Semimembranosus M.

Medial Head Gastrocnemius M.

Deep Popliteal Lymph Nodes

Superior Medial Genicular A.

Medial Sural A.

Middle Genicular A.
Medial Gastrocnemius M. Subtendinous Bursa

Bursa of Semimembranosus M.

Tendon of Insertion of Semimembranosus M. (Deep Pes Anserinus)

Inferior Medial Genicular A., V., and Articular N.

Popliteus M.

Anserina Bursa

Saphenous N.

Great Saphenous V.

Soleus M. and Plantaris Tendon

Sciatic N.

Long and Short (Brevis) Heads of Biceps Femoris M.

Accessory Saphenous V. (Femoropopliteal V.)

Adductor Tendinous Hiatus

Common Peroneal N.

Tibial N.

Popliteal A. and V.

Superior Lateral Genicular A.

Articular N.

Lateral Sural A.

Lateral Sural Cutaneous N.

Neck of Fibula

Deep Peroneal N.

Superficial Peroneal N.

Peroneus Longus M.

Muscular Nn.

Peroneal Communicating Branch

Lateral Head of Gastrocnemius M.

Small Saphenous V.

Medial Sural Cutaneous N.

The Medial Head of the Gastrocnemius M. has been Divided and Retracted Upward and in a Lateral Direction.

7.122a–c Superficial Nerves of the Leg: Right Side. [91]

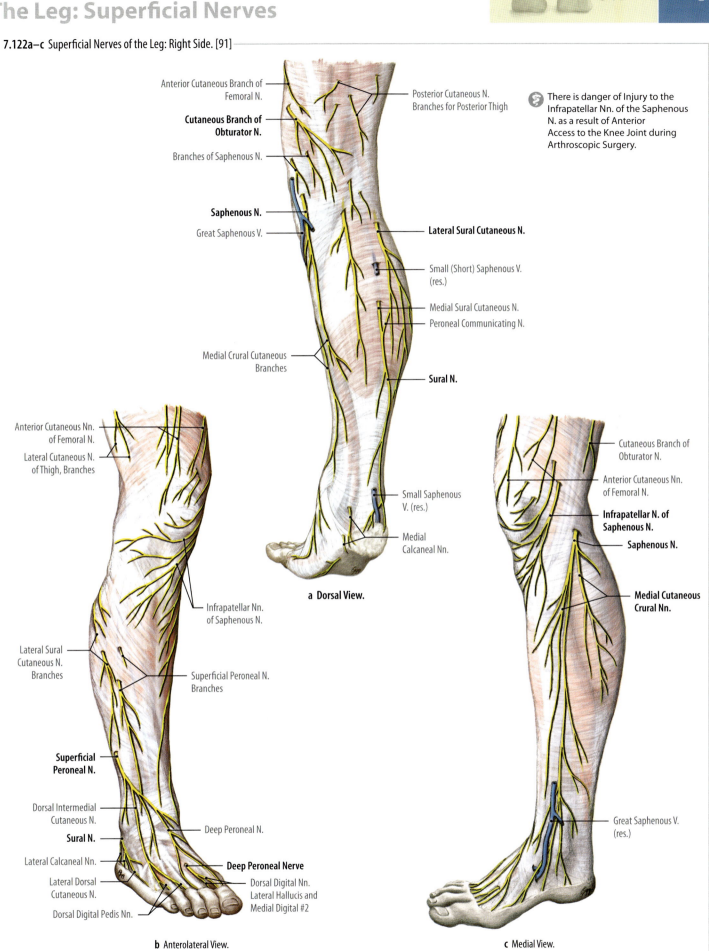

Anterior Cutaneous Branch of Femoral N.

Cutaneous Branch of Obturator N.

Branches of Saphenous N.

Saphenous N.

Great Saphenous V.

Medial Crural Cutaneous Branches

Posterior Cutaneous N. Branches for Posterior Thigh

There is danger of Injury to the Infrapatellar Nn. of the Saphenous N. as a result of Anterior Access to the Knee Joint during Arthroscopic Surgery.

Lateral Sural Cutaneous N.

Small (Short) Saphenous V. (res.)

Medial Sural Cutaneous N.
Peroneal Communicating N.

Sural N.

Small Saphenous V. (res.)

Medial Calcaneal Nn.

a Dorsal View.

Anterior Cutaneous Nn. of Femoral N.

Lateral Cutaneous N. of Thigh, Branches

Lateral Sural Cutaneous N. Branches

Infrapatellar Nn. of Saphenous N.

Superficial Peroneal N. Branches

Superficial Peroneal N.

Dorsal Intermedial Cutaneous N.

Sural N.

Lateral Calcaneal Nn.

Lateral Dorsal Cutaneous N.

Dorsal Digital Pedis Nn.

Deep Peroneal N.

Deep Peroneal Nerve

Dorsal Digital Nn. Lateral Hallucis and Medial Digital #2

b Anterolateral View.

Cutaneous Branch of Obturator N.

Anterior Cutaneous Nn. of Femoral N.

Infrapatellar N. of Saphenous N.

Saphenous N.

Medial Cutaneous Crural Nn.

Great Saphenous V. (res.)

c Medial View.

7.123 Right Leg: Anterolateral View. [46]

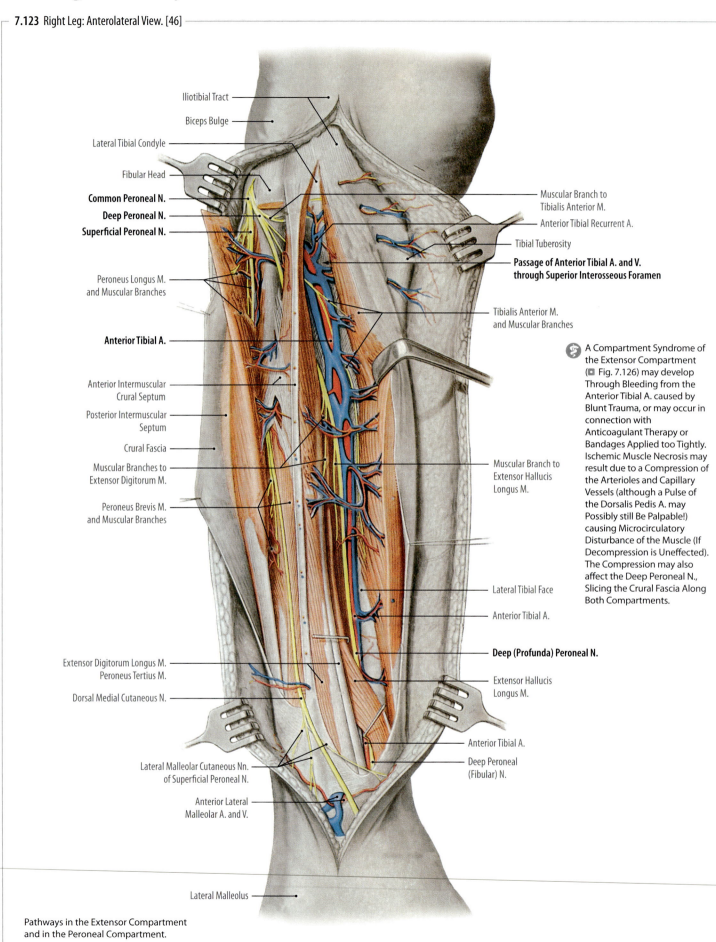

Iliotibial Tract

Biceps Bulge

Lateral Tibial Condyle

Fibular Head

Common Peroneal N.

Deep Peroneal N.

Superficial Peroneal N.

Peroneus Longus M. and Muscular Branches

Anterior Tibial A.

Anterior Intermuscular Crural Septum

Posterior Intermuscular Septum

Crural Fascia

Muscular Branches to Extensor Digitorum M.

Peroneus Brevis M. and Muscular Branches

Extensor Digitorum Longus M. Peroneus Tertius M.

Dorsal Medial Cutaneous N.

Lateral Malleolar Cutaneous Nn. of Superficial Peroneal N.

Anterior Lateral Malleolar A. and V.

Lateral Malleolus

Muscular Branch to Tibialis Anterior M.

Anterior Tibial Recurrent A.

Tibial Tuberosity

Passage of Anterior Tibial A. and V. through Superior Interosseous Foramen

Tibialis Anterior M. and Muscular Branches

Muscular Branch to Extensor Hallucis Longus M.

Lateral Tibial Face

Anterior Tibial A.

Deep (Profunda) Peroneal N.

Extensor Hallucis Longus M.

Anterior Tibial A.

Deep Peroneal (Fibular) N.

A Compartment Syndrome of the Extensor Compartment (🔳 Fig. 7.126) may develop Through Bleeding from the Anterior Tibial A. caused by Blunt Trauma, or may occur in connection with Anticoagulant Therapy or Bandages Applied too Tightly. Ischemic Muscle Necrosis may result due to a Compression of the Arterioles and Capillary Vessels (although a Pulse of the Dorsalis Pedis A. may Possibly still Be Palpable!) causing Microcirculatory Disturbance of the Muscle (If Decompression is Uneffected). The Compression may also affect the Deep Peroneal N., Slicing the Crural Fascia Along Both Compartments.

Pathways in the Extensor Compartment and in the Peroneal Compartment.

7

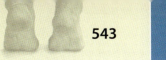

7.124 Muscles and Pathways in the Deep Flexor Compartment of a Right Leg: Medial View. [6]

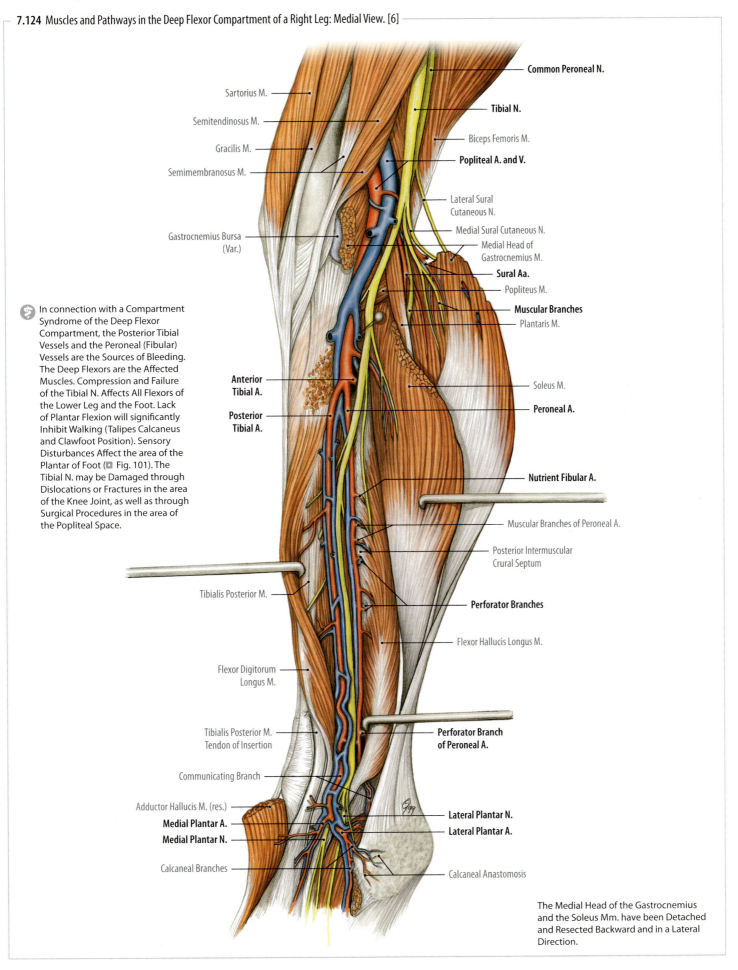

Sartorius M.

Semitendinosus M.

Gracilis M.

Semimembranosus M.

Gastrocnemius Bursa (Var.)

Common Peroneal N.

Tibial N.

Biceps Femoris M.

Popliteal A. and V.

Lateral Sural Cutaneous N.

Medial Sural Cutaneous N.

Medial Head of Gastrocnemius M.

Sural Aa.

Popliteus M.

Muscular Branches

Plantaris M.

In connection with a Compartment Syndrome of the Deep Flexor Compartment, the Posterior Tibial Vessels and the Peroneal (Fibular) Vessels are the Sources of Bleeding. The Deep Flexors are the Affected Muscles. Compression and Failure of the Tibial N. Affects All Flexors of the Lower Leg and the Foot. Lack of Plantar Flexion will significantly Inhibit Walking (Talipes Calcaneus and Clawfoot Position). Sensory Disturbances Affect the area of the Plantar of Foot (☐ Fig. 101). The Tibial N. may be Damaged through Dislocations or Fractures in the area of the Knee Joint, as well as through Surgical Procedures in the area of the Popliteal Space.

Anterior Tibial A.

Posterior Tibial A.

Soleus M.

Peroneal A.

Nutrient Fibular A.

Muscular Branches of Peroneal A.

Posterior Intermuscular Crural Septum

Tibialis Posterior M.

Perforator Branches

Flexor Hallucis Longus M.

Flexor Digitorum Longus M.

Tibialis Posterior M. Tendon of Insertion

Perforator Branch of Peroneal A.

Communicating Branch

Adductor Hallucis M. (res.)

Medial Plantar A.

Medial Plantar N.

Calcaneal Branches

Lateral Plantar N.

Lateral Plantar A.

Calcaneal Anastomosis

The Medial Head of the Gastrocnemius and the Soleus Mm. have been Detached and Resected Backward and in a Lateral Direction.

Pathways and Topography

7.125 Muscles and Pathways of the Distal Area of the Leg of the Right Side with the Ankle and Heel Region: Dorsal View. [46]

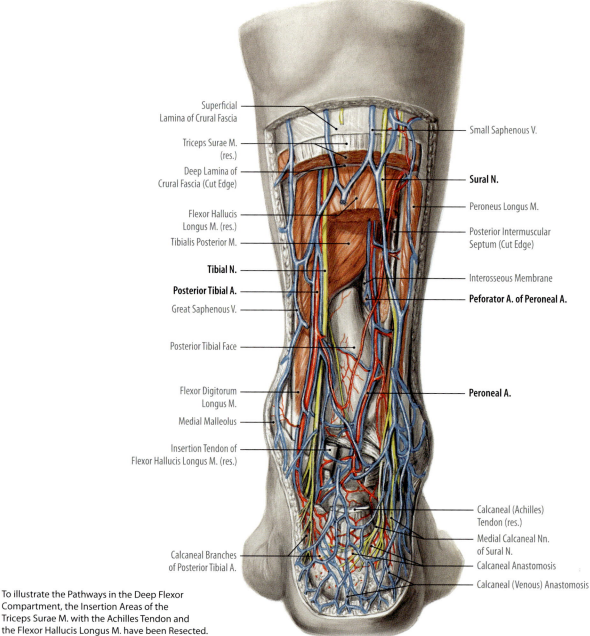

Superficial
Lamina of Crural Fascia

Triceps Surae M.
(res.)

Deep Lamina of
Crural Fascia (Cut Edge)

Flexor Hallucis
Longus M. (res.)

Tibialis Posterior M.

Tibial N.

Posterior Tibial A.

Great Saphenous V.

Posterior Tibial Face

Flexor Digitorum
Longus M.

Medial Malleolus

Insertion Tendon of
Flexor Hallucis Longus M. (res.)

Calcaneal Branches
of Posterior Tibial A.

Small Saphenous V.

Sural N.

Peroneus Longus M.

Posterior Intermuscular
Septum (Cut Edge)

Interosseous Membrane

Peforator A. of Peroneal A.

Peroneal A.

Calcaneal (Achilles)
Tendon (res.)

Medial Calcaneal Nn.
of Sural N.

Calcaneal Anastomosis

Calcaneal (Venous) Anastomosis

To illustrate the Pathways in the Deep Flexor
Compartment, the Insertion Areas of the
Triceps Surae M. with the Achilles Tendon and
the Flexor Hallucis Longus M. have been Resected.

7.126 Muscle Compartments of the Leg and Pathways: Right Side, Inferior View. [46]

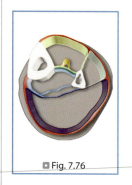

□ Fig. 7.76

ⓘ Note that there are No
Vessels in the Peroneal
Compartment.

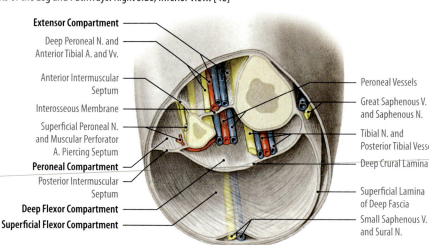

Extensor Compartment

Deep Peroneal N. and
Anterior Tibial A. and Vv.

Anterior Intermuscular
Septum

Interosseous Membrane

Superficial Peroneal N.
and Muscular Perforator
A. Piercing Septum

Peroneal Compartment

Posterior Intermuscular
Septum

Deep Flexor Compartment

Superficial Flexor Compartment

Peroneal Vessels

Great Saphenous V.
and Saphenous N.

Tibial N. and
Posterior Tibial Vessels

Deep Crural Lamina

Superficial Lamina
of Deep Fascia

Small Saphenous V.
and Sural N.

✋ In the Muscle Compartments
of the Leg, Compartment
Syndromes may Develop in
the Extensor Compartment
(most common) and in the
Deep Flexor Compartment.
Swellings and Hematomas
Increase Internal Pressure
Inside the Unextendable
Osteofibrous Spaces, e.g.,
Following Traumatic Muscle
Contusion, in connection
with Fractures of the Bones
of the Lower Leg, or as a
result of Compressing Bandages (□ Fig. 7.123 and □ Fig.
7.124).

Malleolar Region: Pathways

7.127a,b Pathways of the Malleolar Region: Right Side. [46]

A Compression of the Tibial N. or its Terminal Branches (Lateral and Medial Plantar Nn.) at its Passage through the Malleolar Canal Between the Medial Melleolus and the Flexor Retinaculum is called Medial or Posterior Tarsal Tunnel Syndrome. Sensory Disturbances in the area of the Sole of the Foot (◻ Fig. 7.101) and a Paresis of the Short Plantar Muscles of the Foot Occur. The Pulse of the Posterior Tibial A. is Palpable behind the Medial Ankle in its course in the Malleolar Canal.

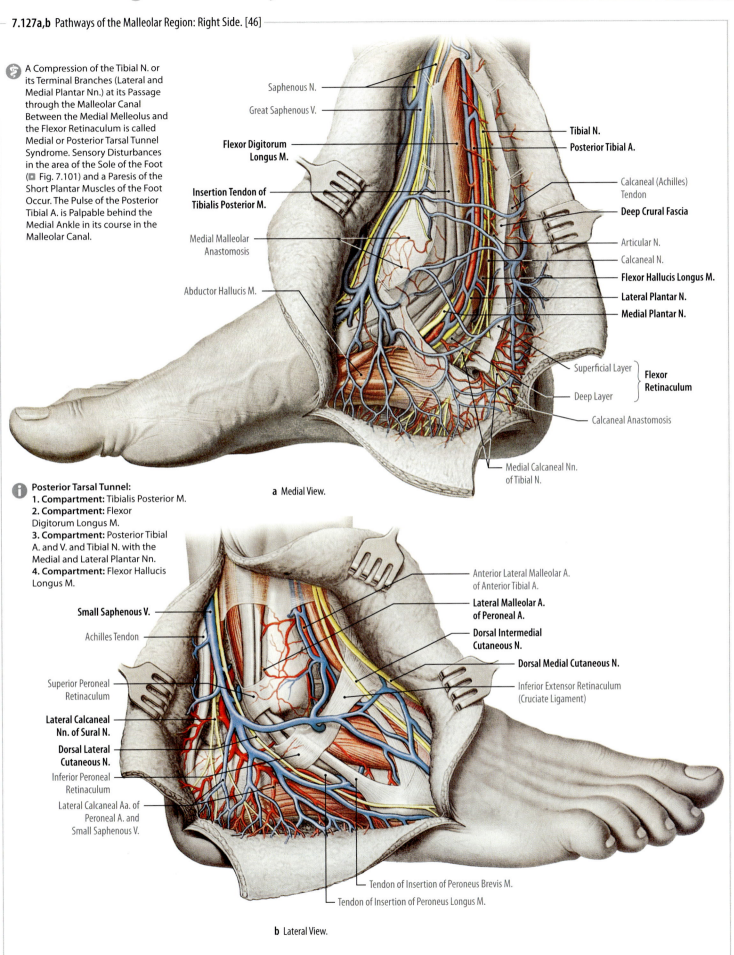

Saphenous N.
Great Saphenous V.
Flexor Digitorum Longus M.
Insertion Tendon of Tibialis Posterior M.
Medial Malleolar Anastomosis
Abductor Hallucis M.

Tibial N.
Posterior Tibial A.
Calcaneal (Achilles) Tendon
Deep Crural Fascia
Articular N.
Calcaneal N.
Flexor Hallucis Longus M.
Lateral Plantar N.
Medial Plantar N.
Superficial Layer } **Flexor Retinaculum**
Deep Layer
Calcaneal Anastomosis
Medial Calcaneal Nn. of Tibial N.

a Medial View.

Posterior Tarsal Tunnel:
1. **Compartment:** Tibialis Posterior M.
2. **Compartment:** Flexor Digitorum Longus M.
3. **Compartment:** Posterior Tibial A. and V. and Tibial N. with the Medial and Lateral Plantar Nn.
4. **Compartment:** Flexor Hallucis Longus M.

Small Saphenous V.
Achilles Tendon
Superior Peroneal Retinaculum
Lateral Calcaneal Nn. of Sural N.
Dorsal Lateral Cutaneous N.
Inferior Peroneal Retinaculum
Lateral Calcaneal Aa. of Peroneal A. and Small Saphenous V.

Anterior Lateral Malleolar A. of Anterior Tibial A.
Lateral Malleolar A. of Peroneal A.
Dorsal Intermedial Cutaneous N.
Dorsal Medial Cutaneous N.
Inferior Extensor Retinaculum (Cruciate Ligament)

Tendon of Insertion of Peroneus Brevis M.
Tendon of Insertion of Peroneus Longus M.

b Lateral View.

Pathways and Topography

7.128 Superficial Pathways on the Dorsum of the Foot: Right Side, Ventral View. [46]

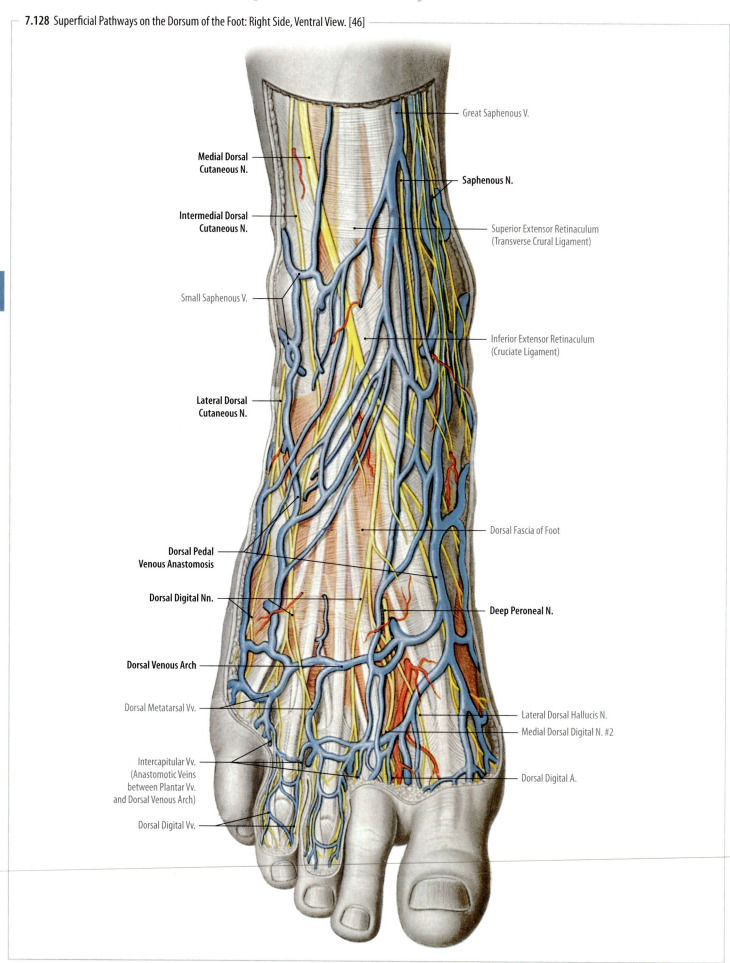

Great Saphenous V.

Medial Dorsal Cutaneous N.

Saphenous N.

Intermedial Dorsal Cutaneous N.

Superior Extensor Retinaculum (Transverse Crural Ligament)

Small Saphenous V.

Inferior Extensor Retinaculum (Cruciate Ligament)

Lateral Dorsal Cutaneous N.

Dorsal Fascia of Foot

Dorsal Pedal Venous Anastomosis

Dorsal Digital Nn.

Deep Peroneal N.

Dorsal Venous Arch

Dorsal Metatarsal Vv.

Lateral Dorsal Hallucis N.

Medial Dorsal Digital N. #2

Intercapitular Vv. (Anastomotic Veins between Plantar Vv. and Dorsal Venous Arch)

Dorsal Digital A.

Dorsal Digital Vv.

7.129 Pathways on the Dorsum of the Foot: Right Side, Ventral View. [46]

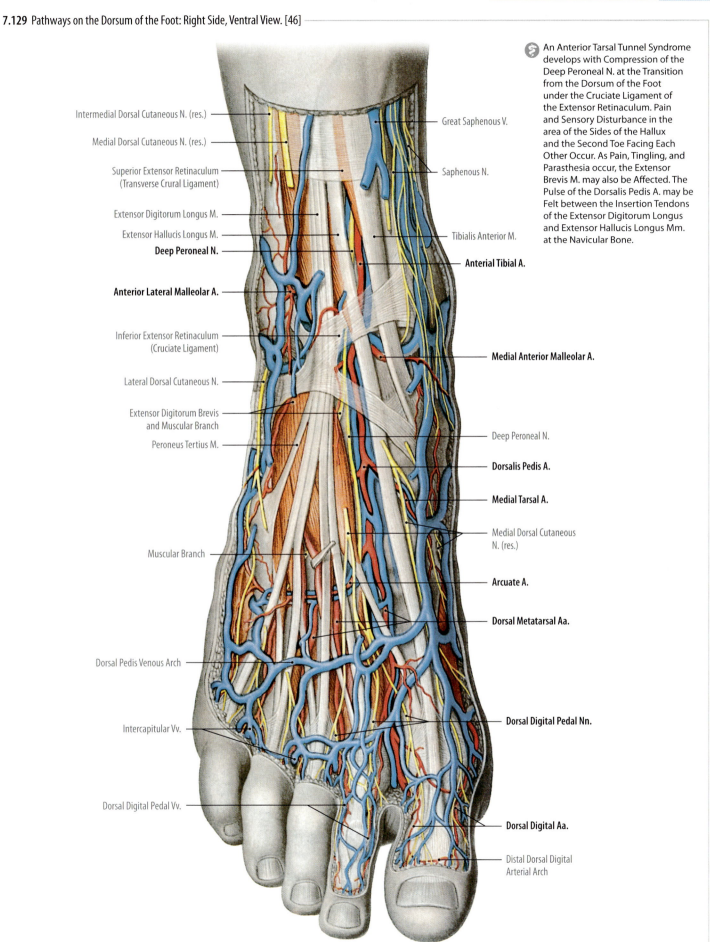

Intermedial Dorsal Cutaneous N. (res.)

Medial Dorsal Cutaneous N. (res.)

Superior Extensor Retinaculum (Transverse Crural Ligament)

Extensor Digitorum Longus M.

Extensor Hallucis Longus M.

Deep Peroneal N.

Anterior Lateral Malleolar A.

Inferior Extensor Retinaculum (Cruciate Ligament)

Lateral Dorsal Cutaneous N.

Extensor Digitorum Brevis and Muscular Branch

Peroneus Tertius M.

Muscular Branch

Dorsal Pedis Venous Arch

Intercapitular Vv.

Dorsal Digital Pedal Vv.

Great Saphenous V.

Saphenous N.

Tibialis Anterior M.

Anterial Tibial A.

Medial Anterior Malleolar A.

Deep Peroneal N.

Dorsalis Pedis A.

Medial Tarsal A.

Medial Dorsal Cutaneous N. (res.)

Arcuate A.

Dorsal Metatarsal Aa.

Dorsal Digital Pedal Nn.

Dorsal Digital Aa.

Distal Dorsal Digital Arterial Arch

An Anterior Tarsal Tunnel Syndrome develops with Compression of the Deep Peroneal N. at the Transition from the Dorsum of the Foot under the Cruciate Ligament of the Extensor Retinaculum. Pain and Sensory Disturbance in the area of the Sides of the Hallux and the Second Toe Facing Each Other Occur. As Pain, Tingling, and Parasthesia occur, the Extensor Brevis M. may also be Affected. The Pulse of the Dorsalis Pedis A. may be Felt between the Insertion Tendons of the Extensor Digitorum Longus and Extensor Hallucis Longus Mm. at the Navicular Bone.

Pathways and Topography

Dorsum of the Foot: Deep Pathways

7.130a–c Muscles and Pathways on the Dorsum of the Foot: Right Side, Ventral View. [46]

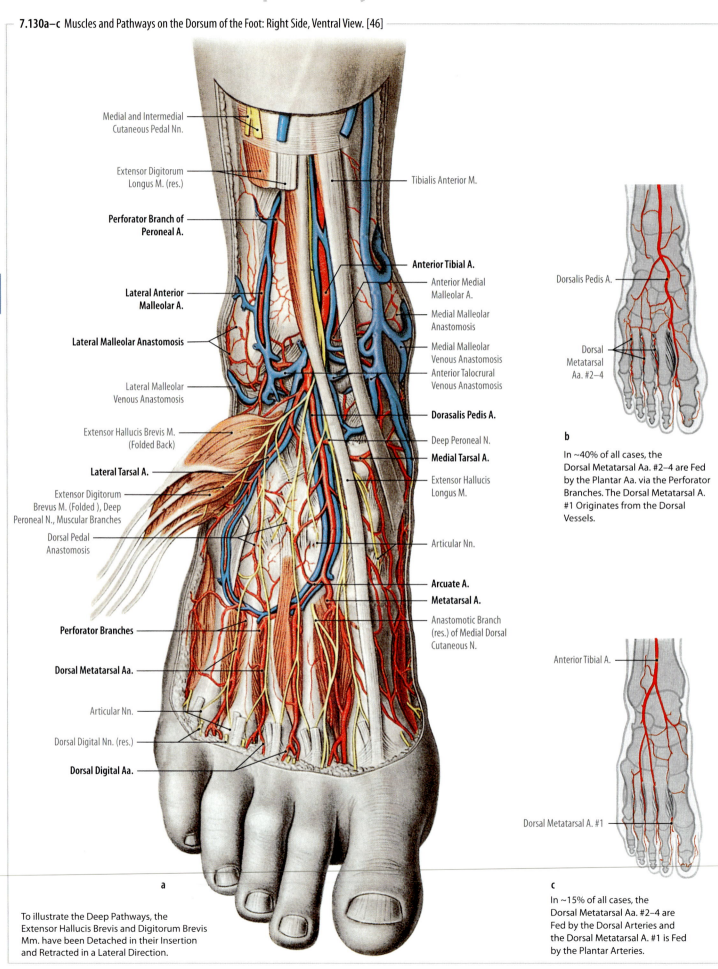

Medial and Intermedial Cutaneous Pedal Nn.

Extensor Digitorum Longus M. (res.)

Perforator Branch of Peroneal A.

Lateral Anterior Malleolar A.

Lateral Malleolar Anastomosis

Lateral Malleolar Venous Anastomosis

Extensor Hallucis Brevis M. (Folded Back)

Lateral Tarsal A.

Extensor Digitorum Brevus M. (Folded), Deep Peroneal N., Muscular Branches

Dorsal Pedal Anastomosis

Perforator Branches

Dorsal Metatarsal Aa.

Articular Nn.

Dorsal Digital Nn. (res.)

Dorsal Digital Aa.

Tibialis Anterior M.

Anterior Tibial A.

Anterior Medial Malleolar A.

Medial Malleolar Anastomosis

Medial Malleolar Venous Anastomosis

Anterior Talocrural Venous Anastomosis

Dorasalis Pedis A.

Deep Peroneal N.

Medial Tarsal A.

Extensor Hallucis Longus M.

Articular Nn.

Arcuate A.

Metatarsal A.

Anastomotic Branch (res.) of Medial Dorsal Cutaneous N.

a

To illustrate the Deep Pathways, the Extensor Hallucis Brevis and Digitorum Brevis Mm. have been Detached in their Insertion and Retracted in a Lateral Direction.

Dorsalis Pedis A.

Dorsal Metatarsal Aa. #2–4

b

In ~40% of all cases, the Dorsal Metatarsal Aa. #2–4 are Fed by the Plantar Aa. via the Perforator Branches. The Dorsal Metatarsal A. #1 Originates from the Dorsal Vessels.

Anterior Tibial A.

Dorsal Metatarsal A. #1

c

In ~15% of all cases, the Dorsal Metatarsal Aa. #2–4 are Fed by the Dorsal Arteries and the Dorsal Metatarsal A. #1 is Fed by the Plantar Arteries.

Sole of the Foot: Arteries · Nerves

7.131 Arteries of the Sole of the Foot: Right Side. [13]

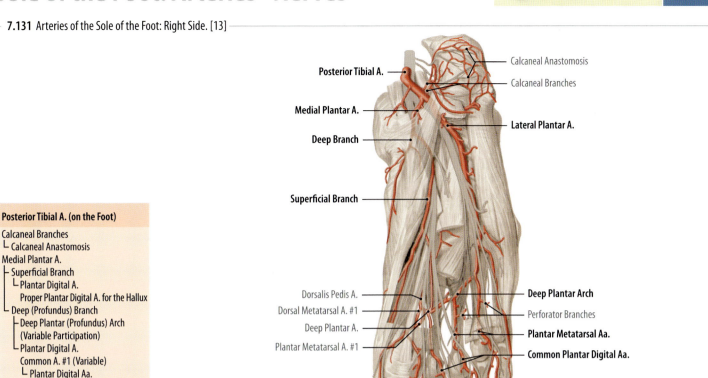

Posterior Tibial A. (on the Foot)
Calcaneal Branches
└ Calcaneal Anastomosis
Medial Plantar A.
├ Superficial Branch
└ Plantar Digital A.
Proper Plantar Digital A. for the Hallux
└ Deep (Profundus) Branch
├ Deep Plantar (Profundus) Arch
(Variable Participation)
└ Plantar Digital A.
Common A. #1 (Variable)
└ Plantar Digital Aa.
Proper Plantar Digital A. for the
Hallux and for Toe #2 (Variable)
Lateral Plantar A.
└ Deep (Profundus) Plantar Arch
└ Plantar Metatarsal Aa.
├ Perforator Branches
├ Plantar Common Digital Aa.
└ Plantar Proper Digital Aa.

Labels in figure:
- Posterior Tibial A.
- Medial Plantar A.
- Deep Branch
- Superficial Branch
- Dorsalis Pedis A.
- Dorsal Metatarsal A. #1
- Deep Plantar A.
- Plantar Metatarsal A. #1
- Medial and Lateral Plantar Digital Aa.
- Calcaneal Anastomosis
- Calcaneal Branches
- Lateral Plantar A.
- Deep Plantar Arch
- Perforator Branches
- Plantar Metatarsal Aa.
- Common Plantar Digital Aa.
- Anastomoses between Plantar Digital Aa. and Dorsal Metatarsal Aa.
- Proper Plantar Digital Aa.

7.132 Nerves of the Sole of the Foot: Right Side. [13]

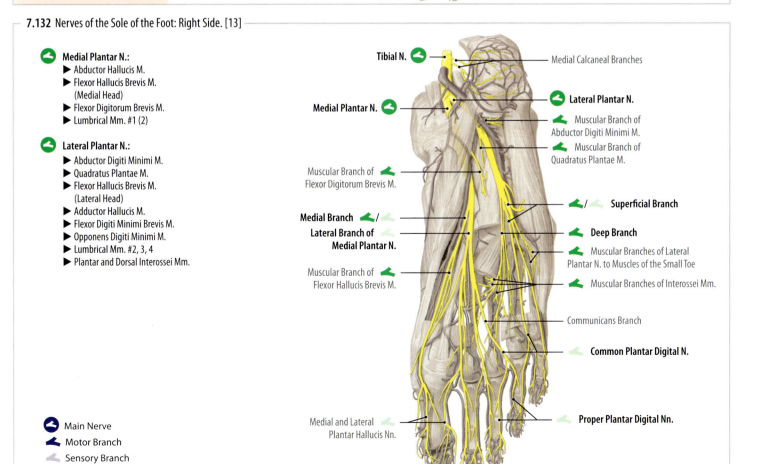

Medial Plantar N.:
▶ Abductor Hallucis M.
▶ Flexor Hallucis Brevis M. (Medial Head)
▶ Flexor Digitorum Brevis M.
▶ Lumbrical Mm. #1 (2)

Lateral Plantar N.:
▶ Abductor Digiti Minimi M.
▶ Quadratus Plantae M.
▶ Flexor Hallucis Brevis M. (Lateral Head)
▶ Adductor Hallucis M.
▶ Flexor Digiti Minimi Brevis M.
▶ Opponens Digiti Minimi M.
▶ Lumbrical Mm. #2, 3, 4
▶ Plantar and Dorsal Interossei Mm.

Labels in figure:
- Tibial N.
- Medial Plantar N.
- Muscular Branch of Flexor Digitorum Brevis M.
- Medial Branch
- Lateral Branch of Medial Plantar N.
- Muscular Branch of Flexor Hallucis Brevis M.
- Medial and Lateral Plantar Hallucis Nn.
- Medial Calcaneal Branches
- Lateral Plantar N.
- Muscular Branch of Abductor Digiti Minimi M.
- Muscular Branch of Quadratus Plantae M.
- Superficial Branch
- Deep Branch
- Muscular Branches of Lateral Plantar N. to Muscles of the Small Toe
- Muscular Branches of Interossei Mm.
- Communicans Branch
- Common Plantar Digital N.
- Proper Plantar Digital Nn.

Main Nerve
Motor Branch
Sensory Branch

Pathways and Topography

7.133 Compartments of the Sole of the Foot on the Planta Pedis: Right Side. [46]

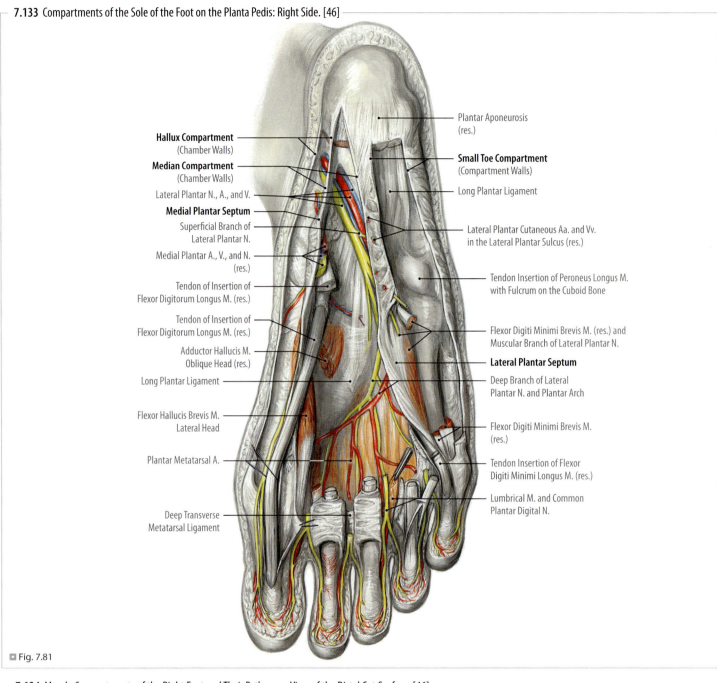

Plantar Aponeurosis (res.)

Hallux Compartment (Chamber Walls)

Median Compartment (Chamber Walls)

Lateral Plantar N., A., and V.

Medial Plantar Septum

Superficial Branch of Lateral Plantar N.

Medial Plantar A., V., and N. (res.)

Tendon of Insertion of Flexor Digitorum Longus M. (res.)

Tendon of Insertion of Flexor Digitorum Longus M. (res.)

Adductor Hallucis M. Oblique Head (res.)

Long Plantar Ligament

Flexor Hallucis Brevis M. Lateral Head

Plantar Metatarsal A.

Deep Transverse Metatarsal Ligament

Small Toe Compartment (Compartment Walls)

Long Plantar Ligament

Lateral Plantar Cutaneous Aa. and Vv. in the Lateral Plantar Sulcus (res.)

Tendon Insertion of Peroneus Longus M. with Fulcrum on the Cuboid Bone

Flexor Digiti Minimi Brevis M. (res.) and Muscular Branch of Lateral Plantar N.

Lateral Plantar Septum

Deep Branch of Lateral Plantar N. and Plantar Arch

Flexor Digiti Minimi Brevis M. (res.)

Tendon Insertion of Flexor Digiti Minimi Longus M. (res.)

Lumbrical M. and Common Plantar Digital N.

◻ Fig. 7.81

7.134 Muscle Compartments of the Right Foot and Their Pathways: View of the Distal Cut Surface. [46]

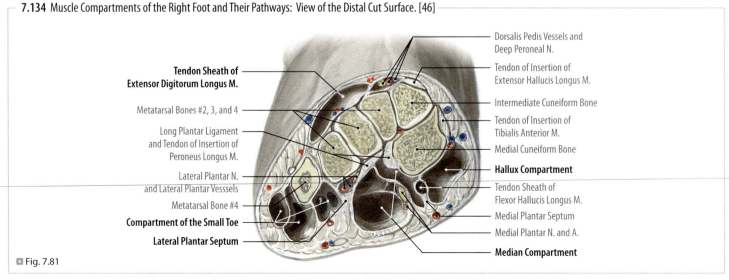

Tendon Sheath of Extensor Digitorum Longus M.

Metatarsal Bones #2, 3, and 4

Long Plantar Ligament and Tendon of Insertion of Peroneus Longus M.

Lateral Plantar N. and Lateral Plantar Vesssels

Metatarsal Bone #4

Compartment of the Small Toe

Lateral Plantar Septum

Dorsalis Pedis Vessels and Deep Peroneal N.

Tendon of Insertion of Extensor Hallucis Longus M.

Intermediate Cuneiform Bone

Tendon of Insertion of Tibialis Anterior M.

Medial Cuneiform Bone

Hallux Compartment

Tendon Sheath of Flexor Hallucis Longus M.

Medial Plantar Septum

Medial Plantar N. and A.

Median Compartment

◻ Fig. 7.81

Plantar Aponeurosis, Pathways

7.135 Fasciae and Pathways on the Planta of the Foot: Right Side. [46]

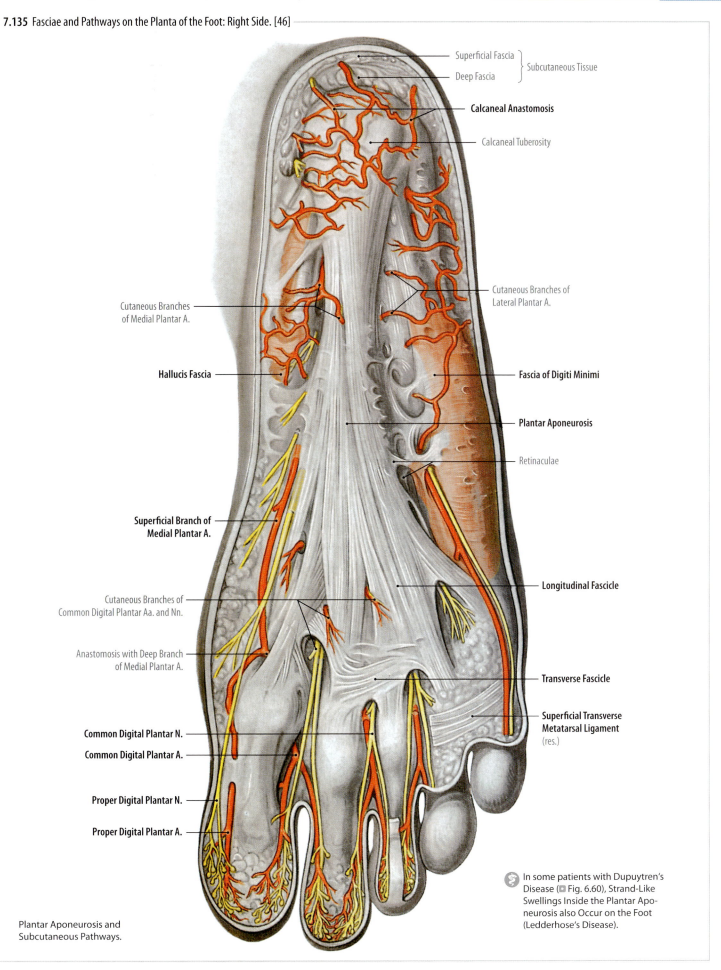

Superficial Fascia
Deep Fascia } Subcutaneous Tissue

Calcaneal Anastomosis

Calcaneal Tuberosity

Cutaneous Branches of
Lateral Plantar A.

Cutaneous Branches
of Medial Plantar A.

Hallucis Fascia

Fascia of Digiti Minimi

Plantar Aponeurosis

Retinaculae

**Superficial Branch of
Medial Plantar A.**

Longitudinal Fascicle

Cutaneous Branches of
Common Digital Plantar Aa. and Nn.

Anastomosis with Deep Branch
of Medial Plantar A.

Transverse Fascicle

Common Digital Plantar N.

Common Digital Plantar A.

**Superficial Transverse
Metatarsal Ligament**
(res.)

Proper Digital Plantar N.

Proper Digital Plantar A.

In some patients with Dupuytren's
Disease (◌ Fig. 6.60), Strand-Like
Swellings Inside the Plantar Apo-
neurosis also Occur on the Foot
(Ledderhose's Disease).

Plantar Aponeurosis and
Subcutaneous Pathways.

Pathways and Topography

7.136a,b Muscles and Pathways on the Plantar of the Right Foot: Superficial Layer. [46]

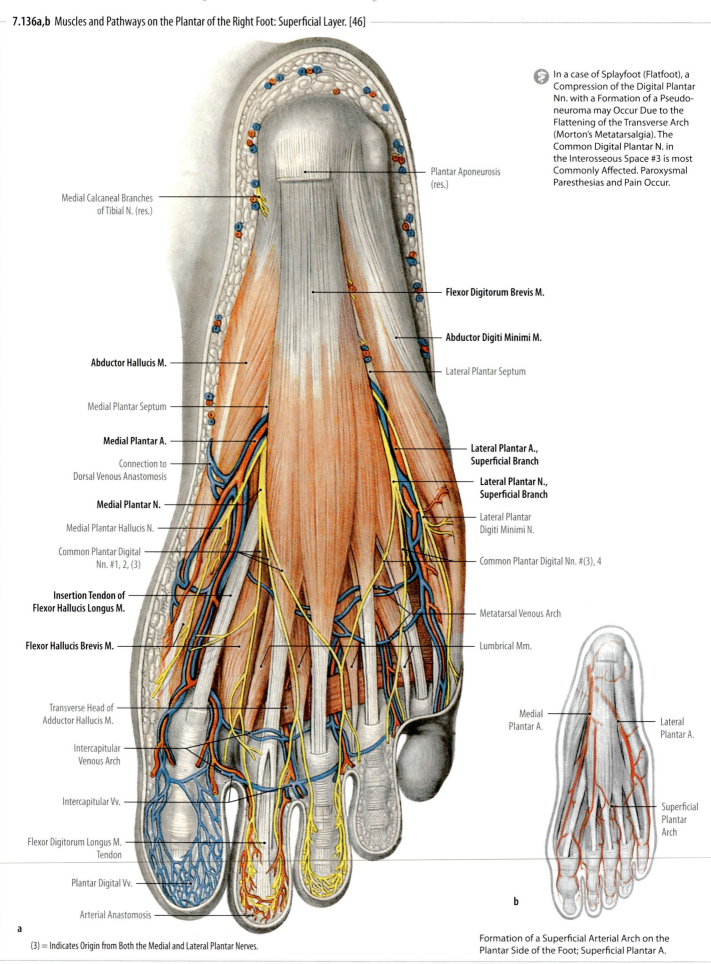

In a case of Splayfoot (Flatfoot), a Compression of the Digital Plantar Nn. with a Formation of a Pseudo-neuroma may Occur Due to the Flattening of the Transverse Arch (Morton's Metatarsalgia). The Common Digital Plantar N. in the Interosseous Space #3 is most Commonly Affected. Paroxysmal Paresthesias and Pain Occur.

Plantar Aponeurosis (res.)

Medial Calcaneal Branches of Tibial N. (res.)

Flexor Digitorum Brevis M.

Abductor Digiti Minimi M.

Abductor Hallucis M.

Lateral Plantar Septum

Medial Plantar Septum

Medial Plantar A.

Lateral Plantar A., Superficial Branch

Connection to Dorsal Venous Anastomosis

Lateral Plantar N., Superficial Branch

Medial Plantar N.

Lateral Plantar Digiti Minimi N.

Medial Plantar Hallucis N.

Common Plantar Digital Nn. #1, 2, (3)

Common Plantar Digital Nn. #(3), 4

Insertion Tendon of Flexor Hallucis Longus M.

Metatarsal Venous Arch

Flexor Hallucis Brevis M.

Lumbrical Mm.

Transverse Head of Adductor Hallucis M.

Medial Plantar A.

Lateral Plantar A.

Intercapitular Venous Arch

Intercapitular Vv.

Superficial Plantar Arch

Flexor Digitorum Longus M. Tendon

Plantar Digital Vv.

Arterial Anastomosis

a

b

(3) = Indicates Origin from Both the Medial and Lateral Plantar Nerves.

Formation of a Superficial Arterial Arch on the Plantar Side of the Foot; Superficial Plantar A.

7

7.137a,b Muscles and Pathways on the Plantar of the Right Foot: Median Layer. [46]

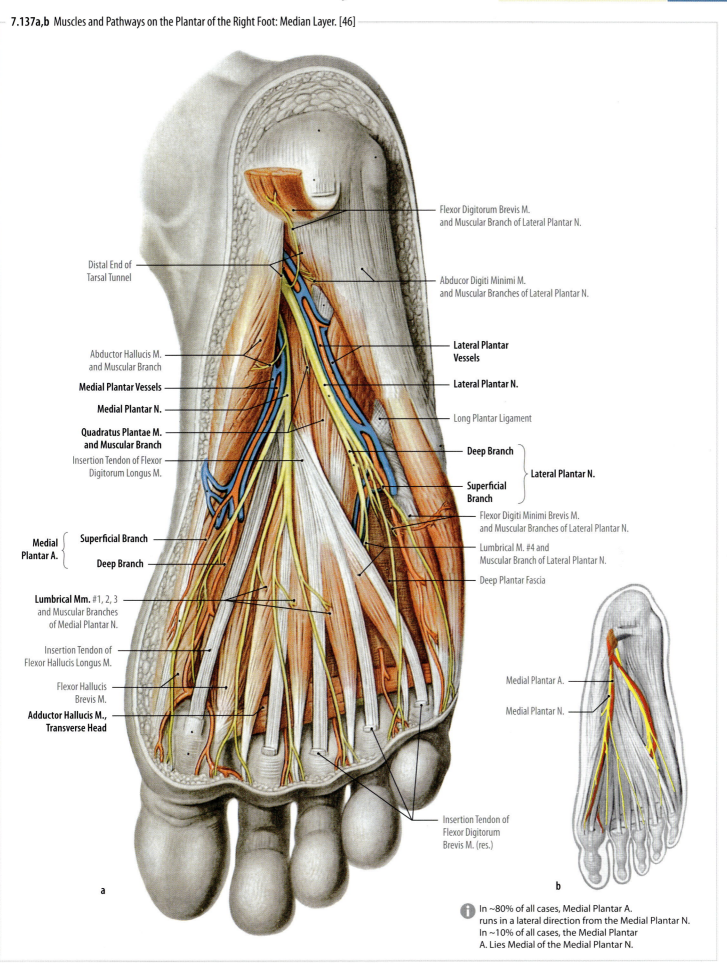

Distal End of Tarsal Tunnel

Abductor Hallucis M. and Muscular Branch

Medial Plantar Vessels

Medial Plantar N.

Quadratus Plantae M. and Muscular Branch

Insertion Tendon of Flexor Digitorum Longus M.

Medial Plantar A. { **Superficial Branch**

Deep Branch

Lumbrical Mm. #1, 2, 3 and Muscular Branches of Medial Plantar N.

Insertion Tendon of Flexor Hallucis Longus M.

Flexor Hallucis Brevis M.

Adductor Hallucis M., Transverse Head

Flexor Digitorum Brevis M. and Muscular Branch of Lateral Plantar N.

Abducor Digiti Minimi M. and Muscular Branches of Lateral Plantar N.

Lateral Plantar Vessels

Lateral Plantar N.

Long Plantar Ligament

Deep Branch

Superficial Branch } **Lateral Plantar N.**

Flexor Digiti Minimi Brevis M. and Muscular Branches of Lateral Plantar N.

Lumbrical M. #4 and Muscular Branch of Lateral Plantar N.

Deep Plantar Fascia

Insertion Tendon of Flexor Digitorum Brevis M. (res.)

a

b

Medial Plantar A.

Medial Plantar N.

In ~80% of all cases, Medial Plantar A. runs in a lateral direction from the Medial Plantar N. In ~10% of all cases, the Medial Plantar A. Lies Medial of the Medial Plantar N.

Pathways and Topography

7.138a–c Muscles and Pathways on the Plantar of the Right Foot: Deep Layer. [46]

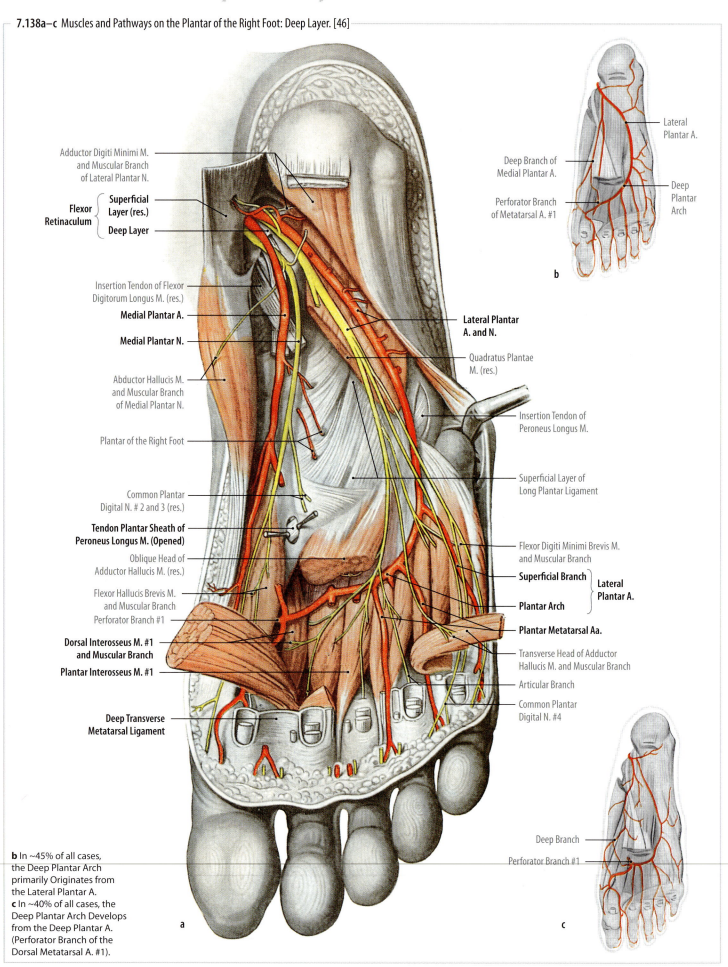

Adductor Digiti Minimi M. and Muscular Branch of Lateral Plantar N.

Flexor Retinaculum { **Superficial Layer (res.)** / **Deep Layer**

Insertion Tendon of Flexor Digitorum Longus M. (res.)

Medial Plantar A.

Medial Plantar N.

Abductor Hallucis M. and Muscular Branch of Medial Plantar N.

Plantar of the Right Foot

Common Plantar Digital N. # 2 and 3 (res.)

Tendon Plantar Sheath of Peroneus Longus M. (Opened)

Oblique Head of Adductor Hallucis M. (res.)

Flexor Hallucis Brevis M. and Muscular Branch

Perforator Branch #1

Dorsal Interosseus M. #1 and Muscular Branch

Plantar Interosseus M. #1

Deep Transverse Metatarsal Ligament

Lateral Plantar A. and N.

Quadratus Plantae M. (res.)

Insertion Tendon of Peroneus Longus M.

Superficial Layer of Long Plantar Ligament

Flexor Digiti Minimi Brevis M. and Muscular Branch

Superficial Branch } Lateral Plantar A.

Plantar Arch

Plantar Metatarsal Aa.

Transverse Head of Adductor Hallucis M. and Muscular Branch

Articular Branch

Common Plantar Digital N. #4

Lateral Plantar A.

Deep Branch of Medial Plantar A.

Perforator Branch of Metatarsal A. #1

Deep Plantar Arch

b

Deep Branch

Perforator Branch #1

a

c

b In ~45% of all cases, the Deep Plantar Arch primarily Originates from the Lateral Plantar A.

c In ~40% of all cases, the Deep Plantar Arch Develops from the Deep Plantar A. (Perforator Branch of the Dorsal Metatarsal A. #1).

554

7.Aa,b Muscles of the Hip Joint: Origins on the Hip Bone.

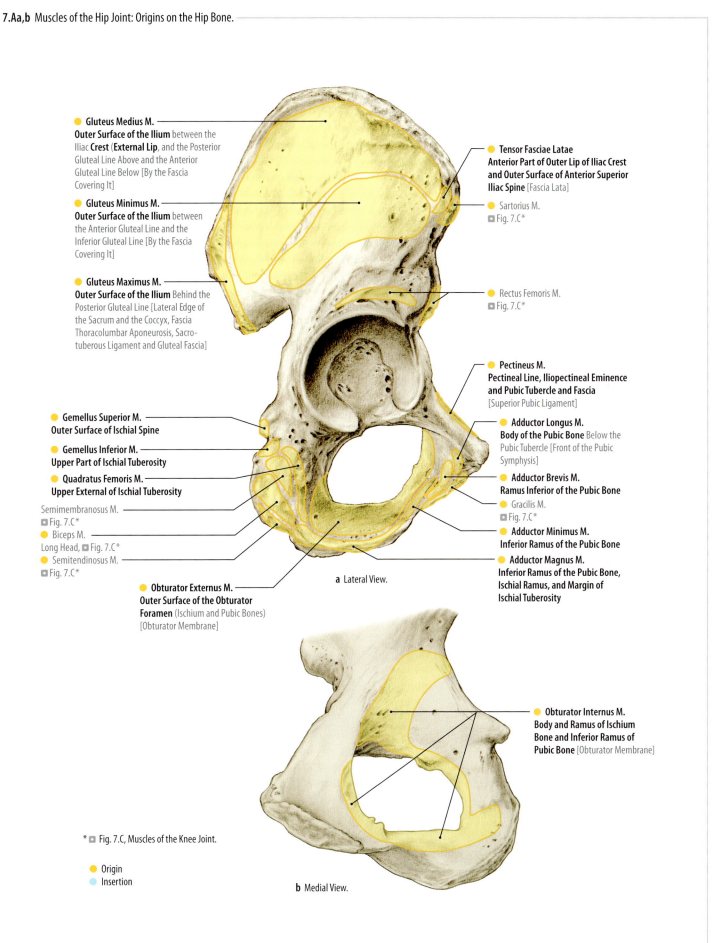

● **Gluteus Medius M.**
Outer Surface of the Ilium between the
Iliac **Crest** (**External Lip**, and the Posterior
Gluteal Line Above and the Anterior
Gluteal Line Below [By the Fascia
Covering It]

● **Gluteus Minimus M.**
Outer Surface of the Ilium between
the Anterior Gluteal Line and the
Inferior Gluteal Line [By the Fascia
Covering It]

● **Gluteus Maximus M.**
Outer Surface of the Ilium Behind the
Posterior Gluteal Line [Lateral Edge of
the Sacrum and the Coccyx, Fascia
Thoracolumbar Aponeurosis, Sacro-
tuberous Ligament and Gluteal Fascia]

● **Gemellus Superior M.**
Outer Surface of Ischial Spine

● **Gemellus Inferior M.**
Upper Part of Ischial Tuberosity

● **Quadratus Femoris M.**
Upper External of Ischial Tuberosity

Semimembranosus M.
▣ Fig. 7.C*
● Biceps M.
Long Head, ▣ Fig. 7.C*
● Semitendinosus M.
▣ Fig. 7.C*

● **Obturator Externus M.**
**Outer Surface of the Obturator
Foramen** (Ischium and Pubic Bones)
[Obturator Membrane]

● **Tensor Fasciae Latae**
**Anterior Part of Outer Lip of Iliac Crest
and Outer Surface of Anterior Superior
Iliac Spine** [Fascia Lata]

● Sartorius M.
▣ Fig. 7.C*

● Rectus Femoris M.
▣ Fig. 7.C*

● **Pectineus M.**
**Pectineal Line, Iliopectineal Eminence
and Pubic Tubercle and Fascia**
[Superior Pubic Ligament]

● **Adductor Longus M.**
Body of the Pubic Bone Below the
Pubic Tubercle [Front of the Pubic
Symphysis]

● **Adductor Brevis M.**
Ramus Inferior of the Pubic Bone

● Gracilis M.
▣ Fig. 7.C*

● **Adductor Minimus M.**
Inferior Ramus of the Pubic Bone

● **Adductor Magnus M.**
**Inferior Ramus of the Pubic Bone,
Ischial Ramus, and Margin of
Ischial Tuberosity**

a Lateral View.

● **Obturator Internus M.**
**Body and Ramus of Ischium
Bone and Inferior Ramus of
Pubic Bone** [Obturator Membrane]

* ▣ Fig. 7.C, Muscles of the Knee Joint.

● Origin
● Insertion

b Medial View.

7.Ac Muscles of the Hip Joint: Origins on the Hip Bone and on the Vertebral Column, Medial View.

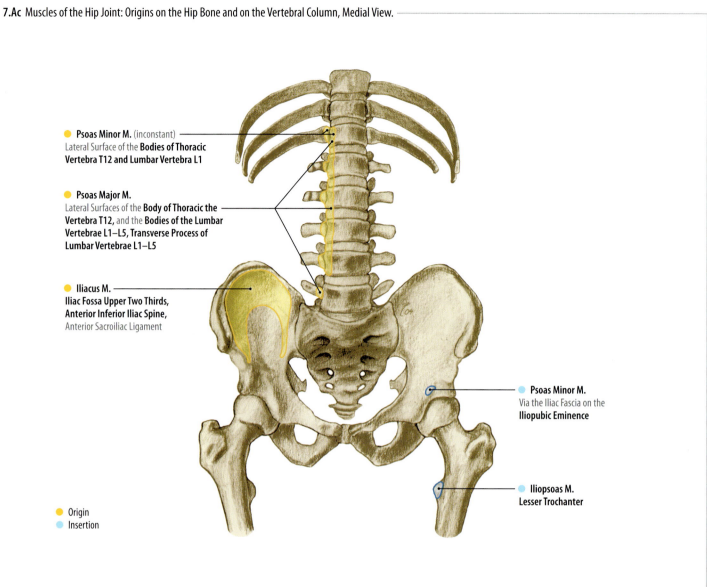

● **Psoas Minor M.** (inconstant)
Lateral Surface of the **Bodies of Thoracic Vertebra T12 and Lumbar Vertebra L1**

● **Psoas Major M.**
Lateral Surfaces of the **Body of Thoracic the Vertebra T12,** and the **Bodies of the Lumbar Vertebrae L1–L5, Transverse Process of Lumbar Vertebrae L1–L5**

● **Iliacus M.**
Iliac Fossa Upper Two Thirds, Anterior Inferior Iliac Spine,
Anterior Sacroiliac Ligament

● **Psoas Minor M.**
Via the Iliac Fascia on the **Iliopubic Eminence**

● **Iliopsoas M.**
Lesser Trochanter

● Origin
● Insertion

7.Ba Muscles of the Hip Joint: Insertions on the Femur, Ventral View.

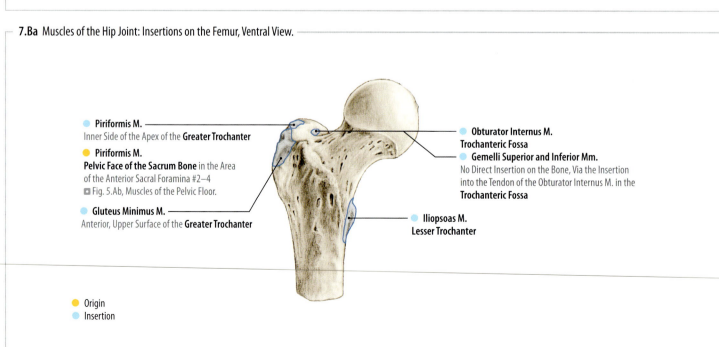

● **Piriformis M.**
Inner Side of the Apex of the **Greater Trochanter**
● **Piriformis M.**
Pelvic Face of the Sacrum Bone in the Area of the **Anterior Sacral Foramina #2–4**
▣ Fig. 5.Ab, Muscles of the Pelvic Floor.
● **Gluteus Minimus M.**
Anterior, Upper Surface of the **Greater Trochanter**

● **Obturator Internus M.**
Trochanteric Fossa
● **Gemelli Superior and Inferior Mm.**
No Direct Insertion on the Bone, Via the Insertion into the Tendon of the Obturator Internus M. in the **Trochanteric Fossa**

● **Iliopsoas M.**
Lesser Trochanter

● Origin
● Insertion

7.Bb Muscles of the Hip Joint: Insertions on the Femur, Dorsal View.

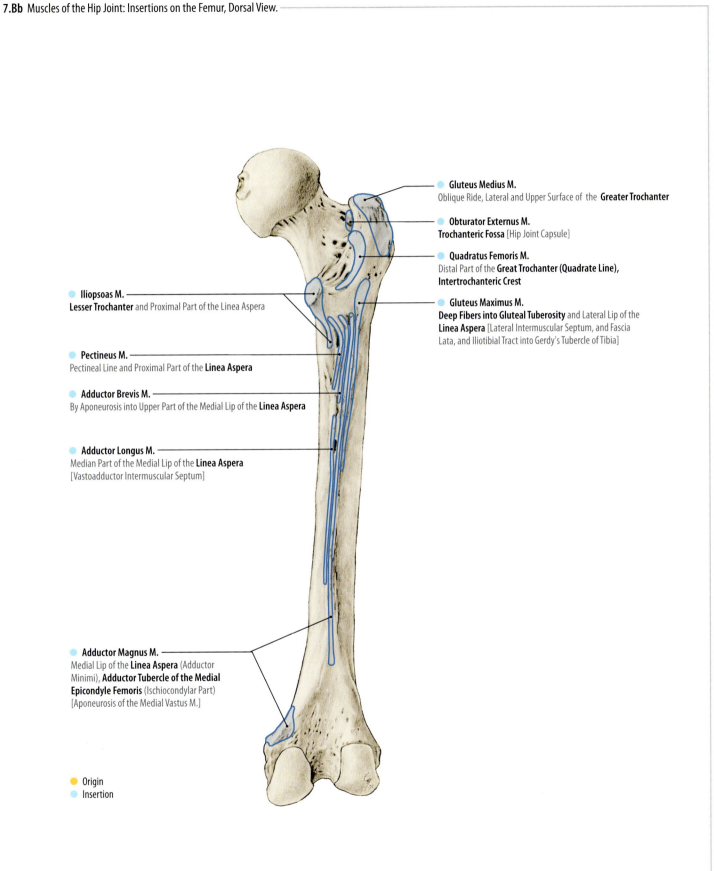

● **Gluteus Medius M.**
Oblique Ride, Lateral and Upper Surface of the **Greater Trochanter**

● **Obturator Externus M.**
Trochanteric Fossa [Hip Joint Capsule]

● **Quadratus Femoris M.**
Distal Part of the **Great Trochanter (Quadrate Line),**
Intertrochanteric Crest

● **Gluteus Maximus M.**
Deep Fibers into Gluteal Tuberosity and Lateral Lip of the
Linea Aspera [Lateral Intermuscular Septum, and Fascia
Lata, and Iliotibial Tract into Gerdy's Tubercle of Tibia]

● **Iliopsoas M.**
Lesser Trochanter and Proximal Part of the Linea Aspera

● **Pectineus M.**
Pectineal Line and Proximal Part of the **Linea Aspera**

● **Adductor Brevis M.**
By Aponeurosis into Upper Part of the Medial Lip of the **Linea Aspera**

● **Adductor Longus M.**
Median Part of the Medial Lip of the **Linea Aspera**
[Vastoadductor Intermuscular Septum]

● **Adductor Magnus M.**
Medial Lip of the **Linea Aspera** (Adductor
Minimi), **Adductor Tubercle of the Medial
Epicondyle Femoris** (Ischiocondylar Part)
[Aponeurosis of the Medial Vastus M.]

● Origin
● Insertion

Muscles of the Lower Limb

7

Function	Innervation	Blood Supply
Dorsal Anterior Group		
Psoas Major M. Flexion in the Hip Joint (outward rotation with a Leg rotated outward) Flexion (sideward inclination) of the Lumbar Spine • *Iliopectineal Bursa*	Anterior Branches of the Lumbar Plexus L 2 –L 3 (4)	Subcostal A. Lumbar Aa. Lumbar Branch of the Iliolumbar A. Lateral Circumflex Femoral A.
Psoas Minor M. (inconstant) (Flexion of the Lumbar Spine)	Anterior Branches of the Lumbar Plexus L1–L2	Lumbar Aa.
Iliacus M. Flexion in the Hip Joint (outward rotation with a Leg rotated outward) • *Iliopectineal Bursa, Iliacus Subtendinous Bursa*	Lumbar Plexus and Femoral N. L3–L4	Iliacus Branch of the Iliolumbar A. Deep Circumflex Iliac A.
Pectineus M. Flexion, adduction, and outward rotation in the Hip Joint	Femoral N. and Anterior Branch of the Obturator N. L2–L3 (L4)	External Pudendal Aa. Superficial Branch of the Medial Circumflex Femoral A. Obturator A.
Dorsal Posterior Group (Gluteal Muscles)		
Gluteus Maximus M. Extension and outward rotation in the Hip Joint (Stabilization of the Pelvis in the sagittal plane) Abduction in the flexed Hip Joint (upper part) Adduction in the Hip Joint, rotate Tibia to lock Knee in extension • *Gluteus Maximus M. Trochanteric Bursa, Subcutaneous Trochanteric Bursa, Ischial Gluteus Maximus M. Bursa, Gluteal Intermuscular Bursae*	Inferior Gluteal N. (L4) L5–S2	Superficial Branch of the Superior Gluteal A. Inferior Gluteal A.
Gluteus Medius M. and Gluteus Minimus M. Abduction in the Hip Joint (stabilization of the Pelvis on the side of the supporting Leg in the frontal plane) Inward rotation and flexion (anterior part) Outward rotation and extension (posterior part) • *Gluteus Medius M. Trochanteric Bursa (Superficial and Deep)* • *Gluteus Minimus M. Trochanteric Bursa*	Superior Gluteal N. L4–S1 (S2)	Superior Gluteal A. Lateral Circumflex Femoral A.
Tensor Fasciae Latae M. Flexion, abduction, and inward rotation in the Hip Joint	Superior Gluteal N. L4–S1	Superior Branch of the Deep Branch of the Superior Gluteal A.
Piriformis M. Outward rotation and abduction in the Hip Joint (extension) • *Piriformis M. Bursa*	Piriformis M. N. of the Sacral Plexus (L5) S1–S2	Superficial Branch of the Superior Gluteal A. Inferior Gluteal A.
Ventral Group		
Obturator Internus M. **Superior and Inferior Gemelli Mm.** Outward rotation, adduction, and extension in the Hip Joint (abduction in the flexed Hip Joint) • *Obturator Internus M. Ischial Bursa*	Obturator Internus M. N. and Muscular Branches of the Sacral Plexus (and Pudendal N.) L5–S2	Inferior Gluteal A. Obturator A. Internal Pudendal A.
Quadratus Femoris M. Outward rotation and adduction in the Hip Joint	Quadratus Formris M. N. of the Sacral Plexus Sciatic N. (tibial portion) (L4) L5–S1 (S2)	Inferior Gluteal A. Medial Circumflex Femoral A. Obturator A.
Obturator Externus M. Adduction and outward rotation in the Hip Joint	Posterior Branch of the Obturator N. L3–L4	Obturator A. Medial Circumflex Femoral A.
Adductor Magnus M. (Adductor Minimus M. Portion) Adduction in the Hip Joint (extension and inward rotation: posterior part)	Posterior Branch of the Obturator N. Sciatic N. (tibial portion) L3–L4 (L5)	Obturator A. Perforator Aa. #2–3 of the Deep Femoral A.
Adductor Brevis M. Adduction and flexion (outward rotation) in the Hip Joint	Anterior Branch of the Obturator N. L2–L4	Obturator A. Perforator A. #1 of the Deep Femoral A.
Adductor Longus M. Adduction and flexion in the Hip Joint	Anterior Branch of the Obturator N. L2–L4	Perforator Aa. #1 and 2 of the Deep Femoral A. External Pudendal Aa. Obturator A.
Gracilis M. Adduction and flexion in the Hip Joint Flexion and inward rotation in the Knee Joint	Anterior Branch of the Obturator N. L2–L4	External Pudendal Aa. Deep Femoral A. Obturator A.

• Bursa = Synovial Bursa assigned to a muscle.

7.C Muscles of the Thigh (Muscles of the Knee Joint): Origins on the Hip Bone, Lateral View.

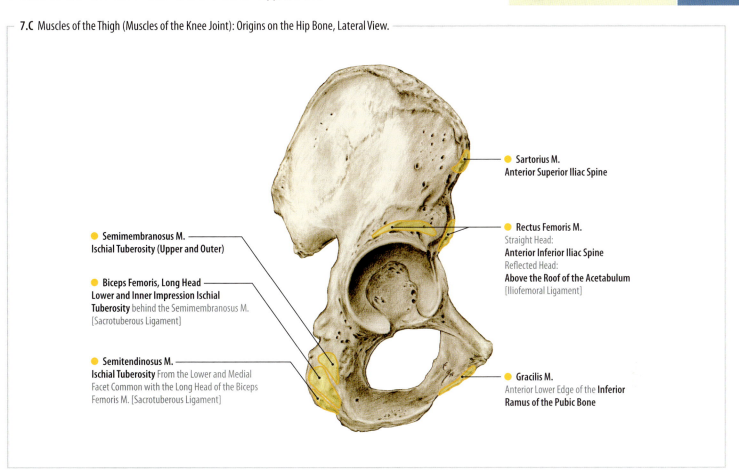

● Sartorius M.
Anterior Superior Iliac Spine

● Rectus Femoris M.
Straight Head:
Anterior Inferior Iliac Spine
Reflected Head:
Above the Roof of the Acetabulum
[Iliofemoral Ligament]

● Semimembranosus M.
Ischial Tuberosity (Upper and Outer)

● Biceps Femoris, Long Head
Lower and Inner Impression Ischial Tuberosity behind the Semimembranosus M.
[Sacrotuberous Ligament]

● Semitendinosus M.
Ischial Tuberosity From the Lower and Medial Facet Common with the Long Head of the Biceps Femoris M. [Sacrotuberous Ligament]

● Gracilis M.
Anterior Lower Edge of the **Inferior Ramus of the Pubic Bone**

7.D Muscles of the Thigh (Muscles of the Knee Joint): Origins on the Femur, Ventral View.

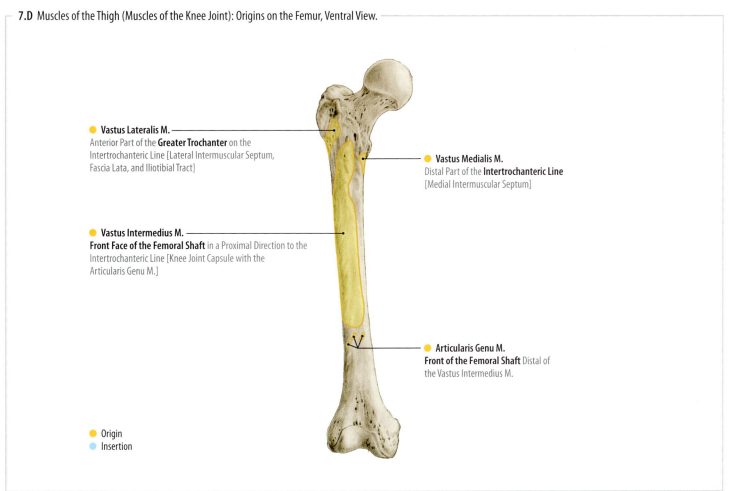

● Vastus Lateralis M.
Anterior Part of the **Greater Trochanter** on the Intertrochanteric Line [Lateral Intermuscular Septum, Fascia Lata, and Iliotibial Tract]

● Vastus Medialis M.
Distal Part of the **Intertrochanteric Line** [Medial Intermuscular Septum]

● Vastus Intermedius M.
Front Face of the Femoral Shaft in a Proximal Direction to the Intertrochanteric Line [Knee Joint Capsule with the Articularis Genu M.]

● Articularis Genu M.
Front of the Femoral Shaft Distal of the Vastus Intermedius M.

● Origin
● Insertion

Muscles of the Lower Limb

7.E Muscles of the Thigh (Muscles of the Knee Joint): Origins on the Femur, Dorsal View.

MA-7:6

7

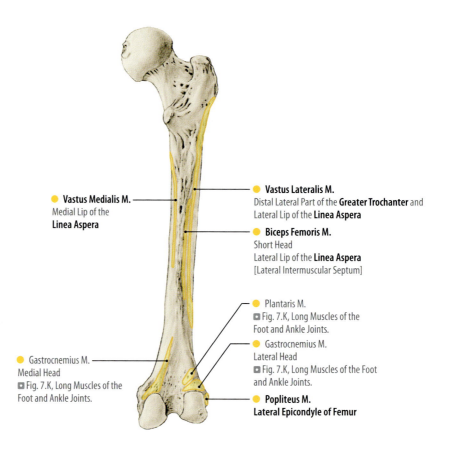

● Vastus Medialis M.
Medial Lip of the
Linea Aspera

● Vastus Lateralis M.
Distal Lateral Part of the **Greater Trochanter** and
Lateral Lip of the **Linea Aspera**

● Biceps Femoris M.
Short Head
Lateral Lip of the **Linea Aspera**
[Lateral Intermuscular Septum]

● Plantaris M.
▣ Fig. 7.K, Long Muscles of the
Foot and Ankle Joints.

● Gastrocnemius M.
Lateral Head
▣ Fig. 7.K, Long Muscles of the Foot
and Ankle Joints.

● Gastrocnemius M.
Medial Head
▣ Fig. 7.K, Long Muscles of the
Foot and Ankle Joints.

● **Popliteus M.**
Lateral Epicondyle of Femur

● Origin
● Insertion

7.F Quadriceps Muscles of the Thigh (the Knee Joint): Insertions on the Patella, Ventral View.

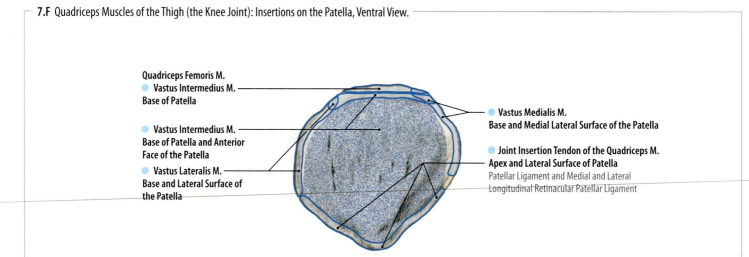

Quadriceps Femoris M.
● Vastus Intermedius M.
Base of Patella

● Vastus Intermedius M.
Base of Patella and Anterior
Face of the Patella

● Vastus Lateralis M.
Base and Lateral Surface of
the Patella

● Vastus Medialis M.
Base and Medial Lateral Surface of the Patella

● **Joint Insertion Tendon of the Quadriceps M.**
Apex and Lateral Surface of Patella
Patellar Ligament and Medial and Lateral
Longitudinal Retinacular Patellar Ligament

7.Ga,b Muscles of the Thigh (the Knee Joint): Insertions on the Tibia and Fibula.

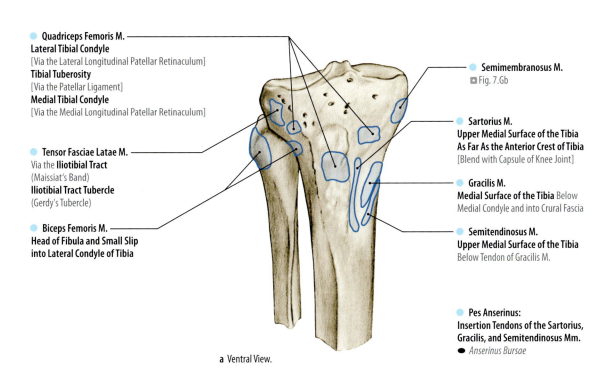

● **Quadriceps Femoris M.**
Lateral Tibial Condyle
[Via the Lateral Longitudinal Patellar Retinaculum]
Tibial Tuberosity
[Via the Patellar Ligament]
Medial Tibial Condyle
[Via the Medial Longitudinal Patellar Retinaculum]

● **Tensor Fasciae Latae M.**
Via the **Iliotibial Tract**
(Maissiat's Band)
Iliotibial Tract Tubercle
(Gerdy's Tubercle)

● **Biceps Femoris M.**
**Head of Fibula and Small Slip
into Lateral Condyle of Tibia**

● **Semimembranosus M.**
▣ Fig. 7.Gb

● **Sartorius M.**
**Upper Medial Surface of the Tibia
As Far As the Anterior Crest of Tibia**
[Blend with Capsule of Knee Joint]

● **Gracilis M.**
Medial Surface of the Tibia Below
Medial Condyle and into Crural Fascia

● **Semitendinosus M.**
Upper Medial Surface of the Tibia
Below Tendon of Gracilis M.

● **Pes Anserinus:**
**Insertion Tendons of the Sartorius,
Gracilis, and Semitendinosus Mm.**
● *Anserinus Bursae*

a Ventral View.

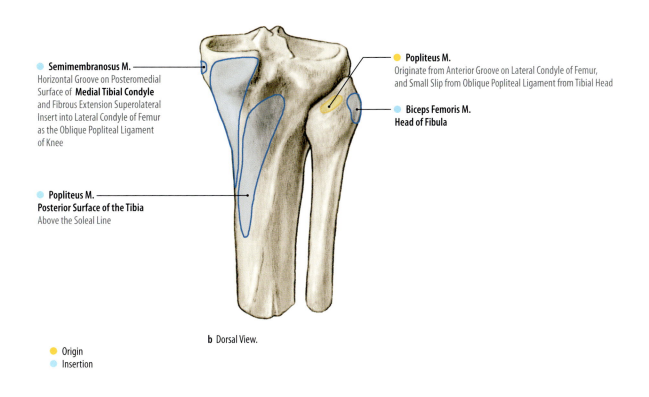

● **Semimembranosus M.**
Horizontal Groove on Posteromedial
Surface of **Medial Tibial Condyle**
and Fibrous Extension Superolateral
Insert into Lateral Condyle of Femur
as the Oblique Popliteal Ligament
of Knee

● **Popliteus M.**
Posterior Surface of the Tibia
Above the Soleal Line

● **Popliteus M.**
Originate from Anterior Groove on Lateral Condyle of Femur,
and Small Slip from Oblique Popliteal Ligament from Tibial Head

● **Biceps Femoris M.**
Head of Fibula

b Dorsal View.

● Origin
● Insertion

Muscles of the Lower Limb

Function	Innervation	Blood Supply
Anterior Muscles		
Quadriceps Femoris M. **Rectus Femoris M.** • *Prepatellar Subtendinous Bursa* **Vastus Lateralis M.** **Vastus Medialis M.** **Vastus Intermedius M.** Extension in the Knee Joint Flexion in the Hip Joint: Rectus Femoris M. • *Deep Infrapatellar Bursa*	Femoral N. L3–L4, parts of the Quadriceps Femoris M.	Lateral Circumflex Femoral A. Perforator Aa. of the Deep Femoral A. Muscular Branches of the Femoral A.
Sartorius M. Flexion and lateral rotation in the Hip Joint Flexion and medial rotation in the Knee Joint • *Subtendinous Sartorial M. Bursa*	Femoral N. (L1)L2–L3	Medial Circumflex Femoral A. Muscular Branches of the Femoral A. Descending Genicular A.
Gracilis M. (▢ p. 65)		
Posterior Muscles		
Biceps Femoris M. **Long Head** • *Superior Bicipital Femoris M. Bursa* **Short Head** Extension in the Hip Joint Flexion and lateral rotation in the Knee Joint • *Inferior Bicipital Femoris M. Bursa*	Sciatic N. –Tibial N. portion L5–S2 –Peroneal N. portion L5–S1	Medial Circumflex Femoral A. Perforator Aa. of the Deep Femoral A. Muscular Branches of the Popliteal A.
Semitendinosus M. Extension in the Hip Joint Flexion and medial rotation in the Knee Joint	Sciatic N. –Tibial N. portion L4–S1	Perforator Aa. of the Deep Femoral A.
Semimembranosus M. Extension in the Hip Joint Flexion and medial rotation in the Knee Joint • *Semimembranosus Bursa M.* (Variant: Gastrocnemiosemimembranosus Bursa	Sciatic N. –Tibial N. portion L4–S1	Medial Circumflex Femoral A. Perforator Aa. of the Deep Femoral A. Muscular Branches of the Popliteal A.
Popliteus M. Medial rotation (with a flexed Knee) and flexion in the Knee Joint • *Subpopliteus Recess*	Tibial N. (L4) L5–S1 (S2)	Muscular Branches of the Popliteal A. Inferior Medial and Lateral Genicular Aa.
Gastrocnemius M. (▢ p. 77)		

• Bursa = Synovial Bursa assigned to a muscle.

◉ Femoral N. L3–L4, parts of the Quadriceps Femoris M.: Segment indicating Quadriceps Femoris M. for Spinal Cord Segment L4, Quadriceps Femoris Reflex [Patellar Tendon Reflex]

7.H Anterior, Lateral Muscles of the Leg to the Toes and Ankle Joints: Origins on the Tibia and Fibula, Ventral View.

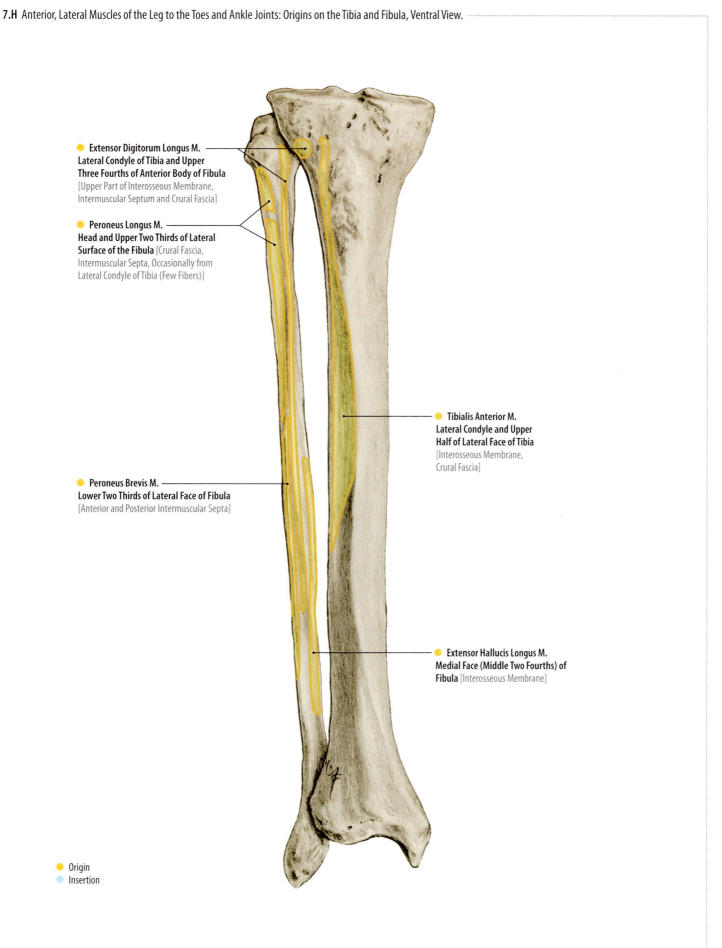

● **Extensor Digitorum Longus M.**
Lateral Condyle of Tibia and Upper
Three Fourths of Anterior Body of Fibula
[Upper Part of Interosseous Membrane,
Intermuscular Septum and Crural Fascia]

● **Peroneus Longus M.**
Head and Upper Two Thirds of Lateral
Surface of the Fibula [Crural Fascia,
Intermuscular Septa, Occasionally from
Lateral Condyle of Tibia (Few Fibers)]

● **Tibialis Anterior M.**
Lateral Condyle and Upper
Half of Lateral Face of Tibia
[Interosseous Membrane,
Crural Fascia]

● **Peroneus Brevis M.**
Lower Two Thirds of Lateral Face of Fibula
[Anterior and Posterior Intermuscular Septa]

● **Extensor Hallucis Longus M.**
Medial Face (Middle Two Fourths) of
Fibula [Interosseous Membrane]

● Origin
● Insertion

Muscles of the Lower Limb

7.la Muscles of the Lower Leg and Long Muscles of the Foot (Anterior, Lateral Muscles of the Toe and Ankle Joints): Insertions on the Skeleton of the Foot, Dorsal View.

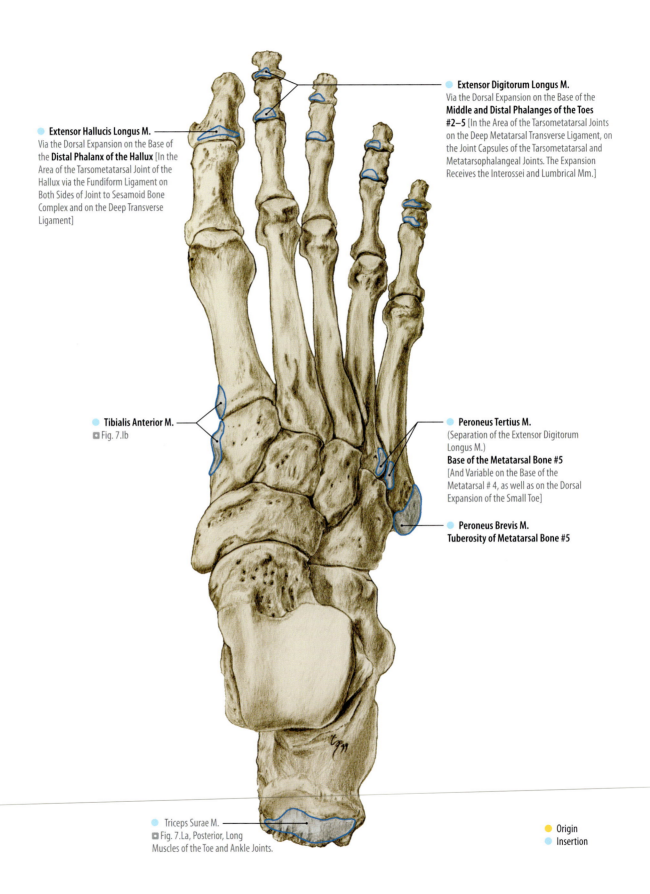

Extensor Digitorum Longus M.
Via the Dorsal Expansion on the Base of the
**Middle and Distal Phalanges of the Toes
#2–5** [In the Area of the Tarsometatarsal Joints
on the Deep Metatarsal Transverse Ligament, on
the Joint Capsules of the Tarsometatarsal and
Metatarsophalangeal Joints. The Expansion
Receives the Interossei and Lumbrical Mm.]

Extensor Hallucis Longus M.
Via the Dorsal Expansion on the Base of
the **Distal Phalanx of the Hallux** [In the
Area of the Tarsometatarsal Joint of the
Hallux via the Fundiform Ligament on
Both Sides of Joint to Sesamoid Bone
Complex and on the Deep Transverse
Ligament]

Tibialis Anterior M.
◪ Fig. 7.lb

Peroneus Tertius M.
(Separation of the Extensor Digitorum
Longus M.)
Base of the Metatarsal Bone #5
[And Variable on the Base of the
Metatarsal # 4, as well as on the Dorsal
Expansion of the Small Toe]

Peroneus Brevis M.
Tuberosity of Metatarsal Bone #5

Triceps Surae M.
◪ Fig. 7.La, Posterior, Long
Muscles of the Toe and Ankle Joints.

● Origin
● Insertion

7

7.Ib Muscles of the Lower Leg and Long Muscles of the Foot (Anterior, Lateral Muscles of the Toe and Ankle Joints): Insertions on the Skeleton of the Foot, Plantar View.

● Flexor Hallucis Longus M.
◻ Fig. 7.Lb

● Flexor Digitorum Longus M.
◻ Fig. 7.Lb

● **Peroneus Longus M.**
Tuberosity Metatarsal #1
(Variable: Bases Metatarsal Bone #2
and Medial Cuneiform Bone)

● **Tibialis Anterior M.**
Lateral and Plantar Surfaces of the
Medial and Planter Cuneiform Bone
and Lateral Surfaces of the **Base of
the Metatarsal Bone #1**
[Tarsometatarsal Capsule #1 Joint]

● Tibialis Posterior M.
◻ Fig. 7.Lb, Posterior Long
Muscles of the Toe and Ankle
Joints.

● Origin
● Insertion

Muscles of the Lower Limb

Function	Innervation	Blood Supply
Anterior Muscles – Extensor Group		
Tibialis Anterior M. Dorsal extension in the upper Ankle Joint Inversion (supination) of the Foot	Deep Peroneal N. L4–L5 🔵 Segment-indicating muscle for Spinal Cord Segment L4	Anterior Tibial A. Anterior Recurrent Tibial A.
Extensor Digitorum Longus M. Dorsal extension in the upper Ankle Joint Extension of the Toes #2–4 (eversion, pronation of the Foot)	Deep Peroneal N. L5–S1	Anterior Tibial A.
[Peroneus Tertius M.] Separation from the Extensor Digitorum Longus M. Dorsal extension in the upper Ankle Joint Eversion (pronation) of the Foot	Deep Peroneal N. L5–S1	Anterior Tibial A.
Extensor Hallucis Longus M. Dorsal extension in the upper Ankle Joint Extension of the Hallux (depending on the original position, eversion (pronation) or inversion (supination) of the Foot) In the stance phase, the Extensors move the lower Leg toward the dorsum of the Foot	Deep Peroneal N. L5–S1	Anterior Tibial A.
Lateral Muscles – Peroneal Group		
Peroneus Longus M.* Plantar flexion in the upper Ankle Joint Eversion (pronation) of the Foot Tension of the Plantar Arch of the Foot	Superficial Peroneal N. L5–S1	Peroneal A. Anterior Tibial A. Inferior Lateralis Genicular A.
Peroneus Brevis M.* Plantar flexion in the upper Ankle Joint Eversion (pronation) of the Foot	Superficial Peroneal N. L5–S2	Peroneal A. Anterior Tibial A.

*The Peronei Mm. effect abduction in the eversion action.

🔵 Deep Peroneal N. L4–L5: Segment indicating Tibialis Anterior M. for Spinal Cord Segment L4.
Deep Peroneal N. L5–S1: Segment indicating Extensor Hallucis Longus M. for Spinal Cord Segment L5.

7

7.J Muscles of the Leg (Posterior Long Muscles of the Toe and Ankle Joints): Origins on the Tibia and Fibula, Dorsal View.

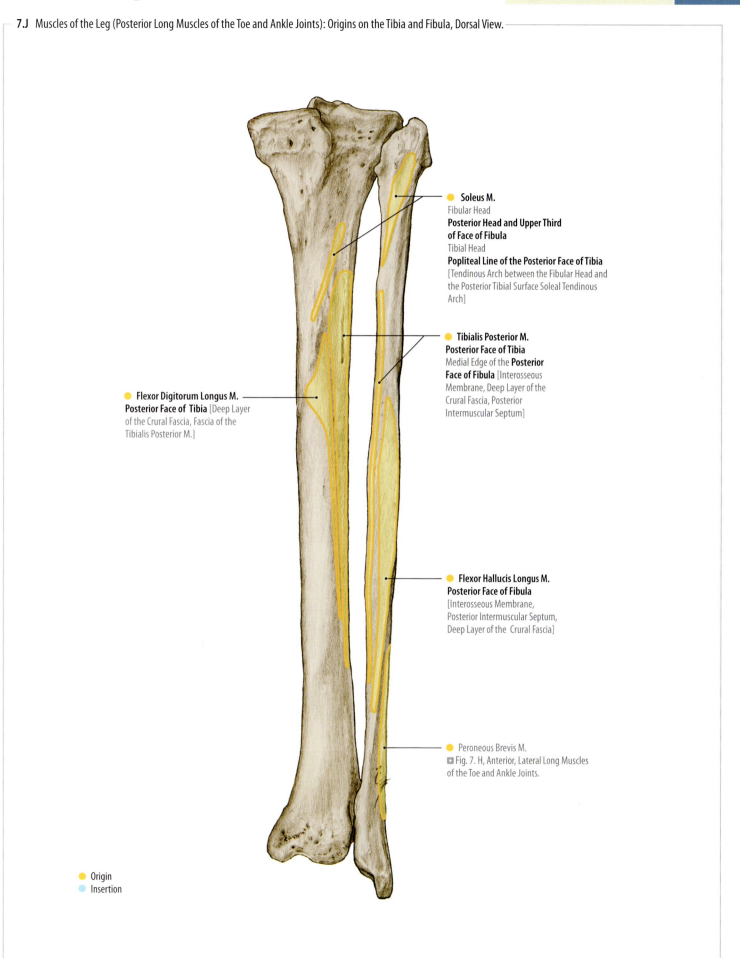

● **Soleus M.**
Fibular Head
**Posterior Head and Upper Third
of Face of Fibula**
Tibial Head
Popliteal Line of the Posterior Face of Tibia
[Tendinous Arch between the Fibular Head and
the Posterior Tibial Surface Soleal Tendinous
Arch]

● **Tibialis Posterior M.**
Posterior Face of Tibia
Medial Edge of the **Posterior
Face of Fibula** [Interosseous
Membrane, Deep Layer of the
Crural Fascia, Posterior
Intermuscular Septum]

● **Flexor Digitorum Longus M.**
Posterior Face of Tibia [Deep Layer
of the Crural Fascia, Fascia of the
Tibialis Posterior M.]

● **Flexor Hallucis Longus M.**
Posterior Face of Fibula
[Interosseous Membrane,
Posterior Intermuscular Septum,
Deep Layer of the Crural Fascia]

● Peroneous Brevis M.
▣ Fig. 7. H, Anterior, Lateral Long Muscles
of the Toe and Ankle Joints.

● Origin
● Insertion

Muscles of the Lower Limb

7.K Posterior Long Muscles of the Toe and Ankle Joints: Origins on the Femur, Dorsal View.

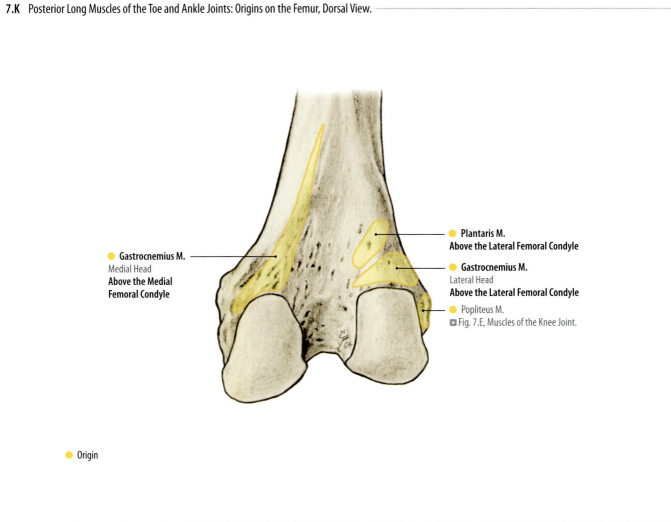

● **Gastrocnemius M.**
Medial Head
**Above the Medial
Femoral Condyle**

● **Plantaris M.
Above the Lateral Femoral Condyle**

● **Gastrocnemius M.**
Lateral Head
Above the Lateral Femoral Condyle

● Popliteus M.
◻ Fig. 7.E, Muscles of the Knee Joint.

● Origin

7.La Muscles of the Leg and Long Muscles of the Foot (Posterior Long Muscles of the Toe and Ankle Joints): Insertions on the Skeleton of the Foot, Dorsal View.

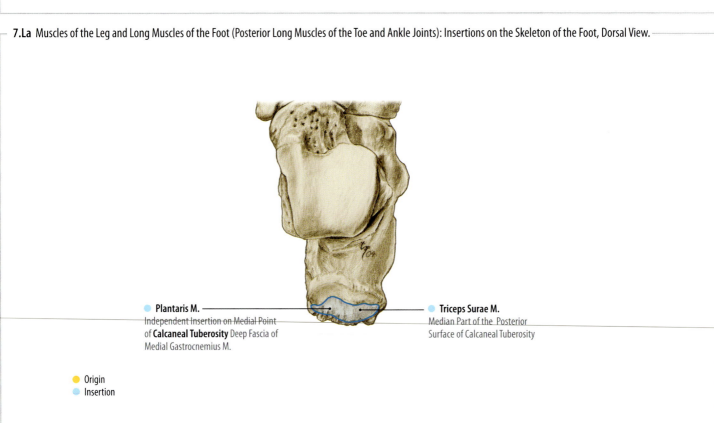

● **Plantaris M.**
Independent Insertion on Medial Point
of **Calcaneal Tuberosity** Deep Fascia of
Medial Gastrocnemius M.

● **Triceps Surae M.**
Median Part of the Posterior
Surface of Calcaneal Tuberosity

● Origin
● Insertion

7.Lb Muscles of the Leg and Long Muscles of the Foot (Muscles of the Toe and Ankle Joints): Insertions on the Skeleton of the Foot, Plantar View.

● **Flexor Hallucis Longus M.**
Base of the **Distal Phalanx of the Hallux**

● **Flexor Digitorum Longus M.**
Distal Phalanx of the Toes #2–4

● Peroneus Longus M.
▣ Fig. 7.Ia, Anterior Muscles of the Foot and
Toe Joints.

● Tibialis Anterior M.
▣ Fig. 7.Ia, Anterior Muscles of the Foot and
Toe Joints

● **Tibialis Posterior M.**
Tuberosity of Navicular Bone,
Medial Cuneiform Bone,
Intermediate and Lateral **Cuboid Bone**,
Base of the **Metatarsal Bones #2, 3, 4**

● Origin
● Insertion

Muscles of the Lower Limb

Function	Innervation	Blood Supply
Posterior Muscles – Superficial Flexor Group (Calf Muscles)		
Triceps Surae M. **Soleus M.** Plantar flexion in the upper Ankle Joint Inversion (supination) of the Foot	Tibial N. (L5) S1–S2	Posterior Tibial A. Peroneal A.

Gastrocnemius M.
Medial Head
Lateral Head
Flexion in the Knee Joint
Plantar flexion in the upper Ankle Joint
Inversion (supination) of the Foot
• *Subtendinous Bursa (Subtendinous Recess)*
  Medial and Lateral Gastrocnemii M.
  Fabella
• *Calcaneal Tendon Bursa*
• *Subcutaneous Calcaneal Bursa*
The Triceps Surae M. lifts the back of the Foot from the ground while walking and affects the Toe stance
	Tibial N. (L5) S1–S2
	🔁 Triceps-Surae-Reflex
	(Achilles Tendon Reflex)
	Segment-indicating muscles
	for the Spinal Cord Segment S1
		Sural Aa. One to Four Branches of the Popliteal A.

Plantaris M. (Flexion in the Knee Joint)	Tibial N. (L5) S1–S2	Sural A. of the Popliteal A.
Posterior Muscles – Deep Flexor Group		
Tibialis Posterior M. Plantar flexion in the upper Ankle Joint Inversion (supination) of the Foot Tension of the longitudinal and transverse arches of the Foot • *Tibialis Posterior M. Subtendinous Bursa*	Tibial N. L4–S1	Posterior Tibial A. Peroneal A.
Flexor Hallucis Longus M. Plantar flexion in the upper Ankle Joint Inversion (supination) of the Foot Plantar flexion of the Hallux (rolling off and pushing off the front of the foot while walking) Tension of the longitudinal arch of the Foot	Tibial N. (L5) S1–S2	Peroneal A.
Flexor Digitorum Longus M. Plantar flexion in the upper Ankle Joint Inversion (supination) of the Foot Plantar flexion of the Toes #2–5 (rolling off and pushing off the front of the foot while walking) Tension of the longitudinal and transverse arches of the Foot	Tibial N. (L5) S1–S2	Posterior Tibial A.

• Bursa = Synovial Bursa assigned to a muscle.
🔁 Tibial N. (L5) S1–S2 : Segment indicating Gastrocnemius M. for the Spinal Cord Segment S1, Triceps Surae Reflex (Achilles Tendon Reflex).

7.Ma Short Muscles of the Foot (Muscles of the Toe Joints): Origins on the Skeleton of the Foot, Dorsal View.

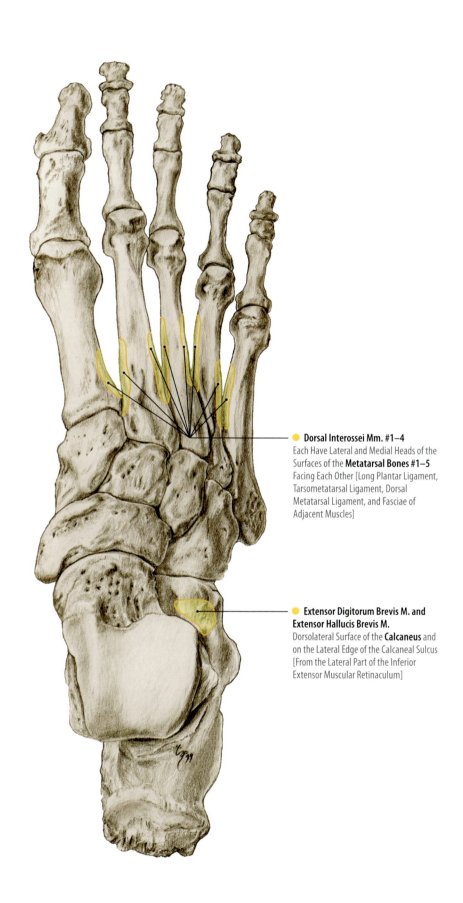

● **Dorsal Interossei Mm. #1–4**
Each Have Lateral and Medial Heads of the
Surfaces of the **Metatarsal Bones #1–5**
Facing Each Other [Long Plantar Ligament,
Tarsometatarsal Ligament, Dorsal
Metatarsal Ligament, and Fasciae of
Adjacent Muscles]

● **Extensor Digitorum Brevis M. and
Extensor Hallucis Brevis M.**
Dorsolateral Surface of the **Calcaneus** and
on the Lateral Edge of the Calcaneal Sulcus
[From the Lateral Part of the Inferior
Extensor Muscular Retinaculum]

● Origin
● Insertion

Muscles of the Lower Limb

7.Mb Short Muscles of the Foot (Muscles of the Toe Joints): Origins on the Skeleton of the Foot, Dorsal View.

7

● **Extensor Digitorum Brevis M.**
Via the Dorsal Expansion in the Lateral Area of
the Base of the **Middle and Distal Phalanges of
the Toes #2–5** [In the Area of the
Tarsometatarsal Joints on the Deep Transverse
Metatarsal Ligament, Joint Capsules of the
Tarsometatarsal and Metatarsophalangeal
Joints]

● **Extensor Hallucis Brevis M.**
Via the Dorsal Expansion on the Base of the
Basal (Proximal) Phalanx of the Hallux
[Joint Capsule]

● **Abductor Hallucis M.**
◨ Fig. 7.Nb

Dorsal Interossei Mm.
● Dorsal Interosseus M. #1
Medial Side of the **Base of the Proximal
Phalanx of the Toe #2**
● Dorsal Interossei Mm. #2–4
Lateral Side of the **Base of the Proximal
Phalanx of the Toes #2–4** [Plantar
Ligament, Joint Capsules of the
Tarsometatarsal Joints of the Toe, Dorsal
Expansion]

● **Abductor Digiti Minimi M.**
**Lateral Surface of the Proximal
Phalanx of the Small Toe**
◨ Fig. 7.Nb

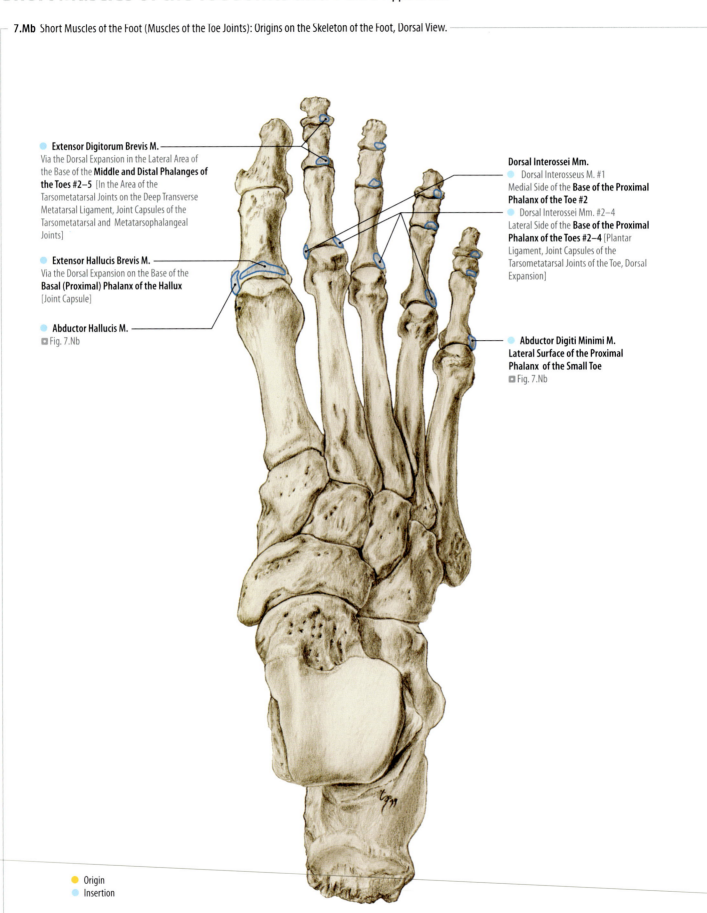

● Origin
● Insertion

7.Na Short Muscles of the Foot (Muscles of the Toe Joints): Origins on the Skeleton of the Foot, Plantar View.

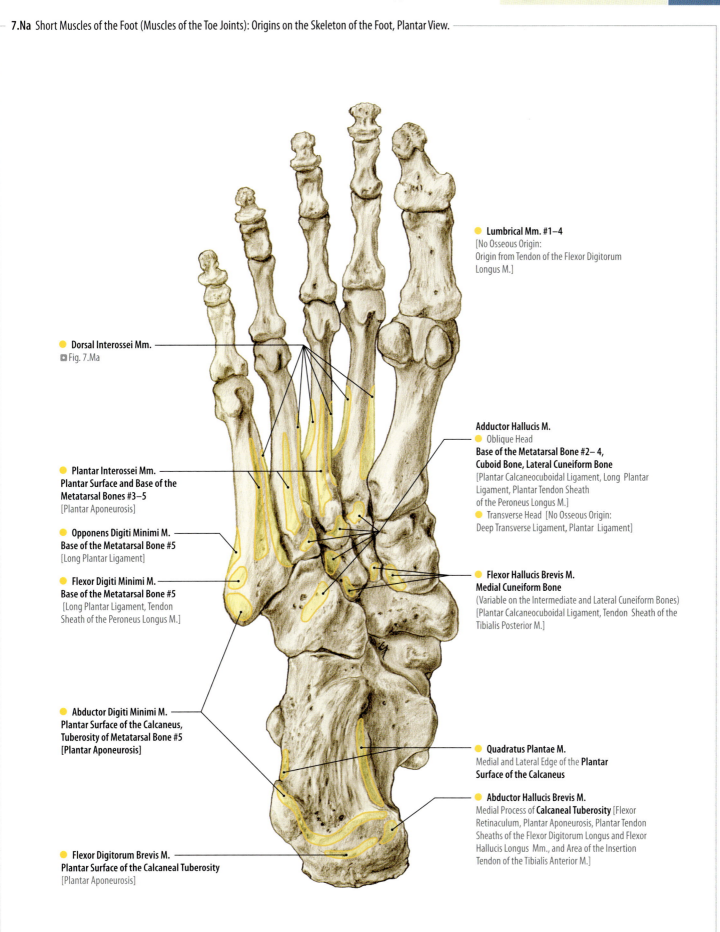

● **Lumbrical Mm. #1–4**
[No Osseous Origin:
Origin from Tendon of the Flexor Digitorum
Longus M.]

● **Dorsal Interossei Mm.**
► Fig. 7.Ma

● **Plantar Interossei Mm.**
**Plantar Surface and Base of the
Metatarsal Bones #3–5**
[Plantar Aponeurosis]

● **Opponens Digiti Minimi M.**
Base of the Metatarsal Bone #5
[Long Plantar Ligament]

● **Flexor Digiti Minimi M.**
Base of the Metatarsal Bone #5
[Long Plantar Ligament, Tendon
Sheath of the Peroneus Longus M.]

● **Abductor Digiti Minimi M.**
**Plantar Surface of the Calcaneus,
Tuberosity of Metatarsal Bone #5**
[Plantar Aponeurosis]

● **Flexor Digitorum Brevis M.**
Plantar Surface of the Calcaneal Tuberosity
[Plantar Aponeurosis]

Adductor Hallucis M.
● Oblique Head
**Base of the Metatarsal Bone #2– 4,
Cuboid Bone, Lateral Cuneiform Bone**
[Plantar Calcaneocuboidal Ligament, Long Plantar
Ligament, Plantar Tendon Sheath
of the Peroneus Longus M.]
● Transverse Head [No Osseous Origin:
Deep Transverse Ligament, Plantar Ligament]

● **Flexor Hallucis Brevis M.**
Medial Cuneiform Bone
(Variable on the Intermediate and Lateral Cuneiform Bones)
[Plantar Calcaneocuboidal Ligament, Tendon Sheath of the
Tibialis Posterior M.]

● **Quadratus Plantae M.**
**Medial and Lateral Edge of the Plantar
Surface of the Calcaneus**

● **Abductor Hallucis Brevis M.**
Medial Process of **Calcaneal Tuberosity** [Flexor
Retinaculum, Plantar Aponeurosis, Plantar Tendon
Sheaths of the Flexor Digitorum Longus and Flexor
Hallucis Longus Mm., and Area of the Insertion
Tendon of the Tibialis Anterior M.]

Muscles of the Lower Limb

7.Nb Short Muscles of the Foot (Muscles of the Toe Joints): Insertions on the Skeleton of the Foot, Plantar View.

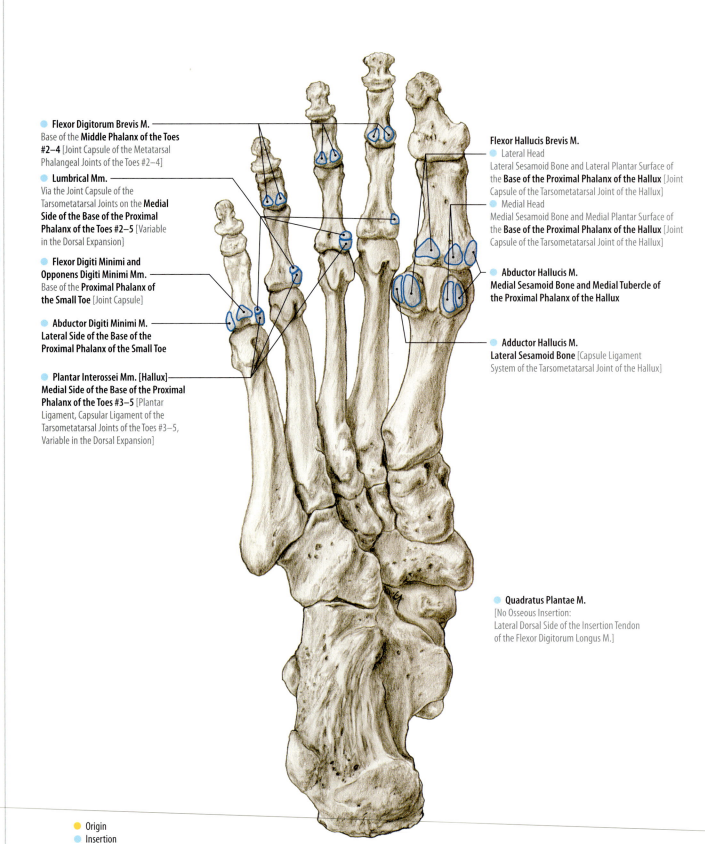

● **Flexor Digitorum Brevis M.**
Base of the **Middle Phalanx of the Toes #2–4** [Joint Capsule of the Metatarsal Phalangeal Joints of the Toes #2–4]

● **Lumbrical Mm.**
Via the Joint Capsule of the Tarsometatarsal Joints on the **Medial Side of the Base of the Proximal Phalanx of the Toes #2–5** [Variable in the Dorsal Expansion]

● **Flexor Digiti Minimi and Opponens Digiti Minimi Mm.**
Base of the **Proximal Phalanx of the Small Toe** [Joint Capsule]

● **Abductor Digiti Minimi M.**
Lateral Side of the Base of the Proximal Phalanx of the Small Toe

● **Plantar Interossei Mm. [Hallux]**
Medial Side of the Base of the Proximal Phalanx of the Toes #3–5 [Plantar Ligament, Capsular Ligament of the Tarsometatarsal Joints of the Toes #3–5, Variable in the Dorsal Expansion]

Flexor Hallucis Brevis M.
● Lateral Head
Lateral Sesamoid Bone and Lateral Plantar Surface of the **Base of the Proximal Phalanx of the Hallux** [Joint Capsule of the Tarsometatarsal Joint of the Hallux]
● Medial Head
Medial Sesamoid Bone and Medial Plantar Surface of the **Base of the Proximal Phalanx of the Hallux** [Joint Capsule of the Tarsometatarsal Joint of the Hallux]

● **Abductor Hallucis M.**
Medial Sesamoid Bone and Medial Tubercle of the Proximal Phalanx of the Hallux

● **Adductor Hallucis M.**
Lateral Sesamoid Bone [Capsule Ligament System of the Tarsometatarsal Joint of the Hallux]

● **Quadratus Plantae M.**
[No Osseous Insertion:
Lateral Dorsal Side of the Insertion Tendon of the Flexor Digitorum Longus M.]

● Origin
● Insertion

Function	Innervation	Blood Supply
Muscles of the Hallux Compartment		
Abductor Hallucis M. Abduction and flexion of the Hallux in the Metatarsophalangeal Joint Tension of the longitudinal arch of the Foot • *Metatarsal Head #1 Subcutaneous Bursa*	Medial Plantar N. of the Tibial N. S1–S2	Medial Plantar A.

Flexor Hallucis Brevis M.
   Medial Head
   Lateral Head
      Flexion of the Hallux in the Metatarsophalangeal Joint
      Tension of the longitudinal arch of the Foot
	Medial Plantar N. (Medial Head) and Lateral Plantar N. (Lateral Head) of the Tibial N. S1–S2 (S3)	Medial Plantar A.

Adductor Hallucis M.
   Oblique Head
   Transverse Head (topographically lies in the median Foot compartment)
      Adduction of the Hallux and flexion (Oblique Head)
      in the Metatarsophalangeal Joint
      Tension of the longitudinal arch (Oblique Head)
      Tension of the transverse arch (Transverse Head)
	Deep Branch of Lateral Plantar N. of the Tibial N. S1–S2 (S3)	Branches from the Deep Plantar Arch Plantar and Dorsal Metatarsal Aa.

Muscles of the Median Compartment		
Flexor Digitorum Brevis M. Flexion of the Metatarsophalangeal and Proximal Interphalangeal Joints of the Toes #2–5 Tension of the longitudinal arch of the Foot	Medial Plantar N. of the Tibial N. S1–S2 (S3) (Lateral Plantar N. for the muscle belly leading to the Small Toe)	Lateral and Medial Plantar Aa.
Quadratus Plantae M. Supports the Flexor Digitorum Longus M. in the flexion of the Toes	Lateral Plantar N. of the Tibial N. S1–S2	Lateral and Medial Plantar Aa.
Lumbrical Mm. Flexion in the Metatarsophalangeal Joints of the Toes #2–5	Medial Plantar N. of the Tibial N. for the Lumbrical Mm. #1 (and 2) Lateral Plantar N. for the Lumbrical Mm. (#2) #3 and #4 S1–S2 (S3)	Medial and Lateral Plantar Aa.
Muscles of the Deep Foot Compartment		
Dorsal Interossei Mm. (#1–4) Flexion of the Metatarsophalangeal Joints of the Toes #3–5 Abduction of the Toes #3–5 (spreading)	Lateral Plantar N. of the Tibial N. S1–S2 (S3)	Dorsal Metatarsal Aa. Plantar Metatarsal Aa.
Plantar Interossei Mm. (#1–3) Flexion of the Metatarsophalangeal Joints of the Toes #3–5 Adduction of the Toes #3–5 to the second Toe The Interossei Mm. fixate the Fibrous Cartilage Plate (Plantar Ligament) during the rolling off of the front of the foot. This allows for the transfer of pressure to the plantar surfaces of the Metatarsal Heads 2–5.	Lateral Plantar N. of the Tibialis N. S1–S2 (S3)	Dorsal Metatarsal Aa. Plantar Metatarsal Aa. ▶

• Bursa = Synovial Bursa assigned to a muscle.

Muscles of the Lower Limb

Function	Innervation	Blood Supply
Muscles of the Small Toe Compartment		
Abductor Digiti Minimi M. Abduction and flexion of the Small Toe in the Metatarsophalangeal Joint Tension of the longitudinal arch of the Foot	Lateral Plantar N. of the Tibial N. S1–S2	Lateral Plantar A.
Flexor Digiti Minimi M. Flexion of the Small Toe in the Metatarsophalangeal Joint Tension of the longitudinal arch of the Foot	Lateral Plantar N. of the Tibial N. S1–S2	Lateral Plantar A.
Opponens Digiti Minimi M. Leading the Metatarsal Bone #5 (in the Tarsometatarsal Joint) in a plantar medial direction Tension of the longitudinal and transverse arches of the Foot	Lateral Plantar N. of the Tibial N. S1–S2	Lateral Plantar A.
Muscles of the Dorsum of the Foot		
Extensor Digitorum Brevis M. Extension of the Metatarsophalangeal, Proximal Interphalangeal and Distal Interphalangeal Joints of the Toes #2–5	Deep Peroneal N. (L4) L5–S1	Lateral Tarsal A. Perforator Branch of the Peroneal A.
Extensor Hallucis Brevis M. Extension of the Hallux in the Metacarpophalangeal Joint	Deep Peroneal N. (L4) L5–S1	Lateral Tarsal A. Perforator Branch of the Peroneal A.

7

Appendix

Glossary

A

abdomen, -inis
between the chest and the pelvis

abducent
efferent, motor nerve

abductor
muscle that pulls a body part away from the midline of the body

accessory
auxiliary or duplicated

acetabulum
cup-shaped depression on hip bone

acromi(o)
indicating combination with the acromion

acoustic
acoustic meatus; nerve

adamantine
very hard; refers to enamel

adductor
muscle that pulls a body part toward the midline of the body

adhesion
adhering due to inflammation

adipose
fat; fatty pad

aditus
inlet to the mastoid air cells

adventitia
outside connective tissue of blood vessels; *tunica adventitia*

equator
orientation line on center of the eyeball and lens

ala
wing, sacrum

albicans
white, corpus albicans

albuginea
white covering, testis

albus
white

alveolus, -i
small cavity, depression; alveolus of lung

ambiguous
bending toward two sides

ampulla
flask-shaped vessel, bottle-shaped dilatation; ampule

amygdala
almond-shaped structure

anastomosis
connection between two vessels; formation of an orifice

anatomic (anatomical)
structure, structural

anconeal (anconal)
cubital

ansa
loop; ansa cervicalis nerve

anserine
goose foot-like, insertion of tendons

antebrachium, -ial
forearm, forearm cutaneous nerves

anteflexion
forward flexion

anterior
lying toward the front

antihelix
rounded edge of (auricle)

antrum
closed cavity

anulus, -ar
small ring, annulus, annular

anus
ring, part of alimentary canal

aorta
main artery of the body

aperture
orifice

apex
tip

aponeurosis
flattened tendon into sheath

apophysis
outgrowth (on bones); independent ossification center

apparatus
mechanism; group or system

appendix
supplementary, accessory, or dependent part attached to a main structure; also called appendage; vermiform appendix of the colon

aqueduct (aquaeduct)
junctional canal between cavities filled with liquid

arachnoid
cobweb-like membrane (one of covering of brain and spinal cord)

arbor
tree-like structure with branching

artery,- ies
blood vessel that carries blood away from the heart

articular
related to joint(s)

articulation
joint

arytenoid
pair of cartilages in the larynx

ascending
rising in its path

aspera
rough, uneven edges on posterior of femur

atrium
vestibule, passageway

auditus
hearing, canal

auricle
auricle; pinna; atrial auricle (blind area of the atrium)

autonomic
autonomous; independent, visceral motor system

avis
bird-like

axilla
pyramidal space between arm and chest (arm pit)

axis
a line around which specified parts of the body are arranged or revolve around; second cervical vertebra

B

basal
toward the body

biceps
two-headed; two bellies

bicuspid
two cusps in heart valve

bifurcation
splitting

bifurcating
two-pronged, dual trace, ligament

biliary
carrying bile

brachium
arm; upper arm

bregma
forehead; point of contact of the coronary and sagittal sutures

brevis
short

bronchus
main branches of the trachea

buccal
cheek

buccinator
deep muscle of the cheek

bulbous
bulb-like

bulla
blister; ethmoid air cells

bursa
sac; synovial sac around tendon to prevent friction

C

cecum (caecum)
blind-ending structure; cecum of ascending colon

calcaneus
heel bone

calcaneus,-al
referring to the heel bone

calcar
spur, spine

calix, -ices
calyx; receptacle of urine in kidney

callosus
callous, thickened places

calvaria
skullcap

calyx (calix)
cup-shaped organ or cavity

canaliculus
canals of small diameter for drainage

canal
main drainage, duct

caninus
canine, tooth

capillary
terminal blood vessel in tissue

capitate
having a head; middle bone in wrist joint

capitulum
knob-like bony prominence in joint; lower end of humerus

capsule
sheath covering structure or joint

caput
head

cardia
orifice of stomach; esophageal opening into stomach

cardiac
referring to the orifice of the stomach; cardiac veins of the heart

carotid
carotid artery to the head area

carpal
related to the wrist

cartilaginous
made of cartilage

caruncle
an outgrowth of tissue

cauda, -al
tail, inferior end of body, located at tail end

caudate
having a tail-like structure

cavity
hollow space

cavum
cavity, cave-like

cella
cavity, chamber, roof part of curve structure

cellular
like a cell; consist of cells

cementum
cement (of the tooth)

centrum
center

cephalic
referring to the head

cerebellum
hind brain

cerebrum
brain, encephalon, forebrain

cervix, -cal
neck, related to the neck

chiasma
crossing; related to optic nerve

choana
funnel; posterior nasal orifice

chorda
string, strand-like

choroid
median vascular layer of the eye

choroidal
referring to the choroid; chorion-like, exterior cover of the germ bud

cingulum
girdle, encircle; refers to intercerebral fibers

circumferential
relating to the circumference

circumflex
bent, going around, as in blood vessels in the arm or thigh

cistern
hollow space containing liquid, especially chyle, lymph, or cerebrospinal fluid

claustrum
barrier, layer of gray matter in putamen

clavicle
collarbone

clinoid
bed-shaped post, related to sphenoid bone

clitoris
female erectile organ

clivus
downward sloped surface in posterior cranial fossa

cluneal
buttocks area, nerves around the buttock area

cochlea
snail-shaped bony structure of the internal ear

colliculus
small hill, mound on the posterior surface of midbrain

collar
neck; neck-shaped part of an organ

column
form a pillar-like or vertical object

comitant
concomitant

commissure
cross-connection

communicans
communicating, connective, linking

common
joint, formed by joining

compact
dense

concha
anatomic structure like shell in shape, as in auricle

condylar
referring to the condyle

condyle
rounded process at end of bone

conical
cone-shaped

conjugate
distance of two points of the ossified pelvis, sagittal diameter of the pelvis

conjunctiva
epithelial membrane covering the eyeball and eyelids

conoid
cone-shaped process

constrictor
an instrument or muscle that constricts a part or a vessel

conus
cone-shaped structure; part of the development of heart or aorta

convergens
convergent, coming together

coracoid
beak-shaped, crooked projection, part of scapula

cornea
transparent tissue on outer surface of the front of the eye

corniculate
having a small horn-like shape

cornu
horn, projection

corona
crown

coronal
referring to the crown; face slices

coronary
corona-like

coronoid
beak-shaped, crooked, hook-like

corpus
body

corpuscle
body

corrugator
muscle that draws skin together causing wrinkling; forehead corrugator

cortex
part of brain; outer portion of an organ

cortical
relating to a cortex

costal
related to rib

coxa
hip

cranial
related to the cranium

cranium
skull

cremaster
the name of a muscle lifting the testicle

crena
cleft, v-shaped cuts, like notches

cribriform
sieve-like; part of ethmoid bone

cricoid
circular, ring-shaped, related to laryngeal cartilage

crista
groin; crest; pia matter at end of spinal cord

cruciate
crossed; cruciform bands

crus
anatomical structure like a leg; a pair of diverging bands

crux
junction or crossing

cubitus
elbow

cuboid
resembling a cube

culmen
portion of the vermis of cerebellum

cumulate
heap, pile, a mass

cuneus
region of the medial surface of occipital lobe of cerebral hemisphere

cupola
dome; apex of the pleura

curvature
a bending, flexure, angulation

cusp
conical elevation of tooth, sail or leaflet of heart valve

cutis
skin

cyst
an abnormal closed cavity

D

declive
posterior sloping portion of the vermis of cerebellum

decussation
crossing over or intersection of parts or fibers.

deferens
to carry away, as in vas deferens

deltoid
a delta form, triangular; name of muscle

dens
tooth-like process protruding upward

dentin
ivory mass of tooth

dentition
teething, teeth eruption

depressor
muscle that lowers or flattens a body part

dermis
thin layer of connective tissue interdigitate with epidermis

descending
running down to periphery

diaphysis
elongated structure, shaft of long bone

digastric
name of a muscle; two bellies

digit
finger, toe

dilator
muscle that enlarges an opening or cavity

disk (disc)
a circular or rounded flat plate; intervertebral disk

distal
toward the periphery, away from the body

distant
space between, gap, distance

diverticulum
outpocketing of a hollow organ

Glossary

dorsal
located toward the back

dorsum
back

ductule
small duct

duct
tube, channel or canal of gland

duodenum
first division of small intestine

dura
hard, outer layer of brain covering

E

ectropion
rolling outward of the margin of part of the eyelid, or the cervix of the uterus

elastic
flexible, ability returning to original shape

ellipsoid
shaped like an ellipse; ellipsoidal

elliptical
ellipsoidal; oval-shaped

embryo
developing organism from the fourth day of fertilization to the end of the second month of pregnancy

eminence
circumscribed raised area on bone

emissary
providing an outlet to the outside or drain

enamel
hard glistening substance covering the exposed part of tooth

endocardium
innermost lining of the heart

endothelium
interior epithelial layer of vessels and heart

enteric

referring to the abdominal viscera, to the intestine

ependyma
cell lining of the cavities of the central nervous system

epicardium
visceral layer of serous pericardium lying on the heart

epicondyle
a projection of long bones near articular surface

epidermis
superficial epithelial surface of skin

epididymis
efferent duct of the testis coiled posterior to the testis

epigastrium
median epigastric area

epiglottis
a leaf-shaped elastic cartilage, serves as diverter valve during swallowing

epiphysis
end of a long bone developed from different ossification center

epiploic
referring to the omental area of great curvature of stomach

epithelium
superficial cell layer

epitympanic
the upper part of the tympanic cavity above tympanic membrane

eponychium
epidermis enclosing the nailbed to the outside (germinal layer-free)

equine
horse-tail like, end of spinal cord

erector
muscle that extends the spine

esophagus (oesophagus)
gullet

ethmoidal
related to ethmoid bone

excavation
natural cavity, pouch

extensor
muscle that straightens a joint, opposite of flexor

externus
lying on the outside, outer

extremities
outermost end of elongated organs, limbs

F

faces
area, surface

fascia
connective tissue coat of muscles or muscle group

fasciola
referring to a small band or group of fibers

fascicle
bundle of muscle fibers and tract in brain

fastigium
fastigial nucleus, roof of fourth ventricle

fenestra
an anatomic aperture, round and oval window (ear)

fetus
an unborn child from nine weeks after fertilization until birth

fibrocartilage
fibrous cartilage as found in the intervertebral disk and articular disk

fibrous
containing fibroblasts and connective tissue

fibula
lateral bone of the leg

fibular
located toward the fibula

filum
fiber, thread

fimbria
fringe-like structure

fissure
a deep furrow, cleft or slit

flaccid

relaxed, flabby or without tone

flexion
act of flexing or bending two ventral surfaces

flexor
muscle that bends or flexes a joint

flexure
a bend in an organ

flocculus
small flake; small lobe of cerebellum

folium
fold cerebellum, vermis

folliculus
sac, follicle; part of cerebellum

fontanelle
cranial growth area

foramen
opening, passage

formation
cell arrangement

fornix
arch-shaped structure, anatomic passage

fossa
groove

fovea
a natural depression on a surface

foveola
small fovea or depression

frenulum
small rein or bridle, band

frontal
located on the plane referring to the forehead

function
performance, capacity of an organ or tissue or muscle

fundiform
sling-shaped, looped

fundus
bottom of sac farthest from opening

funicle
small cord, white column of spinal cord

fusiform
spindle-shaped

G

galea
epicranial aponeurosis between skull and skin

gastrocnemius
referring to superficial calf muscle

gelatinous
jelly-like or resembling gelatin

gemelli
twins, related to name of muscle in buttock

gemellus
twin muscles in buttock

geniculate
having a small knee, knee-shaped

geniculum
small knee, node

genital
pertaining to the organs of reproduction

genu
the knee; a structure bending like a knee

gingiva
gums

glabella
small bald head; hairless area between the eyebrows

glandular
pertaining to a gland

glans
acorn-shaped end of bulbospongiosa; glans penis

glenoid
the socket of the scapula covered by hyaline cartilage; glenoid cavity

glia
supporting cells of the central nervous system

globe
sphere; globe of eyeball

glomus
convolution, cluster

glottis
space between vocal cord

gluteus
related to the gluteal area muscles; buttocks

gracilis
thin, delicate, related muscle

granulation
forming into grains or granules

gubernaculum
a structure that guides

gyrus
prominent elevated convolutions of the surface of the cerebral hemispheres

H

hamate
having a hooked shape, bone in wrist

hamulus
small hook on the medial pterygoid plate

haustra
convexity in the wall of the colon

helicotrema
the apex of cochlea

helix
rounded margin of auricle

hemisphere
half of spherical structure

hiatus
crevice, gaping aperture

hilus
location of vascular entry into and exit from organs

hippocampus
convoluted bulge in the wall of the inferior horn of the lateral ventricle of the brain

horizontal
from side to side

humerus
humeral bone in upper arm

humor
liquid

hyaline
transparent

hyoid
upsilon-shaped (Greek letter); referring to the hyoid bone

hypoglossal
located under the tongue; twelfth cranial nerve

hyponychium
nailbed

hypothenar
the muscle mass in the hand at the base of the little finger

I

ileum
part of the small intestine

ilium
ilium bone; flaring part of hip bone

ilia, -l
pertaining to ilium bone

impar
unpaired

impression
depression

incisure
notch

incisive
referring to the incisor teeth

inclination
leaning or sloping (pelvic-); deviation from long axis (teeth)

index
second finger

indusium
cell layer located on the surface of the corpus callosum

inferior
located further below

infundibulum
funnel, -right atrium

inguinal
relating to groin region

insertion
movable anchoring of muscle

insula
oval region of cerebral cortex overlying the external capsule

intercalated
interposed, inserted between two others

intermediate
interposed, between two others

intermittent
non-continuous, marked by inactivity separating periods of activity

internus
located on the inside; internal

intersection
division, classification

interstitium
interstitial space or gap in the substance of organ or tissue

intestine
part of gastrointestinal system after the stomach

inversion
turning inward,

ischium
the ischial bone of pelvis

isthmus
a narrow connection between two parts

J

jejunum
the second part of small intestine

jugular
the vein that drains blood from the head and neck area

junction
the point of union of two parts

L

labium
lip-shape structure

labrum
an edge, liplike structure, or brim

labyrinth
inner ear structure

lacertus
flat fibrous aponeurosis of biceps brachii M.

lacrimal
tear gland, ducts

lacuna
small space, cavity, gap

lake
tear collection on medial eye

lambdoid
lambda-shaped (Greek letter); suture of the skull

lamella
a thin platelet-like part; a layer of bone around haversian canal

lamina
plate, layer

lateral
located toward the outer side

lemniscus
band; a band of sensory nerve fibers which terminate in the thalamus

ligament
a band of fibrous connective tissue connecting two or more bones

limbus
distinct edge, often a different color; around cornea

limen
threshold or entrance to external opening; outside border of the nose

linea
line

lingual
related to the tongue

lobule
a small lobe

lobe
division of gland or organ; lobes of the lung

locus
place, location to define point; shallow depression in the brain

longitudinal
running lengthwise; a clinical study performed over some time

lucid
clear, lucent, translucent

lumbrical
earthworm-like; small muscle in the hand and foot

lumbar
relating to the loin(s)

lumen
clear width of a hollow organ

lunate
lunar shape; name of carpal bone

lunula
the pale arch area at proximal end of nail

lymph
a yellowish fluid in the intercellular spaces and carried back to venous system

M

macula
a stain spot; sharp vision on the retina

malar
referring to the cheek

malleolus
small hammer; related to the small ossicle in ear

malleus
hammer, bone in middle ear

mandible
lower jaw

manubrium
upper part of sternum, the handle of the malleus

mass
a lump or aggregation of specific material

masseter
one of the mastication muscles

mastoid
nipple-shaped structure behind the ear; name of bony landmark

maxilla
upper jaw

Glossary

meatus
canal, duct, as in the external auditory tube

medial
located toward the median plane of the body

median
located in the middle, symmetrical plane

mediastinum
space between the left and right lung; the space contains the heart, the esophagus, and the aorta

medulla
the most interior portion of a structure or organ

membrane
a thin sheath of a pliable tissue, covering, or envelope

meninges
related to the membranes covering the brain and spinal cord

meniscus
crescent-shaped structure; crescentic interarticular disks of fibrocartilage attached to certain joints like the knee

mental
related to the chin

meridian
line encircling a globular body, as in the eyeball

mesentery
a membranous fold attaching various organs to the body wall; the two layers of peritoneal membrane between abdominal wall and viscera (intestine)

mesothelium
thin flattened cells forming epithelial lining of the peritoneum, pleura, and pericardium

metatarsal
one of the metatarsal bones in the hand

mitral
relating to left atrioventricular valve (bicuspid) of the heart

modiolus
central cone-shaped core of a spiral canal, the axle of the cochlea of the internal ear

molar
grinding tooth

motor
conducive to movement

multifidus
split multiple times; related to muscles of the back

muscular
related to muscle

myocardium
cardiac muscles

myometrium
muscles of the uterus

N

naris
nostril

navicular
tub-shaped; name of bone in this shape in the foot and hand

neonate
a newborn, an infant one month old or less

nerve
distribution of axons or dendrites from and to the central nervous system

nodule
a small node up to 1 cm in diameter

node
circumscribed swelling or mass of tissue

normal
standard

nuchal
back of the neck, or to lines on occipital bone

nucleus
core of cell, collection of neurons in brain

O

obex
the point on the midline of dorsal surface of medulla oblongata

oblique
having a slanting position

oblong
longer in one direction

obstetric
related to child birth

obturator
any structure that blocks off an opening; a foramen in pelvic bone,

ocular
related to the eye

olfactory
sense of smell; first cranial nerve

olive
a nucleus on the lateral side of the medulla oblongata

omentum
double layer of peritoneal membrane between two viscera in the abdomen

omohyoid
connecting scapula and hyoid bone; name of a muscle

operculum
cover, lid, related to clotting during embryo implantation

opponens
opposing, relate to name of muscle in thumb and little finger

ora
seam, edge-like in ora serrata of the retina

oral
related to the mouth area; - cavity

orbicularis
circular; name of muscle around the eye

orbit, -al
eye socket, or related to fascia in the orbit

organ
any part of the body with a specific function

orifice
an aperture, an opening

origin
the fixed point of attachment of a muscle or the site of emergence of a peripheral nerve

oris
the mouth

os
bone

osseous
bony

ostium
a small opening, the mouth of small canal

P

palate
the roof of the mouth, either soft or hard

pallidus, -um
globus, inner part of the lenticular nucleus

pallium
mantle of the brain, cerebral cortex with white substance

palm
flexor side of the hand

palmaris
muscle name related to the palm of the hand and forearm

palpebra
eyelid

pampiniform
twine-shaped, related to venous plexus

papilla
any small nipple-like process; breast nipple

paramedian
parallel to median line or section

parietal
in relation to the walls of a cavity; pertaining to the parietal bone

parotid
salivary gland at the angle of the mandible

pars
part

patella
kneecap; sesamoid bone in the quadriceps tendon

pecten
crest, comblike process

peduncle
stem; neuroanatomy for stalk like

pellucid, -um
thin transparent, related to septum in cerebrum

pelvis
bones which connect lower limbs to vertebral column

penis
male organ of copulation and urination

perforator
a bone-piercing instrument, also used on fetal head; name for blood vessels perforating fascial planes

pericardium
fibroserous membrane around the heart

perineum
area between thighs and pubic bone and coccyx

periodontium
connective tissue around the root of tooth, fibers anchored in cementum

peripheral
toward the surface of the body

peritoneum
serous membrane lining the abdomen and covering the intestine

peroneus, -eal
related to the fibula; name of a muscle group

perpendicular
vertical

petrous
hard, like rock

phalanx
one of the bones in the fingers or toes

pharynx
upper end of the digestive system

pineal
shaped like a pine cone; related to the pineal body

piriformis
pear-shaped

pisiformis
pea-shaped; small bone at medial of wrist

placenta
organ to facilitate exchange between fetus and mother

plantar
sole of the foot

plantaris
related to plantar; muscle name

planus
plane, flat

platysma
thin facial muscle in the neck

pleura
serous membrane covering lungs and thoracic cavity

plexus
interconnections of network of veins or redistribution of nerves

plica
fold

pole
point end of organ or structure

popliteal
hollow area behind the knee, related name

porta
an entrance to an organ

portion
part of an organ

posterior
located toward the back

prepuce
foreskin of penis and clitoris

procerus
slender part of the name of a muscle

process
projection or outgrowth

profundus
deep, located deeply

prominence
part projecting past the surface

promontory
part projecting past the surface

pronator
muscle that extends a part into a prone position

proprio, -ception
proprietary, sense of movement and position of the limbs

prostate
a gland around the urethra

protuberance
a swelling or knoblike projection

proximal
located toward the center of the body

pterygoid
wing-shaped, alar, resembling a wing

pudendum, -al
the external genitalia, related to the area

pulp
soft marrow, parenchyma of an organ (teeth)

pulposus
pulpy, gelatin in form

pulvinar
the expanded posterior part of the thalamus

punctum
tip or end of a sharp process

pupil
circular orifice in the center of the iris

putamen
outermost part and darker area of lenticular nucleus

pylorus
gastric outlet

pyramid
pyramidal shape; relates to an area of the medulla oblongata

Q

quadratus
rectangular in shape; related to the anterior layer of thoracolumbar fascia

R

radial
related to the radius bone in the forearm, name of nerve, artery

radiation
diverging in all direction from a center; ultraviolet or x-ray radiation

radicle
a rootlet

ramus
branch

raphe
the line of union of two contiguous halves, seam

recess
a small hollow or indentation, ancillary chamber

rectum
largest part of the alimentary canal before anal area

rectus
straight

recurrent
re-occurring, turning back on itself

reflex
an involuntary reaction to a stimulus

region
area

renal
related to the kidney

resect
to cut off, to excise a segment of a part

respiratory
related to the respiration system that involves the exchange of oxygen and carbon dioxide between the body cells and the atmosphere

rete
network

retina
the inner layer of neurological sensitive to light perception

retinaculum
a retaining band or ligament

rima
a slit or fissure between two symmetric parts

risorius
muscle on the face

rostrum
beak-shaped structure

rotator
the name of a muscle

ruga, -e
wrinkle; folds of the mucosa of the stomach

S

saccule
smaller of two membranous sacs in vestibule

sagittal
in the direction of line from ventral to dorsal

saliva
secretion from glands around the mouth

saphenous
cutaneous veins of the leg; the cutaneous nerve on medial leg

sartorius
thigh muscle used to cross legs

scala
one of the cavities of the cochlea

scalenus, -e
uneven sides; one of three muscles at root of the neck

scaphoid
boat-shaped; name of a bone

scapula
shoulder blade

sclera
a portion of the fibrous layer of the outer envelope of the eyeball

scrotum
a musculocutaneous sac for the testicle

segment
section of part, as in pleura

sella
saddle, as in Turkish saddle; related to the pituitary

semilunar
like a half-moon

sensory
relating to sensation

septal
related to the septum

septum
a wall dividing two cavities

serosa
outermost cover or serous layer of a viscera

serratus
serrated; several muscles of back and thorax

sesamoid
related to the bone that facilitates the sliding tendon in the knee

sigmoid
shaped like the Greek letter sigma; part of the large intestine

sinus
a channel for the passage of blood or lymph; cavity filled with air connected to the nasal cavity

situs
position of the viscera in the cavities of the body

soleus
halibut-shaped; the muscle in the calf of the leg

Glossary

solitarius
solitary area; nucleus in the brain

sperm
male spermatozoa, all parts of the ejaculate

sphenoidal
wedge-shaped; related to the sphenoid bone

spherical
pertaining to or shaped like a sphere

spheroid
shaped like a sphere

spinalis, -e / spinatus / spinosus
referring to the spine; the spinal cord, or column

spiral
coiled, winding around center

spleno-
related to the spleen

spongiosum
spongy tissue; erectile part of penis

squama
thin plate of bone

stellate
star-shaped, related to the name of the sympathetic ganglion

sternum
lower part of breast bone

stratum
cover, lamina, one layer of differentiated tissue

stria
stripe, band, streak

stroma
connective tissue framework of an organ

styloid
peg-shaped, denoting one of several slender bony processes

subiculum
zone of transition between parahippocampal gyrus and Ammon's horn

substantia
substance; -nigra of midbrain

sulcus
furrow; groove on the surface of the cortex of brain

supercilium, -a
eyebrow

superficial
located near the surface

superior
located above; directed upward

supinator
part of the name of a muscle; assume hand facing forward

sura, -l
calf, fibula, nerves on posterior calf

sustentaculum
support to another; process of calcaneum

suture
sewing together; line between two flat bones of the skull

sympathetic
denoting that part of autonomic nervous system–(vegetative) nerves

symphysis
fibrocartilaginous connection between two bones, as in pubic bones

synchondrosis
cartilaginous joint in which two bones are united

syndesmosis
a form of a fibrous joint in which opposing surfaces are far apart and united with a ligament; like the interosseous membrane between the fibula and tibia

synostosis
union between two bones that are not supposed to be united

synovial
related to synovial membrane in joints; synovial fluid

system
consistent and complex whole made up of correlated semi-independent parts

T

taenia
a coiled bandlike anatomic structure, longitudinal band of large intestine

talus
ankle bone

tarsal
tarsal bones of the foot

tectum
rooflike covering; roof of mesencephalon

tegmen
a structure that covers or roofs over a part; coat, cover, -tympani of middle ear

tegmentum
a covering structure, ceiling, dorsal part of the pons

tela
thin web-like tissue, like -choroid of fourth ventricle in hindbrain

temporalis
name of a muscle in the temporal area

tendinous
related to or resembling a tendon

tendon
fibrous cord or band connecting muscle to bone

tensor
muscle that makes a body part tense or firm

teres
round

terminal
referring to the end, final

tertius
third

testis
male gonad

thalamus
mass of gray matter forming the walls of the diencephalon

theca
sheath or capsule

thenar
the mass of muscle at base of the thumb

thymus
a primary lymphoid organ located in superior mediastinum

thyroid
an endocrine gland; related to name the name of cartilage

tibia
medial bone in the leg

tibialis
related to the tibia

tonsil
lymphoid tissue aggregates in the pharynx

torsion
twisting, turning, rotating about an axis; compromises blood supply

torus
a rounded swelling, bulge

trabecule
a meshwork of supporting bundles, a small piece of spongy substance of bone

trachea
the air tube extend from larynx to bifurcation to bronchi

tract
an elongated area of tube-like structures as in the alimentary tract; fascicles of nerve fibers as in the central nervous system

tragus
a tongue-like projection of one of the cartilages of ear

transversalis
fascial layer lining the inner abdominal wall, deep to a similarly named muscle

transversus
transverse, cross-wise, related to a muscle in the abdomen

trapezius
trapezoid like; related to a muscle on back of neck and chest

trigone
the first three dominant cusps; prominence of floor of fourth ventricle; smooth triangular area of the posterior wall of bladder

trochanter
bony prominence developed from independent osseous centers near the upper end of the femur

trochlea
pulley-like articular surface of bone

truncus
trunk; an embryological derivative to the ascending aorta (- arteriosus); branch of the aorta (truncus arteriosus)

tubal
relating to a tube, as in uterine tubes

tuber
a localized swelling, a knob, related protuberance

tubercle
a nodule, circumscribed, rounded solid elevation

tuberosity
a large tubercle or rounded elevation, as in the heel bone

tubule
small tube, of gland, or in kidney

tube
a hollow cylindrical structure of canal

tunica
coat or covering tissue layer, as in covering to testicle

A

tympanic
related to the ear drum or middle ear cavity

___

ulna
bone of the forearm

ulnar
related to the ulna

umbilicus
the navel

umbo
projecting point of attachment of the handle of malus to the tympanic membrane

uncinate
hooklike; hook-shaped, related to the uncus or specifically to gyrus of the same name

uncus
anterior hooked extremity of the parahippocampal gyrus of the temporal lobe of the brain

ungual
related to a nail (on fingers and toes)

urachus
the part of allantoic stalk between the apex of the bladder and the umbilicus

ureter
the tube that connects the kidney to the bladder

urethra
a canal leading from the bladder to the outside, discharging the urine externally

uterus
a hollow muscular organ in which fertilized ovum is implanted

utricule
a minute pouch in the prostatic part of urethra; of the membranous labyrinth of the internal ear

uvula
a fleshy appending mass of the roof of mouth (palate)

___

vagina
genital canal of the woman

vagus
name of the tenth cranial nerve

valgus
bent outward

vallecula
small valley; trough, space between the posterior tongue and epiglottis

vallum
a slightly raised outer wall of the circular depression, related to nail wall

valve
a fold of the lining membrane of a canal or other hollow organ; prevents a reflux of fluid

vascular
relating to or containing blood vessels

vastus
related to three named muscles in the thigh

velum
any structure resembling a veil or curtain

vena
vein; related to large vein draining into the heart (vena cava)

ventral
related to anterior surface of the body

ventricle
a normal cavity found in the heart chamber; cerebral ventricle; convexity of the larynx

vermis
wormlike area, as in the narrow area between the cerebellar hemisphere

version
displacement of uterus, inclination; conjugate rotation of the eye

vertebra
one of 33 parts making up the vertebral column

vertex
the topmost point of the vault of the skull; in obstetrics the portion of the fetal head at the apex

vertical
denoting any plane or line that passes longitudinally through the body

vesica
any hollow structure or sac; the urinary bladder

vesicle
a small less than 1.0 cm in diameter, circumscribed elevation of skin

vestibule
atrium, a small cavity at entrance of canal

vestigial
vestige; remains of a peritoneal process into the scrotum or labia majora

villus
a minute projection from surface of mucous membrane

vinculum
frenulum or ligament between tendons anchoring and supply path for vessels

viscera
viscus organs like gastrointestinal system, all tissue controlled by autonomic nervous system

vitreous
glassy, resembling glass; as in the vitreous humor (body) behind the lens of the eye

volar
palm of the hand or sole of foot

vomer
plow-share like bone part of the nasal septum

vortex
arranged in a whorl of cardiac muscle fibers on the apex of the heart

vulva
external female genitals

___

xiphoid
sword-shaped; as in the xiphoid process of the sternum

___

Zenker
related to the diverticulum at the pharyngoesophageal junction

zona
belt; or section of a sphere

zygomatic
referring to the zygomatic bone

Appendix: Names Associated with Terms

Physicians and Scientists whose names are associated with medical and, primarily, anatomical terms. This listing was featured in the German edition. A more inclusive list for the clinical edition is in development and will be included in the next edition.

Ackerknecht, Eberhard (Anatomist)
1883–1968
Zurich, Leipzig

Adamkiewicz, Albert (Pathologist)
1850–1921
Vienna, Krakow, Breslau

Alcock, Benjamin (Anatomist)
1801– (unkown)
Dublin, Cork

Aschoff, Ludwig (Pathologist)
1886–1942
Fribourg, Marburg

Bartholin, Caspar Jr. (Anatomist and Physicist)
1655–1738
Copenhagen

Baudeloque, Jean Louis (Gynecologist)
1746–1810
Paris

Bauhin, Caspar (Physician, Anatomist and Botanist)
1560–1624
Basel

Bertin, Exupère Joseph (Anatomist)
1712–1781
Paris

Bichat, Marie Francois Xavier (Physiologist, Anatomist and Pathologist)
1771–1802
Paris

Blandin, Philippe Frederic (Anatomist and Surgeon)
1798–1849
Paris

Bochdalek, Vincenz Alexander (Anatomist)
1801–1883
Vienna, Prague

Böhm, Gottfried (Radiologist)
1880–1952
Munich

Botallo, Leonardo (Physician)
1530–1580
Pavia

Bourgery, Marc-Jean (Anatomist)
1797–1849
Paris

Broca, Paul (Anthropologist and Surgeon)
1824–1880
Paris

Bühler, Anton (Physician)
1869–1959
Würzburg, Zurich

Burdach, Karl Friedrich (Anatomist and Physiologist)
1776–1847
Dorpat, Königsberg

Camper, Pieter (Anatomist)
1722–1789
Amsterdam, Groningen

Cannon, Walter (Physiologist)
1871–1945
Boston

Carabelli-Lunkaszprie, Georg von (Originator of Scientific Dentistry)
1787–1842
Vienna

Chassaignac, Charles Marie Edouard (Surgeon)
1805–1879
Paris

Chievitz, Johan Henrik (Anatomist)
1850–1901
Copenhagen

Chopart, Francois (Surgeon)
1743–1795
Paris

Cleland, John (Anatomist)
1835–1926
Glasgow

Colles, Abraham (Anatomist and Surgeon)
1773–1843
Dublin

Cooper, Astley Paston (Anatomist and Surgeon)
1768–1841
London

Cowper, William (Anatomist and Surgeon)
1666–1709
London

Denonvilliers, Charles Pierre (Surgeon)
1808–1872
Paris

Dorello, Primo D. (Anatomist)
1872–(unknown)
Perugia

Douglas, James (Anatomist, Surgeon and Gynecologist)
1675–1742
London

Dupuytren, Guillaume (Surgeon)
1778–1835
Paris

Edinger, Ludwig (Neurologist)
1855–1918
Frankfurt

Erb, Wilhelm Heinrich (Internist and Neurologist)
1840–1921
Heidelberg

Eustachio, Bartolomeo (Anatomist)
1520–1574
Rome

Fallopio, Gabriele (Anatomist)
1523–1562
Pisa, Padua

Frankenhäuser, Ferdinand (Gynecologist)
1832–1894
Jena

Galen, Claudius (Physician)
130–201/210
Pergamon, Alexandria, Rome

Gasser, Johann Laurentius (Anatomist)
1723–1765
Vienna

Gennari, Francesco (Anatomist)
1750–1801
Parma

Gerdy, Pierre Nicholas (Anatomist and Surgeon)
1797–1856
Paris

Gimbernat, Antonio de (Anatomist and Surgeon)
1734–1816
Barcelona, Madrid

Glaser, Johann Heinrich (Anatomist and Botanist)
1629–1675
Basel

Goll, Friedrich (Anatomist)
1829–1903
Zurich

Gratiolet, Louis-Pierre (Anatomist and Zoologist)
1815–1865
Paris

Grynfeltt, Joseph Kasimir (Gynecologist)
1840–1913
Montpellier

Guyon, Jean Casimir Felix (Surgeon and Urologist)
1831–1920
Paris

Haller, Albrecht von (Anatomist, Botanist and Physiologist)
1708–1777
Berne, Göttingen

Hasner, Josef Ritter von Artha (Ophthalmologist)
1819–1892
Prag

Heister, Lorenz (Anatomist, Botanist and Surgeon)
1683–1758
Altdorf, Helmstedt

Heschl, Richard Ladislaus (Anatomist and Pathologist)
1824–1881
Graz, Vienna, Krakow

Heubner, Johann Leonhard Otto (Pediatrician)
1843–1926
Berlin, Leipzig

Highmore, Nathaneal (Physician)
1613 - 1685
Sherborne

Hilton, John (Surgeon)
1804–1878
London

His, Wilhelm Jr. (Anatomist and Internist)
1863–1934
Berlin, Basel, Göttingen, Leipzig

Holzknecht, Guido (Radiologist)
1872–1931
Vienna

Horner, William Edmund (Anatomist)
1793–1853
Philadelphia

Humphry, Sir George Murray (Anatomist and Surgeon)
1820–1896
Cambridge

Hunter, John (Surgeon)
1728–1793
London

Hyrtl, Josef (Anatomist)
1811 - 1894
Vienna, Prague

Jacobson, Ludwig Levin (Anatomist)
1783–1843
Copenhagen

Kerckring, Theodor (Anatomist)
1640–1693
Amsterdam, Hamburg

Kiesselbach, Wilhelm (Otologist)
1839–1902
Erlangen

Killian, Gustav (Otorhinolaryngologist)
1860–1921
Fribourg, Berlin

Koch, Walter (Pathologist)
1880–1962
Fribourg

Kohlrausch, Otto Ludwig Bernhard (Physician)
1811–1854
Hannover

Krause, Karl Friedrich Theodor (Anatomist)
1797–1868
Hannover

Krönlein, Rudolf Ulrich (Surgeon)
1847–1910
Zurich

Labbé, Ernst Marcel (Internist)
1870–1939
Paris

Laimer, Eduard (Anatomist and Physician)
1857–1934
Graz, Volders

Langer, Karl Ritter von Edenburg (Anatomist)
1819–1887
Vienna

Lanz, Otto (Surgeon)
1865–1935
Berne, Amsterdam, Munich

Larrey, Dominique-Jean Baron de (Surgeon)
1766–1842
Paris

Leonardo, da Vinci (Painter and Universal Scholar)
1452–1519
Milan, Venice, Mantua, Florence, Rome, Amboise

Lisfranc, Jacques (Surgeon)
1790–1847
Paris

Littré, Alexis (Anatomist and Surgeon)
1658–1726
Paris

Lockwood, Charles Banett (Surgeon)
1858–1914
London

Louis, Antoine (Surgeon)
1723–1792
Metz

Louis, Pierre Charles Alexandre (Physician)
1787–1872
Paris

Luschka, Hubert von (Anatomist, Physician and Pharmacologist)
1820–1875
Merseburg, Constance, Tübingen

Mac Burney, Charles (Surgeon)
1845–1914
New York

Mackenrodt, Alwin Karl (Gynecologist)
1859–1925
Berlin

Magendie, Francois (Pathologist and Physiologist)
1783 - 1855
Paris

Maissiat, Jaques Henri (Anatomist)
1805–1878
Paris

Marshall, John (Anatomist and Surgeon)
1818–1891
London

Meckel, Johann Friedrich (Anatomist and Surgeon)
1781–1833
Halle

Merkel, Friedrich Sigismund (Anatomist)
1845–1919
Rostock, Königsberg and Göttingen

Michaelis, Gustav Adolf (Gynecologist)
1798–1848
Kiel

Mohrenheim, Joseph Jakob von (Surgeon, Gynecologist and Ophthalmologist)
1759–1799
Vienna, St. Petersburg

Monro, Alexander (Anatomist and Surgeon)
1733–1817
Edinburgh

Morgagni, Giovanni Battista (Anatomist)
1682–1771
Padua

Müller, Heinrich (Anatomist)
1820–1864
Würzburg
[M. tarsalis superior]

Müller, Johannes (Anatomist and Physiologist)
1801–1858
Berlin
[Ovary]

Nuhn, Anton (Anatomist)
1814–1889
Heidelberg

Oddi, Ruggero (Surgeon)
1864–1913
Bologna

Pacchioni, Antonio (Anatomist)
1665–1726
Tivoli, Rome

Petit, Jean Louis (Anatomist and Surgeon)
1674–1750
Paris

Peyer, Johann Konrad (Anatomist and Physician)
1653–1712
Schaffhausen

Poupart, Francois (Anatomist and Surgeon)
1616–1708
Paris

Appendix: Names Associated with Terms

Prussak, Alexander (Otologist)
1839–1897
St. Petersburg

Reinke, Friedrich Berthold
(Anatomist)
1862–1919
Rostock, Göttingen

Retzius, Anders Adolf
(Anatomist)
1796–1860
Lund

Riolan, Jean (Anatomist, Botanist and Pharmacologist)
1580–1657
Paris

Robert, Cesar Alphonse
(Surgeon)
1801–1862
Paris

Rolando, Luigi
(Anatomist)
1773–1831
Sassari, Turin

Rosenmüller, Johann Christian
(Surgeon and Anatomist)
1771–1820
Leipzig

Rosenthal, Friedrich Christian
(Anatomist and Physiologist)
1780–1829
Greifswald

Rotter, Josef (Surgeon)
1857–1924
Munich, Berlin

Santorini, Giovanni Domenico
(Anatomist and Surgeon)
1681–1737
Pisa, Venice

Scarpa, Antonio
(Anatomist and Surgeon)
1747–1832
Modena

Schlemm, Friedrich
(Anatomist)
1795–1858
Berlin

Shrapnell, Henry Jones
(Anatomist)
1761–1841
London

Sibson, Francis (Internist)
1814–1876
London

Skene, Alexander Johnston
Chalmers (Gynecologist)
1837–1900
New York

Spieghel, Adriaan van den
(Anatomist and Botanist)
1578–1625
Amsterdam, Padua, Venice

Stenon, Nicolaus (Anatomist,
Geologist and Bishop)
original name: Stensen, Niels
1638–1686
Copenhagen, Florence, Münster,
Hamburg, Schwerin
Beatification in Rome 1988

Sylvius, Franciscus de la Boe
(Anatomist)
1614–1672
Amsterdam

Tawara, Sunao
(Pathologist)
1873–1952
Fukuoka, Jena

Tenon, Jacques René
(Ophthalmologist, Surgeon
and Pathologist)
1724–1816
Paris

Thebesius, Adam Christian
(Physician)
1686 - 1732
Hirschberg

Todaro, Francesco (Anatomist)
1839–1918
Florence, Messina, Rome

Treitz, Wenzel (Pathologist)
1819–1872
Krakow, Prague

Trolard, Paulin (Anatomist)
1842–1910
Algiers

Valsalva, Antonio Maria
(Anatomist and Surgeon)
1666–1723
Bologna

Vater, Abraham (Anatomist
and Botanist)
1684–1751
Wittenberg

Vicq D'Azyr, Felix (Anatomist)
1748–1794
Paris

Vidius (Vidianus), Guido
(Anatomist and Philosopher)
1500–1569
Florence, Pisa, Paris

Virchow, Rudolf (Pathologist
and Social Politician)
1821–1902
Würzburg, Berlin

Waldeyer, Heinrich Willhelm
Gottfried von (Anatomist)
1836–1921
Berlin, Breslau, Strassburg

Ward, Frederick Oldfield
1818–1877
London

Weitbrecht, Josias (Anatomist)
1702–1747
St. Petersburg

Wernicke, Karl (Neurologist
and Psychiatrist)
1848 - 1905
Berlin, Breslau, Halle

Westphal, Karl Friedrich Otto
(Neurologist and Psychiatrist)
1833–1890
Berlin

Willis, Thomas (Anatomist)
1622–1675
London, Oxford

Winslow, Jakob Benignus
(Anatomist)
1669–1760
Odense, Copenhagen, Paris

Wirsung, Johann Georg
(Anatomist)
1600–1643
Augsburg, Padua

Wrisberg, Heinrich August
(Anatomist)
1739–1808
Göttingen

Zinn, Johann Gottfried
(Anatomist and Botanist)
1727–1759
Göttingen

Illustration Credits

Photos: Bernhard N. Tillmann

Chapter 1	1.5; 1.6a-e
Chapter 2	2.1a-c; 2.3; 2.4; 2.5a-d; 2.6a,b; 2.7; 2.8; 2.9; 2.18; 2.19; 2.25; 2.27a,b; 2.29; 2.30; 2.31; 2.91; 2.92; 2.114; 2.93;2.94; 2.130; 2.131; 2.133a-f; 2.140; 2.141; 2.142; 2.145; 2.171; 2.172; 2.173; 2.175; 2.177a,b; 2.190a,b
Chapter 3	3.41
Chapter 4	4.3a-d; 4.5a,b; 4.6; 4.7a,b; 4.8a-d; 4.9a-c; 4.10; 4.11a-d; 4.12a-d; 4.13a,b 4.14a,b; 4.15; 4.23; 4.24
Chapter 5	5.14; 5.176a,b; 5.179b
Chapter 6	6.1a,b; 6.2a,b; 6.3a-c; 6.4a,b; 6.5; 6.6; 6.7; 6.8; 6.9; 6.11; 6.21; 6.25
Chapter 7	7.1a,b; 7.2a,b; 7.3a,b; 7.4a,b; 7.5a,b; 7.6a,b; 7.7; 7.8a,b; 7.9; 7.11; 7.12a,b; 7.13a,b; 7.14a,b; 7.15a,b; 7.16; 7.17; 7.18; 7.19; 7.20; 7.21; 7.29; 7.34; 7.42

Illustrations: Alwalid I. Elbermani

Chapter 3	3.9; 3.10
Chapter 4	4.39

Illustrations: Claudia Sperlich

Chapter 1	1.3d
Chapter 2	2.33a,b; 2.34; 2.35; 2.36; 2.37; 2.38; 2.39; 2.51a,b; 2.54; 2.55; 2.56; 2.57; 2.58; 2.59a; 2.60a; 2.61; 2.65; 2.68; 2.69; 2.70; 2.75; 2.76; 2.77; 2.83; 2.85; 2.95; 2.100; 2.103; 2.104a,b; 2.105; 2.108a,b; 2.115; 2.116; 2.117; 2.119; 2.127a,b; 2.128; 2.129; 2.143a-c; 2.153; 2.156; 2.159; 2.161; 2.162; 2.163; 2.164; 2.166; 2.167; 2.179a,b; 2.180; 2.181; 2.182; 2.184a-c; 2.187b; 2.190c; 2.194a; 2.205
Chapter 3	3.7; 3.8; 3.43b; 3.53a; 3.54; 3.55; 3.56; 3.60; 3.62a,b; 3.63; 3.64; 3.65
Chapter 4	4.16; 4.17; 4.18; 4.19; 4.20; 4.21; 4.22a-c; 4.30; 4.31; 4.32; 4.33; 4.34; 4.35a,b; 4.36; 4.37a,b, 4.38; 4.42; 4.44; 4.48; 4.56a,b; 4.55; 4.59; 4.60; 4.68; 4.69; 4.74; 4.78; 4.80a,b; 4.82; 4.83; 4.85a,b
Chapter 5	5.7; 5.8; 5.22; 5.23; 5.39; 5.42; 5.44; 5.45; 5.51a,b; 5.52a,b; 5.54; 5.55a,b; 5.65a,b; 5.66; 5.70;5.92b; 5.95; 5.106a,b; 5.109a,b; 5.127; 5.129; 5.131;5.134b,c; 5.155a,b; 5.156; 5.157; 5.158a,b; 5.160a,b; 5.161a-c; 5.163; 5.165; 5.178a,b; 5.182; 5.185; 5.187; 5.203a,b; 5.204; 5.205; 5.206; 5.207; 5.208; 5.209; 5.212; 5.216; 5.219; 5.222; 5.225; 5.227; 5.237; 5.243; 5.246b; 2.247
Chapter 6	6.14; 6.16; 6.29; 6.30; 6.32; 6.33; 6.34; 6.38; 6.39; 6.41; 6.42; 6.45; 6.46; 6.47; 6.49; 6.50a,b; 6.52; 6.58; 6.59; 6.60; 6.61; 6.64a,b; 6.65; 6.85; 6.86; 6.87; 6.96; 6.97; 6.98; 6.99; 6.106; 6.107
Chapter 7	7.27; 7.31a,b; 7.32a,b; 7.43; 7.45; 7.46; 7.47; 7.48; 7.49; 7.58; 7.59a,b; 7.61; 7.62; 7.64; 7.65; 7.66; 7.68; 7.69; 7.70; 7.72; 7.74a,b; 7.75a,b; 7.77; 7.78; 7.80; 7.82a,b; 7.83a,b; 7.84; 7.85; 7.102; 7.104; 7.105; 7.113; 7.114; 7.121; 7.122a-c; 7.124

Illustration Credits and References

The following lists:
- persons and institutes that provided preparations,
- colleagues in private practices and clinics that offered materials of various imaging processes and diverse clinical illustrations,
- master illustrations of other works on the basis of which further anatomical and clinical contents were included and expanded upon.

We have made intensive efforts to clarify all third party rights. In the event that, despite careful research, third party rights have been infringed upon, please nofity us accordingly.

1   Preparation of the Scientific Collection of the Anatomical Institute of the Christian-Albrechts-University in Kiel, Klaws fecit

2   Rauber, A., and F. Kopsch. Anatomie des Menschen. Lehrbuch und Atlas. Ed. H. Leonhardt, B. Tillmann, G. Töndury, K. Zilles, Vol. II: Innere Organe. Stuttgart, New York: Thieme, 1987.

3   Grosser, O., and R. Ortmann. Grundriss der Entwicklungsgeschichte des Menschen. 7th ed. Berlin, Heidelberg, New York: Springer, 1970.

4   Quain, J., A. Thomson, and E. A. Schaefer. Quain's Elements of Anatomy. London: Longmans, Green & Company, 1882.

5   Krstić, R. V. Human Microscopic Anatomy: An Atlas for Students of Medicine and Biology. Vol. III. Berlin, Heidelberg, New York, Tokyo: Springer, 1991.

6   Preparation of the Scientific Collection of the Anatomical Institute of the Christian-Albrechts-University in Kiel

7   Zilles, K., and G. Rehkämper. 1998). Funktionelle Neuroanatomie: Lehrbuch und Atlas. 3rd ed. Berlin, Heidelberg, New York, Tokyo: Springer, 1998.

8   Preparation of the Scientific Collection of the Anatomical Institute of the Christian-Albrechts-University in Kiel, Gundlach fecit

9   Preparation of the Collection of the Institute for Anatomy, University Clinic Charité of the Humboldt-University in Berlin (Director: Prof. Dr. med. R. Nitsch)

10 Clinic for Diagnostic Radiology of the Christian-Albrechts-University in Kiel (Director: Prof. Dr. med. M. Heller)

11 Preparation and Photograph: Ms. Prof. Dr. C. Schmolke, Bonn

12 Braus, H. Anatomie des Menschen. Ein Lehrbuch für Ärzte und Studierende. Continued by C. Elze, 3rd ed. Vol. I. Berlin, Göttingen, Heidelberg: Springer, 1954.

13 Braus, H. Anatomie des Menschen. Continued by C. Elze. 2nd ed. Vol. III. Berlin, Göttingen, Heidelberg: Springer, 1960.

14 Corning, H. K. Lehrbuch der topographischen Anatomie für Studierende und Ärzte. 1st ed. Wiesbaden: Bergmann, 1907.

15 Hafferl. Lehrbuch der topographischen Anatomie. 2nd ed. Berlin, Göttingen, Heidelberg: Springer, 1957.

16 Tillmann, B. "Topographie und Struktur der Orbitawände und des Canalis opticus." Deutsche Gesellschaft für Hals-Nasen-Ohrenheilkunde, Kopf- und Hals-Chirurgie. Ed. W. Steiner. Berlin, Heidelberg, New York, Tokyo: Springer, 1998. 39–50.

17 Henle, J. Lehrbuch der systematischen Anatomie des Menschen. Vol. III. Braunschweig: Vieweg, 1868.

18 Tillmann, B. Farbatlas der Anatomie: Zahnmedizin – Humanmedizin; Kopf, Hals, Rumpf. Stuttgart, New York: Thieme, 1997.

19 Photograph: Clinic for Tooth Preservation Studies and Periodontology of the Christian-Albrechts-University in Kiel (Director: Prof. Dr. Dr. H.-K. Albers)

20 von Lanz, T., and W. Wachsmuth. Praktische Anatomie. Ein Lehr- und Hilfsbuch der anatomischen Grundlagen ärztlichen Handelns. Vol. I, Part 2: Hals. Berlin, Göttingen, Heidelberg: Springer, 1955.

21 Frick, H., H. Leonhardt, and D. Starck. Allgemeine Anatomie. Spezielle Anatomie I. Extremitäten – Rumpfwand – Kopf – Hals. 4th ed. Stuttgart, New York: Thieme, 1992.

22 According to W. Platzer, Atlas der topographischen Anatomie, Stuttgart, New York: Thieme, 1982 and H. K. Corning, 1922 [23], as well as following own X-Ray images

23 Corning, H. K. Lehrbuch der topographischen Anatomie für Studierende und Ärzte. 12th and 13th. ed. Munich: Bergmann, 1922.

24 Photographs: Dr. med. M. Bosse, Clinic for Otorhinolaryngology of the Christian-Albrechts-University in Kiel (former director: Prof. Dr. med. H. Rudert). Endoscope provided by the company Karl Stortz, Tuttlingen.

25 Photograph: W. Klüglein, Clinic for Ophthalmology of the Christian-Albrechts-University in Kiel (former director: Prof. Dr. med. R. Rochels)

26 Paulsen, F. "The human nasolacrimal ducts." Adv Anat Embryol Cell Biol 170 (2003): 1–106.

27 Photography: Priv. Doz. Dr. med. A. Thale, W. Klüglein, Clinic for Ophthalmology of the Christian-Albrechts-University in Kiel (former director: Prof. Dr. med. R. Rochels)

28 Photograph: Prof. Dr. med. S. Müller-Hülsbeck, Clinic for Diagnostic Radiology of the Christian-Albrechts-University in Kiel (Director: Professor Dr. med. M. Heller). *(Fig. 5.48: Flash 3D; TR 4.1 ms, TE 1.8 ms; FA 30°; Matrix 512×200; FOV 440 mm, effective layer thickness 3.5 mm, data acquisition time 23 seconds)*

29 Priv. Doz. Dr. med. A. Thale, Clinic for Ophthalmology of the Christian-Albrechts-University in Kiel (former director: Prof. Dr. med. R. Rochels)

30 Toldt, C., and F. Hochstetter. Anatomischer Atlas. Vol. III. Munich: Urban and Schwarzenberg, 1979.

31 Spalteholz, W., and R. Spanner. Handatlas der Anatomie des Menschen. Founded by W. Spalteholz. Ed. and arr. by R. Spanner. 16th ed. Part 2: Gefäß-System, Eingeweide, Nervensystem, Sinnesorgane. Amsterdam: Scheltema & Holkema, 1961.

32 Ritter, K., and H. Bräuer. Exempla otologica. Munich: Medical Service, 1988.

33 Photograph: Dr. med. H. Bolte, Clinic for Diagnostic Radiology of the Christian-Albrechts-University in Kiel (Director: Prof. Dr. med. M. Heller)

34 Hirschfeld, L., and J.-B. Leveillé. Systeme Nerveux et des Organes des Sens De L'Homme. Paris: Chez J-B Bailliére, 1853.

35 Preparation of the Scientific Collection of the Anatomical Institute of the Christian-Albrechts-University in Kiel, Tillmann fecit

36 [23] there according to König and Krönlein

37 Preparation of the Scientific Collection of the Anatomical Institute of the Christian-Albrechts-University in Kiel, Klaws et Tillmann fecerunt

38 Ferner, H. "Zur Anatomie der intrakranialen Abschnitte des Nervus trigeminus." Z Anat-Entwickl-Gesch 114 (1948): 108-122.

39 Feneis, H. Anatomisches Bildwörterbuch der internationalen Nomenklatur. 8th ed. Stuttgart: Thieme, 1998.

40 Preparation of the Scientific Collection of the Anatomical Institute of the Christian-Albrechts-University in Kiel, Gundlach et Tillmann fecerunt

41 Nieuwenhuys, R., J. Voogd, and C. van Huijzen. Das Zentralnervensystem des Menschen. Atlas mit Begleittext. Trans. by W. Lange. 2nd ed. Berlin, Heidelberg, New York, Tokyo: Springer, 1991.

42 Original illustrations: Prof. Dr. med. K. Zilles, Director of the C. and O. Vogt–Institute for Brain Research, Heinrich-Heine-University in Düsseldorf, and the Institute for Medicine, Research Center Jülich GmbH, Jülich

43 C. and O. Vogt–Institute for Brain Research, Heinrich-Heine-University Düsseldorf, and Institute for Medicine, Research Center Jülich GmbH, Jülich (Director: Prof. Dr. med. K. Zilles), Blohm et Machus fecerunt

44 Tillmann, B., F. Wustrow. "Kehlkopf." Hals-Nasen-Ohren-Heilkunde in Praxis und Klinik. Eds. J. Berendes, R. Link and F. Zöllner. Vol. IV/1. Stuttgart, New York: Thieme, 1982. 1–101.

45 Tillmann, B. (1997) [18], there according to a preparation of the Anatomical Institute of the Christian-Albrechts-University in Kiel

46 von Lanz, T., and W. Wachsmuth. Praktische Anatomie. Ein Lehr- und Hilfsbuch der anatomischen Grundlagen ärztlichen Handelns. Eds. J. Lang and W. Wachsmuth. Bein und Statik. 2nd ed. Vol. I. Part 4. Berlin, Heidelberg, New York: Springer, 1972.

47 Heimer, L. The Human Brain and Spinal Cord. Functional Neuroanatomy and Dissection Guide. New York, Heidelberg, Berlin: Springer, 1983.

48 Braus, H. Anatomie des Menschen. Ein Lehrbuch für Ärzte und Studierende. Continued by C. Elze. 3rd ed. Vol. II. Berlin, Göttingen, Heidelberg: Springer, 1956.

49 Photograph: Dr. med. W. Brenner, Clinic for Nuclear Medicine of the Christian-Albrechts-University in Kiel (Director: Prof. Dr. med. E. Henze)

50 Photograph: Dr. med. M. Höpfner, Clinic for General Internal Medicine of the Christian-Albrechts-University in Kiel (Director: Prof. Dr. med. U.R. Fölsch)

51 Lippert, H., R. Pabst. Arterial Variations in Man. Munich: Bergmann, 1985.

52 [18], there according to Zöllner, as well as Härle and Münker

53 Krmpotić-Nemanić, J., W. Draf, and J. Helms. Chirurgische Anatomie des Kopf-Hals-Bereiches. Berlin, Heidelberg, New York, Tokyo: Springer, 1985.

54 Preparation of the Collection of the Center for Anatomy of the University of Cologne

55 Rauber, F., and A. Kopsch. Anatomie des Menschen. Lehrbuch und Atlas. Eds. H. Leonhardt and B. Tillmann. 3rd ed. Vol. I: Bewegungsapparat. Stuttgart: Thieme, 2003.

56 von Lanz, T., and W. Wachsmuth. Praktische Anatomie. Ein Lehr- und Hilfsbuch der anatomischen Grundlagen ärztlichen Handelns. 2nd ed. Vol. I. Part 3: Arm. Berlin, Göttingen, Heidelberg: Springer, 1959.

57 von Lanz, T., and W. Wachsmuth. Praktische Anatomie. Ein Lehr- und Hilfsbuch der anatomischen Grundlagen ärztlichen Handelns. Vol. II. Part 6: Bauch. H. von Loeweneck, G. Feifel. Berlin, Heidelberg, New York, Tokyo: Springer, 1993.

58 von Lanz, T., and W. Wachsmuth. Praktische Anatomie. Ein Lehr- und Hilfsbuch der anatomischen Grundlagen ärztlichen Handelns. Vol. II. Part 7: Rücken. Berlin, Heidelberg, New York: Springer, 1982.

59 Clemens, H. J. Die Venensysteme der menschlichen Wirbelsäule. Morphologie und funktionelle Bedeutung. Berlin: de Gruyter, 1961.

60 Section Neuroradiology of the Clinic for Neurosurgery of the Christian-Albrechts-University in Kiel (Director: Professor Dr. med. O. Jansen)

61 Sappey. Anatomie, physiologie et pathologie des vaisseaux lymphatiques confedérés chez l'homme et les vertèbres. 1874. Owner of copy: State and University Library of Lower Saxony, Göttingen

62 Mamma-Center of the Clinic of the Christian-Albrechts-University in Kiel, Photograph: Prof. Dr. med. I. Schreer (Directors: Prof. Dr. med. W. Jonat, Prof. Dr. med. M. Heller)

63 Duus, P. Neurologisch-topische Diagnostik. Anatomie, Physiologie, Klinik. 6th ed. Stuttgart: Thieme, 1995.

64 [58] there according to Rothmann and Simeone, 1975

65 [13], [46], [47]

66 Hansen, K., and H. Schliack. Segmentale Innervation. Ihre Bedeutung für Klinik und Praxis. 2nd ed. Stuttgart: Thieme, 1962.

67 Netter, F. H. Atlas der Anatomie des Menschen. 3rd ed. Stuttgart: Thieme, 2003.

Illustration Credits and References

68 Own preparations

69 Preparation of the Scientific Collection of the Center of Anatomy of the University of Cologne, Photograph: I. Koch

70 Pernkopf, E. Atlas der topographischen und angewandten Anatomie des Menschen. 3rd ed. Munich: Urban & Schwarzenberg, 1994.

71 Photograph: Priv.-Doz. Dr. med. B. Bewig, Clinic for General Internal Medicine of the Christian-Albrechts-University in Kiel (Director: Prof. Dr. med. U. R. Fölsch)

72 von Hayek, H. Die menschliche Lunge. 2nd supplemented and expanded ed. Berlin, Heidelberg, New York: Springer, 1970.

73 Photograph: Dr. med. C. Hilbert, Clinic for Diagnostic Radiology of the Christian-Albrechts-University in Kiel (Director: Prof. Dr. med. M. Heller)

74 Photograph: Dr. med. W. Kroll, Cardiological Group Practice, Kiel

75 Photograph: Dr. med. S. Schmidt, Dipl.-Mathematician A. Schumm, Radiological Group Practice, Kiel
(Fig. 5-49, 5-124, 5-141, 5-170a,b: Multislice Computer-Tomography Mx 8000, Company Marcons)

76 Preparation of the Collection of the Anatomical Institute of the Christian-Albrechts-University in Kiel, Koch fecit

77 Rein, H., and M. Schneider. Einführung in die Physiologie des Menschen. 13th and 14th ed. Berlin, Göttingen, Heidelberg: Springer, 1960.

78 Spalteholz, W., and R. Spanner. Handatlas der Anatomie des Menschen. Founded by W. Spalteholz. Ed. and arr. by R. Spanner. 16th ed. Part 1: Bewegungsapparat. Amsterdam: Scheltema & Holkema, 1960.

79 Rauber, F., and A. Kopsch. Anatomie des Menschen. Lehrbuch und Atlas. Ed. H. Leonhardt, B. Tillmann, G. Töndury and K. Zilles. Vol. III: Nervensystem, Sinnesorgane. Stuttgart, New York: Thieme, 1997.

80 [23] there according to Braune

81 Preparation, Dr. med. Philip Steven, Anatomical Institute in Kiel, Section of the Vestibular Fold and the Vocal Fold of the Left Side. Staining: Orcein-picroindigocarmine (OPIC), magnification: x 3.5

82 Photograph: Dr. med. Dipl.-Biol. W. U. Kampen, Clinic for Nuclear Medicine of the Christian-Albrechts-University in Kiel (Director: Prof. Dr. med. E. Henze)

83 Bargmann, W., and W. Doerr. Das Herz des Menschen. Vol. I. Stuttgart: Thieme, 1963.

84 Photograph: Dr. J. Biederer, Clinic for Diagnostic Radiology of the Christian-Albrechts-University in Kiel (Director: Prof. Dr. M. Heller)

85 Fölsch, U. R. Pankreaschirurgie. Eds. L. F. Hollender and H.-J. Peiper. Berlin, Heidelberg, New York, Tokyo: Springer, 1988.

86 Hollender, L. F., and H.-J. Peiper. Die Praxis der Chirurgie. Pankreaschirurgie. Berlin, Heidelberg, New York, Tokyo: Springer, 1988.

87 Photograph: Prof. Dr. med. U. R. Fölsch, Director of the Clinic for General Internal Medicine of the Christian-Albrechts-University in Kiel (Fig. 5-134: Prograde Optics, Company Olympus)

88 Rouviére, H. Anatomie Humaine. Descriptive et Topographique. Paris: Tome I. Masson, 1924.

89 Photograph: Dr. med. J. Blume, Clinic for Diagnostic Radiology of the Christian-Albrechts-University in Kiel (Director: Prof. Dr. med. M. Heller)

90 [57], there according to S. Deiler, "Präparatorische, röntgenologische und histologische Untersuchungen der Mesenterien und ihrer Äste im Gebiet des Colon transversum und des Colon descendens im höheren Alter." Medical Dissertation, University of Munich, 1983.

91 Rauber, F., and A. Kopsch. Anatomie des Menschen. Lehrbuch und Atlas. Ed. and arr. by H. Leonhardt, B. Tillmann, and Zilles. Vol. IV. Topographie der Organsysteme, Systematik der peripheren Leitungsbahnen. Präparieratlas. Stuttgart, New York: Thieme, 1988.

92 Own observations

93 Ortmann, R. "Über die Bedeutung, Häufigkeit und Variationsbilder der linken retroaortären Nierenvenen." Z Anat-Entwickl-Gesch 127 (1968): 346–358.

94 [13], there according to Hirt, 1924

95 Photograph: Dr. med. H. Bertermann, Department of Urology in the City Hospital of Kiel

96 Photograph: Prof. Dr. med. M. Heller, Director of the Clinic for Diagnostic Radiology of the Christian-Albrechts-University in Kiel

97 Dudenhausen, J. W., W. Pschyrembel, and M. Obladen. Praktische Geburtshilfe mit geburtshilflichen Operationen. Berlin: de Gruyter, 2001.

98 Staubesand, J. "Der Feinbau des Glomus coccygicum und der Glomerula caudalia. Ein Beitrag zur Histophysiologie vasaler Glomusorgane I, II, III." Acta anat 19 (1953): 1105, 209, 309.

99 Martius, H. Lehrbuch der Gynäkologie. 8th ed. Stuttgart: Thieme, 1964.

100 von Hayek, H. "Die Entwicklung der Harn- und Geschlechtsorgane," pp 1-52, "Die Harnblase," pp 253-278, "Gefäße," pp 501-517. Handbuch der Urologie. Vol. I: Anatomie und Embryologie. Eds. C. E. Alken, V. A. Dix, W. E. Goodwin and E. Wildbolz. Berlin, Heidelberg, New York: Springer, 1969.

101 Cytoscopic Photograph: Priv.-Doz. Dr. J. Seiferth, Cologne

102 von Lanz, T., and W. Wachsmuth. Praktische Anatomie. Ein Lehr- und Hilfsbuch der anatomischen Grundlagen ärztlichen Handelns. Vol. II. Part 8: Becken. Berlin, Heidelberg, New York, Tokyo: Springer, 1984.

A

103   Photograph: Dr. med. J. M. Doniec, Clinic for General Surgery and Thoracic Surgery of the Christian-Albrechts-University in Kiel (Director: Prof. Dr. med. B. Kremer)

104   Colposcopic Photographs: Dr. med. M. Löning, Clinic for Gynecology and Obstetrics, University Clinic Lübeck (Director: Prof. Dr. med. K. Diedrich)

105   Antoine, T. Weibels Lehrbuch der Frauenheilkunde in zwei Bänden. Erster Band: Geburtshilfe. 8th revised ed. Vienna: Urban & Schwarzenberg, 1948.

106   Photograph: Prof. Dr. med. L. Mettler, Clinic for Gynecology and Obstetrics of the Christian-Albrechts-University in Kiel (Director: Prof. Dr. med. Jonat)

107   [32] there according to Breckwoldt

108   Original Preparation: Prof. Dr. A. F. Holstein, Anatomical Institute of the University of Hamburg

109   Photograph: Dr. med. F. Pries, Praxis Clinic Kronshagen

110   Preparation of the Collection of the Anatomical Institute of the Christian-Albrechts-University in Kiel, Klaws et Gundlach fecerunt

111   Kaplan and Spinner, 1980, and according to own observations

112   Schmidt, H.-M., and U. Lanz. Chirurgische Anatomie der Hand. Stuttgart: Hippokrates, 1992 and own observations

Bibliography

Antoine, T. Weibels Lehrbuch der Frauenheilkunde in zwei Bänden. Erster Band: Geburtshilfe. 8th rev. ed. Vienna: Urban & Schwarzenberg, 1948.

Bargmann, W., and W. Doerr. Das Herz des Menschen. Vol. I. Stuttgart: Thieme, 1963.

Bertermann, H. "Transrektale Sonographie von Prostata und Samenblasen." Ultraschalldiagnostik – Lehrbuch und Atlas. Eds. Braun, Günther, Schwerk. Landsberg/Lech: ecomed, 1997.

Bojsen-Møller, F., and L. Schmidt. "The palmar aponeurosis and the central spaces of the hand." J Anat 117 (1974): 55-68.

Bojsen-Møller, F., and K. E. Flagstad. "Plantar aponeurosis and internal architecture of the ball of the foot." J Anat 121 (1976): 55.

Braune, W. Topographisch-Anatomischer Atlas. Nach Durchschnitten an gefrorenen Cadavern. Leipzig: Veit & Comp, 1875.

Braus, H. Anatomie des Menschen. Ein Lehrbuch für Ärzte und Studierende. Continued by C. Elze. 3rd ed. Vol. I. Berlin: Springer, 1954.

Braus, H. Anatomie des Menschen. Ein Lehrbuch für Ärzte und Studierende. Continued by C. Elze. 3rd ed. Vol. II. Berlin: Springer, 1956.

Braus, H. Anatomie des Menschen. Continued by C. Elze. 2nd ed. Vol. III. Berlin: Springer, 1960.

Corning, H. K. Lehrbuch der topographischen Anatomie für Studierende und Ärzte. 12th and 13th ed. Munich: Bergmann, 1922.

Clemens, H. J. Die Venensysteme der menschlichen Wirbelsäule. Morphologie und funktionelle Bedeutung. Berlin: de Gruyter, 1961.

Deiler, S. "Präparatorische, röntgenologische und histologische Untersuchungen der Mesenterien und ihrer Äste im Gebiet des Colon transversum und des Colon descendens im höheren Alter." Medical Dissertation, University of Munich, 1983

Duus, P. Neurologisch-topische Diagnostik. Anatomie, Physiologie, Klinik. 6th ed. Stuttgart: Thieme, 1995.

Dudenhausen, J. W., W. Pschyrembel, and M. Obladen. Praktische Geburtshilfe mit geburtshilflichen Operationen. Berlin: de Gruyter, 2001.

Feneis, H., continued by W. Dauber. Anatomisches Bildwörterbuch der internationalen Nomenklatur. 8th ed. Stuttgart: Thieme, 1998.

Ferner, H. "Zur Anatomie der intrakranialen Abschnitte des Nervus trigeminus." Z Anat - Entwickl-Gesch 114 (1948): 108-122.

Fischer, M., and B. Tillmann. "Tendinous insertions in the human thyroid cartilage plate: macroscopic and histologic studies." Anat Embryol 183 (1991): 251-257.

Fölsch, U. R. Pankreaschirurgie. Eds. L. F. Hollender, H.-J. Peiper. Berlin, Heidelberg, New York: Springer, 1988.

Frick, H., H. Leonhardt, and D. Starck. Allgemeine Anatomie Spezielle Anatomie I, Extremitäten – Rumpfwand – Kopf – Hals. 4th rev. ed. Stuttgart, New York: Thieme, 1992.

Frick, H., H. Leonhardt, and D. Starck. Allgemeine Anatomie Spezielle Anatomie II, Eingeweide – Nervensystem – Systematik der Muskeln und Leitungsbahnen. 4th rev. ed. Stuttgart: Thieme, 1992.

Grosser, O., and R. Ortmann. Grundriß der Entwicklungsgeschichte des Menschen. 7th ed. Berlin, Heidelberg, New York: Springer, 1970.

Hafferl. Lehrbuch der topographischen Anatomie. 2nd ed. Berlin: Springer, 1957.

Hansen, K., and H. Schliack. Segmentale Innervation. Ihre Bedeutung für Klinik und Praxis. 2nd ed. Stuttgart: Thieme, 1962.

Häuslmaier, B. Lebensdaten von Ärzten deren Namen mit medizinischen, vor allem mit anatomischen Begriffen verbunden werden. Inaugural Dissertation, Faculty of Medicine of the University of Munich, 1987.

Hayek, H. von. "Die Entwicklung der Harn- und Geschlechtsorgane," pp 1-52, "Die Harnblase," pp 253-278, "Gefäße," pp 501-517. Hdb der Urologie. Vol. I. Anatomie und Embryologie. Eds. C. E. Alken, V. A. Dix, W. E. Goodwin, E. Wildbolz. Berlin, Heidelberg, New York: Springer, 1969.

Hayek, H. von. Die menschliche Lunge. 2nd supplemented and expanded ed. Berlin, Heidelberg, New York: Springer, 1970.

Heimer, L. The Human Brain and Spinal Cord. Functional Neuroanatomy and Dissection Guide. New York, Heidelberg, Berlin: Springer, 1983.

Henkel, A. Die Aponeurosis plantaris. Arch Anat Physiol Anat Abt (Suppl). 1913. 113.

Henle, J. Lehrbuch der systematischen Anatomie des Menschen. Vol. III. Braunschweig: Vieweg, 1868.

Hirschfeld, L., and J.-B. Leveillé. Systeme Nerveux et des Organes des Sens De L'Homme. Paris: Chez J-B Bailliére, 1853.

Hollender, L. F., and H.-J. Peiper. Die Praxis der Chirurgie. Pankreaschirurgie. Berlin, Heidelberg, New York, Tokyo: Springer, 1988.

Jänig, W., and H.-J. Häbler. "Organization of the autonomic nervous system: structure and function." Handbook of Clinical Neurology. Vol 74 (30): The Autonomic Nervous System. Part 1. Normal Function. Ed. O. Appenzeller. Elsevier Science B.V., 1999. 1-52.

Koebke, J., and E. Stümpel. "Untersuchungen zu einer Funktionsanalyse der Metacarpophalangealgelenke II-V der menschlichen Hand." Verh Anat Ges 75 (1981): 275-276.

Koebke, J., and B. Tillmann. "Das Corpus adiposum des Obturatoriuskanales." Anat Anz 161 (1986): 317-325.

Krey, H. F., G. Grunau, and H. Bräuer. "Exempla ophthalmologica." Bildatlas zur Physiologie und Pathophysiologie des Auges. 1986.

Krmpotić-Nemanić, J., W. Draf, and J. Helms. Chirurgische Anatomie des Kopf-Hals-Bereiches. Berlin, Heidelberg, New York: Springer, 1985.

Krstić, R. V. Human Microscopic Anatomy: An Atlas for Students of Medicine and Biology. Vol. III. Berlin, Heidelberg, New York: Springer, 1991.

Lanz, T. von, and W. Wachsmuth. Praktische Anatomie. Ein Lehr- und Hilfsbuch der anatomischen Grundlagen ärztlichen Handelns. Vol. I/1: Kopf. Berlin, Heidelberg, New York: Springer, 1979.

Lanz, T. von, and W. Wachsmuth. Praktische Anatomie. Ein Lehr- und Hilfsbuch der anatomischen Grundlagen ärztlichen Handelns. Vol. I/ 2: Hals. Berlin: Springer, 1955.

Lanz, T. von, and W. Wachsmuth. Praktische Anatomie. Ein Lehr- und Hilfsbuch der anatomischen Grundlagen ärztlichen Handelns. 2nd ed. Vol. I/3: Arm. Berlin: Springer, 1959.

Lanz, T. von, and W. Wachsmuth. Praktische Anatomie. Ein Lehr- und Hilfsbuch der anatomischen Grundlagen ärztlichen Handelns. Eds. J. Lang and Wachsmuth. Bein und Statik. 2nd ed. Vol. I/4. Berlin, Heidelberg, New York: Springer, 1972.

Lanz, T. von, and W. Wachsmuth. Praktische Anatomie. Ein Lehr- und Hilfsbuch der anatomischen Grundlagen ärztlichen Handelns. Vol. II/6. Bauch. Feifel G. von Loeweneck. Berlin, Heidelberg, New York: Springer, 1993.

A

Lanz, T. von, and W. Wachsmuth. Praktische Anatomie. Ein Lehr- und Hilfsbuch der anatomischen Grundlagen ärztlichen Handelns. Vol. II/7: Rücken. Berlin, Heidelberg, New York: Springer, 1982.

Lanz, T. von, and W. Wachsmuth. Praktische Anatomie. Ein Lehr- und Hilfsbuch der anatomischen Grundlagen ärztlichen Handelns. Vol. II/8: Becken. Berlin: Springer, 1984.

Lippert, H., and R. Pabst. Arterial variations in man. Munich: Bergmann, 1985.

Martius, H. Lehrbuch der Gynäkologie. 8th rev. ed. Stuttgart: Thieme, 1964.

Netter, F. H. Atlas der Anatomie des Menschen. 3rd ed. Stuttgart: Thieme, 2003.

Nieuwenhuys, R., J. Voogd, and C. van Huijzen. Das Zentralnervensystem des Menschen. Atlas mit Begleitext. Trans. W. von Lange. 2nd ed. Berlin, Heidelberg, New York: Springer, 1991.

Ortmann, R. "Über die Bedeutung, Häufigkeit und Variationsbild der linken retro-aortären Nierenvenen." Z Anat-Entwickl-Gesch 127 (1968): 346-358.

Paulsen, F. "The human nasolacrimal ducts." Adv Anat Embryol Cell Biol 170 (2003): 1-106.

Paulsen, F., B. Tillmann, C. Christofides, W. Richter, and J. Koebke. "Curving and looping of the internal carotid artery in relation to the pharynx: frequency, embryology and clinical implications." J Anat 197 (2000): 373-381.

Pernkopf. Anatomie: Atlas der topographischen und angewandten Anatomie des Menschen. Ed. W. Platzer. 3rd rev. and expanded ed. Munich, Vienna, Baltimore: Urban & Schwarzenberg, 1994.

Platzer, W. Atlas der topographischen Anatomie. Stuttgart, New York: Thieme, 1982.

Quain, J., A. Thomson, and E. A. Schaefer. Quain's elements of anatomy. London: Longmans, Green & Company, 1882.

Rauber/Kopsch. Anatomie des Menschen. Lehrbuch und Atlas. Eds. H. Leonhardt, B. Tillmann, G. Töndury, and K. Zilles

Vol. I. Bewegungsapparat. Ed. and arr. by B. Tillmann. 3rd ed. Stuttgart, New York: Thieme, 2003.

Vol. II. Innere Organe. Ed. and arr. by H. Leonhardt. Stuttgart, New York: Thieme, 1987.

Vol. III. Nervensystem, Sinnesorgane. Ed. and arr. by H. Leonhardt, G. Töndury, and K. Zilles. Stuttgart, New York: Thieme, 1997.

Vol. IV. Topographie der Organsysteme, Systematik der peripheren Leitungsbahnen. Präparieratlas. Ed. and arr. by H.Leonhardt, B. Tillmann, and K. Zilles. Stuttgart, New York: Thieme, 1988.

Rein, H., and M. Schneider. Einführung in die Physiologie des Menschen. 13th and 14th revised ed. Ed. M. Schneider. Berlin, Heidelberg, New York: Springer, 1960.

Rouviére, H. Anatomie Humaine. Descriptive et Topographique. Paris: Tome I. Masson, 1924.

Ritter, K., and H. Bräuer. Exempla otologica. Munich: Medical Service, 1988.

Sappey. Anatomie, physiologie et pathologie des vaisseaux lymphatiques confédérés chez l'homme et les vertèbres. 1874. Owner of copy: State and University Library of Lower Saxony, Göttingen.

Schmidt, R. F., and G. Thews. Physiologie des Menschen. 27th ed. Berlin, Heidelberg, New York: Springer, 1997.

Schmidt, H.-M., and U. Lanz. Chirurgische Anatomie der Hand. Stuttgart: Hippokrates, 1992.

Spalteholz-Spanner. Handatlas der Anatomie des Menschen. Founded by W. Spalteholz, ed. and arr. by R. Spanner. 16th ed. Part 1: Bewegungsapparat. Amsterdam: Scheltema & Holkema NV, 1960.

Spalteholz-Spanner. Handatlas der Anatomie des Menschen. Founded by W. Spalteholz. Ed. and arr. by R. Spanner. 16th ed. Part 2: Gefäß-System, Eingeweide, Nervensystem, Sinnesorgane. Amsterdam, Scheltema & Holkema NV, 1961.

Staubesand, J. "Der Feinbau des Glomus coccygicum und der Glomerula caudalia. Ein Beitrag zur Histophysiologie vasaler Glomusorgane I, II, III." Acta anat 19 (1953):1105, 209, 309.

Steven, P., F. Paulsen, and B. Tillmann. "Orcein-Picroindigocarmine – A New Multiple Stain." Arch Histol Cytol 63 (2000): 397-400.

Tandler, J. Lehrbuch der systematischen Anatomie. Vol. 2. Die Eingeweide. Leipzig: FCW Vogel, 1923.

Terminologia Anatomica. International Anatomicla Terminologie, FCAT. Federative Committee on Anatomomicla Terminology. Stuttgart, New York: Thieme, 1998.

Tillmann, B. "Verlaufsvarianten des N. gluteus inferior." Anat Anz 145 (1979): 293-302.

Tillmann, B. Farbatlas der Anatomie: Zahnmedizin – Humanmedizin; Kopf, Hals, Rumpf. Stuttgart, New York: Thieme, 1997.

Tillmann, B. "Topographie und Struktur der Orbitawände und des Canalis opticus." Deutsche Gesellschaft für Hals-Nasen-Ohrenheilkunde, Kopf- und Hals-Chirurgie. Ed. W. Steiner. Berlin, Heidelberg, New York: Springer, 1998. 39-50.

Tillmann, B., and C. Christofides. "Die gefährliche Schleife der Arteria carotis interna." HNO 43 (1995): 601-604.

Tillmann, B., and F. Paulsen. "Functional and clinical anatomy of the anterior commissure." Adv Oto Rhino Laryngol 49 (1995): 201-206.

Tillmann, B., and M. Schünke. Taschenatlas zum Präparierkurs. Eine klinisch orientierte Anleitung. Stuttgart, New York: Thieme, 1993.

Tillmann, B., F. Wustrow. "Kehlkopf." Hals-Nasen-Ohren-Heilkunde in Praxis und Klinik. J. Berendes, R. Link, and F. Zöllner. Vol. IV/1. Stuttgart: Thieme, 1982. 1-101.

Töndury, G. Angewandte und topographische Anatomie. 5th ed. Stuttgart: Thieme, 1981.

Toldt, C., and F. Hochstetter. Anatomischer Atlas. Vol. III. Munich, Berlin, Vienna: Urban u. Schwarzenberg, 1979.

Treutner, K. H., B. Klosterhalfen, G. Winkeltau, S. Moench, and V. Schumpelick. "Vascular Anatomy of the Spleen: The Basis for Organ-Preserving Surgery." Clinical Anat 2 (1993): 1-8.

Wolf, J. H. Kompendium der medizinischen Terminologie. Berlin, Heidelberg, New York: Springer, 1982.

Zidorn, T., and B. Tillmann. "Morphological variants of the suprapatellar bursa." Ann Anat 174 (1992): 287-291.

Zilles, K., and G. Rehkämper. Funktionelle Neuroanatomie: Lehrbuch und Atlas. 3rd completely rev. and updated ed. Berlin, Heidelberg, New York: Springer, 1998.

Subject Index

Terms in *italics* refer to clinical terms. Page numbers followed by the letter T refer to structures that can only be found in the tables. The notation MA-1 through MA-7 refers the reader to the Muscle Addenda at the ends of Chapters 2–7.

A

A

Subject Index

A

A

Subject Index

A

D

Subject Index

Subject Index

A

A

A

598

A

A

Subject Index

A

Subject Index

A

A

A

A

Subject Index

A